With the compliments of
The Author

DUODECIMAL ARITHMETIC

We are in the imaginative sphere of art, and the mathematician is engaged in a work of creation which resembles music in its orderliness, and is yet reproducing on another plane the order of the universe, and so becoming as it were a music of the spheres.

HAVELOCK ELLIS

ERRATA

Terry Duodecimal Arithmetic

Page	3	line 14(16)	should read	100 minutes = 1 Degree
"	6	" 18(20)	" "	.41$\dot{6}$
"	8	" 1	" "	Any power of any number
"	8	" 24(28)	" "	duodecimals
"	1£(23)	" .770	" "	.92£
"	23(27)	" 281	" "	5.7.£
"	27(31)	" 1χ(22)	" "	627 070 £
"	4χ(58)	" 3	" "	one dozen and four places
"	6χ(82)	" 1£(23)	" "	$(2\pi N)^{2n - 1}$ instead of $\chi^{2n - 1}$
"	χ8(128)	" .0408	" "	9 020 035
"	209(297)	" 14(16)	" "	536 186
"	20χ(298)	" £(11)	" "	£.593 χ40 9(1)
"	25χ(358)	" .0279	" "	617 668
"	265(365)	" .00χχ	" "	4££ 854
"	267(367)	" .0224	" "	22χ 1χ4
"	267(367)	" .0290	" "	4χ1 600
"	272(374)	" 16(18)	" "	-.2χ9 50£ 7χ9
"	279(381)	" χ(10)	" "	.859 χ69 650 4
"	279(381)	" 30(36)	" "	1.3χ8 £11 668 4
"	28χ(394)	" 37(43)	" "	DN + 1: (N + 1)
"	295(401)	" 7	" "	$\frac{(n + 1)n(n - 1)}{3!}$
"	299(405)	" 33(39)	" "	3£0 etc. (n column)
"	29£(407)	" E_1 .5χ2	" "	.08£ 020

Note: The powers of 1:π given on page 27(31) are the 2nd to the 10th powers inclusive. The value of 1:π is given on page 60(72).

DUODECIMAL ARITHMETIC

GEORGE S. TERRY

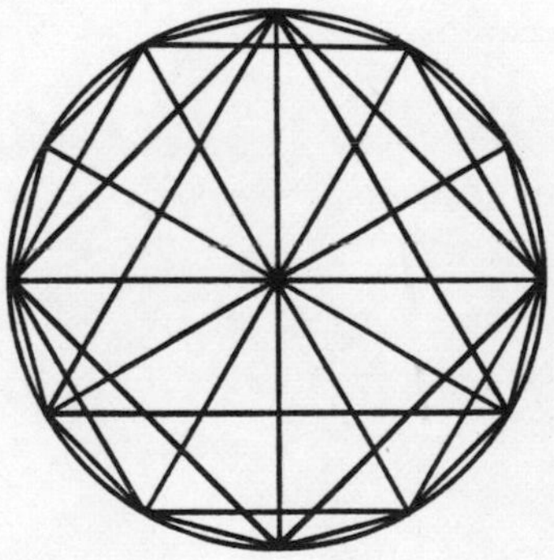

MDCCCCXXXVIII
LONGMANS, GREEN AND CO.
LONDON · NEW YORK · TORONTO

LONGMANS, GREEN AND CO.
114 FIFTH AVENUE, NEW YORK
221 EAST 20TH STREET, CHICAGO
88 TREMONT STREET, BOSTON

LONGMANS, GREEN AND CO. LTD.
39 PATERNOSTER ROW, LONDON, E.C.4
CHITTARANJAN AVENUE, CALCUTTA
53 NICOL ROAD, BOMBAY
36A MOUNT ROAD, MADRAS

LONGMANS, GREEN AND CO.
215 VICTORIA STREET, TORONTO

TERRY

DUODECIMAL ARITHMETIC

FIRST EDITION

PRINTED IN THE UNITED STATES OF AMERICA

TO

THE MEMORY OF MY FATHER

THOMAS ROBERT TERRY, M.A. F.R.A.S.

<u>CONTENTS</u>

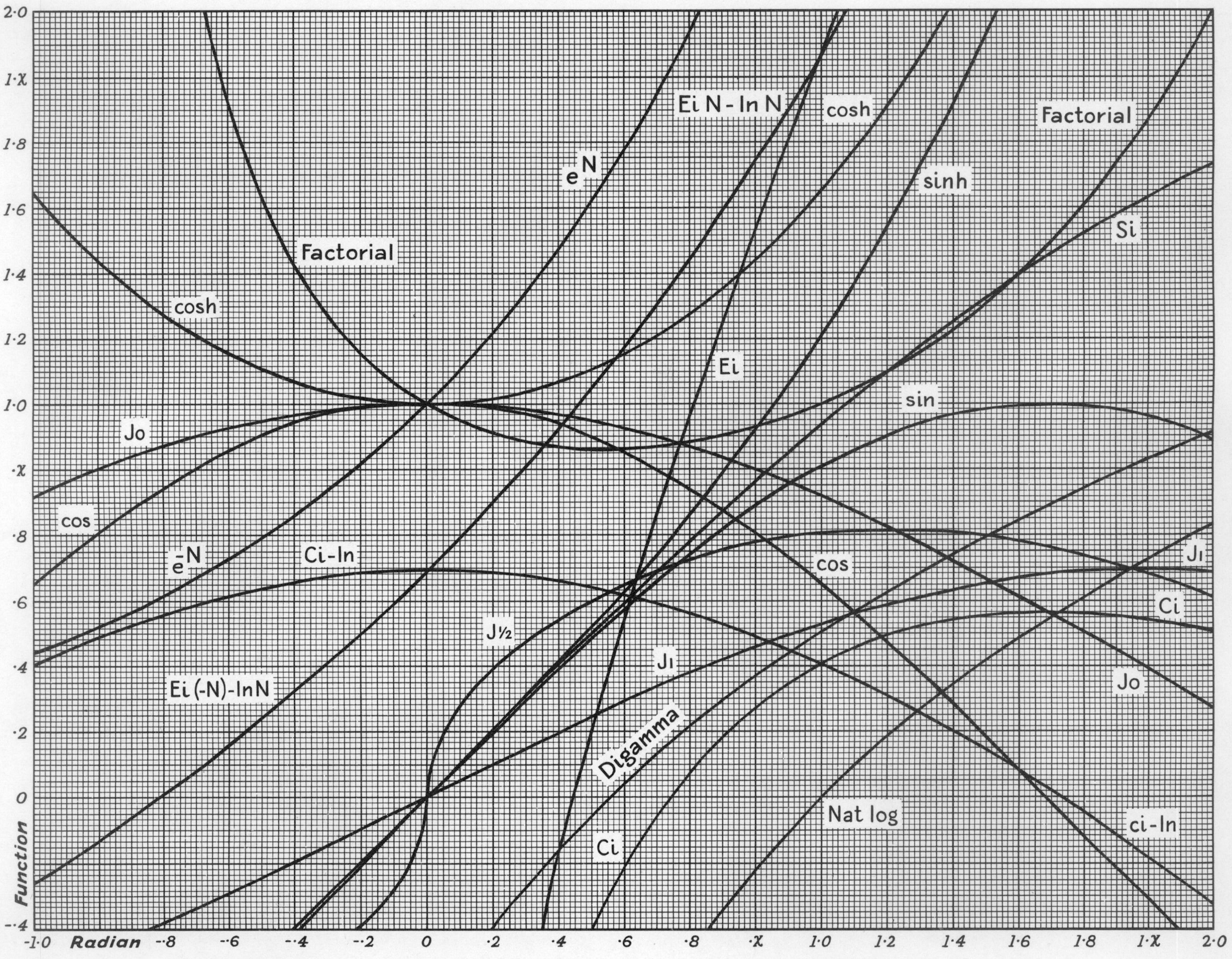

Factorial
cosh
Jo
cos
e^-N
Ci-In
Ei (-N)-InN
Factorial
e^N
Ei N - In N
cosh
sinh
Si
Ei
sin
J½
J1
Digamma
Ci
cos
Nat log
J1
Ci
Jo
ci-In
Function
Radian

Introduction

The duodecimal system of arithmetic consists in counting by dozens rather than by tens. It has been in use from the earliest times usually, as it is today, mixed with the decimal. The Babylonians, for instance, used such units as sixty and six hundred rather than units made up of continued finger counting.

The reason for the present method of counting, based on the number of fingers on the human hand, is physiological. It was convenient for keeping account of small numbers of things. It is much less convenient for dividing things into groups. The interesting thing is that the system has never seemed quite satisfactory. Had it been so, there would have been no reason for the British shilling, the linear foot, the present calendar and clock, or the universal habit of buying eggs by the dozen.

The practical value of the dozen commercially has been illustrated when it was attempted to introduce a system of selling things by tens, to be in line with a decimal money system. This proved a failure, the dozen being much more convenient to the customer who might often want to divide his dozen into threes or fours, as when planting shrubs.

The obvious requirement of a number base is that it should split up into useful subdivisions and build up into useful aggregates. By this test, ten is a poor base. Eight, twelve or sixteen are all better and have all been advocated, yet none heretofore has been tested arithmetically to find out whether the new base actually makes computation easier. This seems the more strange in the case of twelve because, as arithmetical requirements increase with an increasingly complex civilisation, the duodecimal element does not seem to die out, the system we use does not tend to become uniform, we still work with twelve months and the dozen, we still have no standard method of dividing the circle.

In order to count by dozens instead of by tens it is necessary to introduce two new symbols, one to represent ten and one to represent eleven. Count as follows:-

1, 2, 3, 4, 5, 6, 7, 8, 9, Ӿ, Ɛ, 10

One dozen is then written *10*, meaning one dozen and no units. One dozen and a half are represented by *16*, namely, one dozen and six units. One quarter is *.3*, one third is *.4*, three times four is *10*.

Flexibility is the fundamental advantage of the system, just as a dozen eggs is a convenient number to put in a box because the box may have several different shapes. The box of a dozen eggs is more adaptable than the box of ten eggs when all the eggs are in one plane.

The box of a dozen is still more adaptable if we are not limited to putting all the eggs in one plane. For instance, with ten eggs we can have a single row of ten or two rows of five. With a dozen eggs we can have a single row, two rows of six, or three rows of four. Using a two-layer egg box does not give us any new shapes with ten eggs, but with a dozen it gives us the choice of two floors with six on a floor or four floors with three on a floor.

Books on counting by dozens

Counting by dozens instead of by tens is no innovation. It has been considered by a number of writers during the last hundred years.

Isaac Pitman attempted to introduce the duodecimal system of counting among learners of shorthand by using it in his instruction journals in 1857-1858.

Thomas Leech in his book, "Dozens vs. Tens," published in 1866, explains the system and gives a short table of duodecimal logarithms. Although this table is quite short and contains certain errors, it has a practical value which, so far as I have been able to discover, has not been used. It could be used to construct a simple duodecimal slide rule reading in feet and inches which would multiply into square feet and square inches, an instrument which would probably be a convenience to anyone who has occasion to use square feet and square inches.

John W. Nystrom in his book, "On the French Metric System," published in 1876, suggests a simplified system of weights and measures using twelve as a number base.

Herbert Spencer in a series of letters to the London Times, reprinted in Appleton's Popular Science Monthly, June, 1896, sets forth the advantages of the duodecimal division of the circle.

Rear Admiral G. Elbrow in his book, "The New English System of Weights and Measures and of Arithmetic," published in 1913, shows how to convert whole numbers and simple decimals to the base twelve. The simplification of weights and measures which is suggested by Admiral Elbrow is remarkable. Retaining the yard as the fundamental standard of length, he uses as the working standard one twelfth of this called the Palm (in effect three inches) and introduces a new unit called the Quin (in effect one quarter inch).

From these are derived the standards of weight and volume, namely the weight and volume of one cubic palm of water at maximum density and standard pressure, which he calls respectively the Pound and the Pint - which have slightly different values from their present ones (as do the mile, the ounce, the gallon and the bushel). Specific gravity is then the weight of a cubic palm of the substance in pounds or what is exactly the same thing, the weight of a cubic yard of the substance in tons. The only tables which need to be learned on this system are as follows:-

Linear Measure	Square Measure
10 Quins = *1* Palm	*100* sq. Quins = *1* sq. Palm
10 Palms = *1* Yard	*100* sq. Palms = *1* sq. Yard
1000 Yards = *1* Mile	*1,000,000* sq. Yards = *1* sq. Mile

Weight Standard, *1* Pound, the weight of *1* cubic Palm of water at maximum density and standard pressure.

10 Ounces = *1* Pound
1000 Pounds = *1* Ton

Volume Standard, *1* Pint, the volume of *1* cubic Palm of water.

10 Ounces = *1* Pint
10 Pints = *1* Gallon
10 Gallons = *1* Bushel or Barrel
10 Bushels = *1* cubic Yard

Time and the Circle

100 Seconds = *1* Minute
10 Minutes = *1* Degree
100 Degrees = *1* Day or Circle

F. Emerson Andrews in his book, "New Numbers," published in 1935, shows the advantages of the system in arithmetical simplicity, gives methods of converting whole numbers and decimals to a number of places, and gives a six-place logarithm table for numbers from *1* to *100*.

All the above writers lay stress upon the convenience of twelve as a base for a system of counting because of the large number of factors which it contains, and point out the simplification of the arithmetic of surface and volume in terms of feet and inches.

It was the work of Mr. Andrews which led me to enquire further into the system arithmetically as it appeared to be worthwhile, assuming the simplifications which he claimed for the system, to produce, for instance, a workable table of logarithms, and do some calculations in the system in order to become accustomed to it.

It is to Mr. Andrews that we are indebted, first, for demonstrating clearly that twelve is the best available base for a system of counting; and second, that the advantages of the decimal point are likely to be greater in the twelve system than in the ten.

Advantages of twelve as a base

The advantage of twelve as a base over eight or sixteen is that it divides into three as well as into four. This advantage, as will be shown later, increases as we go further with the system. It may not seem to be of much value that three times two is half the number base, but it will soon appear that the fact that four times three times two is twice the number base causes a great simplification in computation. It may not seem to make much difference whether one quarter and three quarters are represented in decimal form by one figure or by two, but when combined with other simple fractions, themselves, on the average, shortened, there is no small saving of work.

There is another probably less important advantage in the fact that the base is larger than the present one. As we explore further outwards, we need larger numbers to express what we see; as we divide more finely, we need more numbers to express the fineness of our division.

In each case the base twelve has an advantage over the base ten because it uses less figures to express the same result. So would a base of two dozen be better than either, its only disadvantage being the large number of new digits required and the labor of learning a multiplication table to two dozen.

For instance, a light year is expressed

decimally as 5,880,000,000,000 miles

duodecimally as *7Ɛ0,000,000,000* miles

Similarly, if two tenth metres or two ten thousand millionths of a metre be expressed

decimally as .000 000 000 2

they are expressed fairly closely

duodecimally as *.000 000 001*

And it will be observed from the conversion table that the possible error in the result so expressed decimally is half what it is expressed duodecimally with one less place. In other words, with nine duodecimal places we express results with but twice the possible error of ten decimal places; with one dozen duodecimal places, with about the same possible error as with thirteen decimal places, and so on.

The great disadvantage of the duodecimal system is that we are accustomed to another system which, because of habit, appears simple to us. Had we grown a second thumb alongside our little finger, our present system would probably never have been heard of, for it has arithmetically nothing which I have been able to discover to recommend it. It is exceedingly convenient for dividing a number of things into five equal parts, but unfortunately this is an operation which is very seldom required. Nevertheless, the method is in use and the question is:-

How much trouble is it to change back and forth between it and another for purposes of experiment? How hard is the new system to learn?

The answers can only be given from the best estimate which can be made from experience. To change back and forth at first was difficult, and looking back four years I think the chief reason was that one does not at first trust the new numbers. One expects them not to work. One is continually surprised when they come out right and check themselves correctly. In about six months, one believes in the integrity of the strange-looking digits and after that, having learned simple addition and carrying from the dozen, conversion offers no further difficulty.

Nor is it limited to any number of figures. For instance, the conversion of π to a gross of places, given a ten-place decimal machine and the three-figure whole number table, is probably a matter of three hours' work. This, from the point of view of the new system, is important, for next to habit, the disadvantage of any new system is the fact that much work has been done on the old. Is this then wasted? By no means. All that has been done is very easily converted to the new, where it will be found, as far as my experience goes, that further calculations may be more easily accomplished because of the better folding up of the numbers in their formulae, and the results turned back again, given a duodecimal machine.

How hard then is it to get a machine which will also believe in these new numbers? Far easier than I had at first supposed, and certainly far easier than adapting a machine to carry over for degrees, minutes and seconds. The Monroe Calculating Machine Company found that their older type of machine could, at small expense, be converted to compute duodecimally, because there was room on the keyboard for the two extra keys on each row and because dials for reading pence were already in existence.

How hard is it then to learn to calculate by the new system? Again one can answer only from experience and only from experience superimposed on the decimal multiplication table. There is no doubt at all that one who had not yet learned any numeration would find the duodecimal multiplication table the easier to learn. One need learn only the *5* times, *7* times, χ times and Ɛ times, about half the tables which must now be completely learned to twelve times. This is, however, not the existing condition.

I, myself, have not learned the new table by rote though I have done a good deal of duodecimal multiplication by hand. I think I should have done so, but at least I am in a position to give the beginner's point of view. At first, carrying over from the dozens seems hard and again one does not trust the results one writes down. At present, I multiply more easily duodecimally than decimally. How much to assign to habit, how much to the system, I do not know, but I can say positively that some is due to the simpler system.

Conversion to and from the present base

If it be found, in certain cases, simpler to calculate duodecimally rather than decimally, then it is essential to be able to convert numbers easily from one system to the other.

Suppose we have a number expressed in the ten system as 75. In order to express it on the twelve system, we need to know how many dozens it contains and how many units are left. That is, we divide it by twelve and put down the number of dozens and the number of units left over, namely, six dozen and three.

Conversely, if we have a whole number expressed duodecimally by *69*, we know that this means six dozen and nine and we can write down six dozen, namely, 72 and add 9, obtaining the result 81. It is, however, simpler, especially with larger numbers to find how many sets of ten the number contains by dividing duodecimally by *X*, when we get 8 sets and 1 left over.

Similarly, if we have a decimal, say .7 and wish to know its duodecimal equivalent, it is necessary to find how many twelfths it contains. That is, we multiply it by twelve and put down the whole number as the number of twelfths, that is, the first duodecimal place, in this case *8*. We have a decimal of a twelfth left over, in this case .4. If we wish to go further, it is necessary to find how many twelfths of a twelfth this decimal contains. That is, we multiply it by twelve and put down the whole number as the second duodecimal place, in this case *.4*.

Conversely, if we have a duodecimal, say *.5*, we know this is five twelfths and we may divide this out decimally and obtain *.416*, but it is simpler to find how many tenths it contains by multiplying duodecimally by *X*, when we get the whole number 4 and *.2* duodecimally left. Multiplying again by *X*, we get 1 and *.8* duodecimally left.

In order to show the relative work, suppose we have *.5555* duodecimally. This is evidently, decimally

$$\frac{5}{12} + \frac{5}{144} + \frac{5}{1728} + \frac{5}{20736}$$

which is	.41666	or it is		*.5555*
	.03472			*X*
	.00289		4	*.6662*
	.00024			*X*
			5	*.5518*
	.4545			*X*
			4	*.63*
				X
			5	*.3*

Arithmetical Simplifications

Multiplication Table

The duodecimal multiplication table is easy to learn and easy to use because of the consistent endings of the three, four, six, eight and nine times. Of the dozen tables there are only four, namely the *5*, *7*, *X* and *Ɛ* times which have to be learned by rote. With the present table all except 2, 5 and 10 have to be learned, that is, nine tables. There is thus about half the work required to learn the duodecimal multiplication table.

Looking at the corresponding tables up to a dozen, in the ten system the product ends in zero thirty two times; in the twelve system, three dozen and three times.

Consider, for instance, three times four, three times eight, four times nine, eight times nine, all ending in *0* so that the carry can be written down direct, all being gains over the decimal table.

Simple division is correspondingly easier, for instance, by three and by four because the carry is self evident. This came as a surprise to me when I was doing divisions by three with a considerable number of figures, and, being inexpert at any division, lost my place. To pick up and go on is easy duodecimally; decimally, it is harder.

Factors

Factors are consequently simpler because all numbers have an obvious factor, except those ending in *1*, *5*, *7* or *£*. For instance, any number ending in *3*, *6*, *9* or *0* has *3* as a factor. Any number ending in *4*, *8* or *0* has *4* as a factor. It follows that prime numbers end in *1*, *5*, *7* or *£*.

Prime Numbers

Suppose, for instance, we wish to know whether a million and one is prime. Expressed in the twelve system (see conversion of whole numbers), 1,000,001 is *402,855*.

We know at once a great deal more about this number when expressed in the twelve system than we did before. For instance:-

1. The number *402,855* is not a square since all squares end in *0*, *1*, *4* or *9* (see table of squares).

2. The number is not any power of any number except, perhaps, an odd power of a number ending in *5* (see table of powers).

3. From the prime factor table we know that if numbers which end in *1*, *5*, *7* or *£* have factors, the factors must also end in *1*, *5*, *7* or *£*. Therefore, if the number has two factors, they must be a pair ending in *1* and *5* or *7* and *£* (see multiplication table). Our search for possible factors is therefore much reduced.

Powers

Powers of whole numbers are simpler because of their more consistent endings. In the first place, all squares end in either *0*, *1*, *4* or *9*, a considerable help in determining at sight whether or not a number is a perfect square.

Secondly, any power of any number ends as follows:-

Number ends *2*	Any power ends *4* or *8*
3	*3* or *9*
4	*4*
5	*1* or *5*
6	*0*

Any number of any power ends:- (concluded)

Number ends	*7*	Any power ends	*1* or *7*
	8		*4* or *8*
	9		*9*
	X		*4*
	Ɛ		*1* or *Ɛ*

This should be compared with the corresponding table on the ten system.

Fractions

Assuming a child were taught the duodecimal multiplication table, he would probably have an easier time with fractions especially when putting the simple fractions into duodecimal form.

Of the eleven fractions from one half to one twelfth, five can be expressed exactly by a one place duodecimal, two by two place duodecimals, - seven in all. Decimally, three can be expressed exactly by one place, one by two places, one by three places, - five in all.

Factorials

The greater simplicity of the duodecimal multiplication table is demonstrated when we multiply together successive numbers to form factorials. For instance, *4*! is *20* and thenceforward every factorial is expressed with fewer significant figures duodecimally than it is decimally. The factorial of one dozen decimally is 479,001,600; duodecimally, *114,500,000*. The saving of work in using the second figure need hardly be emphasized. In fact, as soon as a table of factorials was made, it was at once found easier to work duodecimally rather than, as we had been doing, decimally with subsequent conversion.

The fact that the reciprocal factorials up to *4* are all one figure decimals and that those up to *6* are expressed as fractions with only one significant figure shortens the work of calculating, for instance, the sines and cosines of angles in circular measure.

Reciprocals

There is a point concerning reciprocals which may be of more theoretical than practical interest, though I have found it of use when a considerable number of places of reciprocals was needed to calculate Euler's constant.

The reciprocal of any prime number except *2* or *3* is a recurring decimal which recurs on a number of places one less than the prime number or on a simple fraction of this number. For instance, the reciprocal of *5* is a four-place recurring duodecimal, the reciprocal of *7* is a six-place recurring duodecimal.

I give for comparison the number of places in the recurring decimals and duodecimals produced by the primes up to one gross. In the decimal table, the primes end *1*, *3*, *7* or *9*, any of which endings may or may not produce the full number of places of recurrence. In the duodecimal table, the primes end *1*, *5*, *7* or *Ɛ*, of which only those ending *5* or *7* may produce the full number of places.

Reciprocals of Prime Numbers

Number of places in the Recurring Decimal

Decimal		Duodecimal	
Prime	**Places**	**Prime**	**Places**
3	1	*3*	-
5	-	*5*	*4*
7	6	*7*	*6*
11	2	*Ɛ*	*1*
13	6	*11*	*2*
17	16	*15*	*14*
19	18	*17*	*6*
23	22	*1Ɛ*	*Ɛ*
29	28	*25*	*4*
31	15	*27*	*26*
37	3	*31*	*9*
41	5	*35*	*34*
43	21	*37*	*36*
47	46	*3Ɛ*	*1Ɛ*
53	13	*45*	*44*
59	58	*4Ɛ*	*25*
61	60	*51*	*13*
67	33	*57*	*56*
71	35	*5Ɛ*	*2Ɛ*
73	8	*61*	*30*
79	13	*67*	*22*
83	41	*6Ɛ*	*35*
89	44	*75*	*8*
97	96	*81*	*14*
101	4	*85*	*84*
103	34	*87*	*86*
107	53	*8Ɛ*	*45*
109	108	*91*	*46*
113	112	*95*	*94*
127	42	*X7*	*X6*
131	130	*XƐ*	*55*
137	8	*Ɛ5*	*Ɛ4*
139	46	*Ɛ7*	*Ɛ6*

Interpolation

From the experience gained in making the tables in this book it appears that duodecimal interpolation is likely to be found easier than decimal interpolation because the coefficients are usually shorter.

For instance, Everett coefficients for second differences are:-

	Duodecimal	Decimal
Interval one quarter	.07X6	.0546875
	.0576	.0390625
Interval one half	.09	.0625

Everett coefficients for fourth differences:-

Interval one quarter	.0142XX6	.00939 94140 625
	.0113576	.00769 04296 875
Interval one half	.0183	.01171 875

Similarly, the Bessel coefficients for average second differences for an interval of one quarter are:-

	.116	.09375
For an interval of one half	.16	.125

For average fourth difference:-

For an interval of one half	.0346	.02343 75

These were the intervals most frequently used in the work which has been done and they may perhaps unduly favor the duodecimal system.

Six point Lagrange coefficients for interpolating without differences are, for an interval of one half:-

Multiply V_{-2} by	+ .0183	+ .01171 875
Multiply V_{-1} by	- .1209	- .09765 625
Multiply V_0 by	+ .7046	+ .58593 75
Multiply V_1 by	+ .7046	+ .58593 75
Multiply V_2 by	- .1209	- .09765 625
Multiply V_3 by	+ .0183	+ .01171 875

It is also probable that as we deal with more complex formulae the saving of work is relatively greater. For instance, the expression for the factorial or gamma function expressed decimally is:-

$$(x)! = \sqrt{2\pi} \cdot e^{-x} \cdot x^{x+\frac{1}{2}} \left[1 + \frac{1}{12x} + \frac{1}{288x^2} - \frac{139}{51840x^3} - \frac{571}{2488320x^4} + \frac{163879}{209018880x^5} + \text{etc.}\right]$$

Expressed duodecimally, the contents of the bracket becomes:-

$$\left[1 + \frac{1}{10x} + \frac{1}{200x^2} - \frac{\text{Ɛ}7}{26{,}000x^3} - \frac{3\text{Ɛ}7}{\text{X}00{,}000x^4} + \frac{7\text{XX}07}{5\text{X}{,}000{,}000x^5} + \text{etc.}\right]$$

The Circle

It is perhaps strange that, since the circle has always been divided semi-duodecimally, namely, into thirty dozen degrees and subsequently five dozen minutes, five dozen seconds, that it has not appeared desirable to divide it completely duodecimally, not necessarily with a view towards the adoption of the system, but for experiment, to find out whether it might be convenient for computation.

That it is a very convenient form of division has been quite clearly demonstrated in the work which we have done. That the present systems do not quite satisfy the existing scheme of things is clear from the diversity of approach to the problem at the present time.

The two usual methods of dividing the circle now in use are (1) to degrees, minutes and seconds and decimals of a second; (2) to degrees and decimals of a degree.

The fact that there are two methods has practical disadvantages, apart from the work of converting from one to the other, for it is difficult to compare the results given in tables of the trigonometrical functions under the two systems and requires double work to check the value for any desired angle interpolated from each table. I speak of this feelingly, having performed this work in the construction of the tables which I give for the duodecimal circle.

Things would be simpler if there were one universal system, so I feel doubly apologetic for suggesting a third. I would not do so, were it not for the fact that the duodecimal division of the circle seems to be one of the chief reasons why it may be worthwhile to experiment with the system as a whole.

There are certain obvious advantages in dividing the circle duodecimally and expressing results in terms of the circle itself rather than in any subdivision, notably the fact that angle and time are expressed by the same duodecimal, the longitude of Washington, for instance, measured from Greenwich being the same as the time interval between them. At present the longitude may be expressed in angle as

77 degrees 3 minutes 1.476 seconds;

or in time as:

5 hours 8 minutes 12.098 seconds;

and it is not obvious that these two values express the same thing, nor is the error between the two results apparent. Duodecimally, the above results are:-

.269 X12 Ɛ07
.269 X12 XX7

From the point of view of computations there is a simplification if we have to deal with angle in connection with its trigonometrical function, or the logarithm of the angle in connection with its logarithmic function. There is, I believe, in any computation less chance of error because there are no conversions.

Let there be what commercial or practical subdivisions you will; for calculations, there need be one unit only, namely, the circle, whether we deal with time or with angle. Here, again, we are so accustomed to conversion of hours to degrees or vice versa, and to double entries giving both hours and minutes or degrees and minutes that it may appear of no particular value to avoid this continual transposition. Certainly I am in no position to offer an opinion on either navigation or astronomy. I give the tables in the hope that in the future someone may find them a saving of labor, which I am rash enough to believe that in time they will.

The tables of the higher mathematical functions such as Digamma, Exponential integrals, etc., are obviously too short to be at all comprehensive, but it has not been possible to include more within the reasonable limits of one volume. It is hoped that enough has been given to provoke a study of the advantages of the numerical system in the summation of power factorial series. The advantage is due to the shortness of the earlier terms, as for instance in the Bessel coefficients for *.55*.

J_0		J_1
+	*1.0*	
	.286	+
-	*74 03*	
	9 Ɛ24 09	-
+	*1 154 Ɛ00 23*	
	101 873 220 5	+
-	*χ Ɛ67 285 6*	
	750 χ18 6	-
+	*50 384 5*	
	2 880 0	+
-	*158 4*	
	8 0	-
+	*4*	

Aside from this advantage in the construction of the tables there is a real advantage in their use, which may be observed from their comparison with corresponding decimal tables. For instance, the nine place Digamma table has a fourth difference at *0* of about *210*. The corresponding nine place decimal table at this point has a fourth difference of about 250. When it is remembered that the nine place duodecimal table corresponds in accuracy much more nearly with a ten place decimal table than with a nine, the real saving of work in using duodecimal tables will be seen. This advantage is due to the cumulative effect of the smaller interval of tabulation.

The tables have been prepared with care. No table is presented which has not been computed and subtracted out at least to three more places than those given. I shall be grateful for having my attention drawn to errors occurring in the book and for criticism of the method of presentation. I am deeply indebted to those friends who have helped me with the work for their loyal support and for their belief in the potential value of an untried system to research in the future.

George S. Terry

Hingham, Massachusetts December, 1937

Notation

1 2 3 4 5 6 7 8 9 X Ɛ 10

15 represents a dozen and five
324 represents three gross, two dozen and four

Nomenclature

In preparing this work it has been necessary to have names for the new digits and to use them continuously.

The system suggested by Andrews in "New Numbers" has been followed as closely as possible, the only changes being:-

1. It was found easier to call Ɛ "el" rather than "elf."

2. The use of eleven and twelve was found confusing and it seemed better to follow the alternative system given by Andrews counting as follows:-

   dec (*X*) el (*Ɛ*) do (*10*) do-one (*11*) do-two (*12*)
   do-dec (*1X*) do-el (*1Ɛ*) two-do (*20*) two-do-one (*21*)
   dec-do (*X0*) el-do (*Ɛ0*) gro (*1000*) and me-gro (*10,000*)

Addition

$$\begin{array}{r} 2 \\ \underline{7} \\ 9 \end{array} \qquad \begin{array}{r} 7 \\ \underline{8} \\ 13 \end{array} \qquad \begin{array}{r} 235 \\ \underline{X1Ɛ} \\ 1054 \end{array}$$

Subtraction

$$\begin{array}{r} 7 \\ \underline{2} \\ 5 \end{array} \qquad \begin{array}{r} 11 \\ \underline{6} \\ 7 \end{array} \qquad \begin{array}{r} 447 \\ \underline{1ƐX} \\ 249 \end{array}$$

Multiplication Table

2 × 1 = 2	3 × 1 = 3	4 × 1 = 4	5 × 1 = 5	6 × 1 = 6
2 = 4	2 = 6	2 = 8	2 = χ	2 = 10
3 = 6	3 = 9	3 = 10	3 = 13	3 = 16
4 = 8	4 = 10	4 = 14	4 = 18	4 = 20
5 = χ	5 = 13	5 = 18	5 = 21	5 = 26
6 = 10	6 = 16	6 = 20	6 = 26	6 = 30
7 = 12	7 = 19	7 = 24	7 = 2Ɛ	7 = 36
8 = 14	8 = 20	8 = 28	8 = 34	8 = 40
9 = 16	9 = 23	9 = 30	9 = 39	9 = 46
χ = 18	χ = 26	χ = 34	χ = 42	χ = 50
Ɛ = 1χ	Ɛ = 29	Ɛ = 38	Ɛ = 47	Ɛ = 56
7 × 1 = 7	8 × 1 = 8	9 × 1 = 9	χ × 1 = χ	Ɛ × 1 = Ɛ
2 = 12	2 = 14	2 = 16	2 = 18	2 = 1χ
3 = 19	3 = 20	3 = 23	3 = 26	3 = 29
4 = 24	4 = 28	4 = 30	4 = 34	4 = 38
5 = 2Ɛ	5 = 34	5 = 39	5 = 42	5 = 47
6 = 36	6 = 40	6 = 46	6 = 50	6 = 56
7 = 41	7 = 48	7 = 53	7 = 5χ	7 = 65
8 = 48	8 = 54	8 = 60	8 = 68	8 = 74
9 = 53	9 = 60	9 = 69	9 = 76	9 = 83
χ = 5χ	χ = 68	χ = 76	χ = 84	χ = 92
Ɛ = 65	Ɛ = 74	Ɛ = 83	Ɛ = 92	Ɛ = χ1

Multiplication

```
 371        4Ɛ2        2419
   2          8           Ɛ
 ---       ----       -----
 722       3354       21973
```

Division

```
2)722      8)3354      Ɛ)21973
  371         4Ɛ2         2419
```

Conversion of Whole Numbers

Decimal to Duodecimal

Example:

Find the duodecimal equivalent of 10 38623

Divide decimally, extracting the remainder

12) 10 38623

12) 86551 + *Ɛ*

12) 7212 + *7*

12) 601 + *0*

12) 50 + *1*

12) 4 + *2*

0 + *4*

Answer *421 07Ɛ*

Duodecimal to Decimal

Example:

Find the decimal equivalent of *4 2 1 0 7 Ɛ*

Divide duodecimally, extracting the remainder

χ) *4 2 1 0 7 Ɛ*

χ) *5 0 1 3 2* + 3

χ) *6 0 1 6* + 2

χ) *7 2 6* + 6

χ) *8 7* + 8

χ) *χ* + 3

χ) *1* + 0

0 + 1

Answer 10 38623

Conversion Table - Whole Numbers

Decimal to Duodecimal

0	0	50	42	100	84	150	106	200	148	250	18χ	300	210	350	252	400	294
1	1	1	3	1	5	1	7	1	9	1	Ɛ	1	1	1	3	1	5
2	2	2	4	2	6	2	8	2	χ	2	190	2	2	2	4	2	6
3	3	3	5	3	7	3	9	3	Ɛ	3	1	3	3	3	5	3	7
4	4	4	6	4	8	4	χ	4	150	4	2	4	4	4	6	4	8
5	5	5	7	5	9	5	Ɛ	5	1	5	3	5	5	5	7	5	9
6	6	6	8	6	χ	6	110	6	2	6	4	6	6	6	8	6	χ
7	7	7	9	7	Ɛ	7	1	7	3	7	5	7	7	7	9	7	Ɛ
8	8	8	χ	8	90	8	2	8	4	8	6	8	8	8	χ	8	2χ0
9	9	9	Ɛ	9	1	9	3	9	5	9	7	9	9	9	Ɛ	9	1
10	χ	60	50	110	2	160	4	210	6	260	8	310	χ	360	260	410	2
1	Ɛ	1	1	1	3	1	5	1	7	1	9	1	Ɛ	1	1	1	3
2	10	2	2	2	4	2	6	2	8	2	χ	2	220	2	2	2	4
3	1	3	3	3	5	3	7	3	9	3	Ɛ	3	1	3	3	3	5
4	2	4	4	4	6	4	8	4	χ	4	1χ0	4	2	4	4	4	6
5	3	5	5	5	7	5	9	5	Ɛ	5	1	5	3	5	5	5	7
6	4	6	6	6	8	6	χ	6	160	6	2	6	4	6	6	6	8
7	5	7	7	7	9	7	Ɛ	7	1	7	3	7	5	7	7	7	9
8	6	8	8	8	χ	8	120	8	2	8	4	8	6	8	8	8	χ
9	7	9	9	9	Ɛ	9	1	9	3	9	5	9	7	9	9	9	Ɛ
20	8	70	χ	120	χ0	170	2	220	4	270	6	320	8	370	χ	420	2Ɛ0
1	9	1	Ɛ	1	1	1	3	1	5	1	7	1	9	1	Ɛ	1	1
2	χ	2	60	2	2	2	4	2	6	2	8	2	χ	2	270	2	2
3	Ɛ	3	1	3	3	3	5	3	7	3	9	3	Ɛ	3	1	3	3
4	20	4	2	4	4	4	6	4	8	4	χ	4	230	4	2	4	4
5	1	5	3	5	5	5	7	5	9	5	Ɛ	5	1	5	3	5	5
6	2	6	4	6	6	6	8	6	χ	6	1Ɛ0	6	2	6	4	6	6
7	3	7	5	7	7	7	9	7	Ɛ	7	1	7	3	7	5	7	7
8	4	8	6	8	8	8	χ	8	170	8	2	8	4	8	6	8	8
9	5	9	7	9	9	9	Ɛ	9	1	9	3	9	5	9	7	9	9
30	6	80	8	130	χ	180	130	230	2	280	4	330	6	380	8	430	χ
1	7	1	9	1	Ɛ	1	1	1	3	1	5	1	7	1	9	1	Ɛ
2	8	2	χ	2	Ɛ0	2	2	2	4	2	6	2	8	2	χ	2	300
3	9	3	Ɛ	3	1	3	3	3	5	3	7	3	9	3	Ɛ	3	1
4	χ	4	70	4	2	4	4	4	6	4	8	4	χ	4	280	4	2
5	Ɛ	5	1	5	3	5	5	5	7	5	9	5	Ɛ	5	1	5	3
6	30	6	2	6	4	6	6	6	8	6	χ	6	240	6	2	6	4
7	1	7	3	7	5	7	7	7	9	7	Ɛ	7	1	7	3	7	5
8	2	8	4	8	6	8	8	8	χ	8	200	8	2	8	4	8	6
9	3	9	5	9	7	9	9	9	Ɛ	9	1	9	3	9	5	9	7
40	4	90	6	140	8	190	χ	240	180	290	2	340	4	390	6	440	8
1	5	1	7	1	9	1	Ɛ	1	1	1	3	1	5	1	7	1	9
2	6	2	8	2	χ	2	140	2	2	2	4	2	6	2	8	2	χ
3	7	3	9	3	Ɛ	3	1	3	3	3	5	3	7	3	9	3	Ɛ
4	8	4	χ	4	100	4	2	4	4	4	6	4	8	4	χ	4	310
5	9	5	Ɛ	5	1	5	3	5	5	5	7	5	9	5	Ɛ	5	1
6	χ	6	80	6	2	6	4	6	6	6	8	6	χ	6	290	6	2
7	Ɛ	7	1	7	3	7	5	7	7	7	9	7	Ɛ	7	1	7	3
8	40	8	2	8	4	8	6	8	8	8	χ	8	250	8	2	8	4
9	1	9	3	9	5	9	7	9	9	9	Ɛ	9	1	9	3	9	5

Conversion Table - Whole Numbers

Decimal to Duodecimal

450	316	500	358	550	39X	600	420	650	462	700	4X4	750	526	800	568	850	5XX
1	7	1	9	1	Ɛ	1	1	1	3	1	5	1	7	1	9	1	Ɛ
2	8	2	X	2	3X0	2	2	2	4	2	6	2	8	2	X	2	5Ɛ0
3	9	3	Ɛ	3	1	3	3	3	5	3	7	3	9	3	Ɛ	3	1
4	X	4	360	4	2	4	4	4	6	4	8	4	X	4	570	4	2
5	Ɛ	5	1	5	3	5	5	5	7	5	9	5	Ɛ	5	1	5	3
6	320	6	2	6	4	6	6	6	8	6	X	6	530	6	2	6	4
7	1	7	3	7	5	7	7	7	9	7	Ɛ	7	1	7	3	7	5
8	2	8	4	8	6	8	8	8	X	8	4Ɛ0	8	2	8	4	8	6
9	3	9	5	9	7	9	9	9	Ɛ	9	1	9	3	9	5	9	7
460	4	510	6	560	8	610	X	660	470	710	2	760	4	810	6	860	8
1	5	1	7	1	9	1	Ɛ	1	1	1	3	1	5	1	7	1	9
2	6	2	8	2	X	2	430	2	2	2	4	2	6	2	8	2	X
3	7	3	9	3	Ɛ	3	1	3	3	3	5	3	7	3	9	3	Ɛ
4	8	4	X	4	3Ɛ0	4	2	4	4	4	6	4	8	4	X	4	600
5	9	5	Ɛ	5	1	5	3	5	5	5	7	5	9	5	Ɛ	5	1
6	X	6	370	6	2	6	4	6	6	6	8	6	X	6	580	6	2
7	Ɛ	7	1	7	3	7	5	7	7	7	9	7	Ɛ	7	1	7	3
8	330	8	2	8	4	8	6	8	8	8	X	8	540	8	2	8	4
9	1	9	3	9	5	9	7	9	9	9	Ɛ	9	1	9	3	9	5
470	2	520	4	570	6	620	8	670	X	720	500	770	2	820	4	870	6
1	3	1	5	1	7	1	9	1	Ɛ	1	1	1	3	1	5	1	7
2	4	2	6	2	8	2	X	2	480	2	2	2	4	2	6	2	8
3	5	3	7	3	9	3	Ɛ	3	1	3	3	3	5	3	7	3	9
4	6	4	8	4	X	4	440	4	2	4	4	4	6	4	8	4	X
5	7	5	9	5	Ɛ	5	1	5	3	5	5	5	7	5	9	5	Ɛ
6	8	6	X	6	400	6	2	6	4	6	6	6	8	6	X	6	610
7	9	7	Ɛ	7	1	7	3	7	5	7	7	7	9	7	Ɛ	7	1
8	X	8	380	8	2	8	4	8	6	8	8	8	X	8	590	8	2
9	Ɛ	9	1	9	3	9	5	9	7	9	9	9	Ɛ	9	1	9	3
480	340	530	2	580	4	630	6	680	8	730	X	780	550	830	2	880	4
1	1	1	3	1	5	1	7	1	9	1	Ɛ	1	1	1	3	1	5
2	2	2	4	2	6	2	8	2	X	2	510	2	2	2	4	2	6
3	3	3	5	3	7	3	9	3	Ɛ	3	1	3	3	3	5	3	7
4	4	4	6	4	8	4	X	4	490	4	2	4	4	4	6	4	8
5	5	5	7	5	9	5	Ɛ	5	1	5	3	5	5	5	7	5	9
6	6	6	8	6	X	6	450	6	2	6	4	6	6	6	8	6	X
7	7	7	9	7	Ɛ	7	1	7	3	7	5	7	7	7	9	7	Ɛ
8	8	8	X	8	410	8	2	8	4	8	6	8	8	8	X	8	620
9	9	9	Ɛ	9	1	9	3	9	5	9	7	9	9	9	Ɛ	9	1
490	X	540	390	590	2	640	4	690	6	740	8	790	X	840	5X0	890	2
1	Ɛ	1	1	1	3	1	5	1	7	1	9	1	Ɛ	1	1	1	3
2	350	2	2	2	4	2	6	2	8	2	X	2	560	2	2	2	4
3	1	3	3	3	5	3	7	3	9	3	Ɛ	3	1	3	3	3	5
4	2	4	4	4	6	4	8	4	X	4	520	4	2	4	4	4	6
5	3	5	5	5	7	5	9	5	Ɛ	5	1	5	3	5	5	5	7
6	4	6	6	6	8	6	X	6	4X0	6	2	6	4	6	6	6	8
7	5	7	7	7	9	7	Ɛ	7	1	7	3	7	5	7	7	7	9
8	6	8	8	8	X	8	460	8	2	8	4	8	6	8	8	8	X
9	7	9	9	9	Ɛ	9	1	9	3	9	5	9	7	9	9	9	Ɛ

Conversion Table - Whole Numbers

Decimal to Duodecimal

900	630	950	672	1000	6Ɛ4	1050	736	1100	778	1150	7ƐX	1200	840	1250	882
1	1	1	3	1	5	1	7	1	9	1	Ɛ	1	1	1	3
2	2	2	4	2	6	2	8	2	X	2	800	2	2	2	4
3	3	3	5	3	7	3	9	3	Ɛ	3	1	3	3	3	5
4	4	4	6	4	8	4	X	4	780	4	2	4	4	4	6
5	5	5	7	5	9	5	Ɛ	5	1	5	3	5	5	5	7
6	6	6	8	6	X	6	740	6	2	6	4	6	6	6	8
7	7	7	9	7	Ɛ	7	1	7	3	7	5	7	7	7	9
8	8	8	X	8	700	8	2	8	4	8	6	8	8	8	X
9	9	9	Ɛ	9	1	9	3	9	5	9	7	9	9	9	Ɛ
910	X	960	680	1010	2	1060	4	1110	6	1160	8	1210	X	1260	890
1	Ɛ	1	1	1	3	1	5	1	7	1	9	1	Ɛ	1	1
2	640	2	2	2	4	2	6	2	8	2	X	2	850	2	2
3	1	3	3	3	5	3	7	3	9	3	Ɛ	3	1	3	3
4	2	4	4	4	6	4	8	4	X	4	810	4	2	4	4
5	3	5	5	5	7	5	9	5	Ɛ	5	1	5	3	5	5
6	4	6	6	6	8	6	X	6	790	6	2	6	4	6	6
7	5	7	7	7	9	7	Ɛ	7	1	7	3	7	5	7	7
8	6	8	8	8	X	8	750	8	2	8	4	8	6	8	8
9	7	9	9	9	Ɛ	9	1	9	3	9	5	9	7	9	9
920	8	970	X	1020	710	1070	2	1120	4	1170	6	1220	8	1270	X
1	9	1	Ɛ	1	1	1	3	1	5	1	7	1	9	1	Ɛ
2	X	2	690	2	2	2	4	2	6	2	8	2	X	2	8X0
3	Ɛ	3	1	3	3	3	5	3	7	3	9	3	Ɛ	3	1
4	650	4	2	4	4	4	6	4	8	4	X	4	860	4	2
5	1	5	3	5	5	5	7	5	9	5	Ɛ	5	1	5	3
6	2	6	4	6	6	6	8	6	X	6	820	6	2	6	4
7	3	7	5	7	7	7	9	7	Ɛ	7	1	7	3	7	5
8	4	8	6	8	8	8	X	8	7X0	8	2	8	4	8	6
9	5	9	7	9	9	9	Ɛ	9	1	9	3	9	5	9	7
930	6	980	8	1030	X	1080	760	1130	2	1180	4	1230	6	1280	8
1	7	1	9	1	Ɛ	1	1	1	3	1	5	1	7	1	9
2	8	2	X	2	720	2	2	2	4	2	6	2	8	2	X
3	9	3	Ɛ	3	1	3	3	3	5	3	7	3	9	3	Ɛ
4	X	4	6X0	4	2	4	4	4	6	4	8	4	X	4	8Ɛ0
5	Ɛ	5	1	5	3	5	5	5	7	5	9	5	Ɛ	5	1
6	660	6	2	6	4	6	6	6	8	6	X	6	870	6	2
7	1	7	3	7	5	7	7	7	9	7	Ɛ	7	1	7	3
8	2	8	4	8	6	8	8	8	X	8	830	8	2	8	4
9	3	9	5	9	7	9	9	9	Ɛ	9	1	9	3	9	5
940	4	990	6	1040	8	1090	X	1140	7Ɛ0	1190	2	1240	4	1290	6
1	5	1	7	1	9	1	Ɛ	1	1	1	3	1	5	1	7
2	6	2	8	2	X	2	770	2	2	2	4	2	6	2	8
3	7	3	9	3	Ɛ	3	1	3	3	3	5	3	7	3	9
4	8	4	X	4	730	4	2	4	4	4	6	4	8	4	X
5	9	5	Ɛ	5	1	5	3	5	5	5	7	5	9	5	Ɛ
6	X	6	6Ɛ0	6	2	6	4	6	6	6	8	6	X	6	900
7	Ɛ	7	1	7	3	7	5	7	7	7	9	7	Ɛ	7	1
8	670	8	2	8	4	8	6	8	8	8	X	8	880	8	2
9	1	9	3	9	5	9	7	9	9	9	Ɛ	9	1	9	3

Conversion Table - Whole Numbers

Decimal to Duodecimal

1300	904	1350	946	1400	988	1450	X0X	1500	X50	1550	X92	1600	Ɛ14	1650	Ɛ56	1700	Ɛ98
1	5	1	7	1	9	1	Ɛ	1	1	1	3	1	5	1	7	1	9
2	6	2	8	2	X	2	X10	2	2	2	4	2	6	2	8	2	X
3	7	3	9	3	Ɛ	3	1	3	3	3	5	3	7	3	9	3	Ɛ
4	8	4	X	4	990	4	2	4	4	4	6	4	8	4	X	4	ƐX0
5	9	5	Ɛ	5	1	5	3	5	5	5	7	5	9	5	Ɛ	5	1
6	X	6	950	6	2	6	4	6	6	6	8	6	X	6	Ɛ60	6	2
7	Ɛ	7	1	7	3	7	5	7	7	7	9	7	Ɛ	7	1	7	3
8	910	8	2	8	4	8	6	8	8	8	X	8	Ɛ20	8	2	8	4
9	1	9	3	9	5	9	7	9	9	9	Ɛ	9	1	9	3	9	5
1310	2	1360	4	1410	6	1460	8	1510	X	1560	XX0	1610	2	1660	4	1710	6
1	3	1	5	1	7	1	9	1	Ɛ	1	1	1	3	1	5	1	7
2	4	2	6	2	8	2	X	2	X60	2	2	2	4	2	6	2	8
3	5	3	7	3	9	3	Ɛ	3	1	3	3	3	5	3	7	3	9
4	6	4	8	4	X	4	X20	4	2	4	4	4	6	4	8	4	X
5	7	5	9	5	Ɛ	5	1	5	3	5	5	5	7	5	9	5	Ɛ
6	8	6	X	6	9X0	6	2	6	4	6	6	6	8	6	X	6	ƐƐ0
7	9	7	Ɛ	7	1	7	3	7	5	7	7	7	9	7	Ɛ	7	1
8	X	8	960	8	2	8	4	8	6	8	8	8	X	8	Ɛ70	8	2
9	Ɛ	9	1	9	3	9	5	9	7	9	9	9	Ɛ	9	1	9	3
1320	920	1370	2	1420	4	1470	6	1520	8	1570	X	1620	Ɛ30	1670	2	1720	4
1	1	1	3	1	5	1	7	1	9	1	Ɛ	1	1	1	3	1	5
2	2	2	4	2	6	2	8	2	X	2	XƐ0	2	2	2	4	2	6
3	3	3	5	3	7	3	9	3	Ɛ	3	1	3	3	3	5	3	7
4	4	4	6	4	8	4	X	4	X70	4	2	4	4	4	6	4	8
5	5	5	7	5	9	5	Ɛ	5	1	5	3	5	5	5	7	5	9
6	6	6	8	6	X	6	X30	6	2	6	4	6	6	6	8	6	X
7	7	7	9	7	Ɛ	7	1	7	3	7	5	7	7	7	9	7	ƐƐƐ
8	8	8	X	8	9Ɛ0	8	2	8	4	8	6	8	8	8	X		
9	9	9	Ɛ	9	1	9	3	9	5	9	7	9	9	9	Ɛ		
1330	X	1380	970	1430	2	1480	4	1530	6	1580	8	1630	X	1680	Ɛ80		
1	Ɛ	1	1	1	3	1	5	1	7	1	9	1	Ɛ	1	1		
2	930	2	2	2	4	2	6	2	8	2	X	2	Ɛ40	2	2		
3	1	3	3	3	5	3	7	3	9	3	Ɛ	3	1	3	3		
4	2	4	4	4	6	4	8	4	X	4	Ɛ00	4	2	4	4		
5	3	5	5	5	7	5	9	5	Ɛ	5	1	5	3	5	5		
6	4	6	6	6	8	6	X	6	X80	6	2	6	4	6	6		
7	5	7	7	7	9	7	Ɛ	7	1	7	3	7	5	7	7		
8	6	8	8	8	X	8	X40	8	2	8	4	8	6	8	8		
9	7	9	9	9	Ɛ	9	1	9	3	9	5	9	7	9	9		
1340	8	1390	X	1440	X00	1490	2	1540	4	1590	6	1640	8	1690	X		
1	9	1	Ɛ	1	1	1	3	1	5	1	7	1	9	1	Ɛ		
2	X	2	980	2	2	2	4	2	6	2	8	2	X	2	Ɛ90		
3	Ɛ	3	1	3	3	3	5	3	7	3	9	3	Ɛ	3	1		
4	940	4	2	4	4	4	6	4	8	4	X	4	Ɛ50	4	2		
5	1	5	3	5	5	5	7	5	9	5	Ɛ	5	1	5	3		
6	2	6	4	6	6	6	8	6	X	6	Ɛ10	6	2	6	4		
7	3	7	5	7	7	7	9	7	Ɛ	7	1	7	3	7	5		
8	4	8	6	8	8	8	X	8	X90	8	2	8	4	8	6		
9	5	9	7	9	9	9	Ɛ	9	1	9	3	9	5	9	7		

Conversion of Decimals to Duodecimals

Example: Find the duodecimal equivalent of .1

Multiply decimally, extracting the whole number

```
      .1
      12
  1)  .2
      12
  2)  .4
      12
  4)  .8
      12
  9)  .6
      12
  7)  .2
      12
  2)  .4
```

Answer $.12\dot{4}\ 9\dot{7}$

Conversion of Duodecimals to Decimals

Example: Find the decimal equivalent of .1

Multiply duodecimally, extracting the whole number

```
      .1
       χ
  0)  .χ
       χ
  8)  .4
       χ
  3)  .4
       χ
  3)  .4
```

Answer $.08\dot{3}$

Conversion of Decimals to Duodecimals

Multiplication Method

Using the three place conversion table for whole numbers and for decimals.

Example:

Find the duodecimal equivalent of.11577 17827

Multiply the decimal by 1728 and convert the whole number from the whole number conversion table for the first three places.

Multiply the remaining decimal by 1728 and convert the whole number for the next three places.

Convert the remaining decimal from the decimal conversion table.

.11577 17827
1728
1 4 8 = 200) .05364 05056
1728
0 7 8 = 92) .69079 etc. = *8 3 5*

Answer *.148 078 835*

Conversion of Duodecimals to Decimals

Example:

Find the decimal equivalent of *.1 4 8 0 7 8 8 3 5*

Multiply duodecimally by *6 ℰ 4* and proceed as above.

.1 4 8 0 7 8 8 3 5
6 ℰ 4
115 = *9 7*) *.9 3 1 7 8 2 4 8 8*
6 ℰ 4
771 = *5 4 3*) *.9 4 8 3 3* etc. = 783

Answer .11577 1783

Conversion Table - Decimals to Duodecimals

Decimal	0	1	2	3	4	5	6	7	8	9
.00	.000	.002	.003	.005	.007	.009	.00X	.010	.012	.014
1	.015	.017	.019	.01X	.020	.022	.024	.025	.027	.029
2	.02Ɛ	.030	.032	.034	.035	.037	.039	.03Ɛ	.040	.042
3	.044	.046	.047	.049	.04Ɛ	.050	.052	.054	.056	.057
4	.059	.05Ɛ	.061	.062	.064	.066	.067	.069	.06Ɛ	.071
5	.072	.074	.076	.078	.079	.07Ɛ	.081	.082	.084	.086
6	.088	.089	.08Ɛ	.091	.093	.094	.096	.098	.09X	.09Ɛ
7	.0X1	.0X3	.0X4	.0X6	.0X8	.0XX	.0XƐ	.0Ɛ1	.0Ɛ3	.0Ɛ5
8	.0Ɛ6	.0Ɛ8	.0ƐX	.0ƐƐ	.101	.103	.105	.106	.108	.10X
9	.110	.111	.113	.115	.116	.118	.11X	.120	.121	.123
.10	.125	.127	.128	.12X	.130	.131	.133	.135	.137	.138
1	.13X	.140	.142	.143	.145	.147	.148	.14X	.150	.152
2	.153	.155	.157	.159	.15X	.160	.162	.163	.165	.167
3	.169	.16X	.170	.172	.174	.175	.177	.179	.17X	.180
4	.182	.184	.185	.187	.189	.18Ɛ	.190	.192	.194	.195
5	.197	.199	.19Ɛ	.1X0	.1X2	.1X4	.1X6	.1X7	.1X9	.1XƐ
6	.1Ɛ0	.1Ɛ2	.1Ɛ4	.1Ɛ6	.1Ɛ7	.1Ɛ9	.1ƐƐ	.201	.202	.204
7	.206	.207	.209	.20Ɛ	.211	.212	.214	.216	.218	.219
8	.21Ɛ	.221	.222	.224	.226	.228	.229	.22Ɛ	.231	.233
9	.234	.236	.238	.23X	.23Ɛ	.241	.243	.244	.246	.248
.20	.24X	.24Ɛ	.251	.253	.255	.256	.258	.25X	.25Ɛ	.261
1	.263	.265	.266	.268	.26X	.270	.271	.273	.275	.276
2	.278	.27X	.280	.281	.283	.285	.287	.288	.28X	.290
3	.291	.293	.295	.297	.298	.29X	.2X0	.2X2	.2X3	.2X5
4	.2X7	.2X8	.2XX	.2Ɛ0	.2Ɛ2	.2Ɛ3	.2Ɛ5	.2Ɛ7	.2Ɛ9	.2ƐX
5	.300	.302	.303	.305	.307	.309	.30X	.310	.312	.314
6	.315	.317	.319	.31X	.320	.322	.324	.325	.327	.329
7	.32Ɛ	.330	.332	.334	.335	.337	.339	.33Ɛ	.340	.342
8	.344	.346	.347	.349	.34Ɛ	.350	.352	.354	.356	.357
9	.359	.35Ɛ	.361	.362	.364	.366	.367	.369	.36Ɛ	.371
.30	.372	.374	.376	.378	.379	.37Ɛ	.381	.382	.384	.386
1	.388	.389	.38Ɛ	.391	.393	.394	.396	.398	.39X	.39Ɛ
2	.3X1	.3X3	.3X4	.3X6	.3X8	.3XX	.3XƐ	.3Ɛ1	.3Ɛ3	.3Ɛ5
3	.3Ɛ6	.3Ɛ8	.3ƐX	.3ƐƐ	.401	.403	.405	.406	.408	.40X
4	.410	.411	.413	.415	.416	.418	.41X	.420	.421	.423
5	.425	.427	.428	.42X	.430	.431	.433	.435	.437	.438
6	.43X	.440	.442	.443	.445	.447	.448	.44X	.450	.452
7	.453	.455	.457	.459	.45X	.460	.462	.463	.465	.467
8	.469	.46X	.470	.472	.474	.475	.477	.479	.47X	.480
9	.482	.484	.485	.487	.489	.48Ɛ	.490	.492	.494	.495
.40	.497	.499	.49Ɛ	.4X0	.4X2	.4X4	.4X6	.4X7	.4X9	.4XƐ
1	.4Ɛ0	.4Ɛ2	.4Ɛ4	.4Ɛ6	.4Ɛ7	.4Ɛ9	.4ƐƐ	.501	.502	.504
2	.506	.507	.509	.50Ɛ	.511	.512	.514	.516	.518	.519
3	.51Ɛ	.521	.522	.524	.526	.528	.529	.52Ɛ	.531	.533
4	.534	.536	.538	.53X	.53Ɛ	.541	.543	.544	.546	.548
5	.54X	.54Ɛ	.551	.553	.555	.556	.558	.55X	.55Ɛ	.561
6	.563	.565	.566	.568	.56X	.570	.571	.573	.575	.576
7	.578	.57X	.580	.581	.583	.585	.587	.588	.58X	.590
8	.591	.593	.595	.597	.598	.59X	.5X0	.5X2	.5X3	.5X5
9	.5X7	.5X8	.5XX	.5Ɛ0	.5Ɛ2	.5Ɛ3	.5Ɛ5	.5Ɛ7	.5Ɛ9	.5ƐX

Conversion Table - Decimals to Duodecimals

Decimal	0	1	2	3	4	5	6	7	8	9
.50	.600	.602	.603	.605	.607	.609	.60X	.610	.612	.614
1	.615	.617	.619	.61X	.620	.622	.624	.625	.627	.629
2	.62Ɛ	.630	.632	.634	.635	.637	.639	.63Ɛ	.640	.642
3	.644	.646	.647	.649	.64Ɛ	.650	.652	.654	.656	.657
4	.659	.65Ɛ	.661	.662	.664	.666	.667	.669	.66Ɛ	.671
5	.672	.674	.676	.678	.679	.67Ɛ	.681	.682	.684	.686
6	.688	.689	.68Ɛ	.691	.693	.694	.696	.698	.69X	.69Ɛ
7	.6X1	.6X3	.6X4	.6X6	.6X8	.6XX	.6XƐ	.6Ɛ1	.6Ɛ3	.6Ɛ5
8	.6Ɛ6	.6Ɛ8	.6ƐX	.6ƐƐ	.701	.703	.705	.706	.708	.70X
9	.710	.711	.713	.715	.716	.718	.71X	.720	.721	.723
.60	.725	.727	.728	.72X	.730	.731	.733	.735	.737	.738
1	.73X	.740	.742	.743	.745	.747	.748	.74X	.750	.752
2	.753	.755	.757	.759	.75X	.760	.762	.763	.765	.767
3	.769	.76X	.770	.772	.774	.775	.777	.779	.77X	.780
4	.782	.784	.785	.787	.789	.78Ɛ	.790	.792	.794	.795
5	.797	.799	.79Ɛ	.7X0	.7X2	.7X4	.7X6	.7X7	.7X9	.7XƐ
6	.7Ɛ0	.7Ɛ2	.7Ɛ4	.7Ɛ6	.7Ɛ7	.7Ɛ9	.7ƐƐ	.801	.802	.804
7	.806	.807	.809	.80Ɛ	.811	.812	.814	.816	.818	.819
8	.81Ɛ	.821	.822	.824	.826	.828	.829	.82Ɛ	.831	.833
9	.834	.836	.838	.83X	.83Ɛ	.841	.843	.844	.846	.848
.70	.84X	.84Ɛ	.851	.853	.855	.856	.858	.85X	.85Ɛ	.861
1	.863	.865	.866	.868	.86X	.870	.871	.873	.875	.876
2	.878	.87X	.880	.881	.883	.885	.887	.888	.88X	.890
3	.891	.893	.895	.897	.898	.89X	.8X0	.8X2	.8X3	.8X5
4	.8X7	.8X8	.8XX	.8Ɛ0	.8Ɛ2	.8Ɛ3	.8Ɛ5	.8Ɛ7	.8Ɛ9	.8ƐX
5	.900	.902	.903	.905	.907	.909	.90X	.910	.912	.914
6	.915	.917	.919	.91X	.920	.922	.924	.925	.927	.929
7	.92X	.930	.932	.934	.935	.937	.939	.93Ɛ	.940	.942
8	.944	.946	.947	.949	.94Ɛ	.950	.952	.954	.956	.957
9	.959	.95Ɛ	.961	.962	.964	.966	.967	.969	.96Ɛ	.971
.80	.972	.974	.976	.978	.979	.97Ɛ	.981	.982	.984	.986
1	.988	.989	.98Ɛ	.991	.993	.994	.996	.998	.99X	.99Ɛ
2	.9X1	.9X3	.9X4	.9X6	.9X8	.9XX	.9XƐ	.9Ɛ1	.9Ɛ3	.9Ɛ5
3	.9Ɛ6	.9Ɛ8	.9ƐX	.9ƐƐ	.X01	.X03	.X05	.X06	.X08	.X0X
4	.X10	.X11	.X13	.X15	.X16	.X18	.X1X	.X20	.X21	.X23
5	.X25	.X27	.X28	.X2X	.X30	.X31	.X33	.X35	.X37	.X38
6	.X3X	.X40	.X42	.X43	.X45	.X47	.X48	.X4X	.X50	.X52
7	.X53	.X55	.X57	.X59	.X5X	.X60	.X62	.X63	.X65	.X67
8	.X69	.X6X	.X70	.X72	.X74	.X75	.X77	.X79	.X7X	.X80
9	.X82	.X84	.X85	.X87	.X89	.X8Ɛ	.X90	.X92	.X94	.X95
.90	.X97	.X99	.X9Ɛ	.XX0	.XX2	.XX4	.XX6	.XX7	.XX9	.XXƐ
1	.XƐ0	.XƐ2	.XƐ4	.XƐ6	.XƐ7	.XƐ9	.XƐƐ	.Ɛ01	.Ɛ02	.Ɛ04
2	.Ɛ06	.Ɛ07	.Ɛ09	.Ɛ0Ɛ	.Ɛ11	.Ɛ12	.Ɛ14	.Ɛ16	.Ɛ18	.Ɛ19
3	.Ɛ1Ɛ	.Ɛ21	.Ɛ22	.Ɛ24	.Ɛ26	.Ɛ28	.Ɛ29	.Ɛ2Ɛ	.Ɛ31	.Ɛ33
4	.Ɛ34	.Ɛ36	.Ɛ38	.Ɛ3X	.Ɛ3Ɛ	.Ɛ41	.Ɛ43	.Ɛ44	.Ɛ46	.Ɛ48
5	.Ɛ4X	.Ɛ4Ɛ	.Ɛ51	.Ɛ53	.Ɛ55	.Ɛ56	.Ɛ58	.Ɛ5X	.Ɛ5Ɛ	.Ɛ61
6	.Ɛ63	.Ɛ65	.Ɛ66	.Ɛ68	.Ɛ6X	.Ɛ70	.Ɛ71	.Ɛ73	.Ɛ75	.Ɛ76
7	.Ɛ78	.Ɛ7X	.Ɛ80	.Ɛ81	.Ɛ83	.Ɛ85	.Ɛ87	.Ɛ88	.Ɛ8X	.Ɛ90
8	.Ɛ91	.Ɛ93	.Ɛ95	.Ɛ97	.Ɛ98	.Ɛ9X	.ƐX0	.ƐX2	.ƐX3	.ƐX5
9	.ƐX7	.ƐX8	.ƐXX	.ƐƐ0	.ƐƐ2	.ƐƐ3	.ƐƐ5	.ƐƐ7	.ƐƐ9	.ƐƐX

Conversion Table

Decimals to Duodecimals

Addition Method

.1	= .124 972 497	.01	= .015 343 X10	.001	= .001 889 Ɛ98
.2	= .249 724 972	2	= .02X 687 81Ɛ	2	= .003 557 Ɛ75
.3	= .372 497 24X	3	= .043 X0Ɛ 62Ɛ	3	= .005 225 Ɛ51
.4	= .497 249 725	4	= .059 153 43X	4	= .006 XƐ3 Ɛ29
.5	= .600 000 000	5	= .072 497 24X	5	= .008 781 Ɛ06
.6	= .724 972 497	6	= .087 81Ɛ 059	6	= .00X 44Ɛ XX2
.7	= .849 724 972	7	= .0X0 Ɛ62 X69	7	= .010 119 X7Ɛ
.8	= .972 497 24X	8	= .0Ɛ6 2X6 878	8	= .011 9X7 X57
.9	= .X97 249 725	9	= .10Ɛ 62X 688	9	= .013 675 X33
.0001	= .000 20X 722	.00001	= .000 025 X3X	.00000 1	= .000 002 ƐX0
2	= .000 419 244	2	= .000 04Ɛ 878	2	= .000 005 Ɛ80
3	= .000 627 966	3	= .000 075 6Ɛ5	3	= .000 008 Ɛ5Ɛ
4	= .000 836 488	4	= .000 09Ɛ 533	4	= .000 00Ɛ Ɛ3Ɛ
5	= .000 X44 ƐXX	5	= .000 105 371	5	= .000 012 Ɛ1Ɛ
6	= .001 053 710	6	= .000 12Ɛ 1XƐ	6	= .000 015 XƐƐ
7	= .001 262 232	7	= .000 155 029	7	= .000 018 X9X
8	= .001 470 954	8	= .000 17X X66	8	= .000 01Ɛ X7X
9	= .001 67Ɛ 476	9	= .000 1X4 8X4	9	= .000 022 X5X
.00000 01	= .000 000 370	.00000 001	= .000 000 044	.00000 0001	= .000 000 005
2	= .000 000 720	2	= .000 000 087	2	= .000 000 00X
3	= .000 000 X90	3	= .000 000 10Ɛ	3	= .000 000 013
4	= .000 001 240	4	= .000 000 152	4	= .000 000 019
5	= .000 001 5Ɛ0	5	= .000 000 196	5	= .000 000 022
6	= .000 001 960	6	= .000 000 21X	6	= .000 000 027
7	= .000 002 110	7	= .000 000 261	7	= .000 000 030
8	= .000 002 480	8	= .000 000 2X5	8	= .000 000 035
9	= .000 002 830	9	= .000 000 328	9	= .000 000 03X

.00000 00001 = .000 000 000 624

Example - Find the duodecimal equivalent of .31830 98862

.3	= .3 7 2 4 9 7 2 4 X
.01	= .0 1 5 3 4 3 X 1 0
.008	= .0 1 1 9 X 7 X 5 7
.0003	= .0 0 0 6 2 7 9 6 6
.00000	= .0 0 0 0 0 0 0 0 0
.00000 9	= .0 0 0 0 2 2 X 5 X
.00000 08	= .0 0 0 0 0 2 4 8 0
.00000 008	= .0 0 0 0 0 0 2 X 5
.00000 0006	= .0 0 0 0 0 0 0 2 7
Answer	.3 9 X 0 5 8 2 8(9)

Conversion Table - Duodecimals to Decimals

Addition Method

.1	= .08333 33333	.01	= .00694 44444	.001	= .00057 87037
2	= .16666 66667	2	= .01388 88889	2	= .00115 74074
3	= .25	3	= .02083 33333	3	= .00173 61111
4	= .33333 33333	4	= .02777 77778	4	= .00231 48148
5	= .41666 66667	5	= .03472 22222	5	= .00289 35185
6	= .5	6	= .04166 66667	6	= .00347 22222
7	= .58333 33333	7	= .04861 11111	7	= .00405 09259
8	= .66666 66667	8	= .05555 55556	8	= .00462 96296
9	= .75	9	= .06250 00000	9	= .00520 83333
Χ	= .83333 33333	Χ	= .06944 44444	Χ	= .00578 70370
Ɛ	= .91666 66667	Ɛ	= .07638 88889	Ɛ	= .00636 57407
.000 1	= .00004 82253	.000 01	= .00000 40188	.000 001	= .00000 03349
2	= .00009 64506	2	= .00000 80376	2	= .00000 06698
3	= .00014 46759	3	= .00001 20563	3	= .00000 10047
4	= .00019 29012	4	= .00001 60751	4	= .00000 13396
5	= .00024 11265	5	= .00002 00939	5	= .00000 16745
6	= .00028 93519	6	= .00002 41127	6	= .00000 20094
7	= .00033 75772	7	= .00002 81314	7	= .00000 23443
8	= .00038 58025	8	= .00003 21502	8	= .00000 26792
9	= .00043 40278	9	= .00003 61690	9	= .00000 30141
Χ	= .00048 22531	Χ	= .00004 01878	Χ	= .00000 33490
Ɛ	= .00053 04784	Ɛ	= .00004 42065	Ɛ	= .00000 36839
.000 000 1	= .00000 00279	.000 000 01	= .00000 00023	.000 000 001	= .00000 00002
2	= .00000 00558	2	= .00000 00047	2	= .00000 00004
3	= .00000 00837	3	= .00000 00070	3	= .00000 00006
4	= .00000 01116	4	= .00000 00093	4	= .00000 00008
5	= .00000 01395	5	= .00000 00116	5	= .00000 00010
6	= .00000 01674	6	= .00000 00140	6	= .00000 00012
7	= .00000 01954	7	= .00000 00163	7	= .00000 00014
8	= .00000 02233	8	= .00000 00186	8	= .00000 00016
9	= .00000 02512	9	= .00000 00209	9	= .00000 00017
Χ	= .00000 02791	Χ	= .00000 00233	Χ	= .00000 00019
Ɛ	= .00000 03070	Ɛ	= .00000 00256	Ɛ	= .00000 00021

.000 000 000 1 = .00000 00000 1615

Example: Find the decimal equivalent of .3 9 Χ 0 5 8 2 8 9

.3	= .2 5 0 0 0 0 0 0 0 0
.0 9	= .0 6 2 5 0 0 0 0 0 0
.0 0 Χ	= .0 0 5 7 8 7 0 3 7 0
.0 0 0 0	= .0 0 0 0 0 0 0 0 0 0
.0 0 0 0 5	= .0 0 0 0 2 0 0 9 3 9
.0 0 0 0 0 8	= .0 0 0 0 0 2 6 7 9 2
.0 0 0 0 0 0 2	= .0 0 0 0 0 0 0 5 5 8
.0 0 0 0 0 0 0 8	= .0 0 0 0 0 0 0 1 8 6
.0 0 0 0 0 0 0 0 9	= .0 0 0 0 0 0 0 0 1 7
Answer	.3 1 8 3 0 9 8 8 6(2)

Factors

Any number ending in *3*, *6*, *9* or *0* is divisible by *3*.
Any number ending in *4*, *8* or *0* is divisible by *4*.
Any number ending in *6* or *0* is divisible by *6*.

Any number whose digits add up to a multiple of *£* is divisible by *£*.

All prime numbers (except *2* and *3*) end in *1*, *5*, *7* or *£*.

Since it is obvious by inspection if a number is divisible by *2*, *3*, *4* or *6*, a table of prime factors need only contain those numbers ending with *1*, *5*, *7* or *£* which have factors. Those not appearing are prime.

Since the factors in the following prime factor table all end in *1*, *5*, *7* or *£*, the table may be easily extended by multiplication.

Prime Factors

21	5.5	101	5.25	201	15.15	305	17.1Ɛ	405	7.6Ɛ	501	7.87
2Ɛ	5.7	10Ɛ	5.27	207	5.4Ɛ	311	5.75	407	Ɛ.45	505	5.5.25
41	7.7	115	7.1Ɛ	20Ɛ	11.1Ɛ	317	Ɛ.35	411	17.27	50Ɛ	15.37
47	5.Ɛ	121	11.11	211	7.37	31Ɛ	5.7.11	417	5.7.15	515	Ɛ.57
55	5.11	127	5.5.7	215	5.51	331	7.57	425	5.Ɛ.Ɛ	521	5.105
65	7.Ɛ	135	5.31	227	Ɛ.25	335	Ɛ.37	42Ɛ	11.3Ɛ	525	7.8Ɛ
71	5.15	137	Ɛ.15	22Ɛ	15.17	337	5.5.17	43Ɛ	7.75	52Ɛ	5.107
77	7.11	14Ɛ	7.25	231	5.5.11	341	11.31	441	5.5.5.5	537	7.91
7Ɛ	5.17	151	5.35	235	7.3Ɛ	345	5.81	445	15.31	53Ɛ	11.4Ɛ
97	5.1Ɛ	155	Ɛ.17	23Ɛ	5.57	351	15.25	44Ɛ	5.X7	547	5.5.27
9Ɛ	7.15	15Ɛ	5.37	245	Ɛ.27	355	7.5Ɛ	451	7.7.11	54Ɛ	17.35
X1	Ɛ.Ɛ	161	7.27	247	7.7.7	361	5.85	461	Ɛ.4Ɛ	551	Ɛ.5Ɛ
X5	5.5.5	165	11.15	257	5.5Ɛ	367	7.61	467	5.XƐ	555	5.111
Ɛ1	7.17	177	5.3Ɛ	261	17.17	36Ɛ	5.87	475	5.7.17	55Ɛ	7.95
ƐƐ	Ɛ.11	185	5.7.7	265	5.61	371	Ɛ.3Ɛ	477	1Ɛ.25	561	11.51
		187	11.17	26Ɛ	7.45	37Ɛ	15.27	47Ɛ	Ɛ.51	567	15.3Ɛ
		191	Ɛ.1Ɛ	275	11.25	381	1Ɛ.1Ɛ	487	7.81	56Ɛ	Ɛ.61
		197	7.31	281	5.7Ɛ	385	11.35	491	5.Ɛ5	571	5.7.1Ɛ
		1X1	5.45	287	15.1Ɛ	387	5.8Ɛ	495	11.45	57Ɛ	5.117
		1XƐ	5.5.Ɛ	28Ɛ	5.67	38Ɛ	7.7.Ɛ	49Ɛ	5.Ɛ7	581	17.37
		1ƐƐ	7.35	297	11.27	395	5.91	4X1	15.35	595	7.7.15
				29Ɛ	Ɛ.31	39Ɛ	17.25	4X7	17.31	597	5.11Ɛ
				2X5	7.4Ɛ	3X1	7.67	4XƐ	7.85	5X1	25.25
				2X7	5.6Ɛ	3X7	11.37	4Ɛ5	1Ɛ.27	5X5	5.11.11
				2Ɛ5	5.5.15	3Ɛ1	5.95	4Ɛ7	5.Ɛ.11	5X7	7.Ɛ.Ɛ
				2Ɛ7	7.51	3ƐƐ	5.5.1Ɛ			5XƐ	1Ɛ.31

601	5.125	707	5.7.25	805	11.75	911	7.Ɛ.15	X01	Ɛ.XƐ	Ɛ01	5.225
605	Ɛ.67	715	5.5.35	807	17.51	915	11.85	X05	5.15.15	Ɛ05	7.16Ɛ
607	11.57	717	11.67	811	5.175	917	5.19Ɛ	X15	27.3Ɛ	Ɛ07	31.37
60Ɛ	5.5.5.7	725	15.51	815	7.11Ɛ	925	5.5.45	X1Ɛ	7.Ɛ.17	Ɛ0Ɛ	5.Ɛ.25
621	7.X7	72Ɛ	7.105	81Ɛ	5.5.3Ɛ	92Ɛ	Ɛ.Ɛ.Ɛ	X21	5.205	Ɛ17	7.171
625	17.3Ɛ	731	5.Ɛ.17	821	Ɛ.8Ɛ	931	27.37	X25	11.95	Ɛ27	5.15.17
627	5.12Ɛ	73Ɛ	5.157	827	7.11.11	935	7.13Ɛ	X2Ɛ	5.5.4Ɛ	Ɛ35	5.5.5.11
62Ɛ	25.27	741	7.107	831	25.35	937	11.87	X31	7.157	Ɛ3Ɛ	7.175
631	15.45	74Ɛ	Ɛ.81	837	5.17Ɛ	93Ɛ	15.67	X47	5.11.1Ɛ	Ɛ41	1Ɛ.5Ɛ
635	5.131	755	25.31	83Ɛ	Ɛ.91	941	5.1X5	X51	17.67	Ɛ47	Ɛ.105
641	Ɛ.6Ɛ	757	5.5.37	845	5.181	945	17.5Ɛ	X55	5.7.37	Ɛ4Ɛ	27.45
645	7.XƐ	75Ɛ	11.6Ɛ	847	15.5Ɛ	947	7.141	X57	Ɛ.Ɛ5	Ɛ51	5.7.3Ɛ
64Ɛ	11.5Ɛ	761	1Ɛ.3Ɛ	84Ɛ	7.125	94Ɛ	5.1X7	X61	15.75	Ɛ55	15.81
651	5.5.31	765	5.7.27	857	1Ɛ.45	951	1Ɛ.4Ɛ	X65	31.35	Ɛ57	11.X7
657	7.7.17	777	7.111	861	5.5.7.7	957	25.3Ɛ	X67	7.7.27	Ɛ5Ɛ	5.237
65Ɛ	5.Ɛ.15	781	5.11.15	86Ɛ	5.11.17	961	31.31	X71	5.5.51	Ɛ65	Ɛ.107
667	1Ɛ.35	787	Ɛ.85	875	15.61	967	5.5.5.Ɛ	X75	Ɛ.Ɛ7	Ɛ75	7.17Ɛ
671	11.61	78Ɛ	5.167	877	Ɛ.95	96Ɛ	7.145	X7Ɛ	5.217	Ɛ77	5.5.57
677	5.13Ɛ	795	17.4Ɛ	87Ɛ	25.37	975	5.1Ɛ1	X81	25.45	Ɛ7Ɛ	1Ɛ.61
67Ɛ	7.Ɛ5	79Ɛ	7.7.1Ɛ	885	7.12Ɛ	977	17.61	X85	1Ɛ.57	Ɛ81	35.35
681	27.27	7X5	Ɛ.87	887	5.18Ɛ	97Ɛ	11.8Ɛ	X8Ɛ	7.11.15	Ɛ85	5.241
685	5.141	7X7	5.16Ɛ	891	11.81	981	7.147	X97	5.21Ɛ	Ɛ87	7.181
691	7.Ɛ7	7XƐ	15.57	895	5.Ɛ.1Ɛ	985	Ɛ.X7	XX1	7.167	Ɛ8Ɛ	17.75
697	Ɛ.75	7Ɛ1	7.117	897	7.131	98Ɛ	1Ɛ.51	XX5	5.221	Ɛ9Ɛ	11.XƐ
6X1	5.145	7Ɛ5	5.171	89Ɛ	27.35	991	5.1Ɛ5	XƐ1	Ɛ.Ɛ.11	ƐX1	5.Ɛ.27
6X5	1Ɛ.37	7Ɛ7	27.31	8X1	17.57	997	15.6Ɛ	XƐ5	17.6Ɛ	ƐX7	25.4Ɛ
6XƐ	5.147			8Ɛ1	5.195	99Ɛ	5.1Ɛ7			ƐXƐ	5.7.7.7
6Ɛ5	7.Ɛ.11			8ƐƐ	5.7.31	9X1	11.91			ƐƐ1	15.85
6Ɛ7	15.4Ɛ					9X5	7.7.25			ƐƐƐ	Ɛ.111
6ƐƐ	17.45					9Ɛ7	5.7.35				

Fractions

$$\frac{1}{4} + \frac{1}{3} + \frac{1}{6} = \frac{3}{10} + \frac{4}{10} + \frac{2}{10} = \frac{9}{10}$$

One half	1:2	=	.6
One third	1:3	=	.4
One quarter	1:4	=	.3
One fifth	1:5	=	$.\dot{2}49\dot{7}$
One sixth	1:6	=	.2
One seventh	1:7	=	$.\dot{1}86X3\dot{5}$
One eighth	1:8	=	.16
One ninth	1:9	=	.14
One decth	1:X	=	$.1\dot{2}49\dot{7}$
One elth	1:Ɛ	=	$.\dot{1}$

Factorials

1! =	1
2! =	2
3! =	6
4! =	20
5! =	χ0
6! =	500
7! =	2 Ɛ00
8! =	1Ɛ 400
9! =	156·10^{3}
χ! =	127·10^{4}
Ɛ! =	1 145·10^{4}
10! =	1 145·10^{5}
11! =	12 595·10^{5}
12! =	14χ 8Ɛχ·10^{5}
13! =	1 915 296·10^{5}
14! =	2 41χ Ɛ88·10^{6}
15! =	33 χ86 734·10^{6}
16! =	4 Ɛχ0 9χƐ·10^{8}
17! =	7χ 8Ɛ3 835·10^{8}
18! =	1 11χ χχ1 984·10^{8}
19! =	1 Ɛ04 0Ɛ9 1Ɛ7·10^{9}
1χ! =	36 275 969 72χ·10^{9}
1Ɛ! =	68Ɛ 041 404 χ52·10^{9}
20! =	1 15χ 082 809 8χ4·$10^{χ}$

Reciprocal Factorials

1:2! =	.6
1:3! =	.2
1:4! =	.06
1:5! =	.012497 249724 972497 249724 χ
1:6! =	.002497 249724 972497 249724 χ
1:7! =	.000414 559Ɛ39 310414 559Ɛ39 3
1:8! =	.000062 0828χƐ 7χ7662 0828χƐ 8
1:9! =	.000008 28χƐ7χ 766208 28χƐ7χ 8
1:χ! =	9χ5χ92 31χ273 28111Ɛ χ
1:Ɛ! =	0χ931Ɛ 146472 584568 9
1:10! =	00χ931 Ɛ14647 258456 9
1:11! =	0009Ɛ3 χ10422 498041 5
1:12! =	000086 336037 041520 1
1:13! =	000006 99χ002 χ50χ8Ɛ 2
1:14! =	514460 219980 8
1:15! =	037396 444133 7
1:16! =	0024χ6 42χχ8χ 2
1:17! =	162 χ3Ɛ388 1
1:18! =	χ Ɛ39695 2
1:19! =	630557 1
1:1χ! =	034Ɛ1χ 8
1:1Ɛ! =	001943 1
1:20! =	0000χ8 2

Powers

1	2	3	4	5	6
2	4	9	14	21	30
3	8	23	54	χ5	160
4	14	69	194	441	900
5	28	183	714	1 985	4 600
6	54	509	2 454	9 061	23 000
7	χ8	1 323	9 594	39 265	116 000
8	194	3 969	31 Ɛ14	16χ 081	690 000
9	368	Ɛ 483	107 854	7χ2 345	3 460 000
χ	714	2χ 209	426 994	3 32Ɛ 4χ1	18 300 000
Ɛ	1 228	86 623	1 4χ3 314	14 429 025	χ1 600 000
10	2 454	217 669	5 751 054	69 919 101	509 000 000

1	7	8	9	χ
2	41	54	69	84
3	247	368	509	6Ɛ4
4	1 481	2 454	3 969	5 954
5	9 887	16 Ɛ68	2χ 209	49 χ54
6	58 101	107 854	217 669	402 854
7	338 707	851 768	1 727 Ɛ09	3 423 054
8	1 Ɛ20 141	5 751 054	12 4ƐƐ 369	29 5χ6 454
9	11 620 947	38 Ɛ48 368	χ9 8Ɛ5 809	23χ χ93 854
χ	7χ 725 581	25Ɛ 716 454	813 873 069	1 Ɛ30 Ɛ91 054
Ɛ	472 252 387	1 7Ɛ8 902 Ɛ68	6 0Ɛ9 553 509	17 469 96χ 454
10	2 823 504 201	11 39χ 01Ɛ 854	46 8χ1 0Ɛ6 969	141 981 Ɛ87 854

1	Ɛ		π	π:4
2	χ1		9.χ52 814 9Ɛ3	.749 Ɛ01 075 509
3	92Ɛ		27.00χ χ1χ 098	.599 204 χ17 984
4	8 581		81.4χχ χχƐ 347	.469 617 77χ 1χ2
5	79 24Ɛ		216.02χ 022 554	.370 4χ9 498 784
6	715 261		681.480 639 957	.299 704 87Ɛ 998
7	6 639 36Ɛ		1 8Ɛ8.362 845	.226 668 535 779
8	5Ɛ 956 341		5 5χ8.645 719	.18χ 229 23Ɛ Ɛ5χ
9	559 809 08Ɛ		15 301.123 794	.144 5Ɛ4 332 21Ɛ
χ	5 03χ 483 821		46 240.06χ 057	.10χ 3Ɛ1 545 750
Ɛ	47 366 374 5χƐ		122 310.027 086	.0χ1 25Ɛ Ɛ89 440
10	428 2Ɛ9 391 501		386 χ65.221 80χ	.07Ɛ 244 082 52χ

Reciprocal Powers

	1:2	1:3	1:4	1:5
1	.6	.4	.3	.249 724 972 497 2
2	.3	.14	.09	.059 153 43X 0Ɛ6 3
3	.16	.054	.023	.011 9X7 X56 996 1
4	.09	.019 4	.006 9	.002 921 6X8 691 3
5	.046	.007 14	.001 83	677 621 867 5
6	.023	.002 454	509	13Ɛ 129 Ɛ38 8
7	.011 6	959 4	132 3	032 279 231 9
8	.006 9	31Ɛ 14	039 69	007 789 055 2
9	.003 46	107 854	00Ɛ 483	001 641 983 5
X	.001 83	042 699 4	002 X20 9	380 440 8
Ɛ	X16	014 X33 14	866 23	089 809 9
10	509	005 751 054	217 669	019 174 4

	1:6	1:7	1:8	1:9
1	.2	.186 X35 186 X35 2	.16	.14
2	.04	.02Ɛ 322 547 X05 Ɛ	.023	.019 4
3	.008	.005 055 5XƐ 4X4 3	.003 46	.002 454
4	.001 4	877 785 084 0	509	31Ɛ 14
5	28	129 7Ɛ5 X47 5	077 16	042 699 4
6	054	021 469 4XƐ 4	00Ɛ 483	005 751 054
7	00X 8	003 761 416 9	001 510 46	75X 947 1
8	001 94	627 071 0	217 669	09Ɛ X46 1
9	368	0X7 X45 3	032 53X 2	011 39X 0
X	071 4	016 324 2	004 97Ɛ 9	001 591 1
Ɛ	012 28	002 739 2	726 0	1Ɛ8 1
10	002 454	458 2	0X9 9	027 7

	1:X	1:Ɛ		1:π
1	.124 972 497 249 7	.111 111 111 111 1		.127 0ƐƐ 524 723
2	.015 343 X0Ɛ 62X 7	.012 345 678 9Ɛ0 1		.047 892 695 835
3	.001 889 Ɛ98 428 3	.001 36Ɛ 4Ɛ7 421 1		.015 8X6 085 647
4	20X 722 050 X	14Ɛ Ɛ43 Ɛ35 7		.005 791 5X6 783
5	025 X39 978 6	016 65X 214 X		.001 969 XX4 896
6	002 Ɛ9Ɛ 944 5	001 828 68X 3		.000 6X4 782 7ƐX
7	36Ɛ Ɛ8X 1	1X0 940 Ɛ		222 83Ɛ 332
8	043 721 0	020 0X2 3		084 206 17X
9	005 1Ɛ0 1	002 231 4		027 X75 6XX
X	623 7	247 9		00X 196 12X
Ɛ	075 2	027 3		003 292 675
10	008 Ɛ	002 X		

N	Square	Cube	N	Square	Cube	N	Square	Cube
0	----	----	40	1 400	54 000	80	5 400	368 000
1	1	1	41	1 481	58 101	81	5 541	380 201
2	4	8	42	1 544	60 408	82	5 684	394 808
3	9	23	43	1 609	64 923	83	5 809	3X9 623
4	14	54	44	1 694	69 454	84	5 954	402 854
5	21	X5	45	1 761	72 1X5	85	5 XX1	418 2X5
6	30	160	46	1 830	77 160	86	6 030	432 160
7	41	247	47	1 901	80 347	87	6 181	448 447
8	54	368	48	1 994	85 768	88	6 314	462 Ɛ68
9	69	509	49	1 X69	8Ɛ 209	89	6 469	479 Ɛ09
X	84	6Ɛ4	4X	1 Ɛ44	94 XƐ4	8X	6 604	495 2Ɛ4
Ɛ	X1	92Ɛ	4Ɛ	2 021	9X X2Ɛ	8Ɛ	6 761	4Ɛ0 ƐƐƐ
10	100	1 000	50	2 100	X5 000	90	6 900	509 000
11	121	1 331	51	2 1X1	XƐ 431	91	6 X61	525 531
12	144	1 708	52	2 284	Ɛ5 Ɛ08	92	7 004	542 308
13	169	1 Ɛ53	53	2 369	100 853	93	7 169	55Ɛ 553
14	194	2 454	54	2 454	107 854	94	7 314	579 054
15	201	2 X15	55	2 541	112 Ɛ15	95	7 481	597 015
16	230	3 460	56	2 630	11X 460	96	7 630	5Ɛ5 460
17	261	3 Ɛ77	57	2 721	126 077	97	7 7X1	614 177
18	294	4 768	58	2 814	131 Ɛ68	98	7 954	633 368
19	309	5 439	59	2 909	13X 139	99	7 Ɛ09	652 X39
1X	344	6 1Ɛ4	5X	2 X04	146 5Ɛ4	9X	8 084	672 9Ɛ4
1Ɛ	381	7 05Ɛ	5Ɛ	2 Ɛ01	153 15Ɛ	9Ɛ	8 241	693 25Ɛ
20	400	8 000	60	3 000	160 000	X0	8 400	6Ɛ4 000
21	441	9 061	61	3 101	169 161	X1	8 581	715 261
22	484	X 208	62	3 204	176 608	X2	8 744	736 X08
23	509	Ɛ 483	63	3 309	184 183	X3	8 909	758 X83
24	554	10 854	64	3 414	192 054	X4	8 X94	77Ɛ 454
25	5X1	12 145	65	3 521	1X0 245	X5	9 061	7X2 345
26	630	13 760	66	3 630	1XX 760	X6	9 230	805 760
27	681	15 2X7	67	3 741	1Ɛ9 3X7	X7	9 401	829 4X7
28	714	16 Ɛ68	68	3 854	208 368	X8	9 594	851 768
29	769	18 969	69	3 969	217 669	X9	9 769	876 369
2X	804	1X 8Ɛ4	6X	3 X84	227 0Ɛ4	XX	9 944	89Ɛ 4Ɛ4
2Ɛ	861	20 98Ɛ	6Ɛ	3 ƐX1	236 X8Ɛ	XƐ	9 Ɛ21	904 Ɛ8Ɛ
30	900	23 000	70	4 100	247 000	Ɛ0	X 100	92Ɛ 000
31	961	25 391	71	4 221	257 491	Ɛ1	X 2X1	955 591
32	X04	27 908	72	4 344	268 108	Ɛ2	X 484	980 508
33	X69	2X 3Ɛ3	73	4 469	279 0Ɛ3	Ɛ3	X 669	9X7 9Ɛ3
34	Ɛ14	31 054	74	4 594	28X 454	Ɛ4	X 854	X13 854
35	Ɛ81	33 X75	75	4 701	29Ɛ Ɛ75	Ɛ5	X X41	X40 075
36	1 030	36 X60	76	4 830	2Ɛ1 X60	Ɛ6	Ɛ 030	X68 X60
37	1 0X1	3X 017	77	4 961	304 117	Ɛ7	Ɛ 221	X96 217
38	1 154	41 368	78	4 X94	316 768	Ɛ8	Ɛ 414	Ɛ03 Ɛ68
39	1 209	44 899	79	5 009	329 599	Ɛ9	Ɛ 609	Ɛ32 299
3X	1 284	48 3Ɛ4	7X	5 144	340 7Ɛ4	ƐX	Ɛ 804	Ɛ60 ƐƐ4
3Ɛ	1 341	50 0ƐƐ	7Ɛ	5 281	354 1ƐƐ	ƐƐ	Ɛ X01	Ɛ90 2ƐƐ

Higher Roots

	2	3	5	7
2	1.4Ɛ7 917 0X0 8	1.894 Ɛ97 ƐƐ9 7	2.29Ɛ Ɛ13 254 0	2.78Ɛ X37 0ƐƐ 1
3	1.315 188 11X 4	1.538 25X 183 7	1.862 X08 998 1	1.XƐ5 665 XX3 7
4	1.232 Ɛ49 502 5	1.396 213 Ɛ41 X	1.5Ɛ3 Ɛ67 650 9	1.762 883 708 1
5	1.194 Ɛ4X XXX 6	1.2Ɛ4 758 7X2 1	1.468 20X 83X 3	1.586 177 06Ɛ 2
6	1.157 745 872 9	1.24Ɛ 276 649 4	1.383 779 356 X	1.471 Ɛ85 383 7
7	1.12Ɛ X49 757 6	1.205 782 830 X	1.312 829 892 6	1.3X1 930 068 0
8	1.110 492 784 9	1.192 448 X65 Ɛ	1.281 0XX 2Ɛ4 X	1.337 X17 836 3
9	1.0Ɛ6 415 123 9	1.168 421 220 8	1.242 447 00X 5	1.2X9 0Ɛ6 574 3
X	1.0X4 036 4Ɛ1 9	1.148 7Ɛ1 Ɛ33 X	1.211 8X9 453 8	1.26Ɛ 247 36Ɛ 9
Ɛ	1.094 483 79Ɛ 4	1.131 5Ɛ2 47Ɛ 7	1.1X8 315 4X1 5	1.23X 482 29Ɛ 1
10	1.086 903 X21 Ɛ	1.119 802 3X4 0	1.188 029 964 2	1.214 262 97Ɛ 0

	Ɛ	11	15	17
2	3.397 164 684 3	3.732 486 505 3	4.158 887 518 3	4.438 216 605 3
3	2.283 054 Ɛ72 7	2.427 133 90X 8	2.6X3 211 832 Ɛ	2.802 ƐƐ8 766 4
4	1.9X2 Ɛ6Ɛ 589 X	1.X95 214 944 2	2.044 941 565 2	2.107 86X 399 X
5	1.747 499 523 6	1.806 2X6 418 Ɛ	1.919 3X8 0Ɛ8 3	1.975 9Ɛ0 953 0
6	1.5X8 Ɛ76 417 9	1.649 886 5X5 5	1.72X X75 XX4 8	1.772 891 523 6
7	1.4X9 Ɛ69 620 5	1.538 8Ɛ9 968 3	1.52X 172 909 2	1.633 74Ɛ 796 Ɛ
8	1.423 Ɛ38 618 X	1.465 196 33Ɛ 7	1.512 425 592 0	1.540 9X7 Ɛ51 1
9	1.37Ɛ 684 686 5	1.3Ɛ5 995 969 7	1.453 408 264 7	1.478 939 1Ɛ0 6
X	1.330 30X 925 Ɛ	1.361 306 5XƐ X	1.3Ɛ1 Ɛ84 410 9	1.413 770 1Ɛ0 0
Ɛ	1.2Ɛ0 X93 897 3	1.319 946 Ɛ61 2	1.363 789 696 9	1.382 446 124 6
10	1.27X 269 580 0	1.2X3 967 391 7	1.324 206 648 3	1.340 668 32X 3

	1Ɛ		π	1:π
2	4.967 244 241 6		1.932 972 X0X 9	.692 Ɛ05 0X0 0
3	2.X16 251 372 4		1.56X 993 Ɛ39 2	.823 X26 356 3
4	2.234 269 Ɛ18 4		1.3Ɛ8 66X 118 1	.901 Ɛ40 X36 3
5	1.X57 141 40Ɛ 0		1.310 6X0 487 1	.966 49X 6X9 2
6	1.82X 086 469 1		1.263 293 627 4	.9XƐ X38 Ɛ28 8
7	1.694 524 X45 7		1.217 005 Ɛ4Ɛ 4	.X23 38X 386 Ɛ
8	1.591 206 Ɛ48 2		1.1X1 9Ɛ1 074 6	.X49 745 7Ɛ7 4
9	1.500 248 ƐX7 8		1.176 464 923 Ɛ	.X69 747 277 7
X	1.450 461 64Ɛ 6		1.155 6XƐ 1ƐƐ 3	.X85 114 139 8
Ɛ	1.3Ɛ5 Ɛ22 659 0		1.139 625 082 5	.X99 269 921 8
10	1.36Ɛ ƐX7 Ɛ85 3		1.124 Ɛ62 2XX 4	.XXX 93X Ɛ62 1

Square Roots

The following parallel table of square roots may be used to obtain six figures of the root by direct proportion. It is necessary to find by inspection the first figure of the root and use the column indicated. Results will be within one of the correct sixth figure, except for second column roots of numbers beginning with one. These will be within two and may be checked within one by using a factor.

Example:

Find the square root of *3.18 481*

Root *3.18*	*1.93 159*	
		348
Add *.481* (*348*)	*13X*	
Root *3.18 481*	*1.93 297*	

Check, using factor

Multiply by *9* *24.3 360*(*9*)		
Root *24.3*	*5.39 454*	
		1 165
Add *.3609* (*1165*)	*3Ɛ5*	
	5.39 849	
Divide root by *3*	*1.93 297*	

To nine places, using log table *1.93 297 36Ɛ*

Example:

Find the square root of *.107 497*

Root *.107*	*.366 98X*	
		1 832
Add *.497* (*1832*)	*813*	
Root *.107 497*	*.367 5X1*	

Check, using factor

Multiply by *4* *.425 724*		
Root *.425*	*.712 574*	
		X18
Add *.724* (*X18*)	*60Ɛ*	
	.712 Ɛ83	
Divide root by *2*	*.367 5X2*	

To nine places, using log table *.367 5X1 751*

Note: $\sqrt{2}$ = *1.4Ɛ7 917 0X0 7Ɛ8*

$\sqrt{3}$ = *1.894 Ɛ97 ƐƐ9 687*

N	Square Root		N	Square Root		N	Square Root	
100	100 000	356 9Ɛ7	140	11X 33X	400 000	180	135 XX1	457 ƐX3
1	5ƐƐ	8 687	1	862	1 5Ɛ9	1	136 359	9 3Ɛ2
2	ƐƐ6	X 349	2	11Ɛ 183	2 ƐXƐ	2	814	X 7ƐX
3	101 5XƐ	360 000	3	6X2	4 596	3	137 08X	460 000
4	ƐX0	1 865	4	120 000	5 Ɛ77	4	543	1 3ƐX
5	102 58Ɛ	3 501	5	518	7 551	5	9Ɛ6	2 7Ɛ3
6	Ɛ77	5 14X	6	X31	8 Ɛ20	6	138 267	3 ƐX3
7	103 560	6 98X	7	121 345	X 4X6	7	718	5 38X
8	Ɛ43	8 600	8	857	Ɛ X64	8	Ɛ87	6 771
9	104 522	X 224	9	122 168	411 419	9	139 435	7 Ɛ50
X	XƐƐ	Ɛ X3Ɛ	X	676	2 987	X	8X1	9 325
Ɛ	105 495	371 648	Ɛ	Ɛ83	4 32Ɛ	Ɛ	13X 148	X 6Ɛ7
110	X69	3 249	150	123 489	5 889	190	5Ɛ2	Ɛ X83
1	106 439	4 X40	1	992	7 220	1	X56	471 248
2	X07	6 625	2	124 296	8 76X	2	13Ɛ 2Ɛ9	2 607
3	107 393	8 202	3	797	X 0Ɛ1	3	75Ɛ	3 983
4	958	9 992	4	125 097	Ɛ 62X	4	140 000	5 136
5	108 31X	Ɛ 555	5	595	420 Ɛ62	5	45Ɛ	6 4X4
6	89X	381 10Ɛ	6	X91	2 48Ɛ	6	8Ɛ9	7 84Ɛ
7	109 258	2 879	7	126 388	3 9Ɛ2	7	141 156	8 Ɛ20
8	812	4 419	8	881	5 310	8	5Ɛ2	X 34X
9	10X 187	5 Ɛ72	9	127 174	6 824	9	X48	Ɛ 6X3
X	739	7 6ƐX	X	666	8 132	X	142 2X1	480 X34
Ɛ	10Ɛ 0X8	9 239	Ɛ	Ɛ55	9 636	Ɛ	735	2 181
120	655	X 970	160	128 444	X Ɛ35	1X0	Ɛ88	3 506
1	110 000	390 497	1	930	430 42X	1	143 41X	4 846
2	564	1 ƐƐ6	2	129 217	1 919	2	86X	5 Ɛ82
3	Ɛ06	3 708	3	701	3 203	3	144 0Ɛ9	7 2Ɛ6
4	111 466	5 213	4	ƐX5	4 6X3	4	547	8 626
5	X03	6 911	5	12X 487	5 Ɛ7X	5	994	9 952
6	112 35Ɛ	8 404	6	967	7 44Ɛ	6	145 21Ɛ	Ɛ 076
7	8Ɛ3	9 XXƐ	7	12Ɛ 247	8 917	7	666	490 396
8	113 246	Ɛ 58X	8	724	X 199	8	XXƐ	1 6Ɛ1
9	797	3X1 061	9	130 000	Ɛ 656	9	146 333	2 X05
X	114 125	2 729	X	496	440 Ɛ0X	X	776	4 115
Ɛ	671	4 1X9	Ɛ	96Ɛ	2 378	Ɛ	ƐƐ8	5 421
130	ƐƐ7	5 862	170	131 243	3 822	1Ɛ0	147 438	6 724
1	115 53X	7 30Ɛ	1	715	5 082	1	878	7 X24
2	X80	8 971	2	ƐX5	6 518	2	148 0Ɛ6	9 120
3	116 3ƐƐ	X 408	3	132 474	7 96X	3	533	X 414
4	939	Ɛ X57	4	941	9 1Ɛ7	4	970	Ɛ 705
5	117 274	3Ɛ1 4X0	5	133 209	X 63X	5	149 1X7	4X0 9Ɛ1
6	7X9	2 Ɛ19	6	694	Ɛ X78	6	621	2 096
7	118 121	4 54Ɛ	7	Ɛ59	451 2Ɛ2	7	X56	3 377
8	652	5 Ɛ75	8	134 420	2 722	8	14X 289	4 654
9	Ɛ81	7 595	9	8X3	3 Ɛ4X	9	700	5 929
X	119 4XX	8 ƐXX	X	135 163	5 370	X	Ɛ32	6 ƐƐƐ
Ɛ	X15	X 5Ɛ9	Ɛ	623	6 78X	Ɛ	14Ɛ 362	8 289

N	Square Root		N	Square Root		N	Square Root	
200	14Ɛ 792	4X9 553	240	163 Ɛ69	535 Ɛ87	280	177 199	57X 706
1	150 000	X 815	1	164 35X	7 139	1	55X	Ɛ 792
2	429	Ɛ X94	2	74Ɛ	8 2X8	2	91X	580 857
3	856	4Ɛ1 14Ɛ	3	Ɛ3X	9 454	3	178 099	1 91X
4	151 081	2 403	4	165 329	X 5Ɛ9	4	458	2 99Ɛ
5	4X7	3 673	5	717	Ɛ 760	5	816	3 X59
6	910	4 920	6	Ɛ04	540 8ƐƐ	6	Ɛ93	4 Ɛ15
7	152 134	5 Ɛ84	7	166 2Ɛ0	1 X58	7	179 350	5 Ɛ8X
8	558	7 226	8	698	2 ƐƐ2	8	708	7 041
9	97X	8 484	9	X82	4 145	9	X83	8 0Ɛ2
X	153 19Ɛ	9 71X	X	167 268	5 295	X	17X 23X	9 161
Ɛ	5ƐƐ	X 971	Ɛ	651	6 423	Ɛ	5Ɛ4	X 209
210	X1X	500 000	250	X35	7 569	290	969	Ɛ 273
1	154 238	1 248	1	168 218	8 6Ɛ1	1	17Ɛ 122	590 317
2	655	2 490	2	5ƐƐ	9 832	2	496	1 378
3	X71	3 711	3	9X1	X 971	3	849	2 417
4	155 289	4 94Ɛ	4	169 182	Ɛ XX8	4	180 000	3 474
5	6X3	5 Ɛ85	5	562	551 021	5	372	4 50Ɛ
6	XƐ8	7 1Ɛ8	6	942	2 154	6	724	5 563
7	156 310	8 428	7	16X 120	3 283	7	X94	6 5Ɛ6
8	723	9 654	8	4ƐX	4 3Ɛ0	8	181 244	7 646
9	Ɛ36	X 878	9	897	5 516	9	5Ɛ4	8 693
X	157 347	Ɛ X9X	X	16Ɛ 074	6 63X	X	963	9 71Ɛ
Ɛ	757	511 0Ɛ8	Ɛ	44Ɛ	7 75Ɛ	Ɛ	182 111	X 764
220	Ɛ67	2 313	260	826	8 879	2X0	47Ɛ	Ɛ 7X7
1	158 375	3 527	1	170 000	9 995	1	828	5X0 828
2	783	4 737	2	395	X XXX	2	Ɛ94	1 867
3	Ɛ8Ɛ	5 945	3	76X	560 000	3	183 340	2 8X4
4	159 397	6 Ɛ4Ɛ	4	Ɛ42	1 110	4	6X7	3 91X
5	7X2	8 151	5	171 315	2 219	5	X51	4 953
6	ƐX8	9 351	6	6X7	3 324	6	184 1Ɛ7	5 985
7	15X 3Ɛ1	X 54X	7	X79	4 428	7	560	6 9Ɛ5
8	7Ɛ5	Ɛ 743	8	172 249	5 529	8	905	7 XƐ3
9	ƐƐ8	520 935	9	61X	6 628	9	185 069	8 X4Ɛ
X	15Ɛ 3ƐX	1 Ɛ24	X	9X9	7 725	X	411	9 X75
Ɛ	800	3 110	Ɛ	173 178	8 81Ɛ	Ɛ	773	X X98
230	160 000	4 ƐƐ5	270	545	9 912	2Ɛ0	Ɛ16	Ɛ XƐX
1	400	5 497	1	913	X X03	1	186 277	5Ɛ0 Ɛ19
2	7ƐX	6 676	2	174 09Ɛ	Ɛ XƐ1	2	618	1 Ɛ37
3	ƐƐ8	7 851	3	467	570 Ɛ99	3	979	2 Ɛ52
4	161 3Ɛ5	8 X26	4	832	2 083	4	187 118	3 Ɛ67
5	7Ɛ1	9 ƐƐ7	5	ƐƐ8	3 166	5	478	4 Ɛ7Ɛ
6	ƐX8	Ɛ 186	6	175 382	4 246	6	816	5 Ɛ90
7	162 3X2	530 352	7	747	5 324	7	Ɛ74	6 Ɛ9Ɛ
8	798	1 516	8	Ɛ0Ɛ	6 400	8	188 312	7 ƐX8
9	Ɛ90	2 698	9	176 293	7 495	9	66Ɛ	8 ƐƐ3
X	163 384	3 857	X	655	8 568	X	X07	9 ƐƐ8
Ɛ	777	4 X12	Ɛ	X18	9 638	Ɛ	189 163	X ƐƐƐ

N	Square Root	N	Square Root	N	Square Root
300	189 4ƐX 600 000	340	19X XX7 63X 8X0	380	1XƐ 8X5 677 231
1	854 0 ƐƐƐ	1	19Ɛ 220 Ɛ 826	1	1Ɛ0 000 8 113
2	ƐXX 1 ƐƐ8	2	554 640 76Ɛ	2	317 8 ƐƐ4
3	18X 344 2 ƐƐ3	3	888 1 6Ɛ2	3	631 9 X93
4	698 3 ƐX8	4	1X0 000 2 633	4	946 X 971
5	X31 4 Ɛ9Ɛ	5	333 3 573	5	1Ɛ1 060 Ɛ 84X
6	18Ɛ 184 5 Ɛ90	6	666 4 4Ɛ1	6	375 680 724
7	517 6 Ɛ7Ɛ	7	998 5 429	7	689 1 5ƐX
8	86X 7 Ɛ69	8	1X1 109 6 364	8	9X1 2 492
9	190 000 8 Ɛ54	9	43X 7 299	9	1Ɛ2 0Ɛ5 3 365
X	351 9 Ɛ39	X	76Ɛ 8 210	X	408 4 236
Ɛ	6X2 X Ɛ21	Ɛ	X9Ɛ 9 142	Ɛ	71Ɛ 5 106
310	X33 Ɛ Ɛ02	350	1X2 20Ɛ X 072	390	X31 5 Ɛ94
1	191 182 610 XX1	1	53X X ƐX1	1	1Ɛ3 143 6 X61
2	512 1 X7Ɛ	2	869 Ɛ Ɛ09	2	455 7 928
3	860 2 X57	3	Ɛ97 650 X34	3	766 8 7Ɛ2
4	ƐXX 3 X31	4	1X3 305 1 95X	4	X76 9 677
5	192 338 4 X05	5	632 2 882	5	1Ɛ4 187 X 53X
6	685 5 997	6	95Ɛ 3 7X4	6	497 Ɛ 400
7	X11 6 967	7	1X4 087 4 705	7	7X6 690 280
8	193 159 7 935	8	3Ɛ3 5 624	8	XƐ5 1 13Ɛ
9	4X5 8 901	9	71X 6 541	9	1Ɛ5 204 1 ƐƐ8
X	830 9 888	X	X45 7 459	X	512 2 X75
Ɛ	Ɛ76 X 851	Ɛ	1X5 170 8 373	Ɛ	820 3 92Ɛ
320	194 300 Ɛ 813	360	496 9 288	3X0	Ɛ2X 4 7X5
1	645 620 794	1	800 X 19Ɛ	1	1Ɛ6 237 5 659
2	98X 1 754	2	Ɛ25 Ɛ 0Ɛ0	2	543 6 50Ɛ
3	195 112 2 711	3	1X6 249 660 000	3	850 7 381
4	456 3 688	4	572 0 Ɛ0X	4	Ɛ58 8 230
5	799 4 642	5	895 1 X17	5	1Ɛ7 263 9 09Ɛ
6	Ɛ1Ɛ 5 5Ɛ6	6	ƐƐ9 2 922	6	56X 9 Ɛ48
7	196 262 6 568	7	1X7 320 3 828	7	875 X 9Ɛ4
8	5X3 7 518	8	642 4 730	8	Ɛ7Ɛ Ɛ 85X
9	924 8 487	9	964 5 632	9	1Ɛ8 285 6X0 703
X	197 065 9 433	X	1X8 086 6 533	X	58Ɛ 1 567
Ɛ	3X5 X 39X	Ɛ	3X7 7 433	Ɛ	894 2 409
330	724 Ɛ 343	370	707 8 331	3Ɛ0	Ɛ99 3 26X
1	X63 630 2X7	1	X28 9 229	1	1Ɛ9 2X1 4 10X
2	198 1X2 1 248	2	1X9 147 X 124	2	5X5 4 Ɛ68
3	520 2 1X8	3	467 Ɛ 019	3	8X9 5 X05
4	859 3 146	4	786 Ɛ Ɛ11	4	ƐƐ0 6 861
5	Ɛ96 4 0X2	5	XX4 670 X03	5	1ƐX 2Ɛ3 7 6Ɛ7
6	199 313 5 039	6	1XX 202 1 8Ɛ4	6	5Ɛ5 8 550
7	64Ɛ 5 Ɛ92	7	520 2 7X3	7	8Ɛ7 9 3X4
8	986 6 Ɛ25	8	839 3 691	8	ƐƐ9 X 236
9	19X 101 7 X76	9	Ɛ55 4 579	9	1ƐƐ 2ƐX Ɛ 087
X	438 8 X06	X	1XƐ 272 5 464	X	5ƐƐ Ɛ Ɛ17
Ɛ	772 9 954	Ɛ	58X 6 349	Ɛ	900 6Ɛ0 966

N	Square Root	
400	200 000	6Ɛ1 7Ɛ3
1	300	2 63Ɛ
2	5ƐƐ	3 485
3	8ƐX	4 30X
4	ƐƐ9	5 152
5	201 2Ɛ7	5 Ɛ95
6	5Ɛ5	6 X16
7	8Ɛ3	7 856
8	ƐƐ0	8 695
9	202 2X9	9 513
X	5X5	X 34Ɛ
Ɛ	8X2	Ɛ 186
410	Ɛ99	700 000
1	203 295	0 X35
2	590	1 868
3	886	2 69X
4	Ɛ81	3 50Ɛ
5	204 277	4 33X
6	570	5 168
7	865	5 Ɛ95
8	Ɛ5X	6 X01
9	205 253	7 828
X	547	8 651
Ɛ	83Ɛ	9 475
420	Ɛ32	X 298
1	206 225	Ɛ 0ƐX
2	518	Ɛ Ɛ1X
3	80X	710 939
4	Ɛ00	1 757
5	207 1Ɛ2	2 574
6	4X4	3 390
7	795	4 1X6
8	X85	4 ƐƐƐ
9	208 175	5 X13
X	465	6 826
Ɛ	755	7 638
430	X44	8 448
1	209 133	9 257
2	422	X 065
3	710	X X72
4	9ƐX	Ɛ 87X
5	20X 0X8	720 684
6	395	1 48X
7	682	2 292
8	96X	3 095
9	20Ɛ 056	3 X97
X	342	4 897
Ɛ	62X	5 697

N	Square Root	
440	20Ɛ 915	726 495
1	210 000	7 292
2	2X7	8 08X
3	591	8 X85
4	877	9 87Ɛ
5	Ɛ60	X 674
6	211 245	Ɛ 467
7	52X	730 259
8	813	1 04Ɛ
9	XƐ7	1 X3Ɛ
X	212 19Ɛ	2 82X
Ɛ	483	3 618
450	766	4 404
1	X49	5 1Ɛ0
2	213 130	5 Ɛ96
3	412	6 980
4	6Ɛ4	7 764
5	996	8 547
6	214 077	9 329
7	358	X 10X
8	639	X XXX
9	919	Ɛ 889
X	ƐƐ9	740 666
Ɛ	215 299	1 443
460	578	2 21X
1	858	2 ƐƐ5
2	Ɛ36	3 98X
3	216 215	4 762
4	4Ɛ3	5 535
5	791	6 307
6	X6Ɛ	7 098
7	217 148	7 X68
8	425	8 837
9	701	9 605
X	99X	X 391
Ɛ	218 076	Ɛ 159
470	351	Ɛ Ɛ24
1	629	750 8X9
2	904	1 671
3	Ɛ9Ɛ	2 435
4	219 275	3 1Ɛ7
5	550	3 Ɛ78
6	825	4 939
7	XƐƐ	5 6Ɛ8
8	21X 194	6 476
9	469	7 233
X	742	7 ƐXƐ
Ɛ	X16	8 966

N	Square Root	
480	21Ɛ 0XƐ	759 720
1	382	X 495
2	656	Ɛ 249
3	929	760 000
4	220 000	0 972
5	293	1 723
6	565	2 493
7	837	3 241
8	Ɛ09	3 ƐXƐ
9	221 19X	4 958
X	46Ɛ	5 704
Ɛ	740	6 46Ɛ
490	X11	7 214
1	222 0X1	7 Ɛ79
2	371	8 921
3	641	9 684
4	910	X 425
5	Ɛ9Ɛ	Ɛ 186
6	223 26X	Ɛ Ɛ26
7	539	770 885
8	807	1 623
9	X95	2 37Ɛ
X	224 163	3 117
Ɛ	430	3 X72
4X0	6Ɛ9	4 808
1	986	5 561
2	225 053	6 2Ɛ5
3	31Ɛ	7 048
4	5X7	7 99X
5	873	8 72Ɛ
6	Ɛ3X	9 47Ɛ
7	226 205	X 20X
8	490	X Ɛ58
9	757	Ɛ 8X5
X	X21	780 631
Ɛ	227 0X7	1 379
4Ɛ0	371	2 103
1	637	2 X48
2	900	3 791
3	Ɛ85	4 514
4	228 249	5 256
5	512	5 Ɛ98
6	796	6 919
7	X5X	7 658
8	229 122	8 397
9	3X5	9 115
X	668	9 X52
Ɛ	92Ɛ	X 789

N	Square Root		N	Square Root		N	Square Root	
500	229 ƐƐ1	78Ɛ 504	540	238 679	800 000	580	246 957	82Ɛ 555
1	22X 274	790 23X	1	92Ɛ	0 900	1	ƐƐ9	830 222
2	536	0 Ɛ74	2	ƐX1	1 5ƐX	2	247 260	0 XXX
3	7Ɛ7	1 8X8	3	239 252	2 2Ɛ8	3	502	1 776
4	X79	2 61Ɛ	4	503	2 ƐƐ5	4	765	2 440
5	22Ɛ 13X	3 351	5	774	3 8Ɛ1	5	X07	3 106
6	3ƐƐ	4 083	6	X25	4 5X9	6	248 068	3 98Ɛ
7	67Ɛ	4 9Ɛ3	7	23X 096	5 2X3	7	30X	4 654
8	940	5 723	8	346	5 Ɛ99	8	56Ɛ	5 317
9	230 000	6 451	9	5Ɛ6	6 892	9	810	5 Ɛ9X
X	280	7 17Ɛ	X	866	7 586	X	X71	6 860
Ɛ	53Ɛ	7 XX8	Ɛ	Ɛ16	8 279	Ɛ	249 112	7 521
510	7ƐƐ	8 814	550	23Ɛ 185	8 Ɛ70	590	372	8 1X2
1	X7X	9 53Ɛ	1	434	9 861	1	612	8 X62
2	231 139	X 265	2	6X3	X 552	2	872	9 721
3	3Ɛ7	X Ɛ8X	3	952	Ɛ 242	3	Ɛ12	X 39Ɛ
4	676	Ɛ 8Ɛ3	4	240 000	Ɛ Ɛ31	4	24X 172	Ɛ 058
5	934	7X0 616	5	26X	810 81Ɛ	5	411	Ɛ 915
6	ƐƐ1	1 339	6	518	1 509	6	670	840 591
7	232 26Ɛ	2 05X	7	786	2 1Ɛ6	7	90Ɛ	1 249
8	528	2 97Ɛ	8	X33	2 XX1	8	Ɛ6X	1 Ɛ03
9	7X5	3 69Ɛ	9	241 0X0	3 788	9	24Ɛ 208	2 779
X	X62	4 3ƐX	X	349	4 473	X	466	3 432
Ɛ	233 11X	5 118	Ɛ	5Ɛ6	5 158	Ɛ	705	4 0X6
520	397	5 X35	560	863	5 X41	5X0	962	4 95X
1	653	6 751	1	Ɛ0Ɛ	6 725	1	250 000	5 611
2	90X	7 469	2	242 177	7 408	2	259	6 283
3	Ɛ86	8 183	3	423	8 0XX	3	4Ɛ7	6 Ɛ34
4	234 241	8 X99	4	68Ɛ	8 98Ɛ	4	754	7 7X5
5	4Ɛ8	9 7Ɛ2	5	936	9 670	5	9Ɛ0	8 455
6	773	X 506	6	ƐX1	X 350	6	251 049	9 104
7	X29	Ɛ 219	7	243 248	Ɛ 02Ɛ	7	2X5	9 972
8	235 0X3	Ɛ ƐƐƐ	8	4Ɛ3	Ɛ 909	8	541	X 620
9	359	7Ɛ0 840	9	759	820 5X6	9	799	Ɛ 289
X	613	1 551	X	X03	1 283	X	X35	Ɛ Ɛ35
Ɛ	889	2 260	Ɛ	244 069	1 Ɛ5Ɛ	Ɛ	252 091	850 7X1
530	Ɛ42	2 Ɛ6Ɛ	570	313	2 836	5Ɛ0	328	1 448
1	236 1Ɛ7	3 879	1	579	3 510	1	583	2 0Ɛ2
2	46Ɛ	4 586	2	822	4 1X5	2	81X	2 957
3	724	5 292	3	X87	4 X7X	3	X75	3 600
4	998	5 Ɛ99	4	245 130	5 752	4	253 10Ɛ	4 264
5	237 050	6 8X3	5	394	6 425	5	365	4 Ɛ07
6	304	7 5X9	6	639	7 0Ɛ7	6	5ƐƐ	5 769
7	577	8 2Ɛ1	7	8X1	7 989	7	855	6 40Ɛ
8	82X	8 ƐƐ5	8	Ɛ45	8 65X	8	XXƐ	7 070
9	XX1	9 8Ɛ8	9	246 1X9	9 32X	9	254 144	7 911
X	238 154	X 5ƐX	X	450	9 ƐƐ9	X	39X	8 570
Ɛ	407	Ɛ 300	Ɛ	6Ɛ4	X 888	Ɛ	633	X 20Ɛ

N	Square Root		N	Square Root		N	Square Root	
600	254 887	859 X6X	640	262 485	887 443	680	26Ɛ 981	8Ɛ3 Ɛ85
1	Ɛ20	X 707	1	711	8 074	1	270 000	4 790
2	255 174	Ɛ 364	2	958	8 8X4	2	23X	5 396
3	409	860 000	3	ƐX3	9 514	3	479	5 ƐX0
4	661	0 857	4	263 229	X 143	4	6Ɛ7	6 7X5
5	8Ɛ5	1 4Ɛ2	5	474	X 971	5	934	7 3X9
6	Ɛ48	2 148	6	6ƐX	Ɛ 59Ɛ	6	Ɛ72	7 ƐƐ1
7	256 1X0	2 9X1	7	944	890 208	7	271 1Ɛ0	8 7Ɛ5
8	433	3 636	8	Ɛ8X	0 X35	8	429	9 3Ɛ7
9	686	4 28X	9	264 214	1 660	9	666	9 ƐƐ9
X	919	4 Ɛ21	X	459	2 288	X	8X3	X 7ƐƐ
Ɛ	Ɛ6Ɛ	5 774	Ɛ	6X3	2 XƐ2	Ɛ	Ɛ20	Ɛ 400
610	257 202	6 406	650	928	3 718	690	272 158	900 000
1	454	7 057	1	Ɛ71	4 341	1	395	0 800
2	6X6	7 8X7	2	265 1Ɛ6	4 Ɛ66	2	611	1 3ƐƐ
3	938	8 537	3	43X	5 78X	3	849	1 ƐƐ9
4	Ɛ89	9 186	4	683	6 3Ɛ1	4	X85	2 7Ɛ7
5	258 21Ɛ	9 X14	5	907	7 014	5	273 101	3 3Ɛ5
6	470	X 662	6	Ɛ4Ɛ	7 836	6	339	3 ƐƐ1
7	701	Ɛ 2XƐ	7	266 193	8 457	7	574	4 7XX
8	952	Ɛ Ɛ37	8	417	9 078	8	7XƐ	5 3X5
9	ƐX2	870 783	9	65X	9 898	9	X27	5 ƐX0
X	259 233	1 40X	X	8X1	X 4Ɛ8	X	274 062	6 797
Ɛ	483	2 054	Ɛ	Ɛ25	Ɛ 116	Ɛ	298	7 390
620	713	2 89X	660	267 168	Ɛ 935	6X0	513	7 Ɛ86
1	963	3 523	1	3XX	8X0 552	1	749	8 77X
2	ƐƐ2	4 167	2	631	1 16Ɛ	2	984	9 372
3	25X 242	4 9XƐ	3	873	1 988	3	ƐƐX	9 Ɛ66
4	491	5 631	4	XƐ6	2 5X3	4	275 234	X 759
5	720	6 274	5	268 138	3 1ƐƐ	5	469	Ɛ 34Ɛ
6	96Ɛ	6 XƐ5	6	37X	3 X15	6	6X3	Ɛ Ɛ41
7	ƐƐX	7 736	7	5ƐƐ	4 62Ɛ	7	918	910 732
8	25Ɛ 248	8 376	8	841	5 244	8	Ɛ52	1 323
9	496	8 ƐƐ6	9	X82	5 X59	9	276 187	1 Ɛ13
X	724	9 835	X	269 103	6 671	X	400	2 702
Ɛ	972	X 473	Ɛ	344	7 284	Ɛ	635	3 2Ɛ1
630	260 000	Ɛ 0Ɛ0	670	585	7 X97	6Ɛ0	869	3 X9Ɛ
1	24X	Ɛ 929	1	806	8 6X9	1	XX2	4 689
2	497	880 565	2	X46	9 2ƐƐ	2	277 116	5 276
3	724	1 1X1	3	26X 087	9 Ɛ10	3	34X	5 X63
4	971	1 X18	4	307	X 720	4	582	6 64Ɛ
5	ƐƐX	2 652	5	547	Ɛ 330	5	7Ɛ6	7 236
6	261 246	3 288	6	787	Ɛ Ɛ3Ɛ	6	X29	7 X21
7	493	3 Ɛ00	7	X06	8Ɛ0 74X	7	278 061	8 608
8	71Ɛ	4 735	8	26Ɛ 046	1 358	8	294	9 1Ɛ1
9	967	5 368	9	285	1 Ɛ65	9	507	9 997
X	ƐƐ2	5 Ɛ9Ɛ	X	504	2 772	X	73X	X 57Ɛ
Ɛ	262 23X	6 811	Ɛ	743	3 37X	Ɛ	971	Ɛ 163

N	Square Root		N	Square Root		N	Square Root	
700	278 £X4	91£ 947	740	285 £54	946 X0£	780	292 875	971 249
1	279 216	920 52X	1	286 17£	7 590	1	X95	1 9X9
2	448	1 110	2	3X6	8 150	2	293 0£4	2 54X
3	67£	1 8£2	3	611	8 910	3	314	3 0X9
4	8£1	2 493	4	837	9 490	4	534	3 849
5	£22	3 074	5	X62	X 04£	5	753	4 3X7
6	27X 154	3 854	6	287 088	X 809	6	972	4 £46
7	386	4 434	7	2£2	£ 387	7	£91	5 6X3
8	5£7	5 013	8	518	£ £44	8	294 1£0	6 241
9	828	5 7£1	9	742	950 701	9	40£	6 999
X	X59	6 38£	X	967	1 279	X	62X	7 536
£	27£ 08X	6 £69	£	£91	1 X35	£	849	8 092
710	2££	7 746	750	288 1£6	2 5£0	790	X67	8 829
1	52£	8 322	1	41£	3 167	1	295 085	9 384
2	760	8 X£X	2	644	3 921	2	2X3	9 £1X
3	990	9 695	3	869	4 497	3	501	X 674
4	280 000	X 270	4	X92	5 050	4	71£	£ 20X
5	230	X X46	5	289 0£6	5 805	5	939	£ 962
6	460	£ 61£	6	31£	6 379	6	£57	980 4£7
7	68£	930 1£4	7	543	6 £31	7	296 174	1 04£
8	8££	0 989	8	767	7 6X4	8	391	1 7X2
9	£2X	1 561	9	98£	8 257	9	5X£	2 335
X	281 159	2 134	X	££3	8 X09	X	808	2 X88
£	388	2 907	£	28X 217	9 57X	£	X25	3 61X
720	5£7	3 499	760	43X	X 130	7X0	297 041	4 170
1	826	4 06£	1	662	X 8X0	1	25X	4 901
2	X54	4 840	2	885	£ 450	2	476	5 452
3	282 082	5 411	3	XX8	960 000	3	693	5 £X2
4	2£1	5 £X1	4	28£ 10£	0 76£	4	8X£	6 731
5	51£	6 770	5	332	1 31X	5	£07	7 281
6	749	7 33£	6	555	1 X88	6	298 123	7 X10
7	976	7 £0X	7	777	2 635	7	33£	8 55X
8	£X4	8 698	8	99X	3 1X3	8	557	9 0X8
9	283 211	9 265	9	290 000	3 94£	9	772	9 835
X	43£	9 X32	X	222	4 4£7	X	98X	X 382
£	668	X 5££	£	444	5 063	£	£X5	X £0X
730	895	£ 186	770	666	5 80X	7£0	299 200	£ 656
1	£01	£ 952	1	888	6 375	1	417	990 1X2
2	284 12X	940 518	2	XX9	6 £1£	2	632	0 929
3	357	1 0X3	3	291 10£	7 684	3	849	1 473
4	583	1 868	4	330	8 229	4	X63	1 ££X
5	7X£	2 432	5	551	8 992	5	29X 07X	2 743
6	X17	2 ££6	6	772	9 536	6	294	3 288
7	285 043	3 77X	7	993	X 09X	7	4XX	3 X11
8	26£	4 342	8	££3	X 841	8	704	4 555
9	496	4 £05	9	292 214	£ 3X4	9	91X	5 099
X	702	5 688	X	434	£ £46	X	£34	5 820
£	929	6 24X	£	654	970 6X8	£	29£ 14X	6 363

N	Square Root		N	Square Root		N	Square Root	
800	29Ɛ 363	996 XX6	840	2X7 838	X00 000	880	2Ɛ3 Ɛ12	X24 626
1	579	7 628	1	X47	0 725	1	2Ɛ4 117	5 133
2	792	8 169	2	2X8 056	1 249	2	320	5 83Ɛ
3	9X7	8 8XX	3	265	1 970	3	526	6 347
4	2X0 000	9 42Ɛ	4	474	2 494	4	72Ɛ	6 X52
5	215	9 Ɛ6Ɛ	5	683	2 ƐƐ7	5	934	7 559
6	42X	X 6XƐ	6	892	3 719	6	Ɛ38	8 063
7	642	Ɛ 22X	7	XX0	4 23Ɛ	7	2Ɛ5 141	8 769
8	857	Ɛ 969	8	2X9 0XƐ	4 961	8	346	9 273
9	X6Ɛ	9X0 4X7	9	2Ɛ9	5 482	9	54X	9 978
X	2X1 083	1 025	X	507	5 ƐX2	X	753	X 481
Ɛ	297	1 762	Ɛ	715	6 703	Ɛ	957	X Ɛ85
810	4XƐ	2 29Ɛ	850	923	7 223	890	Ɛ5Ɛ	Ɛ 689
1	703	2 X17	1	Ɛ31	7 942	1	2Ɛ6 163	X30 191
2	917	3 554	2	2XX 13X	8 461	2	367	0 894
3	Ɛ2X	4 08Ɛ	3	348	8 Ɛ80	3	56Ɛ	1 397
4	2X2 142	4 806	4	555	9 69X	4	772	1 X99
5	355	5 341	5	762	X 1Ɛ8	5	976	2 59Ɛ
6	568	5 X77	6	96Ɛ	X 915	6	Ɛ79	3 0X1
7	77Ɛ	6 5Ɛ1	7	Ɛ78	Ɛ 432	7	2Ɛ7 181	3 7X2
8	992	7 126	8	2XƐ 185	Ɛ Ɛ4X	8	384	4 2X3
9	ƐX5	7 85Ɛ	9	392	X10 666	9	587	4 9X3
X	2X3 1Ɛ8	8 394	X	59Ɛ	1 182	X	78X	5 4X3
Ɛ	40X	8 Ɛ08	Ɛ	7X7	1 899	Ɛ	991	5 ƐX3
820	621	9 63Ɛ	860	9Ɛ4	2 3Ɛ4	8X0	Ɛ94	6 6X2
1	833	X 172	1	2Ɛ0 000	2 Ɛ0X	1	2Ɛ8 196	7 1X1
2	X45	X 8X5	2	208	3 624	2	399	7 8X0
3	2X4 057	Ɛ 417	3	414	4 13X	3	59Ɛ	8 39X
4	269	Ɛ Ɛ49	4	620	4 853	4	7X2	8 X97
5	47Ɛ	9Ɛ0 67X	5	828	5 368	5	9X4	9 594
6	690	1 1XƐ	6	X34	5 X80	6	ƐX6	X 091
7	8X2	1 920	7	2Ɛ1 03Ɛ	6 594	7	2Ɛ9 1X8	X 78X
8	XƐ3	2 450	8	247	7 0X7	8	3XX	Ɛ 286
9	2X5 105	2 Ɛ7Ɛ	9	452	7 7ƐX	9	5XƐ	Ɛ 982
X	316	3 6XX	X	659	8 311	X	7Ɛ1	X40 479
Ɛ	527	4 219	Ɛ	864	8 X23	Ɛ	9Ɛ3	0 Ɛ74
830	738	4 947	870	X6Ɛ	9 535	8Ɛ0	ƐƐ4	1 66X
1	948	5 475	1	2Ɛ2 076	X 046	1	2ƐX 1Ɛ5	2 164
2	Ɛ59	5 ƐX2	2	281	X 757	2	3Ɛ6	2 85X
3	2X6 169	6 70Ɛ	3	487	Ɛ 268	3	5Ɛ7	3 353
4	37X	7 238	4	692	Ɛ 978	4	7Ɛ8	3 X48
5	58X	7 964	5	898	X20 488	5	9Ɛ9	4 541
6	79X	8 48Ɛ	6	XX3	0 Ɛ97	6	ƐƐX	5 035
7	9XX	8 ƐƐ7	7	2Ɛ3 0X9	1 6X6	7	2ƐƐ 1ƐƐ	5 729
8	ƐƐX	9 721	8	2Ɛ3	2 1Ɛ5	8	3ƐƐ	6 220
9	2X7 20X	X 248	9	4Ɛ9	2 903	9	5ƐƐ	6 913
X	419	X 972	X	702	3 410	X	800	7 406
Ɛ	629	Ɛ 497	Ɛ	908	3 Ɛ1X	Ɛ	X00	7 XƐ8

N	Square Root		N	Square Root		N	Square Root	
900	300 000	X48 5XX	940	307 Ɛ16	X6Ɛ Ɛ52	980	313 86X	X92 Ɛ17
1	200	9 09Ɛ	1	308 111	X70 62X	1	X60	3 599
2	400	9 791	2	308	1 105	2	314 052	4 05Ɛ
3	600	X 281	3	502	1 7X0	3	243	4 721
4	7ƐƐ	X 972	4	6Ɛ9	2 276	4	435	5 1X2
5	9ƐƐ	Ɛ 462	5	8Ɛ3	2 950	5	626	5 864
6	ƐƐX	Ɛ Ɛ51	6	XX9	3 426	6	818	6 324
7	301 1Ɛ9	X50 640	7	309 0X3	3 XƐƐ	7	X09	6 9X5
8	3Ɛ8	1 12Ɛ	8	299	4 594	8	ƐƐX	7 465
9	5Ɛ8	1 819	9	493	5 069	9	315 1XƐ	7 Ɛ25
X	7Ɛ6	2 307	X	689	5 741	X	3X0	8 5X4
Ɛ	9Ɛ5	2 9Ɛ5	Ɛ	883	6 215	Ɛ	591	9 063
910	ƐƐ4	3 4X2	950	X78	6 8X8	990	782	9 722
1	302 1Ɛ3	3 Ɛ8Ɛ	1	30X 072	7 380	1	972	X 1X0
2	3Ɛ1	4 678	2	267	7 X52	2	Ɛ63	X 85X
3	5Ɛ0	5 164	3	461	8 525	3	316 153	Ɛ 318
4	7XX	5 850	4	656	8 ƐƐ7	4	344	Ɛ 995
5	9X8	6 337	5	84Ɛ	9 689	5	534	XX0 452
6	ƐX6	6 X22	6	X44	X 15X	6	724	0 Ɛ0Ɛ
7	303 1X4	7 509	7	30Ɛ 039	X 82Ɛ	7	914	1 587
8	3X2	7 ƐƐ3	8	232	Ɛ 300	8	Ɛ04	2 043
9	5X0	8 699	9	426	Ɛ 990	9	317 0Ɛ4	2 6ƐƐ
X	799	9 182	X	61Ɛ	X80 460	X	2X4	3 176
Ɛ	997	9 867	Ɛ	813	0 Ɛ30	Ɛ	493	3 831
920	Ɛ94	X 350	960	X08	1 5ƐƐ	9X0	683	4 2X7
1	304 192	X X34	1	310 000	2 08X	1	873	4 962
2	38Ɛ	Ɛ 518	2	1Ɛ4	2 758	2	X62	5 418
3	588	X60 000	3	3X8	3 226	3	318 051	5 X91
4	785	0 6X3	4	5X0	3 8Ɛ4	4	240	6 547
5	982	1 186	5	794	4 382	5	42Ɛ	6 ƐƐƐ
6	Ɛ7Ɛ	1 869	6	988	4 X4Ɛ	6	61X	7 674
7	305 177	2 34Ɛ	7	Ɛ7Ɛ	5 517	7	809	8 128
8	374	2 X30	8	311 173	5 ƐX4	8	9Ɛ8	8 7X0
9	570	3 512	9	366	6 670	9	ƐX7	9 254
X	769	3 ƐƐ3	X	55X	7 138	X	319 195	9 907
Ɛ	965	4 694	Ɛ	751	7 803	Ɛ	384	X 37X
930	Ɛ61	5 174	970	944	8 28X	9Ɛ0	572	X X31
1	306 159	5 854	1	Ɛ37	8 955	1	761	Ɛ 4X3
2	355	6 333	2	312 12X	9 41Ɛ	2	94Ɛ	Ɛ Ɛ55
3	551	6 X12	3	321	9 XX5	3	Ɛ39	XƐ0 606
4	748	7 4Ɛ1	4	514	X 56X	4	31X 127	1 078
5	944	7 Ɛ90	5	706	Ɛ 034	5	315	1 729
6	Ɛ40	8 66X	6	8Ɛ9	Ɛ 6Ɛ9	6	503	2 199
7	307 137	9 147	7	XXƐ	X90 181	7	6Ɛ1	2 84X
8	332	9 825	8	313 0X2	0 845	8	89X	3 2Ɛ9
9	529	X 302	9	294	1 309	9	X88	3 969
X	724	X 99X	X	486	1 991	X	31Ɛ 075	4 418
Ɛ	91Ɛ	Ɛ 476	Ɛ	678	2 454	Ɛ	263	4 X87

N	Square Root	N	Square Root	N	Square Root
X00	31Ɛ 450 XƐ5 536	X40	326 X8Ɛ Ɛ17 624	X80	332 376 Ɛ39 211
1	639 5 ƐX4	1	327 074 8 07Ɛ	1	556 9 855
2	826 6 652	2	258 8 715	2	737 X 299
3	X13 7 100	3	441 9 170	3	917 X 921
4	320 000 7 769	4	625 9 806	4	XƐ7 Ɛ 364
5	1X9 8 216	5	80X X 25Ɛ	5	333 098 Ɛ 9X7
6	395 8 883	6	9Ɛ2 X 8Ɛ5	6	278 Ɛ40 42X
7	582 9 32Ɛ	7	Ɛ96 Ɛ 34X	7	458 0 X70
8	76Ɛ 9 997	8	328 17X Ɛ 9X2	8	638 1 4Ɛ2
9	957 X 443	9	362 Ɛ20 437	9	817 1 Ɛ34
X	Ɛ43 X XXX	X	546 0 X8Ɛ	X	9Ɛ7 2 576
Ɛ	321 130 Ɛ 555	Ɛ	72X 1 523	Ɛ	Ɛ97 2 ƐƐ7
X10	318 Ɛ00 000	X50	912 1 Ɛ76	X90	334 176 3 638
1	504 0 666	1	XƐ5 2 60X	1	356 4 079
2	6Ɛ0 1 110	2	329 099 3 060	2	535 4 6Ɛ9
3	898 1 776	3	281 3 6Ɛ3	3	714 5 139
4	X83 2 220	4	464 4 145	4	8Ɛ4 5 779
5	322 06Ɛ 2 885	5	647 4 797	5	X93 6 1Ɛ9
6	257 3 329	6	82X 5 229	6	335 072 6 838
7	442 3 992	7	X12 5 87X	7	251 7 277
8	629 4 436	8	ƐƐ5 6 30Ɛ	8	430 7 8Ɛ6
9	815 4 X9X	9	32X 198 6 960	9	60X 8 334
X	X00 5 541	X	37X 7 3Ɛ0	X	7X9 8 972
Ɛ	ƐX7 5 ƐX4	Ɛ	561 7 X40	Ɛ	988 9 3Ɛ0
X20	323 192 6 647	X60	744 8 490	XX0	Ɛ66 9 X29
1	379 7 0XX	1	926 8 Ɛ20	1	336 145 X 467
2	564 7 750	2	Ɛ09 9 56Ɛ	2	323 X XX3
3	74Ɛ 8 1Ɛ2	3	32Ɛ 0XƐ 9 ƐƐX	3	502 Ɛ 520
4	935 8 853	4	292 X 648	4	6X0 Ɛ Ɛ58
5	Ɛ20 9 2Ɛ5	5	474 Ɛ 097	5	87X Ɛ50 594
6	324 106 9 956	6	656 Ɛ 725	6	X58 1 010
7	2Ɛ1 X 3Ɛ6	7	838 Ɛ30 172	7	337 036 1 648
8	497 X X56	8	X1X 0 800	8	214 2 083
9	681 Ɛ 4Ɛ6	9	330 000 1 249	9	3Ɛ1 2 6ƐX
X	867 Ɛ Ɛ56	X	1X2 1 896	X	58Ɛ 3 134
Ɛ	X51 Ɛ10 5Ɛ5	Ɛ	384 2 322	Ɛ	769 3 76X
X30	325 037 1 054	X70	565 2 96X	XƐ0	946 4 1X4
1	221 1 6Ɛ3	1	747 3 3Ɛ6	1	Ɛ24 4 81X
2	407 2 151	2	928 3 X42	2	338 101 5 254
3	5Ɛ0 2 7Ɛ0	3	Ɛ0X 4 489	3	29X 5 889
4	796 3 249	4	331 0XƐ 4 Ɛ14	4	478 6 302
5	97Ɛ 3 8X7	5	290 5 55Ɛ	5	655 6 936
6	Ɛ65 4 344	6	471 5 ƐX5	6	832 7 36X
7	326 14X 4 9X1	7	652 6 62Ɛ	7	X0Ɛ 7 9X2
8	333 5 439	8	833 7 075	8	ƐX8 8 416
9	518 5 X95	9	X14 7 6ƐX	9	339 184 8 X49
X	701 6 531	X	ƐƐ5 8 143	X	361 9 481
Ɛ	8X6 6 Ɛ89	Ɛ	332 195 8 788	Ɛ	53X 9 XƐ3

N	Square Root	
Ɛ00	339 716	Ɛ5X 526
1	8Ɛ3	X Ɛ58
2	X8Ɛ	Ɛ 58X
3	33X 068	Ɛ60 000
4	244	0 631
5	420	1 063
6	5Ɛ8	1 693
7	794	2 104
8	970	2 734
9	Ɛ48	3 164
X	33Ɛ 123	3 794
Ɛ	2ƐƐ	4 203
Ɛ10	497	4 833
1	672	5 261
2	849	5 890
3	X25	6 2ƐX
4	340 000	6 928
5	197	7 356
6	372	7 984
7	549	8 3Ɛ1
8	724	8 X1X
9	8ƐƐ	9 446
X	X96	9 X73
Ɛ	341 070	X 49Ɛ
Ɛ20	247	X Ɛ07
1	422	Ɛ 532
2	5Ɛ8	Ɛ Ɛ59
3	792	Ɛ70 584
4	969	0 ƐXƐ
5	Ɛ43	1 615
6	342 119	2 040
7	2Ɛ3	2 665
8	489	3 08Ɛ
9	663	3 6Ɛ4
X	839	4 119
Ɛ	X12	4 742
Ɛ30	ƐX8	5 167
1	343 181	5 78Ɛ
2	357	6 1Ɛ3
3	530	6 816
4	706	7 23X
5	89Ɛ	7 861
6	X74	8 284
7	344 049	8 8X6
8	222	9 308
9	3Ɛ7	9 92X
X	590	X 350
Ɛ	765	X 972

N	Square Root	
Ɛ40	344 939	Ɛ7Ɛ 393
1	Ɛ12	Ɛ 9Ɛ4
2	345 0X6	Ɛ80 414
3	27Ɛ	0 X35
4	453	1 455
5	628	1 X75
6	800	2 494
7	994	2 XƐ4
8	Ɛ68	3 513
9	346 140	3 Ɛ31
X	314	4 550
Ɛ	4X8	4 Ɛ6X
Ɛ50	67Ɛ	5 588
1	853	5 ƐX6
2	X27	6 603
3	ƐƐX	7 020
4	347 192	7 639
5	365	8 056
6	538	8 672
7	710	9 08X
8	8X3	9 6X6
9	X76	X 101
X	348 049	X 718
Ɛ	220	Ɛ 133
Ɛ60	3Ɛ2	Ɛ 74X
1	585	Ɛ90 165
2	758	0 77Ɛ
3	92X	1 195
4	Ɛ01	1 7XX
5	349 093	2 204
6	266	2 819
7	438	3 232
8	60X	3 846
9	7X0	4 25Ɛ
X	972	4 873
Ɛ	Ɛ44	5 286
Ɛ70	34X 116	5 89X
1	2X8	6 2Ɛ1
2	47X	6 904
3	64Ɛ	7 317
4	821	7 92X
5	9Ɛ3	8 340
6	Ɛ84	8 952
7	34Ɛ 155	9 363
8	327	9 975
9	4Ɛ8	X 386
X	689	X 997
Ɛ	85X	Ɛ 3X8

N	Square Root	
Ɛ80	34Ɛ X2Ɛ	Ɛ9Ɛ 9Ɛ8
1	350 000	ƐX0 408
2	191	0 X18
3	362	1 428
4	532	1 X37
5	703	2 446
6	893	2 X55
7	X64	3 463
8	351 034	3 X72
9	205	4 480
X	395	4 X89
Ɛ	565	5 497
Ɛ90	735	5 XX4
1	905	6 4Ɛ1
2	X95	6 XƐX
3	352 065	7 507
4	235	7 Ɛ13
5	404	8 51Ɛ
6	594	8 Ɛ27
7	764	9 532
8	933	9 Ɛ39
9	Ɛ03	X 544
X	353 092	X Ɛ4Ɛ
Ɛ	261	Ɛ 555
ƐX0	430	Ɛ Ɛ5Ɛ
1	600	ƐƐ0 565
2	78Ɛ	0 Ɛ6Ɛ
3	95X	1 575
4	Ɛ29	1 Ɛ7X
5	354 0Ɛ7	2 583
6	286	2 Ɛ87
7	455	3 590
8	623	3 Ɛ94
9	7Ɛ2	4 598
X	980	4 Ɛ9Ɛ
Ɛ	Ɛ4Ɛ	5 5X3
ƐƐ0	355 119	5 ƐX6
1	2X7	6 5X9
2	476	6 ƐXƐ
3	644	7 5Ɛ2
4	812	7 ƐƐ4
5	9X0	8 5Ɛ6
6	Ɛ6X	8 Ɛ27
7	356 137	9 5Ɛ9
8	305	9 ƐƐX
9	493	X 5ƐƐ
X	660	X ƐƐƐ
Ɛ	82X	Ɛ 600
1000	9Ɛ7	1000 000

Cube Roots

The following parallel table of cube roots may be used to obtain six figures of the root by direct proportion. It is necessary to find by inspection the first figure of the root and use the column indicated. Results will be within one of the correct sixth figure, except for third column roots of numbers beginning with one. These will be within two and may be checked within one by using a factor.

Example:

Find the cube root of *3.18 481*

Root *3.18*	*1.56 X11*	
		1X4
Add *.481 (1X4)*	*88*	
Root *3.18 481*	*1.56 X99*	

Check, using factor

Multiply by *8* *21.1 714(8)*		
Root *21.1*	*2.Ɛ1 639*	
		571
Add *.7148 (571)*	*339*	
	2.Ɛ1 976	
Divide root by *2*	*1.56 X99*	

To nine places, using log table *1.56 X99 38Ɛ*

Example:

Find the cube root of *.107 497*

Root *.107*	*.53X 989*	
		1 832
Add *.497 (1832)*	*813*	
Root *.107 497*	*.53Ɛ 5X0*	

Check, using factor

Multiply by *8* *.84Ɛ 248*		
Root *.84Ɛ*	*.X7X X82*	
		509
Add *.248 (509)*	*101*	
	.X7X Ɛ83	
Divide root by *2*	*.53Ɛ 5X2*	

To nine places, using log table *.53Ɛ 5X1 57X*

N	Cube Root			N	Cube Root			N	Cube Root		
100	100 000	235 817	52X 935	140	112 5XƐ	262 X35	592 89Ɛ	180	122 893	286 X62	626 X72
1	3ƐƐ	6 533	530 625	1	926	3 5X0	4 213	1	Ɛ74	7 503	8 15Ɛ
2	7Ɛ7	7 244	2 303	2	113 05Ɛ	4 143	5 73Ɛ	2	123 254	7 Ɛ61	9 441
3	Ɛ20	7 Ɛ50	3 Ɛ90	3	392	4 8X2	7 059	3	533	8 5Ɛ9	X 71X
4	101 3X3	8 852	5 847	4	704	5 43X	8 570	4	811	9 052	Ɛ 9Ɛ1
5	793	9 54X	7 4Ɛ1	5	X34	5 Ɛ92	9 X76	5	XXX	9 6X4	631 07Ɛ
6	Ɛ81	X 240	9 145	6	114 163	6 722	Ɛ 374	6	124 185	X 134	2 342
7	102 368	X Ɛ28	X 989	7	490	7 26Ɛ	5X0 865	7	460	X 782	3 600
8	751	Ɛ 80Ɛ	540 5ƐƐ	8	7Ɛ7	7 9Ɛ4	2 14X	8	735	Ɛ 209	4 874
9	Ɛ34	240 4X8	2 221	9	Ɛ21	8 535	3 628	9	X0X	Ɛ 851	5 Ɛ23
X	103 314	1 180	3 X32	X	115 246	9 073	4 XƐ9	X	125 0X1	290 294	7 187
Ɛ	6Ɛ1	1 X4X	5 633	Ɛ	568	9 7XX	6 382	Ɛ	373	0 913	8 427
110	X88	2 713	7 224	150	88X	X 321	7 840	190	644	1 351	9 680
1	104 261	3 393	8 X04	1	ƐXX	X X51	9 0Ɛ1	1	914	1 988	X 911
2	634	4 049	X 594	2	116 308	Ɛ 579	X 557	2	ƐX3	2 400	Ɛ Ɛ57
3	X04	4 8ƐX	550 154	3	625	270 0X2	Ɛ 9Ɛ5	3	126 271	2 X32	641 199
4	105 192	5 566	1 904	4	941	0 804	5Ɛ1 248	4	53Ɛ	3 462	2 415
5	55X	6 209	3 464	5	117 057	1 322	2 693	5	806	3 X8Ɛ	3 647
6	924	6 X66	4 ƐƐ5	6	36Ɛ	1 X39	3 Ɛ12	6	X91	4 4Ɛ6	4 875
7	106 0X7	7 6ƐƐ	6 737	7	683	2 551	5 346	7	127 157	4 Ɛ1Ɛ	5 X99
8	468	8 34Ɛ	8 269	8	994	3 062	6 773	8	420	5 542	7 0Ɛ7
9	827	8 Ɛ95	9 98Ɛ	9	118 0X5	3 76Ɛ	7 Ɛ94	9	6X4	5 Ɛ62	8 311
X	ƐX4	9 817	Ɛ 4X3	X	3Ɛ4	4 275	9 3XX	X	967	6 580	9 521
Ɛ	107 35Ɛ	X 454	560 ƐX8	Ɛ	701	4 978	X 7Ɛ8	Ɛ	128 029	6 Ɛ98	X 728
120	714	Ɛ 089	2 6X1	160	X0X	5 478	600 000	1X0	2XX	7 5Ɛ1	Ɛ 92X
1	X87	Ɛ 8Ɛ8	4 188	1	119 114	5 Ɛ75	1 3Ɛ8	1	56X	8 004	650 Ɛ27
2	108 237	250 523	5 864	2	41X	6 66Ɛ	2 7XX	2	829	8 615	2 11Ɛ
3	5X6	1 145	7 332	3	722	7 162	3 Ɛ94	3	XX8	9 024	3 30X
4	953	1 963	8 9Ɛ1	4	X25	7 851	5 374	4	129 165	9 631	4 4Ɛ4
5	109 0Ɛ9	2 578	X 462	5	11X 127	8 33X	6 748	5	421	X 037	5 695
6	462	3 189	Ɛ Ɛ04	6	427	8 X23	7 Ɛ16	6	698	X 640	6 871
7	805	3 995	571 558	7	726	9 506	9 299	7	953	Ɛ 042	7 X44
8	Ɛ66	4 599	2 ƐX2	8	X24	9 ƐX6	X 655	8	12X 008	Ɛ 642	9 012
9	10X 305	5 198	4 61X	9	11Ɛ 120	X 683	Ɛ X06	9	280	2X0 040	X 198
X	662	5 993	6 048	X	417	Ɛ 159	611 171	X	534	0 638	Ɛ 358
Ɛ	9Ɛ9	6 586	7 669	Ɛ	711	Ɛ 830	2 512	Ɛ	7X7	1 031	660 514
130	10Ɛ 152	7 174	9 07Ɛ	170	X06	280 300	3 867	1Ɛ0	X58	1 625	1 687
1	4X6	7 95Ɛ	X 684	1	120 0Ɛ9	0 989	4 ƐƐ6	1	12Ɛ 109	2 017	2 835
2	837	8 541	580 080	2	3XƐ	1 454	6 33Ɛ	2	379	2 606	3 99Ɛ
3	Ɛ87	9 11Ɛ	1 66X	3	6X0	1 Ɛ17	7 67X	3	628	2 ƐƐ4	4 Ɛ40
4	110 315	9 8Ɛ5	3 04X	4	990	2 598	8 9Ɛ1	4	897	3 59Ɛ	6 098
5	661	X 487	4 622	5	121 07X	3 056	X 11Ɛ	5	Ɛ44	3 Ɛ85	7 230
6	9X8	Ɛ 055	5 ƐX8	6	368	3 712	Ɛ 443	6	130 1Ɛ0	4 568	8 37Ɛ
7	111 131	Ɛ 81Ɛ	7 565	7	654	4 186	620 760	7	458	4 Ɛ4X	9 505
8	474	260 3X0	8 Ɛ15	8	93Ɛ	4 839	1 X73	8	702	5 529	X 647
9	7Ɛ5	0 Ɛ5X	X 477	9	122 025	5 2X8	3 180	9	968	5 Ɛ07	Ɛ 785
X	Ɛ35	1 715	Ɛ X12	X	309	5 955	4 482	X	131 011	6 4X2	670 8ƐX
Ɛ	112 273	2 287	591 35Ɛ	Ɛ	5Ɛ1	6 3ƐƐ	5 77Ɛ	Ɛ	275	6 X78	1 X2X

N	Cube Root			N	Cube Root			N	Cube Root		
200	131 519	2χ7 450	672 Ɛ56	240	13χ ƐƐ3	305 329	6Ɛ5 119	280	147 831	321 208	732 7Ɛ3
1	77Ɛ	7 χ21	4 07χ	1	13Ɛ 226	5 851	6 108	1	χ40	1 69χ	3 6χ0
2	χ21	8 3Ɛ1	5 199	2	458	6 175	7 0Ɛ3	2	148 04Ɛ	1 Ɛ69	4 586
3	132 081	8 97Ɛ	6 2Ɛ4	3	68χ	6 697	8 097	3	259	2 438	5 469
4	321	9 347	7 407	4	8ƐƐ	6 ƐƐ7	9 077	4	467	2 906	6 349
5	581	9 912	8 515	5	Ɛ30	7 516	χ 054	5	674	3 192	7 227
6	81Ɛ	χ 296	9 61Ɛ	6	140 160	7 χ34	Ɛ 02χ	6	881	3 65χ	8 102
7	χ78	χ 858	χ 721	7	38Ɛ	8 350	700 000	7	χ89	3 Ɛ24	8 Ɛ97
8	133 115	Ɛ 219	Ɛ 81Ɛ	8	5Ɛχ	8 866	0 Ɛ8Ɛ	8	149 095	4 3χ9	9 χ69
9	371	Ɛ 798	680 914	9	828	9 180	1 Ɛ57	9	2χ0	4 871	χ 938
χ	608	2Ɛ0 155	1 χ05	χ	χ55	9 693	2 Ɛ1Ɛ	χ	4χ7	5 133	Ɛ 805
Ɛ	862	0 710	2 χƐ2	Ɛ	141 082	9 Ɛχ6	3 χχ1	Ɛ	6Ɛ1	5 5Ɛ5	740 68Ɛ
210	χƐ8	1 085	3 Ɛ97	250	2χχ	χ 4Ɛ7	4 χ5Ɛ	290	8Ɛ7	5 χ75	1 552
1	134 151	1 639	5 078	1	516	χ χ06	5 χ16	1	Ɛ00	6 334	2 413
2	3χ5	1 Ɛχχ	6 155	2	741	Ɛ 314	6 989	2	14χ 104	6 7Ɛ3	3 291
3	638	2 55χ	7 22χ	3	967	Ɛ 821	7 93χ	3	309	7 070	4 149
4	88χ	2 Ɛ09	8 2Ɛχ	4	Ɛ91	310 129	8 8χ7	4	510	7 528	5 002
5	Ɛ20	3 475	9 387	5	142 1Ɛ6	0 633	9 851	5	714	7 9χ2	5 χ74
6	135 171	3 χ20	χ 44Ɛ	6	41χ	0 Ɛ37	χ 7Ɛ5	6	916	8 258	6 924
7	401	4 385	Ɛ 510	7	642	1 43Ɛ	Ɛ 754	7	Ɛ19	8 711	7 792
8	650	4 928	690 588	8	866	1 941	710 6Ɛ1	8	14Ɛ 11χ	8 Ɛ84	8 639
9	89Ɛ	5 28χ	1 641	9	χ88	2 241	1 647	9	320	9 436	9 4χ1
χ	Ɛ28	5 829	2 6Ɛ2	χ	143 0χχ	2 740	2 59χ	χ	521	9 8χ8	χ 343
Ɛ	136 176	6 187	3 75Ɛ	Ɛ	310	3 03χ	3 529	Ɛ	721	χ 158	Ɛ 1χ3
220	402	6 724	4 804	260	531	3 537	4 476	2χ0	921	χ 607	750 040
1	64χ	7 07Ɛ	5 865	1	751	3 χ32	5 3ƐƐ	1	Ɛ20	χ χ75	0 χ97
2	894	7 614	6 902	2	971	4 328	6 342	2	150 11Ɛ	Ɛ 322	1 92Ɛ
3	Ɛ1Ɛ	7 Ɛ67	7 958	3	Ɛ90	4 821	7 281	3	31χ	Ɛ 78χ	2 780
4	137 164	8 4Ɛ9	8 9χχ	4	144 1χƐ	5 114	8 1Ɛχ	4	518	330 035	3 610
5	3χ9	8 χ49	9 χ38	5	409	5 606	9 133	5	715	0 49Ɛ	4 458
6	631	9 397	χ χ82	6	627	5 χƐ7	χ 066	6	913	0 943	5 2χ3
7	874	9 924	Ɛ Ɛ04	7	844	6 3χ6	χ Ɛ95	7	Ɛ0Ɛ	1 1χ7	6 127
8	χƐ7	χ 26Ɛ	6χ0 Ɛ43	8	χ60	6 894	Ɛ Ɛ02	8	151 107	1 64χ	6 Ɛ68
9	138 139	χ 7Ɛ5	1 Ɛ7χ	9	145 078	7 181	720 χ28	9	303	1 χχƐ	7 9χ8
χ	37χ	Ɛ 139	2 ƐƐ1	χ	293	7 669	1 94χ	χ	4Ɛχ	2 350	8 824
Ɛ	5Ɛχ	Ɛ 67Ɛ	4 021	Ɛ	4χχ	7 Ɛ53	2 86χ	Ɛ	6Ɛ5	2 7χƐ	9 65Ɛ
230	83χ	300 000	5 049	270	704	8 438	3 787	2Ɛ0	8Ɛ0	3 04χ	χ 493
1	χ79	0 53Ɛ	6 072	1	91χ	8 920	4 6χ2	1	χχ6	3 4χ7	Ɛ 305
2	139 0Ɛ8	0 χ79	7 093	2	Ɛ33	9 202	5 5Ɛ5	2	152 09Ɛ	3 944	760 134
3	335	1 3Ɛ5	8 0Ɛ0	3	146 148	9 6χ4	6 505	3	294	4 19Ɛ	0 Ɛ61
4	572	1 92Ɛ	9 106	4	360	9 Ɛ84	7 413	4	489	4 636	1 988
5	7χƐ	2 264	χ 118	5	573	χ 463	8 31χ	5	681	4 χ8Ɛ	2 7Ɛ1
6	χ27	2 798	Ɛ 126	6	786	χ 940	9 222	6	875	5 324	3 613
7	13χ 062	3 10χ	6Ɛ0 132	7	999	Ɛ 219	χ 123	7	χ68	5 777	4 433
8	298	3 63χ	1 135	8	ƐχƐ	Ɛ 6Ɛ4	Ɛ 021	8	153 05Ɛ	6 009	5 250
9	512	3 Ɛ69	2 135	9	147 200	Ɛ Ɛ8χ	Ɛ Ɛ19	9	251	6 45Ɛ	6 068
χ	747	4 496	3 132	χ	411	320 462	730 χ12	χ	443	6 8χƐ	6 χ81
Ɛ	97Ɛ	4 χ02	4 127	Ɛ	621	0 936	1 904	Ɛ	635	7 13Ɛ	7 893

N	Cube Root					
300	153	826	337	589	768	6X4
1		X17		X17	9	4Σ2
2	154	007	338	263	X	2ΣX
3		1Σ7		6XΣ	Σ	104
4		3X6		Σ35	Σ	Σ08
5		595	339	37Σ	770	909
6		784		804	1	709
7		972	33X	047	2	506
8		Σ60		48X	3	301
9	155	149		910	4	0Σ5
X		336	33Σ	151	4	XX8
Σ		522		590	5	898
310		70X		X0Σ	6	686
1		8Σ6	340	249	7	472
2		XX1		687	8	258
3	156	088		Σ03	9	040
4		273	341	33X	9	X22
5		459		774	X	802
6		643		ΣXX	Σ	59Σ
7		828	342	422	780	377
8		X11		856	1	150
9		ΣΣ5	343	088	1	Σ23
X	157	199		4ΣX	2	8Σ4
Σ		381		92Σ	3	683
320		564	344	15Σ	4	450
1		747		58X	5	217
2		92X		9Σ8	5	ΣX0
3		Σ10	345	226	6	963
4	158	0Σ2		652	7	724
5		293		X7X	8	4X3
6		474	346	2X4	9	260
7		655		70X	X	017
8		835		Σ33	X	990
9		X15	347	357	Σ	743
X		ΣΣ4		77X	790	4Σ4
Σ	159	193		ΣX0	1	263
330		372	348	402	2	010
1		550		823	2	977
2		72X	349	042	3	720
3		908		461	4	483
4		XX5		87Σ	5	224
5	15X	082	34X	098	5	Σ83
6		25X		4Σ5	6	921
7		436		910	7	678
8		612	34Σ	127	8	412
9		7XX		541	9	165
X		985		956	9	XΣ7
Σ		Σ5Σ	350	16X	X	847

N	Cube Root					
340	15Σ	136	350	581	79Σ	595
1		310		994	7X0	321
2		4X5	351	1X6	1	067
3		67X		5Σ7	1	9XΣ
4		853		X07	2	732
5		X28	352	216	3	472
6	160	000		625	4	1Σ1
7		194		X32	4	Σ2X
8		367	353	23Σ	5	865
9		53X		647	6	59X
X		711		X53	7	312
Σ		8X4	354	259	8	043
350		X76		663	8	973
1	161	047		X68	9	6X1
2		219	355	270	X	409
3		3XX		673	Σ	134
4		57Σ		X76	Σ	X58
5		74Σ	356	278	7Σ0	77Σ
6		91Σ		679	1	4X0
7		XXΣ		X79	2	1ΣΣ
8	162	07X	357	278	2	Σ19
9		249		677	3	835
X		418		X75	4	54Σ
Σ		5X6	358	272	5	263
360		774		66Σ	5	Σ76
1		942		X66	6	886
2		Σ0Σ	359	261	7	595
3	163	098		657	8	2X3
4		265		X51	8	ΣXX
5		431	35X	246	9	8Σ4
6		5ΣX		639	X	5Σ9
7		785		X31	Σ	2ΣΣ
8		951	35Σ	223	800	000
9		Σ18		615	0	8ΣΣ
X	164	0X3		X06	1	5Σ9
Σ		269	360	1Σ6	2	2Σ4
370		433		5X6	2	ΣXΣ
1		5Σ9		994	3	8X3
2		783	361	182	4	596
3		948		570	5	287
4		Σ11		958	5	Σ76
5	165	095	362	144	6	864
6		259		52Σ	7	551
7		421		916	8	237
8		5X5	363	100	8	Σ20
9		768		4X5	9	803
X		92Σ		889	X	4X5
Σ		XΣ2	364	071	Σ	185

N	Cube Root					
380	166	074	364	454	80Σ	X64
1		236		836	810	741
2		3Σ8	365	017	1	418
3		57X		3Σ8	2	0Σ2
4		73Σ		798	2	986
5		900		Σ78	3	658
6		X80	366	357	4	329
7	167	041		735	4	ΣΣ8
8		201		Σ12	5	886
9		380	367	2XΣ	6	553
X		540		687	7	219
Σ		6ΣΣ		X62	7	XX2
390		879	368	239	8	766
1		X38		613	9	428
2		ΣΣ6		9X8	X	0X8
3	168	174	369	181	X	967
4		332		555	Σ	625
5		4XΣ		928	820	2X1
6		668	36X	0ΣΣ	0	Σ57
7		825		491	1	810
8		9X1		862	2	483
9		Σ59	36Σ	033	3	135
X	169	115		403	3	9X6
Σ		291		792	4	654
3X0		448		Σ61	5	302
1		603	370	32Σ	5	Σ6X
2		77X		6Σ8	6	814
3		934		X85	7	479
4		XXΣ	371	251	8	120
5	16X	064		619	8	982
6		21X		9X4	9	623
7		393	372	16X	X	282
8		548		533	X	Σ1Σ
9		701		8Σ8	Σ	777
X		876	373	081	830	412
Σ		X2X		444	1	067
3Σ0		ΣX2		807	1	8ΣΣ
1	16Σ	156		Σ8X	2	551
2		309	374	350	3	1X2
3		480		711	3	X32
4		633		X91	4	680
5		7X6	375	251	5	309
6		958		611	5	Σ54
7		Σ0X		98Σ	6	79X
8	170	080	376	149	7	422
9		231		507	8	065
X		3X2		884	8	8X7
Σ		553	377	040	9	527

N	Cube Root						N	Cube Root						N	Cube Root					
400	170	704	377	3Ɛ8	83X	166	440	176	925	389	594	866	638	480	180	77Ɛ	39X	Ɛ11	891	375
1		875		773	X	9X3	1		X85		928	7	224	1		911	39Ɛ	245	1	Ɛ16
2		X25		Ɛ29	Ɛ	61Ɛ	2	177	026	38X	07Ɛ	7	X0X	2		X63		578	2	675
3		Ɛ95	378	2X3	840	256	3		186		412	8	5Ɛ3	3		ƐƐ5		8Ɛ0	3	214
4	171	144		658	0	X8Ɛ	4		326		765	9	196	4	181	146	3X0	022	3	971
5		2Ɛ4		X11	1	703	5		486		XƐ6	9	979	5		298		354	4	509
6		463	379	185	2	336	6		625	38Ɛ	248	X	55X	6		429		686	5	064
7		612		538	2	Ɛ67	7		784		598	Ɛ	13X	7		57X		9Ɛ7	5	7ƐƐ
8		780		8XƐ	3	797	8		923		928	Ɛ	919	8		70Ɛ	3X1	128	6	354
9		92Ɛ	37X	061	4	405	9		X82	390	078	870	4Ɛ6	9		85Ɛ		458	6	XX8
X		X99		413	5	032	X	178	020		407	1	093	X		9XƐ		788	7	63Ɛ
Ɛ	172	047		784	5	85X	Ɛ		17Ɛ		756	1	86X	Ɛ		Ɛ40		XƐ7	8	191
410		1Ɛ4		Ɛ34	6	485	450		319		XX4	2	444	490	182	090	3X2	226	8	922
1		362	37Ɛ	2X4	7	0XX	1		477	391	232	3	019	1		21Ɛ		555	9	472
2		50Ɛ		654	7	911	2		614		57Ɛ	3	7Ɛ1	2		36Ɛ		883	X	001
3		678		X02	8	534	3		772		907	4	384	3		4ƐX		Ɛ20	X	74Ɛ
4		824	380	170	9	155	4		90Ɛ	392	054	4	Ɛ55	4		649	3X3	319	Ɛ	297
5		991		51X	9	975	5		X68		39Ɛ	5	725	5		798		646	Ɛ	X23
6		Ɛ39		887	X	593	6	179	005		726	6	2Ɛ5	6		927		972	8X0	56X
7	173	0X4	381	033	Ɛ	1Ɛ0	7		161		X71	6	X83	7		X76	3X4	09X	1	0Ɛ4
8		250		39Ɛ	Ɛ	X08	8		2ƐX	393	1Ɛ7	7	64Ɛ	8	183	004		405	1	838
9		3Ɛ7		747	850	623	9		456		540	8	217	9		152		730	2	380
X		562		XƐ1	1	238	X		5Ɛ1		885	8	9X1	X		2X0		X56	2	Ɛ03
Ɛ		709	382	257	1	X50	Ɛ		749	394	00X	9	567	Ɛ		42X	3X5	180	3	644
420		874		601	2	662	460		8X5		352	X	12Ɛ	4X0		577		4X6	4	185
1		X1X		966	3	274	1		X40		696	X	8Ɛ2	1		705		80Ɛ	4	904
2		Ɛ84	383	10X	3	X84	2		Ɛ97		X19	Ɛ	474	2		852		Ɛ34	5	443
3	174	12X		472	4	692	3	17X	132	395	15Ɛ	880	035	3		99Ɛ	3X6	258	5	Ɛ81
4		294		816	5	2X0	4		288		4X1	0	7Ɛ5	4		Ɛ28		580	6	6Ɛ9
5		439		Ɛ78	5	XX8	5		422		823	1	373	5	184	075		8X3	7	235
6		5X2	384	31X	6	6Ɛ3	6		579		Ɛ64	1	Ɛ31	6		201	3X7	006	7	96Ɛ
7		747		680	7	2Ɛ9	7		713	396	2X5	2	6X9	7		349		328	8	4X5
8		8XƐ		X21	7	Ɛ01	8		868		625	3	264	8		495		64X	9	01X
9		X54	385	182	8	704	9		X02		964	3	X1X	9		621		970	9	751
X		ƐƐ8		522	9	306	X		Ɛ57	397	0X3	4	593	X		769	3X8	091	X	284
Ɛ	175	160		881	9	Ɛ06	Ɛ	17Ɛ	0Ɛ0		422	5	147	Ɛ		8Ɛ4		3Ɛ2	X	9Ɛ6
430		304	386	020	X	706	470		245		760	5	8ƐX	4Ɛ0		X40		712	Ɛ	526
1		467		37X	Ɛ	304	1		39X		X9X	6	46Ɛ	1		Ɛ87		X32	8Ɛ0	056
2		60X		718	Ɛ	Ɛ00	2		532	398	217	7	020	2	185	112	3X9	151	0	784
3		771		X75	860	6Ɛ8	3		686		554	7	78Ɛ	3		258		470	1	2Ɛ2
4		914	387	212	1	2Ɛ2	4		81X		890	8	33X	4		3X3		78Ɛ	1	X1Ɛ
5		X76		56X	1	XX7	5		972	399	008	8	XX7	5		529		XX9	2	547
6	176	018		906	2	69Ɛ	6		Ɛ06		343	9	653	6		674	3XX	207	3	071
7		17X	388	061	3	292	7	180	059		67X	X	1ƐX	7		7Ɛ9		524	3	797
8		320		3Ɛ7	3	X83	8		1Ɛ0		9Ɛ4	X	964	8		943		841	4	300
9		482		751	4	673	9		343	39X	12X	Ɛ	509	9		X89		Ɛ59	4	X24
X		623		XX7	5	262	X		496		464	890	071	X	186	012	3XƐ	276	5	547
Ɛ		784	389	240	5	X50	Ɛ		629		799	0	813	Ɛ		158		591	6	069

N	Cube Root					
500	186	2X1	3XƐ	8X8	8Ɛ6	78X
1		426	3Ɛ0	003	7	2XX
2		56X		319	7	X09
3		6Ɛ3		633	8	527
4		837		949	9	044
5		97Ɛ	3Ɛ1	062	9	760
6		Ɛ03		377	X	278
7	187	047		68Ɛ	X	992
8		18Ɛ		9X3	Ɛ	4X8
9		312	3Ɛ2	0Ɛ6	900	000
X		456		40X	0	714
Ɛ		599		720	1	226
510		720		X32	1	938
1		862	3Ɛ3	144	2	449
2		9X5		456	2	Ɛ58
3		Ɛ27		767	3	667
4	188	069		X77	4	175
5		1Ɛ0	3Ɛ4	188	4	882
6		331		497	5	38X
7		473		7X7	5	X96
8		5Ɛ5		X26	6	5X0
9		736	3Ɛ5	205	7	0X5
X		877		513	7	7XX
Ɛ		9Ɛ8		821	8	2Ɛ1
520		Ɛ39		Ɛ2X	8	9Ɛ4
1	189	07X	3Ɛ6	237	9	4Ɛ6
2		1ƐX		544	9	ƐƐ6
3		33X		850	X	6Ɛ6
4		47X		Ɛ58	Ɛ	1Ɛ5
5		5ƐX	3Ɛ7	263	Ɛ	8Ɛ4
6		73X		56X	910	3Ɛ1
7		87X		875	0	XX9
8		9Ɛ9		Ɛ7Ɛ	1	5X5
9		Ɛ39	3Ɛ8	285	2	09Ɛ
X	18X	078		58Ɛ	2	795
Ɛ		1Ɛ7		894	3	28X
530		335		Ɛ99	3	982
1		474	3Ɛ9	2X1	4	475
2		5Ɛ2		5X5	4	Ɛ67
3		731		8X9	5	658
4		86Ɛ		ƐƐ0	6	148
5		9X9	3ƐX	2Ɛ3	6	838
6		Ɛ26		5Ɛ5	7	327
7	18Ɛ	064		8Ɛ7	7	X14
8		1X1		ƐƐ9	8	501
9		31Ɛ	3ƐƐ	2ƐX	8	ƐX9
X		458		5ƐƐ	9	694
Ɛ		595		900	X	17Ɛ

N	Cube Root					
540	18Ɛ	712	400	000	91X	864
1		84X		300	Ɛ	349
2		987		5ƐƐ	Ɛ	X31
3		Ɛ03		8ƐX	920	514
4	190	03Ɛ		ƐƐ9	0	ƐƐ6
5		177	401	2Ɛ7	1	697
6		2Ɛ3		5Ɛ5	2	177
7		42X		8Ɛ3	2	857
8		566		ƐƐ0	3	335
9		6X1	402	2X9	3	X13
X		818		5X5	4	4Ɛ0
Ɛ		953		8X1	4	Ɛ88
550		X8X		Ɛ99	5	663
1	191	005	403	295	6	13X
2		13Ɛ		590	6	813
3		276		886	7	2X8
4		3Ɛ0		Ɛ81	7	980
5		526	404	276	8	453
6		660		570	8	Ɛ26
7		796		865	9	5Ɛ7
8		90Ɛ		Ɛ5X	X	088
9		X45	405	253	X	757
X		Ɛ7X		547	Ɛ	226
Ɛ	192	0Ɛ3		83X	Ɛ	8Ɛ5
560		228		Ɛ32	930	382
1		361	406	225	0	X4Ɛ
2		495		518	1	516
3		60X		80X	1	ƐX1
4		742		Ɛ00	2	667
5		876	407	1Ɛ2	3	131
6		9XX		4X3	3	7Ɛ5
7		Ɛ22		794	4	279
8	193	056		X84	4	940
9		189	408	175	5	402
X		301		464	5	X83
Ɛ		434		754	6	544
570		567		X43	7	003
1		69X	409	132	7	682
2		811		420	8	140
3		943		70Ɛ	8	7Ɛ9
4		X76		9Ɛ8	9	276
5		ƐX8	40X	0X6	9	932
6	194	11X		393	X	3X9
7		250		680	X	X63
8		382		968	Ɛ	518
9		4Ɛ4	40Ɛ	054	Ɛ	Ɛ91
X		626		340	940	645
Ɛ		757		627	1	0Ɛ8

N	Cube Root					
580	194	888	40Ɛ	912	941	76X
1		9ƐX		ƐƐ9	2	21Ɛ
2		ƐƐƐ	410	2X4	2	890
3	195	05Ɛ		58X	3	340
4		190		873	3	9XƐ
5		301		Ɛ59	4	459
6		431	411	242	4	Ɛ07
7		561		526	5	574
8		691		80Ɛ	6	020
9		801		XƐ3	6	687
X		931	412	196	7	132
Ɛ		X61		47X	7	798
590		Ɛ90		761	8	241
1	196	100		X44	8	8X5
2		22Ɛ	413	126	9	348
3		35X		408	9	9XƐ
4		489		6XX	X	451
5		5Ɛ8		98Ɛ	X	XƐ3
6		727	414	070	Ɛ	553
7		855		351	Ɛ	ƐƐ3
8		984		631	950	652
9		XƐ2		911	1	0Ɛ0
X	197	020		ƐƐ1	1	74X
Ɛ		14X	415	291	2	1X6
5X0		278		570	2	842
1		3X5		84X	3	29X
2		513		Ɛ29	3	934
3		640	416	207	4	38X
4		76X		4X5	4	X23
5		897		782	5	478
6		X04		X60	5	Ɛ0Ɛ
7		Ɛ31	417	138	6	562
8	198	059		415	6	ƐƐ4
9		186		6Ɛ1	7	646
X		2Ɛ2		989	8	096
Ɛ		41Ɛ	418	065	8	726
5Ɛ0		547		340	9	176
1		673		617	9	804
2		79Ɛ		8Ɛ2	X	252
3		906		Ɛ88	X	89Ɛ
4		X32	419	262	Ɛ	328
5		Ɛ59		538	Ɛ	973
6	199	085		811	960	3ƐX
7		1Ɛ0		XX6	0	X45
8		317	41X	17Ɛ	1	48X
9		442		453	1	Ɛ13
X		569		727	2	557
Ɛ		693		9ƐƐ	2	Ɛ9X

N	Cube Root					
600	199	7ƐX	41Ɛ	093	963	621
1		924		366	964	063
2		X4X		639		6X4
3		Ɛ74		910	965	125
4	19X	09X		ƐX2		765
5		204	420	274	966	1X4
6		32X		546		822
7		454		817	967	260
8		579		XX8		899
9		6X2	421	179	968	316
X		807		449		951
Ɛ		931		719	969	388
610		X55		9X9		X03
1		Ɛ7X	422	079	96X	438
2	19Ɛ	0X3		348		X71
3		207		617	96Ɛ	4X6
4		330		8X6		Ɛ19
5		454		Ɛ74	970	550
6		578	423	242		Ɛ82
7		6X0		510	971	5Ɛ4
8		804		79X	972	025
9		928		X67		655
X		X4Ɛ	424	134	973	084
Ɛ		Ɛ73		400		6Ɛ3
620	1X0	096		688	974	121
1		1Ɛ9		954		74Ɛ
2		321		020	975	177
3		444	425	2X8		7X4
4		566		573	976	20Ɛ
5		689		83X		836
6		7Ɛ0		Ɛ04	977	260
7		912	426	18X		885
8		X34		454	978	2XX
9		Ɛ57		71X		912
X	1X1	079		9X3	979	336
Ɛ		19Ɛ	427	068		958
630		300		331	97X	37Ɛ
1		422		5Ɛ6		9X0
2		544		87X	97Ɛ	401
3		665		Ɛ42		X21
4		787	428	206	980	440
5		8X8		489		X5Ɛ
6		X09		750	981	479
7		Ɛ2X		X13		X97
8	1X2	04Ɛ	429	095	982	4Ɛ4
9		16Ɛ		357		Ɛ10
X		290		619	983	528
Ɛ		3Ɛ0		89Ɛ		Ɛ43

N	Cube Root					
640	1X2	511	429	Ɛ60	984	559
1		631	42X	222		Ɛ73
2		751		4X2	985	588
3		871		763		ƐX0
4		991		X23	986	5Ɛ4
5		XƐ0	42Ɛ	0X3	987	007
6	1X3	010		363		619
7		12Ɛ		622	988	02Ɛ
8		24Ɛ		8X1		640
9		36X		Ɛ60	989	051
X		489	430	21Ɛ		661
Ɛ		5X8		499	98X	070
650		707		757		67Ɛ
1		826		X15	98Ɛ	089
2		944	431	092		696
3		X63		350	990	0X3
4		Ɛ81		609		6XƐ
5	1X4	0X0		885	991	0Ɛ6
6		1ƐX		Ɛ42		701
7		318	432	1ƐX	992	107
8		436		476		711
9		553		731	993	116
X		671		9X8		71X
Ɛ		78Ɛ	433	063	994	122
660		8X8		31X		725
1		X05		595	995	128
2		Ɛ23		84Ɛ		72X
3	1X5	040		Ɛ05	996	12Ɛ
4		159	434	17Ɛ		730
5		276		434	997	130
6		392		6X9		72Ɛ
7		4XƐ		962	998	12X
8		607	435	017		728
9		724		28Ɛ	999	126
X		840		543		723
Ɛ		958		7Ɛ7	99X	11Ɛ
670		X74		X6X		717
1		Ɛ90	436	122	99Ɛ	112
2	1X6	0X8		395		709
3		204		647	9X0	103
4		31Ɛ		8ƐX		6Ɛ8
5		437		Ɛ70	9X1	0Ɛ1
6		552	437	222		6X5
7		669		494	9X2	099
8		784		745		690
9		89Ɛ		9Ɛ7	9X3	082
X		9Ɛ6	438	067		674
Ɛ		Ɛ11		318	9X4	065

N	Cube Root					
680	1X7	028	438	589	9X4	656
1		142		839	9X5	046
2		259		XX9		635
3		373	439	158	9X6	024
4		489		408		612
5		5X3		677	9X7	000
6		6Ɛ9		926		5X9
7		813		Ɛ94		Ɛ96
8		929	43X	243	9X8	582
9		X43		4Ɛ1		Ɛ69
X		Ɛ58		75Ɛ	9X9	554
Ɛ	1X8	072		X08		Ɛ3X
690		187	43Ɛ	076	9XX	523
1		2X0		323		Ɛ08
2		3Ɛ5		58Ɛ	9XƐ	4Ɛ1
3		50X		838		X95
4		623		XX4	9Ɛ0	478
5		738	440	150		X5Ɛ
6		851		3Ɛ8	9Ɛ1	441
7		965		664		XƐ2
8		X7X		90Ɛ	9Ɛ2	403
9		Ɛ92		Ɛ76		9X4
X	1X9	0X6	441	221	9Ɛ3	384
Ɛ		1ƐX		488		963
6X0		312		732	9Ɛ4	342
1		426		998		920
2		53X	442	042	9Ɛ5	2Ɛ9
3		652		2X8		896
4		765		551	9Ɛ6	273
5		879		7Ɛ6		84X
6		990		X5Ɛ	9Ɛ7	226
7		XX3	443	103		801
8		ƐƐ7		368	9Ɛ8	197
9	1XX	10X		610		770
X		221		874	9Ɛ9	145
Ɛ		333		Ɛ17		71X
6Ɛ0		446	444	17Ɛ	9ƐX	0Ɛ2
1		559		422		685
2		66Ɛ		685	9ƐƐ	058
3		782		927		62X
4		894		Ɛ8X	X00	000
5		9X6	445	230		591
6		XƐ8		492		Ɛ62
7	1XƐ	00X		734	X01	532
8		120		995		Ɛ01
9		232	446	036	X02	490
X		343		297		X5Ɛ
Ɛ		455		538	X03	429

N	Cube Root					
700	1XƐ	566	446	799	X03	9Ɛ6
1		678		X39	X04	383
2		789	447	099		94Ɛ
3		89X		339	X05	317
4		9XƐ		598		8X2
5		Ɛ00		837	X06	268
6	1Ɛ0	011		X96		832
7		122	448	135	X07	1Ɛ8
8		232		394		781
9		343		632	X08	145
X		453		890		709
Ɛ		564		Ɛ2X	X09	091
710		674	449	188		653
1		784		425	X0X	016
2		894		683		597
3		9X4		91Ɛ		Ɛ59
4		XƐ4		Ɛ78	X0Ɛ	519
5	1Ɛ1	004	44X	215		X9X
6		113		471	X10	459
7		223		709		X18
8		332		965	X11	397
9		441	44Ɛ	000		955
X		551		258	X12	312
Ɛ		660		4Ɛ3		88Ɛ
720		76Ɛ		74X	X13	248
1		87X		9X4		804
2		988	450	03Ɛ	X14	17Ɛ
3		X97		295		736
4		ƐX6		52Ɛ	X15	0Ɛ1
5	1Ɛ2	0Ɛ4		785		666
6		203		X1X	X16	020
7		311	451	073		595
8		41Ɛ		308		Ɛ49
9		529		561	X17	501
X		637		7Ɛ6		X74
Ɛ		745		X4X	X18	427
730		853	452	0X2		999
1		961		336	X19	34Ɛ
2		X6X		58X		900
3		Ɛ78		822	X1X	270
4	1Ɛ3	085		X75		821
5		193	453	108	X1Ɛ	190
6		2X0		35Ɛ		73Ɛ
7		3X9		5Ɛ1	X20	0XX
8		4Ɛ6		844		658
9		603		X96	X21	006
X		710	454	128		573
Ɛ		819		379		Ɛ20

N	Cube Root					
740	1Ɛ3	925	454	60Ɛ	X22	488
1		X32		860		X33
2		Ɛ3X		XƐ1	X23	39X
3	1Ɛ4	047	455	142		945
4		153		393	X24	2XƐ
5		25Ɛ		623		855
6		367		873	X25	1ƐX
7		473		Ɛ03		762
8		57Ɛ	456	153	X26	106
9		687		3X2		66X
X		792		632	X27	011
Ɛ		89X		881		574
750		9X5		Ɛ0Ɛ		Ɛ16
1		XƐ1	457	15X	X28	477
2		ƐƐ8		3X9		X18
3	1Ɛ5	103		637	X29	379
4		20Ɛ		885		919
5		316		Ɛ12	X2X	279
6		421	458	160		818
7		527		3X9	X2Ɛ	177
8		632		637		715
9		739		883	X30	072
X		843		Ɛ10		610
Ɛ		94X	459	159		Ɛ68
760		X54		3X5	X31	504
1		Ɛ5X		631		X60
2	1Ɛ6	065		879	X32	3Ɛ7
3		16Ɛ		Ɛ04		952
4		275	45X	150	X33	2X8
5		37Ɛ		397		842
6		484		622	X34	197
7		58X		869		730
8		694		XƐ4	X35	085
9		799	45Ɛ	13X		618
X		8X3		384		Ɛ70
Ɛ		9X8		60X	X36	503
770		XƐ2		854		X55
1		ƐƐ7		X99	X37	3X7
2	1Ɛ7	100	460	123		938
3		205		368	X38	289
4		30X		5Ɛ1		81X
5		413		835	X39	16X
6		517		X7X		6ƐX
7		620	461	102	X3X	049
8		724		346		597
9		829		58X		Ɛ25
X		931		812	X3Ɛ	473
Ɛ		X36		X55		X00

N	Cube Root					
780	1Ɛ7	Ɛ3X	462	099	X40	349
1	1Ɛ8	042		320		895
2		146		563	X41	221
3		24X		7X5		768
4		352		X28	X42	0Ɛ3
5		455	463	06X		63X
6		559		2Ɛ0		Ɛ84
7		661		532	X43	509
8		764		773		X52
9		867		9Ɛ5	X44	397
X		96Ɛ	464	036		91Ɛ
Ɛ		X72		277	X45	262
790		Ɛ75		4Ɛ8		7X5
1	1Ɛ9	078		739	X46	128
2		17Ɛ		979		66X
3		282		ƐƐ9		ƐƐ0
4		385	465	239	X47	531
5		487		479		X72
6		58X		6Ɛ9	X48	3Ɛ3
7		690		938		933
8		793		Ɛ77	X49	272
9		895	466	1Ɛ6		7Ɛ1
X		997		435	X4X	130
Ɛ		X9X		674		66X
7X0		ƐX0		8Ɛ2		ƐX7
1	1ƐX	0X2		Ɛ31	X4Ɛ	525
2		1X4	467	16Ɛ		X61
3		2X5		3X8	X50	39X
4		3X7		626		916
5		4X9		864	X51	251
6		5XX		XX1		788
7		6Ɛ0	468	11X	X52	103
8		7Ɛ1		357		639
9		8Ɛ3		593		Ɛ72
X		9Ɛ4		810	X53	4X7
Ɛ		XƐ5		X48		X20
7Ɛ0		ƐƐ6	469	084	X54	354
1	1ƐƐ	0Ɛ7		300		888
2		1Ɛ8		538	X55	200
3		2Ɛ9		773		733
4		3Ɛ9		9XƐ	X56	065
5		4ƐX	46X	026		597
6		5ƐX		261		Ɛ09
7		6ƐƐ		497	X57	43X
8		7ƐƐ		712		96Ɛ
9		900		948	X58	29Ɛ
X		X00		Ɛ82		80Ɛ
Ɛ		Ɛ00	46Ɛ	1Ɛ8	X59	13X

N	Cube Root					
800	200	000	46Ɛ	432	X59	669
1		100		668		Ɛ98
2		200		8X1	X5X	506
3		300		Ɛ16		X34
4		3ƐƐ	470	14Ɛ	X5Ɛ	361
5		4ƐƐ		384		88X
6		5ƐƐ		5Ɛ9	X60	1Ɛ6
7		6ƐX		831		722
8		7Ɛ9		X65	X61	04X
9		8Ɛ9	471	09X		575
X		9Ɛ8		311		X9Ɛ
Ɛ		XƐ7		545	X62	406
810		ƐƐ6		779		92Ɛ
1	201	0Ɛ5		9Ɛ0	X63	255
2		1Ɛ4	472	023		77X
3		2Ɛ3		256	X64	0X2
4		3Ɛ1		489		606
5		4Ɛ0		6ƐƐ		Ɛ2X
6		5XƐ		932	X65	451
7		6X9		Ɛ64		974
8		7X7	473	196	X66	296
9		8X6		408		7Ɛ8
X		9X4		639	X67	11X
Ɛ		XX2		86Ɛ		63Ɛ
820		ƐX0		XX0		Ɛ5Ɛ
1	202	09X	474	111	X68	480
2		198		342		9X0
3		296		573	X69	2ƐƐ
4		394		7X3		81X
5		491		X14	X6X	139
6		58Ɛ	475	044		657
7		689		274		Ɛ74
8		786		4X4	X6Ɛ	492
9		883		713		9XƐ
X		981		943	X70	307
Ɛ		X7X		Ɛ72		823
830		Ɛ77	476	1X1	X71	13Ɛ
1	203	074		410		656
2		171		63Ɛ		Ɛ71
3		26X		869	X72	487
4		367		X97		9X1
5		463	477	106	X73	2Ɛ7
6		560		334		810
7		659		561	X74	125
8		755		78Ɛ		639
9		851		9Ɛ9		Ɛ51
X		94X	478	026	X75	465
Ɛ		X46		253		978

N	Cube Root					
840	203	Ɛ42	478	480	X76	28Ɛ
1	204	03X		6X9		7X1
2		136		915	X77	0Ɛ3
3		232		Ɛ42		604
4		32X	479	16X		Ɛ15
5		426		396	X78	426
6		522		602		936
7		619		829	X79	246
8		715		X55		756
9		810	47X	080	X7X	065
X		908		2X7		573
Ɛ		X03		512		X82
850		XƐX		739	X7Ɛ	38Ɛ
1		ƐƐ5		964		899
2	205	0Ɛ0		Ɛ8X	X80	1X6
3		1X7	47Ɛ	1Ɛ4		6Ɛ3
4		2X2		41X		ƐƐƐ
5		399		644	X81	507
6		494		86X		X12
7		58Ɛ		X94	X82	319
8		685	480	0Ɛ9		824
9		780		322	X83	12X
X		876		547		634
Ɛ		971		770		Ɛ39
860		X67		995	X84	443
1		Ɛ61		ƐƐ9		947
2	206	058	481	222	X85	250
3		152		446		753
4		248		66X	X86	057
5		342		892		55X
6		438		XƐ6		X61
7		531	482	119	X87	363
8		627		340		865
9		721		564	X88	167
X		816		787		668
Ɛ		910		9X9		Ɛ68
870		X05	483	010	X89	469
1		XƐƐ		232		969
2		ƐƐ4		455	X8X	268
3	207	0X9		677		768
4		1X2		899	X8Ɛ	066
5		297		XƐƐ		565
6		390	484	120		X63
7		485		342	X90	361
8		57X		563		85X
9		673		784	X91	157
X		768		9X5		653
Ɛ		860	485	006		Ɛ4Ɛ

N	Cube Root					
880	207	955	485	227	X92	447
1		X49		447		942
2		Ɛ42		667	X93	239
3	208	036		888		734
4		12X		XX7	X94	02X
5		223	486	107		524
6		317		327		X1X
7		40Ɛ		546	X95	313
8		503		766		807
9		5Ɛ7		985	X96	100
X		6XX		ƐX4		5Ɛ4
Ɛ		7X2	487	203		XX7
890		896		421	X97	39X
1		989		640		891
2		X81		85X	X98	184
3		Ɛ74		X78		676
4	209	068	488	096		Ɛ67
5		15Ɛ		2Ɛ4	X99	459
6		252		512		94X
7		346		72Ɛ	X9X	23X
8		439		948		72X
9		530		Ɛ66	X9Ɛ	01X
X		623	489	183		50X
Ɛ		716		39Ɛ		9Ɛ9
8X0		808		5Ɛ8	XX0	2X7
1		8ƐƐ		815		796
2		9Ɛ2		X31	XX1	084
3		XX5	48X	049		571
4		Ɛ97		265		X5Ɛ
5	20X	08X		481	XX2	347
6		180		699		834
7		272		8Ɛ4	XX3	120
8		365		Ɛ10		608
9		457	48Ɛ	127		XƐ3
X		549		342	XX4	39X
Ɛ		63Ɛ		559		885
8Ɛ0		731		774	XX5	16Ɛ
1		823		98X		655
2		915		ƐX5		Ɛ3Ɛ
3		X07	490	1ƐƐ	XX6	424
4		XƐ8		415		909
5		ƐXX		62Ɛ	XX7	1Ɛ1
6	20Ɛ	09Ɛ		845		695
7		191		X5Ɛ		Ɛ79
8		282	491	074	XX8	461
9		374		289		944
X		465		4X3	XX9	226
Ɛ		556		6Ɛ8		709

N	Cube Root					
900	20Ɛ	647	491	911	XX9	ƐXƐ
1		739		Ɛ25	XXX	490
2		82X	492	13X		971
3		91X		352	XXƐ	252
4		X0Ɛ		566		733
5		Ɛ00		77X	XƐ0	013
6		ƐƐ1		992		4Ɛ3
7	210	0X2		ƐX6		992
8		192	493	1ƐX	XƐ1	271
9		283		411		750
X		373		625	XƐ2	02X
Ɛ		464		838		508
910		554		X4Ɛ		9X6
1		644	494	062	XƐ3	283
2		735		274		760
3		825		487	XƐ4	039
4		915		699		515
5		X05		8XƐ		9Ɛ1
6		XƐ5		Ɛ01	XƐ5	289
7		ƐX5	495	113		764
8	211	094		325	XƐ6	03Ɛ
9		184		537		515
X		274		748		9XƐ
Ɛ		363		959	XƐ7	285
920		453		Ɛ6Ɛ		75Ɛ
1		542	496	180	XƐ8	034
2		632		390		509
3		721		5X1		9X1
4		810		7Ɛ2	XƐ9	275
5		900		X02		749
6		9XƐ	497	012	XƐX	020
7		X9X		222		4Ɛ3
8		Ɛ89		432		986
9	212	078		642	XƐƐ	258
X		167		852		72X
Ɛ		255		X61	Ɛ00	000
930		344	498	071		491
1		433		280		962
2		522		48Ɛ	Ɛ01	233
3		610		69X		703
4		6ƐƐ		8X8		Ɛ93
5		7X9		XƐ7	Ɛ02	463
6		897	499	105		932
7		986		314	Ɛ03	201
8		X74		522		690
9		Ɛ62		730		Ɛ5X
X	213	050		93X	Ɛ04	428
Ɛ		13X		Ɛ47		8Ɛ5

N	Cube Root					
940	213	228	49X	155	Ɛ05	182
1		316		362		64Ɛ
2		404		570		Ɛ18
3		4Ɛ2		779	Ɛ06	3X4
4		59Ɛ		986		870
5		689		Ɛ93	Ɛ07	138
6		777	49Ɛ	19Ɛ		603
7		864		3X8		X8X
8		952		5Ɛ4	Ɛ08	354
9		X3Ɛ		800		81X
X		Ɛ28		X08	Ɛ09	0X4
Ɛ	214	016	4X0	014		56X
950		103		220		X33
1		1Ɛ0		428	Ɛ0X	2Ɛ8
2		299		633		780
3		386		83Ɛ	Ɛ0Ɛ	045
4		473		X46		508
5		560	4X1	051		990
6		649		258	Ɛ10	253
7		735		463		716
8		822		669		Ɛ99
9		90Ɛ		874	Ɛ11	45Ɛ
X		9Ɛ7		X7X		921
Ɛ		XX4	4X2	084	Ɛ12	1X2
960		Ɛ90		28X		664
1	215	079		494		Ɛ24
2		165		69X	Ɛ13	3X5
3		251		8X4		865
4		339		XX9	Ɛ14	125
5		426	4X3	0Ɛ3		5X5
6		512		2Ɛ8		X64
7		5ƐX		501	Ɛ15	323
8		6X6		706		7X2
9		791		90Ɛ	Ɛ16	060
X		879		Ɛ13		51X
Ɛ		965	4X4	118		998
970		X51		320	Ɛ17	255
1		Ɛ38		524		712
2	216	024		728		Ɛ8Ɛ
3		10Ɛ		930	Ɛ18	447
4		1Ɛ7		Ɛ34		903
5		2X2	4X5	138	Ɛ19	17Ɛ
6		38X		33Ɛ		636
7		475		543		XƐ1
8		560		746	Ɛ1X	368
9		647		949		822
X		732		Ɛ50	Ɛ1Ɛ	098
Ɛ		819	4X6	153		552

N	Cube Root					
980	216	904	4X6	355	Ɛ1Ɛ	X08
1		9XƐ		558	Ɛ20	281
2		X96		75X		736
3		Ɛ81		961		ƐXX
4	217	068		Ɛ63	Ɛ21	462
5		152	4X7	165		916
6		239		367	Ɛ22	18X
7		323		568		641
8		40X		76X		XƐ4
9		4Ɛ4		96Ɛ	Ɛ23	367
X		59Ɛ		Ɛ70		819
Ɛ		685	4X8	172	Ɛ24	08Ɛ
990		76Ɛ		373		541
1		855		574		9Ɛ2
2		93Ɛ		774	Ɛ25	263
3		X25		975		714
4		Ɛ0Ɛ		Ɛ75		Ɛ84
5		ƐƐ5	4X9	176	Ɛ26	434
6	218	09Ɛ		376		8X4
7		185		576	Ɛ27	154
8		26Ɛ		776		603
9		355		976		X72
X		43X		Ɛ75	Ɛ28	320
Ɛ		524	4XX	175		78X
9X0		609		374	Ɛ29	038
1		6Ɛ3		573		4X6
2		798		772		953
3		882		971	Ɛ2X	200
4		967		Ɛ70		669
5		X50	4XƐ	16Ɛ		Ɛ15
6		Ɛ35		36X	Ɛ2Ɛ	381
7	219	01X		568		829
8		103		766	Ɛ30	095
9		1X8		964		540
X		291		Ɛ62		9X7
Ɛ		376	4Ɛ0	160	Ɛ31	251
9Ɛ0		45Ɛ		35X		6Ɛ7
1		544		558		Ɛ61
2		628		755	Ɛ32	407
3		711		953		870
4		7Ɛ6		Ɛ50	Ɛ33	115
5		89X	4Ɛ1	149		57X
6		983		346		X22
7		X67		543	Ɛ34	287
8		Ɛ4Ɛ		73Ɛ		72X
9	21X	034		938		Ɛ92
X		118		Ɛ34	Ɛ35	435
Ɛ		200	4Ɛ2	131		898

N	Cube Root					
X00	21X	2X4	4Ɛ2	329	Ɛ36	13Ɛ
1		388		525		5X1
2		470		721		X43
3		554		919	Ɛ37	2X5
4		638		Ɛ14		746
5		720	4Ɛ3	110		ƐX7
6		804		307	Ɛ38	448
7		8X8		503		8X8
8		98Ɛ		6ƐX	Ɛ39	148
9		X73		8Ɛ5		5X8
X		Ɛ56		XXƐ		X48
Ɛ	21Ɛ	03X	4Ɛ4	0X6	Ɛ3X	2X7
X10		121		2X1		746
1		205		497		ƐX5
2		2X8		692	Ɛ3Ɛ	443
3		38Ɛ		888		8X2
4		473		X82	Ɛ40	13Ɛ
5		556	4Ɛ5	078		599
6		639		272		X36
7		720		467	Ɛ41	293
8		803		661		730
9		8X6		856		Ɛ88
X		989		X50	Ɛ42	424
Ɛ		X6Ɛ	4Ɛ6	045		880
X20		Ɛ52		23X	Ɛ43	117
1	220	035		433		572
2		118		628		X09
3		1ƐX		820	Ɛ44	264
4		2X1		X15		6ƐX
5		383	4Ɛ7	009		Ɛ54
6		466		202	Ɛ45	3XX
7		548		3Ɛ6		843
8		62X		5XX	Ɛ46	098
9		711		7X2		531
X		7Ɛ3		996		986
Ɛ		895		Ɛ89	Ɛ47	21X
X30		977	4Ɛ8	181		672
1		X59		374		Ɛ06
2		Ɛ3Ɛ		567	Ɛ48	359
3	221	021		75Ɛ		7Ɛ0
4		103		952	Ɛ49	043
5		1X5		Ɛ45		496
6		286	4Ɛ9	137		928
7		368		32X	Ɛ4X	17X
8		44X		520		60Ɛ
9		52Ɛ		713		X61
X		611		905	Ɛ4Ɛ	2Ɛ2
Ɛ		6Ɛ2		XƐ7		743

N	Cube Root					
X40	221	794	4ƐX	0X9	Ɛ4Ɛ	Ɛ93
1		875		29Ɛ	Ɛ50	423
2		957		491		873
3		X38		683	Ɛ51	103
4		Ɛ19		874		552
5		ƐƐX		X66		9X2
6	222	09Ɛ	4ƐƐ	057	Ɛ52	230
7		180		248		67Ɛ
8		261		439		Ɛ09
9		342		62X	Ɛ53	357
X		423		81Ɛ		7X5
Ɛ		504		X0Ɛ	Ɛ54	032
X50		5X5	500	000		47Ɛ
1		686		1Ɛ0		908
2		766		3X1	Ɛ55	155
3		847		591		5X1
4		928		781		X29
5		X08		971	Ɛ56	275
6		XX9		Ɛ61		700
7		Ɛ89	501	150		Ɛ47
8	223	069		340	Ɛ57	392
9		14X		52Ɛ		819
X		22X		71Ɛ	Ɛ58	063
Ɛ		30X		90X		4X9
X60		3XX		XƐ9		933
1		48X	502	0X8	Ɛ59	178
2		56X		297		602
3		64X		485		X47
4		72X		674	Ɛ5X	28Ɛ
5		80X		863		714
6		8XX		X51		Ɛ58
7		98X	503	03Ɛ	Ɛ5Ɛ	3X0
8		X6X		229		823
9		Ɛ49		417	Ɛ60	066
X	224	029		605		4X9
Ɛ		108		7Ɛ3		930
X70		1X8		9X0	Ɛ61	173
1		287		Ɛ8X		5Ɛ5
2		367	504	177		X37
3		446		365	Ɛ62	278
4		525		552		6ƐX
5		605		73Ɛ		Ɛ3Ɛ
6		6X4		928	Ɛ63	380
7		783		Ɛ15		800
8		862	505	101	Ɛ64	040
9		941		2XX		480
X		X20		496		900
Ɛ		XƐƐ		682	Ɛ65	140

N	Cube Root					
X80	224	Ɛ9X	505	86Ɛ	Ɛ65	57Ɛ
1	225	079		X57		9ƐX
2		158	506	043	Ɛ66	238
3		236		22Ɛ		677
4		315		416		XƐ5
5		3Ɛ4		602	Ɛ67	333
6		492		7X9		770
7		571		995		ƐXX
8		64Ɛ		Ɛ80	Ɛ68	427
9		72X	507	167		863
X		808		352	Ɛ69	0X0
Ɛ		8X7		539		518
X90		985		724		954
1		X63		90Ɛ	Ɛ6X	190
2		Ɛ41		XƐ5		607
3	226	01Ɛ	508	0X0		X42
4		0Ɛ9		286	Ɛ6Ɛ	279
5		197		470		6Ɛ4
6		275		656		Ɛ2X
7		353		840	Ɛ70	364
8		431		X26		79X
9		50Ɛ	509	010	Ɛ71	014
X		5X9		1Ɛ5		449
Ɛ		687		39Ɛ		882
XX0		764		584	Ɛ72	0Ɛ7
1		842		76X		52Ɛ
2		91Ɛ		953		964
3		9Ɛ9		Ɛ38	Ɛ73	198
4		X96	50X	121		60Ɛ
5		Ɛ74		306		X43
6	227	051		4XX	Ɛ74	276
7		12Ɛ		693		6X9
8		208		877		Ɛ20
9		2X5		X60	Ɛ75	352
X		382	50Ɛ	044		784
Ɛ		45Ɛ		228		ƐƐ6
XƐ0		538		410	Ɛ76	428
1		615		5Ɛ4		859
2		6Ɛ2		798	Ɛ77	08X
3		78Ɛ		980		4ƐƐ
4		868		Ɛ63		930
5		945	510	147	Ɛ78	160
6		X22		32X		590
7		XƐƐ		511		X00
8		Ɛ97		6Ɛ4	Ɛ79	22Ɛ
9	228	074		897		65Ɛ
X		150		X7X		X8X
Ɛ		229	511	061	Ɛ7X	2Ɛ8

N	Cube Root					
Ɛ00	228	305	511	244	Ɛ7X	727
1		3X2		426		Ɛ55
2		47X		609	Ɛ7Ɛ	383
3		557		7XƐ		7Ɛ1
4		633		991	Ɛ80	01Ɛ
5		70Ɛ		Ɛ73		448
6		7X7	512	155		875
7		883		337	Ɛ81	0X2
8		95Ɛ		519		50X
9		X38		6ƐƐ		936
X		Ɛ14		8X0	Ɛ82	162
Ɛ		ƐXƐ		X82		58X
Ɛ10	229	087	513	063		9Ɛ5
1		163		244	Ɛ83	221
2		23Ɛ		425		648
3		317		606		X72
4		3Ɛ2		7X7	Ɛ84	299
5		48X		988		703
6		566		Ɛ69		Ɛ29
7		641	514	149	Ɛ85	353
8		719		32X		778
9		7Ɛ4		50X		ƐX1
X		890		6XX	Ɛ86	406
Ɛ		967		88Ɛ		82Ɛ
Ɛ20		X42		X6Ɛ	Ɛ87	053
1		Ɛ1X	515	04X		477
2		ƐƐ5		22X		89Ɛ
3	22X	090		40X	Ɛ88	103
4		167		5XX		527
5		242		789		94X
6		319		968	Ɛ89	171
7		3Ɛ4		Ɛ48		593
8		48Ɛ	516	127		9Ɛ6
9		566		306	Ɛ8X	218
X		641		4X5		63X
Ɛ		718		683		X60
Ɛ30		7Ɛ2		862	Ɛ8Ɛ	281
1		889		X41		6X2
2		964	517	01Ɛ		Ɛ03
3		X3X		1ƐX	Ɛ90	324
4		Ɛ15		398		744
5		ƐXƐ		576		Ɛ65
6	22Ɛ	086		754	Ɛ91	385
7		160		932		7X4
8		237		Ɛ10	Ɛ92	004
9		311	518	0XX		423
X		3X7		287		842
Ɛ		482		465	Ɛ93	061

N	Cube Root					
Ɛ40	22Ɛ	558	518	642	Ɛ93	47Ɛ
1		632		820		899
2		708		9Ɛ9	Ɛ94	0Ɛ7
3		7X2		Ɛ96		515
4		878	519	173		933
5		952		350	Ɛ95	150
6		X28		529		569
7		Ɛ02		705		986
8		Ɛ98		8X2	Ɛ96	1X2
9	230	071		X7X		5ƐƐ
X		147	51X	057		X17
Ɛ		221		233	Ɛ97	233
Ɛ50		2Ɛ6		40Ɛ		64X
1		390		5X7		X65
2		465		783	Ɛ98	281
3		53Ɛ		95Ɛ		697
4		614		Ɛ37		XƐ2
5		6XX	51Ɛ	112	Ɛ99	308
6		783		2XX		723
7		858		485		Ɛ38
8		932		660	Ɛ9X	352
9		X07		838		767
X		XX0		X13		Ɛ81
Ɛ		Ɛ75		ƐXX	Ɛ9Ɛ	396
Ɛ60	231	04X	520	184		7XX
1		123		35Ɛ	ƐX0	003
2		1Ɛ8		536		417
3		291		711		82Ɛ
4		366		8X7	ƐX1	043
5		43Ɛ		X81		456
6		514	521	058		869
7		5X9		232	ƐX2	080
8		681		408		493
9		756		5X2		8X6
X		82Ɛ		778	ƐX3	0Ɛ8
Ɛ		903		951		50X
Ɛ70		998		Ɛ27		920
1		X70	522	101	ƐX4	132
2		Ɛ45		296		543
3	232	019		46Ɛ		954
4		0Ɛ1		645	ƐX5	165
5		186		81X		576
6		25X		9Ɛ3		986
7		332		Ɛ88	ƐX6	196
8		406	523	160		5X6
9		49X		335		9Ɛ6
X		573		50X	ƐX7	206
Ɛ		647		6X2		615

N	Cube Root					
Ɛ80	232	71Ɛ	523	877	ƐX7	X24
1		7Ɛ3		X4Ɛ	ƐX8	233
2		886	524	023		641
3		95X		1Ɛ7		X50
4		X32		38Ɛ	ƐX9	25X
5		Ɛ06		563		668
6		Ɛ9X		737		X75
7	233	071		90Ɛ	ƐXX	283
8		145		XX2		690
9		219	525	076		X99
X		2Ɛ0		249	ƐXƐ	2X6
Ɛ		384		421		6Ɛ2
Ɛ90		457		5Ɛ4		XƐX
1		52Ɛ		787	ƐƐ0	306
2		602		95X		712
3		695		Ɛ31		Ɛ1X
4		769	526	104	ƐƐ1	325
5		840		296		730
6		913		469		Ɛ37
7		9X6		63Ɛ	ƐƐ2	342
8		X79		812		748
9		Ɛ50		9X4		Ɛ52
X	234	023		Ɛ76	ƐƐ3	358
Ɛ		0Ɛ6	527	148		762
ƐX0		189		31X		Ɛ68
1		260		4Ɛ0	ƐƐ4	371
2		333		682		776
3		406		854		Ɛ7Ɛ
4		499		X25	ƐƐ5	383
5		56Ɛ		ƐƐ7		788
6		642	528	188		Ɛ90
7		715		359	ƐƐ6	394
8		7X7		52Ɛ		797
9		87X		700		Ɛ9Ɛ
X		950		891	ƐƐ7	3X2
Ɛ		X23		X62		7X5
ƐƐ0		XƐ5	529	033		ƐX8
1		Ɛ88		203	ƐƐ8	3XƐ
2	235	05X		394		7Ɛ1
3		130		564		ƐƐ3
4		203		735	ƐƐ9	3Ɛ5
5		295		905		7Ɛ7
6		367		X95		ƐƐ8
7		439	52X	065	ƐƐX	3Ɛ9
8		50Ɛ		236		7ƐX
9		5X1		405		ƐƐƐ
X		673		595	ƐƐƐ	400
Ɛ		745		765		800
1000		817		935	1000	000

Reciprocals

In the following table the reciprocals of numbers from *1* to *100* are given to one dozen and seven places for the purpose of such summations as are required for Euler's constant. No differences are given for the first part of the nine place table but by the use of a factor, six figures of any reciprocal may be obtained by direct proportion or eight figures by direct proportion after increasing the book difference by $\frac{1 - \text{Interval}}{2}$ of the second difference.

Example:

Find the reciprocal of *3.18 480 949(4)*

(a) To six places by direct proportion

Multiply by *3*	*9.51 202 424(0)*		
Reciprocal *9.51*		*.133 452 0*	
			175 4
Subtract	*.2024 (1754)*	*33 2*	
		.133 41X X	
Multiply by *3*		*.39X 058(6)*	

(b) To eight places, using second difference

Reciprocal *9.51*	*.133 451 Ɛ80*		*(416)*
		175 3Ɛ6	
Add to book diff. *416* $\frac{1 - .202}{2}$		*187*	
Corrected difference		*175 581*	
Mult. by int. *.202 424*	*33 291*		
Subtract from reciprocal *9.51*	*.133 41X 8XƐ*		
Multiply by *3*	*.39X 058 28(9)*		
Result by division	*.39X 058 289*		

Example:

Find the reciprocal of *1.05 149 0Ɛ4(6)*

(a) To six places by direct proportion

Multiply by *6*	*6.26 846 583(0)*		
Reciprocal *6.26*		*.1Ɛ2 403 X*	
			389 5
Subtract	*.8466 (3895)*	*273 3*	
		.1Ɛ2 150 7	
Multiply by *6*		*.Ɛ70 863(6)*	

(b) To eight places, using second difference

Reciprocal *6.26*	*.1Ɛ2 403 X48*		*(1253)*
		389 482	
Add to book diff. *1253* $\frac{1 - .8466}{2}$		*222*	
Corrected difference		*389 6X4*	
Mult. by int. *.846 583*	*273 3Ɛ2*		
Subtract from reciprocal *6.26*	*.1Ɛ2 150 656*		
Multiply by *6*	*.Ɛ70 863 29(0)*		
Result by division	*.Ɛ70 863 293*		

N	Reciprocal	N	Reciprocal	N	Reciprocal
		40	.030 000 000 000 000 0	80	.016 000 000 000 000 0
1	1.000 000 000 000 000 0	1	.02Ɛ 322 547 X05 X64 5	1	.015 993 40Ɛ X62 287 Ɛ
2	.600 000 000 000 000 0	2	.02X 687 81Ɛ 059 153 4	2	.015 771 283 Ɛ02 Ɛ32 2
3	.400 000 000 000 000 0	3	.029 X70 857 921 4Ɛ3 6	3	.015 555 555 555 555 5
4	.300 000 000 000 000 0	4	.029 292 929 292 929 3	4	.015 343 X0Ɛ 62X 687 8
5	.249 724 972 497 249 7	5	.028 72Ɛ 3X2 320 552 6	5	.015 138 246 217 Ɛ63 7
6	.200 000 000 000 000 0	6	.028 000 000 000 000 0	6	.014 Ɛ36 429 X70 857 9
7	.186 X35 186 X35 186 X	7	.027 502 750 275 027 5	7	.014 93X 176 X59 XX0 3
8	.160 000 000 000 000 0	8	.026 X35 186 X35 186 X	8	.014 747 474 747 474 7
9	.140 000 000 000 000 0	9	.026 395 826 395 826 4	9	.014 559 Ɛ39 310 414 5
X	.124 972 497 249 724 X	X	.025 962 596 259 625 X	X	.014 375 7Ɛ1 170 287 3
Ɛ	.111 111 111 111 111 1	Ɛ	.025 355 X94 330 73X 4	Ɛ	.014 196 486 344 59Ɛ 9
10	.100 000 000 000 000 0	50	.024 972 497 249 724 X	90	.014 000 000 000 000 0
1	.0Ɛ0 Ɛ0Ɛ 0Ɛ0 Ɛ0Ɛ 0Ɛ0 Ɛ	1	.024 3Ɛ2 683 192 Ɛ4Ɛ 0	1	.013 X2X 422 509 2Ɛ8 0
2	.0X3 518 6X3 518 6X3 5	2	.023 X55 047 8XX 093 6	2	.013 861 386 138 613 9
3	.097 249 724 972 497 2	3	.023 518 6X3 518 6X3 5	3	.013 698 90Ɛ 813 698 9
4	.090 000 000 000 000 0	4	.023 000 000 000 000 0	4	.013 518 6X3 518 6X3 5
5	.085 792 14Ɛ 364 29X 7	5	.022 702 270 227 022 7	5	.013 360 779 039 X61 Ɛ
6	.080 000 000 000 000 0	6	.022 222 222 222 222 2	6	.013 1X8 X13 1X8 X13 2
7	.076 Ɛ45 076 Ɛ45 076 Ɛ	7	.021 95X Ɛ13 065 458 9	7	.013 039 0Ɛ3 299 855 1
8	.072 497 249 724 972 5	8	.021 4Ɛ3 642 9X7 085 8	8	.012 X91 2X9 12X 912 Ɛ
9	.06X 351 86X 351 86X 3	9	.021 063 169 484 210 6	9	.012 929 292 929 292 9
X	.066 666 666 666 666 7	X	.020 828 XƐ7 X76 620 8	X	.012 788 Ɛ48 176 37Ɛ 2
Ɛ	.063 169 484 210 631 7	Ɛ	.020 408 142 854 X99 8	Ɛ	.012 630 376 90X X83 3
20	.060 000 000 000 000 0	60	.020 000 000 000 000 0	X0	.012 497 249 724 972 5
1	.059 153 43X 0Ɛ6 2X6 9	1	.01Ɛ 807 X82 768 X63 0	1	.012 345 678 9Ɛ0 123 4
2	.056 565 656 565 656 6	2	.01Ɛ 427 175 61Ɛ 427 2	2	.012 1Ɛ7 341 6X7 585 6
3	.054 000 000 000 000 0	3	.01Ɛ 059 153 43X 0Ɛ6 3	3	.012 070 361 90X 653 3
4	.051 86X 351 86X 351 9	4	.01X 8X1 31X 8X1 31X 9	4	.011 Ɛ28 623 X55 047 9
5	.04Ɛ 704 Ɛ70 4Ɛ7 04Ɛ 7	5	.01X 537 01X 537 01X 5	5	.011 9X7 X56 996 06X Ɛ
6	.049 724 972 497 249 7	6	.01X 1X1 X1X 1X1 X1X 2	6	.011 86X 351 86X 351 9
7	.047 8XX 093 598 167 0	7	.019 X59 323 412 6ƐX 2	7	.011 733 827 8Ɛ8 722 1
8	.046 000 000 000 000 0	8	.019 724 972 497 249 7	8	.011 600 000 000 000 0
9	.044 444 444 444 444 4	9	.019 400 000 000 000 0	9	.011 48Ɛ 1Ɛ5 376 503 4
X	.042 9X7 085 792 14Ɛ 4	X	.019 0X6 532 773 97X X	X	.011 361 136 113 611 4
Ɛ	.041 455 9Ɛ3 931 041 4	Ɛ	.018 99Ɛ 864 406 Ɛ33 Ɛ	Ɛ	.011 235 930 336 X53 9
30	.040 000 000 000 000 0	70	.018 6X3 518 6X3 518 7	Ɛ0	.011 111 111 111 111 1
1	.03X 852 32Ɛ 03X 852 3	1	.018 3Ɛ5 282 313 2Ɛ6 Ɛ	1	.010 ƐXƐ 010 ƐXƐ 011 0
2	.039 582 639 582 639 6	2	.018 114 8Ɛ1 Ɛ53 765 0	2	.010 X8Ɛ 567 632 82X 5
3	.038 383 838 383 838 4	3	.017 X41 7X4 17X 417 X	3	.010 972 497 249 724 X
4	.037 249 724 972 497 2	4	.017 777 777 777 777 8	4	.010 857 921 4Ɛ3 642 X
5	.036 190 X65 327 739 8	5	.017 4ƐX 470 174 ƐX4 7	5	.010 743 606 381 903 2
6	.035 186 X35 186 X35 2	6	.017 249 724 972 497 2	6	.010 631 694 842 106 3
7	.034 229 5X3 XX7 30X 1	7	.016 ƐX5 016 ƐX5 017 0	7	.010 521 X95 Ɛ59 4Ɛ0 7
8	.033 333 333 333 333 3	8	.016 948 421 063 169 5	8	.010 414 559 Ɛ39 310 4
9	.032 497 249 724 972 5	9	.016 6Ɛ7 431 1Ɛ2 862 4	9	.010 309 236 X88 206 2
X	.031 694 842 106 316 9	X	.016 471 954 410 309 2	X	.010 204 081 428 54X X
Ɛ	.030 923 6X8 820 616 5	Ɛ	.016 233 4Ɛ1 481 016 2	Ɛ	.010 101 010 101 010 1

N	Reciprocal	d	N	Reciprocal	d	N	Reciprocal	d
100	1 000 000 000		140	900 000 000		180	724 972 497	
1	ƐƐ0 0ƐƐ 010		1	8Ɛ5 350 528		1	720 5Ɛ8 4Ɛ9	
2	Ɛχ0 3Ɛ4 139		2	8χχ 780 5Ɛ3		2	718 293 χ50	
3	Ɛ90 899 674		3	8χ4 08χ 409		3	714 000 000	
4	Ɛ81 369 891		4	899 674 1Ɛ6		4	70Ɛ 978 095	
5	Ɛ72 01Ɛ 240		5	893 134 253		5	707 783 3Ɛ7	
6	Ɛ62 χ68 782		6	888 888 889		6	703 619 0χ6	
7	Ɛ53 χ88 χ98		7	882 4Ɛ4 059		7	6ƐƐ 500 6ƐƐ	
8	Ɛ45 076 Ɛ45		8	878 1Ɛ0 591		8	6Ɛ7 431 1Ɛ3	
9	Ɛ36 429 χ71		9	871 Ɛ78 502		9	6Ɛ3 3χχ 154	
χ	Ɛ27 960 Ɛ28		χ	867 χ12 311		χ	6χƐ 3Ɛ2 94Ɛ	
Ɛ	Ɛ19 44Ɛ 560		Ɛ	861 934 525		Ɛ	6χ7 442 5χ0	
110	Ɛ0Ɛ 0Ɛ0 Ɛ0Ɛ		150	857 921 4Ɛ4		190	6χ3 518 6χ3	
1	Ɛ00 Ɛ00 Ɛ01		1	851 993 831		1	69Ɛ 638 48Ɛ	
2	χƐ2 χ77 181		2	847 Ɛ09 953		2	697 7χ1 3χ6	
3	χχ4 Ɛ93 491		3	842 106 317		3	693 98χ 890	
4	χ97 249 725		4	838 383 838		4	690 000 000	
5	χ89 659 920		5	832 700 833		5	688 274 642	
6	χ80 000 000		6	828 χƐ7 χ77		6	684 56Ɛ 87χ	
7	χ72 6Ɛ0 623		7	823 36Ɛ Ɛ3χ		7	680 8χ8 Ɛχ4	
8	χ65 327 73χ		8	819 89Ɛ 66χ		8	679 067 907	
9	χ58 0χ5 80χ		9	814 285 4χχ		9	675 467 547	
χ	χ4χ Ɛχ3 220		χ	80χ 924 318		χ	671 8χ7 618	
Ɛ	χ42 018 840		Ɛ	805 436 χ47		Ɛ	66χ 167 485	
120	χ35 186 χ35		160	800 000 000		1χ0	666 666 667	
1	χ28 466 483		1	7Ɛ6 836 578		1	662 Ɛχ4 530	
2	χ1Ɛ 874 117		2	7Ɛ1 521 126		2	65Ɛ 560 65Ɛ	
3	χ13 1χ8 χ13		3	7χ8 276 8χ6		3	657 Ɛ56 406	
4	χ06 845 6Ɛ9		4	7χ3 07χ 308		4	654 589 392	
5	9Ɛχ 403 3Ɛ5		5	799 Ɛ2χ 64Ɛ		5	651 038 Ɛ72	
6	9Ɛ2 09Ɛ 20χ		6	794 χ46 5χ1		6	649 724 972	
7	9χ5 χ92 31χ		7	78Ɛ χ09 05χ		7	646 248 3χ9	
8	999 999 99χ		8	786 χ35 187		8	642 9χ7 086	
9	991 9Ɛ7 151		9	781 Ɛ05 915		9	63Ɛ 580 63Ɛ	
χ	985 Ɛ23 60χ		χ	779 039 χ62		χ	638 190 31χ	
Ɛ	97χ 158 468		Ɛ	774 214 5Ɛ1		Ɛ	634 χ15 979	
130	972 497 24χ		170	76Ɛ 450 76Ɛ		1Ɛ0	631 694 842	
1	966 919 593		1	766 729 3Ɛ2		1	62χ 388 5χ8	
2	95Ɛ 260 95Ɛ		2	761 χ65 775		2	627 0Ɛ4 8Ɛ9	
3	953 8χ2 907		3	759 240 759		3	623 χ55 048	
4	948 421 063		4	754 675 467		4	620 828 χƐ8	
5	941 055 473		5	74Ɛ Ɛ47 007		5	619 633 Ɛ7Ɛ	
6	935 981 670		6	747 474 747		6	616 471 954	
7	92χ 79Ɛ 437		7	742 χ39 418		7	613 321 Ɛ4Ɛ	
8	923 6χ8 821		8	73χ 458 40χ		8	610 204 081	
9	918 6χ3 519		9	735 Ɛ10 914		9	609 117 857	
χ	911 785 684		χ	731 619 946		χ	606 060 606	
Ɛ	906 951 09χ		Ɛ	729 17χ 717		Ɛ	603 016 090	

N	Reciprocal	d	N	Reciprocal	d	N	Reciprocal	d
200	600 000 000		240	518 6X3 519		280	460 000 000	
1	5Ɛ9 015 Ɛ30		1	516 45X 0Ɛ1		1	45X 397 6X8	
2	5Ɛ6 05Ɛ 606		2	514 233 241		2	458 786 274	
3	5Ɛ3 114 3Ɛ6		3	512 026 701		3	456 Ɛ87 993	
4	5Ɛ0 1Ɛ8 07Ɛ		4	50Ɛ X38 069		4	455 3X0 2Ɛ8	
5	5X9 30X 3X2		5	509 867 482		5	453 807 4X1	
6	5X6 44X 938		6	507 6Ɛ4 508		6	452 045 204	
7	5X3 5Ɛ9 0X3		7	505 55X Ɛ4X		7	450 495 523	
8	5X0 794 X46		8	503 422 95X		8	44X 938 0Ɛ9	
9	599 999 99X		9	501 303 90Ɛ		9	449 1Ɛ1 011	
X	597 00Ɛ 720		X	4ƐƐ 201 7Ɛ9		X	447 678 127	
Ɛ	594 269 X58		Ɛ	4Ɛ9 118 402		Ɛ	445 Ɛ55 30X	
210	591 534 3X1		250	4Ɛ7 04Ɛ 705		290	444 444 444	
1	58X 826 750		1	4Ɛ4 Ɛ9Ɛ 2Ɛ1		1	442 945 3X1	
2	587 Ɛ44 54X		2	4Ɛ2 Ɛ47 16Ɛ		2	441 258 02Ɛ	
3	585 289 609		3	4Ɛ0 Ɛ0Ɛ 0Ɛ1		3	43Ɛ 780 440	
4	582 639 583		4	4XX XXX XXƐ		4	43X 0Ɛ6 2X7	
5	57Ɛ X14 077		5	4X8 XX6 561		5	438 641 681	
6	579 214 Ɛ36		6	4X6 XƐ9 687		6	436 Ɛ9X 261	
7	576 63Ɛ X16		7	4X4 Ɛ28 066		7	435 548 124	
8	573 X90 574		8	4X2 Ɛ71 905		8	433 Ɛ07 166	
9	571 346 636		9	4X1 012 630		9	432 497 24X	
X	56X 825 890		X	49Ɛ 08X 234		X	430 X78 273	
Ɛ	568 129 974		Ɛ	499 160 728		Ɛ	42Ɛ 46X 100	
220	565 656 566		260	497 249 725		2X0	429 X70 858	
1	562 ƐX7 530		1	495 351 045		1	428 483 ƐX7	
2	560 560 560		2	493 46X 8X7		2	426 XX7 X16	
3	559 Ɛ39 310		3	491 5X2 6Ɛ4		3	425 520 213	
4	557 539 6X0		4	48Ɛ 730 490		4	423 Ɛ64 X87	
5	554 Ɛ61 176		5	489 894 064		5	422 5Ɛ9 XX9	
6	552 5X7 846		6	487 X51 464		6	421 063 169	
7	550 055 005		7	486 024 301		7	41Ɛ 718 580	
8	549 724 972		8	484 210 632		8	41X 1X1 X1X	
9	547 216 X11		9	482 412 070		9	418 877 1ƐX	
X	544 92X X70		X	480 628 838		X	417 360 417	
Ɛ	542 464 821		Ɛ	47X 858 390		Ɛ	415 X55 370	
230	540 000 000		270	478 XX0 936		2Ɛ0	414 559 Ɛ39	
1	539 778 72X		1	477 139 Ɛ36		1	413 072 241	
2	537 356 311		2	475 3XƐ 81X		2	411 795 Ɛ7Ɛ	
3	534 Ɛ54 898		3	473 675 X33		3	410 309 237	
4	532 773 97Ɛ		4	471 954 410		4	40X X4Ɛ 935	
5	530 3Ɛ3 2Ɛ5		5	470 047 005		5	409 5X1 77X	
6	52X 052 X05		6	46X 351 86X		6	408 142 855	
7	527 912 434		7	468 670 422		7	406 8Ɛ2 X8X	
8	525 5Ɛ1 710		8	466 9X2 942		8	405 472 16X	
9	523 2Ɛ0 3X8		9	465 128 X70		9	404 040 404	
X	521 00X 420		X	463 486 64Ɛ		X	402 819 523	
Ɛ	51X 947 54Ɛ		Ɛ	461 837 744		Ɛ	401 405 419	

N	Reciprocal	d	N	Reciprocal	d	N	Reciprocal	d
300	400 000 000		340	372 497 24X		380	333 333 333	
1	3ƐX 805 3X3		1	371 3X4 X0Ɛ		1	332 46Ɛ X12	
2	3Ɛ9 419 29X		2	370 2ƐX 25Ɛ		2	331 5Ɛ2 276	
3	3Ɛ8 03Ɛ 804		3	36Ɛ 21Ɛ 308		3	330 73X 458	
4	3Ɛ6 870 673		4	36X 147 Ɛ26		4	32Ɛ 890 330	
5	3Ɛ5 4XƐ 984		5	369 080 246		5	32X X27 X69	
6	3Ɛ4 139 453		6	368 000 000		6	329 Ɛ89 203	
7	3Ɛ2 995 1ƐƐ		7	366 Ɛ47 363		7	329 134 131	
8	3Ɛ1 63Ɛ 164		8	365 X9X 049		8	328 2X4 7X7	
9	3Ɛ0 2Ɛ3 225		9	364 X38 209		9	327 45X 963	
X	3XX Ɛ75 325		X	363 9X1 7ƐX		X	326 61X 597	
Ɛ	3X9 845 386		Ɛ	362 952 575		Ɛ	325 7X3 842	
310	3X8 523 2Ɛ0		350	361 90X 653		390	324 972 497	
1	3X7 20Ɛ 004		1	360 891 9XƐ		1	323 Ɛ46 695	
2	3X5 Ɛ04 62Ɛ		2	35Ɛ 860 360		2	323 124 1Ɛ5	
3	3X4 807 894		3	35X 835 X83		3	322 307 1Ɛ1	
4	3X3 518 6X3		4	359 816 6Ɛ7		4	321 4Ɛ3 643	
5	3X2 236 Ɛ86		5	358 802 399		5	320 6X5 2X7	
6	3X0 Ɛ62 X69		6	357 7Ɛ5 088		6	31Ɛ 8X0 320	
7	39Ɛ 898 27Ɛ		7	356 7Ɛ2 923		7	31X XX0 6X2	
8	39X 61X Ɛ31		8	355 7Ɛ7 485		8	31X 0X6 16Ɛ	
9	399 36X Ɛ73		9	354 806 X94		9	319 2Ɛ4 Ɛ02	
X	398 108 2Ɛ6		X	353 821 2Ɛ0		X	318 508 X9X	
Ɛ	396 X72 872		Ɛ	352 842 476		Ɛ	317 726 07X	
320	395 826 396		360	351 86X 352		3X0	316 948 421	
1	394 5X6 Ɛ9X		1	350 8X0 XX0		1	315 Ɛ73 907	
2	393 374 7Ɛ7		2	34Ɛ 91X 246		2	315 1X4 2Ɛ4	
3	392 14Ɛ 364		3	34X 962 169		3	314 419 965	
4	390 Ɛ32 998		4	349 9Ɛ0 7Ɛ3		4	313 658 45X	
5	38Ɛ 923 214		5	348 X45 904		5	312 89Ɛ Ɛ5X	
6	38X 720 38Ɛ		6	347 XX5 446		6	311 Ɛ28 624	
7	389 526 203		7	346 Ɛ4Ɛ 563		7	311 17X 037	
8	388 338 834		8	346 000 000		8	310 414 55X	
9	387 157 9X0		9	345 076 Ɛ45		9	30Ɛ 673 952	
X	385 Ɛ83 604		X	344 138 321		X	30X 917 Ɛ9Ɛ	
Ɛ	384 9Ɛ7 824		Ɛ	343 203 XƐ8		Ɛ	309 Ɛ85 044	
330	383 838 384		370	342 295 X3Ɛ		3Ɛ0	309 236 X88	
1	382 685 3X4		1	341 372 096		1	308 4Ɛ1 673	
2	381 51X 80X		2	340 454 5Ɛ2		2	307 770 Ɛ85	
3	380 380 380		3	33Ɛ 541 13X		3	306 X35 187	
4	37Ɛ 22X 205		4	33X 633 X63		4	306 102 041	
5	37X 0X4 265		5	339 730 915		5	305 393 734	
6	378 Ɛ66 468		6	338 833 883		6	304 669 X29	
7	377 X34 759		7	337 940 899		7	303 948 8XƐ	
8	376 90X X83		8	336 X53 90X		8	303 030 303	
9	375 7Ɛ1 170		9	335 Ɛ70 907		9	302 318 433	
X	374 69Ɛ 369		X	335 093 842		X	301 609 046	
Ɛ	373 595 405		Ɛ	334 200 668		Ɛ	300 902 307	

N	Reciprocal	d	N	Reciprocal	d	N	Reciprocal	d
400	300 000 000		440	292 929 293		480	26X 351 86X	
1	2ƐƐ 302 2Ɛ5		1	292 16X 869		1	269 89X Ɛ71	
2	2ƐX 608 Ɛ76		2	291 5Ɛ3 876		2	269 22Ɛ 057	
3	2Ɛ9 918 18Ɛ		3	290 X40 291		3	268 781 Ɛ06	
4	2Ɛ9 02Ɛ 903		4	290 290 290		4	268 117 721	
5	2Ɛ8 347 924		5	28Ɛ 723 850		5	267 674 086	
6	2Ɛ7 668 1Ɛ9		6	28X Ɛ7X 766		6	267 013 361	
7	2Ɛ6 990 Ɛ15		7	28X 418 ƐƐ4		7	266 575 34Ɛ	
8	2Ɛ6 0ƐX 03Ɛ		8	289 87X 950		8	265 Ɛ1X 035	
9	2Ɛ5 42Ɛ 543		9	289 123 Ɛ93		9	265 485 5Ɛ8	
X	2Ɛ4 765 1Ɛ1		X	288 590 699		X	264 X33 841	
Ɛ	2Ɛ3 XX3 194		Ɛ	287 X40 642		Ɛ	264 3X4 72X	
410	2Ɛ3 225 47X		450	287 2Ɛ3 X23		490	263 958 264	
1	2Ɛ2 56Ɛ X36		1	286 76X 618		1	263 312 609	
2	2Ɛ1 8ƐX 652		2	286 028 603		2	262 88Ɛ 585	
3	2Ɛ1 051 499		3	285 4X9 977		3	262 24Ɛ 139	
4	2Ɛ0 3X8 523		4	284 972 497		4	261 811 48Ɛ	
5	2XƐ 747 738		5	284 23X 340		5	261 196 3X5	
6	2XX XXX XXƐ		6	283 709 507		6	260 761 X66	
7	2XX 256 390		7	282 Ɛ9Ɛ 992		7	260 130 076	
8	2X9 605 970		8	282 475 536		8	25Ɛ 700 9ƐX	
9	2X8 979 41Ɛ		9	281 952 356		9	25Ɛ 094 25Ɛ	
X	2X8 134 Ɛ2X		X	281 232 410		X	25X 66X 201	
Ɛ	2X7 4Ɛ4 66X		Ɛ	280 715 6ƐƐ		Ɛ	25X 046 848	
420	2X6 878 1Ɛ0		460	280 000 000		4X0	259 625 962	
1	2X6 043 906		1	27Ɛ 4X9 6Ɛ2		1	259 007 530	
2	2X5 413 386		2	27X 99X 375		2	258 5XƐ 756	
3	2X4 7X6 981		3	27X 292 1X7		3	257 Ɛ96 402	
4	2X3 Ɛ82 285		4	279 789 167		4	257 583 696	
5	2X3 361 669		5	279 087 254		5	256 Ɛ73 379	
6	2X2 744 904		6	278 588 44X		6	256 565 656	
7	2X1 Ɛ2Ɛ 9X5		7	277 X90 731		7	255 Ɛ5X 313	
8	2X1 31X 8X1		8	277 397 X9Ɛ		8	255 555 555	
9	2X0 711 58X		9	276 8X6 2Ɛ6		9	254 Ɛ53 147	
X	29Ɛ Ɛ08 039		X	276 1Ɛ7 759		X	254 553 291	
Ɛ	29Ɛ 306 444		Ɛ	275 710 027		Ɛ	253 Ɛ55 955	
430	29X 708 579		470	275 027 503		4Ɛ0	253 55X 943	
1	299 Ɛ12 3Ɛ5		1	274 545 987		1	252 Ɛ66 240	
2	299 31Ɛ Ɛ09		2	273 X67 218		2	252 574 033	
3	298 731 290		3	273 38Ɛ 618		3	251 Ɛ84 305	
4	297 Ɛ46 298		4	272 8Ɛ6 966		4	251 596 X62	
5	297 362 Ɛ01		5	272 225 025		5	250 ƐXƐ X70	
6	296 783 319		6	271 756 1Ɛ4		6	250 607 316	
7	295 ƐX7 301		7	271 08X 276		7	250 025 002	
8	295 412 X46		8	270 605 210		8	24Ɛ 645 118	
9	294 842 106		9	26Ɛ Ɛ43 01Ɛ		9	24Ɛ 067 646	
X	294 074 X98		X	26Ɛ 483 885		X	24X 690 374	
Ɛ	293 4XƐ 354		Ɛ	26X X07 368		Ɛ	24X 0Ɛ7 488	

N	Reciprocal	d	N	Reciprocal	d	N	Reciprocal	d
500	249 724 972		540	230 000 000		580	214 Ɛ36 42X	
1	249 154 616		1	22Ɛ 6Ɛ3 Ɛ46		1	214 699 476	
2	248 786 622		2	22Ɛ 1X9 954		2	214 241 ƐƐ4	
3	248 1ƐX 97Ɛ		3	22X 8X5 615		3	213 9X8 214	
4	247 835 454		4	22X 3X3 138		4	213 553 Ɛ09	
5	247 272 250		5	229 XX2 6Ɛ1		5	213 101 28X	
6	246 8Ɛ1 358		6	229 5X3 XX7		6	212 870 107	
7	246 332 75Ɛ		7	229 0X7 112		7	212 420 5Ɛ5	
8	245 976 246		8	228 7Ɛ0 15X		8	211 Ɛ92 544	
9	245 400 000		9	228 2Ɛ6 ƐƐ5		9	211 745 Ɛ27	
X	244 X48 032		X	227 X03 851		X	211 2ƐX Ɛ55	
Ɛ	244 496 308		Ɛ	227 512 298		Ɛ	210 X75 5ƐƐ	
510	243 Ɛ26 832		550	227 022 702		590	210 631 695	
1	243 579 395		1	226 734 8Ɛ8		1	210 1XƐ 190	
2	243 012 161		2	226 248 871		2	20Ɛ 96X 2X0	
3	242 669 13X		3	225 962 596		3	20Ɛ 52X 9Ɛ7	
4	242 106 317		4	225 47X 05Ɛ		4	20Ɛ 0Ɛ0 Ɛ0Ɛ	
5	241 765 69X		5	224 Ɛ97 473		5	20X 874 614	
6	241 207 036		6	224 6Ɛ6 607		6	20X 439 6ƐƐ	
7	240 86X 753		7	224 217 48Ɛ		7	20X 004 180	
8	240 314 41X		8	223 93X 074		8	209 790 20X	
9	23Ɛ 980 240		9	223 462 56X		9	209 359 817	
X	23Ɛ 42X 1X6		X	222 Ɛ88 765		X	208 Ɛ28 796	
Ɛ	23X X9X 282		Ɛ	222 6Ɛ4 652		Ɛ	208 6Ɛ9 0ƐX	
520	23X 550 479		560	222 222 222		5X0	208 28X Ɛ7Ɛ	
1	23X 004 780		1	221 951 685		1	207 X62 38X	
2	239 67X Ɛ79		2	221 482 7Ɛ0		2	207 637 120	
3	239 137 459		3	220 ƐƐ5 590		3	207 211 3X8	
4	238 7Ɛ5 X0Ɛ		4	220 72X 015		4	206 9X8 Ɛ9Ɛ	
5	238 276 43Ɛ		5	220 264 2Ɛ5		5	206 586 0Ɛ3	
6	237 938 Ɛ18		6	21Ɛ 9X0 220		6	206 164 719	
7	237 401 64Ɛ		7	21Ɛ 519 983		7	205 944 64X	
8	236 X88 206		8	21Ɛ 059 153		8	205 525 X78	
9	236 554 9Ɛ4		9	21X 79X 142		9	205 108 798	
X	236 023 602		X	21X 320 940		X	204 8Ɛ0 99Ɛ	
Ɛ	235 6Ɛ4 21Ɛ		Ɛ	219 X65 140		Ɛ	204 496 47X	
530	235 186 X35		570	219 5XƐ 131		5Ɛ0	204 081 428	
1	234 85Ɛ 636		1	219 136 905		1	203 869 85X	
2	234 336 211		2	218 884 072		2	203 457 545	
3	233 X12 970		3	218 412 ƐX5		3	203 046 69X	
4	233 4Ɛ1 481		4	217 Ɛ63 693		4	202 837 095	
5	232 Ɛ91 Ɛ34		5	217 6Ɛ5 92Ɛ		5	202 428 Ɛ25	
6	232 674 536		6	217 249 725		6	202 020 202	
7	232 158 X77		7	216 9X3 06Ɛ		7	201 814 920	
8	231 843 325		8	216 53X 137		8	201 40X 872	
9	231 32Ɛ 6Ɛ0		9	216 096 937		9	201 006 030	
X	230 X19 982		X	215 835 060		X	200 802 80Ɛ	
Ɛ	230 509 Ɛ4X		Ɛ	215 394 XX1		Ɛ	200 400 801	

N	Reciprocal	d
600	200 000 000	3ƐƐ 401
1	1ƐƐ 800 7ƐƐ	χ 00χ
2	402 7Ɛ1	8 821
3	005 Ɛ90	7 441
4	1Ɛχ 80χ 74Ɛ	6 069
5	414 6χ2	4 8χ0
6	01Ɛ χ02	3 520
7	1Ɛ9 828 4χ2	2 166
8	436 338	0 9Ɛχ
9	045 53χ	3χƐ 658
χ	1Ɛ8 855 χχ2	χ 302
Ɛ	467 7χ0	8 Ɛ74
610	07χ 828	7 832
1	1Ɛ7 892 ƐƐ6	6 4Ɛ6
2	4χ8 700	5 187
3	103 535	3 χ63
4	1Ɛ6 91Ɛ 692	2 746
5	538 Ɛ48	1 435
6	157 713	0 130
7	1Ɛ5 977 5χ3	39χ χ30
8	598 773	9 73χ
9	1ƐƐ 035	8 452
χ	1Ɛ4 χ22 7χ3	7 171
Ɛ	647 632	5 χ98
620	271 756	4 809
1	1Ɛ3 χ98 Ɛ49	3 547
2	705 602	2 28Ɛ
3	333 333	1 01χ
4	1Ɛ2 Ɛ62 315	38Ɛ 974
5	792 561	χ 715
6	403 χ48	9 482
7	036 586	8 234
8	1Ɛ1 86χ 352	6 ƐƐ3
9	4χ3 35Ɛ	5 978
χ	119 5χ3	4 748
Ɛ	1Ɛ0 954 χ57	3 523
630	591 534	2 304
1	20Ɛ 230	1 0Ɛ0
2	1χƐ χ4χ 140	37Ɛ χχ4
3	68χ 258	χ 8χ2
4	30Ɛ 576	9 6χ5
5	1χχ Ɛ51 χ91	8 4Ɛ6
6	795 597	7 30Ɛ
7	41χ 288	6 12Ɛ
8	064 159	4 Ɛ56
9	1χ9 8χƐ 203	3 988
χ	537 437	2 804
Ɛ	184 833	1 646

N	Reciprocal	d
640	1χ8 χ13 1χ9	370 493
1	662 916	36Ɛ 327
2	2Ɛ3 5χƐ	χ 185
3	1χ7 Ɛ45 426	9 029
4	798 3Ɛ9	7 χ97
5	430 522	6 950
6	085 792	5 80Ɛ
7	1χ6 91Ɛ Ɛ83	4 695
8	577 4χχ	3 564
9	213 Ɛ46	2 43χ
χ	1χ5 χ71 708	1 31χ
Ɛ	710 3χχ	0 205
650	370 1χ5	35Ɛ 0Ɛ4
1	011 0Ɛ1	9 ƐχƐ
2	1χ4 873 102	8 χƐ0
3	516 212	7 9Ɛ6
4	17χ 418	6 907
5	1χ3 χ23 711	5 821
6	689 χƐ0	4 742
7	335 36χ	3 668
8	1χ2 Ɛχ1 902	2 599
9	84Ɛ 325	1 513
χ	4Ɛ9 χ12	0 453
Ɛ	169 57Ɛ	34Ɛ 399
660	1χ1 χ1χ 1χ2	χ 329
1	68Ɛ χ75	9 283
2	342 7Ɛ2	8 222
3	1χ0 ƐƐ6 590	7 187
4	86Ɛ 405	6 136
5	525 28Ɛ	5 0χƐ
6	1χ0 1χ0	4 069
7	19Ɛ χ58 133	3 031
8	715 102	1 ƐƐχ
9	393 104	0 Ɛ91
χ	052 133	33Ɛ Ɛ6χ
Ɛ	19χ 912 185	χ Ɛ51
670	593 234	9 Ɛ38
1	255 2Ɛ8	8 Ɛ2χ
2	199 Ɛ18 38χ	7 Ɛ24
3	7χ0 466	6 Ɛ24
4	465 542	5 Ɛ2Ɛ
5	12Ɛ 613	4 Ɛ39
6	198 9Ɛ6 696	3 Ɛ52
7	682 744	2 Ɛ6Ɛ
8	34Ɛ 795	1 Ɛ93
9	019 802	1 000
χ	197 8χ8 802	0 031
Ɛ	578 791	32Ɛ 068

N	Reciprocal	d
680	197 249 725	32χ 0χ9
1	196 Ɛ1Ɛ 638	9 132
2	7Ɛ2 506	8 182
3	486 344	7 215
4	15Ɛ 12Ɛ	6 272
5	195 χ34 χ79	5 315
6	70Ɛ 764	4 380
7	3χ7 3χ4	3 431
8	083 Ɛ73	2 4χ7
9	194 961 688	1 565
χ	640 123	0 629
Ɛ	31Ɛ 6Ɛ6	31Ɛ 6Ɛ6
690	000 000	χ 788
1	193 8χ1 434	9 862
2	583 792	8 943
3	266 χ4Ɛ	7 χ27
4	192 Ɛ4Ɛ 024	6 Ɛ14
5	834 110	6 008
6	51χ 104	5 102
7	205 002	4 203
8	191 χƐ0 9ƐƐ	3 308
9	799 6Ɛ3	2 416
χ	487 299	1 529
Ɛ	175 970	0 644
6χ0	190 χ65 328	30Ɛ 765
1	755 783	χ 88χ
2	446 χƐ5	9 9Ɛ7
3	139 0Ɛχ	8 Ɛ2χ
4	18Ɛ χ30 190	8 065
5	724 127	7 1χ5
6	418 Ɛ42	6 32χ
7	112 814	5 476
8	18χ χ09 35χ	4 609
9	704 951	3 762
χ	401 1χƐ	2 902
Ɛ	0Ɛχ 4χ9	1 χ65
6Ɛ0	189 9Ɛ8 644	1 011
1	6Ɛ7 633	0 182
2	3Ɛ7 471	2ƐƐ 336
3	0Ɛ8 137	χ 4Ɛ4
4	188 9Ɛ9 843	9 676
5	700 189	8 841
6	403 548	7 χ0Ɛ
7	107 739	6 Ɛχ3
8	187 χ10 756	6 17χ
9	716 598	5 35Ɛ
χ	421 239	4 543
Ɛ	128 8Ɛ6	3 72Ɛ

N	Reciprocal	d	N	Reciprocal	d	N	Reciprocal	d
700	186 Ӿ35 187	2Ɛ2 921	740	177 777 778	281 280	780	169 484 211	254 574
1	742 466	1 Ɛ16	1	4Ɛ6 4Ɛ8	0 5Ɛ1	1	22Ɛ 859	3 9Ɛ5
2	450 550	1 114	2	235 Ɛ07	27Ɛ 927	2	168 Ɛ97 Ӿ64	3 240
3	15Ɛ 438	0 315	3	176 Ɛ76 1Ӿ0	Ɛ 063	3	944 824	2 688
4	185 Ӿ6Ɛ 123	2ӾƐ 520	4	8Ɛ7 139	Ӿ 3Ӿ3	4	6Ɛ2 158	1 Ɛ17
5	77Ɛ 803	Ӿ 72Ɛ	5	638 956	9 728	5	460 241	1 36Ӿ
6	491 094	9 941	6	37Ɛ 22Ӿ	8 Ӿ73	6	20Ӿ Ӿ93	0 804
7	1Ӿ3 353	8 Ɛ58	7	102 377	8 201	7	167 Ɛ7Ӿ 28Ɛ	0 060
8	184 Ӿ26 3Ɛ7	8 177	8	175 Ӿ46 176	7 554	8	92Ӿ 22Ɛ	24Ɛ 4ƐƐ
9	80Ӿ 240	7 39Ӿ	9	78Ӿ 822	6 8ӾӾ	9	69Ӿ 930	Ӿ 961
Ӿ	522 Ӿ62	6 606	Ӿ	513 Ɛ34	6 047	Ӿ	44Ɛ Ɛ8Ɛ	Ӿ 207
Ɛ	238 458	5 835	Ɛ	259 ӾӾ9	5 3Ӿ7	Ɛ	201 984	9 672
710	183 Ɛ52 823	4 Ӿ69	750	174 ƐӾ4 702	4 750	790	166 Ɛ74 312	8 Ɛ21
1	869 976	4 0Ӿ5	1	92Ɛ Ɛ72	3 ӾƐ8	1	927 3Ɛ1	8 393
2	585 891	3 324	2	678 076	3 266	2	69Ɛ 01Ӿ	7 848
3	2Ӿ2 569	2 569	3	404 Ӿ10	2 619	3	453 392	7 103
4	000 000	1 7Ɛ5	4	152 3Ɛ3	1 992	4	208 28Ɛ	6 581
5	182 91Ӿ 407	0 Ӿ44	5	173 ӾӾ0 621	1 150	5	165 Ɛ81 90Ӿ	5 Ӿ43
6	639 583	0 099	6	82Ɛ 491	0 510	6	937 Ӿ87	5 306
7	359 4Ӿ6	29Ɛ 335	7	57Ӿ Ɛ81	26Ɛ 893	7	6Ɛ2 781	4 791
8	07Ӿ 171	Ӿ 596	8	30Ɛ 2ӾӾ	Ɛ 05Ɛ	8	469 Ɛ20	4 05Ɛ
9	181 99Ɛ 797	9 839	9	060 24Ɛ	Ӿ 42Ӿ	9	225 Ɛ51	3 52Ɛ
Ӿ	701 Ɛ5Ӿ	8 ӾӾ5	Ӿ	172 9Ɛ1 Ӿ21	9 7ƐƐ	Ӿ	164 ƐӾ2 622	2 Ӿ02
Ɛ	425 075	8 156	Ɛ	744 222	8 Ɛ94	Ɛ	95Ɛ 820	2 298
720	148 Ɛ1Ɛ	7 409	760	497 24Ӿ	8 371	7Ӿ0	719 544	1 774
1	180 Ӿ71 712	6 685	1	22Ӿ Ӿ99	7 750	1	497 990	1 054
2	797 049	5 945	2	171 Ɛ83 349	6 Ɛ33	2	256 938	0 536
3	501 304	5 009	3	918 416	6 31Ӿ	3	016 402	23Ɛ Ӿ1Ɛ
4	228 2Ɛ7	4 294	4	672 0Ɛ8	5 706	4	163 996 5Ӿ3	Ɛ 307
5	17Ɛ Ɛ54 023	3 564	5	408 5Ɛ2	4 ӾƐ8	5	757 298	Ӿ 7Ɛ5
6	880 67Ɛ	2 837	6	163 6Ɛ6	4 2ӾƐ	6	518 6Ӿ3	Ӿ 0Ӿ5
7	5Ӿ9 Ӿ44	1 Ɛ12	7	170 ӾƐƐ 407	3 6Ӿ6	7	29Ӿ 5ƐӾ	9 59Ӿ
8	317 Ɛ32	1 1Ɛ1	8	857 921	2 ӾӾ4	8	061 020	8 Ӿ93
9	046 941	0 494	9	5Ɛ4 Ӿ39	2 2Ӿ5	9	162 Ӿ24 149	8 391
Ӿ	17Ӿ 976 469	28Ɛ 77Ɛ	Ӿ	352 754	1 6ӾӾ	Ӿ	7Ӿ7 978	7 891
Ɛ	6Ӿ6 8ӾӾ	Ӿ Ӿ68	Ɛ	0Ɛ1 066	0 ӾƐ6	Ɛ	570 0Ӿ7	7 192
730	417 Ӿ42	Ӿ 15Ɛ	770	16Ɛ Ӿ50 170	0 305	7Ɛ0	334 Ɛ15	6 698
1	149 8Ӿ3	9 455	1	7ӾƐ Ӿ67	25Ɛ 716	1	0ƐӾ 439	5 ƐӾ3
2	179 Ӿ80 44Ӿ	8 752	2	550 351	Ӿ Ɛ30	2	161 Ӿ84 456	5 4Ɛ2
3	7Ɛ3 8Ɛ8	7 Ӿ53	3	2Ɛ1 421	Ӿ 347	3	84Ӿ Ɛ64	4 Ӿ02
4	527 Ӿ65	7 158	4	053 096	9 767	4	616 162	4 316
5	260 909	6 465	5	16Ӿ 9Ɛ5 52Ɛ	8 Ɛ8Ӿ	5	3Ӿ1 Ӿ48	3 830
6	178 Ɛ96 464	5 776	6	758 561	8 3Ɛ3	6	16Ӿ 218	3 149
7	910 8ӾӾ	4 Ӿ89	7	500 16Ӿ	7 81Ɛ	7	160 Ɛ37 08Ɛ	2 668
8	647 Ӿ21	4 1Ӿ5	8	264 54Ɛ	7 04Ɛ	8	904 623	1 Ɛ8Ӿ
9	383 838	3 504	9	009 500	6 481	9	692 655	1 4Ɛ2
Ӿ	100 334	2 827	Ӿ	169 973 03Ɛ	5 8Ɛ7	Ӿ	461 163	0 Ӿ19
Ɛ	177 Ӿ39 709	1 Ɛ51	Ɛ	719 344	5 133	Ɛ	230 346	0 346

N	Reciprocal	d	N	Reciprocal	d	N	Reciprocal	d
800	160 000 000	22Ɛ 876	840	153 43X 0Ɛ6	20X 424	880	147 474 747	1XƐ X24
1	15Ɛ 990 346	Ɛ 1X9	1	22Ɛ 892	9 X2Ɛ	1	284 923	Ɛ 4XX
2	761 159	X 722	2	021 X63	9 437	2	095 435	X Ɛ76
3	532 637	X 05X	3	152 X14 628	8 X45	3	146 XX6 47Ɛ	X 642
4	304 599	9 598	4	807 7X3	8 456	4	8Ɛ7 X39	X 111
5	097 001	8 Ɛ18	5	5ƐƐ 349	7 X69	5	709 928	9 7X2
6	15X X6X 0X5	8 45Ɛ	6	3Ɛ3 4X0	7 481	6	520 146	9 274
7	841 846	7 9X5	7	1X8 01Ɛ	6 X98	7	332 X92	8 948
8	615 X61	7 330	8	151 ƐX1 143	6 4Ɛ6	8	146 146	8 422
9	3XX 731	6 87Ɛ	9	996 849	5 Ɛ14	9	145 Ɛ59 924	7 XƐX
X	183 X72	6 210	X	790 935	5 536	X	971 X26	7 598
Ɛ	159 Ɛ59 862	5 763	Ɛ	587 3ƐƐ	4 Ɛ59	Ɛ	786 44X	7 077
810	934 0ƐƐ	5 0ƐX	850	382 462	4 582	890	59Ɛ 393	6 758
1	70Ɛ 001	4 655	1	179 XX0	3 ƐXX	1	3Ɛ4 837	6 23Ɛ
2	4X6 568	3 Ɛ24	2	150 Ɛ75 XƐ2	3 617	2	20X 5Ɛ8	5 924
3	282 574	3 554	3	972 497	3 046	3	024 894	5 40X
4	05Ɛ 020	2 XƐ9	4	76Ɛ 451	2 678	4	144 X3Ɛ 486	4 XƐ6
5	158 X38 123	2 462	5	568 995	2 0Ɛ0	5	856 590	4 5X4
6	815 881	1 X0X	6	366 8X5	1 725	6	671 ƐX8	4 094
7	5Ɛ3 X73	1 378	7	165 180	1 161	7	489 Ɛ14	3 785
8	392 6Ɛ7	0 92X	8	14Ɛ Ɛ64 01Ɛ	0 79Ɛ	8	2X6 34Ɛ	3 279
9	171 989	0 2X1	9	963 440	0 21X	9	103 092	2 971
X	157 Ɛ51 6X8	21Ɛ 856	X	763 222	1ƐƐ 860	X	143 Ɛ20 321	2 467
Ɛ	931 X52	Ɛ 213	Ɛ	563 582	Ɛ 2X3	Ɛ	939 X76	1 Ɛ64
820	712 83Ɛ	X 791	860	364 29Ɛ	X 92X	8X0	757 Ɛ12	1 662
1	4Ɛ4 06X	X 151	1	165 571	X 374	1	576 470	1 162
2	295 Ɛ19	9 715	2	14X Ɛ67 1Ɛ9	9 X03	2	395 30X	0 863
3	078 404	9 099	3	969 3Ɛ6	9 452	3	1Ɛ4 667	0 366
4	156 X5Ɛ 327	8 665	4	76Ɛ Ɛ64	8 XX3	4	014 301	19Ɛ X6X
5	842 882	8 034	5	573 081	8 537	5	142 X34 453	Ɛ 575
6	626 84X	7 603	6	376 746	7 Ɛ90	6	854 X9X	Ɛ 082
7	40Ɛ 247	6 Ɛ95	7	17X 776	7 628	7	675 X18	X 78X
8	1Ɛ4 272	6 56Ɛ	8	149 Ɛ83 14X	7 085	8	497 24X	X 29Ɛ
9	155 Ɛ99 903	5 Ɛ45	9	988 085	6 724	9	2Ɛ8 Ɛ6Ɛ	9 9XƐ
X	983 97X	5 523	X	791 561	6 186	X	11Ɛ 180	9 502
Ɛ	76X 457	4 Ɛ02	Ɛ	597 397	5 829	Ɛ	141 Ɛ41 87X	9 017
830	555 555	4 4X3	870	3X1 76X	5 291	8Ɛ0	964 863	8 730
1	341 072	3 X88	1	1X8 499	4 939	1	788 133	8 248
2	129 1X6	3 472	2	148 ƐƐ3 760	4 3X5	2	5XƐ XX7	7 966
3	154 Ɛ15 934	2 X5X	3	9ƐƐ 377	3 X54	3	414 141	7 484
4	902 X96	2 449	4	807 523	3 505	4	238 879	6 ƐX5
5	6Ɛ0 649	1 X39	5	614 01X	2 Ɛ77	5	061 894	6 707
6	49X 810	1 431	6	421 063	2 62Ɛ	6	140 X87 189	6 22Ɛ
7	289 39Ɛ	0 X26	7	22X 634	2 0X6	7	8Ɛ0 Ɛ5X	5 954
8	078 575	0 421	8	038 54X	1 762	8	717 206	5 47Ɛ
9	153 X68 154	20Ɛ X1Ɛ	9	147 X46 9X8	1 220	9	541 947	4 ƐX8
X	858 335	Ɛ 41X	X	855 788	0 89Ɛ	X	368 95Ɛ	4 715
Ɛ	648 Ɛ17	X X21	Ɛ	664 XX9	0 362	Ɛ	194 246	4 246

N	Reciprocal	d	N	Reciprocal	d	N	Reciprocal	d
900	140 000 000	193 977	940	135 186 X35	179 X45	980	12X 912 X91	165 8Ɛ8
1	13Ɛ X28 245	3 4XX	1	008 Ɛ20	9 616	1	769 195	5 51Ɛ
2	854 957	3 022	2	134 X4Ɛ 596	9 1X8	2	603 876	5 142
3	681 935	2 758	3	892 3XX	8 981	3	45X 734	4 967
4	4XƐ 199	2 294	4	715 629	8 556	4	2Ɛ5 989	4 590
5	318 Ɛ05	1 X12	5	559 093	8 130	5	151 3Ɛ9	4 1Ɛ8
6	147 0Ɛ3	1 550	6	3X0 Ɛ63	7 909	6	129 ƐX9 201	3 X23
7	13X Ɛ75 763	1 090	7	225 256	7 4X6	7	X45 39X	3 651
8	9X4 693	0 812	8	069 970	7 084	8	8X1 949	3 280
9	813 X81	0 355	9	133 XƐ2 8X8	6 865	9	73X 689	2 XXX
X	643 728	18Ɛ X9X	X	938 043	6 446	X	597 79Ɛ	2 720
Ɛ	473 84X	Ɛ 625	Ɛ	781 7Ɛ9	6 029	Ɛ	435 07Ɛ	2 352
910	2X4 225	Ɛ 171	950	607 790	5 810	990	292 929	1 Ɛ84
1	115 074	X 8ƐX	1	451 Ɛ80	5 3Ɛ6	1	130 965	1 7Ɛ9
2	139 Ɛ46 376	X 449	2	298 786	4 ƐX1	2	128 Ɛ8Ɛ 168	1 433
3	977 Ɛ29	9 Ɛ99	3	123 7X5	4 789	3	X29 935	1 068
4	7X9 Ɛ50	9 730	4	132 Ɛ6Ɛ 018	4 376	4	888 889	0 8X5
5	620 420	9 283	5	9Ɛ6 862	3 Ɛ64	5	727 ƐX4	0 521
6	453 159	8 X18	6	842 8ƐX	3 754	6	587 683	0 15Ɛ
7	286 341	8 573	7	68Ɛ 166	3 346	7	427 524	15Ɛ 99X
8	0Ɛ9 98X	8 10X	8	517 X20	2 Ɛ37	8	287 746	Ɛ 61X
9	138 Ɛ31 880	7 868	9	364 XX5	2 730	9	128 128	Ɛ 25Ɛ
X	966 014	7 407	X	1Ɛ2 375	2 324	X	127 Ɛ88 X89	X XX2
Ɛ	79X 809	6 Ɛ68	Ɛ	040 051	1 Ɛ1Ɛ	Ɛ	X29 ƐX7	X 725
920	613 861	6 709	960	131 X8X 132	1 716	9X0	88Ɛ 482	X 36X
1	449 154	6 271	1	918 618	1 314	1	731 114	9 ƐƐ4
2	282 XX3	5 X15	2	767 304	0 Ɛ11	2	593 120	9 83X
3	0Ɛ9 08X	5 580	3	5Ɛ6 3Ɛ3	0 710	3	435 4X2	9 487
4	137 Ɛ33 70X	5 128	4	445 8X3	0 312	4	298 017	9 113
5	96X 5X2	4 894	5	295 591	16Ɛ Ɛ13	5	13X Ɛ04	8 961
6	7X5 90X	4 444	6	125 67X	Ɛ 716	6	126 ƐX2 163	8 5Ɛ1
7	621 486	3 ƐƐ3	7	130 Ɛ75 Ɛ64	Ɛ 31X	7	X45 772	8 241
8	459 493	3 765	8	X06 846	X Ɛ25	8	8X9 531	7 X92
9	295 92X	3 318	9	857 921	X 72Ɛ	9	751 65Ɛ	7 725
X	112 612	2 X90	X	6X9 1Ɛ2	X 337	X	5Ɛ5 Ɛ36	7 378
Ɛ	136 Ɛ4Ɛ 742	2 646	Ɛ	53X X77	9 Ɛ44	Ɛ	45X 77X	7 011
930	989 0Ɛ8	2 201	970	390 Ɛ33	9 753	9Ɛ0	303 769	6 866
1	806 XƐ7	1 97X	1	223 3X0	9 363	1	168 Ɛ03	6 502
2	645 139	1 538	2	076 039	8 Ɛ74	2	012 601	6 159
3	483 801	1 0Ɛ7	3	12Ɛ Ɛ09 085	8 786	3	125 X78 464	5 9Ɛ6
4	302 706	0 878	4	960 4ƐƐ	8 399	4	922 66X	5 654
5	141 X4X	0 43X	5	7Ɛ4 122	7 ƐƐ2	5	789 016	5 2Ɛ3
6	135 Ɛ81 610	0 002	6	648 130	7 808	6	633 923	4 Ɛ53
7	X01 60X	17Ɛ 787	7	4X0 524	7 424	7	49X 990	4 7Ɛ4
8	841 X43	Ɛ 352	8	335 100	7 03Ɛ	8	346 198	4 456
9	682 6Ɛ1	X Ɛ19	9	18X 081	6 859	9	1Ɛ1 942	4 0ƐX
X	503 794	X 6X6	X	023 424	6 477	X	059 844	3 962
Ɛ	345 0XX	X 275	Ɛ	12X X78 Ɛ69	6 098	Ɛ	124 Ɛ05 XX2	3 607

N	Reciprocal	d	N	Reciprocal	d	N	Reciprocal	d
χ00	124 972 497	153 271	χ40	11Ɛ 286 23χ	142 098	χ80	116 000 000	132 16Ɛ
1	81Ɛ 226	152 Ɛ19	1	144 162	141 982	1	115 χ89 χ51	131 χ8χ
2	688 309	785	2	002 3χ0	669	2	957 Ɛ83	7χ9
3	535 744	433	3	11χ χ80 933	354	3	826 396	50χ
4	3χ3 311	0χ1	4	93Ɛ 59Ɛ	042	4	6Ɛ4 χ88	22Ɛ
5	251 230	151 950	5	7Ɛχ 559	140 92χ	5	583 859	130 Ɛ51
6	0ƐƐ 4χ0	602	6	679 82Ɛ	619	6	452 908	873
7	123 Ɛ69 χ9χ	272	7	539 212	309	7	322 055	597
8	χ18 828	150 Ɛ25	8	3Ɛ8 Ɛ05	13Ɛ ƐƐ8	8	1Ɛ1 67χ	2ƐƐ
9	887 903	799	9	278 Ɛ09	8χχ	9	081 37Ɛ	024
χ	737 126	451	χ	139 21Ɛ	59Ɛ	χ	114 Ɛ51 357	12Ɛ 94Ɛ
Ɛ	5χ6 895	107	Ɛ	119 ƐƐ9 840	292	Ɛ	χ21 608	674
χ10	456 78χ	14Ɛ 981	χ50	χ7χ 56χ	13χ Ɛ86	χ90	8Ɛ1 Ɛ54	3χ1
1	306 χ09	639	1	93Ɛ 5χ4	87Ɛ	1	782 773	108
2	177 390	2Ɛ6	2	800 925	574	2	653 667	12χ χ35
3	028 096	14χ Ɛ73	3	682 371	26χ	3	524 832	763
4	122 χ99 123	832	4	544 103	139 Ɛ65	4	3Ɛ6 08Ɛ	492
5	94χ 4Ɛ1	4Ɛ1	5	406 15χ	862	5	287 7Ɛ9	200
6	800 000	172	6	288 4Ɛ8	55Ɛ	6	159 5Ɛ9	129 Ɛ31
7	671 χ4χ	149 χ33	7	14χ Ɛ59	258	7	02Ɛ 688	862
8	524 017	6Ɛ6	8	011 901	138 Ɛ57	8	113 Ɛ01 χ26	593
9	396 521	379	9	118 χ94 966	856	9	994 453	305
χ	249 164	042	χ	958 110	557	χ	867 14χ	039
Ɛ	100 122	148 907	Ɛ	81Ɛ 775	258	Ɛ	73χ 111	128 970
χ20	121 Ɛ73 417	592	χ60	6χ3 519	137 Ɛ5Ɛ	χχ0	611 361	6χ5
1	χ26 χ45	259	1	567 57χ	861	1	4χ4 878	41χ
2	89χ 7χ8	147 Ɛ25	2	42Ɛ 919	565	2	378 45χ	154
3	752 883	7Ɛ3	3	2Ɛ4 374	26χ	3	250 306	127 χ8Ɛ
4	607 090	481	4	179 106	136 Ɛ73	4	124 437	807
5	47Ɛ 80Ɛ	150	5	042 153	879	5	112 ƐƐ8 830	543
6	334 67Ɛ	146 χ20	6	117 Ɛ07 496	585	6	χ91 2χ9	280
7	1χ9 85Ɛ	6Ɛ2	7	990 Ɛ11	290	7	966 029	126 ƐƐχ
8	063 169	383	8	856 841	135 Ɛ9χ	8	83Ɛ 02Ɛ	938
9	120 Ɛ18 9χ6	057	9	720 863	8χ7	9	714 2Ɛ3	678
χ	992 94Ɛ	145 92χ	χ	5χ6 Ɛ78	5Ɛ6	χ	5χ9 837	3Ɛ7
Ɛ	849 021	604	Ɛ	471 582	305	Ɛ	483 440	139
χ30	703 619	299	χ70	338 279	015	χƐ0	359 303	125 χ7χ
1	57χ 340	144 Ɛ75	1	203 264	134 927	1	233 445	800
2	435 387	84Ɛ	2	08χ 539	638	2	109 845	543
3	2Ɛ0 738	529	3	116 Ɛ55 Ɛ01	34χ	3	111 Ɛχ4 302	286
4	168 20Ɛ	206	4	χ21 773	062	4	χ7Ɛ 038	00Ɛ
5	024 005	143 χχ5	5	8χ9 711	133 977	5	956 029	124 954
6	11Ɛ χχ0 120	784	6	775 956	68Ɛ	6	831 295	69χ
7	958 558	465	7	642 287	3χ6	7	708 7Ɛ7	425
8	815 0Ɛ3	146	8	50χ χχ1	100	8	5χ4 392	16Ɛ
9	691 Ɛ69	142 χ28	9	397 9χ1	132 χ18	9	480 223	123 χƐ8
χ	54Ɛ 141	70Ɛ	χ	264 Ɛ85	734	χ	358 327	844
Ɛ	408 632	3Ɛ4	Ɛ	132 451	451	Ɛ	234 6χ3	592

N	Reciprocal	d	N	Reciprocal	d	N	Reciprocal	d
Ɛ00	111 111 111	123 320	Ɛ40	108 579 215	115 411	Ɛ80	104 145 59Ɛ	108 309
1	110 ƐX9 9Ɛ1	06X	1	463 X04	187	1	039 292	0X9
2	X86 943	122 9ƐX	2	34X 839	114 Ɛ43	2	103 Ɛ31 1X5	107 X88
3	963 Ɛ45	74Ɛ	3	235 8Ɛ6	8ƐX	3	X25 319	869
4	841 3Ɛ6	49Ɛ	4	120 ƐƐ8	678	4	919 670	649
5	71X Ɛ17	231	5	008 540	434	5	812 023	42Ɛ
6	5Ɛ8 8X6	121 Ɛ83	6	107 XƐ4 108	1Ɛ3	6	706 7Ɛ4	211
7	496 923	916	7	99Ɛ Ɛ15	113 Ɛ70	7	5ƐƐ 5X3	106 ƐƐ3
8	375 009	66X	8	887 Ɛ65	930	8	4Ɛ4 5Ɛ0	997
9	253 55Ɛ	403	9	774 235	6Ɛ0	9	3X9 815	77X
X	132 158	157	X	660 745	470	X	2X3 057	562
Ɛ	011 001	120 XƐ1	Ɛ	549 295	231	Ɛ	198 6Ɛ5	346
Ɛ10	10Ɛ XƐ0 110	848	Ɛ50	436 064	112 ƐƐ3	Ɛ90	092 36Ɛ	130
1	98Ɛ 484	5X3	1	323 071	975	1	102 Ɛ88 23Ɛ	105 Ɛ16
2	86X XX1	33X	2	210 2Ɛ8	737	2	X82 325	900
3	74X 763	097	3	0Ɛ9 781	4ƐƐ	3	978 625	6X7
4	62X 688	11Ɛ X35	4	106 ƐX7 282	283	4	872 Ɛ3X	492
5	50X 853	792	5	X94 ƐƐƐ	048	5	769 668	27X
6	3XƐ 081	531	6	982 Ɛ73	111 X10	6	664 3XX	067
7	28Ɛ 750	290	7	871 163	797	7	55Ɛ 343	104 X54
8	170 480	030	8	75Ɛ 588	561	8	456 4XƐ	841
9	051 450	11X 990	9	64X 027	328	9	351 86X	62Ɛ
X	10X Ɛ32 680	732	X	538 8ƐƐ	0Ɛ3	X	249 23Ɛ	41X
Ɛ	X13 Ɛ4X	494	Ɛ	427 808	110 X80	Ɛ	144 X21	209
Ɛ20	8Ɛ5 676	236	Ɛ60	316 948	848	ƐX0	040 814	103 Ɛ28
1	797 440	119 Ɛ9X	1	206 100	616	1	101 Ɛ38 818	9X9
2	679 462	941	2	0Ɛ5 6X6	3X4	2	X34 X2Ɛ	79X
3	55Ɛ 721	6X6	3	105 ƐX5 302	172	3	931 251	58Ɛ
4	442 037	44Ɛ	4	X95 150	10Ɛ Ɛ41	4	829 882	380
5	324 7X8	1Ɛ6	5	985 20Ɛ	912	5	726 502	173
6	207 5Ɛ2	118 Ɛ5Ɛ	6	875 4Ɛ9	6X1	6	623 34Ɛ	102 Ɛ66
7	0XX 653	907	7	765 X18	472	7	520 3X5	958
8	109 Ɛ91 948	673	8	656 566	244	8	419 649	751
9	X75 295	420	9	547 322	016	9	316 XƐ8	545
X	958 X75	188	X	438 308	10X 9X9	X	214 573	33Ɛ
Ɛ	840 8X9	117 Ɛ37	Ɛ	329 51Ɛ	780	Ɛ	112 234	133
Ɛ30	724 972	8X4	Ɛ70	21X 95Ɛ	553	ƐƐ0	010 101	101 Ɛ29
1	609 08X	654	1	110 408	328	1	100 Ɛ0X 194	924
2	4Ɛ1 636	404	2	002 0X0	101	2	X08 470	71Ɛ
3	396 232	174	3	104 XƐ3 Ɛ9Ɛ	109 X96	3	906 951	516
4	27Ɛ 07X	116 Ɛ26	4	9X6 105	871	4	805 437	312
5	164 154	896	5	898 454	647	5	704 125	10Ɛ
6	049 47X	64X	6	78X X09	422	6	603 016	100 Ɛ08
7	108 Ɛ32 X30	400	7	681 5X7	1ƐX	7	502 10X	905
8	X18 630	174	8	574 3X9	108 Ɛ97	8	401 405	703
9	902 478	115 Ɛ28	9	467 412	973	9	300 902	501
X	7X8 550	8X1	X	35X 65Ɛ	751	X	200 401	301
Ɛ	692 86Ɛ	656	Ɛ	251 Ɛ0X	52Ɛ	Ɛ	100 100	100

THE DUODECIMAL CIRCLE

Duodecimal Circle

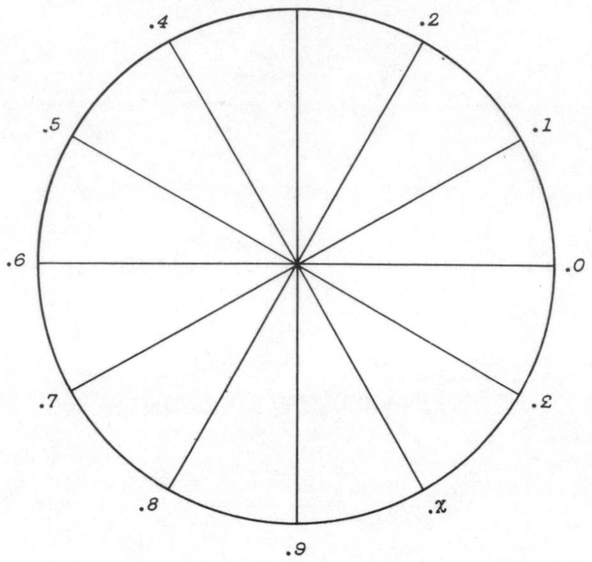

Constants

π	3 .184 809 493 Ɛ91 866 457 3χ6 212
1:π	.39χ 058 288 6Ɛ3 742 178 522 878
√π	1 .932 972 χ0χ 88Ɛ 8Ɛ3 107 939 185
log π	.564 062 958 849 980 059 1Ɛ8 χχ1
ln π	1 .18χ 115 159 429 χ62 931 59χ 729
e	2 .875 236 069 821 9Ɛχ 719 710 09Ɛ
1:e	.44Ɛ 842 160 564 χ44 4Ɛ6 χ08 Ɛ59
M	.49Ɛ 494 439 904 549 679 Ɛ59 Ɛ60
1:M	2 .599 Ɛ03 5Ɛ8 169 131 06Ɛ 881 096
C (Euler)	.6Ɛ1 518 8χ6 760 Ɛ38 1Ɛ7 543 345

Duodecimal Circle

Angles are expressed in terms of the circle.

A right angle is .3, the complete circle 1.0.

$\sin .1 = \frac{1}{2}$	$\sin .16 = \frac{1}{\sqrt{2}}$	$\sin .2 = \frac{\sqrt{3}}{2}$
$\cos .1 = \frac{\sqrt{3}}{2}$	$\cos .16 = \frac{1}{\sqrt{2}}$	$\cos .2 = \frac{1}{2}$
$\tan .1 = \frac{1}{\sqrt{3}}$	$\tan .16 = 1$	$\tan .2 = \frac{1}{\sqrt{3}}$

$\sin(.3 - A) = \cos A$	$\sin(.3 + A) = \cos A$
$\cos(.3 - A) = \sin A$	$\cos(.3 + A) = -\sin A$
$\tan(.3 - A) = \cot A$	$\tan(.3 + A) = -\cot A$
$\sin(.6 - A) = \sin A$	$\sin(.6 + A) = -\sin A$
$\cos(.6 - A) = -\cos A$	$\cos(.6 + A) = -\cos A$
$\tan(.6 - A) = -\tan A$	$\tan(.6 + A) = \tan A$
$\sin(.9 - A) = -\cos A$	$\sin(.9 + A) = -\cos A$
$\cos(.9 - A) = -\sin A$	$\cos(.9 + A) = \sin A$
$\tan(.9 - A) = \cot A$	$\tan(.9 + A) = -\cot A$
$\sin(1 - A) = -\sin A$	$\sin(1 + A) = \sin A$
$\cos(1 - A) = \cos A$	$\cos(1 + A) = \cos A$
$\tan(1 - A) = -\tan A$	$\tan(1 + A) = \tan A$

Conversion of Angles

Degrees, etc., to Circle

Example:

Find the duodecimal equivalent of
57 deg. 17 min. 44.8062 sec.

i. e., 57.29577 95 deg.

```
     45 deg. = .1 6
     10  "   = .0 4
      2  "   = .0 0 9   7 2 4   9 7 2
     15 min. = .0 0 1   2 4 9   7 2 5
      2  "   = .0 0 0   1 Ɛ 0   5 9 1
     40 sec. = .0 0 0   0 7 8   1 Ɛ 0
      4  "   =          0 0 9   2 7 1
(.981) .8062 =              1   Χ 3 5
               .1 Χ Ɛ   0 2 Χ   1 4(2)
```

```
     45 deg.  = .1 6
     10  "    = .0 4
      2  "    = .0 0 9   7 2 4   9 7 2
       .2     =          Ɛ 6 2   Χ 6 9
       .09    =          5 2 2   5 Ɛ 5
       .005   =          0 3 5   5 8 0
(.943)   .78  =          0 0 6   5 7 1
                .1 Χ Ɛ   0 2 Χ   1 4(5)
```

Alternative:

Multiply decimally by 4.8 (i. e., 1728:360) and convert the whole number for the first three duodecimal places from the whole number conversion table. Multiply the remaining decimal by 1728 and convert the whole number for the second three places. Convert the remaining decimal from the three place decimal table, previously given, for the third three places.

```
                   5 7.2 9 5 7 7   9 5
                                   4.8
                 2 2 9 1 8 3 1 1   8 0
                 4 5 8 3 6 6 2   3 6
.1 Χ Ɛ = 2 7 5) .0 1 9 7 4   1 6
                           1 7 2 8
                     1 5 7 9 3   2 8
                     3 9 4 8 3   2
                 1 3 8 1 9 1 2
                 1 9 7 4 1 6
0 2 Χ =      3 4) .1 1 3 5          = 1 4 4
```

Answer .1 Χ Ɛ 0 2 Χ 1 4 4

Note: 1 radian = .1 Χ Ɛ 0 2 Χ 1 4 4 3 5 8

Conversion Table

Degrees, Minutes, Seconds to Duodecimal of Circle

Deg.	Circle	Min.	Circle	Sec.	Circle
1	.004̇ 972̇	1	.000 0Ɛ6 2X7	1	.000 002 379
2	.009̇ 724̇	2	.000 1Ɛ0 591	2	.000 004 737
3	.012̇ 497̇	3	.000 2X6 878	3	.000 006 XƐ4
4	.017̇ 249̇	4	.000 3X0 Ɛ63	4	.000 009 271
5	.02	5	.000 4̇97 2̇	5	.000 00Ɛ 62Ɛ
10	.04	10	.000 9̇72 4̇	10	.000 01Ɛ 059
15	.06	15	.001 2̇49 7̇	15	.000 02X 688
20	.08	20	.001 7̇24 9̇	20	.000 03X 0Ɛ6
25	.0X	25	.002	25	.000 049 725
30	.1	30	.002 4̇97 2̇	30	.000 059 153
35	.12	35	.002 9̇72 4̇	35	.000 068 782
40	.14	40	.003 2̇49 7̇	40	.000 078 1Ɛ0
45	.16	45	.003 7̇24 9̇	45	.000 087 81Ɛ
60	.2	50	.004	50	.000 097 24X
90	.3	55	.004 4̇97 2̇	55	.000 0X6 878

1 Second = .000 002 379 38Ɛ

Decimals of Degrees

Deg.		Deg.		Deg.	
.1	.000 591 534	.01	.000 06X Ɛ3Ɛ	.001	.000 008 365
.2	.000 Ɛ62 X69	.02	.000 119 X7X	.002	.000 014 709
.3	.001 534 3X1	.03	.000 188 9ƐX	.003	.000 020 X72
.4	.001 Ɛ05 915	.04	.000 237 939	.004	.000 029 217
.5	.002 497 24X	.05	.000 2X6 878	.005	.000 035 580
.6	.002 X68 782	.06	.000 355 7Ɛ7	.006	.000 041 924
.7	.003 43X 0Ɛ6	.07	.000 404 737	.007	.000 04X 089
.8	.003 X0Ɛ 62Ɛ	.08	.000 473 676	.008	.000 056 432
.9	.004 3X0 Ɛ63	.09	.000 522 5Ɛ5	.009	.000 062 797

.001 Degree = .000 008 364 882

Conversion of Angles

Circle to Degrees, etc.

Example:

Find the decimal equivalent of *.1XƐ 02X 144* of the circle.

```
.1              =  30.
.0X             =  25.
.00Ɛ            =   2.29166 7
.000 0          =   0.
.000 02         =   0.00289 4
.000 00X        =    .00120 6
   (.113).144   =         01 3
                   ___________
                   57.29578(0)
```

Alternative:

Multiply duodecimally by *260* (the equivalent of 360) and convert the whole number of degrees. Multiply the remaining decimal by *6Ɛ4* (the equivalent of 1000) and convert the whole number of seconds and the duodecimal of seconds.

```
                 .1XƐ 02X 144
                          260
                Ɛ 561 508 200
               39 X05 828 8
  57  =   49)  .367 134 X
                      6Ɛ 4
                1 224 517 4
               33 062 152
              193 678 5
 295  =  207)  .943 0        = 779(5)

        Answer  57.29577 9(5)
```

Alternative to Minutes and Seconds:

Multiply duodecimally by *260* and convert the whole number of degrees. Multiply the remaining duodecimal by *50* (the equivalent of 60 minutes) and convert the whole number of minutes. Multiply the remaining duodecimal by *50* and convert the whole number and duodecimal of a second.

```
                    .1XƐ 02X 144
                             260
                   Ɛ 561 508 200
                  39 X05 828 8
  57 deg.  =  49)  .367 134 X
                          5 0
  17 min.  =  15)  .8Ɛ6 502 0
                          5 0
  44 sec.  =  38)  .981 0X      = .806

    Answer  57 deg. 17 min. 44.806 sec.
```

Conversion Table

Duodecimal Circle to Degrees

Circle	Degrees	Circle	Degrees	Circle	Degrees
.1	30	*.01*	2.5	*.001*	.208$\dot{3}$
.2	60	*2*	5.0	*2*	.416$\dot{6}$
.3	90	*3*	7.5	*3*	.625
.4	120	*4*	10.0	*4*	.833$\dot{3}$
.5	150	*5*	12.5	*5*	1.041$\dot{6}$
.6	180	*6*	15.0	*6*	1.25
.7	210	*7*	17.5	*7*	1.458$\dot{3}$
.8	240	*8*	20.0	*8*	1.666$\dot{6}$
.9	270	*9*	22.5	*9*	1.875
.χ	300	*χ*	25.0	*χ*	2.083$\dot{3}$
.Ɛ	330	*Ɛ*	27.5	*Ɛ*	2.291$\dot{6}$

Circle	Degrees	Circle	Degrees	Circle	Degrees
.000 1	.01736 $\dot{1}$	*.000 01*	.00144 7	*.000 001*	.00012 1
2	.03472 $\dot{2}$	*2*	.00289 4	*2*	.00024 1
3	.05208 $\dot{3}$	*3*	.00434 0	*3*	.00036 2
4	.06944 $\dot{4}$	*4*	.00578 7	*4*	.00048 2
5	.08680 $\dot{5}$	*5*	.00723 4	*5*	.00060 3
6	.10416 $\dot{6}$	*6*	.00868 1	*6*	.00072 3
7	.12152 $\dot{7}$	*7*	.01012 7	*7*	.00084 4
8	.13888 $\dot{8}$	*8*	.01157 4	*8*	.00096 5
9	.15625 $\dot{0}$	*9*	.01302 1	*9*	.00108 5
χ	.17361 $\dot{1}$	*χ*	.01446 8	*χ*	.00120 6
Ɛ	.19097 $\dot{2}$	*Ɛ*	.01591 4	*Ɛ*	.00132 6

.000 001 = .00012 05633

Conversion of Time

Hours, etc., to Circle

Example:

Find the duodecimal equivalent of 5 hours, 8 minutes, 12.098 seconds.

5 hours	=	.2 6
5 min.	=	.0 0 6
3	=	.0 0 3 7 2 4 9 7 2
10 sec.	=	.0 0 0 2 4 9 7 2 5
2	=	.0 0 0 0 5 9 1 5 3
(.1 2 1) .098	=	.0 0 0 0 0 3 4 6 9
		.2 6 9 X 1 2 X X(7)

Alternative:

Convert to seconds. Multiply decimally by .02 (i. e., 1728:864000) and convert the whole number for the first three duodecimal places. Convert the remaining decimal from the three place decimal table for the next three places.

```
              18492.098 seconds
                    .02
2 6 9 = 369)    .84196 = X 1 3

        Answer  .2 6 9  X 1 3
```

For further places, remultiply the remaining decimal by 1728 and convert the whole number for the second three places and the decimal for the third three places.

```
                 .84196
                   1728
                6 73568
               16 8392
              589 372
              841 96
X 1 2 = 1454)  .907    = X X 7

Answer  .2 6 9  X 1 2  X X 7
```

Conversion Table

Hours, Minutes, Seconds to Duodecimal of Circle

Hrs.	Circle	Min.	Circle	Sec.	Circle
1	.06	1	.001 $\dot{2}$49 $\dot{7}$	1	.000 02X 688
2	.10	2	.002 $\dot{4}$97 $\dot{2}$	2	.000 059 153
3	.16	3	.003 $\dot{7}$24 $\dot{9}$	3	.000 087 81Ɛ
4	.20	4	.004 $\dot{9}$72 $\dot{4}$	4	.000 0Ɛ6 2X7
5	.26	5	.006	5	.000 $\dot{1}$24 9$\dot{7}$
6	.30	10	.01	10	.000 $\dot{2}$49 7$\dot{2}$
7	.36	15	.016	15	.000 $\dot{3}$72 4$\dot{9}$
8	.40	20	.02	20	.000 $\dot{4}$97 2$\dot{4}$
9	.46	25	.026	25	.000 6
10	.50	30	.03	30	.000 $\dot{7}$24 9$\dot{7}$
11	.56	35	.036	35	.000 $\dot{8}$49 7$\dot{2}$
12	.60	40	.04	40	.000 $\dot{9}$72 4$\dot{9}$
15	.76	45	.046	45	.000 $\dot{X}$97 2$\dot{4}$
18	.90	50	.05	50	.001
21	.X6	55	.056	55	.001 $\dot{1}$24 9$\dot{7}$

1 Second = .000 02X 687 81Ɛ

Conversion of Time

Circle to Hours, etc.

Example:

Find the decimal equivalent in hours, etc., of *.269 X12 XX7*

.2	=	4	0	0
.06	=	1	0	0
.009	=	0	7	30
.000 X	=			41.6667
.000 01	=			.3472
.000 002	=			.0579
(.907).*XX7*	=			.0262
		5	8	12.098(0)

Answer 5 hrs. 8 min. 12.098(0) sec.

Alternative:

Multiply duodecimally by *20* (the equivalent of 24 hours) and convert the whole number for hours. Multiply the remaining duodecimal by *50* (the equivalent of 60 minutes) and convert the whole number by minutes. Multiply the remaining duodecimal by *50* and convert the whole number for seconds. Convert the remaining duodecimal for decimal of a second.

```
                   .269 X12 XX7
                             20
  5 hrs. =  5)   .178 259 920
                             50
  8 min. =  8)   .250 509 X00
                             50
 12 sec. = 10)   .121 412        = .098
```

Answer 5 hrs. 8 min. 12.098 sec.

Conversion Table

Duodecimal of Circle to Hours, Minutes, Seconds

Circle	H.	M.	S.	Circle	H.	M.	S.	Circle	H.	M.	S.
.1	2	0	0	*.01*	0	10	0	*.001*	0	0	50
.2	4			*2*	0	20	0	*2*	0	1	40
.3	6			*3*	0	30	0	*3*	0	2	30
.4	8			*4*	0	40	0	*4*	0	3	20
.5	10			*5*	0	50	0	*5*	0	4	10
.6	12			*6*	1	0	0	*6*	0	5	0
.7	14			*7*	1	10	0	*7*	0	5	50
.8	16			*8*	1	20	0	*8*	0	6	40
.9	18			*9*	1	30	0	*9*	0	7	30
.χ	20			*χ*	1	40	0	*χ*	0	8	20
.Ɛ	22			*Ɛ*	1	50	0	*Ɛ*	0	9	10

Circle	Sec.	Circle	Sec.	Circle	Sec.
.000 1	$4.1\dot{6}$	*.000 01*	$.347\dot{2}$	*.000 001*	.0289
2	$8.3\dot{3}$	*2*	$.694\dot{4}$	*2*	.0579
3	12.5	*3*	$1.041\dot{6}$	*3*	.0868
4	$16.6\dot{6}$	*4*	$1.388\dot{8}$	*4*	.1157
5	$20.8\dot{3}$	*5*	$1.736\dot{1}$	*5*	.1447
6	25	*6*	$2.083\dot{3}$	*6*	.1736
7	$29.1\dot{6}$	*7*	$2.430\dot{5}$	*7*	.2025
8	$33.3\dot{3}$	*8*	$2.777\dot{7}$	*8*	.2315
9	37.5	*9*	3.125	*9*	.2604
χ	$41.6\dot{6}$	*χ*	$3.472\dot{2}$	*χ*	.2894
Ɛ	$45.8\dot{3}$	*Ɛ*	$3.819\dot{4}$	*Ɛ*	.3183

.000 001 = .02893 51851

Natural Sines, Cosines, Tangents

The following tables of natural sines, cosines and tangents were derived from Andoyer's tables of natural functions. Twelve duodecimal places were calculated.

(a) The tables may be used to seven places by direct proportion, results being within one in the seventh place except for natural tangents of angles between *.1200* and *.1600* where the result will be within two.

(b) The tables may be read to nine places by direct proportion after increasing for sine (decreasing for cosine and tangent) the book difference by $\frac{1 - \text{Interval}}{2}$ of the second difference.

The table of N cotangent N may be read to eight places by direct proportion, or to nine places by direct proportion after decreasing the book differences by $\frac{1 - \text{Interval}}{2}$ of the second difference.

Note: The extended values on the opposite page are given in order that the tables may be checked or extended by multiplication or from the expansions:-

$$\sin N = 2\pi N - \frac{(2\pi N)^3}{3!} + \frac{(2\pi N)^5}{5!} - \frac{(2\pi N)^7}{7!} + \cdots$$

$$\cos N = 1 - \frac{(2\pi N)^2}{2!} + \frac{(2\pi N)^4}{4!} - \frac{(2\pi N)^6}{6!} + \cdots$$

$$\tan N = 2\pi N + \frac{1}{3}(2\pi N)^3 + \frac{2}{13}(2\pi N)^5 + \frac{15}{223}(2\pi N)^7 + \cdots$$

$$\cdots + \frac{2^{2n}(2^{2n} - 1) B_n \chi^{2n - 1}}{(2n)!}$$

Extended Values

N	Sin	N	Cos	N	Tan
.0001	.000 634 941 661 4	.0001	.ƐƐƐ ƐƐƐ X43 167 9	.0001	.000 634 941 745 4
2	.001 069 682 Ɛ36 7	2	.ƐƐƐ ƐƐƐ 550 627 1	2	.001 069 683 622 X
3	.001 6X2 404 077 9	3	.ƐƐƐ ƐƐX 924 1ƐX 2	3	.001 6X2 405 ƐX8 5
4	.002 117 144 898 9	4	.ƐƐƐ ƐƐ9 982 0X5 1	4	.002 117 149 3Ɛ2 5
5	.002 74Ɛ X84 X11 7	5	.ƐƐƐ ƐƐ8 6X6 2X4 1	5	.002 74Ɛ X91 990 9
6	.003 184 804 292 2	6	.ƐƐƐ ƐƐ7 094 7Ɛ7 8	6	.003 184 817 897 7
7	.003 7Ɛ9 542 912 5	7	.ƐƐƐ ƐƐ5 349 424 1	7	.003 7Ɛ9 563 463 1
8	.004 232 280 346 4	8	.ƐƐƐ ƐƐ3 288 365 X	8	.004 232 2Ɛ1 043 4
9	.004 866 ƐƐ8 7X5 Ɛ	9	.ƐƐƐ ƐƐ0 X91 601 7	9	.004 867 040 Ɛ90 4
X	.005 29Ɛ 933 8X4 Ɛ	X	.ƐƐƐ ƐXX 360 Ɛ73 Ɛ	X	.005 29Ɛ 993 61X 4
Ɛ	.005 914 669 477 6	Ɛ	.ƐƐƐ ƐX7 4Ɛ6 841 7	Ɛ	.005 914 728 Ɛ01 5
.001	.006 349 3X1 555 7	.001	.ƐƐƐ ƐX4 316 827 3	.001	.006 349 485 591 8
2	.010 696 5Ɛ6 X39 9	2	.ƐƐƐ Ɛ55 063 234 5	2	.010 697 0X3 0X7 6
3	.016 X23 478 204 Ɛ	3	.ƐƐƐ X92 422 X51 2	3	.016 X25 3X8 Ɛ44 5
4	.021 16Ɛ X19 416 8	4	.ƐƐƐ 998 217 Ɛ85 X	4	.021 174 533 454 9
5	.027 4Ɛ7 892 42Ɛ 8	5	.ƐƐƐ 86X 649 801 3	5	.027 504 852 934 9
6	.031 842 X93 223 4	6	.ƐƐƐ 709 500 004 6	6	.031 856 49Ɛ 963 X
7	.037 Ɛ89 253 9Ɛ5 2	7	.ƐƐƐ 534 9Ɛ7 Ɛ37 0	7	.037 ƐX9 9XƐ 3ƐƐ 1
8	.042 312 608 392 X	8	.ƐƐƐ 328 943 41X 3	8	.042 343 316 734 4
9	.048 656 7X8 819 9	9	.ƐƐƐ 0X9 324 Ɛ92 0	9	.048 69X ƐƐ3 249 6
X	.052 999 628 ƐƐ0 6	X	.ƐƐX X36 368 613 9	X	.052 X39 397 14Ɛ 5
Ɛ	.059 11X Ɛ41 430 9	Ɛ	.ƐƐX 74Ɛ X5X 5ƐX 7	Ɛ	.059 19X 620 X09 8
.01	.063 45X 961 X88 9	.01	.ƐƐX 432 008 503 4	.01	.063 542 X63 451 X
2	.106 731 7X0 ƐƐ0 6	2	.ƐƐ5 511 519 Ɛ92 1	2	.107 21Ɛ 8ƐƐ 100 X
3	.169 671 156 056 4	3	.ƐX9 272 5XƐ 984 2	3	.16Ɛ 5Ɛ4 302 415 0
4	.210 092 81Ɛ 352 Ɛ	4	.Ɛ99 8Ɛ8 23X 5X6 2	4	.214 839 662 706 4
5	.272 011 283 485 X	5	.Ɛ87 058 30Ɛ 334 7	5	.27Ɛ 108 870 546 8
6	.313 2X5 63Ɛ 787 9	6	.Ɛ71 153 08Ɛ Ɛ86 0	6	.327 024 002 535 0
7	.373 752 858 021 3	7	.Ɛ54 033 67Ɛ X0Ɛ 7	7	.394 X05 17Ɛ X4X 6
8	.413 016 813 62X 7	8	.Ɛ33 957 169 798 1	8	.444 Ɛ35 367 590 9
9	.471 33X 733 42X 6	9	.Ɛ10 569 603 572 5	9	.4Ɛ7 917 0X0 7Ɛ8 6
X	.50X 34Ɛ 44Ɛ 3XƐ 5	X	.XX6 124 674 4ƐƐ 5	X	.571 943 258 651 0
Ɛ	.565 X99 Ɛ7X 172 6	Ɛ	.X78 908 1X5 064 3	Ɛ	.62Ɛ 658 X73 403 9
.10	.600 000 000 000 0	.10	.X48 5X9 ƐƐX 943 6	.10	.6Ɛ1 7Ɛ2 7ƐƐ 22X 4
1	.654 554 04X 350 Ɛ	1	.X15 469 443 197 7	1	.778 X35 732 684 3
2	.6X7 182 08X 7X2 8	2	.99Ɛ 5Ɛ2 X93 50X Ɛ	2	.849 Ɛ60 609 Ɛ87 X
3	.737 Ɛ33 X78 555 7	3	.962 XƐ8 469 518 1	3	.925 Ɛ36 138 172 2
4	.786 8X1 626 Ɛ77 7	4	.923 884 54X 445 2	4	.X09 Ɛ6X 0X6 39Ɛ 2
5	.813 505 673 313 4	5	.8X2 022 3Ɛ8 545 9	5	.XƐƐ 506 283 753 8
6	.859 X69 650 3ƐX 3	6	.859 X69 650 3ƐX 3	6	1.000 000 000 000 0

Natural Sines

Example:

Find sin .1572 49724(Ӿ)

(a) To seven places by direct proportion

Sin	.1572	.840 276 52	
			462 9Ɛ
Interval	.49725		
Add	.49725 (4629Ɛ)	198 40	
Sin	.1572 497(2)	.840 452 9(2)	

(b) To nine places, using second difference

Sin	.1572	.840 276 516		(235)
Add to book diff.	235 $\frac{1 - .497}{2}$		462 9Ӿ8 / 83	
Corrected difference			462 Ӿ6Ɛ	
Multiply by	.497 24Ӿ	198 429		
Add to sin	.1572	.840 452 943		

Example:

Find the angle whose sine is .840 452 943

(a) To seven places by direct proportion

Sin	.1572	.840 276(5)	
			462(Ӿ)
Difference		198(4)	
Int. $\frac{1984}{462Ӿ}$ =	.497(2)		
Angle is	.1572 497(2)		

(b) To nine places, using second difference

Sin	.1572	.840 276 516		(235)
Add to book diff.	235 $\frac{1 - .497}{2}$		462 9Ӿ8 / 83	
Corrected difference			462 Ӿ6Ɛ	
Int. $\frac{198429}{462Ӿ6Ɛ}$ =	.49724(9)			
Angle is	.1572 49725			

Example:

Find sin .1649 72497(2) (second half quadrant)

Sin .1649 72497(2) = cos .1572 49724(Ӿ)
Proceed as for cosine
Sin .1649 72497(2) = .877 029 174

Example:

Find the angle whose sine is .877 029 174

This value being greater than .859 Ӿ69 650 (sin .16), the angle is in the second half quadrant
Proceed as in cosine example to find angle whose cosine is .877 029 174
This angle is .1572 49724(Ӿ)
Angle required is .3 - .1572 49724(Ӿ) = .1649 72497

Natural Cosines

Example:

Find cos .1572 49724(X)

(a) To seven places by direct proportion

Cos	.1572	.877 1Ɛ8 63	
			444 65
Interval	.49725		
Subtract	.49725 (44465)	18Ɛ 50	
Cos	.1572 497(2)	.877 029 1(3)	

(b) To nine places, using second difference

Cos	.1572	.877 1Ɛ8 634		(244)
			444 646	
Subtract from book diff. $244 \frac{1 - .497}{2}$			86	
Corrected difference			444 580	
Multiply by	.497 24X	18Ɛ 480		
Sub. from cos .1572		.877 029 174		

Example:

Find the angle whose cosine is .877 029 174

(a) To seven places by direct proportion

Cos	.1572	.877 1Ɛ8(6)	
			444(6)
Difference		18Ɛ(4)	
Int. $\frac{18Ɛ4}{4446}$ =	.497(0)		
Angle is	.1572 497(0)		

(b) To nine places, using second difference

Cos	.1572	.877 1Ɛ8 634		(244)
			444 646	
Subtract from book diff. $244 \frac{1 - .497}{2}$			86	
Corrected difference			444 580	
Int. $\frac{18Ɛ\ 480}{444\ 580}$ =	.49724(X)			
Angle is	.1572 49725			

Example:

Find cos .1649 72497(2) (second half quadrant)

Cos .1649 72497(2) = sin .1572 49724(X)
Proceed as for sine
Cos .1649 72497(2) = .840 452 943

Example:

Find the angle whose cosine is .840 452 943

This value being less than .859 X69 650 (cos .16), the angle is in the second half quadrant
Proceed as in sine example to find the angle whose sine is .840 452 943
This angle is .1572 49725
Angle required is .3 - .1572 49725 = .1649 72497

Natural Tangents

Example:

Find tan .1572 49724(X)

(a) To seven places by direct proportion

Tan	.1572	.Ɛ70 37Ɛ X9	
			1 018 78
Interval	.49725		
Add	.49725 (101878)	4X3 56	
Tan	.1572 497(2)	.Ɛ70 863 4(3)	

(b) To nine places, using second difference

Tan	.1572	.Ɛ70 37Ɛ X95		(1 033)
			1 018 778	
Subtract from book diff.	1033 $\frac{1 - .4972}{2}$		382	
Corrected difference			1 018 3Ɛ6	
Multiply by	.497 24X	4X3 3ƐX		
Add to tan	.1572	.Ɛ70 863 293		

Example:

Find the angle whose tangent is .Ɛ70 863 293

(a) To seven places by direct proportion

Tan	.1572	.Ɛ70 37Ɛ(Ɛ)	
			1 018(8)
Difference		4X3(4)	
Int. $\frac{4X34}{10188}$ =	.497(1)		
Angle is	.1572 497(1)		

(b) To nine places, using second difference

Tan	.1572	.Ɛ70 37Ɛ X95		(1 033)
			1 018 778	
Subtract from book diff.	1033 $\frac{1 - .4971}{2}$		382	
Corrected difference			1 018 3Ɛ6	
Int. $\frac{4X33ƐX}{10183Ɛ6}$ =	.49724(X)			
Angle is	.1572 49725			

Example:

Find tan .1649 72497(2) (second half quadrant)

Tan .1649 72497 = $\frac{1}{\tan .1572\ 49724(X)}$

Proceed as above

Tan .1649 72497 = $\frac{1}{.Ɛ70\ 863\ 293}$

(see reciprocal table) = 1.051 490 Ɛ4(6)

Example:

Find the angle whose tangent is 1.051 490 Ɛ4(6)

This value being greater than unity, the angle is in the second half quadrant

Proceed as above to find the angle whose tangent is $\frac{1}{1.051\ 490\ Ɛ46}$

(see reciprocal table) = .Ɛ70 863 293

This angle is .1572 49725

Angle required = .3 - .1572 49725 = .1649 72497

Natural Tangents and Cotangents

Alternative: (Using N Cot N Table)

Find tan .1649 72497(2)

Tan .1649 72497(2) = cot .1572 49724(χ)

(a) To eight figures by direct proportion

N cot .1572 .162 880 649 68 078
Subtract .49725 (68078) 28 031
N cot N .162 854 618
Divide by N 1.051 490 χ(£)

(b) To nine figures, using second difference

N cot .1572 .162 880 649 (54)
Subtract from book diff. 54 $\frac{1 - .4χ}{2}$ 68 078
17
Corrected difference 68 061
Subtract .49725 (68061) 28 025
N cot N .162 854 624
Divide by N 1.051 490 £4(£)

Example:

Find cot .1572 49724(χ)

Tan .1572 40724(χ) = .£70 863 293
Cot .1572 49724(χ) = 1.051 490 £4(6) (see reciprocal table)

Example:

Find cot .1649 72497(2)

Cot .1649 72497(2) = tan .1572 49724(χ)
Cot .1649 72497(2) = .£70 863 293 (see previous example)

For cotangents greater than 1 (first half quadrant) find the reciprocal and proceed as for the tangent

Example:

Find the angle whose cotangent is 1.051 490 £4(6)

Reciprocal = .£70 863 293 = tan .1572 49725 (see previous example)
Angle required = .1572 49725

For cotangents less than 1 (second half quadrant) proceed as for tangent

Example:

Find the angle whose cotangent is .£70 863 293

.£70 863 293 = tan .1572 49725 (see previous example)
Angle required = .3 - .1572 49725 = .1649 72497

N	Sine	d	N	Sine	d	N	Sine	d
.0000	.000 000 000	634 942	.0040	.021 16Ɛ X19	634 821	.0080	.042 312 608	634 486
1	634 942	941	1	7X4 63X	816	1	946 X92	473
2	.001 069 683	941	2	.022 219 254	80X	2	.043 37Ɛ 345	461
3	6X2 404	941	3	851 X62	804	3	9Ɛ3 7X6	44Ɛ
4	.002 117 145	940	4	.023 286 666	7Ɛ7	4	.044 428 035	439
5	74Ɛ X85	93Ɛ	5	8ƐƐ 261	7Ɛ0	5	X60 472	426
6	.003 184 804	93Ɛ	6	.024 333 X51	7X5	6	.045 494 898	414
7	7Ɛ9 543	939	7	968 636	798	7	Ɛ09 0Ɛ0	400
8	.004 232 280	939	8	.025 3X1 212	791	8	.046 541 4Ɛ0	3XX
9	866 ƐƐ9	937	9	X15 9X3	784	9	Ɛ75 89X	397
X	.005 29Ɛ 934	935	X	.026 44X 567	778	X	.047 5XX 075	383
Ɛ	914 669	934	Ɛ	X83 123	76Ɛ	Ɛ	.048 022 438	371
.0010	.006 349 3X1	933	.0050	.027 4Ɛ7 892	763	.0090	656 7X9	358
1	982 114	930	1	Ɛ30 435	756	1	.049 08X Ɛ45	345
2	.007 3Ɛ6 X44	92Ɛ	2	.028 564 Ɛ8Ɛ	74X	2	703 28X	332
3	X2Ɛ 773	928	3	Ɛ99 719	740	3	.04X 137 600	319
4	.008 464 49Ɛ	926	4	.029 612 259	733	4	76Ɛ 919	305
5	X99 205	924	5	.02X 046 990	725	5	.04Ɛ 1X4 022	2Ɛ1
6	.009 511 Ɛ29	921	6	67Ɛ 4Ɛ5	718	6	818 313	299
7	Ɛ46 84X	91X	7	.02Ɛ 0Ɛ4 011	70Ɛ	7	.050 250 5Ɛ0	284
8	.00X 57Ɛ 568	917	8	728 720	701	8	884 874	270
9	ƐƐ4 283	915	9	.030 161 221	6Ɛ3	9	.051 2Ɛ8 Ɛ24	256
X	.00Ɛ 628 Ɛ98	911	X	795 914	6X5	X	931 17X	242
Ɛ	.010 061 8X9	90X	Ɛ	.031 20X 3Ɛ9	696	Ɛ	.052 365 400	229
.0020	696 5Ɛ7	906	.0060	842 X93	688	.00X0	999 629	213
1	.011 10Ɛ 301	903	1	.032 277 55Ɛ	67X	1	.053 411 840	1ƐƐ
2	744 004	8ƐƐ	2	8Ɛ0 019	670	2	X45 X3Ɛ	1X4
3	.012 178 903	8Ɛ8	3	.033 324 689	660	3	.054 47X 023	18Ɛ
4	7Ɛ1 5ƐƐ	8Ɛ3	4	959 129	652	4	XƐ2 1Ɛ2	175
5	.013 226 2Ɛ2	8XƐ	5	.034 391 77Ɛ	642	5	.055 526 367	160
6	85X ƐX1	8X7	6	X06 201	633	6	Ɛ5X 507	145
7	.014 293 888	8X2	7	.035 43X 834	624	7	.056 592 650	12Ɛ
8	908 56X	89X	8	X73 258	615	8	.057 006 77Ɛ	114
9	.015 341 248	895	9	.036 4X7 871	605	9	63X 893	0ƐX
X	975 Ɛ21	890	X	Ɛ20 276	5Ɛ5	X	.058 072 991	0X4
Ɛ	.016 3XX 7Ɛ1	887	Ɛ	.037 554 86Ɛ	5X5	Ɛ	6X6 X75	088
.0030	X23 478	882	.0070	Ɛ89 254	595	.00Ɛ0	.059 11X Ɛ41	072
1	.017 458 13X	879	1	.038 601 829	585	1	752 ƐƐ3	057
2	X90 9Ɛ7	873	2	.039 036 1Ɛ2	574	2	.05X 187 04X	03Ɛ
3	.018 505 66X	869	3	66X 766	564	3	7ƐƐ 089	024
4	Ɛ3X 317	864	4	.03X 0X3 10X	554	4	.05Ɛ 233 0Ɛ1	008
5	.019 572 Ɛ7Ɛ	85X	5	717 662	543	5	867 0Ɛ9	633 ƐƐ1
6	ƐX7 819	854	6	.03Ɛ 14Ɛ ƐX5	531	6	.060 29Ɛ 0XX	Ɛ95
7	.01X 620 471	84X	7	784 516	521	7	913 083	Ɛ79
8	.01Ɛ 055 0ƐƐ	843	8	.040 1Ɛ8 X37	510	8	.061 347 040	Ɛ61
9	689 942	839	9	831 347	4ƐX	9	97X ƐX1	Ɛ45
X	.020 102 57Ɛ	833	X	.041 265 845	4X8	X	.062 3Ɛ2 Ɛ26	Ɛ28
Ɛ	737 1Ɛ2	827	Ɛ	89X 131	497	Ɛ	X26 X52	Ɛ10

N	Sine	d	N	Sine	d	N	Sine	d
.0100	.063 45X 962	633 XƐ3	.0140	.084 583 642	633 2X6	.0180	.0X5 677 656	632 464
1	X92 855	X96	1	ƐƐ6 928	283	1	.0X6 0X9 XƐX	435
2	.064 506 72Ɛ	X7X	2	.085 629 ƐXƐ	260	2	720 333	407
3	Ɛ3X 5X9	X60	3	.086 061 24Ɛ	237	3	.0X7 152 73X	398
4	.065 572 449	X43	4	694 486	213	4	784 Ɛ16	369
5	ƐX6 290	X26	5	.087 107 699	1XX	5	.0X8 1Ɛ7 283	339
6	.066 61X 0Ɛ6	X08	6	73X 887	187	6	829 600	30Ɛ
7	.067 051 Ɛ02	9XX	7	.088 171 X52	162	7	.0X9 25Ɛ 90Ɛ	29Ɛ
8	685 8Ɛ0	991	8	7X4 ƐƐ4	139	8	891 ƐXX	26Ɛ
9	.068 0Ɛ9 681	973	9	.089 218 131	114	9	.0XX 304 259	240
X	731 434	954	X	84Ɛ 245	0XƐ	X	936 499	210
Ɛ	.069 165 188	937	Ɛ	.08X 282 334	087	Ɛ	.0XƐ 368 6X9	1X0
.0110	798 Ɛ03	918	.0150	8Ɛ5 3ƐƐ	060	.0190	99X 889	170
1	.06X 210 81Ɛ	8Ɛ9	1	.08Ɛ 328 45Ɛ	038	1	.0Ɛ0 410 X39	13Ɛ
2	844 518	89Ɛ	2	95Ɛ 497	012	2	X42 Ɛ78	10Ɛ
3	.06Ɛ 278 1Ɛ7	880	3	.090 392 4X9	632 ƐX8	3	.0Ɛ1 475 087	09Ɛ
4	8XƐ X77	861	4	X05 495	Ɛ83	4	XX7 166	069
5	.070 323 718	842	5	.091 438 458	Ɛ58	5	.0Ɛ2 519 213	039
6	957 35X	823	6	X6Ɛ 3Ɛ4	Ɛ32	6	Ɛ4Ɛ 250	008
7	.071 38X Ɛ81	803	7	.092 4X2 326	Ɛ08	7	.0Ɛ3 581 258	631 Ɛ97
8	X02 784	7X4	8	Ɛ15 232	XX2	8	ƐƐ3 233	Ɛ66
9	.072 436 368	784	9	.093 548 114	X77	9	.0Ɛ4 625 199	Ɛ34
X	X69 Ɛ30	764	X	Ɛ7X Ɛ8Ɛ	X51	X	.0Ɛ5 057 111	Ɛ02
Ɛ	.073 4X1 694	744	Ɛ	.094 5Ɛ1 X20	X25	Ɛ	689 013	X91
.0120	Ɛ15 218	724	.0160	.095 024 845	9ƐƐ	.01X0	.0Ɛ6 0ƐX XX4	X5Ɛ
1	.074 548 940	704	1	657 644	993	1	730 943	X29
2	Ɛ80 444	6X4	2	.096 08X 417	968	2	.0Ɛ7 162 770	9Ɛ7
3	.075 5Ɛ3 Ɛ28	683	3	701 183	941	3	794 567	984
4	.076 027 5XƐ	662	4	.097 133 Ɛ04	915	4	.0Ɛ8 206 32Ɛ	952
5	65Ɛ 051	642	5	766 819	8XX	5	838 081	920
6	.077 092 693	620	6	.098 199 507	881	6	.0Ɛ9 269 9X1	8X8
7	706 0Ɛ3	600	7	810 188	856	7	89Ɛ 689	876
8	.078 139 6Ɛ3	59X	8	.099 242 X22	82X	8	.0ƐX 311 343	843
9	771 091	579	9	875 650	801	9	942 Ɛ86	810
X	.079 1X4 64X	557	X	.09X 2X8 251	795	X	.0ƐƐ 374 796	799
Ɛ	817 ƐX5	535	Ɛ	91X X26	768	Ɛ	9X6 373	765
.0130	.07X 24Ɛ 51X	514	.0170	.09Ɛ 351 592	740	.01Ɛ0	.100 417 Ɛ18	731
1	882 X32	4Ɛ2	1	984 112	712	1	X49 649	6ƐX
2	.07Ɛ 2Ɛ6 324	490	2	.0X0 3Ɛ6 824	6X6	2	.101 47Ɛ 147	686
3	929 7Ɛ4	469	3	X29 30X	679	3	XƐ0 811	652
4	.080 361 061	447	4	.0X1 45Ɛ 987	64Ɛ	4	.102 522 263	61X
5	994 4X8	424	5	X92 416	622	5	Ɛ53 881	5X5
6	.081 407 910	402	6	.0X2 504 X38	5Ɛ4	6	.103 585 266	571
7	X3Ɛ 112	39Ɛ	7	Ɛ37 430	587	7	ƐƐ6 817	539
8	.082 472 4Ɛ1	378	8	.0X3 569 9Ɛ7	559	8	.104 628 154	503
9	XX5 869	355	9	ƐX0 354	52Ɛ	9	.105 059 657	48Ɛ
X	.083 519 002	332	X	.0X4 612 883	500	X	68X Ɛ26	456
Ɛ	Ɛ50 334	30X	Ɛ	.0X5 045 183	493	Ɛ	.106 100 380	421

N	Sine	d	N	Sine	d	N	Sine	d
.0200	.106 731 7X1	631 3X7	.0240	.127 760 873	630 0Ɛ6	.0280	.148 737 701	62X 78Ɛ
1	.107 162 Ɛ88	373	1	.128 190 969	075	1	.149 166 290	743
2	794 33Ɛ	338	2	800 X22	035	2	794 X13	6Ɛ8
3	.108 205 677	303	3	.129 230 X57	62Ɛ ƐƐ4	3	.14X 203 50Ɛ	671
4	836 97X	289	4	860 X4Ɛ	Ɛ74	4	831 Ɛ80	625
5	.109 268 047	252	5	.12X 290 X03	Ɛ32	5	.14Ɛ 260 5X5	599
6	899 299	219	6	900 935	XƐ2	6	88X Ɛ82	552
7	.10X 30X 4Ɛ6	1X3	7	.12Ɛ 330 827	X70	7	.150 2Ɛ9 514	505
8	93Ɛ 699	168	8	960 697	X2Ɛ	8	927 X19	47X
9	.10Ɛ 370 845	131	9	.130 390 506	9XX	9	.151 356 297	431
X	9X1 976	0Ɛ7	X	X00 2Ɛ4	968	X	984 708	3X5
Ɛ	.110 412 X71	080	Ɛ	.131 430 060	927	Ɛ	.152 3Ɛ2 XƐ1	358
.0210	X43 Ɛ31	044	.0250	X5Ɛ 987	8X4	.0290	X21 249	30Ɛ
1	.111 474 Ɛ75	00X	1	.132 48Ɛ 66Ɛ	863	1	.153 44Ɛ 558	283
2	XX5 Ɛ83	630 Ɛ93	2	XƐƐ 312	820	2	X79 81Ɛ	235
3	.112 516 Ɛ56	Ɛ57	3	.133 52X Ɛ32	79X	3	.154 4X7 X54	1X9
4	Ɛ47 XƐ1	Ɛ1Ɛ	4	Ɛ5X 710	758	4	Ɛ16 041	15Ɛ
5	.113 578 X10	XX4	5	.134 58X 268	715	5	.155 544 1X0	112
6	ƐX9 8Ɛ4	X67	6	ƐƐ9 981	693	6	Ɛ72 2Ɛ2	084
7	.114 61X 75Ɛ	X30	7	.135 629 454	64Ɛ	7	.156 5X0 376	036
8	.115 04Ɛ 58Ɛ	9Ɛ4	8	.136 058 XX3	609	8	.157 00X 3Ɛ0	629 ƐX9
9	680 383	977	9	688 4Ɛ0	585	9	638 399	Ɛ5X
X	.116 0Ɛ1 13X	93Ɛ	X	.137 0Ɛ7 X75	542	X	.158 066 337	Ɛ11
Ɛ	721 X79	903	Ɛ	727 3Ɛ7	4ƐƐ	Ɛ	694 248	X82
.0220	.117 152 780	885	.0260	.138 156 8Ɛ6	477	.02X0	.159 102 10X	X34
1	783 445	849	1	786 171	433	1	72Ɛ Ɛ42	9X5
2	.118 1Ɛ4 092	810	2	.139 1Ɛ5 5X4	3Ɛ0	2	.15X 159 927	957
3	824 8X2	792	3	824 994	367	3	787 682	907
4	.119 255 474	756	4	.13X 254 13Ɛ	324	4	.15Ɛ 1Ɛ5 389	879
5	886 00X	718	5	883 463	29Ɛ	5	823 046	82X
6	.11X 2Ɛ6 726	69X	6	.13Ɛ 2Ɛ2 742	256	6	.160 250 874	79X
7	927 204	661	7	921 998	213	7	87X 452	74Ɛ
8	.11Ɛ 357 865	622	8	.140 350 ƐXƐ	189	8	.161 2X7 ƐX1	6ƐƐ
9	988 287	5X5	9	980 178	144	9	915 6X0	670
X	.120 3Ɛ8 870	567	X	.141 3XƐ 300	100	X	.162 343 150	61Ɛ
Ɛ	X29 217	528	Ɛ	X1X 400	076	Ɛ	970 76Ɛ	590
.0230	.121 459 743	4XX	.0270	.142 449 476	031	.02Ɛ0	.163 39X 13Ɛ	540
1	X8X 031	46Ɛ	1	X78 4X7	62X ƐX8	1	X07 67Ɛ	4XƐ
2	.122 4ƐX 4X0	431	2	.143 4X7 493	Ɛ62	2	.164 434 Ɛ6X	45Ɛ
3	Ɛ2X 911	3Ɛ1	3	Ɛ16 435	Ɛ18	3	X62 409	40Ɛ
4	.123 55Ɛ 102	373	4	.144 545 351	X93	4	.165 48Ɛ 818	379
5	Ɛ8Ɛ 475	333	5	Ɛ74 224	X48	5	XƐ8 Ɛ95	329
6	.124 5ƐƐ 7X8	2Ɛ5	6	.145 5X3 070	X03	6	.166 526 302	298
7	.125 02Ɛ XX1	274	7	.146 011 X73	978	7	Ɛ53 59X	247
8	660 155	236	8	640 82Ɛ	931	8	.167 580 825	1Ɛ6
9	.126 090 38Ɛ	1Ɛ5	9	.147 06Ɛ 560	8X7	9	ƐX9 X1Ɛ	164
X	700 584	176	X	69X 247	861	X	.168 616 Ɛ83	112
Ɛ	.127 130 73X	135	Ɛ	.148 108 XX8	815	Ɛ	.169 044 095	081

N	Sine	d	N	Sine	d	N	Sine	d
.0300	.169 671 156	629 02Ɛ	.0340	.18χ 538 268	627 258	.0380	.1χƐ 347 914	625 251
1	.16χ 09χ 185	628 Ɛ99	1	Ɛ63 504	1ƐƐ	1	970 Ɛ65	1χ9
2	707 162	Ɛ47	2	.18Ɛ 58χ 703	161	2	.1Ɛ0 396 152	146
3	.16Ɛ 134 0χ9	χƐ5	3	ƐƐ5 864	105	3	9ƐƐ 298	0χ2
4	760 Ɛχ2	χ62	4	.190 620 969	068	4	.1Ɛ1 424 37χ	03χ
5	.170 189 χ44	χ10	5	.191 047 χ15	00χ	5	χ49 3Ɛ8	624 Ɛ95
6	7Ɛ6 854	979	6	672 χ23	626 Ɛ71	6	.1Ɛ2 472 391	Ɛ31
7	.171 223 611	926	7	.192 099 994	Ɛ13	7	χ97 302	χ89
8	850 337	893	8	704 8χ7	χ75	8	.1Ɛ3 500 18Ɛ	χ24
9	.172 279 00χ	840	9	.193 12Ɛ 760	χ18	9	Ɛ24 ƐƐ3	980
χ	8χ5 84χ	7χ9	χ	756 578	979	χ	.1Ɛ4 549 973	917
Ɛ	.173 312 437	756	Ɛ	.194 181 335	91Ɛ	Ɛ	Ɛ72 68χ	871
.0310	93χ Ɛ91	701	.0350	7χ8 054	880	.0390	.1Ɛ5 597 33Ɛ	808
1	.174 367 692	66Ɛ	1	.195 212 914	823	1	ƐƐƐ Ɛ47	763
2	994 141	616	2	839 537	783	2	.1Ɛ6 624 6χχ	6Ɛχ
3	.175 400 757	582	3	.196 264 0Ɛχ	725	3	.1Ɛ7 049 1χ8	654
4	χ29 119	52Ɛ	4	88χ 823	686	4	671 840	5χχ
5	.176 455 648	496	5	.197 2Ɛ5 2χ9	626	5	.1Ɛ8 096 22χ	545
6	χ81 Ɛ22	441	6	91Ɛ 913	588	6	6Ɛχ 773	49χ
7	.177 4χχ 363	3χχ	7	.198 346 29Ɛ	528	7	.1Ɛ9 123 051	434
8	Ɛ16 751	354	8	970 807	489	8	747 485	38χ
9	.178 542 χχ5	300	9	.199 397 094	429	9	.1Ɛχ 16Ɛ 853	324
χ	Ɛ6Ɛ 1χ5	266	χ	χ01 501	389	χ	793 Ɛ77	279
Ɛ	.179 597 44Ɛ	212	Ɛ	.19χ 427 88χ	320	Ɛ	.1ƐƐ 1Ɛ8 234	212
.0320	.17χ 003 661	178	.0360	χ51 ƐƐ7	289	.03χ0	820 446	167
1	62Ɛ 819	123	1	.19Ɛ 478 284	229	1	.200 244 5Ɛ1	100
2	.17Ɛ 057 940	089	2	χχ2 4Ɛ1	189	2	868 6Ɛ1	055
3	683 χ09	034	3	.1χ0 508 67χ	128	3	.201 290 746	623 Ɛχχ
4	.180 0χƐ χ41	627 Ɛ9χ	4	Ɛ32 7χ6	088	4	8Ɛ4 734	Ɛ43
5	717 χ1Ɛ	Ɛ44	5	.1χ1 558 872	027	5	.202 318 677	χ97
6	.181 143 963	χχχ	6	Ɛ82 899	625 Ɛ85	6	940 552	χ2Ɛ
7	76Ɛ 851	χ53	7	.1χ2 5χ8 862	Ɛ25	7	.203 364 381	983
8	.182 197 6χ4	9Ɛ9	8	.1χ3 012 787	χ84	8	988 144	917
9	803 4χ1	963	9	638 64Ɛ	χ22	9	.204 3χƐ χ5Ɛ	86Ɛ
χ	.183 22Ɛ 244	908	χ	.1χ4 062 471	981	χ	χ13 70χ	803
Ɛ	856 Ɛ50	871	Ɛ	688 232	91Ɛ	Ɛ	.205 437 311	756
.0330	.184 282 801	816	.0370	.1χ5 0Ɛ1 Ɛ51	879	.03Ɛ0	χ5χ χ67	6χχ
1	8χχ 417	780	1	717 80χ	818	1	.206 482 555	641
2	.185 315 Ɛ97	723	2	.1χ6 141 426	775	2	χχ5 Ɛ96	595
3	941 6Ɛχ	689	3	766 Ɛ9Ɛ	713	3	.207 509 56Ɛ	527
4	.186 369 187	631	4	.1χ7 190 6Ɛ2	671	4	Ɛ30 χ96	47χ
5	994 7Ɛ8	595	5	7Ɛ6 163	60χ	5	.208 554 354	411
6	.187 400 191	53χ	6	.1χ8 21Ɛ 771	568	6	Ɛ77 765	363
7	χ27 70Ɛ	4χ1	7	845 119	505	7	.209 59χ Ɛ08	2Ɛ6
8	.188 452 ƐƐ0	446	8	.1χ9 26χ 622	462	8	.20χ 002 202	248
9	χ7χ 436	3χ9	9	893 χ84	3ƐƐ	9	625 44χ	19Ɛ
χ	.189 4χ5 823	351	χ	.1χχ 2Ɛ9 283	358	χ	.20Ɛ 048 629	130
Ɛ	Ɛ10 Ɛ74	2Ɛ4	Ɛ	922 61Ɛ	2Ɛ5	Ɛ	66Ɛ 759	082

N	Sine	d	N	Sine	d	N	Sine	d
.0400	.210 092 81Ɛ	623 014	.0440	.230 947 Ɛ01	620 765	.0480	.251 522 529	61X 085
1	6Ɛ5 833	622 Ɛ66	1	.231 368 666	6Ɛ0	1	Ɛ40 5Ɛ2	006
2	.211 118 799	XƐ7	2	989 156	637	2	.252 55X 5Ɛ8	619 Ɛ45
3	73Ɛ 694	X48	3	.232 3X9 791	581	3	Ɛ78 541	X86
4	.212 162 520	99X	4	X0X 152	508	4	.253 596 407	X05
5	785 2ƐX	92X	5	.233 42X 65X	452	5	ƐƐ4 210	944
6	.213 1X8 028	880	6	X4X XƐ0	398	6	.254 611 Ɛ54	884
7	80X 8X8	810	7	.234 46Ɛ 288	322	7	.255 02Ɛ 818	803
8	.214 231 4Ɛ8	761	8	X8Ɛ 5XX	268	8	649 41Ɛ	742
9	854 059	6Ɛ1	9	.235 4XƐ 856	1Ɛ1	9	.256 066 Ɛ61	681
X	.215 276 74X	641	X	Ɛ0Ɛ X47	137	X	684 622	600
Ɛ	899 18Ɛ	592	Ɛ	.236 52Ɛ Ɛ82	081	Ɛ	.257 0X2 022	53Ɛ
.0410	.216 2ƐƐ 761	522	.0450	Ɛ50 043	005	.0490	6ƐƐ 561	479
1	922 083	472	1	.237 570 048	61Ɛ Ɛ4Ɛ	1	.258 118 X1X	3Ɛ7
2	.217 344 535	401	2	Ɛ8Ɛ Ɛ97	X94	2	736 215	336
3	966 936	351	3	.238 5XƐ X6Ɛ	X19	3	.259 153 54Ɛ	273
4	.218 389 087	2X1	4	.239 00Ɛ 888	961	4	770 802	1Ɛ2
5	9XƐ 368	22Ɛ	5	62Ɛ 629	8X6	5	.25X 189 9Ɛ4	130
6	.219 411 597	180	6	.23X 04Ɛ 313	82X	6	7X6 Ɛ24	069
7	X33 757	10X	7	66X Ɛ41	773	7	.25Ɛ 203 Ɛ91	618 ƐX7
8	.21X 455 865	059	8	.23Ɛ 08X 6Ɛ4	6Ɛ7	8	820 Ɛ78	Ɛ24
9	X77 902	621 ƐX7	9	6XX 1XƐ	63X	9	.260 239 XX0	X61
X	.21Ɛ 499 8X9	Ɛ37	X	.240 109 829	583	X	856 941	99X
Ɛ	XƐƐ 824	X85	Ɛ	729 1Ɛ0	506	Ɛ	.261 273 71Ɛ	918
.0420	.220 521 6X9	X13	.0460	.241 148 6Ɛ6	44X	.04X0	890 437	854
1	Ɛ43 500	961	1	767 Ɛ44	392	1	.262 2X9 08Ɛ	791
2	.221 565 261	8Ɛ0	2	.242 187 316	314	2	905 860	70X
3	Ɛ86 Ɛ51	839	3	7X6 62X	258	3	.263 322 36X	645
4	.222 5X8 78X	788	4	.243 205 886	19Ɛ	4	93X 9Ɛ3	583
5	.223 00X 356	714	5	824 X65	122	5	.264 357 376	4ƐX
6	62Ɛ X6X	663	6	.244 243 Ɛ87	064	6	973 874	436
7	.224 051 511	5Ɛ0	7	863 02Ɛ	61X ƐX7	7	.265 390 0XX	372
8	672 Ɛ01	538	8	.245 282 016	Ɛ2X	8	9X8 460	2XX
9	.225 094 439	486	9	8X0 Ɛ44	X70	9	.266 404 74X	226
X	6Ɛ5 903	413	X	.246 2ƐƐ 9Ɛ4	9Ɛ1	X	X20 974	160
Ɛ	.226 117 116	360	Ɛ	91X 7X5	934	Ɛ	.267 438 Ɛ14	099
.0430	738 476	2X8	.0470	.247 339 519	876	.04Ɛ0	X54 ƐƐ1	013
1	.227 159 762	235	1	958 193	7Ɛ8	1	.268 471 004	617 Ɛ4X
2	77X 997	182	2	.248 376 98Ɛ	739	2	X88 Ɛ52	X85
3	.228 19Ɛ Ɛ59	109	3	995 508	67Ɛ	3	.269 4X4 X17	X00
4	801 066	056	4	.249 3Ɛ3 Ɛ87	600	4	Ɛ00 817	937
5	.229 222 100	620 ƐX1	5	X12 587	541	5	.26X 518 552	871
6	843 0X1	Ɛ2X	6	.24X 430 Ɛ08	482	6	Ɛ34 203	7X7
7	.22X 264 00Ɛ	X74	7	X4Ɛ 38X	404	7	.26Ɛ 54Ɛ 9XX	721
8	884 X83	X01	8	.24Ɛ 469 792	344	8	Ɛ67 50Ɛ	657
9	.22Ɛ 2X5 884	948	9	X87 Ɛ16	284	9	.270 582 Ɛ66	592
X	906 610	893	X	.250 4X6 19X	205	X	Ɛ9X 538	507
Ɛ	.230 327 2X3	81X	Ɛ	Ɛ04 3X3	146	Ɛ	.271 5Ɛ5 X43	440

N	Sine	d	N	Sine	d	N	Sine	d
.0500	.272 011 283	617 376	.0540	.292 607 373	614 437	.0580	.2Ɛ2 XƐƐ 861	611 290
1	628 639	2Ɛ0	1	.293 01Ɛ 7XX	367	1	.2Ɛ3 510 Ɛ31	1Ɛ3
2	.273 043 929	224	2	633 Ɛ55	295	2	Ɛ22 124	118
3	65X Ɛ51	15X	3	.294 048 22X	203	3	.2Ɛ4 533 240	03Ɛ
4	.274 076 0XƐ	093	4	660 431	131	4	Ɛ44 27Ɛ	610 Ɛ62
5	691 182	007	5	.295 074 562	05Ɛ	5	.2Ɛ5 555 221	X86
6	.275 0X8 189	616 Ɛ40	6	688 601	613 Ɛ8X	6	Ɛ66 0X7	9X9
7	703 109	X74	7	.296 0X0 58Ɛ	XƐ7	7	.2Ɛ6 576 X94	910
8	.276 119 Ɛ81	9X9	8	6Ɛ4 486	X24	8	Ɛ87 7X4	833
9	734 96X	921	9	.297 108 2XX	952	9	.2Ɛ7 598 417	755
X	.277 14Ɛ 68Ɛ	855	X	720 040	880	X	ƐX8 Ɛ70	679
Ɛ	766 324	789	Ɛ	.298 133 900	7X9	Ɛ	.2Ɛ8 5Ɛ9 629	59Ɛ
.0510	.278 180 XƐ1	701	.0550	747 4X9	716	.0590	.2Ɛ9 00X 008	501
1	797 5Ɛ2	634	1	.299 15Ɛ 003	642	1	61X 509	424
2	.279 1Ɛ2 026	568	2	772 645	570	2	.2ƐX 02X 931	345
3	808 592	49Ɛ	3	.29X 185 ƐƐ5	498	3	63Ɛ 076	268
4	.27X 222 X71	413	4	799 491	405	4	.2ƐƐ 04Ɛ 322	18X
5	839 284	345	5	.29Ɛ 1Ɛ0 896	331	5	65Ɛ 4Ɛ0	0XƐ
6	.27Ɛ 253 609	279	6	804 007	259	6	.300 06Ɛ 59Ɛ	011
7	869 886	1XƐ	7	.2X0 217 264	185	7	67Ɛ 5Ɛ0	60Ɛ Ɛ32
8	.280 283 X75	122	8	82X 429	0Ɛ2	8	.301 08Ɛ 522	X53
9	899 Ɛ97	054	9	.2X1 241 51Ɛ	019	9	69Ɛ 375	975
X	.281 2Ɛ4 02Ɛ	615 Ɛ87	X	854 538	612 Ɛ45	X	.302 0XƐ 12X	895
Ɛ	909 ƐƐ6	XƐ9	Ɛ	.2X2 267 481	X70	Ɛ	6ƐX X03	7Ɛ7
.0520	.282 323 XƐ3	X2Ɛ	.0560	87X 331	998	.05X0	.303 10X 5ƐX	717
1	939 922	962	1	.2X3 291 109	903	1	71X 115	638
2	.283 353 684	893	2	8X3 X10	82X	2	.304 129 751	558
3	969 357	804	3	.2X4 2Ɛ6 63X	755	3	739 0X9	478
4	.284 382 Ɛ5Ɛ	736	4	909 193	680	4	.305 148 565	399
5	998 695	668	5	.2X5 31Ɛ 853	5X7	5	757 942	2Ɛ8
6	.285 3Ɛ2 141	599	6	932 23X	511	6	.306 167 03X	219
7	X07 71X	50X	7	.2X6 344 74Ɛ	438	7	776 257	138
8	.286 421 028	43Ɛ	8	956 Ɛ87	362	8	.307 185 393	058
9	X36 467	370	9	.2X7 369 329	288	9	794 42Ɛ	60X Ɛ77
X	.287 44Ɛ 817	2X0	X	97Ɛ 5Ɛ5	1Ɛ2	X	.308 1X3 3X6	X97
Ɛ	X64 XƐ7	211	Ɛ	.2X8 391 7X7	118	Ɛ	7Ɛ2 281	9Ɛ6
.0530	.288 47X 108	142	.0570	9X3 903	042	.05Ɛ0	.309 201 077	915
1	X93 24X	072	1	.2X9 3Ɛ5 945	611 Ɛ67	1	80Ɛ 990	834
2	.289 4X8 300	614 ƐX2	2	X07 8Ɛ0	X91	2	.30X 21X 604	752
3	Ɛ01 2X2	Ɛ12	3	.2XX 419 781	9Ɛ6	3	829 156	672
4	.28X 516 1Ɛ4	X41	4	X2Ɛ 577	91Ɛ	4	.30Ɛ 237 808	58Ɛ
5	ƐƐƐ 035	972	5	.2XƐ 441 296	844	5	846 197	4XX
6	.28Ɛ 543 9X7	8X1	6	X52 Ɛ1X	769	6	.310 254 685	409
7	Ɛ58 688	811	7	.2Ɛ0 464 687	692	7	862 X92	326
8	.290 571 299	740	8	X76 159	5Ɛ7	8	.311 271 1Ɛ8	244
9	Ɛ85 X19	66Ɛ	9	.2Ɛ1 487 754	51Ɛ	9	87Ɛ 440	163
X	.291 59X 488	59X	X	X99 073	443	X	.312 289 5X3	07Ɛ
Ɛ	ƐƐ2 X66	509	Ɛ	.2Ɛ2 4XX 4Ɛ6	367	Ɛ	897 662	609 Ɛ9X

N	Sine	d	N	Sine	d	N	Sine	d
.0600	.313 2X5 640	609 XƐ6	.0640	.333 573 X46	606 4Ɛ6	.0680	.353 719 X45	602 890
1	8Ɛ3 536	X14	1	Ɛ7X 340	40X	1	.354 120 715	798
2	.314 301 34X	931	2	.334 584 74X	31Ɛ	2	723 2Ɛ1	6X4
3	90Ɛ 07Ɛ	84X	3	Ɛ8X X69	232	3	.355 125 995	5XƐ
4	.315 318 909	767	4	.335 595 09Ɛ	144	4	728 384	4Ɛ8
5	926 474	684	5	Ɛ9Ɛ 223	056	5	.356 12X 880	402
6	.316 333 Ɛ38	5X0	6	.336 5X5 279	605 Ɛ68	6	731 082	30X
7	941 518	4Ɛ9	7	ƐXƐ 225	X7X	7	.357 133 390	215
8	.317 34X X15	414	8	.337 5Ɛ5 0X3	98Ɛ	8	735 5X5	120
9	958 229	331	9	ƐƐX X72	8X1	9	.358 137 705	027
X	.318 365 55X	249	X	.338 604 753	7Ɛ2	X	739 730	601 Ɛ32
Ɛ	972 7X7	165	Ɛ	.339 00X 345	704	Ɛ	.359 13Ɛ 662	X38
.0610	.319 37Ɛ 950	081	.0650	613 X49	615	.0690	741 49X	943
1	988 X11	608 Ɛ98	1	.33X 019 462	525	1	.35X 143 221	849
2	.31X 395 9X9	XƐ3	2	622 987	436	2	744 X6X	754
3	9X2 8X0	X0Ɛ	3	.33Ɛ 028 201	347	3	.35Ɛ 146 602	659
4	.31Ɛ 3XƐ 6XƐ	926	4	631 548	258	4	748 05Ɛ	563
5	9Ɛ8 415	841	5	.340 036 7X4	168	5	.360 149 602	46X
6	.320 405 056	758	6	63Ɛ 950	078	6	74X X70	372
7	X11 7Ɛ2	673	7	.341 044 X08	604 Ɛ89	7	.361 150 222	279
8	.321 41X 265	589	8	649 995	X98	8	751 49Ɛ	181
9	X26 832	4X4	9	.342 052 871	9X8	9	.362 152 660	087
X	.322 433 116	3ƐX	X	657 659	8Ɛ8	X	753 727	600 Ɛ90
Ɛ	X3Ɛ 514	315	Ɛ	.343 060 355	808	Ɛ	.363 154 6Ɛ7	X96
.0620	.323 447 829	22X	.0660	664 Ɛ61	716	.06X0	755 591	999
1	X53 X57	145	1	.344 069 677	627	1	.364 156 36X	8X3
2	.324 45Ɛ ƐX0	05X	2	672 0X2	535	2	757 051	7X7
3	X68 03X	607 Ɛ73	3	.345 076 617	444	3	.365 157 838	6Ɛ0
4	.325 473 ƐƐ1	X8X	4	67X X5Ɛ	354	4	758 328	5Ɛ3
5	X7Ɛ X7Ɛ	9X2	5	.346 083 1Ɛ3	262	5	.366 158 91Ɛ	4Ɛ8
6	.326 487 861	8Ɛ8	6	687 455	170	6	759 217	400
7	X93 559	811	7	.347 08Ɛ 605	07Ɛ	7	.367 159 617	304
8	.327 49Ɛ 16X	726	8	693 684	603 Ɛ8X	8	759 91Ɛ	208
9	XX6 894	63Ɛ	9	.348 097 652	X97	9	.368 159 Ɛ27	10Ɛ
X	.328 4Ɛ2 313	553	X	69Ɛ 529	9X6	X	75X 036	013
Ɛ	XƐ9 866	468	Ɛ	.349 0X3 313	8Ɛ4	Ɛ	.369 15X 049	5ƐƐ Ɛ16
.0630	.329 505 112	381	.0670	6X7 007	801	.06Ɛ0	759 Ɛ63	X19
1	Ɛ10 493	294	1	.34X 0XX 808	70Ɛ	1	.36X 159 980	920
2	.32X 517 767	1X9	2	6Ɛ2 317	618	2	759 6X0	823
3	Ɛ22 954	101	3	.34Ɛ 0Ɛ5 933	526	3	.36Ɛ 159 303	726
4	.32Ɛ 529 X55	015	4	6Ɛ9 259	433	4	758 X29	629
5	Ɛ34 X6X	606 Ɛ28	5	.350 100 690	341	5	.370 158 456	52Ɛ
6	.330 53Ɛ 996	X40	6	703 X11	249	6	757 985	431
7	Ɛ46 816	953	7	.351 107 05X	156	7	.371 157 1Ɛ6	334
8	.331 551 569	867	8	70X 1Ɛ4	062	8	756 52X	236
9	Ɛ58 214	77X	9	.352 111 256	602 Ɛ70	9	.372 155 764	137
X	.332 562 992	690	X	714 206	X77	X	754 89Ɛ	03X
Ɛ	Ɛ69 462	5X4	Ɛ	.353 117 081	984	Ɛ	.373 153 919	5ƐX Ɛ3Ɛ

N	Sine	d	N	Sine	d	N	Sine	d
.0700	.373 752 858	5ƐX X41	.0740	.393 649 739	5Ɛ6 98X	.0780	.3Ɛ3 3Ɛ9 9ƐX	5Ɛ2 6Ɛ5
1	.374 151 699	942	1	.394 044 507	885	1	9Ɛ0 4Ɛ3	5X6
2	750 41Ɛ	843	2	63Ɛ 190	77Ɛ	2	.3Ɛ4 3X2 X99	496
3	.375 14Ɛ 062	745	3	.395 035 94Ɛ	676	3	995 373	386
4	749 7X7	645	4	630 405	571	4	.3Ɛ5 387 739	276
5	.376 148 230	547	5	.396 026 976	467	5	979 9Ɛ3	166
6	746 777	447	6	621 221	361	6	.3Ɛ6 36Ɛ Ɛ59	055
7	.377 145 002	348	7	.397 017 582	257	7	961 ƐƐ2	5Ɛ1 Ɛ45
8	743 34X	248	8	611 819	151	8	.3Ɛ7 353 Ɛ37	X35
9	.378 141 596	148	9	.398 007 96X	047	9	945 970	923
X	73Ɛ 722	049	X	601 9Ɛ5	5Ɛ5 Ɛ41	X	.3Ɛ8 337 693	813
Ɛ	.379 139 76Ɛ	5Ɛ9 Ɛ49	Ɛ	ƐƐ7 936	X36	Ɛ	929 2X6	701
.0710	737 6Ɛ8	X48	.0750	.399 5Ɛ1 770	92Ɛ	.0790	.3Ɛ9 31X 9X7	5Ɛ1
1	.37X 135 544	948	1	ƐX7 49Ɛ	824	1	910 398	49Ɛ
2	733 290	848	2	.39X 5X1 103	71X	2	.3ƐX 301 877	38X
3	.37Ɛ 130 Ɛ18	748	3	Ɛ96 821	612	3	8Ɛ3 045	278
4	72X 664	647	4	.39Ɛ 590 233	508	4	.3ƐƐ 2X4 301	166
5	.380 128 0XƐ	546	5	Ɛ85 73Ɛ	400	5	895 467	055
6	725 635	445	6	.3X0 57X Ɛ3Ɛ	2Ɛ4	6	.400 286 500	5Ɛ0 Ɛ42
7	.381 122 X7X	344	7	Ɛ74 233	1X9	7	877 442	X31
8	720 202	243	8	.3X1 569 420	0X2	8	.401 268 273	91X
9	.382 119 445	141	9	Ɛ62 502	5Ɛ4 Ɛ95	9	858 Ɛ91	808
X	716 586	040	X	.3X2 557 497	X89	X	.402 249 799	6Ɛ6
Ɛ	.383 113 606	5Ɛ8 Ɛ3Ɛ	Ɛ	Ɛ50 364	981	Ɛ	83X 293	5X2
.0720	710 545	X39	.0760	.3X3 545 125	875	.07X0	.403 22X 875	490
1	.384 109 382	936	1	Ɛ39 99X	769	1	81Ɛ 145	379
2	706 0Ɛ8	835	2	.3X4 532 547	660	2	.404 20Ɛ 502	266
3	.385 102 931	733	3	Ɛ26 ƐX7	553	3	7ƐƐ 768	153
4	6ƐƐ 464	630	4	.3X5 51Ɛ 53X	446	4	.405 1XƐ 8ƐƐ	03Ɛ
5	.386 0Ɛ7 X94	52X	5	Ɛ13 984	33X	5	79Ɛ 93X	5XƐ Ɛ28
6	6Ɛ4 402	428	6	.3X6 508 102	230	6	.406 18Ɛ 866	X15
7	.387 0Ɛ0 82X	325	7	Ɛ00 332	124	7	77Ɛ 67Ɛ	900
8	6X8 Ɛ53	221	8	.3X7 4Ɛ4 456	015	8	.407 16Ɛ 37Ɛ	7X9
9	.388 0X5 174	11Ɛ	9	XX8 46Ɛ	5Ɛ3 Ɛ09	9	75X Ɛ68	695
X	6X1 293	018	X	.3X8 4X0 378	9ƐX	X	.408 14X 641	580
Ɛ	.389 099 2XƐ	5Ɛ7 Ɛ15	Ɛ	X94 176	8Ɛ1	Ɛ	73X 001	469
.0730	695 204	X11	.0770	.3X9 487 X67	7X3	.07Ɛ0	.409 129 46X	354
1	.38X 091 015	90X	1	X7Ɛ 64X	695	1	718 802	23Ɛ
2	688 923	806	2	.3XX 473 123	587	2	.40X 107 X41	127
3	.38Ɛ 084 529	702	3	X66 6XX	478	3	6Ɛ6 Ɛ68	012
4	680 02Ɛ	5ƐX	4	.3XƐ 459 Ɛ66	36X	4	.40Ɛ 0X5 Ɛ7X	5XX XƐ9
5	.390 077 629	4Ɛ7	5	X51 314	260	5	694 X77	9X4
6	672 Ɛ24	3Ɛ2	6	.3Ɛ0 444 574	150	6	.410 083 85Ɛ	88X
7	.391 06X 316	2XX	7	X37 704	042	7	672 529	776
8	665 604	1X5	8	.3Ɛ1 42X 746	5Ɛ2 Ɛ33	8	.411 061 0X3	65Ɛ
9	.392 060 7X9	0X1	9	X21 679	X23	9	64Ɛ 742	547
X	657 88X	5Ɛ6 Ɛ98	X	.3Ɛ2 414 4X0	915	X	.412 03X 089	430
Ɛ	.393 052 866	X93	Ɛ	X07 1Ɛ5	805	Ɛ	628 4Ɛ9	317

N	Sine	d	N	Sine	d	N	Sine	d
.0800	.413 016 814	5XX 200	.0840	.432 693 599	5X5 6X9	.0880	.451 ƐX3 795	5X0 978
1	604 X14	0X6	1	.433 079 086	588	1	.452 584 551	851
2	ƐƐ2 XƐX	5X9 Ɛ90	2	662 652	467	2	Ɛ65 1X2	725
3	.414 5X0 X8X	X76	3	.434 047 XƐ9	347	3	.453 545 907	5ƐƐ
4	Ɛ8X 944	95Ɛ	4	631 244	225	4	Ɛ26 306	493
5	.415 578 6X3	844	5	.435 016 469	105	5	.454 506 799	367
6	Ɛ66 327	72X	6	5ƐƐ 572	5X4 ƐX3	6	XX6 Ɛ44	240
7	.416 553 X55	612	7	ƐX4 555	X81	7	.455 487 184	114
8	Ɛ41 467	4Ɛ8	8	.436 589 416	960	8	X67 298	59Ɛ ƐX8
9	.417 52X 963	3X0	9	Ɛ72 176	83Ɛ	9	.456 447 284	X7Ɛ
X	Ɛ18 143	285	X	.437 556 9Ɛ5	718	X	X27 143	954
Ɛ	.418 505 408	169	Ɛ	Ɛ3Ɛ 511	5Ɛ7	Ɛ	.457 406 X97	827
.0810	XƐ2 575	052	.0850	.438 523 Ɛ08	494	.0890	9X6 702	6ƐƐ
1	.419 49Ɛ 607	5X8 Ɛ36	1	Ɛ08 3X0	372	1	.458 386 201	592
2	X88 541	X19	2	.439 4Ɛ0 752	250	2	965 793	465
3	.41X 475 35X	902	3	X94 9X2	12X	3	.459 345 038	338
4	X62 060	7X6	4	.43X 478 Ɛ10	006	4	924 374	20Ɛ
5	.41Ɛ 44X 846	689	5	X60 Ɛ16	5X3 XX4	5	.45X 303 583	0X3
6	X37 313	571	6	.43Ɛ 444 9ƐX	981	6	8X2 666	59X Ɛ74
7	.420 423 884	455	7	X28 77Ɛ	85Ɛ	7	.45Ɛ 281 61X	X48
8	X10 119	337	8	.440 410 41X	736	8	860 466	91X
9	.421 3Ɛ8 454	21Ɛ	9	9Ɛ3 Ɛ54	614	9	.460 23Ɛ 184	7Ɛ0
X	9X4 673	102	X	.441 397 568	4Ɛ0	X	819 974	682
Ɛ	.422 390 775	5X7 ƐX5	Ɛ	97X X58	389	Ɛ	.461 1Ɛ8 436	554
.0820	978 75X	X87	.0860	.442 362 225	265	.08X0	796 98X	426
1	.423 364 625	96X	1	945 48X	141	1	.462 175 1Ɛ4	2Ɛ8
2	950 393	850	2	.443 328 60Ɛ	019	2	753 4Ɛ0	18X
3	.424 338 023	733	3	90Ɛ 628	5X2 XƐ5	3	.463 131 67X	05Ɛ
4	923 756	615	4	.444 2Ɛ2 521	990	4	70Ɛ 719	599 Ɛ30
5	.425 30Ɛ 16Ɛ	4Ɛ7	5	895 2Ɛ1	869	5	.464 0X9 649	X02
6	8Ɛ6 666	399	6	.445 277 Ɛ5X	744	6	687 44Ɛ	893
7	.426 2X1 X43	27Ɛ	7	85X 6X2	61Ɛ	7	.465 065 122	763
8	889 102	160	8	.446 241 101	4Ɛ6	8	642 885	635
9	.427 274 262	042	9	823 5Ɛ7	392	9	.466 020 2ƐX	505
X	85Ɛ 2X4	5X6 Ɛ24	X	.447 205 989	268	X	5Ɛ9 803	396
Ɛ	.428 246 208	X04	Ɛ	7X8 035	144	Ɛ	Ɛ96 Ɛ99	266
.0830	831 010	8X6	.0870	.448 18X 179	01X	.08Ɛ0	.467 574 243	137
1	.429 217 8Ɛ6	787	1	770 197	5X1 XƐ4	1	Ɛ51 37X	006
2	802 481	667	2	.449 152 08Ɛ	98Ɛ	2	.468 52X 384	598 X97
3	.42X 1X8 Ɛ28	549	3	733 X5X	866	3	Ɛ07 25Ɛ	967
4	793 475	429	4	.44X 115 704	73Ɛ	4	.469 4X4 006	836
5	.42Ɛ 179 8X2	309	5	6Ɛ7 243	616	5	X80 840	706
6	763 ƐXƐ	1XX	6	.44Ɛ 098 859	4XƐ	6	.46X 459 346	596
7	.430 14X 199	089	7	67X 148	385	7	X35 920	465
8	734 266	5X5 Ɛ6X	8	.450 05Ɛ 511	25Ɛ	8	.46Ɛ 412 185	334
9	.431 11X 214	X4X	9	640 770	134	9	9XX 4Ɛ9	203
X	704 062	92X	X	.451 021 8X4	00X	X	.470 386 700	092
Ɛ	.432 0X9 990	809	Ɛ	602 8Ɛ2	5X0 XX3	Ɛ	962 792	597 Ɛ61

N	Sine	d	N	Sine	d	N	Sine	d
.0900	.471 33X 733	597 X30	.0940	.490 513 X17	592 88X	.0980	.4XƐ 51X X99	589 514
1	916 563	8ƐX	1	XX6 6X5	752	1	XX8 3Ɛ1	393
2	.472 2Ɛ2 261	789	2	.491 479 237	616	2	.4Ɛ0 475 784	251
3	889 X2X	657	3	X4Ɛ 851	49Ɛ	3	X42 X15	10X
4	.473 265 485	526	4	.492 422 130	362	4	.4Ɛ1 40Ɛ Ɛ23	588 Ɛ87
5	840 9XƐ	3Ɛ3	5	9Ɛ4 492	226	5	998 XXX	X45
6	.474 218 1X2	281	6	.493 386 6Ɛ8	0X9	6	.4Ɛ2 365 933	903
7	7Ɛ3 463	14Ɛ	7	958 7X5	591 Ɛ71	7	932 636	77Ɛ
8	.475 18X 5Ɛ2	019	8	.494 32X 756	X35	8	.4Ɛ3 2ƐƐ 1Ɛ5	638
9	765 60Ɛ	596 XX6	9	900 58Ɛ	8Ɛ7	9	887 831	4Ɛ6
X	.476 140 4Ɛ5	974	X	.495 292 286	77X	X	.4Ɛ4 254 127	372
Ɛ	717 269	840	Ɛ	863 X44	642	Ɛ	820 499	22Ɛ
.0910	.477 0Ɛ1 XX9	70X	.0950	.496 235 486	504	.0990	.4Ɛ5 1X8 708	0X7
1	688 5Ɛ7	597	1	806 98X	387	1	774 7Ɛ3	587 Ɛ63
2	.478 062 Ɛ92	464	2	.497 198 155	249	2	.4Ɛ6 140 756	X20
3	639 436	331	3	769 3X2	110	3	708 576	898
4	.479 013 767	1Ɛ9	4	.498 13X 4Ɛ2	590 Ɛ92	4	.4Ɛ7 094 252	754
5	5X9 964	085	5	70Ɛ 484	X54	5	65Ɛ 9X6	60Ɛ
6	Ɛ83 X29	595 Ɛ52	6	.499 0X0 318	916	6	.4Ɛ8 027 3Ɛ5	487
7	.47X 559 97Ɛ	X1X	7	671 032	798	7	5Ɛ2 880	343
8	Ɛ33 799	8X6	8	.49X 041 80X	659	8	Ɛ7X 003	1ƐƐ
9	.47Ɛ 509 483	772	9	612 267	51Ɛ	9	.4Ɛ9 545 202	075
X	XX3 035	63X	X	ƐX2 786	3X1	X	Ɛ10 277	586 Ɛ31
Ɛ	.480 478 673	505	Ɛ	.49Ɛ 572 Ɛ67	262	Ɛ	.4ƐX 497 1X8	9X8
.0920	X51 Ɛ78	391	0960	Ɛ43 209	123	.09X0	X61 Ɛ94	863
1	.481 427 349	259	1	.4X0 513 330	58Ɛ ƐX5	1	.4ƐƐ 428 837	719
2	X00 5X6	123	2	XX3 315	X65	2	9Ɛ3 354	595
3	.482 395 709	594 ƐXƐ	3	.4X1 473 17X	926	3	.500 379 929	44X
4	96X 6Ɛ8	X76	4	X42 XX4	7X7	4	944 177	305
5	.483 343 572	941	5	.4X2 412 68Ɛ	667	5	.501 30X 480	180
6	918 2Ɛ3	807	6	9X2 136	528	6	894 640	035
7	.484 2Ɛ0 XƐX	692	7	.4X3 371 662	3X8	7	.502 25X 675	585 XƐ0
8	885 590	559	8	940 X4X	268	8	824 565	965
9	.485 259 Ɛ29	422	9	.4X4 310 0Ɛ6	128	9	.503 1XX 30X	81Ɛ
X	832 34Ɛ	2X9	X	89Ɛ 222	58X ƐX8	X	773 Ɛ29	695
Ɛ	.486 206 638	174	Ɛ	.4X5 26X 20X	X68	Ɛ	.504 139 602	54X
.0930	79X 7Ɛ0	039	.0970	839 076	927	.09Ɛ0	702 Ɛ50	404
1	.487 172 829	593 Ɛ02	1	.4X6 207 9X1	7X7	1	.505 088 354	279
2	746 72Ɛ	989	2	796 588	666	2	651 611	132
3	.488 11X 4Ɛ8	852	3	.4X7 165 032	526	3	.506 016 743	584 ƐX7
4	6Ɛ2 14X	718	4	733 558	3X5	4	59Ɛ 72X	X5Ɛ
5	.489 085 866	5X0	5	.4X8 101 941	263	5	Ɛ64 589	915
6	659 246	466	6	68Ɛ ƐX4	123	6	.507 529 2X2	789
7	.48X 030 6Ɛ0	32Ɛ	7	.4X9 05X 107	589 ƐX1	7	XƐ1 X6Ɛ	641
8	603 X1Ɛ	1Ɛ4	8	628 0X8	X5Ɛ	8	.508 476 4Ɛ0	4Ɛ6
9	Ɛ97 013	079	9	ƐƐ5 Ɛ47	91Ɛ	9	X3X,9X6	36X
X	.48Ɛ 56X 090	592 Ɛ41	X	.4XX 583 866	798	X	.509 403 154	221
Ɛ	Ɛ41 011	X06	Ɛ	Ɛ51 442	657	Ɛ	987 375	096

N	Sine	d	N	Sine	d	N	Sine	d
.0X00	.50X 34Ɛ 44Ɛ	583 Ɛ4X	.0X40	.528 Ɛ98 X82	57X 373	.0X80	.547 637 208	574 58X
1	913 399	X01	1	.529 557 235	221	1	ƐXƐ 796	432
2	.50Ɛ 297 19X	875	2	Ɛ15 456	089	2	.548 564 008	295
3	85X X53	728	3	.52X 493 523	579 Ɛ37	3	Ɛ18 2X1	138
4	.510 222 57Ɛ	5X0	4	X51 45X	9X4	4	.549 490 419	573 Ɛ9X
5	7X5 Ɛ5Ɛ	452	5	.52Ɛ 40Ɛ 242	850	5	X44 3Ɛ7	X42
6	.511 169 3Ɛ1	306	6	988 X92	6ƐX	6	.54X 3Ɛ8 239	8X4
7	730 6Ɛ7	179	7	.530 346 590	566	7	96Ɛ Ɛ21	746
8	.512 0Ɛ3 874	02Ɛ	8	903 Ɛ36	413	8	.54Ɛ 323 667	5X9
9	676 8X3	582 XX2	9	.531 281 349	27Ɛ	9	897 054	44Ɛ
X	.513 039 785	954	X	83X 608	127	X	.550 24X 4X3	2Ɛ1
Ɛ	600 519	807	Ɛ	.532 1Ɛ7 733	578 Ɛ94	Ɛ	801 794	153
.0X10	Ɛ83 124	679	.0X50	774 707	X3Ɛ	.0X90	.551 174 927	572 ƐƐ5
1	.514 545 7X1	52Ɛ	1	.533 131 546	8X8	1	727 920	X57
2	Ɛ08 110	3X1	2	6XX 232	753	2	.552 09X 777	8Ɛ8
3	.515 48X 4Ɛ1	253	3	.534 066 985	5ƐƐ	3	651 473	75X
4	X50 744	104	4	623 384	466	4	.553 004 011	5ƐƐ
5	.516 412 848	581 Ɛ76	5	Ɛ9Ɛ 82X	312	5	576 610	461
6	994 802	X28	6	.535 557 Ɛ40	179	6	Ɛ28 X71	301
7	.517 356 62X	899	7	Ɛ14 0Ɛ9	024	7	.554 49Ɛ 172	162
8	918 307	74X	8	.536 490 121	577 X8Ɛ	8	X51 314	004
9	.518 299 X55	5ƐƐ	9	X47 ƐƐ0	936	9	.555 403 318	571 X63
X	85Ɛ 454	470	X	.537 403 926	7X0	X	975 17Ɛ	905
Ɛ	.519 220 904	321	Ɛ	97Ɛ 506	648	Ɛ	.556 326 X84	765
.0X20	7X2 025	192	.0X60	.538 336 Ɛ52	4Ɛ1	.0XX0	898 629	605
1	.51X 163 1Ɛ7	042	1	8Ɛ2 443	358	1	.557 24X 032	465
2	724 239	580 XƐ3	2	.539 269 79Ɛ	203	2	7ƐƐ 497	306
3	.51Ɛ 0X5 130	962	3	824 9X2	068	3	.558 170 7X1	165
4	665 X92	813	4	.53X 19Ɛ X4X	576 Ɛ12	4	721 946	005
5	.520 026 6X5	683	5	756 960	978	5	.559 092 94Ɛ	570 X65
6	5X7 168	533	6	.53Ɛ 111 718	822	6	643 7Ɛ4	905
7	Ɛ67 69Ɛ	3X3	7	688 33X	688	7	ƐƐ4 4Ɛ9	763
8	.521 527 X82	252	8	.540 042 X06	530	8	.55X 565 060	604
9	XX8 114	102	9	5Ɛ9 336	396	9	Ɛ15 664	462
X	.522 468 216	57Ɛ Ɛ71	X	Ɛ73 710	240	X	.55Ɛ 485 Ɛ06	301
Ɛ	X28 187	X20	Ɛ	.541 529 950	0X4	Ɛ	X36 207	160
.0X30	.523 3X7 ƐX7	890	.0X70	XX3 X34	575 Ɛ49	.0XƐ0	.560 3X6 367	56Ɛ ƐƐƐ
1	967 877	73Ɛ	1	.542 459 981	9Ɛ3	1	956 366	X5X
2	.524 327 3Ɛ6	5X9	2	X13 774	856	2	.561 306 204	8Ɛ8
3	8X6 9X3	458	3	.543 389 40X	700	3	875 Ɛ00	757
4	.525 266 23Ɛ	307	4	942 Ɛ0X	563	4	.562 225 657	5Ɛ4
5	825 546	175	5	.544 2Ɛ8 471	408	5	795 04Ɛ	453
6	.526 1X4 6ƐƐ	023	6	871 879	270	6	.563 144 4X2	2Ɛ1
7	763 722	57X X92	7	.545 226 Ɛ29	115	7	6Ɛ3 793	14Ɛ
8	.527 122 5Ɛ4	940	8	7X0 042	574 Ɛ78	8	.564 062 922	56X ƐX9
9	6X1 334	7XX	9	.546 154 ƐƐX	X20	9	611 90Ɛ	X46
X	.528 05Ɛ Ɛ22	657	X	709 X1X	883	X	Ɛ80 755	8X4
Ɛ	61X 579	505	Ɛ	.547 082 6X1	727	Ɛ	.565 52Ɛ 439	741

N	Sine	d	N	Sine	d	N	Sine	d
.0Ɛ00	.565 χ99 Ɛ7χ	56χ 59Ɛ	.0Ɛ40	.584 139 13Ɛ	564 3χ5	.0Ɛ80	.5χ2 188 57Ɛ	559 Ɛχ8
1	.566 448 559	437	1	6χ1 524	238	1	726 567	χ36
2	9Ɛ6 994	295	2	.585 045 760	08Ɛ	2	.5χ3 084 3χ1	883
3	.567 365 069	131	3	5χ9 82Ɛ	563 Ɛ22	3	622 064	70Ɛ
4	913 19χ	569 Ɛ8χ	4	Ɛ51 751	974	4	Ɛ7Ɛ 773	558
5	.568 281 168	χ27	5	.586 4Ɛ5 505	807	5	.5χ4 519 10Ɛ	3χ4
6	82χ Ɛ93	883	6	χ59 110	65χ	6	χ76 4Ɛ3	231
7	.569 198 856	720	7	.587 400 76χ	4χƐ	7	.5χ5 413 724	079
8	746 376	578	8	964 059	342	8	970 7χ1	558 Ɛ05
9	.56χ 0Ɛ3 932	413	9	.588 307 39Ɛ	194	9	.5χ6 309 6χ6	951
χ	661 145	270	χ	86χ 573	026	χ	866 437	799
Ɛ	.56Ɛ 00χ 3Ɛ5	108	Ɛ	.589 211 599	562 χ77	Ɛ	.5χ7 203 014	625
.0Ɛ10	577 501	568 Ɛ64	.0Ɛ50	774 454	90χ	.0Ɛ90	75Ɛ 639	471
1	Ɛ24 465	9ƐƐ	1	.58χ 117 162	75χ	1	.5χ8 0Ɛ7 χχχ	2Ɛ7
2	.570 491 264	856	2	679 900	5Ɛ0	2	654 1χ5	144
3	χ39 χƐχ	6Ɛ2	3	.58Ɛ 020 2Ɛ0	442	3	ƐƐ0 329	557 Ɛ8χ
4	.571 3χ6 5Ɛ0	549	4	582 732	292	4	.5χ9 548 2Ɛ7	χ16
5	952 Ɛ39	3χ4	5	Ɛ24 χ04	124	5	χχ4 111	860
6	.572 2ƐƐ 321	240	6	.590 486 Ɛ28	561 Ɛ74	6	.5χχ 43Ɛ 971	6χ8
7	867 561	096	7	χ28 χχ0	χ06	7	997 459	532
3	.573 213 637	567 Ɛ30	8	.591 38χ 8χ6	855	8	.5χƐ 332 98Ɛ	379
9	77Ɛ 567	988	9	930 53Ɛ	6χ7	9	88χ 148	203
χ	.574 127 333	821	χ	.592 292 026	536	χ	.5Ɛ0 225 34Ɛ	04χ
Ɛ	692 Ɛ54	678	Ɛ	833 560	387	Ɛ	780 399	556 χ94
.0Ɛ20	.575 03χ 610	513	.0Ɛ60	.593 194 927	218	.0Ɛχ0	.5Ɛ1 117 271	91χ
1	5χ5 Ɛ23	368	1	735 Ɛ43	067	1	671 Ɛ8Ɛ	764
2	Ɛ51 28Ɛ	202	2	.594 096 Ɛχχ	560 χƐ7	2	.5Ɛ2 008 733	5χχ
3	.576 4Ɛ8 491	058	3	637 χχ5	946	3	563 121	433
4	χ63 529	566 χƐ2	4	Ɛ98 82Ɛ	797	4	χƐ9 554	27χ
5	.577 40χ 41Ɛ	948	5	.595 539 406	626	5	.5Ɛ3 453 812	102
6	975 167	7χ0	6	χ99 χ30	475	6	9χ9 914	555 Ɛ49
7	.578 31Ɛ 947	637	7	.596 43χ 2χ5	305	7	.5Ɛ4 343 861	991
8	886 382	48Ɛ	8	99χ 5χχ	153	8	899 632	816
9	.579 230 851	324	9	.597 33χ 741	55Ɛ Ɛχ3	9	.5Ɛ5 233 248	660
χ	796 Ɛ75	17χ	χ	89χ 724	χ32	χ	788 8χ8	4χ4
Ɛ	.57χ 141 133	012	Ɛ	.598 23χ 556	880	Ɛ	.5Ɛ6 122 190	32χ
.0Ɛ30	6χ7 145	565 χ66	.0Ɛ70	79χ 216	70Ɛ	.0ƐƐ0	677 4Ɛχ	171
1	.57Ɛ 050 ƐχƐ	900	1	.599 139 925	559	1	.5Ɛ7 010 66Ɛ	554 ƐƐ7
2	5Ɛ6 8χƐ	754	2	699 282	3χ8	2	565 666	χ3χ
3	Ɛ60 443	5χ8	3	.59χ 038 66χ	236	3	χƐχ 4χ4	883
4	.580 505 χ2Ɛ	440	4	597 8χ4	084	4	.5Ɛ8 453 167	707
5	χ6Ɛ 26Ɛ	294	5	Ɛ36 968	55χ Ɛ13	5	9χ7 872	54Ɛ
6	.581 414 543	128	6	.59Ɛ 495 87Ɛ	960	6	.5Ɛ9 340 201	393
7	979 66Ɛ	564 Ɛ80	7	χ34 61Ɛ	7χχ	7	894 594	216
8	.582 322 62Ɛ	χ14	8	.5χ0 393 209	637	8	.5Ɛχ 228 7χχ	05Ɛ
9	887 443	867	9	931 844	485	9	780 849	553 χχ1
χ	.583 230 0χχ	6ƐƐ	χ	.5χ1 290 109	312	χ	.5ƐƐ 114 72χ	926
Ɛ	794 7χ9	552	Ɛ	82χ 41Ɛ	160	Ɛ	668 454	768

N	Sine	d	N	Sine	d	N	Sine	d
.1000	.600 000 000	553 5Ɛ0	.1040	.619 80Ɛ 859	548 9Ɛ4	.1080	.637 1χƐ 804	542 001
1	553 5Ɛ0	432	1	.61χ 158 651	831	1	731 805	541 χ34
2	χχ6 χ22	275	2	6χ5 282	66χ	2	.638 073 639	866
3	.601 43χ 097	0Ɛ9	3	.61Ɛ 031 930	4χ7	3	5Ɛ5 2χ3	69χ
4	991 194	552 Ɛ3χ	4	57χ 217	323	4	Ɛ36 981	510
5	.602 324 112	982	5	Ɛ06 53χ	160	5	.639 478 291	343
6	876 χ94	803	6	.620 452 69χ	547 Ɛ99	6	9Ɛ9 614	176
7	.603 209 697	646	7	99χ 677	χ15	7	.63χ 33χ 78χ	540 Ɛχ8
8	760 121	488	8	.621 326 490	851	8	87Ɛ 776	χ1χ
9	.604 0Ɛ2 5χ9	30χ	9	872 121	689	9	.63Ɛ 200 594	851
χ	644 8Ɛ7	150	χ	.622 1Ɛ9 7χχ	505	χ	741 225	683
Ɛ	Ɛ96 χ47	551 Ɛ92	Ɛ	745 0Ɛ3	341	Ɛ	.640 081 8χ8	4Ɛ4
.1010	.605 528 χ19	χ14	.1050	.623 090 434	178	.1090	602 1χ0	327
1	χ7χ 831	854	1	617 5Ɛ0	546 ƐƐ5	1	Ɛ42 507	158
2	.606 410 485	697	2	Ɛ62 5χ5	χ2Ɛ	2	.641 482 663	53Ɛ Ɛ8χ
3	961 Ɛ60	517	3	.624 4χ9 414	867	3	χ02 631	9ƐƐ
4	.607 2Ɛ3 477	359	4	χ34 07Ɛ	6χ2	4	.642 342 430	831
5	844 814	19χ	5	.625 37χ 761	51χ	5	882 061	661
6	.608 195 9Ɛ2	01χ	6	905 07Ɛ	354	6	.643 201 702	493
7	726 χ10	550 χ60	7	.626 24Ɛ 413	18Ɛ	7	740 Ɛ95	304
8	.609 077 870	8χ0	8	795 5χ2	006	8	.644 080 299	135
9	608 550	720	9	.627 11Ɛ 5χ8	545 χ40	9	5ƐƐ 412	53χ Ɛ65
χ	Ɛ59 070	561	χ	665 428	877	χ	Ɛ3χ 377	996
Ɛ	.60χ 4χ9 611	3χ1	Ɛ	ƐχƐ 0χ3	6Ɛ2	Ɛ	.645 479 151	807
.1020	χ39 9Ɛ2	222	.1060	.628 534 795	527	.10χ0	9Ɛ7 958	637
1	.60Ɛ 38χ 014	061	1	χ7χ 100	362	1	.646 336 393	467
2	91χ 075	54Ɛ χχ2	2	.629 403 462	197	2	874 83χ	298
3	.610 269 Ɛ57	921	3	948 639	012	3	.647 1Ɛ2 Ɛ16	107
4	7Ɛ9 878	760	4	.62χ 291 64Ɛ	544 χ47	4	731 021	539 Ɛ37
5	.611 149 418	5χ1	5	816 496	881	5	.648 06χ Ɛ58	967
6	698 9Ɛ9	41Ɛ	6	.62Ɛ 15Ɛ 157	6Ɛ6	6	5χ8 903	797
7	.612 028 218	25Ɛ	7	6χ3 851	530	7	Ɛ26 49χ	606
8	577 477	09Ɛ	8	.630 028 181	365	8	.649 463 χχ4	436
9	Ɛ06 556	54χ Ɛ19	9	570 526	19χ	9	9χ1 31χ	264
χ	.613 455 473	958	χ	χƐ4 704	013	χ	.64χ 31χ 582	094
Ɛ	9χ4 20Ɛ	797	Ɛ	.631 438 717	543 χ48	Ɛ	857 656	538 Ɛ03
.1030	.614 332 9χ6	615	.1070	980 563	881	.10Ɛ0	.64Ɛ 194 559	932
1	881 3ƐƐ	454	1	.632 304 224	6Ɛ6	1	711 28Ɛ	761
2	.615 20Ɛ 853	293	2	847 91χ	52χ	2	.650 049 χ30	58Ɛ
3	759 Ɛ26	111	3	.633 18Ɛ 248	362	3	586 3ƐƐ	3Ɛχ
4	.616 0χ8 037	549 Ɛ4Ɛ	4	712 5χχ	197	4	Ɛ02 7Ɛ9	229
5	635 Ɛ86	989	5	.634 055 785	00χ	5	.651 43χ χ26	056
6	Ɛ83 953	807	6	598 793	542 χ43	6	976 χ80	537 χ85
7	.617 511 55χ	644	7	Ɛ1Ɛ 616	877	7	.652 2Ɛ2 945	8Ɛ3
8	χ5χ Ɛχ2	483	8	.635 462 291	6χχ	8	82χ 638	721
9	.618 3χ8 465	300	9	9χ4 97Ɛ	523	9	.653 166 159	54Ɛ
χ	935 765	139	χ	.636 327 2χ2	355	χ	6χ1 6χ8	378
Ɛ	.619 282 8χ2	548 Ɛ77	Ɛ	869 637	189	Ɛ	.654 018 χ64	1χ6

N	Sine	d	N	Sine	d	N	Sine	d
.1100	.654 554 04X	537 014	.1140	.671 675 024	52Ɛ X34	.1180	.68X 546 XX4	524 664
1	X8Ɛ 062	536 X41	1	ƐX4 X58	857	1	X6Ɛ 548	481
2	.655 405 XX3	86X	2	.672 514 6Ɛ3	67Ɛ	2	.68Ɛ 393 X09	29Ɛ
3	940 751	697	3	X44 172	4X1	3	8Ɛ8 0X8	0Ɛ8
4	.656 277 228	504	4	.673 373 653	305	4	.690 220 1X4	523 Ɛ16
5	7Ɛ1 730	331	5	8X2 958	129	5	744 0ƐX	934
6	.657 127 X61	159	6	.674 211 X85	52X Ɛ4Ɛ	6	.691 067 X32	750
7	661 ƐƐX	535 Ɛ87	7	740 X14	972	7	58Ɛ 582	56X
8	Ɛ97 Ɛ85	9Ɛ2	8	.675 06Ɛ 786	794	8	XƐ2 Ɛ30	386
9	.658 511 977	81Ɛ	9	59X 35X	5Ɛ7	9	.692 416 2Ɛ6	1X4
X	X47 596	648	X	Ɛ08 955	41X	X	939 49X	000
Ɛ	.659 381 022	473	Ɛ	.676 437 173	240	Ɛ	.693 260 49X	522 X19
.1110	8Ɛ6 495	2X0	.1150	965 3Ɛ3	063	.1190	783 2Ɛ7	836
1	.65X 22Ɛ 775	107	1	.677 293 456	529 X84	1	.694 0X5 Ɛ31	652
2	764 880	534 Ɛ33	2	801 31X	8X6	2	608 583	46X
3	.65Ɛ 099 7Ɛ3	95Ɛ	3	.678 12Ɛ 004	709	3	Ɛ2X X31	286
4	612 552	787	4	658 711	52X	4	.695 451 0Ɛ7	0X2
5	Ɛ47 119	5Ɛ1	5	Ɛ86 03Ɛ	350	5	973 199	521 XƐƐ
6	.660 47Ɛ 70X	419	6	.679 4Ɛ3 38Ɛ	171	6	.696 295 098	916
7	9Ɛ3 Ɛ27	245	7	X20 540	528 Ɛ92	7	7Ɛ6 9Ɛ2	732
8	.661 328 170	06Ɛ	8	.67X 349 512	9Ɛ4	8	.697 118 524	549
9	860 21Ɛ	533 X96	9	876 306	815	9	639 X71	365
X	.662 194 0Ɛ5	901	X	.67Ɛ 1X2 Ɛ1Ɛ	636	X	Ɛ5Ɛ 216	180
Ɛ	707 9Ɛ6	728	Ɛ	70Ɛ 555	457	Ɛ	.698 480 396	520 Ɛ98
.1120	.663 03Ɛ 522	552	.1160	.680 037 9Ɛ0	278	.11X0	9X1 372	9Ɛ2
1	572 X74	378	1	564 068	099	1	.699 302 164	80X
2	XX6 230	1X3	2	X90 145	527 XƐ9	2	822 972	624
3	.664 419 413	00X	3	.681 3Ɛ8 042	919	3	.69X 143 396	43Ɛ
4	950 421	532 X33	4	923 95Ɛ	73X	4	663 815	256
5	.665 283 254	859	5	.682 24Ɛ 499	55X	5	Ɛ83 X6Ɛ	070
6	7Ɛ5 XƐ1	683	6	776 X37	37Ɛ	6	.69Ɛ 4X3 Ɛ1Ɛ	51Ɛ X87
7	.666 128 574	4X9	7	.683 0X2 1Ɛ6	19X	7	X03 9X6	8X1
8	65X X61	312	8	609 394	526 ƐƐX	8	.6X0 323 687	6Ɛ7
9	Ɛ91 173	138	9	Ɛ34 392	X19	9	843 182	511
X	.667 503 2XƐ	531 Ɛ61	X	.684 45Ɛ 1XƐ	83X	X	.6X1 162 693	327
Ɛ	X35 250	987	Ɛ	985 X29	658	Ɛ	681 9ƐX	141
.1130	.668 367 017	7XƐ	.1170	.685 2Ɛ0 485	479	.11Ɛ0	ƐX0 Ɛ3Ɛ	51X Ɛ56
1	898 806	615	1	816 942	297	1	.6X2 4ƐƐ X95	970
2	.669 20X 21Ɛ	439	2	.686 141 019	0Ɛ7	2	X1X 845	786
3	73Ɛ 658	262	3	667 114	525 Ɛ15	3	.6X3 339 40Ɛ	59Ɛ
4	.66X 070 8ƐX	087	4	Ɛ91 029	935	4	857 9XX	3Ɛ4
5	5X1 985	530 XXƐ	5	.687 4Ɛ6 962	753	5	.6X4 176 1X2	209
6	Ɛ12 874	914	6	X20 4Ɛ5	572	6	694 3XƐ	022
7	.66Ɛ 443 588	738	7	.688 345 X67	390	7	ƐƐ2 411	519 X37
8	974 104	560	8	86Ɛ 237	1XƐ	8	.6X5 510 248	850
9	.670 2X4 664	384	9	.689 194 426	009	9	X29 X98	664
X	814 X28	1X8	X	6Ɛ9 433	524 X28	X	.6X6 347 540	479
Ɛ	.671 145 014	010	Ɛ	.68X 022 25Ɛ	845	Ɛ	864 9Ɛ9	292

N	Sine	d	N	Sine	d	N	Sine	d
.1200	.6X7 182 08Ɛ	519 0X5	.1240	.703 756 Ɛ0X	511 541	.1280	.71Ɛ X82 000	505 7Ɛ5
1	69Ɛ 174	518 XƐX	1	.704 068 44Ɛ	34Ɛ	1	.720 387 7Ɛ5	5Ɛ9
2	ƐƐ8 072	912	2	579 79X	15X	2	891 1Ɛ2	402
3	.6X8 514 984	725	3	X8X 938	510 Ɛ68	3	.721 196 5Ɛ4	206
4	X31 4X9	53X	4	.705 39Ɛ 8X4	977	4	69Ɛ 7ƐX	010
5	.6X9 349 X27	351	5	8Ɛ0 65Ɛ	784	5	ƐX4 80X	504 X14
6	866 178	165	6	.706 201 223	592	6	.722 4X9 622	818
7	.6XX 182 321	517 Ɛ78	7	711 7Ɛ5	3X1	7	9Ɛ2 23X	621
8	69X 299	990	8	.707 021 Ɛ96	1XX	8	.723 2Ɛ6 85Ɛ	424
9	ƐƐ6 069	7X2	9	532 184	50Ɛ ƐƐ7	9	7ƐƐ 083	229
X	.6XƐ 511 84Ɛ	5Ɛ6	X	X42 17Ɛ	X05	X	.724 103 2Ɛ0	031
Ɛ	X29 245	409	Ɛ	.708 351 Ɛ84	813	Ɛ	607 321	503 X35
.1210	.6Ɛ0 344 652	220	.1250	861 797	61Ɛ	.1290	Ɛ0Ɛ 156	838
1	85Ɛ 872	032	1	.709 171 1Ɛ6	429	1	.725 412 992	640
2	.6Ɛ1 176 8X4	516 X45	2	680 623	236	2	916 412	443
3	691 729	858	3	Ɛ8Ɛ 859	043	3	.726 219 855	247
4	ƐX8 385	66X	4	.70X 49X 8X0	50X X50	4	720 XX0	04X
5	.6Ɛ2 502 X33	480	5	9X9 730	858	5	.727 023 Ɛ2X	502 X51
6	X19 2Ɛ3	292	6	.70Ɛ 2Ɛ8 388	665	6	526 97Ɛ	855
7	.6Ɛ3 333 585	0X5	7	806 X31	471	7	X29 614	657
8	849 66X	515 XƐ6	8	.710 115 2X2	27X	8	.728 330 06Ɛ	45X
9	.6Ɛ4 163 564	909	9	623 560	086	9	832 509	261
X	679 271	719	X	Ɛ31 626	509 X92	X	.729 134 76X	063
Ɛ	Ɛ92 98X	530	Ɛ	.711 43Ɛ 4Ɛ8	89X	Ɛ	636 811	501 X66
.1220	.6Ɛ5 4X8 2ƐX	341	.1260	949 196	6X5	.12X0	Ɛ38 677	868
1	X01 63Ɛ	152	1	.712 256 87Ɛ	4Ɛ2	1	.72X 43X 323	66X
2	.6Ɛ6 316 791	514 Ɛ64	2	764 171	2Ɛ9	2	93Ɛ 991	470
3	82Ɛ 735	974	3	.713 071 46X	105	3	.72Ɛ 241 241	273
4	.6Ɛ7 144 4X9	786	4	57X 573	508 Ɛ10	4	742 4Ɛ4	074
5	659 073	596	5	X87 483	918	5	.730 043 568	500 X76
6	Ɛ71 649	3X7	6	.714 394 19Ɛ	722	6	544 422	878
7	.6Ɛ8 485 X34	1Ɛ8	7	8X0 901	52X	7	X45 09X	679
8	99X 030	009	8	.715 1X9 22Ɛ	335	8	.731 345 757	47Ɛ
9	.6Ɛ9 2Ɛ2 039	513 X18	9	6Ɛ5 564	13Ɛ	9	846 016	280
X	805 X55	82X	X	.716 001 6X3	507 Ɛ46	X	.732 146 296	081
Ɛ	.6ƐX 119 683	639	Ɛ	509 629	951	Ɛ	646 357	4ƐƐ X82
.1230	631 100	449	.1270	X15 37X	757	.12Ɛ0	Ɛ46 219	884
1	Ɛ44 549	259	1	.717 320 Ɛ15	562	1	.733 445 XX1	684
2	.6ƐƐ 457 7X6	069	2	828 477	368	2	945 565	485
3	96X 853	512 X79	3	.718 133 823	172	3	.734 244 X2X	285
4	.700 281 710	889	4	63X 995	506 Ɛ78	4	744 0Ɛ3	086
5	794 399	697	5	Ɛ45 951	982	5	.735 043 179	4ƐX X87
6	.701 0X6 X74	4X8	6	.719 450 713	788	6	542 044	886
7	5Ɛ9 360	2Ɛ6	7	957 29Ɛ	591	7	X40 90X	687
8	Ɛ0Ɛ 656	106	8	.71X 261 870	397	8	.736 33Ɛ 395	487
9	.702 421 760	511 Ɛ14	9	768 047	1X1	9	839 860	287
X	933 674	924	X	.71Ɛ 072 228	505 ƐX5	X	.737 137 Ɛ27	087
Ɛ	.703 245 398	732	Ɛ	578 211	9XƐ	Ɛ	635 ƐƐ2	4Ɛ9 X86

N	Sine	d	N	Sine	d	N	Sine	d
.1300	.737 Ɛ33 X78	4Ɛ9 887	.1340	.753 925 305	4Ɛ1 77X	.1380	.76Ɛ 44X X28	4X5 496
1	.738 431 743	685	1	.754 216 X83	574	1	934 302	286
2	92Ɛ 208	485	2	708 437	36X	2	.770 219 588	077
3	.739 228 691	284	3	ƐƐ9 7X5	163	3	702 643	4X4 X68
4	725 955	084	4	.755 4XX 948	4Ɛ0 Ɛ59	4	ƐX7 4XƐ	858
5	.73X 022 X19	4Ɛ8 X82	5	99Ɛ 8X5	953	5	.771 490 147	648
6	51Ɛ 89Ɛ	881	6	.756 290 638	748	6	974 793	438
7	X18 560	680	7	781 184	542	7	.772 259 00Ɛ	229
8	.73Ɛ 315 020	47Ɛ	8	.757 071 706	337	8	741 238	018
9	811 49Ɛ	27X	9	561 X41	130	9	.773 025 254	4X3 X08
X	.740 109 759	077	X	X51 Ɛ71	4XƐ Ɛ25	X	509 060	7Ɛ8
Ɛ	605 814	4Ɛ7 X77	Ɛ	.758 341 X96	91X	Ɛ	9Ɛ0 858	5X7
.1310	Ɛ01 68Ɛ	874	.1350	831 7Ɛ4	713	.1390	.774 294 243	397
1	.741 3Ɛ9 343	673	1	.759 121 307	508	1	777 61X	186
2	8Ɛ4 9Ɛ6	470	2	610 813	300	2	.775 05X 7X4	4X2 Ɛ75
3	.742 1Ɛ0 266	26Ɛ	3	XƐƐ Ɛ13	0Ɛ5	3	541 759	965
4	6X7 515	068	4	.75X 3XƐ 008	4XX XX9	4	X24 502	753
5	ƐX2 581	4Ɛ6 X66	5	899 XƐ5	8X1	5	.776 307 055	543
6	.743 499 427	863	6	.75Ɛ 188 796	696	6	7X9 598	331
7	994 08X	661	7	677 270	489	7	.777 08Ɛ 909	120
8	.744 28X 72Ɛ	45Ɛ	8	Ɛ65 739	282	8	571 X29	4X1 Ɛ0X
9	784 Ɛ8X	257	9	.760 453 9ƐƐ	075	9	X53 937	8Ɛ9
X	.745 07Ɛ 225	055	X	941 X74	4X9 X69	X	.778 335 634	6X7
Ɛ	575 27X	4Ɛ5 X51	Ɛ	.761 22Ɛ 921	861	Ɛ	817 11Ɛ	496
.1320	X6Ɛ 10Ɛ	84Ɛ	.1360	719 582	654	.13X0	.779 0Ɛ8 5Ɛ5	284
1	.746 364 95X	647	1	.762 007 016	447	1	599 879	071
2	85X 3X5	444	2	4Ɛ4 461	23Ɛ	2	X7X 92X	4X0 X60
3	.747 153 829	240	3	9X1 6X0	031	3	.77X 35Ɛ 78X	849
4	648 X69	039	4	.763 28X 711	4X8 X25	4	840 417	637
5	Ɛ41 XX6	4Ɛ4 X35	5	777 536	818	5	.77Ɛ 120 X52	425
6	.748 436 91Ɛ	832	6	.764 064 152	60X	6	601 277	212
7	92Ɛ 551	629	7	550 760	402	7	XX1 489	000
8	.749 223 Ɛ7X	426	8	X38 Ɛ62	1Ɛ3	8	.780 381 489	49Ɛ 9X8
9	718 3X4	221	9	.765 325 155	4X7 ƐX7	9	861 275	796
X	.74X 010 605	019	X	811 140	998	X	.781 140 X4Ɛ	583
Ɛ	504 622	4Ɛ3 X15	Ɛ	.766 0Ɛ8 Ɛ18	78Ɛ	Ɛ	620 412	370
.1330	9Ɛ8 437	810	.1370	5X4 6X7	581	.13Ɛ0	XƐƐ 782	158
1	.74Ɛ 2Ɛ0 047	608	1	X90 068	373	1	.782 39X 91X	49X Ɛ46
2	7X3 653	403	2	.767 377 41Ɛ	165	2	879 864	932
3	.750 096 X56	1ƐX	3	862 584	4X6 Ɛ57	3	.783 158 596	71X
4	58X 054	4Ɛ2 Ɛ25	4	.768 149 51Ɛ	948	4	637 0Ɛ4	507
5	X81 049	9Ɛ0	5	634 267	73X	5	Ɛ15 5ƐƐ	2Ɛ3
6	.751 373 X39	7X7	6	Ɛ1X 9X5	530	6	.784 3Ɛ3 8Ɛ2	09Ɛ
7	866 624	5X2	7	.769 405 315	320	7	891 991	499 X87
8	.752 159 006	398	8	8XƐ 635	112	8	.785 16Ɛ 858	873
9	64Ɛ 3X2	193	9	.76X 195 747	4X5 Ɛ04	9	649 50Ɛ	65Ɛ
X	Ɛ41 575	4Ɛ1 Ɛ89	X	67Ɛ 64Ɛ	8Ɛ4	X	Ɛ26 Ɛ6X	447
Ɛ	.753 433 542	983	Ɛ	Ɛ65 343	6X5	Ɛ	.786 404 3Ɛ5	232

N	Sine	d	N	Sine	d	N	Sine	d
.1400	.786 8X1 627	499 01X	.1440	.7X1 X56 208	490 590	.1480	.7Ɛ8 925 999	483 975
1	.787 17X 645	498 X05	1	.7X2 326 798	373	1	.7Ɛ9 1X9 752	751
2	657 44X	7Ɛ0	2	7Ɛ6 Ɛ4Ɛ	154	2	671 2X3	52Ɛ
3	Ɛ34 03X	598	3	.7X3 087 0X3	48Ɛ Ɛ36	3	Ɛ34 812	307
4	.788 410 616	382	4	557 019	919	4	.7ƐX 3Ɛ7 Ɛ19	0X3
5	8X8 998	16X	5	X26 936	6Ɛ9	5	87Ɛ 000	482 X81
6	.789 184 Ɛ46	497 Ɛ54	6	.7X4 2Ɛ6 433	4X0	6	.7ƐƐ 141 X81	858
7	660 X9X	93Ɛ	7	785 913	281	7	604 719	635
8	Ɛ38 819	726	8	.7X5 054 Ɛ94	062	8	X87 152	411
9	.78X 414 343	510	9	524 036	48X X43	9	.800 349 563	1XX
X	8XƐ 853	2Ɛ6	X	9Ɛ2 X79	825	X	80Ɛ 751	481 Ɛ85
Ɛ	.78Ɛ 186 Ɛ49	0X1	Ɛ	.7X6 281 6X2	606	Ɛ	.801 091 716	961
.1410	662 02X	496 X87	.1450	750 0X8	3X6	.1490	553 477	739
1	Ɛ38 XƐ5	871	1	.7X7 01X 492	188	1	X14 ƐƐ4	514
2	.790 413 766	657	2	4X8 65X	489 Ɛ68	2	.802 296 508	2Ɛ0
3	8XX 201	441	3	976 606	949	3	757 7Ɛ8	088
4	.791 184 642	226	4	.7X8 244 353	729	4	.803 018 884	480 X63
5	65X 868	010	5	711 X80	50X	5	499 727	83X
6	Ɛ34 878	495 9Ɛ6	6	Ɛ9Ɛ 38X	2XX	6	95X 365	615
7	.792 40X 672	79Ɛ	7	.7X9 468 678	08X	7	.804 21X 97X	3Ɛ0
8	8X4 251	585	8	935 746	488 X6X	8	69Ɛ 16X	188
9	.793 179 816	369	9	.7XX 202 5Ɛ4	84X	9	Ɛ5Ɛ 336	47Ɛ Ɛ62
X	652 Ɛ83	153	X	68Ɛ 242	62X	X	.805 41Ɛ 298	938
Ɛ	Ɛ28 116	494 Ɛ37	Ɛ	Ɛ57 870	40X	Ɛ	89Ɛ 014	714
1420	.794 401 051	921	.1460	.7XƐ 424 07X	1X9	.14X0	.806 15X 728	4XX
1	895 972	705	1	8Ɛ0 267	487 Ɛ89	1	61X 016	284
2	.795 16X 477	4XX	2	.7Ɛ0 178 234	969	2	X99 29X	05X
3	642 965	292	3	643 ƐX1	747	3	.807 358 338	47X X35
4	Ɛ17 037	077	4	Ɛ0Ɛ 728	527	4	817 171	80Ɛ
5	.796 3XƐ 0Ɛ2	493 X5Ɛ	5	.7Ɛ1 397 053	306	5	.808 095 980	5X4
6	882 Ɛ51	843	6	862 359	0X5	6	554 364	37Ɛ
7	.797 156 794	627	7	.7Ɛ2 129 442	486 X84	7	X12 723	154
8	62X 1ƐƐ	410	8	5Ɛ4 306	863	8	.809 290 877	479 Ɛ2X
9	Ɛ01 60Ɛ	1Ɛ3	9	X7X Ɛ69	641	9	74X 7X5	904
X	.798 394 802	492 Ɛ97	X	.7Ɛ3 345 5XX	420	X	.80X 008 4X9	699
Ɛ	867 799	97Ɛ	Ɛ	80Ɛ X0X	1ƐƐ	Ɛ	485 Ɛ86	472
.1430	.799 13X 558	762	.1470	7Ɛ4 096 009	485 Ɛ98	.14Ɛ0	943 438	247
1	611 0ƐX	545	1	55Ɛ ƐX5	977	1	.80Ɛ 200 683	021
2	XX3 643	329	2	X25 960	755	2	679 6X4	478 9Ɛ5
3	.79X 375 970	110	3	.7Ɛ5 2XƐ 4Ɛ5	534	3	Ɛ36 499	78Ɛ
4	847 X80	491 XƐ4	4	774 X29	311	4	.810 3Ɛ3 068	563
5	.79Ɛ 119 974	896	5	.7Ɛ6 03X 13X	0XX	5	86Ɛ 60Ɛ	338
6	5XƐ 64X	679	6	503 228	484 X89	6	.811 127 947	111
7	X81 107	460	7	988 0Ɛ5	866	7	5X3 X58	477 XX5
8	.7X0 352 567	243	8	.7Ɛ7 250 95Ɛ	644	8	X5Ɛ 941	879
9	823 7XX	025	9	715 3X3	421	9	.812 317 5ƐX	652
X	.7X1 0Ɛ4 813	490 X07	X	Ɛ99 804	1ƐX	X	793 050	425
Ɛ	585 61X	7XX	Ɛ	.7Ɛ8 461 X02	483 Ɛ97	Ɛ	.813 04X 475	1ƐX

N	Sine	d	N	Sine	d	N	Sine	d
.1500	.813 505 673	476 Ɛ92	.1540	.829 9XX 674	46X 027	.1580	.843 Ɛ92 111	460 Ɛ00
1	980 645	966	1	.82X 258 69Ɛ	469 9Ɛ6	1	.844 433 011	886
2	.814 237 3XƐ	739	2	706 495	785	2	893 897	650
3	6Ɛ1 Ɛ28	511	3	Ɛ74 05X	553	3	.845 134 327	416
4	Ɛ68 439	2X5	4	.82Ɛ 421 5Ɛ1	322	4	594 741	19X
5	.815 422 722	077	5	88X 913	0Ɛ0	5	X34 91Ɛ	45Ɛ Ɛ65
6	898 799	475 X50	6	.830 137 X03	468 X7Ɛ	6	.846 294 884	929
7	.816 152 629	822	7	5X4 882	848	7	734 5Ɛ1	6Ɛ3
8	608 24Ɛ	5Ɛ6	8	X51 50X	617	8	Ɛ94 0X4	478
9	X81 845	388	9	.831 2Ɛ9 Ɛ25	3X5	9	.847 433 560	241
X	.817 337 011	160	X	766 30X	172	X	892 7X1	006
Ɛ	7Ɛ0 171	474 Ɛ32	Ɛ	.832 012 480	467 Ɛ40	Ɛ	.848 131 7X7	45X 98X
.1510	.818 065 0X3	905	.1550	47X 400	90X	.1590	590 575	753
1	519 9X8	697	1	926 10X	698	1	X2Ɛ 108	518
2	992 483	46X	2	.833 191 7X6	465	2	.849 289 624	2X0
3	.819 246 931	240	3	639 04Ɛ	232	3	727 904	065
4	6ƐX Ɛ71	013	4	XX4 281	466 ƐƐƐ	4	Ɛ85 969	459 X29
5	Ɛ72 Ɛ84	473 9X5	5	.834 34Ɛ 280	989	5	.84X 423 796	7Ɛ1
6	.81X 426 969	776	6	7Ɛ6 049	756	6	881 387	575
7	89X 523	549	7	.835 060 7X3	522	7	.84Ɛ 11X 940	33X
8	.81Ɛ 151 X70	31Ɛ	8	507 105	2XƐ	8	578 07X	101
9	605 18Ɛ	0Ɛ0	9	971 3Ɛ4	079	9	X15 17Ɛ	458 X85
X	X78 27Ɛ	472 X82	X	.836 217 471	465 X44	X	.850 272 044	848
Ɛ	.820 32Ɛ 141	853	Ɛ	681 2Ɛ5	811	Ɛ	70X 890	610
.1520	7X1 994	625	1560	Ɛ26 Ɛ06	59X	.15X0	Ɛ67 2X0	394
1	.821 054 3Ɛ9	3Ɛ6	1	.837 390 4X4	366	1	.851 403 674	156
2	506 7Ɛ3	187	2	835 84X	132	2	85Ɛ 80X	457 Ɛ1Ɛ
3	978 97X	471 Ɛ59	3	.838 09X 980	464 XƐX	3	.852 0Ɛ7 729	8X1
4	.822 22X 917	929	4	543 87X	886	4	553 40X	664
5	6X0 644	6ƐX	5	9X8 544	652	5	9XX X72	427
6	Ɛ52 142	48Ɛ	6	839 250 Ɛ96	41X	6	.853 246 299	1XƐ
7	.823 403 611	260	7	6Ɛ5 3Ɛ4	1X6	7	6X1 488	456 Ɛ70
8	874 871	030	8	Ɛ59 59X	463 Ɛ71	8	Ɛ38 438	934
9	.824 125 8X1	470 X01	9	.83X 401 54Ɛ	938	9	.854 393 170	6Ɛ6
X	596 6X2	791	X	865 287	704	X	829 866	478
Ɛ	X47 273	562	Ɛ	.83Ɛ 108 98Ɛ	48Ɛ	Ɛ	.855 084 122	23Ɛ
.1530	.825 2Ɛ7 815	331	.1570	570 25X	257	.15Ɛ0	51X 361	001
1	767 Ɛ46	102	1	X13 4Ɛ5	021	1	974 362	455 984
2	.826 018 048	46Ɛ X91	2	.840 276 516	462 9X8	2	.856 20X 126	745
3	487 Ɛ19	862	3	719 302	774	3	663 86Ɛ	507
4	937 77Ɛ	631	4	Ɛ7Ɛ X76	539	4	XƐ9 176	289
5	.827 1X7 1Ɛ0	401	5	.841 422 3Ɛ3	305	5	.857 352 443	04Ɛ
6	656 5Ɛ1	190	6	884 6Ɛ8	08Ɛ	6	7X7 492	454 X10
7	Ɛ05 781	46X Ɛ60	7	.842 126 787	461 X56	7	.858 040 2X2	792
8	.828 374 721	92Ɛ	8	588 621	820	8	494 X74	553
9	823 450	6ƐX	9	X2X 241	5X6	9	929 407	315
X	.829 091 Ɛ4X	489	X	.843 28Ɛ 827	370	X	.859 181 720	095
Ɛ	540 417	259	Ɛ	730 Ɛ97	136	Ɛ	615 7Ɛ5	453 X57
						.1600	X69 650	

N	Cosine	d	N	Cosine	d	N	Cosine	d
.0000	1.000 000 000	179	.0040	.ƐƐƐ 998 218	11 368	.0080	.ƐƐƐ 328 943	22 551
1	.ƐƐƐ ƐƐƐ χ43	4Ɛ2	1	986 χ70	6χ1	1	306 3Ɛ2	887
2	ƐƐƐ 551	829	2	975 38Ɛ	χ17	2	2χ3 727	23 001
3	ƐƐχ 924	Ɛ62	3	963 574	12 151	3	280 726	336
4	ƐƐ9 982	1 298	4	951 423	486	4	259 3Ɛ0	66Ɛ
5	ƐƐ8 6χ6	611	5	93χ Ɛ59	800	5	235 941	9χ6
6	ƐƐ7 095	948	6	928 359	Ɛ36	6	211 Ɛ57	24 11χ
7	ƐƐ5 349	2 081	7	915 423	13 26Ɛ	7	1χ9 χ39	454
8	ƐƐ3 288	3Ɛ6	8	902 174	5χ5	8	185 5χ5	78χ
9	ƐƐ0 χ92	731	9	8χχ 78Ɛ	91Ɛ	9	160 χ17	Ɛ03
χ	Ɛχχ 361	χ66	χ	896 χ70	14 054	χ	137 Ɛ14	25 239
Ɛ	Ɛχ7 4Ɛ7	3 1χ0	Ɛ	882 χ18	38χ	Ɛ	112 897	572
.0010	Ɛχ4 317	516	.0050	86χ 64χ	704	.0090	0χ9 325	8χƐ
1	Ɛχ0 χ01	850	1	855 Ɛ46	χ39	1	083 639	26 021
2	Ɛ99 171	Ɛ85	2	841 109	15 173	2	059 618	356
3	Ɛ95 1χ8	4 2ƐƐ	3	827 Ɛ56	4χ9	3	033 282	690
4	Ɛ90 χχ9	634	4	812 669	823	4	008 7Ɛ2	χ06
5	Ɛ88 475	96Ɛ	5	7Ɛ8 χ46	Ɛ58	5	.ƐƐχ Ɛχ1 9χ8	27 13Ɛ
6	Ɛ83 706	5 0χ4	6	7χ2 χχχ	16 291	6	Ɛ76 869	474
7	Ɛ7χ 622	41χ	7	788 819	607	7	Ɛ4Ɛ 3Ɛ5	7χχ
8	Ɛ75 204	754	8	772 212	941	8	Ɛ23 807	Ɛ24
9	Ɛ6Ɛ 670	χ89	9	757 491	17 077	9	χƐ7 8χ3	28 259
χ	Ɛ65 7χ3	6 203	χ	740 416	3Ɛ0	χ	χ8Ɛ 646	592
Ɛ	Ɛ5Ɛ 5χ0	539	Ɛ	725 026	726	Ɛ	χ63 074	907
.0020	Ɛ55 063	872	.0060	709 500	χ5Ɛ	.00χ0	χ36 369	29 042
1	Ɛ4χ 3Ɛ1	Ɛχ9	1	6Ɛ1 661	18 196	1	χ09 327	376
2	Ɛ43 404	7 322	2	695 487	50χ	2	99Ɛ Ɛ71	6Ɛ0
3	Ɛ38 0χ2	657	3	678 Ɛ79	845	3	972 481	χ25
4	Ɛ30 647	992	4	660 334	Ɛ7χ	4	944 658	2χ 15Ɛ
5	Ɛ24 875	8 107	5	643 376	19 2Ɛ3	5	916 4Ɛ9	494
6	Ɛ18 76χ	441	6	626 083	629	6	8χ8 025	80χ
7	Ɛ10 329	776	7	608 656	963	7	879 417	Ɛ43
8	Ɛ03 773	χƐ1	8	5χχ 8Ɛ3	1χ 098	8	84χ 494	2Ɛ 278
9	χƐ6 882	9 226	9	590 817	412	9	81Ɛ 218	5Ɛ2
χ	χχ9 658	560	χ	572 405	748	χ	7χƐ 826	927
Ɛ	χχ0 0Ɛ8	895	Ɛ	553 879	χ81	Ɛ	77Ɛ χƐƐ	30 061
.0030	χ92 423	χ 00Ɛ	.0070	534 9Ɛ8	1Ɛ 1Ɛ7	.00Ɛ0	74Ɛ χ5χ	395
1	χ84 414	345	1	515 801	530	1	71Ɛ 685	710
2	χ76 08Ɛ	67Ɛ	2	4Ɛ6 291	866	2	6χχ Ɛ75	χ44
3	χ67 610	9Ɛ4	3	496 627	Ɛχ0	3	67χ 131	31 17χ
4	χ58 818	Ɛ 12χ	4	476 647	20 315	4	648 Ɛ73	4Ɛ3
5	χ49 6χχ	464	5	456 332	64χ	5	617 680	829
6	χ3χ 246	799	6	435 8χ4	984	6	5χ5 χ53	Ɛ62
7	χ2χ 669	Ɛ14	7	414 Ɛ20	21 0Ɛχ	7	573 χƐ1	32 297
8	χ1χ 755	10 248	8	3Ɛ3 χ22	433	8	541 816	610
9	χ0χ 509	583	9	392 5χƐ	769	9	50Ɛ 206	946
χ	9Ɛ9 Ɛ46	8Ɛ8	χ	370 χ42	χχ3	χ	498 480	33 07Ɛ
Ɛ	9χ9 24χ	11 032	Ɛ	34χ Ɛ5Ɛ	22 218	Ɛ	465 401	3Ɛ5

N	Cosine	d
.0100	.ƐƐX 432 008	33 729
1	3ƐX 49Ɛ	X63
2	386 638	34 199
3	352 45Ɛ	511
4	319 Ɛ4X	847
5	2X5 303	Ɛ80
6	270 343	35 2Ɛ5
7	237 04X	62Ɛ
8	201 61Ɛ	964
9	187 877	36 099
X	151 79X	412
Ɛ	117 388	747
.0110	0X0 841	X81
1	065 980	37 1Ɛ6
2	02X 786	52Ɛ
3	.ƐƐ9 ƐƐ3 257	864
4	Ɛ77 5Ɛ3	Ɛ9X
5	Ɛ3Ɛ 615	38 312
6	Ɛ03 303	648
7	X86 877	981
8	X49 XƐ6	39 0Ɛ6
9	X10 X00	430
X	993 590	764
Ɛ	955 X28	X9X
.0120	917 Ɛ4X	3X 212
1	899 938	548
2	85Ɛ 3Ɛ0	881
3	820 72Ɛ	ƐƐ6
4	7X1 735	3Ɛ 32Ɛ
5	762 406	664
6	722 962	99X
7	6X2 Ɛ84	40 112
8	662 X72	447
9	622 627	781
X	5X1 X66	XƐ5
Ɛ	560 Ɛ71	41 22Ɛ
.0130	51Ɛ 942	564
1	49X 39X	898
2	458 702	42 012
3	416 6Ɛ0	347
4	394 365	67Ɛ
5	351 8X6	9Ɛ5
6	30X XƐ1	43 12X
7	287 983	462
8	244 521	798
9	200 945	Ɛ11
X	178 X34	44 245
Ɛ	134 7XƐ	57Ɛ

N	Cosine	d
.0140	.ƐƐ9 0Ɛ0 230	44 8Ɛ3
1	067 539	45 029
2	022 510	361
3	.ƐƐ8 Ɛ99 16Ɛ	696
4	Ɛ53 695	X0Ɛ
5	Ɛ09 886	46 144
6	X83 742	479
7	X39 285	7Ɛ2
8	9Ɛ2 693	Ɛ26
9	967 769	47 260
X	920 509	594
Ɛ	894 Ɛ35	90X
.0150	849 227	48 042
1	801 1X5	377
2	774 X2X	6XƐ
3	728 33Ɛ	X25
4	69Ɛ 516	49 159
5	652 379	492
6	604 XX7	807
7	577 2X0	Ɛ40
8	529 360	4X 274
9	49Ɛ 0X8	5X9
X	450 6ƐƐ	922
Ɛ	401 999	4Ɛ 057
.0160	372 942	38Ɛ
1	323 573	704
2	293 X6Ɛ	X39
3	244 032	50 172
4	1Ɛ3 X80	4X6
5	163 596	81Ɛ
6	112 977	Ɛ53
7	081 X24	51 288
8	030 758	601
9	.ƐƐ7 Ɛ9Ɛ 157	936
X	Ɛ49 421	52 06X
Ɛ	XƐ7 373	3X3
.0170	X64 Ɛ90	717
1	X12 475	X50
2	97Ɛ 625	53 184
3	928 461	4ƐX
4	894 Ɛ63	831
5	841 332	Ɛ67
6	7X9 387	54 29X
7	755 0X9	614
8	700 695	948
9	667 949	55 080
X	612 889	3Ɛ5
Ɛ	579 494	729

N	Cosine	d
.0180	.ƐƐ7 523 967	55 X62
1	489 Ɛ05	56 197
2	433 92X	50X
3	399 420	844
4	342 798	Ɛ77
5	2X7 821	57 2Ɛ1
6	250 530	624
7	1Ɛ4 Ɛ08	959
8	159 16Ɛ	58 092
9	101 099	406
X	064 893	73X
Ɛ	008 155	X72
.0190	.ƐƐ6 Ɛ6Ɛ 2X3	59 1X7
1	Ɛ12 0Ɛ8	520
2	X74 798	853
3	X16 Ɛ45	Ɛ88
4	978 Ɛ79	5X 300
5	91X 879	635
6	880 244	969
7	821 497	5Ɛ 0X1
8	782 3Ɛ6	415
9	722 ƐX1	74X
X	683 453	X82
Ɛ	623 591	60 1Ɛ6
.01X0	583 397	52Ɛ
1	522 X68	862
2	482 206	Ɛ97
3	421 22Ɛ	61 30Ɛ
4	37Ɛ Ɛ20	643
5	31X 499	977
6	278 722	62 0Ɛ0
7	216 632	424
8	174 20X	757
9	111 673	X90
X	06X 7X3	63 204
Ɛ	007 59Ɛ	538
.01Ɛ0	.ƐƐ5 Ɛ64 063	871
1	Ɛ00 3Ɛ2	ƐX4
2	X58 40X	64 318
3	9Ɛ4 0Ɛ2	651
4	94Ɛ 661	984
5	8X6 899	65 0Ɛ9
6	841 7X0	430
7	798 370	764
8	732 808	X99
9	688 92Ɛ	66 210
X	622 71Ɛ	545
Ɛ	578 196	878

N	Cosine	d	N	Cosine	d	N	Cosine	d
.0200	.ƐƐ5 511 51X	66 ƐƐ0	.0240	.ƐƐ3 075 9X7	78 116	.0280	.ƐƐ0 395 X17	89 211
1	466 52X	67 324	1	.ƐƐ2 ƐƐ9 891	449	1	308 806	545
2	3ƐƐ 206	659	2	Ɛ41 444	781	2	23Ɛ 281	876
3	353 769	990	3	X84 883	XƐ3	3	171 607	ƐX9
4	2X7 999	68 104	4	X07 990	79 227	4	0X3 61X	8X 320
5	23Ɛ 895	437	5	94X 765	55X	5	015 2ƐX	652
6	193 45X	770	6	891 207	891	6	.ƐXƐ Ɛ46 868	985
7	126 8XX	XX3	7	813 536	7X 004	7	X77 XX3	8Ɛ 026
8	079 X07	69 218	8	755 532	338	8	9X8 9X9	42X
9	010 7XƐ	54Ɛ	9	697 1Ɛ6	66Ɛ	9	919 57Ɛ	75Ɛ
X	.ƐƐ4 Ɛ63 260	883	X	618 747	9X2	X	849 X20	X92
Ɛ	XƐ5 599	ƐƐ7	Ɛ	559 965	7Ɛ 114	Ɛ	779 Ɛ4X	90 205
.0210	X47 5X2	6X 32X	.0250	49X 851	449	.0290	6X9 945	537
1	999 274	662	1	41Ɛ 404	77Ɛ	1	619 40X	869
2	92X 812	997	2	35Ɛ 845	XƐ2	2	548 761	Ɛ9Ɛ
3	87Ɛ X37	6Ɛ 109	3	29Ɛ 953	80 225	3	477 782	91 312
4	810 92X	442	4	21Ɛ 72X	559	4	3X6 470	644
5	761 4X8	775	5	15Ɛ 191	88Ɛ	5	314 X28	976
6	6Ɛ1 933	XX9	6	09X 502	81 002	6	243 072	92 0X8
7	641 X46	70 221	7	019 500	336	7	170 Ɛ86	41Ɛ
8	591 825	554	8	.ƐƐ1 Ɛ58 186	668	8	09X 767	751
9	521 291	888	9	X96 71X	9X0	9	008 016	X83
X	470 605	71 000	X	X14 93X	82 112	X	.ƐXX Ɛ35 153	93 1Ɛ5
Ɛ	3ƐƐ 605	333	Ɛ	952 828	445	Ɛ	X61 Ɛ5X	527
.0220	34X 292	667	.0260	890 3X3	778	.02X0	98X 633	859
1	298 827	99Ɛ	1	809 827	XƐ0	1	8Ɛ6 996	Ɛ90
2	226 X48	72 112	2	746 937	83 222	2	822 X06	94 302
3	174 936	445	3	683 715	554	3	74X 704	633
4	102 4Ɛ1	77X	4	600 181	888	4	676 091	966
5	04Ɛ 933	XƐ1	5	538 4Ɛ5	ƐƐƐ	5	5X1 327	95 098
6	.ƐƐ3 Ɛ98 X42	73 224	6	474 4Ɛ6	84 331	6	508 24Ɛ	40X
7	Ɛ25 81X	558	7	3Ɛ0 185	664	7	432 X41	73Ɛ
8	X72 282	88Ɛ	8	327 721	997	8	359 302	X72
9	9ƐX 5Ɛ3	74 003	9	262 946	85 10X	9	283 450	96 1X4
X	946 5Ɛ0	337	X	199 838	441	X	1X9 268	516
Ɛ	892 275	66X	Ɛ	114 3Ɛ7	773	Ɛ	112 952	847
.0230	819 807	9X1	.0270	04X 844	XX6	.02Ɛ0	038 107	Ɛ7X
1	764 X26	75 115	1	.ƐƐ0 Ɛ84 95X	86 219	1	.ƐX9 Ɛ61 149	97 2XƐ
2	6XƐ 911	448	2	XƐX 741	550	2	X85 X5X	621
3	636 485	780	3	X34 1Ɛ1	882	3	9XX 439	953
4	580 905	XƐ3	4	969 52Ɛ	ƐƐ5	4	912 6X6	98 085
5	506 X12	76 226	5	8X2 536	87 327	5	836 621	3Ɛ7
6	450 7X8	55X	6	817 20Ɛ	65X	6	75X 226	729
7	396 24X	891	7	74Ɛ 771	991	7	681 6Ɛ9	X5X
8	31Ɛ 579	77 005	8	683 9X0	88 103	8	5X4 85Ɛ	99 190
9	264 574	338	9	5Ɛ7 899	436	9	507 68Ɛ	502
X	1X9 238	66Ɛ	X	52Ɛ 463	769	X	42X 189	834
Ɛ	131 789	9X2	Ɛ	462 8Ɛ6	X9Ɛ	Ɛ	350 555	Ɛ65

N	Cosine	d	N	Cosine	d	N	Cosine	d
.0300	.ƐX9 272 5Ɛ0	9X 297	.0340	.ƐX5 908 X9X	XƐ 325	.0380	.ƐX1 Ɛ22 405	100 334
1	194 315	609	1	819 775	656	1	X22 091	663
2	0Ɛ5 908	93X	2	72X 11Ɛ	986	2	921 62X	992
3	016 Ɛ8X	9Ɛ 070	3	63X 355	Ɛ0 0Ɛ8	3	820 858	101 103
4	.ƐX8 Ɛ37 Ɛ1X	3X2	4	54X 259	428	4	71Ɛ 755	432
5	X58 738	713	5	459 X31	758	5	61X 323	761
6	979 025	X45	6	369 295	X89	6	518 782	X91
7	899 1X0	X0 176	7	278 408	Ɛ1 1ƐX	7	416 8Ɛ1	102 201
8	7Ɛ9 026	4X8	8	187 20X	52Ɛ	8	314 6Ɛ0	530
9	718 73X	819	9	095 89Ɛ	85X	9	212 180	85Ɛ
X	637 Ɛ21	Ɛ4Ɛ	X	.ƐX4 ƐX4 041	Ɛ90	X	10Ɛ 521	Ɛ8Ɛ
Ɛ	556 Ɛ92	X1 280	Ɛ	XƐ2 071	Ɛ2 300	Ɛ	008 552	103 2ƐƐ
.0310	475 912	5Ɛ2	.0350	9ƐƐ 971	630	.0390	.ƐX0 Ɛ05 253	62X
1	394 320	923	1	909 341	961	1	X01 825	959
2	2Ɛ2 5Ɛ9	X2 055	2	816 5X0	Ɛ3 091	2	8Ɛ9 X88	104 088
3	210 564	386	3	723 50Ɛ	402	3	7Ɛ5 X00	3Ɛ8
4	12X 19X	6Ɛ7	4	630 109	732	4	6Ɛ1 604	728
5	047 6X3	X29	5	538 597	X63	5	5X8 X98	X56
6	.ƐX7 Ɛ64 876	X3 15X	6	444 734	Ɛ4 193	6	4X4 042	105 186
7	X81 718	490	7	350 561	503	7	39X X78	4Ɛ5
8	99X 248	801	8	258 05X	833	8	295 583	825
9	8Ɛ6 647	Ɛ32	9	163 427	Ɛ64	9	18Ɛ 95X	Ɛ53
X	812 715	X4 263	X	06X 483	Ɛ5 294	X	085 X07	106 283
Ɛ	72X 472	595	Ɛ	.ƐX3 Ɛ75 1XƐ	605	Ɛ	.Ɛ9Ɛ Ɛ7Ɛ 744	5Ɛ2
.0320	645 X99	905	.0360	X7Ɛ 7X6	934	.03X0	X75 152	921
1	561 194	X5 037	1	985 X72	Ɛ6 065	1	96X 431	107 050
2	478 159	368	2	88Ɛ X09	395	2	863 3X1	37Ɛ
3	392 9Ɛ1	69X	3	795 634	705	3	758 022	6XX
4	2X9 313	X0X	4	69X Ɛ2Ɛ	X35	4	650 534	X19
5	203 505	X6 140	5	5X4 0Ɛ6	Ɛ7 166	5	544 717	108 149
6	119 385	471	6	4X8 Ɛ50	495	6	438 58X	477
7	032 Ɛ14	7X1	7	3Ɛ1 677	806	7	330 113	7X6
8	.ƐX6 Ɛ48 333	Ɛ13	8	2Ɛ5 X71	Ɛ35	8	223 529	Ɛ15
9	X61 420	X7 244	9	1Ɛ9 Ɛ38	Ɛ8 266	9	116 614	109 244
X	976 198	575	X	101 892	596	X	009 390	573
Ɛ	88X 823	8X6	Ɛ	005 2Ɛ8	905	Ɛ	.Ɛ9X XƐƐ X19	8X2
.0330	7X2 Ɛ39	X8 017	.0370	.ƐX2 Ɛ08 5Ɛ3	Ɛ9 036	.03Ɛ0	9Ɛ2 137	10X 011
1	6Ɛ6 Ɛ22	348	1	X0Ɛ 579	365	1	8X4 126	33Ɛ
2	60X 796	679	2	912 214	696	2	795 9X7	66Ɛ
3	522 119	9XX	3	814 73X	X05	3	687 338	999
4	435 32Ɛ	X9 11X	4	716 935	ƐX 135	4	578 55Ɛ	10Ɛ 107
5	348 211	450	5	618 800	465	5	469 454	437
6	25X 981	780	6	51X 357	795	6	35X 019	765
7	171 201	XƐ2	7	41Ɛ 782	Ɛ05	7	24X 474	X94
8	083 30Ɛ	XX 222	8	320 879	ƐƐ 234	8	13X 5X0	110 202
9	.ƐX5 Ɛ95 0X9	553	9	221 645	565	9	02X 39X	532
X	XX6 756	883	X	122 0X0	894	X	.Ɛ99 Ɛ19 X68	85Ɛ
Ɛ	9Ɛ7 X93	ƐƐ5	Ɛ	022 408	100 003	Ɛ	X09 209	Ɛ8Ɛ

N	Cosine	d	N	Cosine	d	N	Cosine	d
.0400	.£99 8£8 23X	111 2£8	.0440	.£95 254 006	122 235	.0480	.£90 373 516	133 11X
1	7X6 £42	628	1	131 991	562	1	240 3£8	447
2	695 516	956	2	00£ 42£	88£	2	108 £71	772
3	583 780	112 084	3	.£94 XX8 760	££9	3	.£8£ £95 3££	X9£
4	471 6£8	3£3	4	985 763	123 325	4	X61 520	134 206
5	35£ 305	721	5	862 43X	653	5	929 316	532
6	248 7X4	X4£	6	73X 9X7	980	6	7£4 9X4	859
7	135 955	113 17X	7	617 027	124 0X9	7	680 147	£86
8	022 797	4X9	8	4£2 £3X	417	8	547 181	135 2£1
9	.£98 £0£ 2XX	816	9	38X 723	743	9	411 X90	619
X	9£7 694	£45	X	265 £X0	X70	X	298 473	944
£	8X3 74£	114 273	£	141 130	125 199	£	162 72£	136 070
.0410	78£ 498	5X2	.0450	017 £53	507	.0490	028 67£	398
1	676 X£6	90£	1	.£93 X£2 648	833	1	.£8X X£2 2X3	703
2	562 1X7	115 03X	2	988 X15	£60	2	977 7X0	X2£
3	449 169	368	3	862 X75	126 289	3	840 971	137 157
4	333 X01	696	4	738 7X8	5£6	4	705 816	481
5	21X 327	X04	5	612 1£2	922	5	58X 355	7XX
6	104 523	116 133	6	4X7 490	127 050	6	452 767	£14
7	.£97 £XX 3£0	460	7	380 440	378	7	316 853	138 241
8	X93 £50	78X	8	255 084	6X5	8	19X 612	567
9	979 382	X£9	9	129 59£	X12	9	062 067	893
X	862 485	117 226	X	001 789	128 13£	X	.£89 £25 394	£2X
£	747 25£	554	£	.£92 X95 64X	467	£	9X8 396	139 325
.0420	62£ 907	883	.0460	969 1X3	793	.04X0	86£ 071	651
1	514 044	£20	1	840 610	£01	1	731 620	978
2	3£8 054	118 31X	2	713 70£	129 229	2	5£3 864	13X 0X3
3	29£ 936	648	3	5X6 4X2	555	3	475 781	40X
4	183 2XX	976	4	478 £49	882	4	337 373	735
5	066 534	119 0X3	5	34£ 287	£X£	5	1£8 83X	X61
6	.£96 £49 451	412	6	221 298	12X 317	6	079 999	13£ 187
7	X30 03£	73£	7	0£2 £81	643	7	.£88 £3X 812	4£3
8	912 500	X69	8	.£91 £84 53X	970	8	9££ 31£	819
9	7£4 653	11X 196	9	X55 78X	12£ 098	9	87£ 702	£45
X	696 479	504	X	926 6£2	405	X	73£ 779	140 26£
£	577 £75	832	£	7£7 2X9	731	£	5££ 50X	597
.0430	459 343	£60	.0470	687 778	X59	.04£0	47X £33	901
1	33X 3X3	11£ 289	1	557 91£	130 185	1	33X 232	141 028
2	21£ 116	5£6	2	427 756	4£2	2	1£9 206	353
3	0££ 720	924	3	2£7 264	81X	3	077 X73	67X
4	.£95 £9£ 9£8	120 052	4	186 646	£46	4	.£87 £36 3£5	9X4
5	X7£ 966	37£	5	055 700	131 273	5	9£4 611	142 10£
6	95£ 5X7	6X9	6	.£90 £24 449	59X	6	872 502	436
7	83X X£X	X16	7	9£2 X6£	906	7	730 088	761
8	71X 0X4	121 143	8	881 165	132 033	8	5X9 527	X87
9	5£8 £61	471	9	74£ 132	35£	9	466 660	143 1£1
X	497 6£0	79X	X	618 993	686	X	323 46£	519
£	375 £12	£08	£	4X6 309	9£3	£	19£ £52	843

N	Cosine	d	N	Cosine	d	N	Cosine	d
.0500	.Ɛ87 058 30Ɛ	143 Ɛ69	.0540	.Ɛ81 508 4Ɛ9	154 959	.0580	.Ɛ77 545 Ɛ57	165 6X3
1	.Ɛ86 Ɛ14 362	144 294	1	373 760	155 081	1	3X0 474	X07
2	990 08X	5ƐX	2	21X 69Ɛ	3X7	2	236 669	166 12X
3	847 690	925	3	085 2Ɛ4	70Ɛ	3	090 53Ɛ	451
4	702 967	145 04Ɛ	4	.Ɛ80 Ɛ2Ɛ 7X5	X34	4	.Ɛ76 Ɛ26 0XX	775
5	579 918	376	5	995 971	156 159	5	97Ɛ 535	X97
6	434 562	6X0	6	83Ɛ 814	482	6	814 65X	167 1ƐƐ
7	2XX X82	X06	7	6X5 352	7X6	7	669 45Ɛ	522
8	165 078	146 130	8	54X 768	Ɛ10	8	501 Ɛ39	845
9	01X Ɛ48	457	9	3Ɛ3 858	157 233	9	356 2Ɛ4	Ɛ68
X	.Ɛ85 X94 6Ɛ1	780	X	258 625	559	X	1XX 348	168 28Ɛ
Ɛ	949 Ɛ31	XX7	Ɛ	101 088	881	Ɛ	042 079	5Ɛ2
.0510	803 046	147 211	.0550	.Ɛ7Ɛ Ɛ65 407	ƐX6	.0590	.Ɛ75 X95 687	914
1	677 X35	538	1	X09 421	158 30X	1	928 973	169 038
2	530 4Ɛ9	861	2	871 113	633	2	77Ɛ 937	35X
3	3X4 858	Ɛ87	3	714 6X0	957	3	612 599	682
4	258 891	148 2Ɛ2	4	577 945	159 07Ɛ	4	464 Ɛ17	9X4
5	110 59Ɛ	617	5	41X 886	3X4	5	2Ɛ7 133	16X 106
6	.Ɛ84 Ɛ83 Ɛ84	941	6	281 4X2	709	6	149 029	42X
7	X37 243	149 067	7	123 995	X31	7	.Ɛ74 Ɛ9X 7ƐƐ	750
8	8XX 198	391	8	.Ɛ7X Ɛ85 Ɛ64	15X 155	8	X30 06Ɛ	X73
9	760 X07	6Ɛ7	9	X27 X0Ɛ	479	9	881 1Ɛ8	16Ɛ 195
X	613 310	X21	X	889 552	7X1	X	712 023	4Ɛ8
Ɛ	485 4XƐ	14X 147	Ɛ	72X 971	Ɛ06	Ɛ	562 727	81X
.0520	337 364	470	.0560	58Ɛ X67	15Ɛ 22X	.05X0	3Ɛ2 Ɛ09	Ɛ41
1	1X8 XƐ4	796	1	430 839	552	1	242 Ɛ88	170 263
2	05X 31X	XƐƐ	2	291 2X7	876	2	092 925	586
3	.Ɛ83 Ɛ0Ɛ 41Ɛ	14Ɛ 226	3	131 631	Ɛ9X	3	.Ɛ73 Ɛ22 35Ɛ	8X8
4	980 1Ɛ5	54Ɛ	4	.Ɛ79 Ɛ91 653	160 302	4	971 673	171 00Ɛ
5	830 866	874	5	X31 351	627	5	800 664	330
6	6X0 ƐƐ2	Ɛ9X	6	890 926	94X	6	64Ɛ 334	653
7	551 014	150 304	7	72Ɛ Ɛ98	161 072	7	499 8X1	975
8	400 910	629	8	58X Ɛ26	396	8	327 Ɛ28	172 098
9	270 2X3	953	9	429 750	6ƐX	9	175 X50	3Ɛ9
X	11Ɛ 550	151 078	X	288 052	X21	X	003 653	720
Ɛ	.Ɛ82 Ɛ8X 494	3X1	Ɛ	126 231	162 146	Ɛ	.Ɛ72 X50 Ɛ33	X42
.0530	X39 0Ɛ3	707	.0570	.Ɛ78 Ɛ84 0X7	469	.05Ɛ0	89X 0Ɛ1	173 163
1	8X7 5X8	X30	1	X21 83X	791	1	726 Ɛ4X	486
2	755 778	152 155	2	87Ɛ 069	XƐ4	2	573 684	7X8
3	603 623	47Ɛ	3	718 175	163 219	3	3ƐƐ X98	Ɛ0X
4	471 164	7X4	4	574 Ɛ58	540	4	247 Ɛ8X	174 22Ɛ
5	31X 580	Ɛ09	5	411 618	863	5	093 95Ɛ	552
6	187 673	153 232	6	269 975	Ɛ87	6	.Ɛ71 Ɛ1Ɛ 409	873
7	034 441	558	7	105 9XX	164 2XX	7	966 756	Ɛ95
8	.Ɛ81 XX0 XX5	880	8	.Ɛ77 Ɛ61 700	612	8	7Ɛ1 781	175 2Ɛ7
9	949 225	ƐX6	9	9Ɛ9 0XX	936	9	638 486	618
X	7Ɛ5 23Ɛ	154 30Ɛ	X	854 374	165 059	X	482 X6X	93X
Ɛ	660 Ɛ30	633	Ɛ	6XƐ 317	380	Ɛ	309 130	176 060

N	Cosine	d	N	Cosine	d	N	Cosine	d
.0600	.Ɛ71 153 090	176 381	.0640	.Ɛ66 532 070	186 ƐXX	.0680	.Ɛ5Ɛ 4X5 433	197 760
1	.Ɛ70 Ɛ98 90Ɛ	6X3	1	367 082	187 309	1	309 893	X79
2	X22 228	X05	2	19Ɛ 975	629	2	131 X16	198 197
3	867 423	177 126	3	014 348	949	3	.Ɛ5X Ɛ55 83Ɛ	4Ɛ5
4	6Ɛ0 2Ɛ9	447	4	.Ɛ65 X48 5ƐƐ	188 068	4	979 346	812
5	534 X72	769	5	880 553	388	5	7X0 734	Ɛ31
6	379 305	X8X	6	6Ɛ4 187	6X7	6	603 803	199 249
7	201 437	178 1Ɛ0	7	527 6X0	X07	7	426 576	568
8	045 247	511	8	35X 895	189 127	8	249 00X	885
9	.Ɛ6Ɛ X88 936	832	9	191 76X	446	9	06Ɛ 345	ƐX2
X	910 104	Ɛ53	X	004 324	765	X	.Ɛ59 X91 363	19X 300
Ɛ	753 171	179 275	Ɛ	.Ɛ64 X36 77Ɛ	X84	Ɛ	8Ɛ3 063	619
.0610	595 XƐ8	595	.0650	868 8Ɛ7	18X 1X4	.0690	714 646	936
1	418 523	8Ɛ7	1	69X 713	503	1	535 910	19Ɛ 054
2	25X 828	17X 018	2	510 210	822	2	356 878	371
3	0X0 810	339	3	341 5XX	Ɛ42	3	177 507	68X
4	.Ɛ6X Ɛ22 493	65X	4	172 668	18Ɛ 260	4	.Ɛ58 Ɛ97 X39	9X7
5	963 X35	97X	5	.Ɛ63 ƐX3 408	580	5	9Ɛ8 052	1X0 105
6	7X5 077	17Ɛ 0X0	6	X13 X48	89X	6	817 Ɛ49	422
7	625 Ɛ97	401	7	844 16X	ƐƐX	7	637 727	73X
8	466 796	721	8	674 170	190 319	8	456 ƐX9	X58
9	2X7 075	X43	9	4X3 X53	638	9	276 151	1X1 175
X	127 232	180 163	X	313 417	956	X	094 Ɛ98	491
Ɛ	.Ɛ69 Ɛ67 08Ɛ	484	Ɛ	142 681	191 075	Ɛ	.Ɛ57 XƐ3 707	7XƐ
.0620	9X6 807	7X4	.0660	.Ɛ62 Ɛ71 608	395	.06X0	911 Ɛ18	Ɛ07
1	826 023	Ɛ05	1	9X0 233	6Ɛ3	1	730 011	1X2 224
2	665 11X	181 226	2	80X 740	X11	2	549 9X9	541
3	4X3 XƐ4	546	3	638 92Ɛ	192 131	3	367 468	859
4	322 56X	867	4	466 7ƐX	44Ɛ	4	184 80Ɛ	Ɛ76
5	160 903	Ɛ88	5	294 36Ɛ	769	5	.Ɛ56 ƐX1 855	1X3 293
6	.Ɛ68 Ɛ9X 937	182 2X8	6	101 802	X89	6	9ƐX 582	5Ɛ0
7	X18 64Ɛ	608	7	.Ɛ61 Ɛ2X 935	193 1X6	7	816 Ɛ92	908
8	856 043	929	8	957 74Ɛ	506	8	633 286	1X4 024
9	693 316	183 049	9	784 245	823	9	44Ɛ 262	341
X	510 289	369	X	5Ɛ0 622	Ɛ42	X	266 Ɛ21	659
Ɛ	348 Ɛ20	68X	Ɛ	418 6X0	194 261	Ɛ	082 484	976
.0630	185 452	9X9	.0670	244 43Ɛ	57Ɛ	.06Ɛ0	.Ɛ55 X99 70X	1X5 092
1	001 665	184 10X	1	06Ɛ X80	899	1	8Ɛ4 638	3XƐ
2	.Ɛ67 X39 557	42Ɛ	2	.Ɛ60 X97 1X3	ƐƐ7	2	70Ɛ 249	706
3	875 128	74X	3	902 1X8	195 316	3	525 743	X23
4	6Ɛ0 59X	X6X	4	728 X92	634	4	33Ɛ 920	1X6 13Ɛ
5	527 730	185 18Ɛ	5	553 45X	951	5	155 7X1	457
6	362 561	4XX	6	379 709	196 070	6	.Ɛ54 Ɛ6Ɛ 346	773
7	199 073	80Ɛ	7	1X3 659	38X	7	984 793	X8Ɛ
8	013 464	Ɛ2X	8	009 28Ɛ	6X8	8	799 904	1X7 1X7
9	.Ɛ66 X49 536	186 24X	9	.Ɛ5Ɛ X32 7X3	X06	9	5Ɛ2 719	503
X	883 2X8	56X	X	857 999	197 124	X	407 216	81Ɛ
Ɛ	6Ɛ8 93X	88X	Ɛ	680 875	442	Ɛ	21Ɛ 5Ɛ7	Ɛ37

N	Cosine	d	N	Cosine	d	N	Cosine	d
.0700	.Ɛ54 033 680	1X8 253	.0740	.Ɛ48 35Ɛ 41X	1Ɛ8 883	.0780	.Ɛ40 267 678	209 226
1	.Ɛ53 X47 429	56X	1	162 757	Ɛ97	1	05X 452	539
2	85X X7Ɛ	886	2	.Ɛ47 Ɛ65 780	1Ɛ9 2Ɛ2	2	.Ɛ3Ɛ X50 Ɛ15	850
3	672 1Ɛ5	ƐX2	3	968 48X	607	3	843 285	Ɛ64
4	485 213	1X9 2ƐX	4	76X X83	921	4	635 321	20X 277
5	297 Ɛ15	615	5	571 162	1ƐX 036	5	427 066	58Ɛ
6	0XX 500	930	6	373 128	34Ɛ	6	218 697	8X1
7	.Ɛ52 Ɛ00 790	1XX 049	7	174 999	665	7	009 9Ɛ6	ƐƐ5
8	912 743	363	8	.Ɛ46 Ɛ76 334	97X	8	.Ɛ3X 9ƐX X01	20Ɛ 308
9	724 3X0	67Ɛ	9	977 576	1ƐƐ 093	9	7XƐ 6Ɛ5	61Ɛ
X	535 921	997	X	778 4X3	3X9	X	5X0 096	932
Ɛ	346 Ɛ46	1XƐ 0Ɛ1	Ɛ	579 0Ɛ6	702	Ɛ	390 364	210 045
.0710	157 X55	40X	.0750	379 5Ɛ4	X17	.0790	180 31Ɛ	357
1	.Ɛ51 Ɛ68 647	724	1	179 799	200 130	1	.Ɛ39 Ɛ6Ɛ Ɛ84	66Ɛ
2	978 Ɛ23	X3Ɛ	2	.Ɛ45 Ɛ79 669	445	2	95Ɛ 515	982
3	789 0X4	1Ɛ0 157	3	979 224	75Ɛ	3	74X 753	211 094
4	598 Ɛ49	472	4	778 685	X73	4	539 67Ɛ	3X7
5	3X8 697	789	5	577 812	201 188	5	328 294	6Ɛ9
6	1Ɛ7 Ɛ0X	XX4	6	376 646	4X1	6	116 797	X11
7	007 026	1Ɛ1 1ƐX	7	175 165	7Ɛ6	7	.Ɛ38 Ɛ04 986	212 122
8	.Ɛ50 X15 X28	516	8	.Ɛ44 Ɛ73 56Ɛ	Ɛ0X	8	8Ɛ2 864	436
9	824 512	831	9	971 661	202 223	9	6X0 42X	748
X	632 8X1	Ɛ48	X	76Ɛ 43X	538	X	489 8X2	X5X
Ɛ	440 955	1Ɛ2 262	Ɛ	568 Ɛ02	851	Ɛ	276 X44	213 171
.0720	24X 6Ɛ3	579	.0760	366 271	Ɛ65	.07X0	063 893	483
1	058 136	894	1	163 308	203 27X	1	.Ɛ37 X50 410	795
2	.Ɛ4Ɛ X65 462	ƐXƐ	2	.Ɛ43 Ɛ60 04X	592	2	838 837	XX7
3	872 473	1Ɛ3 305	3	958 678	8X7	3	624 950	214 1ƐX
4	67Ɛ 16X	620	4	754 991	ƐƐƐ	4	410 752	510
5	487 74X	936	5	550 992	204 314	5	1Ɛ8 242	822
6	293 X14	1Ɛ4 051	6	348 67X	628	6	.Ɛ36 ƐX3 620	Ɛ34
7	09Ɛ 983	367	7	144 052	940	7	98X 6X8	215 246
8	.Ɛ4X XX7 618	682	8	.Ɛ42 Ɛ3Ɛ 312	205 054	8	775 462	558
9	8Ɛ2 Ɛ56	998	9	936 27X	369	9	55Ɛ Ɛ06	86X
X	6ƐX 17X	1Ɛ5 0Ɛ2	X	730 Ɛ11	681	X	346 258	Ɛ7Ɛ
Ɛ	505 088	409	Ɛ	527 450	995	Ɛ	130 299	216 292
.0730	30Ɛ 87Ɛ	723	.0770	321 677	206 0X8	.07Ɛ0	.Ɛ35 Ɛ16 007	5X3
1	116 158	X39	1	117 58Ɛ	401	1	8ƐƐ 624	8Ɛ5
2	.Ɛ49 Ɛ20 31Ɛ	1Ɛ6 153	2	.Ɛ41 Ɛ11 18X	715	2	6X4 92Ɛ	217 007
3	926 188	469	3	906 675	X29	3	489 924	318
4	72Ɛ 91Ɛ	784	4	6ƐƐ 848	207 140	4	272 608	62X
5	535 157	X99	5	4Ɛ4 708	455	5	056 Ɛ9X	93Ɛ
6	33X 27X	1Ɛ7 1Ɛ4	6	2X9 273	768	6	.Ɛ34 X3Ɛ 25Ɛ	218 051
7	143 086	509	7	0X1 707	X80	7	823 20X	362
8	.Ɛ48 Ɛ47 779	823	8	.Ɛ40 X95 847	208 193	8	606 X68	674
9	94Ɛ Ɛ56	Ɛ39	9	889 674	4X7	9	3XX 3Ɛ4	985
X	754 019	1Ɛ8 253	X	681 189	7ƐƐ	X	191 62Ɛ	219 096
Ɛ	557 986	568	Ɛ	474 58X	Ɛ12	Ɛ	.Ɛ33 Ɛ74 555	3X7

N	Cosine	d	N	Cosine	d	N	Cosine	d
.0800	.Ɛ33 957 16X	219 6Ɛ9	.0840	.Ɛ27 031 1X8	229 XƐ7	.0880	.Ɛ19 XƐ4 X08	23X 217
1	739 671	X0X	1	.Ɛ26 X03 2Ɛ1	22X 205	1	876 7Ɛ1	522
2	51Ɛ 863	21X 11X	2	795 0X8	513	2	638 28Ɛ	82Ɛ
3	301 745	430	3	566 795	822	3	3Ɛ9 660	Ɛ36
4	0X3 315	741	4	337 Ɛ73	Ɛ31	4	17X 726	23Ɛ 243
5	.Ɛ32 X84 794	X52	5	109 042	22Ɛ 240	5	.Ɛ18 Ɛ3Ɛ 4X3	54Ɛ
6	865 942	21Ɛ 162	6	.Ɛ25 X99 X02	549	6	8ƐƐ Ɛ54	857
7	646 7X0	473	7	86X 475	859	7	680 2Ɛ9	Ɛ63
8	427 329	785	8	63X 818	Ɛ66	8	440 356	240 26X
9	207 764	X95	9	40X 872	230 275	9	200 0X8	576
X	.Ɛ31 ƐX7 88Ɛ	220 1X5	X	19X 5Ɛ9	583	X	.Ɛ17 Ɛ7Ɛ 732	882
Ɛ	987 6X6	4Ɛ6	Ɛ	.Ɛ24 Ɛ6X 036	891	Ɛ	93X X70	Ɛ8X
.0810	767 1Ɛ0	807	.0850	939 365	ƐX0	.0890	6Ɛ9 XX2	241 296
1	546 5X5	Ɛ17	1	708 385	231 2X9	1	478 808	5X0
2	325 68X	221 228	2	497 098	5Ɛ8	2	237 228	8X9
3	104 462	538	3	265 6X0	906	3	.Ɛ16 ƐƐ5 53Ɛ	ƐƐ4
4	.Ɛ30 XX2 Ɛ26	849	4	033 996	232 013	4	973 547	242 2ƐƐ
5	881 299	Ɛ59	5	.Ɛ23 X01 983	322	5	731 248	607
6	65Ɛ 340	222 269	6	78Ɛ 661	62Ɛ	6	4XX 841	912
7	439 093	579	7	559 032	939	7	267 Ɛ2Ɛ	243 019
8	216 716	88X	8	326 2Ɛ5	233 047	8	024 Ɛ12	325
9	.Ɛ2Ɛ ƐƐ3 X48	Ɛ9X	9	0Ɛ3 26X	354	9	.Ɛ15 9X1 7X9	62Ɛ
X	990 X6X	223 2XX	X	.Ɛ22 X7Ɛ Ɛ16	662	X	75X 17X	937
Ɛ	769 780	5Ɛ9	Ɛ	848 474	970	Ɛ	516 443	244 042
.0820	546 183	90X	.0860	614 704	234 079	.08X0	292 401	349
1	322 475	224 01X	1	3X0 647	387	1	04X 074	653
2	0ƐX 457	32X	2	168 280	694	2	.Ɛ14 X05 621	95Ɛ
3	.Ɛ2X X96 129	639	3	.Ɛ21 Ɛ33 7X8	9X2	3	780 882	245 065
4	871 6Ɛ0	949	4	8ƐX X06	235 0XƐ	4	537 819	370
5	648 963	225 059	5	685 917	3Ɛ8	5	2Ɛ2 469	677
6	423 906	369	6	450 51Ɛ	705	6	068 9Ɛ2	982
7	1ƐX 559	678	7	216 X16	X13	7	.Ɛ13 X23 030	246 088
8	.Ɛ29 Ɛ94 XX1	988	8	.Ɛ20 ƐX1 003	236 11Ɛ	8	798 Ɛ64	393
9	96Ɛ 115	226 098	9	966 XX4	429	9	552 791	699
X	745 039	3X6	X	730 677	736	X	308 0Ɛ4	9X4
Ɛ	51X 853	6Ɛ7	Ɛ	4Ɛ5 Ɛ41	X42	Ɛ	081 310	247 0XX
.0830	2Ɛ4 158	X05	.0870	27Ɛ 0ƐƐ	237 150	.08Ɛ0	.Ɛ12 X36 222	3Ɛ4
1	089 353	227 115	1	043 Ɛ6Ɛ	458	1	7XX X2X	6ƐƐ
2	.Ɛ28 X62 23X	425	2	.Ɛ1Ɛ X08 713	765	2	563 32Ɛ	X04
3	836 X15	733	3	790 Ɛ6X	X72	3	317 527	248 10Ɛ
4	60Ɛ 2X2	X43	4	555 0Ɛ8	238 17Ɛ	4	08Ɛ 418	416
5	3X3 45Ɛ	228 152	5	318 Ɛ39	487	5	.Ɛ11 X43 002	71Ɛ
6	177 309	461	6	0X0 672	794	6	7Ɛ6 4X3	X25
7	.Ɛ27 Ɛ4X X68	770	7	.Ɛ1X X63 X9X	XX0	7	569 67X	249 12Ɛ
8	922 2Ɛ8	X7X	8	826 ƐƐX	239 1X9	8	320 54Ɛ	435
9	6Ɛ5 43X	229 18X	9	5X9 X11	4Ɛ6	9	093 116	73Ɛ
X	488 270	499	X	370 517	801	X	.Ɛ10 X45 597	X45
Ɛ	25X 993	7X7	Ɛ	132 916	Ɛ0X	Ɛ	7Ɛ7 752	24X 14Ɛ

N	Cosine	d
.0900	.Ɛ10 569 603	24χ 454
1	31Ɛ 16Ɛ	759
2	090 612	χ64
3	.Ɛ0Ɛ χ41 76χ	24Ɛ 169
4	7Ɛ2 601	472
5	563 14Ɛ	778
6	313 593	χ81
7	083 712	250 186
8	.Ɛ0χ χ33 548	490
9	7χ3 078	794
χ	552 4χ4	χ9χ
Ɛ	301 606	251 1χ3
.0910	070 423	4χ8
1	.Ɛ09 χ1χ Ɛ37	7Ɛ1
2	789 346	χƐ6
3	537 450	252 1ƐƐ
4	2χ5 251	503
5	052 94χ	809
6	.Ɛ08 χ00 141	Ɛ11
7	769 230	253 215
8	516 017	51χ
9	282 6Ɛ9	823
χ	02χ χ96	Ɛ27
Ɛ	.Ɛ07 996 Ɛ6Ɛ	254 230
.0920	742 93Ɛ	533
1	4χχ 408	839
2	255 78Ɛ	Ɛ40
3	000 84Ɛ	255 245
4	.Ɛ06 967 606	548
5	712 07χ	851
6	478 429	Ɛ55
7	222 494	256 259
8	.Ɛ05 Ɛ88 237	560
9	931 897	865
χ	697 032	Ɛ68
Ɛ	440 086	257 270
.0930	1χ4 χ16	574
1	.Ɛ04 Ɛ49 462	877
2	8Ɛ1 7χ7	Ɛ7Ɛ
3	655 828	258 282
4	3Ɛ9 566	586
5	160 Ɛχ0	889
6	.Ɛ03 Ɛ04 313	Ɛ91
7	867 342	259 294
8	60χ 06χ	597
9	370 693	89χ
χ	112 9Ɛ5	Ɛχ1
Ɛ	.Ɛ02 χ74 χ14	25χ 2χ5

N	Cosine	d
.0940	.Ɛ02 816 72Ɛ	25χ 5χ7
1	578 144	8χƐ
2	319 455	ƐƐ1
3	07χ 464	25Ɛ 2Ɛ4
4	.Ɛ01 χ1Ɛ 170	5Ɛ7
5	77Ɛ 775	8Ɛ9
6	51Ɛ χ78	260 000
7	27Ɛ χ78	303
8	01Ɛ 775	605
9	.Ɛ00 97Ɛ 170	908
χ	71χ 464	261 00χ
Ɛ	479 456	311
.0950	218 145	613
1	.χƐƐ Ɛ76 732	915
2	914 χ19	262 017
3	672 χ02	31χ
4	410 6χ4	620
5	16χ 084	921
6	.χƐχ Ɛ07 363	263 024
7	864 33Ɛ	325
8	601 016	628
9	359 5χχ	929
χ	0Ɛ5 881	264 02Ɛ
Ɛ	.χƐ9 χ51 852	330
.0960	7χ9 522	632
1	544 χƐ0	934
2	2χ0 178	265 035
3	037 143	337
4	.χƐ8 991 χ08	638
5	728 390	939
6	482 653	266 03Ɛ
7	218 614	340
8	.χƐ7 Ɛ72 294	641
9	907 853	942
χ	660 Ɛ11	267 043
Ɛ	3Ɛ5 χ8χ	344
.0970	14χ 746	645
1	.χƐ6 χχ3 101	946
2	837 377	268 047
3	58Ɛ 330	348
4	322 Ɛχ4	648
5	076 558	949
6	.χƐ5 χ09 80Ɛ	269 049
7	760 782	34χ
8	4Ɛ3 434	64χ
9	245 9χ6	94Ɛ
χ	.χƐ4 Ɛ98 057	26χ 04Ɛ
Ɛ	92χ 008	350

N	Cosine	d
.0980	.χƐ4 67Ɛ 878	26χ 64Ɛ
1	411 229	950
2	162 499	26Ɛ 050
3	.χƐ3 χƐ3 449	350
4	844 0Ɛ9	650
5	594 669	950
6	324 919	270 04Ɛ
7	074 88χ	350
8	.χƐ2 χ04 53χ	64Ɛ
9	753 χχƐ	94Ɛ
χ	4χ3 160	271 04Ɛ
Ɛ	232 111	34χ
.0990	.χƐ1 Ɛ80 983	649
1	90Ɛ 336	94χ
2	659 5χ8	272 048
3	3χ7 560	348
4	135 214	647
5	.χƐ0 χ82 789	947
6	80Ɛ χ42	273 045
7	558 9Ɛ9	345
8	2χ5 674	643
9	032 031	943
χ	.χχƐ 97χ 2χχ	274 041
Ɛ	706 269	341
.09χ0	451 Ɛ28	63Ɛ
1	199 4χ9	93χ
2	.χχχ Ɛ24 76Ɛ	275 039
3	86Ɛ 732	337
4	5Ɛ6 3Ɛ7	636
5	340 981	934
6	087 049	276 033
7	.χχ9 χ11 016	331
8	756 8χ5	62Ɛ
9	4χ0 276	92χ
χ	225 548	277 028
Ɛ	.χχ8 Ɛ6χ 520	326
.09Ɛ0	8Ɛ3 1Ɛ6	624
1	637 792	922
2	37Ɛ χ70	278 020
3	103 χ50	31χ
4	.χχ7 χ47 732	618
5	78Ɛ 116	916
6	512 400	279 013
7	255 3χ9	311
8	.χχ6 Ɛ98 098	60Ɛ
9	91χ 689	908
χ	660 981	27χ 006
Ɛ	3χ2 977	303

N	Cosine	d	N	Cosine	d	N	Cosine	d
.0X00	.XX6 124 674	27X 600	.0X40	.X97 390 Ɛ04	28X 476	.0X80	.X88 244 923	29X 22X
1	.XX5 X66 074	8ƐX	1	102 64X	76Ɛ	1	.X87 Ɛ66 6Ɛ5	521
2	7X7 376	ƐƐ7	2	.X96 X33 X9Ɛ	X66	2	888 194	815
3	528 37Ɛ	27Ɛ 2Ɛ4	3	765 035	28Ɛ 160	3	5X9 57Ɛ	Ɛ08
4	269 087	5Ɛ1	4	495 X95	457	4	30X 673	29Ɛ 1ƐX
5	.XX4 ƐX9 696	8XX	5	206 63X	750	5	02Ɛ 475	4Ɛ2
6	929 9X8	ƐX7	6	.X95 Ɛ36 XXX	X47	6	.X86 94Ɛ Ɛ83	7X5
7	669 X01	280 2X5	7	867 063	290 140	7	670 39X	X98
8	3X9 718	5X1	8	596 Ɛ23	436	8	390 502	2X0 18Ɛ
9	129 137	899	9	306 6X9	730	9	0Ɛ0 333	481
X	.XX3 X68 45X	Ɛ97	X	035 Ɛ79	X26	X	.X85 X0Ɛ X72	774
Ɛ	7X7 483	281 293	Ɛ	.X94 965 153	291 120	Ɛ	72Ɛ 2ƐX	X67
.0X10	526 1Ɛ0	590	.0X50	694 033	415	.0X90	44X 453	2X1 159
1	264 820	889	1	402 81X	70Ɛ	1	169 2Ɛ6	450
2	.XX2 ƐX2 Ɛ53	Ɛ85	2	131 10Ɛ	X04	2	.X84 X87 X66	742
3	920 Ɛ8X	282 281	3	.X93 X5Ɛ 307	292 0ƐX	3	7X6 324	X35
4	65X 909	57X	4	789 209	3Ɛ3	4	504 4XƐ	2X2 127
5	398 34Ɛ	876	5	4Ɛ6 X16	6X9	5	222 384	419
6	115 695	Ɛ72	6	224 329	9X1	6	.X83 Ɛ3Ɛ Ɛ67	70Ɛ
7	.XX1 X52 723	283 26Ɛ	7	.X92 Ɛ51 548	293 097	7	859 458	X02
8	78Ɛ 474	567	8	87X 471	390	8	576 656	2X3 0Ɛ4
9	507 Ɛ09	862	9	5X7 0X1	686	9	293 562	3X5
X	244 267	Ɛ5Ɛ	X	313 617	97X	X	.X82 ƐƐ0 179	698
Ɛ	.XX0 Ɛ80 308	284 257	Ɛ	03Ɛ 859	294 073	Ɛ	908 6X1	989
.0X20	8Ɛ8 071	552	.0X60	.X91 967 7X6	368	.0XX0	624 914	2X4 07Ɛ
1	633 71Ɛ	84Ɛ	1	693 43X	661	1	340 855	371
2	36X X90	Ɛ46	2	3ƐX 999	955	2	058 4X4	662
3	0X5 Ɛ46	285 242	3	126 044	295 04Ɛ	3	.X81 973 X42	954
4	.X9Ɛ X20 904	53X	4	.X90 X50 ƐƐ5	343	4	68Ɛ 0XX	2X5 046
5	757 386	835	5	777 872	637	5	3X6 064	337
6	491 751	Ɛ30	6	4X2 237	930	6	100 929	629
7	207 821	286 228	7	208 507	296 025	7	.X80 X17 300	91X
8	.X9X Ɛ41 5Ɛ5	524	8	.X8Ɛ Ɛ32 4X2	319	8	731 5X2	2X6 00Ɛ
9	877 091	81Ɛ	9	858 185	611	9	447 593	300
X	5Ɛ0 472	Ɛ16	X	581 774	905	X	161 293	5Ɛ1
Ɛ	325 558	287 211	Ɛ	2X6 X6Ɛ	ƐƐX	Ɛ	.X7Ɛ X76 8X2	8X3
.0X30	05X 347	509	.0X70	00Ɛ X71	297 2Ɛ1	.0XƐ0	78Ɛ ƐƐƐ	Ɛ94
1	.X99 992 X3X	803	1	.X8X 934 780	5X6	1	4X5 027	2X7 284
2	707 237	XƐƐ	2	659 196	89X	2	1Ɛ9 963	575
3	43Ɛ 338	288 1Ɛ5	3	381 4Ɛ8	Ɛ91	3	.X7X Ɛ12 3XX	867
4	173 143	4Ɛ1	4	0X5 527	298 286	4	826 743	Ɛ56
5	.X98 XX6 852	7X7	5	.X89 X09 261	579	5	53X 7X9	2X8 248
6	81X 067	XX2	6	730 8X4	871	6	252 561	538
7	551 185	289 199	7	454 033	Ɛ65	7	Ɛ66 025	829
8	283 ƐX8	493	8	177 08X	299 258	8	.X79 879 3Ɛ8	Ɛ19
9	.X97 ƐƐ6 715	78X	9	.X88 X99 X32	550	9	590 49Ɛ	2X9 20X
X	928 Ɛ47	X84	X	800 4X2	844	X	2X3 291	4ƐX
Ɛ	65Ɛ 083	28X 17Ɛ	Ɛ	522 85X	Ɛ37	Ɛ	.X78 ƐƐ5 993	7XX

N	Cosine	d	N	Cosine	d	N	Cosine	d
.0Ɛ00	.X78 908 1X5	2X9 X9X	.0Ɛ40	.X68 ƐX3 330	2Ɛ9 642	.0Ɛ80	.X58 X96 4Ɛ5	309 095
1	61X 307	2XX 18Ɛ	1	8X5 8XX	92Ɛ	1	789 420	37X
2	330 138	47Ɛ	2	5X7 Ɛ7Ɛ	2ƐX 018	2	480 062	664
3	041 879	76X	3	2X9 Ɛ63	304	3	172 5ƐX	949
4	.X77 953 10Ɛ	X5Ɛ	4	.X67 ƐXƐ 85Ɛ	5Ɛ2	4	.X57 X64 871	30X 032
5	664 270	2XƐ 14Ɛ	5	8Ɛ1 269	89X	5	756 83Ɛ	318
6	375 121	43X	6	5Ɛ2 58Ɛ	Ɛ86	6	448 523	602
7	085 8X3	72X	7	2Ɛ3 605	2ƐƐ 273	7	139 Ɛ21	8X6
8	.X76 996 175	X1X	8	.X66 ƐƐ4 352	560	8	.X56 X2Ɛ 237	Ɛ8Ɛ
9	6X6 357	2Ɛ0 109	9	8Ɛ4 9Ɛ2	847	9	720 268	30Ɛ 275
X	3Ɛ6 24X	3Ɛ9	X	5Ɛ5 167	Ɛ35	X	410 ƐƐ3	559
Ɛ	105 X51	6X9	Ɛ	2Ɛ5 232	300 220	Ɛ	101 656	843
.0Ɛ10	.X75 X15 364	997	.0Ɛ50	.X65 ƐƐ5 012	508	.0Ɛ90	.X55 9Ɛ1 X13	Ɛ27
1	724 589	2Ɛ1 088	1	8Ɛ4 706	7Ɛ5	1	6X1 XX8	310 210
2	433 501	376	2	5Ɛ3 Ɛ11	XX1	2	391 898	4Ɛ4
3	142 147	666	3	2Ɛ3 030	301 188	3	081 3X4	79X
4	.X74 X50 6X1	955	4	.X64 ƐƐ1 X64	475	4	.X54 970 806	X81
5	75X 948	2Ɛ2 043	5	8Ɛ0 5XƐ	760	5	65Ɛ 945	311 167
6	468 905	333	6	5XX X4Ɛ	X48	6	34X 79X	44X
7	176 592	622	7	2X9 003	302 134	7	039 350	733
8	.X73 X83 Ɛ70	911	8	.X63 ƐX6 X8Ɛ	420	8	.X53 927 819	X18
9	791 25Ɛ	2Ɛ3 000	9	8X4 66Ɛ	707	9	615 X01	312 0ƐƐ
X	49X 25Ɛ	2XX	X	5X1 Ɛ64	9Ɛ2	X	303 902	3X4
Ɛ	1X6 Ɛ71	599	Ɛ	29Ɛ 172	303 09X	Ɛ	.X52 ƐƐ1 51X	688
.0Ɛ20	.X72 XƐ3 594	887	.0Ɛ60	.X62 Ɛ98 094	385	.0ƐX0	89X X52	96Ɛ
1	7ƐƐ 909	Ɛ77	1	894 90Ɛ	670	1	588 0X3	313 054
2	507 952	2Ɛ4 264	2	591 25Ɛ	958	2	275 04Ɛ	337
3	213 6XX	553	3	289 503	304 043	3	.X51 Ɛ61 914	61Ɛ
4	.X71 Ɛ1Ɛ 157	842	4	.X61 Ɛ85 480	32X	4	84X 2Ɛ5	903
5	826 515	Ɛ2Ɛ	5	881 152	615	5	536 5Ɛ2	ƐX7
6	531 5X6	2Ɛ5 21X	6	578 739	8ƐƐ	6	222 607	314 28X
7	238 388	508	7	273 X3X	ƐX7	7	.X50 Ɛ0X 339	571
8	.X70 Ɛ42 X80	7Ɛ6	8	.X60 Ɛ6X X53	305 292	8	7Ɛ5 988	855
9	849 286	XX4	9	865 781	578	9	4X1 133	Ɛ39
X	553 3X2	2Ɛ6 192	X	560 205	862	X	188 1Ɛ6	315 21Ɛ
Ɛ	259 210	480	Ɛ	256 563	Ɛ4X	Ɛ	.X4Ɛ X72 Ɛ97	503
.0Ɛ30	.X6Ɛ Ɛ62 950	76X	.0Ɛ70	.X5Ɛ Ɛ50 615	306 234	.0ƐƐ0	759 694	7X6
1	868 1X2	X57	1	846 3X1	51X	1	443 XXX	X89
2	571 347	2Ɛ7 145	2	53Ɛ X83	805	2	12X 021	316 170
3	276 202	433	3	235 27X	XXƐ	3	.X4X X13 X71	453
4	.X6X Ɛ7X 98Ɛ	720	4	.X5X Ɛ2X 38Ɛ	307 195	4	6Ɛ9 61X	735
5	883 26Ɛ	X0X	5	823 1Ɛ6	47Ɛ	5	3X2 XX5	X19
6	587 461	2Ɛ8 0Ɛ7	6	517 937	766	6	088 088	317 0ƐƐ
7	28Ɛ 366	3X4	7	210 191	X4Ɛ	7	.X49 970 Ɛ89	3X2
8	.X69 Ɛ92 Ɛ82	692	8	.X59 Ɛ04 342	308 136	8	655 7X7	684
9	896 4Ɛ0	97Ɛ	9	7Ɛ8 208	41Ɛ	9	33X 123	967
X	599 731	2Ɛ9 068	X	4XƐ 9X9	705	X	022 378	318 04X
Ɛ	2X0 685	355	Ɛ	1X3 2X4	9XƐ	Ɛ	.X48 906 32X	32Ɛ

N	Cosine	d	N	Cosine	d	N	Cosine	d
.1000	.X48 5X9 ƐƐƐ	318 612	.1040	.X37 926 697	327 X31	.1080	.X26 890 924	337 130
1	291 5X9	8Ɛ4	1	5ƐX 866	328 111	1	555 7Ɛ4	408
2	.X47 Ɛ74 8Ɛ5	Ɛ96	2	292 755	3XƐ	2	21X 3X8	6X2
3	857 91Ɛ	319 279	3	.X36 Ɛ66 366	68X	3	.X25 XX2 906	97X
4	53X 662	55X	4	839 898	968	4	766 Ɛ48	338 054
5	221 104	840	5	510 Ɛ30	329 047	5	42X XƐ4	32Ɛ
6	.X46 Ɛ03 484	Ɛ22	6	1X3 XX5	325	6	0Ɛ2 785	606
7	7X5 562	31X 204	7	.X35 X76 780	603	7	.X24 976 17Ɛ	8X0
8	487 35X	4X6	8	749 179	8X1	8	639 49Ɛ	Ɛ78
9	168 X74	787	9	41Ɛ 498	Ɛ80	9	300 523	339 251
X	.X45 X4X 2X9	X68	X	0Ɛ1 518	32X 25X	X	.X23 Ɛ83 292	528
Ɛ	72Ɛ 441	31Ɛ 14X	Ɛ	.X34 983 27X	537	Ɛ	845 966	803
.1010	410 2Ɛ3	430	.1050	654 943	816	.1090	508 163	X99
1	0Ɛ0 X83	711	1	326 129	XƐ3	1	18X 286	33X 173
2	.X44 991 372	9Ɛ2	2	.X33 ƐƐ7 236	32Ɛ 191	2	.X22 X50 113	449
3	671 580	320 093	3	888 065	46Ɛ	3	711 886	723
4	351 4X9	375	4	558 7Ɛ6	748	4	393 163	9Ɛ9
5	031 134	655	5	229 06X	X26	5	054 366	33Ɛ 094
6	.X43 910 69Ɛ	937	6	.X32 XƐ9 244	330 103	6	.X21 915 292	369
7	5XƐ 964	321 017	7	789 141	3X1	7	595 Ɛ25	642
8	28X 949	2Ɛ9	8	458 960	67X	8	256 4X3	919
9	.X42 Ɛ69 650	598	9	128 2X2	957	9	.X20 Ɛ16 786	ƐƐ2
X	848 074	87X	X	.X31 9Ɛ7 547	331 035	X	796 794	340 288
Ɛ	526 3Ɛ6	Ɛ5X	Ɛ	686 512	311	Ɛ	456 508	561
.1020	204 458	322 23Ɛ	.1060	355 201	5XX	.10X0	115 Ɛ67	836
1	.X41 XX2 219	51Ɛ	1	023 813	888	1	.X1Ɛ 995 331	Ɛ10
2	77Ɛ 8ƐX	800	2	.X30 8Ɛ1 Ɛ47	Ɛ64	2	654 421	341 1X5
3	459 0ƐX	XX0	3	57Ɛ ƐX3	332 241	3	313 238	47Ɛ
4	136 21X	323 180	4	249 962	51X	4	.X1X Ɛ91 979	753
5	.X40 X13 05X	461	5	.X2Ɛ Ɛ17 444	7Ɛ6	5	850 226	X28
6	6XƐ 7Ɛ9	740	6	7X4 84X	X93	6	50X 3ƐX	342 101
7	388 079	X21	7	471 977	333 170	7	188 2Ɛ9	396
8	064 258	324 100	8	13X 807	448	8	.X19 X45 Ɛ23	66Ɛ
9	.X3Ɛ 940 158	3X1	9	.X2X X07 37Ɛ	724	9	703 474	944
X	617 977	680	X	693 857	X00	X	380 730	343 018
Ɛ	2Ɛ3 2Ɛ7	960	Ɛ	35Ɛ X57	334 099	Ɛ	039 714	2Ɛ1
.1030	.X3X Ɛ8X 557	325 03Ɛ	.1070	027 97X	374	.10Ɛ0	.X18 8Ɛ6 423	585
1	865 518	320	1	.X29 8Ɛ3 606	651	1	572 X5X	85X
2	540 1Ɛ8	5ƐX	2	57X Ɛ75	929	2	22Ɛ 200	Ɛ32
3	216 7ƐX	89X	3	246 248	335 005	3	.X17 XX7 28X	344 206
4	.X39 XƐ0 Ɛ20	Ɛ7X	4	.X28 Ɛ11 243	2X0	4	763 084	49X
5	786 Ɛ62	326 259	5	797 Ɛ63	578	5	41X 7X6	773
6	460 905	538	6	462 5X7	854	6	096 033	X46
7	136 389	817	7	128 953	Ɛ2Ɛ	7	.X16 951 1X9	345 11Ɛ
8	.X38 X0Ɛ 772	XƐ6	8	.X27 9Ɛ2 X24	336 207	8	608 08X	3Ɛ2
9	6X4 878	327 195	9	678 819	4X3	9	282 898	686
X	379 6X3	475	X	342 336	779	X	.X15 Ɛ39 212	959
Ɛ	052 22X	753	Ɛ	007 779	X55	Ɛ	7Ɛ3 475	346 032

N	Cosine	d	N	Cosine	d	N	Cosine	d
.1100	.X15 469 443	346 305	.1140	.X03 881 2X2	355 370	.1180	.9Ɛ1 915 46X	364 2X5
1	123 13X	598	1	527 Ɛ32	640	1	571 185	571
2	.X14 998 762	870	2	192 4Ɛ2	90Ɛ	2	208 814	839
3	651 XƐ2	Ɛ43	3	.X02 X38 7X3	Ɛ9Ɛ	3	.9Ɛ0 X63 Ɛ97	Ɛ04
4	306 Ɛ6Ɛ	347 216	4	6X2 804	356 26X	4	6ƐƐ 093	365 190
5	.X13 Ɛ7Ɛ 955	4XX	5	348 556	53X	5	355 Ɛ03	458
6	834 467	780	6	.X01 ƐƐ2 018	809	6	.9XƐ ƐƐ0 667	723
7	4X8 8X7	X54	7	857 40Ɛ	X98	7	846 Ɛ44	9XƐ
8	160 X53	348 126	8	500 533	357 168	8	4X1 155	366 076
9	.X12 X14 929	3ƐX	9	165 387	436	9	137 09Ɛ	341
X	688 52Ɛ	690	X	.X00 X09 Ɛ51	706	X	.9XX 990 95X	608
Ɛ	33Ɛ X5Ɛ	963	Ɛ	672 447	994	Ɛ	626 352	894
.1110	.X11 ƐƐ3 0Ɛ8	349 035	.1150	316 673	358 064	.1190	27Ɛ 67X	Ɛ5X
1	866 083	308	1	.9ƐƐ Ɛ7X 60Ɛ	332	1	.9X9 Ɛ14 720	367 226
2	518 977	59Ɛ	2	822 299	600	2	769 4Ɛ6	4Ɛ0
3	18Ɛ 398	871	3	485 899	890	3	402 006	777
4	.X10 X41 727	Ɛ43	4	129 009	Ɛ5X	4	056 44Ɛ	X42
5	6Ɛ3 7X4	34X 215	5	.9ƐX 990 06Ɛ	359 228	5	.9X8 8XX 609	368 108
6	365 58Ɛ	4X8	6	632 X43	4Ɛ7	6	542 501	393
7	017 0X3	779	7	295 548	785	7	196 12X	659
8	.X0Ɛ 888 526	X50	8	.9Ɛ9 Ɛ37 983	X54	8	.9X7 X29 691	924
9	539 696	34Ɛ 122	9	799 Ɛ2Ɛ	35X 121	9	680 969	ƐX9
X	1XX 574	3Ɛ3	X	43Ɛ X0X	3Ɛ0	X	313 980	369 275
Ɛ	.X0X X5Ɛ 181	685	Ɛ	0X1 61X	679	Ɛ	.9X6 Ɛ66 707	53X
.1120	70Ɛ 6Ɛ8	957	.1160	.9Ɛ8 942 Ɛ61	948	.11X0	7Ɛ9 189	804
1	37Ɛ 961	350 028	1	5X4 215	35Ɛ 015	1	44Ɛ 585	X8X
2	02Ɛ 935	2ƐX	2	245 200	2X3	2	0X1 6Ɛ7	36X 154
3	.X09 89Ɛ 637	590	3	.9Ɛ7 XX5 Ɛ19	570	3	.9X5 933 563	41X
4	54Ɛ 067	861	4	746 569	83Ɛ	4	585 145	6X3
5	1ƐX 406	Ɛ32	5	3X6 92X	Ɛ07	5	216 662	96X
6	.X08 X69 494	351 203	6	046 X23	360 196	6	.9X4 X67 8Ɛ4	36Ɛ 032
7	718 291	495	7	.9Ɛ6 8X6 849	462	7	6Ɛ8 882	2Ɛ8
8	386 9Ɛ8	765	8	546 3X7	730	8	349 586	582
9	035 253	X37	9	1X5 877	9Ɛ9	9	.9X3 Ɛ9X 004	847
X	.X07 8X3 418	352 107	X	.9Ɛ5 X44 X7X	361 086	X	82X 379	Ɛ10
Ɛ	551 311	398	Ɛ	6X3 9Ɛ4	353	Ɛ	47X 469	370 195
.1130	1ƐX Ɛ35	669	.1170	342 661	620	.11Ɛ0	10X 294	45X
1	.X06 X68 488	93X	1	.9Ɛ4 ƐX1 041	8X9	1	.9X2 959 X36	723
2	715 74X	353 00X	2	83Ɛ 354	Ɛ75	2	5X9 313	9X8
3	382 740	29Ɛ	3	499 39Ɛ	362 243	3	238 527	371 071
4	02Ɛ 461	56Ɛ	4	137 158	50Ɛ	4	.9X1 X87 476	336
5	.X05 897 XƐ2	840	5	.9Ɛ3 994 849	797	5	716 140	5ƐX
6	544 272	Ɛ10	6	632 072	X64	6	364 742	883
7	1Ɛ0 362	354 1X0	7	28Ɛ 20X	363 131	7	.9X0 ƐƐ2 X7Ɛ	Ɛ47
8	.X04 X58 182	470	8	.9Ɛ2 Ɛ28 099	3Ɛ8	8	840 Ɛ34	372 210
9	703 912	740	9	784 8X1	685	9	48X 924	494
X	36Ɛ 192	X10	X	421 218	951	X	118 450	758
Ɛ	016 382	355 0X0	Ɛ	079 487	364 019	Ɛ	.99Ɛ 965 8Ɛ4	X21

N	Cosine	d	N	Cosine	d	N	Cosine	d
.1200	.99Ɛ 5Ɛ2 Ӿ93	373 0Ӿ4	.1240	.988 Ɛ1Ɛ 005	381 966	.1280	.976 09Ɛ 02Ӿ	390 4Ӿ6
1	23Ɛ 9ӾƐ	368	1	759 25Ɛ	382 026	1	.975 90Ӿ 744	762
2	.99Ӿ Ӿ88 643	631	2	397 235	2Ӿ6	2	539 ƐӾ2	Ӿ1Ӿ
3	715 012	8Ɛ4	3	014 Ɛ4Ɛ	566	3	169 184	391 096
4	361 31Ӿ	Ɛ78	4	.987 852 5Ӿ5	826	4	.974 998 0ӾӾ	351
5	.999 ƐӾ9 362	374 23Ɛ	5	48Ɛ 97Ɛ	ӾӾ5	5	606 959	609
6	835 123	503	6	108 Ӿ96	383 165	6	235 350	884
7	480 820	787	7	.986 945 931	424	7	.973 Ӿ63 688	Ɛ40
8	108 055	Ӿ4Ӿ	8	582 509	6Ӿ4	8	691 748	392 1Ɛ7
9	.998 953 207	375 111	9	1ƐӾ Ӿ25	963	9	2ƐƐ 551	472
Ӿ	59Ӿ 0Ɛ6	395	Ӿ	.985 Ӿ37 082	384 022	Ӿ	.972 Ɛ29 09Ɛ	729
Ɛ	224 921	658	Ɛ	673 060	2Ӿ1	Ɛ	756 572	9Ӿ5
.1210	.997 Ӿ6Ɛ 285	91Ӿ	.1250	2ӾӾ 97Ɛ	561	.1290	383 789	393 05Ɛ
1	6Ɛ5 567	ƐӾ2	1	.984 Ɛ26 41Ӿ	81Ɛ	1	.971 ƐƐ0 72Ӿ	316
2	33Ɛ 585	376 265	2	761 7ƐƐ	Ӿ9Ӿ	2	819 414	591
3	.996 Ɛ85 320	527	3	398 921	385 159	3	445 Ӿ43	848
4	80Ӿ 9Ɛ5	7ӾƐ	4	013 784	418	4	072 1Ɛ7	Ɛ03
5	454 206	Ӿ71	5	.983 84Ӿ 368	697	5	.970 89Ӿ 2Ɛ4	394 179
6	099 355	377 133	6	484 891	955	6	506 137	433
7	.995 922 222	3Ɛ6	7	0ƐӾ Ɛ38	386 013	7	131 904	6ӾӾ
8	566 Ӿ28	679	8	.982 934 Ɛ25	292	8	.96Ɛ 959 216	964
9	1ӾƐ 36Ɛ	93Ӿ	9	56Ӿ 853	550	9	584 472	395 01Ӿ
Ӿ	.994 Ӿ33 631	378 001	Ӿ	1Ӿ4 303	80Ӿ	Ӿ	1ӾƐ 454	294
Ɛ	677 630	283	Ɛ	.981 Ӿ19 6Ɛ5	Ӿ89	Ɛ	.96Ӿ Ӿ16 180	54Ɛ
.1220	2ƐƐ 369	546	.1260	652 828	387 146	.12Ӿ0	640 831	804
1	.993 Ɛ42 Ӿ23	807	1	287 6Ӿ2	405	1	267 029	Ӿ7Ӿ
2	786 218	Ӿ89	2	.980 Ɛ00 299	682	2	.969 Ӿ91 16Ɛ	396 134
3	409 34Ɛ	379 14Ɛ	3	734 817	941	3	6Ɛ7 037	3Ӿ9
4	050 200	411	4	368 Ӿ96	ƐƐ9	4	320 84Ӿ	664
5	.992 892 9ӾƐ	692	5	.97Ɛ ƐӾ0 Ӿ99	388 278	5	.968 Ɛ46 1Ӿ6	918
6	515 319	954	6	814 821	535	6	76Ɛ 48Ӿ	Ɛ92
7	157 585	37Ӿ 016	7	448 2Ӿ8	7Ɛ2	7	394 4Ɛ8	397 248
8	.991 999 56Ɛ	296	8	07Ɛ 6Ɛ6	Ӿ70	8	.967 ƐƐ9 270	500
9	61Ɛ 295	559	9	.97Ӿ 8Ɛ2 846	389 129	9	821 970	776
Ӿ	260 938	819	Ӿ	525 719	3Ӿ7	Ӿ	446 1Ɛ6	Ӿ2Ɛ
Ɛ	.990 ӾӾ2 11Ɛ	Ӿ9Ɛ	Ɛ	158 332	663	Ɛ	06Ӿ 387	398 0Ӿ4
.1230	723 240	37Ɛ 15Ɛ	.1270	.979 98Ӿ 88Ɛ	921	.12Ɛ0	.966 892 2Ӿ3	358
1	364 0Ӿ1	421	1	600 Ɛ6Ӿ	Ɛ99	1	4Ɛ5 Ɛ47	612
2	.98Ɛ ƐӾ4 880	6Ӿ2	2	232 Ɛ91	38Ӿ 256	2	119 535	886
3	825 19Ӿ	962	3	.978 Ӿ64 937	513	3	.965 940 86Ɛ	Ɛ3Ɛ
4	465 438	380 023	4	696 424	790	4	563 930	399 1Ɛ3
5	0Ӿ5 415	2Ӿ4	5	307 854	Ӿ48	5	186 739	468
6	.98Ӿ 925 131	564	6	.977 Ɛ38 Ӿ08	38Ɛ 105	6	.964 9Ӿ9 291	720
7	564 789	825	7	769 903	382	7	60Ɛ 771	995
8	1Ӿ3 Ɛ64	ӾӾ6	8	39Ӿ 541	639	8	231 998	39Ӿ 048
9	.989 Ӿ23 07Ӿ	381 165	9	00Ӿ Ɛ04	8Ɛ6	9	.963 Ӿ53 950	301
Ӿ	661 Ɛ15	426	Ӿ	.976 83Ɛ 20Ӿ	Ɛ72	Ӿ	675 64Ɛ	575
Ɛ	2Ӿ0 6ӾƐ	6Ӿ6	Ɛ	46Ɛ 258	390 22Ӿ	Ɛ	297 096	829

N	Cosine	d	N	Cosine	d	N	Cosine	d
.1300	.962 χƐ8 469	39χ χχ0	.1340	.94Ɛ 578 760	3χ9 34χ	.1380	.937 8χ5 494	3Ɛ7 666
1	719 589	39Ɛ 154	1	18Ɛ 412	5Ɛ9	1	4χ9 χ2χ	911
2	33χ 435	408	2	.94χ 9χ1 χ15	869	2	0Ɛ2 119	Ɛ77
3	.961 Ɛ5Ɛ 029	680	3	5Ɛ4 168	Ɛ18	3	.936 8Ɛ6 162	3Ɛ8 223
4	77Ɛ 569	933	4	206 250	3χχ 187	4	4Ɛ9 Ɛ3Ɛ	48χ
5	39Ɛ 836	Ɛχ7	5	.949 χ18 085	436	5	101 671	735
6	.960 ƐƐƐ 84Ɛ	3χ0 259	6	629 84Ɛ	6χ6	6	.935 904 Ɛ38	99Ɛ
7	81Ɛ 5Ɛ2	511	7	23Ɛ 165	954	7	508 159	3Ɛ9 047
8	43Ɛ 0χ1	785	8	.948 χ50 411	3χƐ 004	8	10Ɛ 112	2Ɛ0
9	05χ 518	χ37	9	661 409	272	9	.934 911 χ22	557
χ	.95Ɛ 879 6χ1	3χ1 0χχ	χ	272 157	521	χ	514 487	802
Ɛ	498 5Ɛ3	361	Ɛ	.947 χ82 836	78Ɛ	Ɛ	116 885	χ68
.1310	0Ɛ7 252	614	.1350	693 067	χ3χ	.1390	.933 918 χ19	3Ɛχ 112
1	.95χ 915 83χ	887	1	2χ3 229	3Ɛ0 0χ9	1	51χ 907	378
2	533 Ɛ73	Ɛ39	2	.946 χƐ3 140	356	2	120 54Ɛ	622
3	152 036	3χ2 1χƐ	3	702 9χ6	605	3	.932 921 Ɛ29	888
4	.959 96Ɛ χ47	463	4	312 3χ1	874	4	523 261	Ɛ32
5	589 5χ4	714	5	.945 Ɛ21 729	Ɛ21	5	124 32Ɛ	3ƐƐ 198
6	1χ6 χ90	987	6	730 808	3Ɛ1 190	6	.931 925 153	442
7	.958 χ04 105	3χ3 039	7	33Ɛ 638	439	7	525 911	6χ7
8	621 088	2χ2	8	.944 Ɛ4χ 1ƐƐ	6χ7	8	126 226	950
9	239 999	561	9	758 714	955	9	.930 926 496	ƐƐ6
χ	.957 χ56 438	813	χ	366 97Ɛ	3Ɛ2 002	χ	526 4χ0	400 25Ɛ
Ɛ	672 825	χ85	Ɛ	.943 Ɛ74 979	270	Ɛ	126 241	504
.1320	28χ 960	3χ4 136	.1360	782 709	51χ	.13χ0	.92Ɛ 925 939	76χ
1	.956 χχ6 826	3χ8	1	390 1χƐ	787	1	525 18Ɛ	χ12
2	702 43χ	65χ	2	.942 Ɛ99 624	χ34	2	124 379	401 078
3	319 9χ0	90Ɛ	3	7χ6 7Ɛ0	3Ɛ3 0χ1	3	.92χ 923 301	320
4	.955 Ɛ35 091	Ɛ81	4	3Ɛ3 70Ɛ	34Ɛ	4	521 Ɛχ1	585
5	750 110	3χ5 232	5	000 380	5Ɛ7	5	120 618	829
6	366 χ9χ	4χ3	6	.941 808 985	865	6	.929 91χ 9χƐ	χ93
7	.954 Ɛ81 5Ɛ7	754	7	415 120	Ɛ11	7	518 Ɛ18	402 136
8	797 χ63	χ05	8	021 20Ɛ	3Ɛ4 17χ	8	116 9χ2	39Ɛ
9	3Ɛ2 05χ	3χ6 077	9	.940 829 051	426	9	.928 914 603	644
χ	007 Ɛχ3	327	χ	434 827	694	χ	511 Ɛ7Ɛ	8χ7
Ɛ	.953 821 878	597	Ɛ	040 153	93Ɛ	Ɛ	10Ɛ 294	Ɛ50
.1330	437 2χ1	849	.1370	.93Ɛ 847 414	Ɛχ8	.13Ɛ0	.927 908 344	403 1Ɛ3
1	050 654	χƐ9	1	452 428	3Ɛ5 255	1	505 151	458
2	.952 865 757	3χ7 16χ	2	059 193	500	2	101 8Ɛ5	6ƐƐ
3	47χ 5χ9	419	3	.93χ 863 893	769	3	.926 8Ɛχ 1Ɛ6	963
4	093 190	68Ɛ	4	46χ 126	χ14	4	4Ɛ6 453	404 007
5	.951 8χ7 701	93χ	5	074 312	3Ɛ6 081	5	0Ɛ2 448	26χ
6	4ƐƐ 983	ƐχƐ	6	.939 87χ 251	329	6	.925 8χχ 19χ	512
7	113 994	3χ8 25Ɛ	7	483 Ɛ24	594	7	4χ5 888	775
8	.950 927 735	50χ	8	089 550	840	8	0χ1 113	χ19
9	53Ɛ 227	77Ɛ	9	.938 892 910	χχ7	9	.924 898 2Ɛ6	405 07Ɛ
χ	152 668	χ2χ	χ	497 χ25	3Ɛ7 153	χ	493 237	323
Ɛ	.94Ɛ 965 83χ	3χ9 09χ	Ɛ	0χ0 892	3Ɛχ	Ɛ	089 Ɛ14	586

N	Cosine	d	N	Cosine	d	N	Cosine	d
.1400	.923 884 54X	405 828	.1440	.90Ɛ 51Ɛ 777	413 853	.1480	.8Ɛ6 X38 XƐ1	421 719
1	47X 922	X90	1	107 Ɛ24	XƐ2	1	617 394	973
2	074 X52	406 132	2	.90X 8Ɛ4 032	414 14Ɛ	2	1Ɛ5 621	422 008
3	.922 86X 920	395	3	49Ɛ XX3	3XX	3	.8Ɛ5 993 615	263
4	464 547	637	4	087 6Ɛ5	648	4	571 372	4Ɛ7
5	059 Ɛ10	89X	5	.909 873 069	8X5	5	14X X77	751
6	.921 853 232	Ɛ40	6	45X 384	Ɛ44	6	.8Ɛ4 928 326	9X7
7	448 2Ɛ2	407 1X2	7	045 440	415 1X1	7	505 53Ɛ	423 040
8	041 110	445	8	.908 830 25Ɛ	440	8	0X2 4ƐƐ	294
9	.920 835 887	6X6	9	416 X1Ɛ	698	9	.8Ɛ3 87Ɛ 227	52X
X	42X 1X1	949	X	001 343	936	X	457 8Ɛ9	783
Ɛ	022 454	ƐXX	Ɛ	.907 7X7 609	Ɛ94	Ɛ	034 136	X18
.1410	.91Ɛ 816 466	408 250	.1450	391 635	416 231	.1490	.8Ɛ2 810 31X	424 070
1	40X 216	4Ɛ2	1	.906 Ɛ77 404	48X	1	3X8 26X	305
2	001 924	754	2	760 Ɛ36	727	2	.8Ɛ1 Ɛ83 Ɛ65	559
3	.91X 7Ɛ5 190	9Ɛ5	3	346 40Ɛ	985	3	75Ɛ 608	7Ɛ2
4	3X8 397	409 057	4	.905 Ɛ2Ɛ 646	417 021	4	336 X16	X47
5	.919 Ɛ9Ɛ 340	2Ɛ7	5	714 625	27X	5	.8Ɛ0 Ɛ11 Ɛ8Ɛ	425 09Ɛ
6	792 045	55X	6	2Ɛ9 367	517	6	6X8 XƐ0	332
7	384 6X7	7ƐX	7	.904 XX1 X50	773	7	283 77X	587
8	.918 Ɛ76 XX9	X5Ɛ	8	686 299	X10	8	.8XƐ X5X 1Ɛ3	81Ɛ
9	769 04X	40X 100	9	26X 489	418 069	9	634 594	X73
X	35X Ɛ4X	361	X	.903 X52 420	304	X	20X 721	426 107
Ɛ	.917 Ɛ50 7X9	602	Ɛ	636 118	562	Ɛ	.8XX 9X4 616	35X
.1420	742 1X7	863	.1460	219 776	7Ɛ9	.14X0	57X 278	5Ɛ2
1	333 544	Ɛ03	1	.902 X00 Ɛ79	X55	1	153 886	845
2	.916 Ɛ24 641	40Ɛ 164	2	5X4 124	419 0Ɛ2	2	.8X9 929 041	X99
3	715 499	404	3	187 032	349	3	502 164	427 130
4	306 095	664	4	.901 969 8X5	5X5	4	097 034	383
5	.915 XƐ6 631	905	5	550 300	841	5	.8X8 86Ɛ 871	617
6	6X6 928	Ɛ65	6	132 67Ɛ	X98	6	444 256	869
7	296 983	410 204	7	.900 914 7X3	41X 134	7	018 5X9	Ɛ00
8	.914 X86 77Ɛ	465	8	4Ɛ6 66Ɛ	38Ɛ	8	.8X7 7Ɛ0 6X9	428 154
9	676 316	705	9	098 2X0	627	9	384 555	3X5
X	265 811	964	X	.8ƐƐ 879 875	881	X	.8X6 Ɛ58 170	639
Ɛ	.913 X54 X69	411 004	Ɛ	45X ƐƐ4	Ɛ19	Ɛ	72Ɛ 733	88Ɛ
.1430	643 X65	263	.1470	040 097	41Ɛ 174	.14Ɛ0	302 X64	Ɛ22
1	232 802	503	1	.8ƐX 820 Ɛ23	40Ɛ	1	.8X5 X95 Ɛ42	429 173
2	.912 X21 2ƐƐ	763	2	401 714	666	2	668 98Ɛ	407
3	60Ɛ 758	X01	3	.8Ɛ9 ƐX2 06X	901	3	23Ɛ 584	658
4	1Ɛ9 957	412 061	4	782 369	Ɛ57	4	.8X4 X11 Ɛ28	8XX
5	.911 9X7 8Ɛ6	300	5	362 412	420 1Ɛ2	5	5X4 23X	Ɛ40
6	595 5Ɛ6	55Ɛ	6	.8Ɛ8 Ɛ42 220	448	6	176 2ƐX	42X 192
7	183 057	7ƐX	7	721 994	6X3	7	.8X3 948 128	424
8	.910 970 459	X58	8	301 2Ɛ1	939	8	519 904	676
9	559 601	413 0Ɛ8	9	.8Ɛ7 XX0 574	Ɛ93	9	0XƐ 24X	907
X	146 505	356	X	67Ɛ 5X1	421 229	X	.8X2 880 543	Ɛ59
Ɛ	.90Ɛ 933 16Ɛ	5Ɛ4	Ɛ	25X 374	483	Ɛ	451 5X6	42Ɛ 1XX

N	Cosine	d	N	Cosine	d	N	Cosine	d
.1500	.8X2 022 3Ɛ8	42Ɛ 43Ɛ	.1540	.888 X9X 080	438 Ɛ26	.1580	.873 632 40X	446 601
1	.8X1 7Ɛ2 Ɛ79	690	1	661 086	439 242	1	1X7 X09	846
2	383 4X9	922	2	223 X44	48Ɛ	2	.872 961 183	X89
3	.8X0 Ɛ53 787	Ɛ72	3	.887 9X6 575	717	3	516 2Ɛ6	447 110
4	723 815	430 204	4	568 X5X	963	4	08Ɛ 1X6	354
5	2Ɛ3 611	454	5	12Ɛ 0Ɛ7	ƐƐ0	5	.871 843 X52	597
6	.89Ɛ X83 179	6X5	6	.886 8Ɛ1 107	43X 237	6	3Ɛ8 477	81Ɛ
7	652 694	935	7	472 X90	483	7	.870 Ɛ70 858	X62
8	221 95Ɛ	Ɛ86	8	034 609	710	8	724 9Ɛ6	448 0X4
9	.89X 9Ɛ0 995	431 217	9	.885 7Ɛ5 XƐ9	956	9	298 912	328
X	57Ɛ 77X	466	X	377 163	ƐX3	X	.86Ɛ X50 5X6	56X
Ɛ	14X 314	6Ɛ7	Ɛ	.884 Ɛ38 180	43Ɛ 22X	Ɛ	604 038	7Ɛ1
.1510	.899 918 819	947	.1550	6Ɛ8 Ɛ52	475	.1590	177 447	X34
1	4X6 X92	Ɛ97	1	279 699	701	1	.86X 92X 613	449 076
2	074 XƐ7	432 227	2	.883 X39 Ɛ98	947	2	4X1 559	2Ɛ9
3	.898 842 890	477	3	5ƐX 251	Ɛ93	3	054 260	53Ɛ
4	410 415	706	4	17X 27X	440 21X	4	.869 806 921	781
5	.897 Ɛ99 90Ɛ	956	5	.882 93X 060	465	5	379 160	X03
6	766 Ɛ75	ƐX6	6	4Ɛ9 7Ɛ7	6Ɛ0	6	.868 Ɛ2Ɛ 359	44X 046
7	333 Ɛ8Ɛ	433 235	7	079 107	936	7	6X1 313	287
8	.896 Ɛ00 956	485	8	.881 838 391	Ɛ81	8	253 048	509
9	689 491	713	9	3Ɛ7 410	441 207	9	.867 X04 73Ɛ	74Ɛ
X	255 97X	963	X	.880 Ɛ76 205	452	X	575 Ɛ20	990
Ɛ	.895 X22 017	ƐƐ2	Ɛ	734 973	699	Ɛ	127 220	44Ɛ 012
.1520	5XX 025	434 241	.1560	2Ɛ3 296	922	.15X0	.866 898 20X	254
1	175 9X4	48Ɛ	1	.87Ɛ X71 574	Ɛ69	1	448 Ɛ76	494
2	.894 941 515	71Ɛ	2	62Ɛ 607	442 1Ɛ2	2	.865 ƐƐ9 6X2	716
3	508 9Ɛ6	969	3	1X9 415	438	3	769 Ɛ88	957
4	094 049	ƐƐ7	4	.87X 966 Ɛ99	683	4	31X 231	Ɛ98
5	.893 85Ɛ 052	435 246	5	524 516	908	5	.864 X8X 255	450 219
6	425 X08	494	6	0X1 80X	Ɛ51	6	63X 038	459
7	.892 ƐƐ0 534	723	7	.879 85X 879	443 197	7	1X9 79Ɛ	69Ɛ
8	776 X11	971	8	417 6X2	421	8	.863 959 100	91Ɛ
9	341 060	ƐƐƐ	9	.878 Ɛ94 281	666	9	508 3X1	Ɛ5Ɛ
X	.891 Ɛ07 061	436 248	X	750 817	8XƐ	X	077 442	451 1X0
Ɛ	690 X15	497	Ɛ	308 Ɛ28	Ɛ34	Ɛ	.862 826 262	420
.1530	256 53X	724	.1570	.877 X84 Ɛ24	444 179	.15Ɛ0	394 X42	661
1	.890 X1Ɛ X16	973	1	640 X37	403	1	.861 Ɛ43 3X1	8X0
2	5X5 063	ƐƐƐ	2	1Ɛ8 634	646	2	6Ɛ1 701	Ɛ21
3	16X 064	437 249	3	.876 973 ƐXX	890	3	25Ɛ 7X0	452 160
4	.88Ɛ 932 X17	497	4	52Ɛ 31X	Ɛ14	4	.860 X09 640	3X0
5	4Ɛ7 540	724	5	0X6 406	445 159	5	577 260	620
6	07Ɛ X18	971	6	.875 861 269	3X2	6	124 840	860
7	.88X 844 067	ƐƐX	7	417 X87	625	7	.85Ɛ 891 ƐX0	X9Ɛ
8	408 069	438 247	8	.874 Ɛ92 462	86X	8	43Ɛ 101	453 11X
9	.889 28Ɛ X22	494	9	748 7Ɛ4	XƐ2	9	.85X ƐX7 ƐX3	35X
X	753 54X	720	X	302 902	446 136	X	754 845	599
Ɛ	316 X2X	96X	Ɛ	.873 X78 788	37X	Ɛ	301 268	818
						.1600	.859 X69 650	

N	Tangent	d	N	Tangent	d	N	Tangent	d
.0000	.000 000 000	634 942	.0040	.021 174 533	634 Ɛ84	.0080	.042 343 317	635 677
1	0 634 942	942	1	1 7X9 4Ɛ7	Ɛ95	1	2 978 992	69Ɛ
2	1 069 684	942	2	2 222 490	ƐX8	2	3 3Ɛ2 471	703
3	1 6X2 406	943	3	2 857 478	ƐƐX	3	3 X27 Ɛ74	727
4	2 117 149	945	4	3 290 476	635 011	4	4 461 69Ɛ	751
5	2 74Ɛ X92	946	5	3 905 487	025	5	4 X97 230	775
6	3 184 818	947	6	4 33X 4Ɛ0	038	6	5 510 9X5	79Ɛ
7	3 7Ɛ9 563	94X	7	4 973 528	050	7	5 Ɛ46 584	804
8	4 232 2Ɛ1	950	8	5 3X8 578	064	8	6 580 188	82X
9	4 867 041	953	9	5 X21 620	078	9	6 ƐƐ5 9Ɛ6	855
X	5 29Ɛ 994	955	X	6 456 698	091	X	7 62Ɛ 64Ɛ	87Ɛ
Ɛ	5 914 729	958	Ɛ	6 X8Ɛ 769	0X6	Ɛ	8 065 30X	8X5
.0010	6 349 485	960	.0050	7 504 853	0ƐƐ	.0090	8 69X ƐƐ3	911
1	6 982 225	964	1	7 Ɛ39 952	115	1	9 114 904	938
2	7 3Ɛ6 Ɛ89	968	2	8 572 X67	12X	2	9 74X 640	964
3	7 X2Ɛ 935	970	3	8 ƐX7 Ɛ95	145	3	X 184 3X4	98Ɛ
4	8 464 6X5	975	4	9 621 11X	15X	4	X 7ƐX 173	9Ɛ8
5	8 X99 45X	979	5	X 056 278	176	5	Ɛ 233 Ɛ6Ɛ	X24
6	9 512 217	983	6	X 68Ɛ 432	191	6	Ɛ 869 993	X51
7	9 Ɛ46 Ɛ9X	988	7	Ɛ 104 603	1X7	7	.050 2X3 824	X7X
8	X 57Ɛ 966	992	8	Ɛ 739 7XX	204	8	0 919 6X2	XX8
9	X ƐƐ4 738	998	9	.030 172 9Ɛ2	21Ɛ	9	1 353 58X	Ɛ15
X	Ɛ 629 514	9X2	X	0 7X8 011	237	X	1 989 4X3	Ɛ43
Ɛ	.010 062 2Ɛ6	9X9	Ɛ	1 221 248	254	Ɛ	2 403 426	Ɛ71
.0020	0 697 0X3	9Ɛ4	.0060	1 856 4X0	270	.00X0	2 X39 397	ƐX0
1	1 10Ɛ X97	9ƐƐ	1	2 28Ɛ 750	289	1	3 473 377	636 00X
2	1 744 896	X06	2	2 904 X19	2X7	2	3 XX9 385	03X
3	2 179 6X0	X12	3	3 33X 104	304	3	4 523 403	069
4	2 7Ɛ2 4Ɛ2	X1X	4	3 973 408	322	4	4 Ɛ59 470	099
5	3 227 310	X27	5	4 3X8 72X	340	5	5 593 549	109
6	3 860 137	X33	6	4 X21 X6X	35Ɛ	6	6 009 656	138
7	4 294 Ɛ6X	X40	7	5 457 209	379	7	6 643 792	16X
8	4 909 9XX	X49	8	5 X90 586	398	8	7 079 940	19X
9	5 342 837	X57	9	6 505 962	3Ɛ7	9	7 6Ɛ3 Ɛ1X	210
X	5 977 692	X64	X	6 Ɛ3Ɛ 159	417	X	8 12X 12X	240
Ɛ	6 3Ɛ0 536	X73	Ɛ	7 574 574	437	Ɛ	8 764 36X	273
.0030	6 X25 3X9	X81	.0070	7 ƐX9 9XƐ	457	.00Ɛ0	9 19X 621	2X4
1	7 45X 26X	X8Ɛ	1	8 623 246	478	1	9 814 905	317
2	7 X93 139	X9Ɛ	2	9 058 702	498	2	X 24Ɛ 020	349
3	8 508 018	XX9	3	9 691 Ɛ9X	4Ɛ9	3	X 885 369	380
4	8 Ɛ40 Ɛ05	XƐ9	4	X 107 497	51X	4	Ɛ 2ƐƐ 729	3Ɛ4
5	9 575 X02	Ɛ09	5	X 740 9Ɛ5	540	5	Ɛ 935 Ɛ21	426
6	9 ƐXX 90Ɛ	Ɛ19	6	Ɛ 176 335	562	6	.060 370 347	45Ɛ
7	X 623 828	Ɛ29	7	Ɛ 7XƐ 897	584	7	0 9X6 7X6	492
8	Ɛ 058 755	Ɛ3X	8	.040 225 25Ɛ	5X7	8	1 421 078	507
9	Ɛ 691 693	Ɛ4Ɛ	9	0 85X 846	609	9	1 X57 583	53Ɛ
X	.020 106 622	Ɛ60	X	1 294 253	630	X	2 491 Ɛ02	574
Ɛ	0 73Ɛ 582	Ɛ71	Ɛ	1 909 883	654	Ɛ	2 Ɛ08 476	5X9

N	Tangent	d	N	Tangent	d	N	Tangent	d
.0100	.063 542 X63	636 623	.0140	.084 789 91Ɛ	637 X45	.0180	.0X5 X76 5X5	639 726
1	3 Ɛ79 486	659	1	5 205 764	X91	1	6 4Ɛ4 10Ɛ	784
2	4 5Ɛ3 Ɛ23	692	2	5 841 635	Ɛ18	2	6 Ɛ31 893	821
3	5 02X 5Ɛ5	709	3	6 279 551	Ɛ65	3	7 56Ɛ 4Ɛ4	880
4	5 665 102	743	4	6 8Ɛ5 4Ɛ6	ƐƐ2	4	7 ƐX9 174	91Ɛ
5	6 09Ɛ 845	77Ɛ	5	7 331 4X8	638 03X	5	8 626 X93	979
6	6 716 404	7Ɛ5	6	7 969 526	087	6	9 064 850	X18
7	7 150 ƐƐ9	831	7	8 3X5 5Ɛ1	115	7	9 6X2 668	X78
8	7 787 82X	869	8	8 X21 706	162	8	X 120 524	Ɛ18
9	8 202 497	8X4	9	9 459 868	1Ɛ1	9	X 75X 440	Ɛ77
X	8 839 17Ɛ	922	X	9 X95 X59	23Ɛ	X	Ɛ 198 3Ɛ7	63X 018
Ɛ	9 273 XX1	959	Ɛ	X 512 098	289	Ɛ	Ɛ 816 413	079
.0110	9 8XX 83X	997	.0150	X Ɛ4X 365	318	.0190	.0Ɛ0 254 490	119
1	X 325 615	X14	1	Ɛ 586 681	367	1	0 892 5X9	17Ɛ
2	X 960 429	X51	2	.090 002 X28	3Ɛ7	2	1 310 768	220
3	Ɛ 397 27X	X8Ɛ	3	0 63Ɛ 223	447	3	1 94X 988	282
4	Ɛ X12 149	Ɛ0X	4	1 077 66X	496	4	2 389 04X	324
5	.070 449 057	Ɛ47	5	1 6Ɛ3 Ɛ44	527	5	2 X07 372	387
6	0 X83 ƐX2	Ɛ86	6	2 130 46Ɛ	578	6	3 445 739	429
7	1 4ƐX Ɛ68	637 006	7	2 768 X27	608	7	3 X83 Ɛ66	490
8	1 Ɛ35 Ɛ72	044	8	3 1X5 433	65X	8	4 502 436	533
9	2 570 ƐƐ6	084	9	3 821 X91	6XƐ	9	4 Ɛ40 969	597
X	2 ƐX8 07X	104	X	4 25X 580	741	X	5 57Ɛ 344	63Ɛ
Ɛ	3 623 182	144	Ɛ	4 897 101	793	Ɛ	5 ƐƐ9 983	6X3
.0120	4 05X 306	184	.0160	5 313 894	825	.01X0	6 638 466	747
1	4 695 48X	205	1	5 950 4Ɛ9	878	1	7 076 ƐƐ1	7Ɛ0
2	5 110 693	246	2	6 389 175	90Ɛ	2	7 6Ɛ5 7X1	855
3	5 747 919	287	3	6 X05 X84	962	3	8 134 436	8ƐƐ
4	6 182 ƐX4	309	4	7 442 826	9Ɛ6	4	8 773 135	964
5	6 7ƐX 2Ɛ1	34Ɛ	5	7 X7Ɛ 620	X49	5	9 1Ɛ1 X99	X0X
6	7 235 640	391	6	8 4Ɛ8 469	XX2	6	9 830 8X7	X74
7	7 870 X11	413	7	8 Ɛ35 34Ɛ	Ɛ36	7	X 26Ɛ 75Ɛ	Ɛ1Ɛ
8	8 2X8 224	456	8	9 572 285	Ɛ8Ɛ	8	X 8XX 67X	Ɛ85
9	8 923 67X	499	9	9 ƐXƐ 254	639 024	9	Ɛ 329 643	63Ɛ 031
X	9 35X Ɛ57	520	X	X 628 278	079	X	Ɛ 968 674	098
Ɛ	9 996 477	564	Ɛ	Ɛ 065 335	112	Ɛ	.100 3X7 750	144
.0130	X 411 X1Ɛ	5X8	.0170	Ɛ 6X2 447	169	.01Ɛ0	0 X26 894	1XƐ
1	X X49 407	630	1	.0X0 11Ɛ 5Ɛ4	203	1	1 465 X83	258
2	Ɛ 484 X37	674	2	0 758 7Ɛ7	259	2	1 XX5 11Ɛ	305
3	Ɛ Ɛ00 4XƐ	6Ɛ9	3	1 195 X54	2Ɛ4	3	2 524 424	371
4	.080 537 ƐX8	742	4	1 813 148	34Ɛ	4	2 Ɛ63 795	41Ɛ
5	0 Ɛ73 72X	788	5	2 250 497	3X6	5	3 5X2 ƐƐ4	488
6	1 5XƐ 2Ɛ6	811	6	2 889 881	442	6	4 022 480	536
7	2 026 Ɛ07	857	7	3 307 103	49X	7	4 661 9Ɛ6	5X3
8	2 662 762	8X1	8	3 944 5X1	536	8	5 0X1 399	653
9	3 09X 443	928	9	4 381 Ɛ17	593	9	5 720 X30	700
X	3 716 16Ɛ	972	X	4 9ƐƐ 4XX	62Ɛ	X	6 160 530	770
Ɛ	4 151 Ɛ21	9ƐX	Ɛ	5 438 Ɛ19	688	Ɛ	6 7X0 0X0	81Ɛ

N	Tangent	d	N	Tangent	d	N	Tangent	d
.0200	.107 21Ɛ 8ƐƐ	63Ɛ 88Ɛ	.0240	.128 658 492	642 301	.0280	.149 Ɛ83 585	645 209
1	7 85Ɛ 58χ	93χ	1	9 09χ 793	383	1	χ 608 792	2χ2
2	8 29Ɛ 308	9χχ	2	9 720 Ɛ56	446	2	Ɛ 051 χ74	376
3	8 91Ɛ 0Ɛ6	χ5Ɛ	3	χ 163 3χ0	508	3	Ɛ 697 22χ	450
4	9 35χ Ɛ55	Ɛ10	4	χ 7χ5 8χ8	58Ɛ	4	.150 120 67χ	525
5	9 99χ χ65	Ɛ80	5	Ɛ 228 277	653	5	0 765 Ɛχ3	5ƐƐ
6	χ 41χ χ25	640 032	6	Ɛ 86χ 90χ	716	6	1 1χƐ 5χ2	695
7	χ χ5χ χ57	0χ4	7	.130 2Ɛ1 424	79χ	7	1 835 077	770
8	Ɛ 49χ Ɛ3Ɛ	155	8	0 934 002	863	8	2 27χ 827	846
9	Ɛ Ɛ1Ɛ 094	208	9	1 376 865	927	9	2 904 471	921
χ	.110 55Ɛ 2χ0	27χ	χ	1 9Ɛ9 590	9χƐ	χ	3 34χ 192	9Ɛ9
Ɛ	0 Ɛ9Ɛ 55χ	331	Ɛ	2 440 37Ɛ	χ75	Ɛ	3 993 Ɛ8Ɛ	χ94
.0210	1 61Ɛ 88Ɛ	3χ4	.0250	2 χ83 234	Ɛ3χ	.0290	4 419 χ63	Ɛ70
1	2 060 073	457	1	3 506 172	643 004	1	4 χ63 χ13	646 048
2	2 6χ0 50χ	50Ɛ	2	3 Ɛ49 176	08χ	2	5 4χ9 χ5Ɛ	125
3	3 120 χ19	583	3	4 590 244	154	3	5 Ɛ33 Ɛ84	201
4	3 761 3χ0	637	4	5 013 398	21Ɛ	4	6 57χ 185	29Ɛ
5	4 1χ1 χ17	6Ɛ0	5	5 656 5Ɛ7	2χ6	5	7 004 464	378
6	4 822 507	765	6	6 099 8χ1	371	6	7 64χ 820	456
7	5 263 070	81χ	7	6 721 052	438	7	8 095 076	533
8	5 8χ3 88χ	893	8	7 164 48χ	504	8	8 71Ɛ 5χ9	612
9	6 324 561	949	9	7 7χ7 992	591	9	9 165 ƐƐƐ	6Ɛ1
χ	6 965 2χχ	χ03	χ	8 22Ɛ 363	658	χ	9 7Ɛ0 6Ɛ0	790
Ɛ	7 3χ6 0Ɛ1	χ79	Ɛ	8 872 9ƐƐ	726	Ɛ	χ 237 280	86Ɛ
.0220	7 χ26 Ɛ6χ	Ɛ35	.0260	9 2Ɛ6 525	7Ɛ2	.02χ0	χ 881 Ɛ2Ɛ	94χ
1	8 467 χχ3	ƐχƐ	1	9 93χ 117	880	1	Ɛ 308 879	χ2Ɛ
2	8 χχ8 χ92	641 066	2	χ 381 997	94χ	2	Ɛ 953 6χ8	Ɛ0χ
3	9 529 Ɛ38	122	3	χ χ05 725	χ17	3	.160 39χ 5Ɛ6	ƐχƐ
4	9 Ɛ6Ɛ 05χ	19χ	4	Ɛ 449 540	χχ5	4	0 χ25 5χ5	647 090
5	χ 5Ɛ0 238	255	5	Ɛ χ91 425	Ɛ74	5	1 470 675	171
6	Ɛ 031 491	313	6	.140 515 399	644 043	6	1 χƐ7 826	252
7	Ɛ 672 7χ4	38Ɛ	7	0 Ɛ59 420	112	7	2 542 χ78	334
8	.120 0Ɛ3 Ɛ73	448	8	1 5χ1 532	1χ2	8	2 Ɛ8χ 1Ɛ0	416
9	0 735 3ƐƐ	505	9	2 025 714	271	9	3 615 606	4Ɛ8
χ	1 176 904	583	χ	2 669 985	341	χ	4 060 Ɛ02	59Ɛ
Ɛ	1 7Ɛ8 287	641	Ɛ	3 0Ɛ2 106	411	Ɛ	4 6χ8 4χ1	682
.0230	2 239 908	6ƐƐ	.0270	3 736 517	4χ2	.02Ɛ0	5 133 Ɛ63	765
1	2 87Ɛ 407	77χ	1	4 17χ 9Ɛ9	574	1	5 77Ɛ 708	848
2	3 300 Ɛ85	838	2	4 803 371	644	2	6 207 354	930
3	3 942 801	8Ɛ8	3	5 247 9Ɛ5	716	3	6 853 084	χ15
4	4 384 4Ɛ9	977	4	5 890 50Ɛ	7χ7	4	7 29χ χ99	χƐ9
5	4 χ06 274	χ37	5	6 315 0Ɛ6	87χ	5	7 926 996	Ɛχ1
6	5 448 0χƐ	χƐ6	6	6 959 974	950	6	8 372 977	648 087
7	5 χ89 Ɛχ5	Ɛ77	7	7 3χ2 704	χ23	7	8 9Ɛχ χ42	170
8	6 50Ɛ Ɛ60	642 038	8	7 χ27 527	χƐ6	8	9 446 ƐƐ2	256
9	6 Ɛ51 Ɛ98	0Ɛ9	9	8 470 421	Ɛ8χ	9	9 χ93 248	340
χ	7 594 095	179	χ	8 χƐ5 3χƐ	645 061	χ	χ 51Ɛ 588	426
Ɛ	8 016 252	240	Ɛ	9 53χ 450	135	Ɛ	χ Ɛ67 9Ɛ2	510

N	Tangent	d	N	Tangent	d	N	Tangent	d
.0300	.16Ɛ 5Ɛ4 302	648 5Ɛ8	.0340	.191 146 305	650 296	.0380	.1Ɛ2 X15 372	654 474
1	.170 040 8ƐX	6X3	1	1 796 59Ɛ	394	1	3 469 826	585
2	0 689 3X1	78X	2	2 226 973	492	2	3 Ɛ02 1XƐ	696
3	1 115 Ɛ6Ɛ	876	3	2 877 245	591	3	4 556 885	7X9
4	1 762 825	962	4	3 307 816	691	4	4 ƐXƐ 472	8ƐX
5	2 1XƐ 587	X4Ɛ	5	3 958 2X7	78Ɛ	5	5 644 170	X11
6	2 838 416	Ɛ37	6	4 3X8 X76	88Ɛ	6	6 098 Ɛ81	Ɛ24
7	3 285 351	649 024	7	4 X39 745	98Ɛ	7	6 731 XX5	655 036
8	3 912 375	112	8	5 48X 514	X8Ɛ	8	7 186 Ɛ1Ɛ	14Ɛ
9	4 35Ɛ 487	200	9	5 Ɛ1Ɛ 3X3	Ɛ90	9	7 820 06X	261
X	4 9X8 687	2X9	X	6 570 373	651 091	X	8 275 30Ɛ	376
Ɛ	5 435 974	398	Ɛ	7 001 444	192	Ɛ	8 90X 685	48Ɛ
.0310	5 X83 150	486	.0350	7 652 616	293	.0390	9 363 Ɛ54	5X3
1	6 510 616	575	1	8 0X3 8X9	396	1	9 9Ɛ9 537	6Ɛ8
2	6 Ɛ59 Ɛ8Ɛ	665	2	8 735 083	497	2	X 453 033	811
3	7 5X7 634	754	3	9 186 55X	59X	3	X XX8 844	927
4	8 035 188	844	4	9 817 Ɛ38	6X1	4	Ɛ 542 56Ɛ	X41
5	8 682 X10	933	5	X 269 619	7X4	5	Ɛ Ɛ98 3Ɛ0	Ɛ58
6	9 110 743	X25	6	X 8ƐƐ 201	8X7	6	.200 632 348	656 072
7	9 75X 568	Ɛ15	7	Ɛ 350 XX8	9XƐ	7	1 088 3ƐX	189
8	X 1X8 481	64X 006	8	Ɛ 9X2 897	XƐ3	8	1 722 587	2X4
9	X 836 487	0Ɛ8	9	.1X0 434 78X	ƐƐ7	9	2 178 86Ɛ	3ƐƐ
X	Ɛ 284 583	1X9	X	0 X86 785	652 100	X	2 813 06X	518
Ɛ	Ɛ 912 770	29Ɛ	Ɛ	1 518 885	205	Ɛ	3 269 586	634
.0320	.180 360 X4Ɛ	392	.0360	1 Ɛ6X X8X	30X	.03X0	3 903 ƐƐX	750
1	0 9XƐ 221	484	1	2 601 198	414	1	4 35X 74X	869
2	1 439 6X5	577	2	3 053 5Ɛ0	519	2	4 9Ɛ5 3Ɛ7	986
3	1 X88 060	66X	3	3 6X5 Ɛ09	624	3	5 450 181	XX4
4	2 516 70X	762	4	4 138 531	72Ɛ	4	5 XX7 065	657 002
5	2 Ɛ65 270	856	5	4 78Ɛ 060	835	5	6 542 067	120
6	3 5Ɛ3 Ɛ06	94X	6	5 221 895	940	6	6 Ɛ99 187	23X
7	4 042 854	X42	7	5 874 615	X48	7	7 634 405	359
8	4 691 696	Ɛ37	8	6 307 461	Ɛ54	8	8 08Ɛ 762	478
9	5 120 611	64Ɛ 030	9	6 95X 3Ɛ5	653 060	9	8 727 01X	598
X	5 76Ɛ 641	126	X	7 3Ɛ1 455	169	X	9 182 5Ɛ6	6Ɛ7
Ɛ	6 1ƐX 767	21Ɛ	Ɛ	7 X44 602	275	Ɛ	9 81X 0Ɛ1	817
.0330	6 849 986	315	.0370	8 497 877	382	.03Ɛ0	X 275 908	938
1	7 299 09Ɛ	410	1	8 Ɛ2Ɛ 039	48Ɛ	1	X 911 644	X58
2	7 928 4XƐ	506	2	9 582 508	59X	2	Ɛ 369 4X0	Ɛ7X
3	8 377 9Ɛ5	602	3	X 015 XX6	6X7	3	Ɛ X05 45X	658 09Ɛ
4	8 X07 3Ɛ7	6Ɛ8	4	X 669 591	7Ɛ6	4	.210 461 539	200
5	9 456 XƐ3	7Ɛ4	5	Ɛ 101 187	904	5	0 XƐ9 739	323
6	9 XX6 6X7	8Ɛ1	6	Ɛ 754 X8Ɛ	X13	6	1 555 X60	444
7	X 536 398	9X8	7	.1Ɛ0 1X8 8X2	Ɛ23	7	1 ƐƐ2 2X4	568
8	X Ɛ86 184	XX5	8	0 840 805	654 032	8	2 64X 850	68X
9	Ɛ 616 069	ƐX1	9	1 294 837	142	9	3 0X7 31X	7Ɛ2
X	.190 066 04X	650 09Ɛ	X	1 928 979	252	X	3 743 Ɛ10	915
Ɛ	0 6Ɛ6 129	198	Ɛ	2 381 00Ɛ	363	Ɛ	4 1X0 825	X3X

N	Tangent	d	N	Tangent	d	N	Tangent	d
.0400	.214 839 663	658 Ɛ61	.0440	.236 813 603	661 Ɛ71	.0480	.258 978 127	667 4Ɛ6
1	5 296 604	659 086	1	7 275 574	662 0XX	1	9 423 621	647
2	5 933 68X	1XƐ	2	7 917 662	226	2	9 X8Ɛ 068	797
3	6 390 879	315	3	8 379 888	363	3	X 536 843	928
4	6 X29 Ɛ92	439	4	8 X20 02Ɛ	4X0	4	X ƐX2 56Ɛ	X7X
5	7 487 40Ɛ	564	5	9 482 50Ɛ	61X	5	Ɛ 64X 429	668 00Ɛ
6	7 Ɛ24 973	68X	6	9 Ɛ24 Ɛ29	758	6	.260 0Ɛ6 438	161
7	8 582 441	7Ɛ4	7	X 587 685	896	7	0 762 599	2Ɛ4
8	8 020 035	920	8	Ɛ 02X 35Ɛ	X15	8	1 20X 891	446
9	9 679 955	X46	9	Ɛ 691 174	Ɛ54	9	1 877 117	599
X	X 117 79Ɛ	Ɛ72	X	.240 134 108	663 092	X	2 323 6Ɛ4	731
Ɛ	X 775 751	65X 09X	Ɛ	0 797 19X	213	Ɛ	2 990 225	884
.0410	Ɛ 213 82Ɛ	206	.0450	1 23X 3Ɛ1	352	.0490	3 438 XX9	X19
1	Ɛ 871 X35	332	1	1 8X1 743	493	1	3 XX5 906	Ɛ70
2	.220 310 167	45Ɛ	2	2 345 016	614	2	4 552 876	669 106
3	0 96X 606	589	3	2 9X8 62X	754	3	4 ƐƐƐ 980	25X
4	1 408 Ɛ93	6Ɛ6	4	3 450 182	895	4	5 669 01X	3Ɛ4
5	1 X67 689	823	5	3 XƐ3 X57	X17	5	6 116 412	54X
6	2 506 2Ɛ0	952	6	4 557 872	Ɛ59	6	6 783 960	6X4
7	2 Ɛ65 042	X80	7	4 ƐƐƐ 80Ɛ	664 0X0	7	7 231 444	83X
8	3 603 Ɛ02	ƐXƐ	8	5 663 8XƐ	222	8	7 89Ɛ 082	995
9	4 062 XƐ1	65Ɛ 11X	9	6 107 Ɛ11	364	9	8 348 X57	Ɛ30
X	4 702 00Ɛ	249	X	6 770 275	4X8	X	8 9Ɛ6 987	66X 088
Ɛ	5 161 258	37X	Ɛ	7 214 761	630	Ɛ	9 464 X53	223
.0420	5 800 616	4X9	.0460	7 879 191	774	.04X0	9 Ɛ13 076	37Ɛ
1	6 25Ɛ Ɛ03	619	1	8 321 945	8Ɛ7	1	X 581 435	518
2	6 8ƐƐ 520	74Ɛ	2	8 986 640	X41	2	Ɛ 02Ɛ 951	675
3	7 35Ɛ 06Ɛ	87Ɛ	3	9 42Ɛ 481	Ɛ85	3	Ɛ 69X 406	812
4	7 9ƐX 92X	9Ɛ1	4	9 X94 446	665 10Ɛ	4	.270 149 018	96Ɛ
5	8 45X 71Ɛ	Ɛ22	5	X 539 555	254	5	0 7Ɛ7 987	Ɛ0X
6	8 XƐX 641	660 055	6	X ƐX2 7X9	39X	6	1 266 895	66Ɛ 067
7	9 55X 696	187	7	Ɛ 647 Ɛ87	524	7	1 915 940	206
8	9 ƐƐX 861	2Ɛ9	8	.250 0Ɛ1 4XƐ	66Ɛ	8	2 384 Ɛ46	365
9	X 65X Ɛ5X	431	9	0 756 Ɛ5X	7Ɛ6	9	2 X34 2XƐ	504
X	Ɛ 0ƐƐ 38Ɛ	564	X	1 200 754	941	X	3 4X3 7Ɛ3	663
Ɛ	Ɛ 75Ɛ 933	697	Ɛ	1 866 495	X89	Ɛ	3 Ɛ53 256	804
.0430	.230 200 40X	810	.0470	2 310 362	666 015	.04Ɛ0	4 602 X5X	963
1	0 861 01X	943	1	2 976 377	161	1	5 072 801	Ɛ05
2	1 301 961	X79	2	3 420 518	2X9	2	5 722 706	670 065
3	1 962 81X	ƐƐ2	3	3 X86 805	437	3	6 192 76Ɛ	206
4	2 403 810	661 126	4	4 531 040	584	4	6 842 975	369
5	2 X64 936	261	5	4 Ɛ97 604	711	5	7 2Ɛ3 122	50X
6	3 505 Ɛ97	396	6	5 642 115	860	6	7 963 630	670
7	3 Ɛ67 371	511	7	6 0X8 975	9X9	7	8 414 0X0	813
8	4 608 882	648	8	6 753 762	Ɛ39	8	8 X84 8Ɛ3	976
9	5 06X 30X	782	9	7 1ƐX 69Ɛ	667 087	9	9 535 669	Ɛ19
X	5 70Ɛ X90	8ƐX	X	7 865 766	217	X	9 ƐX6 586	671 081
Ɛ	6 171 78X	X35	Ɛ	8 310 981	366	Ɛ	X 657 647	225

N	Tangent	d	N	Tangent	d	N	Tangent	d
.0500	.27Ɛ 108 870	671 38X	.0540	.2X1 663 260	677 805	.0580	.304 221 Ɛ89	682 602
1	Ɛ 77X 03X	532	1	2 11X X65	983	1	4 8X4 58Ɛ	794
2	.280 22Ɛ 570	697	2	2 796 828	Ɛ41	2	5 367 163	968
3	0 8X1 047	841	3	3 252 769	678 0ƐƐ	3	5 X29 Ɛ0Ɛ	Ɛ3Ɛ
4	1 352 888	9X6	4	3 90X 868	279	4	6 4Ɛ0 X4X	683 113
5	1 X04 672	Ɛ51	5	4 386 Ɛ25	439	5	6 Ɛ73 Ɛ61	2X8
6	2 476 603	672 0Ɛ7	6	4 X43 362	5Ɛ7	6	7 637 249	480
7	2 Ɛ28 6ƐX	262	7	5 4ƐƐ 959	778	7	8 0ƐX 709	654
8	3 59X 960	408	8	5 Ɛ78 515	937	8	8 782 161	82Ɛ
9	4 051 168	575	9	6 635 250	XƐ8	9	9 245 990	X04
X	4 703 721	720	X	7 0Ɛ2 148	679 079	X	9 909 794	Ɛ99
Ɛ	5 176 241	889	Ɛ	7 76Ɛ 205	239	Ɛ	X 391 771	684 175
.0510	5 828 Ɛ0X	X34	.0550	8 228 442	3ƐƐ	.0590	X X55 926	34Ɛ
1	6 29Ɛ 942	ƐX2	1	8 8X5 841	581	1	Ɛ 51X 075	526
2	6 952 924	673 14Ɛ	2	9 363 202	743	2	Ɛ ƐX2 59Ɛ	702
3	7 405 X73	2Ɛ9	3	9 X20 945	905	3	.310 667 0X1	899
4	7 X79 170	467	4	X 49X 64X	X89	4	1 12Ɛ 97X	X76
5	8 530 617	615	5	X Ɛ58 517	67X 04Ɛ	5	1 7Ɛ4 834	685 053
6	8 ƐX4 030	783	6	Ɛ 616 566	214	6	2 279 887	2ƐƐ
7	9 657 7Ɛ3	932	7	.2Ɛ0 094 77X	397	7	2 942 XƐ6	409
8	X 10Ɛ 525	XX2	8	0 752 Ɛ55	55Ɛ	8	3 408 303	5X7
9	X 783 407	674 052	9	1 211 4Ɛ4	724	9	3 X91 8XX	784
X	Ɛ 237 459	201	X	1 890 018	8X9	X	4 557 472	964
Ɛ	Ɛ 8XƐ 65X	372	Ɛ	2 34X 905	X73	Ɛ	5 021 216	Ɛ41
.0520	.290 363 X10	523	.0560	2 X09 778	67Ɛ 038	.05X0	5 6X7 157	686 122
1	0 X18 333	693	1	3 488 7Ɛ4	202	1	6 171 279	300
2	1 490 X06	845	2	3 Ɛ47 9Ɛ6	389	2	6 837 579	4X1
3	1 Ɛ45 64Ɛ	9Ɛ7	3	4 607 183	553	3	7 301 X5X	681
4	2 5ƐX 446	Ɛ69	4	5 086 716	71Ɛ	4	7 988 51Ɛ	861
5	3 073 3Ɛ3	675 120	5	5 746 235	8X6	5	8 453 180	X43
6	3 728 513	292	6	6 205 Ɛ1Ɛ	X72	6	8 Ɛ1X 003	687 024
7	4 1X1 7X5	445	7	6 885 991	680 03X	7	9 5X5 027	206
8	4 857 02X	5Ɛ9	8	7 345 X0Ɛ	207	8	X 070 231	3X8
9	5 310 627	771	9	7 X06 016	394	9	X 737 619	58X
X	5 986 198	925	X	8 486 3XX	561	X	Ɛ 202 ƐX7	772
Ɛ	6 43Ɛ Ɛ01	X9X	Ɛ	8 Ɛ46 94Ɛ	72Ɛ	Ɛ	Ɛ 88X 759	954
.0530	6 XƐ5 99Ɛ	676 052	.0570	9 607 47X	8Ɛ9	.05Ɛ0	.320 356 4Ɛ1	Ɛ38
1	7 56Ɛ X31	208	1	X 088 177	X88	1	0 X22 429	688 121
2	8 026 039	382	2	X 749 043	681 056	2	1 4XX 54X	304
3	8 6X0 3ƐƐ	537	3	Ɛ 20X 099	225	3	1 Ɛ76 852	4XX
4	9 156 936	6Ɛ2	4	Ɛ 88Ɛ 302	3Ɛ5	4	2 643 140	692
5	9 811 428	868	5	.300 350 6Ɛ7	585	5	3 10Ɛ 812	878
6	X 288 094	X24	6	0 X12 080	755	6	3 798 48X	X62
7	X 942 XƐ8	Ɛ9Ɛ	7	1 493 815	925	7	4 265 330	689 048
8	Ɛ 3Ɛ9 X97	677 157	8	1 Ɛ55 53X	XƐ6	8	4 932 378	233
9	Ɛ X75 032	313	9	2 617 434	682 088	9	5 3ƐƐ 5XƐ	41X
X	.2X0 530 345	48Ɛ	X	3 099 500	25X	X	5 X88 X09	605
Ɛ	0 ƐX7 814	648	Ɛ	3 75Ɛ 75X	42Ɛ	Ɛ	6 556 412	7Ɛ0

N	Tangent	d	N	Tangent	d	N	Tangent	d
.0600	.327 024 002	689 999	.0640	.34X 088 X7Ɛ	695 772	.0680	.371 3Ɛ4 Ɛ15	6X1 Ɛ66
1	7 6Ɛ1 99Ɛ	Ɛ86	1	X 762 631	975	1	1 X96 X7Ɛ	6X2 185
2	8 17Ɛ 965	68X 172	2	Ɛ 238 3X6	Ɛ77	2	2 579 044	3X2
3	8 849 Ɛ17	35Ɛ	3	Ɛ 912 361	696 180	3	3 05Ɛ 426	600
4	9 318 276	549	4	.350 3X8 521	383	4	3 741 X26	81Ɛ
5	9 9X6 803	737	5	0 X82 8X4	587	5	4 224 645	X3X
6	X 475 33X	926	6	1 559 26Ɛ	790	6	4 907 483	6X3 059
7	X Ɛ44 064	Ɛ14	7	2 033 X3Ɛ	995	7	5 3XX 520	27X
8	Ɛ 612 Ɛ78	68Ɛ 103	8	2 70X 814	Ɛ9Ɛ	8	5 X91 79X	499
9	.330 0X2 07Ɛ	2Ɛ3	9	3 1X5 7Ɛ3	697 1X4	9	6 575 077	6ƐƐ
X	0 771 372	4X2	X	3 880 997	3XX	X	7 058 776	91Ɛ
Ɛ	1 240 854	693	Ɛ	4 358 185	5Ɛ5	Ɛ	7 740 495	Ɛ41
.0610	1 910 327	883	.0650	4 X33 77X	800	.0690	8 224 416	6X4 163
1	2 39Ɛ ƐXX	X75	1	5 50Ɛ 37X	X07	1	8 908 579	385
2	2 X6Ɛ X63	690 066	2	5 ƐX7 185	698 013	2	9 3Ɛ0 942	5X7
3	3 53Ɛ Ɛ09	257	3	6 683 198	220	3	9 X95 329	80Ɛ
4	4 010 164	44X	4	7 15Ɛ 3Ɛ8	427	4	X 579 Ɛ38	X32
5	4 6X0 5Ɛ2	640	5	7 837 823	635	5	Ɛ 062 96X	6X5 056
6	5 171 032	833	6	8 314 258	841	6	Ɛ 747 X04	27X
7	5 841 865	X26	7	8 9Ɛ0 X99	X50	7	.380 231 082	4X3
8	6 312 68Ɛ	691 01X	8	9 489 929	699 05X	8	0 916 565	708
9	6 9X3 6X9	212	9	9 Ɛ66 987	268	9	1 400 071	932
X	7 474 8ƐƐ	406	X	X 644 033	476	X	1 XX5 9X3	Ɛ57
Ɛ	7 Ɛ46 105	5ƐƐ	Ɛ	Ɛ 121 4X9	687	Ɛ	2 58Ɛ 93X	6X6 182
.0620	8 617 704	7Ɛ4	.0660	Ɛ 7ƐX Ɛ74	895	.06X0	3 075 Ɛ00	3X8
1	9 0X9 2Ɛ8	9XX	1	.360 298 849	XX6	1	3 760 2X8	614
2	9 77Ɛ 0X6	ƐX3	2	0 976 733	69X 0Ɛ6	2	4 246 900	83Ɛ
3	X 251 089	692 19X	3	1 454 829	307	3	4 931 53Ɛ	X66
4	X 923 267	395	4	1 Ɛ32 Ɛ34	518	4	5 418 3X5	6X7 094
5	Ɛ 3Ɛ5 640	58Ɛ	5	2 611 450	72X	5	5 Ɛ03 479	2ƐƐ
6	Ɛ X88 00Ɛ	787	6	3 0XƐ Ɛ7X	940	6	6 5XX 778	529
7	.340 55X 796	983	7	3 78X 8ƐX	Ɛ52	7	7 096 0X5	757
8	1 031 559	Ɛ7Ɛ	8	4 269 850	69Ɛ 165	8	7 781 840	984
9	1 704 518	693 177	9	4 948 9Ɛ5	378	9	8 269 604	ƐƐ3
X	2 197 693	375	X	5 428 171	58Ɛ	X	8 955 5Ɛ7	6X8 221
Ɛ	2 86X X48	572	Ɛ	5 Ɛ07 740	7X4	Ɛ	9 441 818	451
.0630	3 342 3ƐX	76Ɛ	.0670	6 5X7 324	9Ɛ8	.06Ɛ0	9 Ɛ2X 069	680
1	3 X15 Ɛ69	96X	1	7 087 120	6X0 010	1	X 616 729	8Ɛ0
2	4 4X9 917	Ɛ68	2	7 767 130	226	2	Ɛ 103 419	Ɛ20
3	4 Ɛ81 883	694 167	3	8 247 356	43Ɛ	3	Ɛ 7Ɛ0 339	6X9 151
4	5 655 X2X	366	4	8 927 795	655	4	.390 299 48X	383
5	6 12X 194	566	5	9 408 22X	870	5	0 986 851	5Ɛ4
6	6 802 73X	766	6	9 XX8 X9X	X86	6	1 474 245	825
7	7 297 2X4	966	7	X 589 964	6X1 0X1	7	1 Ɛ61 X6X	X59
8	7 970 04X	Ɛ67	8	Ɛ 06X X45	2Ɛ9	8	2 64Ɛ 907	6XX 08Ɛ
9	8 444 ƐƐ5	695 168	9	Ɛ 750 142	514	9	3 139 996	302
X	8 Ɛ1X 161	36X	X	.370 231 656	731	X	3 828 098	536
Ɛ	9 5Ɛ3 50Ɛ	570	Ɛ	0 913 187	94X	Ɛ	4 316 612	76X

N	Tangent	d	N	Tangent	d	N	Tangent	d
.0700	.394 X05 180	6XX 9X2	.0740	.3Ɛ8 71Ɛ 410	6Ɛ8 287	.0780	.420 762 247	706 243
1	5 4Ɛ3 Ɛ62	6XƐ 017	1	9 217 697	518	1	1 268 48X	4Ɛ1
2	5 ƐX2 Ɛ79	251	2	9 913 ƐƐ3	768	2	1 972 97Ɛ	75Ɛ
3	6 692 20X	486	3	X 410 75Ɛ	9ƐƐ	3	2 479 51X	X0X
4	7 181 694	700	4	X Ɛ09 55X	6Ɛ9 051	4	2 Ɛ84 328	707 078
5	7 871 194	937	5	Ɛ 606 5XƐ	2X3	5	3 68Ɛ 3X4	328
6	8 360 Ɛ0Ɛ	Ɛ72	6	.400 103 892	536	6	4 196 710	597
7	8 X50 X81	6Ɛ0 1X9	7	0 801 208	78X	7	4 8X2 0X7	848
8	9 541 06X	424	8	1 2ƐX 996	X21	8	5 3X9 933	XƐ8
9	X 031 492	661	9	1 9Ɛ8 7Ɛ7	6ƐX 076	9	5 XƐ5 82Ɛ	708 169
X	X 721 Ɛ33	899	X	2 4Ɛ6 871	30X	X	6 601 998	41Ɛ
Ɛ	Ɛ 212 810	Ɛ17	Ɛ	2 ƐƐ4 Ɛ7Ɛ	564	Ɛ	7 10X 1Ɛ7	691
.0710	Ɛ 903 727	6Ɛ1 153	.0750	3 6Ɛ3 523	7Ɛ9	.0790	7 816 888	943
1	.3X0 3Ɛ4 87X	392	1	4 1Ɛ2 120	X53	1	8 323 60Ɛ	ƐƐ6
2	0 XX6 050	610	2	4 8Ɛ0 Ɛ73	6ƐƐ 0X9	2	8 X30 605	709 269
3	1 597 660	84X	3	5 3Ɛ0 060	344	3	9 539 872	521
4	2 089 2XX	X89	4	5 XXƐ 3X4	5X0	4	X 047 193	796
5	2 77Ɛ 177	6Ɛ2 109	5	6 5XX 984	837	5	X 754 969	X49
6	3 271 284	349	6	7 0XX 5ƐƐ	X93	6	Ɛ 262 7Ɛ6	70X 103
7	3 963 611	588	7	7 7XX 492	700 130	7	Ɛ 970 8Ɛ9	379
8	4 455 Ɛ99	80X	8	8 2XX 602	389	8	.430 47Ɛ 076	632
9	4 Ɛ48 7X7	X4Ɛ	9	8 9XX 98Ɛ	626	9	0 Ɛ89 6X8	8X9
X	5 63Ɛ 636	6Ɛ3 090	X	9 4XƐ 3Ɛ5	884	X	1 698 395	Ɛ63
Ɛ	6 132 706	312	Ɛ	9 ƐƐ0 079	Ɛ22	Ɛ	2 1X7 338	70Ɛ 21Ɛ
.0720	6 825 X18	555	.0760	X 6Ɛ0 Ɛ9Ɛ	701 181	.07X0	2 8Ɛ6 557	497
1	7 319 371	797	1	Ɛ 1Ɛ2 160	420	1	3 405 X32	753
2	7 X10 Ɛ48	X1X	2	Ɛ 8Ɛ3 580	680	2	3 Ɛ15 585	X0Ɛ
3	8 504 966	6Ɛ4 063	3	.410 3Ɛ5 040	91Ɛ	3	4 625 394	710 089
4	8 ƐƐ8 X09	2X6	4	0 XƐ6 95Ɛ	Ɛ80	4	5 135 461	346
5	9 6Ɛ1 0Ɛ3	52X	5	1 5Ɛ8 91Ɛ	702 221	5	5 845 7X7	604
6	X 1X5 621	774	6	2 0ƐX Ɛ40	482	6	6 356 1XƐ	882
7	X 89X 195	9Ɛ8	7	2 801 402	724	7	6 X66 X71	Ɛ41
8	Ɛ 392 Ɛ91	6Ɛ5 043	8	3 303 Ɛ26	986	8	7 577 9Ɛ2	711 201
9	Ɛ X88 014	288	9	3 X06 8Ɛ0	703 029	9	8 088 ƐƐ3	480
X	.3Ɛ0 581 2X0	513	X	4 509 919	28Ɛ	X	8 79X 473	741
Ɛ	1 076 7Ɛ3	75X	Ɛ	5 010 ƐXƐ	533	Ɛ	9 2XƐ ƐƐ4	X01
.0730	1 770 351	9X5	.0770	5 714 51Ɛ	797	.07Ɛ0	9 X01 9Ɛ5	712 082
1	2 266 136	6Ɛ6 032	1	6 218 0Ɛ6	X40	1	X 513 X77	344
2	2 960 168	279	2	6 91Ɛ Ɛ36	704 0X3	2	Ɛ 026 1ƐƐ	606
3	3 456 425	506	3	7 424 019	34X	3	Ɛ 738 805	889
4	3 Ɛ50 92Ɛ	753	4	7 Ɛ28 367	5Ɛ2	4	.440 24Ɛ 492	Ɛ4Ɛ
5	4 647 482	9X1	5	8 630 959	859	5	0 962 421	713 212
6	5 142 263	6Ɛ7 02X	6	9 135 5Ɛ6	Ɛ04	6	1 475 633	497
7	5 839 291	279	7	9 83X 4ƐX	705 16X	7	1 Ɛ88 Ɛ0X	75Ɛ
8	6 334 54X	507	8	X 343 668	415	8	2 6X0 669	X23
9	6 X2Ɛ X55	757	9	X X48 X81	682	9	3 1Ɛ4 490	714 0X9
X	7 527 5Ɛ0	9X6	X	Ɛ 552 543	929	X	3 908 579	372
Ɛ	8 023 396	6Ɛ8 036	Ɛ	.420 058 270	Ɛ97	Ɛ	4 420 92Ɛ	638

N	Tangent	d
.0800	.444 Ɛ35 367	714 903
1	5 64χ 06χ	Ɛ8χ
2	6 163 038	715 256
3	6 878 292	521
4	7 391 7Ɛ3	7χχ
5	7 χχ7 3χ1	χ76
6	8 601 257	716 144
7	9 117 39Ɛ	411
8	9 831 7Ɛ0	6χ0
9	χ 348 290	96χ
χ	χ χ63 03χ	717 039
Ɛ	Ɛ 57χ 077	309
.0810	.450 095 384	599
1	0 7Ɛ0 961	86χ
2	1 308 60Ɛ	Ɛ3χ
3	1 χ24 549	718 210
4	2 540 759	4χ1
5	3 059 03χ	774
6	3 775 7Ɛ2	χ47
7	4 292 639	719 11χ
8	4 9χƐ 757	3Ɛ1
9	5 508 Ɛ48	686
χ	6 026 612	95Ɛ
Ɛ	6 744 371	71χ 033
.0820	7 262 3χ4	309
1	7 980 6Ɛ1	5χ3
2	8 49Ɛ 094	87χ
3	8 ƐƐ9 952	Ɛ54
4	9 718 8χ6	71Ɛ 230
5	χ 237 Ɛ16	507
6	χ 957 421	7χ4
7	Ɛ 477 005	χ81
8	Ɛ Ɛ96 χ86	720 15χ
9	.460 6Ɛ7 024	438
χ	1 217 460	716
Ɛ	1 937 Ɛ76	9Ɛ5
.0830	2 458 96Ɛ	721 093
1	2 Ɛ79 χ42	374
2	3 69Ɛ 1Ɛ6	653
3	4 200 849	934
4	4 922 581	722 015
5	5 444 596	2Ɛ6
6	5 Ɛ66 890	599
7	6 689 269	87Ɛ
8	7 1χƐ Ɛ28	Ɛ61
9	7 912 χ89	723 245
χ	8 436 112	529
Ɛ	8 Ɛ59 63Ɛ	811

N	Tangent	d
.0840	.469 681 250	723 χƐ6
1	χ 1χ5 146	724 19Ɛ
2	χ 909 325	484
3	Ɛ 431 7χ9	76Ɛ
4	Ɛ Ɛ56 358	χ56
5	.470 67Ɛ 1Ɛ2	725 140
6	1 1χ4 332	428
7	1 909 75χ	715
8	2 433 273	χ01
9	2 Ɛ59 074	726 0χ9
χ	3 683 161	398
Ɛ	4 1χ9 539	685
.0850	4 914 002	974
1	5 43χ 976	727 062
2	5 Ɛ65 χ18	352
3	6 691 16χ	642
4	7 1Ɛ8 7Ɛ0	932
5	7 924 522	728 024
6	8 450 546	314
7	8 Ɛ78 85χ	606
8	9 6χ5 264	8Ɛ8
9	χ 211 Ɛ60	ƐƐ0
χ	χ 93χ Ɛ50	729 2χ2
Ɛ	Ɛ 468 232	596
.0860	Ɛ Ɛ95 808	88χ
1	.480 703 496	Ɛ83
2	1 231 459	72χ 278
3	1 95Ɛ 715	572
4	2 48χ 087	867
5	2 ƐƐ8 932	Ɛ63
6	3 727 895	72Ɛ 259
7	4 256 Ɛ32	555
8	4 986 487	851
9	5 4Ɛ6 118	Ɛ49
χ	6 026 065	730 247
Ɛ	6 756 2Ɛ0	544
.0870	7 286 834	842
1	7 9Ɛ7 476	Ɛ40
2	8 528 3Ɛ6	731 23Ɛ
3	9 059 635	53Ɛ
4	9 78χ Ɛ74	83Ɛ
5	χ 300 7Ɛ3	Ɛ3Ɛ
6	χ χ32 732	732 240
7	Ɛ 564 972	541
8	.490 097 2Ɛ3	843
9	0 809 Ɛ36	Ɛ46
χ	1 340 χ80	733 248
Ɛ	1 χ74 108	550

N	Tangent	d
.0880	.492 5χ7 658	733 853
1	3 11Ɛ 2χƐ	Ɛ58
2	3 853 247	734 261
3	4 387 4χ8	566
4	4 χƐƐ χ52	870
5	5 634 702	Ɛ76
6	6 169 678	735 280
7	6 8χ2 938	588
8	7 418 304	894
9	7 Ɛ51 Ɛ98	Ɛχ0
χ	8 687 Ɛ78	736 2χ9
Ɛ	9 202 265	5Ɛ6
.0890	9 938 85Ɛ	903
1	χ 473 562	737 012
2	χ Ɛχχ 574	321
3	Ɛ 725 895	630
4	.4χ0 261 305	93Ɛ
5	0 999 044	738 050
6	1 515 094	360
7	2 051 434	672
8	2 789 χχ6	983
9	3 306 869	739 096
χ	3 χ43 943	3χ8
Ɛ	4 581 12Ɛ	6ƐƐ
.08χ0	5 0Ɛχ 82χ	χ13
1	5 838 641	73χ 128
2	6 376 769	440
3	6 χƐ4 Ɛχ9	755
4	7 633 742	χ6Ɛ
5	8 172 5Ɛ1	73Ɛ 185
6	8 8Ɛ1 776	49Ɛ
7	9 431 055	7Ɛ7
8	9 Ɛ70 850	Ɛ13
9	χ 6Ɛ0 763	740 2ƐƐ
χ	Ɛ 230 992	547
Ɛ	Ɛ 971 319	865
.08Ɛ0	.4Ɛ0 4Ɛ1 Ɛ82	Ɛ82
1	1 032 Ɛ44	741 2χ1
2	1 774 225	5ƐƐ
3	2 2Ɛ5 824	91Ɛ
4	2 χ37 543	742 03χ
5	3 579 581	35Ɛ
6	4 0ƐƐ 920	67Ɛ
7	4 842 39Ɛ	9χ1
8	5 385 180	743 102
9	5 Ɛ08 282	425
χ	6 64Ɛ 6χ7	747
Ɛ	7 193 232	χ6Ɛ

N	Tangent	d	N	Tangent	d	N	Tangent	d
.0900	.4Ɛ7 917 0χ1	744 192	.0940	.521 477 92χ	755 330	.0980	.547 476 Ɛ07	767 129
1	8 45Ɛ 273	4Ɛ7	1	2 011 05χ	675	1	8 022 034	494
2	8 Ɛχ3 76χ	81Ɛ	2	2 766 713	9ƐƐ	2	8 789 508	840
3	9 728 389	Ɛ45	3	3 300 512	756 146	3	9 335 148	Ɛχ9
4	χ 271 312	745 26Ɛ	4	3 χ56 658	490	4	9 χχ1 135	768 355
5	χ 9Ɛ6 581	595	5	4 5Ɛ0 Ɛ28	818	5	χ 649 48χ	703
6	Ɛ 53Ɛ Ɛ56	900	6	5 147 744	Ɛ63	6	Ɛ 1Ɛ5 Ɛ91	χ71
7	.500 085 856	746 027	7	5 8χ2 6χ7	757 2Ɛ1	7	Ɛ 962 χ42	769 220
8	0 80Ɛ 881	354	8	6 439 998	639	8	.550 510 062	58Ɛ
9	1 356 015	67Ɛ	9	6 Ɛ95 415	986	9	1 079 631	93χ
χ	1 χχ0 694	9χ9	χ	7 731 19Ɛ	758 115	χ	1 827 36Ɛ	76χ 0χƐ
Ɛ	2 627 481	747 116	Ɛ	8 289 2Ɛ4	464	Ɛ	2 395 45χ	460
.0910	3 172 597	444	.0950	8 χ25 758	7Ɛ2	.0990	2 Ɛ43 8Ɛχ	811
1	3 8Ɛ9 χ1Ɛ	772	1	9 582 34χ	Ɛ42	1	3 6Ɛ2 50Ɛ	Ɛ84
2	4 445 591	χχ1	2	χ 11Ɛ 290	759 293	2	4 261 493	76Ɛ 335
3	4 Ɛ91 472	748 211	3	χ 878 563	623	3	4 χ10 808	6χ9
4	5 719 683	541	4	Ɛ 415 Ɛ86	975	4	5 580 2Ɛ5	χ61
5	6 266 004	871	5	Ɛ Ɛ73 93Ɛ	75χ 106	5	6 130 156	770 215
6	6 9Ɛ2 875	Ɛχ3	6	.530 711 χ45	459	6	6 8χ0 36Ɛ	589
7	7 53Ɛ 858	749 313	7	1 270 2χ2	7χƐ	7	7 450 938	943
8	8 088 Ɛ6Ɛ	646	8	1 χ0χ χ91	Ɛ43	8	8 001 67Ɛ	771 0Ɛ9
9	8 816 5Ɛ5	979	9	2 569 χ14	75Ɛ 298	9	8 772 778	474
χ	9 364 372	74χ 0Ɛ0	χ	3 109 0Ɛ0	62Ɛ	χ	9 324 030	82χ
Ɛ	9 χƐ2 462	423	Ɛ	3 868 71Ɛ	985	Ɛ	9 χ95 85χ	Ɛχ6
.0920	χ 640 885	757	.0960	4 408 4χ4	760 11χ	.09χ0	χ 647 844	772 362
1	Ɛ 18Ɛ 420	χ90	1	4 Ɛ68 602	475	1	Ɛ 1Ɛ9 Ɛχ6	71Ɛ
2	Ɛ 91χ 2Ɛ0	74Ɛ 206	2	5 708 χ77	80Ɛ	2	Ɛ 970 705	χ98
3	.510 469 4Ɛ6	53Ɛ	3	6 269 686	Ɛ66	3	.560 523 5χ1	773 256
4	0 ƐƐ8 χ35	875	4	6 χ0χ 630	761 303	4	1 096 837	615
5	1 748 6χχ	ƐƐ0	5	7 56Ɛ 933	65χ	5	1 84χ 250	994
6	2 298 69χ	750 327	6	8 111 391	9Ɛ8	6	2 402 024	774 153
7	2 χ28 χ05	663	7	8 873 189	762 155	7	2 Ɛ76 177	513
8	3 579 468	9χ0	8	9 415 322	4Ɛ2	8	3 72χ 68χ	894
9	4 10χ 248	751 118	9	9 Ɛ77 814	852	9	4 2χ3 362	775 055
χ	4 85Ɛ 364	455	χ	χ 71χ 466	ƐƐ0	χ	4 χ58 3Ɛ7	418
Ɛ	5 3Ɛ0 7Ɛ9	794	Ɛ	Ɛ 281 456	763 350	Ɛ	5 611 813	799
.0930	5 Ɛ42 391	Ɛ12	.0970	Ɛ χ24 7χ6	6Ɛ0	.09Ɛ0	6 187 3Ɛ0	Ɛ61
1	6 694 2χ3	752 251	1	.540 588 296	χ51	1	6 941 351	776 324
2	7 226 534	590	2	1 130 127	764 1Ɛ2	2	7 4Ɛ7 675	6χ8
3	7 978 Ɛ04	910	3	1 894 319	554	3	8 072 161	χ71
4	8 50Ɛ 814	753 051	4	2 438 871	8Ɛ7	4	8 829 012	777 236
5	9 062 865	392	5	2 Ɛχ1 568	765 059	5	9 3χ4 248	601
6	9 7Ɛ6 037	713	6	3 746 605	400	6	9 Ɛ5Ɛ 849	986
7	χ 349 74χ	χ56	7	4 2χƐ χ05	765	7	χ 717 613	778 152
8	χ χχ1 5χ4	754 198	8	4 χ55 56χ	Ɛ09	8	Ɛ 293 765	519
9	Ɛ 635 780	520	9	5 5ƐƐ 477	766 272	9	Ɛ χ50 082	8χ5
χ	.520 18χ 0χ0	863	χ	6 165 729	618	χ	.570 608 967	779 072
Ɛ	0 922 943	Ɛχ7	Ɛ	6 910 145	982	Ɛ	1 185 χ19	440

N	Tangent	d	N	Tangent	d	N	Tangent	d
.0X00	.571 943 259	779 809	.0X40	.598 708 988	791 019	.0X80	.603 X01 641	7X5 1X9
1	2 500 X66	Ɛ97	1	9 299 9X5	411	1	4 5X6 82X	605
2	3 07X X41	77X 367	2	9 X6Ɛ 1Ɛ6	803	2	5 190 233	X22
3	3 839 1X8	737	3	X 640 9Ɛ9	ƐƐ7	3	5 976 055	7X6 241
4	4 3Ɛ7 923	Ɛ06	4	Ɛ 212 9Ɛ4	792 3Ɛ1	4	6 560 296	65X
5	4 Ɛ76 829	77Ɛ 298	5	Ɛ 9X5 1X5	7X5	5	7 146 934	X7X
6	5 735 Ɛ05	668	6	.5X0 577 98X	Ɛ9Ɛ	6	7 931 7Ɛ2	7X7 299
7	6 2Ɛ5 571	X3Ɛ	7	1 14X 969	793 396	7	8 518 X8Ɛ	6ƐX
8	6 X75 3Ɛ0	780 211	8	1 922 143	791	8	9 104 589	Ɛ1X
9	7 635 601	5X4	9	2 4Ɛ5 914	Ɛ88	9	9 8Ɛ0 4X7	7X8 340
X	8 1Ɛ5 ƐX5	978	X	3 089 8X0	794 385	X	X 498 827	763
Ɛ	8 976 961	781 151	Ɛ	3 862 065	782	Ɛ	Ɛ 085 38X	Ɛ85
.0X10	9 537 XƐ2	525	.0X50	4 436 827	Ɛ7Ɛ	.0X90	Ɛ 872 353	7X9 3X8
1	X 0Ɛ9 417	8ƐX	1	5 00Ɛ 7X6	795 379	1	.610 45Ɛ 73Ɛ	811
2	X 87Ɛ 115	782 095	2	5 7X4 Ɛ63	778	2	1 049 350	7XX 036
3	Ɛ 441 1XX	46Ɛ	3	6 37X 71Ɛ	Ɛ78	3	1 837 386	45X
4	.580 003 659	847	4	6 Ɛ54 697	796 377	4	2 425 824	885
5	0 786 2X4	783 022	5	7 72X X52	778	5	3 014 4X9	7XƐ 0Ɛ0
6	1 349 306	3ƐX	6	8 305 60X	Ɛ79	6	3 803 599	517
7	1 Ɛ10 704	798	7	8 XX0 587	797 37Ɛ	7	4 3Ɛ2 XƐ4	943
8	2 694 2X0	Ɛ75	8	9 677 946	781	8	4 ƐX2 837	7Ɛ0 170
9	3 258 255	784 353	9	X 253 507	Ɛ85	9	5 792 9X7	598
X	3 X20 5X8	732	X	X X2Ɛ 490	798 388	X	6 383 383	X07
Ɛ	4 5X5 11X	Ɛ11	Ɛ	Ɛ 607 858	790	Ɛ	6 Ɛ74 18X	7Ɛ1 235
.0X20	5 16X 02Ɛ	785 2Ɛ1	.0X60	.5Ɛ0 1X4 428	Ɛ95	.0XX0	7 765 403	665
1	5 933 320	692	1	0 981 401	799 39Ɛ	1	8 356 X68	X94
2	6 4Ɛ8 9Ɛ2	X73	2	1 55X 7X0	7X4	2	8 Ɛ48 940	7Ɛ2 305
3	7 082 865	786 254	3	2 138 384	ƐƐ0	3	9 73Ɛ 045	736
4	7 848 XƐ9	637	4	2 916 374	79X 3Ɛ7	4	X 331 77Ɛ	Ɛ68
5	8 413 534	X19	5	3 4Ɛ4 76Ɛ	802	5	X Ɛ24 727	7Ɛ3 39X
6	8 Ɛ9X 351	787 201	6	4 093 371	79Ɛ 010	6	Ɛ 717 Ɛ05	811
7	9 765 552	5X5	7	4 872 381	418	7	.620 30Ɛ 716	7Ɛ4 045
8	X 330 Ɛ37	98X	8	5 451 799	827	8	0 Ɛ03 75Ɛ	479
9	X XƐ8 905	788 173	9	6 031 404	7X0 035	9	1 6Ɛ8 018	8Ɛ3
X	Ɛ 684 X78	558	X	6 811 439	444	X	2 2Ɛ0 90Ɛ	7Ɛ5 128
Ɛ	.590 251 414	944	Ɛ	7 3Ɛ1 881	853	Ɛ	2 XX5 X37	562
.0X30	0 X1X 158	789 12X	.0X70	7 Ɛ92 514	7X1 064	.0XƐ0	3 69Ɛ 399	99X
1	1 5X7 286	515	1	8 773 578	475	1	4 295 177	7Ɛ6 215
2	2 174 79Ɛ	902	2	9 354 X31	887	2	4 X8Ɛ 390	651
3	2 942 4X1	78X 0XƐ	3	9 Ɛ36 6Ɛ8	7X2 099	3	5 685 X21	X8X
4	3 510 590	499	4	X 718 795	4XƐ	4	6 280 8XƐ	7Ɛ7 308
5	4 09X X69	886	5	Ɛ 2ƐƐ 084	903	5	6 X77 ƐƐ7	746
6	4 869 733	78Ɛ 075	6	Ɛ XX1 987	7X3 117	6	7 673 741	Ɛ86
7	5 438 7X8	464	7	.600 684 XX2	530	7	8 26Ɛ 707	7Ɛ8 404
8	6 008 050	854	8	1 268 412	945	8	8 X67 Ɛ0Ɛ	845
9	6 797 8X4	790 044	9	1 X50 157	7X4 15Ɛ	9	9 664 754	7Ɛ9 086
X	7 367 928	435	X	2 634 2Ɛ6	576	X	X 261 81X	508
Ɛ	7 Ɛ38 161	827	Ɛ	3 218 870	991	Ɛ	X X5Ɛ 126	949

N	Tangent	d	N	Tangent	d	N	Tangent	d
.0ε00	.62ε 658 χ73	7εχ 191	.0ε40	.657 890 30χ	814 025	.0ε80	.684 517 01ε	82χ 993
1	.630 257 044	614	1	8 4χ4 333	496	1	5 145 9ε2	82ε 271
2	0 χ55 658	χ58	2	9 0ε8 809	947	2	5 975 063	74ε
3	1 654 4ε4	7εε 2χ2	3	9 911 554	815 1ε8	3	6 5χ4 7ε2	830 030
4	2 253 796	726	4	χ 526 750	66χ	4	7 214 822	510
5	2 χ53 300	ε71	5	ε 140 1εχ	ε21	5	7 χ45 132	9ε1
6	3 653 271	800 3ε8	6	ε 956 11ε	816 395	6	8 675 ε23	831 293
7	4 253 669	843	7	.660 570 4ε4	849	7	9 2χ7 1ε6	776
8	4 χ54 2ε0	801 090	8	1 187 141	817 102	8	9 ε18 970	832 059
9	5 655 380	518	9	1 9χ2 243	578	9	χ 74χ χ09	541
χ	6 256 898	966	χ	2 5ε9 7εε	χ32	χ	ε 381 34χ	χ26
ε	6 χ58 642	802 1ε5	ε	3 215 631	818 2χ9	ε	ε ε ε4 174	833 30ε
.0ε10	7 65χ 837	643	.0ε50	3 χ31 91χ	765	.0ε90	.690 827 483	7ε6
1	8 261 27χ	χ92	1	4 64χ 483	819 021	1	1 45ε 079	834 0χ1
2	8 χ64 150	803 323	2	5 267 4χ4	49ε	2	2 093 15χ	589
3	9 667 473	774	3	5 χ84 983	958	3	2 907 727	χ75
4	χ 26ε 027	804 005	4	6 6χ2 71ε	81χ 217	4	3 540 5χ0	835 363
5	χ χ73 030	457	5	7 300 936	697	5	4 175 943	851
6	ε 677 487	8χε	6	7 ε1ε 411	ε56	6	4 9χε 594	836 13ε
7	.640 280 176	805 142	7	8 73χ 367	81ε 417	7	5 625 713	62ε
8	0 χ85 2ε8	596	8	9 359 782	899	8	6 260 142	ε1ε
9	1 68χ 892	χ2ε	9	9 ε79 45ε	820 15χ	9	6 χ97 061	837 410
χ	2 294 701	806 285	χ	χ 799 5ε9	622	χ	7 712 471	902
ε	2 χ9χ 986	71ε	ε	ε 3εχ 01ε	χχ5	ε	8 34χ 173	838 1ε4
.0ε20	3 6χ5 4χ5	ε76	.0ε60	.670 01χ ε04	821 369	.0εχ0	8 ε86 367	6χ8
1	4 2ε0 45ε	807 411	1	0 840 271	833	1	9 802 χ53	ε9ε
2	4 χε7 870	86χ	2	1 461 χχ4	822 0ε7	2	χ 43ε χ32	839 495
3	5 703 51χ	808 107	3	2 083 ε9ε	583	3	ε 079 307	989
4	6 30ε 625	564	4	2 8χ6 562	χ49	4	ε 8ε7 094	83χ 284
5	6 ε17 ε89	χ03	5	3 509 3χε	823 316	5	.6χ0 535 358	77ε
6	7 724 990	809 262	6	4 130 705	7χ1	6	1 173 ε17	83ε 077
7	8 332 032	702	7	4 954 2χ6	824 06ε	7	1 9ε2 ε92	573
8	8 ε3ε 734	ε62	8	5 578 355	539	8	2 632 545	χ70
9	9 749 696	80χ 403	9	6 1χ0 892	χ08	9	3 272 3ε5	840 36ε
χ	χ 357 χ99	865	χ	6 χ05 69χ	825 297	χ	3 χε2 764	869
ε	χ ε66 742	80ε 107	ε	7 62χ 975	768	ε	4 733 411	841 168
.0ε30	ε 775 849	56ε	.0ε70	8 254 521	826 038	.0εε0	5 374 579	669
1	.650 385 1ε8	χ12	1	8 χ7χ 559	509	1	5 εε6 026	ε6χ
2	0 ε95 00χ	810 277	2	9 6χ4 χ66	9χ0	2	6 837 ε94	842 46ε
3	1 7χ5 285	720	3	χ 30ε 846	827 273	3	7 47χ 443	972
4	2 3ε5 9χ5	ε85	4	χ ε36 χε9	747	4	8 101 1ε5	843 275
5	3 006 96χ	811 431	5	ε 762 644	828 01ε	5	8 944 46χ	77χ
6	3 818 19ε	897	6	.680 38χ 663	4ε4	6	9 588 028	844 082
7	4 429 χ76	812 144	7	0 εε6 ε57	98χ	7	χ 210 0χχ	588
8	5 03ε εεχ	5ε0	8	1 823 925	829 265	8	χ χ54 676	χ92
9	5 852 5χχ	χ5χ	9	2 450 ε8χ	740	9	ε 699 548	845 399
χ	6 465 448	813 307	χ	3 07χ 70χ	82χ 018	χ	.6ε0 322 925	8χ5
ε	7 078 753	777	ε	3 8χ8 726	4ε5	ε	0 ε68 60χ	846 1ε1

N	Tangent	d	N	Tangent	d	N	Tangent	d
.1000	.6Ɛ1 7Ɛ2 7ƐƐ	846 6ƐƐ	.1040	.71Ɛ 55Ɛ 030	863 458	.1080	.749 X1X 431	881 2X4
1	2 439 2ƐX	7 009	1	.720 202 488	3 999	1	X 69Ɛ 715	1 858
2	3 084 307	7 518	2	0 X66 265	4 319	2	Ɛ 361 371	2 210
3	3 90Ɛ 823	7 X28	3	1 70X 582	4 85Ɛ	3	.750 023 581	2 786
4	4 557 64Ɛ	8 338	4	2 373 221	5 1X1	4	0 8X6 147	3 132
5	5 1X3 987	8 849	5	3 018 402	5 724	5	1 569 286	3 6Ɛ7
6	5 X30 614	9 15Ɛ	6	3 881 Ɛ26	6 068	6	2 230 981	4 073
7	6 679 773	9 672	7	4 527 Ɛ92	6 5Ɛ1	7	2 XƐ4 X34	4 62Ɛ
8	7 307 225	9 Ɛ86	8	5 192 583	6 Ɛ36	8	3 779 463	4 ƐX9
9	7 Ɛ55 1XƐ	X 49X	9	5 X39 4Ɛ9	7 481	9	4 442 450	5 567
X	8 7X3 689	X 9Ɛ2	X	6 6X4 97X	7 X07	X	5 107 9Ɛ7	5 Ɛ26
Ɛ	9 432 47Ɛ	Ɛ 309	Ɛ	7 350 785	8 354	Ɛ	5 991 921	6 4X7
.1010	X 081 788	Ɛ 824	.1050	7 ƐƐ8 Ɛ19	8 8X1	.1090	6 658 208	6 X68
1	X 911 3Ɛ0	850 13X	1	8 865 7ƐX	9 22X	1	7 323 074	7 429
2	Ɛ 561 52X	0 657	2	9 512 X28	9 779	2	7 ƐXX 4X1	7 9Ɛ1
3	.700 1Ɛ1 Ɛ85	0 Ɛ74	3	X 180 5X5	X 108	3	8 876 292	8 374
4	0 X42 Ɛ39	1 492	4	X X2X 6Ɛ1	X 658	4	9 542 646	8 938
5	1 694 40Ɛ	1 9Ɛ0	5	Ɛ 699 149	X ƐX8	5	X 20Ɛ 382	9 302
6	2 326 1ƐƐ	2 30Ɛ	6	.730 348 135	Ɛ 53Ɛ	6	X X98 684	9 887
7	2 Ɛ78 50X	2 830	7	0 ƐƐ7 674	Ɛ X91	7	Ɛ 766 34Ɛ	X 253
8	3 80Ɛ 13X	3 150	8	1 867 545	870 425	8	.760 434 5X2	X 81Ɛ
9	4 462 28X	3 672	9	2 517 96X	0 978	9	1 103 201	Ɛ 1X8
X	5 0Ɛ5 940	3 Ɛ94	X	3 188 726	1 312	X	1 992 3X9	Ɛ 775
Ɛ	5 949 914	4 4Ɛ8	Ɛ	3 X39 X38	1 867	Ɛ	2 661 Ɛ62	890 144
.1020	6 5X2 210	4 X1Ɛ	.1060	4 6XƐ 6X3	2 202	.10X0	3 332 0X6	0 713
1	7 237 02Ɛ	5 344	1	5 361 8X5	2 75X	1	4 002 7Ɛ9	1 0X4
2	7 X90 373	5 86X	2	6 014 443	3 0Ɛ6	2	4 893 8X1	1 674
3	8 726 021	6 194	3	6 887 539	3 653	3	5 565 355	2 047
4	9 380 1Ɛ5	6 700	4	7 53X Ɛ90	3 Ɛ21	4	6 237 3X0	2 619
5	X 016 8Ɛ5	7 027	5	8 1Ɛ2 Ɛ81	4 550	5	6 Ɛ09 9Ɛ9	2 ƐƐ2
6	X 871 920	7 554	6	8 X67 511	4 XXƐ	6	7 7X0 9XƐ	3 586
7	Ɛ 509 274	7 X81	7	9 720 400	5 450	7	8 474 375	3 Ɛ5Ɛ
8	.710 165 135	8 3Ɛ0	8	X 395 850	5 9Ɛ2	8	9 148 314	4 536
9	0 X01 525	8 91Ɛ	9	Ɛ 04Ɛ 642	6 353	9	9 X20 84X	4 Ɛ11
X	1 65X 244	9 24X	X	Ɛ 905 995	6 8Ɛ6	X	X 6Ɛ5 75Ɛ	5 4X9
Ɛ	2 2Ɛ7 492	9 77Ɛ	Ɛ	.740 580 68Ɛ	7 25X	Ɛ	Ɛ 38Ɛ 048	5 X87
.1030	2 Ɛ55 051	X 0Ɛ1	.1070	1 237 929	7 803	.10Ɛ0	.770 064 Ɛ13	6 464
1	3 7Ɛ3 142	X 623	1	1 XƐ3 530	8 168	1	0 93Ɛ 377	6 X43
2	4 451 765	X Ɛ56	2	2 76Ɛ 698	8 713	2	1 616 1ƐX	7 423
3	5 0Ɛ0 6ƐƐ	Ɛ 48X	3	3 428 1XƐ	9 07X	3	2 2Ɛ1 621	7 X03
4	5 94Ɛ Ɛ89	Ɛ X03	4	4 0X5 269	9 625	4	2 Ɛ89 424	8 3X5
5	6 5XƐ 990	860 338	5	4 962 892	9 Ɛ93	5	3 865 809	8 987
6	7 250 108	0 872	6	5 620 865	X 540	6	4 542 594	9 36Ɛ
7	7 XƐ0 97X	1 1XX	7	6 29Ɛ 1X5	X XXƐ	7	5 21Ɛ 943	9 952
8	8 751 Ɛ68	1 725	8	6 Ɛ5X 094	Ɛ 45X	8	5 XƐ9 695	X 338
9	9 3Ɛ3 691	2 062	9	7 819 532	Ɛ X0X	9	6 797 X11	X 921
X	X 055 733	2 59Ɛ	X	8 499 340	880 380	X	7 476 732	Ɛ 309
Ɛ	X 8Ɛ8 112	2 Ɛ1X	Ɛ	9 159 700	0 931	Ɛ	8 155 X3Ɛ	Ɛ 8Ɛ4

N	Tangent	d	N	Tangent	d	N	Tangent	d
.1100	.778 X35 733	8X0 2X0	.1140	.7X8 634 6X4	900 519	.1180	.818 X66 177	921 X71
1	9 715 X13	0 88X	1	9 335 001	0 Ɛ43	1	9 788 028	2 515
2	X 3Ɛ6 6X1	1 279	2	X 035 Ɛ44	1 569	2	X 4XX 541	2 Ɛ7Ɛ
3	Ɛ 097 95X	1 867	3	X 937 4Ɛ1	1 Ɛ95	3	Ɛ 211 500	3 625
4	Ɛ 979 605	2 258	4	Ɛ 639 486	2 602	4	Ɛ Ɛ34 Ɛ25	4 091
5	.780 65Ɛ 861	2 849	5	.7Ɛ0 33Ɛ X88	3 02Ɛ	5	.820 858 ƐƐ6	4 738
6	1 342 4XX	3 23Ɛ	6	1 042 XƐ7	3 659	6	1 581 732	5 1X7
7	2 025 729	3 832	7	1 946 554	4 089	7	2 2X6 919	5 854
8	2 909 35Ɛ	4 226	8	2 64X 621	4 6Ɛ9	8	3 010 571	6 305
9	3 5Ɛ1 585	4 81X	9	3 353 11X	5 12Ɛ	9	3 936 876	6 974
X	4 296 1X3	5 214	X	4 058 249	5 760	X	4 661 62X	7 426
Ɛ	4 Ɛ7Ɛ 3Ɛ7	5 80Ɛ	Ɛ	4 961 9X9	6 194	Ɛ	5 388 X54	7 X98
.1110	5 865 006	6 205	.1150	5 667 Ɛ81	6 808	.1190	6 0Ɛ4 930	8 550
1	6 54Ɛ 20Ɛ	6 803	1	6 372 789	7 242	1	6 X21 280	9 005
2	7 235 X12	7 1ƐƐ	2	7 079 X0Ɛ	7 877	2	7 74X 285	9 679
3	7 Ɛ21 011	7 7ƐX	3	7 985 686	8 2Ɛ2	3	8 477 942	X 135
4	8 808 80Ɛ	8 1Ɛ8	4	8 691 978	8 92X	4	9 1X5 X77	X 7XƐ
5	9 4Ɛ4 X07	8 7Ɛ9	5	9 39X 6X6	9 368	5	9 Ɛ14 666	Ɛ 269
6	X 1X1 604	9 1Ɛ9	6	X 0X7 X52	9 9X5	6	X 843 913	Ɛ 926
7	X X8X 801	9 7ƐƐ	7	X 9Ɛ5 837	X 424	7	Ɛ 573 639	930 3X4
8	Ɛ 778 400	X 202	8	Ɛ 704 05Ɛ	X X64	8	.830 2X3 X21	0 X64
9	.790 466 602	X 806	9	.800 412 Ɛ03	Ɛ 4X5	9	1 014 885	1 525
X	1 155 208	Ɛ 20X	X	1 122 3X8	Ɛ Ɛ26	X	1 946 1XX	1 ƐX6
Ɛ	1 X44 416	Ɛ 813	Ɛ	1 X32 312	910 56X	Ɛ	2 678 194	2 669
.1120	2 734 029	8Ɛ0 21X	.1160	2 742 880	0 ƐƐ1	.11X0	3 3XX 841	3 131
1	3 424 247	0 825	1	3 453 871	1 635	1	4 121 972	3 7Ɛ5
2	4 114 X70	1 231	2	4 165 2X6	2 080	2	4 X55 567	4 280
3	4 X06 0X1	1 83Ɛ	3	4 X77 366	2 706	3	5 789 827	4 945
4	5 6Ɛ7 920	2 248	4	5 789 X70	3 152	4	6 502 570	5 412
5	6 3X9 Ɛ68	2 858	5	6 4X1 002	3 79X	5	7 237 982	5 X9Ɛ
6	7 0X0 804	3 267	6	7 1Ɛ4 7X0	4 228	6	7 Ɛ71 861	6 568
7	7 993 X6Ɛ	3 878	7	7 Ɛ08 X08	4 877	7	8 8X8 209	7 038
8	8 687 727	4 28X	8	8 821 683	5 306	8	9 623 245	7 707
9	9 37Ɛ 9Ɛ5	4 8X1	9	9 536 989	5 956	9	X 35X 950	8 199
X	X 074 696	5 2Ɛ4	X	X 250 723	6 3X8	X	Ɛ 096 Ɛ29	8 86X
Ɛ	X 969 98X	5 909	Ɛ	X Ɛ66 Ɛ0Ɛ	6 X3Ɛ	Ɛ	Ɛ X13 797	9 341
.1130	Ɛ 663 697	6 322	.1170	Ɛ 881 94X	7 492	.11Ɛ0	.840 750 Ɛ18	9 X16
1	.7X0 359 9Ɛ9	6 939	1	.810 599 220	7 Ɛ26	1	1 48X 932	X 4XƐ
2	1 054 736	7 354	2	1 2Ɛ5 146	8 580	2	2 209 221	X Ɛ85
3	1 94Ɛ X8X	7 971	3	2 011 706	9 017	3	2 Ɛ48 1X6	Ɛ 660
4	2 647 83Ɛ	8 389	4	2 92X 721	9 672	4	3 887 846	940 138
5	3 344 008	8 9X8	5	3 648 193	X 10X	5	4 607 982	0 816
6	4 040 9Ɛ4	9 407	6	4 366 2X1	X 768	6	5 348 598	1 2Ɛ4
7	4 93X 1ƐƐ	9 X27	7	5 084 X49	Ɛ 206	7	6 089 890	1 994
8	5 638 026	X 447	8	5 9X4 053	Ɛ 865	8	6 X0Ɛ 664	2 474
9	6 336 471	X X6X	9	6 703 8Ɛ8	920 306	9	7 751 Ɛ18	2 Ɛ56
X	7 035 31Ɛ	Ɛ 491	X	7 424 002	0 967	X	8 494 X72	3 638
Ɛ	7 934 7Ɛ0	Ɛ XƐ4	Ɛ	8 144 969	1 40X	Ɛ	9 218 4XX	4 120

N	Tangent	d	N	Tangent	d	N	Tangent	d
.1200	.849 Ɛ60 60X	944 805	.1240	.87Ɛ 975 58X	968 X4X	.1280	.8Ɛ2 546 884	992 687
1	X 8X5 213	5 2XX	1	.880 722 418	9 578	1	3 319 34Ɛ	3 241
2	Ɛ 62X 501	5 995	2	1 48Ɛ 994	X 0X8	2	4 0Ɛ0 590	3 9Ɛ7
3	.850 374 296	6 481	3	2 239 X80	X 818	3	4 X84 387	4 574
4	1 0ƐX 757	6 Ɛ6X	4	2 ƐX8 698	Ɛ 349	4	5 858 93Ɛ	5 130
5	1 X45 705	7 659	5	3 957 X25	Ɛ X80	5	6 631 X6Ɛ	5 8XƐ
6	2 791 162	8 147	6	4 707 8X5	970 5Ɛ4	6	7 407 75X	6 46Ɛ
7	3 519 2X9	8 837	7	5 478 299	1 128	7	8 1X2 009	7 02Ɛ
8	4 265 Ɛ24	9 328	8	6 229 405	1 863	8	8 Ɛ79 038	7 7Ɛ0
9	4 ƐƐ3 250	9 X1Ɛ	9	6 Ɛ9Ɛ 068	2 399	9	9 954 828	8 374
X	5 941 06Ɛ	X 512	X	7 951 445	2 Ɛ16	X	X 730 ƐX0	8 Ɛ39
Ɛ	6 68Ɛ 581	Ɛ 007	Ɛ	8 704 35Ɛ	3 653	Ɛ	Ɛ 509 Ɛ19	9 701
.1210	7 41X 588	Ɛ 700	.1250	9 477 9Ɛ2	4 192	.1290	.900 2X7 61X	X 289
1	8 16X 088	950 1Ɛ7	1	X 22Ɛ Ɛ84	4 911	1	1 085 8X7	X X54
2	8 XƐX 283	0 8Ɛ2	2	X ƐX4 895	5 452	2	1 X64 73Ɛ	Ɛ 621
3	9 84X Ɛ75	1 3XƐ	3	Ɛ 95X 127	5 Ɛ93	3	2 844 160	9X0 1Ɛ0
4	X 5X0 364	1 XX8	4	.890 714 0ƐX	6 717	4	3 624 350	0 97Ɛ
5	Ɛ 332 250	2 5X8	5	1 48X 815	7 25Ɛ	5	4 405 10Ɛ	1 550
6	.860 084 838	3 0X8	6	2 245 X74	7 9X5	6	5 1X6 65Ɛ	2 122
7	0 X17 924	3 7X8	7	3 001 859	8 52X	7	5 Ɛ88 781	2 8Ɛ5
8	1 76Ɛ 510	4 2XƐ	8	3 97X 187	9 077	8	6 96Ɛ 476	3 489
9	2 503 7ƐƐ	4 9Ɛ2	9	4 737 242	9 803	9	7 752 943	4 063
X	3 258 5Ɛ1	5 4Ɛ6	X	5 4Ɛ4 X45	X 351	X	8 536 9X6	4 83X
Ɛ	3 ƐƐ1 XX7	5 ƐƐƐ	Ɛ	6 273 196	X XX1	Ɛ	9 31Ɛ 624	5 416
.1220	4 947 XX6	6 706	.1260	7 032 077	Ɛ 630	.12X0	X 104 X3X	5 ƐƐ3
1	5 6X2 5Ɛ0	7 212	1	7 9Ɛ1 6X7	980 182	1	X XXX X31	6 792
2	6 439 802	7 91X	2	8 771 869	0 914	2	Ɛ 895 603	7 371
3	7 195 520	8 428	3	9 532 581	1 468	3	.910 680 974	7 Ɛ52
4	7 Ɛ31 948	8 Ɛ36	4	X 2Ɛ3 X29	2 001	4	1 468 906	8 735
5	8 88X 882	9 647	5	Ɛ 075 X2X	2 757	5	2 255 43Ɛ	9 318
6	9 628 309	X 157	6	Ɛ X38 585	3 2Ɛ2	6	3 042 757	9 Ɛ00
7	X 386 464	X 86X	7	.8X0 7ƐƐ 877	3 X4X	7	3 X30 657	X 6X7
8	Ɛ 125 112	Ɛ 381	8	1 583 705	4 5X8	8	4 81Ɛ 142	Ɛ 291
9	Ɛ X84 493	Ɛ X95	9	2 348 0Ɛ1	5 147	9	5 60X 413	Ɛ X7X
X	.870 824 368	960 5XX	X	3 111 238	5 8X6	X	6 3ƐX 291	9Ɛ0 668
Ɛ	1 584 956	1 106	Ɛ	3 X96 Ɛ22	6 448	Ɛ	7 1XX 939	1 256
.1230	2 325 X60	1 820	.1270	4 861 36X	6 ƐX9	.12Ɛ0	7 Ɛ9Ɛ Ɛ93	1 X46
1	3 087 680	2 339	1	5 628 357	7 751	1	8 991 X19	2 638
2	3 X29 9Ɛ9	2 X58	2	6 3Ɛ3 XX8	8 2Ɛ6	2	9 784 455	3 22X
3	4 790 855	3 576	3	7 180 1X2	8 X5Ɛ	3	X 577 683	3 X22
4	5 534 20Ɛ	4 096	4	7 Ɛ49 041	9 606	4	Ɛ 36Ɛ 4X5	4 617
5	6 298 2X5	4 7Ɛ7	5	8 916 647	X 172	5	.920 163 Ɛ00	5 211
6	7 040 XX0	5 31X	6	9 6X4 7Ɛ9	X 91Ɛ	6	0 Ɛ59 111	5 X09
7	7 9X6 1ƐX	5 X40	7	X 473 518	Ɛ 48X	7	1 952 Ɛ1X	6 606
8	8 750 03X	6 566	8	Ɛ 242 9X6	990 039	8	2 749 524	7 204
9	9 4Ɛ6 5X4	7 08Ɛ	9	.8Ɛ0 012 X23	0 7XX	9	3 544 728	7 X03
X	X 261 673	7 7Ɛ5	X	0 9X3 611	1 360	X	4 340 52Ɛ	8 604
Ɛ	Ɛ 009 268	8 322	Ɛ	1 774 971	1 Ɛ13	Ɛ	5 138 Ɛ33	9 205

N	Tangent	d	N	Tangent	d	N	Tangent	d
.1300	.925 Ɛ36 138	9Ɛ9 X09	.1340	.95X 3XX 045	X26 974	.1380	.993 795 979	X55 67Ɛ
1	6 933 Ɛ45	X 611	1	Ɛ 214 9Ɛ9	7 60Ɛ	1	4 62Ɛ 438	6 36Ɛ
2	7 732 556	Ɛ 216	2	.960 040 408	8 268	2	5 485 7X7	7 063
3	8 531 770	Ɛ X22	3	0 X68 674	8 Ɛ05	3	6 320 84X	7 957
4	9 331 592	X00 629	4	1 895 579	9 763	4	7 178 5X5	8 651
5	X 131 ƐƐƐ	1 237	5	2 703 120	X 404	5	8 015 036	9 348
6	X Ɛ33 236	1 X46	6	3 531 524	Ɛ 066	6	8 X72 382	X 044
7	Ɛ 935 080	2 656	7	4 360 58X	Ɛ 909	7	9 910 406	X 943
8	.930 737 716	3 267	8	5 190 297	X30 571	8	X 76Ɛ 149	Ɛ 642
9	1 53X 981	3 X79	9	6 000 848	1 217	9	Ɛ 60X 78Ɛ	X60 343
X	2 342 83X	4 692	X	6 X31 X63	1 X82	X	.9X0 46X Ɛ12	1 045
Ɛ	3 147 310	5 2X6	Ɛ	7 863 925	2 72X	Ɛ	1 30Ɛ Ɛ57	1 949
.1310	3 Ɛ50 5Ɛ6	5 Ɛ01	.1350	8 696 453	3 398	.1390	2 171 8X4	2 653
1	4 956 4Ɛ7	6 718	1	9 509 82Ɛ	4 047	1	3 014 337	3 359
2	5 761 013	7 335	2	X 341 876	4 8Ɛ8	2	3 X77 694	4 065
3	6 568 348	7 Ɛ54	3	Ɛ 176 572	5 56X	3	4 91Ɛ 739	4 974
4	7 374 2X0	8 773	4	Ɛ ƐXƐ Ɛ20	6 220	4	5 784 4Ɛ1	5 682
5	8 180 X53	9 394	5	.970 X26 140	6 X96	5	6 629 Ɛ73	6 392
6	8 Ɛ8X 227	9 ƐƐ5	6	1 861 016	7 74Ɛ	6	7 494 345	7 0X5
7	9 998 220	X 81X	7	2 698 765	8 407	7	8 33Ɛ 42X	7 9Ɛ9
8	X 7X6 X3X	Ɛ 441	8	3 514 Ɛ70	9 084	8	9 1X7 227	8 711
9	Ɛ 5Ɛ6 27Ɛ	X10 068	9	4 352 034	9 941	9	X 053 938	9 428
X	.940 406 327	0 893	X	5 18Ɛ 975	X 601	X	X Ɛ01 164	X 143
Ɛ	1 216 ƐƐX	1 500	Ɛ	6 00X 376	Ɛ 282	Ɛ	Ɛ 96Ɛ 2X7	X X61
.1320	2 028 4ƐX	2 129	.1360	6 X49 638	Ɛ Ɛ45	.13X0	.9Ɛ0 81X 148	Ɛ 780
1	2 X3X 627	2 959	1	7 889 581	X40 808	1	1 689 908	X70 4X0
2	3 851 384	3 589	2	8 70X 189	1 491	2	2 53X 1X8	1 202
3	4 664 951	4 1ƐƐ	3	9 54Ɛ 65X	2 157	3	3 3XƐ 3XX	1 Ɛ25
4	5 478 Ɛ50	4 X31	4	X 391 7Ɛ5	2 X23	4	4 261 313	2 84X
5	6 291 981	5 667	5	Ɛ 214 618	3 6Ɛ1	5	5 113 Ɛ61	3 574
6	7 0X7 428	6 2X0	6	.980 058 109	4 37Ɛ	6	5 Ɛ87 515	4 2X0
7	7 Ɛ01 708	6 Ɛ16	7	0 XX0 488	5 04Ɛ	7	6 X3Ɛ 7Ɛ5	5 009
8	8 918 622	7 754	8	1 925 517	5 920	8	7 8Ɛ4 802	5 938
9	9 734 176	8 391	9	2 76Ɛ 237	6 5Ɛ4	9	8 76X 53X	6 668
X	X 550 547	9 00Ɛ	X	3 5Ɛ5 82Ɛ	7 287	X	9 624 ƐX6	7 39X
Ɛ	Ɛ 369 556	9 850	Ɛ	4 440 XƐ6	7 Ɛ61	Ɛ	X 4X0 384	8 111
.1330	.950 187 1X6	X 492	.1370	5 288 X57	8 838	.13Ɛ0	Ɛ 358 495	8 X45
1	0 ƐX5 678	Ɛ 114	1	6 115 693	9 514	1	.X00 215 31X	9 780
2	1 X04 790	Ɛ 959	2	6 Ɛ62 ƐX7	X 1Ɛ3	2	1 092 X9X	X 4Ɛ7
3	2 824 529	X20 5X2	3	7 9Ɛ1 19X	X X91	3	1 Ɛ51 395	Ɛ 235
4	3 644 Ɛ0Ɛ	1 22X	4	8 840 06Ɛ	Ɛ 772	4	2 X10 60X	Ɛ Ɛ73
5	4 466 139	1 X75	5	9 68Ɛ 821	X50 454	5	3 890 581	X80 8Ɛ4
6	5 287 ƐƐ2	2 703	6	X 520 075	1 138	6	4 751 275	1 635
7	6 0XX 6Ɛ5	3 352	7	Ɛ 371 1Ɛ1	1 X21	7	5 612 8XX	2 378
8	6 Ɛ11 X47	3 ƐX2	8	.990 203 012	2 707	8	6 495 066	3 101
9	7 935 X29	4 833	9	1 055 719	3 3Ɛ2	9	7 358 167	3 X48
X	8 75X 660	5 487	X	1 XX8 Ɛ0Ɛ	4 0X0	X	8 21Ɛ ƐƐ3	4 793
Ɛ	9 583 Ɛ27	6 11X	Ɛ	2 940 ƐXƐ	4 98X	Ɛ	9 0X4 786	5 520

N	Tangent	d	N	Tangent	d	N	Tangent	d
.1400	.X09 Ɛ6X 0X6	X86 270	.1440	.X45 3X9 332	XƐ8 XX8	.1480	.X81 958 166	Ɛ31 92X
1	X X34 356	6 ƐƐƐ	1	6 2X6 21X	9 8X0	1	2 889 X94	2 78Ɛ
2	Ɛ 8ƐƐ 355	7 952	2	7 1X3 XƐX	X 696	2	3 800 663	3 631
3	.X10 787 0X7	8 6X4	3	8 0X2 594	Ɛ 491	3	4 734 094	4 495
4	1 653 78Ɛ	9 43X	4	8 ƐX1 X65	Ɛ00 28X	4	5 668 569	5 33Ɛ
5	2 521 009	X 194	5	9 XX2 133	1 088	5	6 5X1 8X8	6 1X7
6	3 3XƐ 1X1	X Ɛ30	6	X 9X3 1ƐƐ	1 X88	6	7 517 X93	7 054
7	4 27X 111	Ɛ 88X	7	Ɛ 8X5 087	2 88X	7	8 452 Ɛ27	7 Ɛ03
8	5 149 99Ɛ	X90 629	8	.X50 7X7 955	3 692	8	9 38X X2X	8 974
9	6 01X 408	1 389	9	1 6XƐ 427	4 496	9	X 307 7X2	9 827
X	6 XXƐ 795	2 12Ɛ	X	2 5Ɛ3 901	5 2X2	X	Ɛ 245 409	X 6X0
Ɛ	7 981 904	2 X93	Ɛ	3 4Ɛ8 ƐX3	6 0X9	Ɛ	.X90 183 XX9	Ɛ 555
.1410	8 854 797	3 839	.1450	4 403 090	6 XƐ8	.1490	1 103 442	Ɛ40 412
1	9 728 414	4 5X3	1	5 309 Ɛ88	7 907	1	2 043 854	1 28Ɛ
2	X 600 9Ɛ7	5 34Ɛ	2	6 215 893	8 718	2	2 Ɛ84 Ɛ23	2 14Ɛ
3	Ɛ 496 146	6 0ƐX	3	7 122 3XƐ	9 52Ɛ	3	3 Ɛ07 072	3 010
4	.X20 370 244	6 X68	4	8 02Ɛ 91X	X 344	4	4 X4X 082	3 X94
5	1 247 0Ɛ0	7 81X	5	8 Ɛ3X 062	Ɛ 15Ɛ	5	5 991 Ɛ56	4 958
6	2 122 90X	8 590	6	9 X49 201	Ɛ Ɛ76	6	6 916 8Ɛ2	5 822
7	2 ƐƐƐ 29X	9 345	7	X 959 177	Ɛ10 993	7	7 860 514	6 6Ɛ0
8	3 X98 623	X 0ƐX	8	Ɛ 869 Ɛ4X	1 7Ɛ3	8	8 7X7 004	7 579
9	4 976 721	X X75	9	.X60 77Ɛ 741	2 614	9	9 732 581	8 449
X	5 855 596	Ɛ 832	X	1 692 155	3 437	X	X 67X X0X	9 31Ɛ
Ɛ	6 735 208	XX0 5Ɛ0	Ɛ	2 5X5 590	4 25Ɛ	Ɛ	Ɛ 608 129	X 1Ɛ3
.1420	7 615 7Ɛ8	1 371	.1460	3 4Ɛ9 82Ɛ	5 085	.14X0	.XX0 556 320	Ɛ 088
1	8 4Ɛ6 Ɛ69	2 132	1	4 412 8Ɛ4	5 XƐ0	1	1 4X5 3X8	Ɛ Ɛ63
2	9 399 09Ɛ	2 XƐ5	2	5 328 7X4	6 91X	2	2 435 34Ɛ	Ɛ50 X40
3	X 27Ɛ Ɛ94	3 879	3	6 243 502	7 749	3	3 386 18Ɛ	1 91Ɛ
4	Ɛ 163 851	4 644	4	7 15Ɛ 04Ɛ	8 579	4	4 317 XXX	2 7ƐƐ
5	.X30 048 295	5 410	5	8 077 608	9 3Ɛ0	5	5 26X 6X9	3 6X2
6	0 Ɛ31 6X5	6 199	6	8 Ɛ94 9Ɛ8	X 224	6	6 202 18Ɛ	4 586
7	1 X17 882	6 Ɛ69	7	9 XƐ3 020	Ɛ 05X	7	7 156 755	5 470
8	2 902 82Ɛ	7 938	8	X X12 07X	Ɛ X96	8	8 0Ɛ0 005	6 357
9	3 7XX 567	8 70Ɛ	9	Ɛ 931 Ɛ54	Ɛ20 912	9	9 046 360	7 246
X	4 697 076	9 4X3	X	.X70 852 866	1 751	X	9 ƐX1 5X6	8 135
Ɛ	5 584 559	X 278	Ɛ	1 774 3Ɛ7	2 592	Ɛ	X Ɛ39 71Ɛ	9 026
.1430	6 472 815	Ɛ 053	.1470	2 696 989	3 415	.14Ɛ0	Ɛ X96 745	9 Ɛ19
1	7 361 868	Ɛ X30	1	3 5ƐX 1X2	4 258	1	.XƐ0 X34 662	X X12
2	8 251 698	XƐ0 80X	2	4 522 43X	5 0X2	2	1 993 474	Ɛ 909
3	9 142 2X6	1 5XX	3	5 447 520	5 Ɛ29	3	2 933 181	Ɛ60 805
4	X 033 894	2 38Ɛ	4	6 371 449	6 977	4	3 893 986	1 704
5	X Ɛ26 063	3 172	5	7 298 204	7 805	5	4 835 48X	2 604
6	Ɛ X19 215	3 Ɛ56	6	8 203 X09	8 656	6	5 797 X92	3 506
7	.X40 911 16Ɛ	4 941	7	9 130 463	9 4X9	7	6 73Ɛ 398	4 40X
8	1 805 XƐ0	5 729	8	X 059 950	X 340	8	7 6X3 7X6	5 314
9	2 6ƐƐ 619	6 516	9	X Ɛ88 090	Ɛ 196	9	8 648 XƐX	6 220
X	3 5Ɛ5 Ɛ33	7 305	X	Ɛ XƐ7 266	Ɛ30 032	X	9 5Ɛ3 11X	7 129
Ɛ	4 4Ɛ1 238	8 0Ɛ6	Ɛ	.X80 X27 298	0 X8X	Ɛ	X 55X 247	8 039

N	Tangent	d	N	Tangent	d	N	Tangent	d
.1500	.XƐƐ 506 284	Ɛ68 Ɛ49	.1540	.Ɛ3X 34X 73Ɛ	ƐX6 741	.1580	.Ɛ7X 550 5Ɛ2	1 026 Ɛ23
1	.Ɛ00 473 211	9 X61	1	Ɛ 335 280	7 710	1	Ɛ 577 515	7 Ɛ75
2	1 421 072	X 976	2	.Ɛ40 320 990	8 6X2	2	.Ɛ80 5X3 48X	9 00X
3	2 38Ɛ X28	Ɛ 890	3	1 309 472	9 676	3	1 610 498	X 066
4	3 33Ɛ 6Ɛ8	Ɛ70 7X9	4	2 2Ɛ6 Ɛ28	X 64Ɛ	4	2 63X 542	Ɛ 102
5	4 2Ɛ0 2X5	1 708	5	3 2X5 577	Ɛ 627	5	3 669 644	1 030 162
6	5 261 9Ɛ1	2 628	6	4 294 ƐX2	ƐƐ0 604	6	4 699 7X6	1 204
7	6 214 419	3 54X	7	5 285 5X6	1 5X4	7	5 70X 9XX	2 267
8	7 187 967	4 473	8	6 276 Ɛ8X	2 585	8	6 741 055	3 310
9	8 140 21X	5 398	9	7 269 553	3 569	9	7 774 365	4 379
X	9 0Ɛ5 5Ɛ6	6 305	X	8 260 Ɛ00	4 553	X	8 7X8 722	5 427
Ɛ	X 06Ɛ 8ƐƐ	7 232	Ɛ	9 255 453	5 53X	Ɛ	9 821 Ɛ49	6 497
.1510	Ɛ 026 Ɛ31	8 162	.1550	X 24X 991	6 528	.1590	X 858 424	7 54X
1	Ɛ ƐX3 093	9 094	1	Ɛ 245 2Ɛ9	7 518	1	Ɛ 893 972	8 603
2	.Ɛ10 Ɛ60 167	X 007	2	.Ɛ50 240 815	8 50X	2	.Ɛ90 910 375	9 679
3	1 Ɛ1X 172	X Ɛ41	3	1 239 123	9 501	3	1 949 X32	X 736
4	2 X99 0Ɛ3	Ɛ X77	4	2 236 624	X 4Ɛ7	4	2 988 568	Ɛ 7Ɛ6
5	3 X58 Ɛ6X	Ɛ80 9Ɛ5	5	3 234 Ɛ1Ɛ	Ɛ 4Ɛ3	5	3 X08 162	1 040 877
6	4 X19 963	1 934	6	4 234 412	1 000 4Ɛ1	6	4 X48 X19	1 93X
7	5 99Ɛ 697	2 875	7	5 234 903	1 4Ɛ0	7	5 X8X 757	2 X04
8	6 962 350	3 7Ɛ8	8	6 236 1Ɛ3	2 4Ɛ3	8	6 Ɛ11 55Ɛ	3 X91
9	7 925 Ɛ48	4 741	9	7 238 6X6	3 4Ɛ7	9	7 Ɛ55 430	4 Ɛ5X
X	8 8XX 689	5 688	X	8 23Ɛ ƐX1	4 501	X	8 Ɛ9X 38X	6 02Ɛ
Ɛ	9 874 155	6 614	Ɛ	9 244 4X2	5 509	Ɛ	X 024 3Ɛ9	7 101
.1520	X 83X 769	7 563	.1560	X 249 9XƐ	6 517	.15X0	Ɛ 06Ɛ 4ƐX	8 197
1	Ɛ 806 110	8 4Ɛ3	1	Ɛ 254 306	7 528	1	.ƐX0 0Ɛ7 695	9 271
2	.Ɛ20 792 603	9 446	2	.Ɛ60 25Ɛ 832	8 539	2	1 144 946	X 34Ɛ
3	1 75Ɛ X49	X 39X	3	1 268 16Ɛ	9 553	3	2 193 095	Ɛ 42X
4	2 72X 227	Ɛ 335	4	2 275 702	X 568	4	3 222 503	1 050 510
5	3 6Ɛ9 560	Ɛ90 290	5	3 284 06X	Ɛ 586	5	4 272 X13	1 5Ɛ3
6	4 689 830	1 22Ɛ	6	4 293 634	1 010 5X4	6	5 304 406	2 69X
7	5 65X X5Ɛ	2 18Ɛ	7	5 2X4 018	1 604	7	6 356 XX4	3 787
8	6 631 02X	3 131	8	6 2Ɛ5 620	2 628	8	7 3XX 66Ɛ	4 875
9	7 604 15Ɛ	4 095	9	7 308 048	3 650	9	8 443 324	5 966
X	8 598 234	5 03Ɛ	X	8 31Ɛ 698	4 678	X	9 499 08X	6 X59
Ɛ	9 571 273	5 ƐX7	Ɛ	9 334 154	5 6X4	Ɛ	X 533 Ɛ27	7 Ɛ52
.1530	X 547 25X	6 Ɛ55	.1570	X 349 838	6 714	.15Ɛ0	Ɛ 58Ɛ X79	9 04X
1	Ɛ 522 1Ɛ3	7 Ɛ05	1	Ɛ 364 350	7 745	1	.ƐƐ0 628 Ɛ07	X 149
2	.Ɛ30 4ƐX 0Ɛ8	8 X76	2	.Ɛ70 37Ɛ X95	8 778	2	1 687 054	Ɛ 248
3	1 496 Ɛ72	9 X2Ɛ	3	1 398 651	9 7Ɛ2	3	2 726 2X0	1 060 34X
4	2 474 9X1	X 9X4	4	2 3Ɛ6 243	X 82X	4	3 786 62X	1 454
5	3 453 785	Ɛ 95Ɛ	5	3 414 X71	Ɛ 867	5	4 827 X82	2 55X
6	4 433 524	ƐX0 91X	6	4 434 718	1 020 8X7	6	5 88X 420	3 668
7	5 414 242	1 899	7	5 455 403	1 929	7	6 931 X88	4 777
8	6 3Ɛ5 Ɛ1Ɛ	2 85X	8	6 477 130	2 971	8	7 996 643	5 889
9	7 398 779	3 822	9	7 499 XX1	3 9Ɛ7	9	8 X40 310	6 9X1
X	8 380 39Ɛ	4 7X8	X	8 501 898	4 X44	X	9 XX7 0Ɛ1	7 XƐ7
Ɛ	9 364 Ɛ87	5 774	Ɛ	9 526 720	5 X92	Ɛ	X Ɛ52 ƐX8	9 014

.1600 1·000 000 000

N	N Cot N	d	N	N Cot N	d	N	N Cot N	d
.0000	.1XƐ 02X 144	21	.0040	.1XƐ 000 72X	1 4Ɛ2	.0080	.1XX Ɛ38 094	2 983
1	123	63	1	.1XX ƐƐƐ 238	535	1	Ɛ35 311	X06
2	080	X6	2	ƐƐ9 903	576	2	Ɛ32 507	X47
3	029 Ɛ96	128	3	ƐƐ8 349	5Ɛ9	3	Ɛ2Ɛ 680	X8Ɛ
4	X6X	16X	4	ƐƐ6 950	63Ɛ	4	Ɛ28 7Ɛ1	Ɛ10
5	900	1Ɛ0	5	ƐƐ5 311	681	5	Ɛ25 8X1	Ɛ52
6	710	233	6	ƐƐ3 850	704	6	Ɛ22 94Ɛ	Ɛ95
7	499	275	7	ƐƐ2 148	746	7	Ɛ1Ɛ 976	3 017
8	224	2Ɛ7	8	ƐƐ0 602	788	8	Ɛ18 95Ɛ	05X
9	028 Ɛ29	33X	9	ƐXX X36	80X	9	Ɛ15 901	0X0
X	7XƐ	380	X	ƐX9 228	851	X	Ɛ12 821	122
Ɛ	42Ɛ	402	Ɛ	ƐX7 597	893	Ɛ	Ɛ0Ɛ 6ƐƐ	164
.0010	029	444	.0050	ƐX5 904	915	.0090	Ɛ08 557	1X7
1	027 7X5	487	1	ƐX3 ƐXƐ	957	1	Ɛ05 370	228
2	31X	509	2	ƐX2 254	99X	2	Ɛ02 144	270
3	026 X11	54Ɛ	3	ƐX0 476	X20	3	XƐX X94	2Ɛ1
4	482	591	4	Ɛ9X 656	X62	4	XƐ7 7X3	334
5	025 XƐ1	614	5	Ɛ98 7Ɛ4	XX5	5	XƐ4 46Ɛ	376
6	499	656	6	Ɛ96 90Ɛ	Ɛ27	6	XƐ1 0Ɛ5	3Ɛ8
7	024 X43	698	7	Ɛ94 9X4	Ɛ69	7	XX9 8Ɛ9	43Ɛ
8	367	71X	8	Ɛ92 X37	ƐXƐ	8	XX6 47X	481
9	023 849	761	9	Ɛ90 X48	2 032	9	XX2 ƐƐ9	503
X	0X8	7X3	X	Ɛ8X X16	074	X	X9Ɛ 6Ɛ6	545
Ɛ	022 505	825	Ɛ	Ɛ88 962	0Ɛ6	Ɛ	X98 171	588
.0020	021 8X0	868	.0060	Ɛ86 868	138	.00X0	X94 7X5	60X
1	034	8XX	1	Ɛ84 730	17Ɛ	1	X91 197	651
2	020 346	930	2	Ɛ82 571	201	2	X89 746	692
3	01Ɛ 616	972	3	Ɛ80 370	244	3	X86 074	715
4	01X 864	9Ɛ4	4	Ɛ7X 128	285	4	X82 55Ɛ	757
5	019 X70	X37	5	Ɛ77 X63	308	5	X7X X04	79X
6	035	X79	6	Ɛ75 757	34X	6	X77 226	820
7	018 178	Ɛ00	7	Ɛ73 409	391	7	X73 606	862
8	017 278	Ɛ41	8	Ɛ71 038	412	8	X6Ɛ 964	8X4
9	016 337	Ɛ84	9	Ɛ6X 826	455	9	X68 080	927
X	015 373	1 007	X	Ɛ68 391	497	X	X64 355	969
Ɛ	014 368	048	Ɛ	Ɛ65 XƐ6	51X	Ɛ	X60 5X8	9XƐ
.0030	013 320	08Ɛ	.0070	Ɛ63 598	560	.00Ɛ0	X58 7Ɛ9	X32
1	012 251	111	1	Ɛ61 038	5X2	1	X54 987	X74
2	011 140	153	2	Ɛ5X 656	624	2	X50 Ɛ13	XƐ6
3	00Ɛ ƐX9	195	3	Ɛ58 032	667	3	X49 019	Ɛ39
4	00X X14	218	4	Ɛ55 587	6X9	4	X45 0X0	Ɛ7X
5	009 7Ɛ8	25X	5	Ɛ52 X9X	72Ɛ	5	X41 122	4 001
6	008 55X	2X1	6	Ɛ50 36Ɛ	771	6	X39 121	044
7	007 279	322	7	Ɛ49 7ƐX	7Ɛ4	7	X35 099	086
8	005 Ɛ57	365	8	Ɛ47 006	836	8	X31 013	108
9	004 7Ɛ2	3X7	9	Ɛ44 390	879	9	X28 Ɛ07	14X
X	003 407	42X	X	Ɛ41 713	8ƐX	X	X24 979	190
Ɛ	001 Ɛ99	46Ɛ	Ɛ	Ɛ3X X15	941	Ɛ	X20 7X9	213

N	N Cot N	d	N	N Cot N	d	N	N Cot N	d
.0100	.1XX X18 596	4 256	.0140	.1XX 861 9Ɛ2	5 729	.0180	.1XX 650 088	7 002
1	X14 340	297	1	858 285	76Ɛ	1	645 086	043
2	X10 065	31X	2	852 716	7Ɛ1	2	63X 043	087
3	X07 947	360	3	848 Ɛ25	833	3	632 Ɛ78	108
4	X03 5X7	3X3	4	843 2Ɛ2	876	4	627 X70	14Ɛ
5	9ƐƐ 204	424	5	839 638	8Ɛ8	5	620 921	191
6	9Ɛ6 9X0	467	6	833 940	93Ɛ	6	615 750	214
7	9Ɛ2 535	4XX	7	82X 001	981	7	60X 538	256
8	9XX 047	52Ɛ	8	824 240	X03	8	603 2X2	298
9	9X5 718	572	9	81X 439	X45	9	5Ɛ8 006	31Ɛ
X	9X1 166	5Ɛ5	X	814 5Ɛ4	X88	X	5Ɛ0 8X7	361
Ɛ	998 771	636	Ɛ	80X 728	Ɛ0X	Ɛ	5X5 546	3X4
.0110	994 137	679	.0150	804 81X	Ɛ51	.0190	59X 162	426
1	98Ɛ 67X	6ƐƐ	1	7ƐX 889	Ɛ93	1	592 938	468
2	986 Ɛ7Ɛ	742	2	7Ɛ4 8Ɛ6	6 015	2	587 490	4XƐ
3	982 439	784	3	7XX 8X1	058	3	57Ɛ ƐX1	531
4	979 875	806	4	7X4 845	09X	4	574 670	574
5	975 06Ɛ	848	5	79X 767	120	5	569 0Ɛ8	5Ɛ6
6	970 423	88Ɛ	6	794 647	163	6	561 702	638
7	967 754	911	7	78X 4X4	1X4	7	556 086	67X
8	962 X43	954	8	784 300	228	8	54X 608	701
9	95X 0XƐ	995	9	77X 094	269	9	542 Ɛ07	744
X	955 316	X18	X	773 X27	2Ɛ1	X	537 383	786
Ɛ	950 4ƐX	X5Ɛ	Ɛ	769 736	332	Ɛ	52Ɛ 7Ɛ9	808
.0120	947 65Ɛ	XX0	.0160	763 404	375	.01X0	523 ƐƐ1	84Ɛ
1	942 77Ɛ	Ɛ23	1	759 04Ɛ	3Ɛ7	1	518 362	891
2	939 858	Ɛ66	2	752 854	439	2	510 691	913
3	934 8Ɛ2	ƐX7	3	748 417	480	3	504 97X	956
4	92Ɛ 907	5 02X	4	741 Ɛ57	502	4	4Ɛ9 024	998
5	926 899	071	5	737 655	545	5	4Ɛ1 248	X1Ɛ
6	921 828	0Ɛ2	6	731 110	586	6	4X5 429	X61
7	918 736	135	7	726 746	60X	7	499 588	XX3
8	913 601	177	8	720 138	64Ɛ	8	491 6X5	Ɛ26
9	90X 446	1ƐX	9	715 6X9	692	9	485 77Ɛ	Ɛ68
X	905 248	240	X	70Ɛ 017	714	X	479 813	ƐXƐ
Ɛ	900 008	282	Ɛ	704 503	757	Ɛ	471 824	8 031
.0130	8Ɛ6 946	305	.0170	6Ɛ9 968	799	.01Ɛ0	465 7Ɛ3	073
1	8Ɛ1 641	346	1	6Ɛ3 18Ɛ	81Ɛ	1	459 740	0Ɛ6
2	8X8 2Ɛ7	38X	2	6X8 570	862	2	451 646	138
3	8X2 Ɛ29	40Ɛ	3	6X1 90X	8X4	3	445 50X	17Ɛ
4	899 71X	452	4	697 026	927	4	439 34Ɛ	201
5	894 288	494	5	690 2ƐƐ	969	5	431 14X	243
6	88X 9Ɛ4	517	6	685 552	9XƐ	6	424 Ɛ07	286
7	885 499	559	7	67X 763	X31	7	418 841	309
8	87Ɛ Ɛ40	59Ɛ	8	673 932	X74	8	410 534	34X
9	876 561	621	9	668 X7X	XƐ7	9	404 1X6	391
X	870 Ɛ40	664	X	661 Ɛ83	Ɛ38	X	3Ɛ7 X15	414
Ɛ	867 498	6X6	Ɛ	657 047	Ɛ7Ɛ	Ɛ	3XƐ 601	456

N	N Cot N	d	N	N Cot N	d	N	N Cot N	d
.0200	.1ᘔᘔ 3ᘔ3 167	8 498	.0240	.1ᘔᘔ 09ᘔ Ɛ80	9 976	.0280	.1ᘔ9 93Ɛ 622	Ɛ 257
1	396 88Ɛ	51Ɛ	1	091 206	9Ɛ8	1	930 387	298
2	38ᘔ 370	561	2	083 40ᘔ	ᘔ3Ɛ	2	921 0ᘔƐ	31Ɛ
3	381 ᘔ0Ɛ	5ᘔ4	3	075 58Ɛ	ᘔ81	3	911 990	362
4	375 427	626	4	067 70ᘔ	Ɛ04	4	902 62ᘔ	3ᘔ4
5	368 ᘔ01	669	5	059 806	Ɛ46	5	8Ɛ3 246	427
6	360 354	6ᘔᘔ	6	04Ɛ 880	Ɛ89	6	8ᘔ3 ᘔ1Ɛ	46ᘔ
7	353 866	732	7	041 8Ɛ3	ᘔ 00Ɛ	7	894 571	4Ɛ0
8	347 134	774	8	033 8ᘔ4	052	8	885 081	532
9	33ᘔ 580	7Ɛ6	9	025 852	094	9	875 74Ɛ	575
ᘔ	331 986	838	ᘔ	017 77ᘔ	117	ᘔ	866 196	5Ɛ8
Ɛ	325 14ᘔ	87Ɛ	Ɛ	009 663	159	Ɛ	856 79ᘔ	63ᘔ
.0210	318 48Ɛ	902	.0250	.1ᘔ9 ƐƐƐ 506	19Ɛ	.0290	847 160	681
1	30Ɛ 789	944	1	ƐƐ1 327	222	1	837 69Ɛ	703
2	302 ᘔ45	986	2	Ɛᘔ3 105	265	2	827 Ɛ98	746
3	2Ɛ6 07Ɛ	ᘔ09	3	Ɛ94 ᘔ60	2ᘔ7	3	818 452	788
4	2ᘔ9 272	ᘔ4Ɛ	4	Ɛ86 775	32ᘔ	4	808 886	80Ɛ
5	2ᘔ0 423	ᘔ92	5	Ɛ78 447	370	5	7Ɛ9 077	851
6	293 551	Ɛ14	6	Ɛ6ᘔ 097	3Ɛ2	6	7ᘔ9 426	895
7	286 639	Ɛ57	7	Ɛ5Ɛ 8ᘔ5	435	7	799 751	916
8	279 6ᘔ2	Ɛ99	8	Ɛ51 470	478	8	789 ᘔ37	959
9	270 705	9 01Ɛ	9	Ɛ42 ƐƐ4	4Ɛᘔ	9	77ᘔ 09ᘔ	9ᘔ0
ᘔ	263 6ᘔ6	062	ᘔ	Ɛ34 6Ɛ6	541	ᘔ	76ᘔ 2Ɛᘔ	ᘔ22
Ɛ	256 644	0ᘔ4	Ɛ	Ɛ26 175	583	Ɛ	75ᘔ 498	ᘔ65
.0220	249 560	127	.0260	Ɛ17 7Ɛ2	605	.02ᘔ0	74ᘔ 633	ᘔᘔ8
1	240 435	169	1	Ɛ09 1ᘔ9	648	1	73ᘔ 747	Ɛ2ᘔ
2	233 288	1Ɛ0	2	ᘔƐƐ 761	68Ɛ	2	72ᘔ 819	Ɛ71
3	226 098	232	3	ᘔƐ0 092	711	3	71ᘔ 868	ƐƐ3
4	218 ᘔ66	275	4	ᘔᘔ1 581	754	4	70ᘔ 875	10 036
5	20Ɛ 7Ɛ1	2Ɛ7	5	ᘔ92 ᘔ29	796	5	6Ɛᘔ 83Ɛ	078
6	202 4Ɛ6	339	6	ᘔ84 253	819	6	6ᘔᘔ 783	0ƐƐ
7	1Ɛ5 179	380	7	ᘔ75 636	85Ɛ	7	69ᘔ 684	142
8	1ᘔ7 9Ɛ9	402	8	ᘔ66 997	8ᘔ1	8	68ᘔ 542	184
9	19ᘔ 5Ɛ7	445	9	ᘔ58 0Ɛ6	925	9	67ᘔ 37ᘔ	206
ᘔ	191 172	487	ᘔ	ᘔ49 391	966	ᘔ	66ᘔ 174	24ᘔ
Ɛ	183 8ᘔ7	50ᘔ	Ɛ	ᘔ3ᘔ 627	9ᘔᘔ	Ɛ	659 Ɛ26	290
.0230	176 399	550	.0270	ᘔ2Ɛ 839	ᘔ2Ɛ	.02Ɛ0	649 856	312
1	168 ᘔ49	593	1	ᘔ20 ᘔ0ᘔ	ᘔ73	1	639 544	355
2	15Ɛ 476	615	2	ᘔ11 Ɛ57	ᘔƐ4	2	629 1ᘔƐ	398
3	151 ᘔ61	658	3	ᘔ03 063	Ɛ38	3	618 ᘔ13	41ᘔ
4	144 405	69ᘔ	4	9Ɛ4 127	Ɛ7ᘔ	4	608 5Ɛ5	461
5	136 927	720	5	9ᘔ5 169	Ɛ 000	5	5Ɛ8 154	4ᘔ3
6	129 207	763	6	996 169	043	6	5ᘔ7 871	527
7	11Ɛ 664	7ᘔ6	7	987 126	085	7	597 346	568
8	111 ᘔ7ᘔ	828	8	978 061	108	8	586 99ᘔ	5Ɛ0
9	104 252	86ᘔ	9	968 Ɛ55	14Ɛ	9	576 3ᘔᘔ	631
ᘔ	0Ɛ6 5ᘔ4	8Ɛ1	ᘔ	959 ᘔ06	191	ᘔ	565 979	675
Ɛ	0ᘔ8 8Ɛ3	933	Ɛ	94ᘔ 835	213	Ɛ	555 304	6Ɛ7

N	N Cot N	d	N	N Cot N	d	N	N Cot N	d
.0300	.1X9 544 809	10 73X	.0340	.1X9 0£2 41X	12 025	.0380	.1X8 804 519	13 515
1	534 08£	780	1	0X0 3£5	068	1	7£1 004	557
2	523 50£	803	2	08X 349	0XX	2	799 669	59X
3	512 908	846	3	078 25£	131	3	786 08£	621
4	502 082	888	4	066 12X	174	4	772 66X	664
5	4£1 3£6	90£	5	053 £76	1£7	5	75£ 006	6X6
6	4X0 6X7	951	6	041 97£	239	6	747 520	729
7	48£ 956	994	7	02£ 742	280	7	733 9£3	770
8	47X £82	X17	8	019 482	303	8	720 243	7£3
9	46X 167	X59	9	007 17£	345	9	708 650	836
X	459 30X	XX0	X	.1X8 ££4 X36	388	X	6£4 X16	878
£	448 42X	£23	£	£X2 66X	40£	£	6X1 15X	8££
.0310	437 507	£65	.0350	£90 25£	451	.0390	689 45£	942
1	426 562	£X8	1	£79 X0X	494	1	675 719	985
2	415 576	11 02X	2	£67 536	517	2	661 954	X08
3	404 548	071	3	£55 01£	55X	3	649 £48	X4X
4	3£3 497	0£4	4	£42 681	5X0	4	636 0£X	X92
5	3X2 3X3	136	5	£30 0X1	623	5	622 228	£14
6	391 269	179	6	£19 67X	666	6	60X 314	£57
7	380 0£0	200	7	£07 014	6X9	7	5£6 379	£99
8	36X X£0	242	8	X£4 527	72£	8	5X2 3X0	14 021
9	359 86X	285	9	XX1 9£8	772	9	58X 37£	063
X	348 5X5	308	X	X8£ 246	7£5	X	576 318	0X6
£	337 299	34X	£	X78 651	837	£	562 232	129
.0320	325 £4£	391	.0360	X65 X16	87£	.03X0	54X 105	170
1	314 77X	413	1	X53 157	901	1	535 £55	1£3
2	303 367	457	2	X40 456	943	2	521 962	236
3	2£1 £10	498	3	X29 713	987	3	509 728	278
4	2X0 634	520	4	X16 948	X09	4	4£5 470	2££
5	28£ 114	562	5	X03 £3£	X50	5	4X1 171	342
6	279 772	5X5	6	9£1 0X£	X92	6	488 X2£	385
7	268 189	627	7	99X 219	£16	7	474 666	408
8	256 762	66£	8	987 303	£58	8	460 25X	44£
9	245 0£3	6£0	9	974 367	£9£	9	447 X0£	491
X	233 603	734	X	961 388	13 022	X	433 53X	514
£	221 X8£	776	£	94X 366	064	£	41£ 026	558
.0330	210 315	7£9	.0370	937 302	0X7	.03£0	406 68X	59X
1	1£X 718	83£	1	924 217	12X	1	3£2 0£0	620
2	1X8 X99	883	2	911 0X9	171	2	399 690	664
3	197 216	905	3	8£9 £38	1£4	3	385 028	6X7
4	185 511	947	4	8X6 944	236	4	370 541	729
5	173 786	98X	5	893 70X	279	5	357 X14	771
6	161 9£8	X11	6	880 451	300	6	343 263	7£3
7	14£ £X7	X54	7	869 151	342	7	32X 670	836
8	13X 153	X96	8	855 X0£	386	8	315 X36	879
9	128 279	£19	9	842 645	408	9	301 179	900
X	116 360	£60	X	82£ 239	44£	X	2X8 479	942
£	104 400	£X2	£	817 9XX	491	£	293 737	986

N	N Cot N	d	N	N Cot N	d	N	N Cot N	d
.0400	.1χ8 27χ 971	14 χ08	.0440	.1χ7 899 3χƐ	16 306	.0480	.1χ7 25Ɛ χ45	17 808
1	265 Ɛ65	χ50	1	883 0χ5	348	1	244 239	84Ɛ
2	251 115	χ92	2	868 959	390	2	228 5χχ	892
3	238 243	Ɛ15	3	852 589	412	3	210 918	915
4	223 32χ	Ɛ58	4	838 177	455	4	1Ɛ5 003	959
5	20χ 392	Ɛ9Ɛ	5	821 922	499	5	199 266	99Ɛ
6	1Ɛ5 3Ɛ3	15 022	6	807 445	51Ɛ	6	181 487	χ22
7	1χ0 391	065	7	7Ɛ0 Ɛ26	563	7	165 665	χ66
8	187 328	0χ7	8	796 583	5χ5	8	149 7ƐƐ	χχ9
9	172 241	12Ɛ	9	77Ɛ Ɛ9χ	629	9	131 912	Ɛ30
χ	159 112	171	χ	765 571	66Ɛ	χ	115 9χ2	Ɛ73
Ɛ	143 Ɛ61	1Ɛ4	Ɛ	74χ Ɛ02	6Ɛ3	Ɛ	0Ɛ9 χ2Ɛ	ƐƐ6
.0410	12χ 969	238	.0450	734 40Ɛ	735	.0490	0χ1 χ35	18 039
1	115 731	27χ	1	719 896	779	1	085 9Ɛ8	081
2	100 473	301	2	703 119	7ƐƐ	2	069 937	103
3	0χ7 172	344	3	6χ8 51χ	843	3	051 834	147
4	091 χ2χ	387	4	691 897	885	4	035 6χ9	18χ
5	078 663	409	5	677 012	909	5	019 51Ɛ	211
6	063 256	451	6	660 305	950	6	001 30χ	254
7	049 χ05	494	7	645 575	992	7	.1χ6 Ɛχ5 076	297
8	034 531	516	8	62χ 7χ3	χ16	8	Ɛ88 99Ɛ	31Ɛ
9	01Ɛ 017	55χ	9	613 989	χ59	9	Ɛ70 680	361
χ	005 679	5χ0	χ	5Ɛ8 Ɛ30	χχ0	χ	Ɛ54 31Ɛ	3χ5
Ɛ	.1χ7 ƐƐ0 099	624	Ɛ	5χ2 050	Ɛ23	Ɛ	Ɛ37 Ɛ36	428
.0420	Ɛ96 675	666	.0460	587 129	Ɛ65	.04χ0	Ɛ1Ɛ 70χ	46Ɛ
1	Ɛ81 00Ɛ	6χ9	1	570 184	Ɛχ9	1	Ɛ03 25Ɛ	4Ɛ3
2	Ɛ67 522	730	2	555 197	17 030	2	χχ6 968	535
3	Ɛ51 9Ɛ2	774	3	53χ 167	074	3	χ8χ 433	579
4	Ɛ38 23χ	7Ɛ6	4	523 0Ɛ3	0Ɛ6	4	χ71 χ76	600
5	Ɛ22 644	839	5	507 ƐƐ9	139	5	χ55 476	643
6	Ɛ08 χ07	880	6	4Ɛ0 χ80	180	6	χ38 χ33	686
7	χƐ3 147	902	7	495 900	203	7	χ20 369	709
8	χ99 445	946	8	47χ 6Ɛ9	247	8	χ03 860	751
9	χ83 6ƐƐ	989	9	463 472	289	9	9χ7 10Ɛ	794
χ	χ69 932	χ10	χ	448 1χ5	311	χ	98χ 537	817
Ɛ	χ53 Ɛ22	χ53	Ɛ	430 χ94	353	Ɛ	971 920	85χ
.0430	χ3χ 08Ɛ	χ95	.0470	415 741	397	.04Ɛ0	955 082	8χ1
1	χ24 1Ɛ6	Ɛ19	1	3Ɛχ 366	41χ	1	938 3χ1	925
2	χ0χ 299	Ɛ60	2	3χ2 Ɛ48	461	2	91Ɛ 678	968
3	9Ɛ4 339	Ɛχ2	3	387 6χ7	4χ4	3	902 910	9χƐ
4	99χ 357	16 026	4	370 203	527	4	8χ5 Ɛ21	χ32
5	984 331	068	5	354 898	56χ	5	889 0χƐ	χ75
6	96χ 285	0Ɛ0	6	339 32χ	5Ɛ1	6	870 236	χƐ9
7	954 195	132	7	321 939	634	7	853 339	Ɛ40
8	93χ 063	176	8	306 305	678	8	836 3Ɛ9	Ɛ83
9	923 χχ9	1Ɛ8	9	2χχ 849	6Ɛχ	9	819 436	19 006
χ	909 8Ɛ1	240	χ	293 14Ɛ	742	χ	800 430	04χ
Ɛ	8Ɛ3 671	282	Ɛ	277 609	784	Ɛ	7χ3 3χ2	091

N	N Cot N	d
.0500	.1X6 786 311	19 114
1	769 1Ɛ9	157
2	750 062	19Ɛ
3	732 X83	221
4	715 862	265
5	6Ɛ8 5Ɛ9	2X8
6	69Ɛ 311	330
7	681 ƐX1	373
8	664 82X	3Ɛ6
9	647 434	439
X	629 ƐƐ7	480
Ɛ	610 737	504
.0510	5Ɛ3 233	547
1	595 8X8	58X
2	578 31X	612
3	55X 908	655
4	541 273	698
5	523 797	71Ɛ
6	506 078	763
7	4X8 515	7X6
8	48X 92Ɛ	829
9	471 102	871
X	453 451	8Ɛ4
Ɛ	435 759	937
.0520	417 X22	97X
1	3ƐX 064	X02
2	3X0 262	X45
3	382 419	X88
4	364 551	Ɛ10
5	346 641	Ɛ53
6	328 6XX	Ɛ96
7	30X 714	1X 01X
8	2Ɛ0 6Ɛ6	061
9	292 655	0X4
X	274 571	128
Ɛ	256 445	16Ɛ
.0530	238 296	1Ɛ2
1	21X 0X4	236
2	1ƐƐ X6X	278
3	1X1 7Ɛ2	301
4	183 4Ɛ1	343
5	165 16X	387
6	146 9X3	40Ɛ
7	128 594	451
8	10X 143	495
9	0XƐ 86X	519
X	091 351	55Ɛ
Ɛ	072 9Ɛ2	5X4

N	N Cot N	d
.0540	.1X6 054 40X	1X 626
1	035 9X4	66X
2	017 336	6Ɛ1
3	.1X5 ƐƐ8 845	735
4	Ɛ9X 110	778
5	Ɛ7Ɛ 554	7ƐƐ
6	Ɛ60 955	843
7	Ɛ42 112	886
8	Ɛ23 448	90X
9	Ɛ04 73X	951
X	XX5 9X9	994
Ɛ	X87 015	X18
.0550	X68 1Ɛ9	X5Ɛ
1	X49 35X	XX2
2	X2X 478	Ɛ26
3	X0Ɛ 552	Ɛ6X
4	9Ɛ0 5X4	ƐƐ0
5	991 5Ɛ4	1Ɛ 035
6	972 57Ɛ	077
7	953 504	0ƐƐ
8	934 405	143
9	915 282	186
X	8Ɛ6 0Ɛ8	209
Ɛ	896 XXƐ	251
.0560	877 85X	294
1	858 586	318
2	839 26X	35Ɛ
3	819 Ɛ0Ɛ	3X2
4	7ƐX 729	426
5	79Ɛ 303	46X
6	77Ɛ X55	4Ɛ1
7	760 564	534
8	741 030	578
9	721 674	5ƐƐ
X	702 075	643
Ɛ	6X2 632	686
.0570	682 Ɛ68	70X
1	663 45X	751
2	643 909	795
3	624 134	818
4	604 518	860
5	5X4 878	8X3
6	584 Ɛ95	927
7	565 26X	96X
8	545 500	9Ɛ1
9	525 70Ɛ	X35
X	505 896	X79
Ɛ	4X5 X19	Ɛ00

N	N Cot N	d
.0580	.1X5 485 Ɛ19	1Ɛ Ɛ44
1	465 Ɛ95	Ɛ87
2	446 00X	20 00Ɛ
3	425 ƐƐƐ	052
4	405 Ɛ69	096
5	3X5 X93	119
6	385 976	161
7	365 815	1X4
8	345 631	228
9	325 405	270
X	305 155	2Ɛ3
Ɛ	2X4 X62	336
.0590	284 728	37X
1	264 36X	402
2	243 Ɛ68	445
3	223 723	489
4	203 256	510
5	1X2 946	554
6	182 3Ɛ2	597
7	161 X17	61Ɛ
8	141 3Ɛ8	663
9	120 955	6X6
X	100 26Ɛ	72X
Ɛ	09Ɛ 741	771
.05X0	07X Ɛ90	7Ɛ5
1	05X 397	839
2	039 75X	880
3	018 X9X	903
4	.1X4 ƐƐ8 197	948
5	Ɛ97 44Ɛ	98Ɛ
6	Ɛ76 680	X12
7	Ɛ55 86X	X56
8	Ɛ34 X14	X9X
9	Ɛ13 Ɛ36	Ɛ21
X	XƐ3 015	Ɛ65
Ɛ	X92 070	ƐX9
.05Ɛ0	X71 083	21 030
1	X50 053	074
2	X2X Ɛ9Ɛ	0Ɛ8
3	X09 XX3	13Ɛ
4	9X8 964	182
5	987 7X2	207
6	966 597	24X
7	945 349	292
8	924 077	315
9	902 962	359
X	8X1 605	3X1
Ɛ	880 224	424

N	N Cot N	d	N	N Cot N	d	N	N Cot N	d
.0600	.1X4 85X X00	21 468	.0640	.1X3 Ɛ96 X22	22 998	.0680	.1X3 275 910	24 314
1	839 554	4Ɛ0	1	Ɛ74 046	X20	1	251 5Ɛ8	358
2	818 064	533	2	Ɛ51 226	X63	2	229 260	3X0
3	7Ɛ6 731	577	3	Ɛ2X 383	XX8	3	204 X80	424
4	795 176	5ƐƐ	4	Ɛ07 497	Ɛ2Ɛ	4	1X0 658	468
5	773 777	642	5	XX4 568	Ɛ73	5	178 1Ɛ0	4Ɛ0
6	752 135	686	6	X81 5Ɛ5	ƐƐ7	6	153 900	534
7	730 66Ɛ	70X	7	X5X 5ƐX	23 03Ɛ	7	12Ɛ 388	578
8	70X Ɛ61	752	8	X37 57Ɛ	083	8	106 X10	600
9	6X9 40Ɛ	795	9	X14 4Ɛ8	106	9	0X2 410	644
X	687 836	819	X	9Ɛ1 3Ɛ2	14Ɛ	X	079 988	688
Ɛ	666 019	860	Ɛ	98X 263	192	Ɛ	055 300	711
.0610	644 379	8X4	.0650	967 091	216	.0690	030 7XƐ	754
1	622 695	928	1	943 X77	25X	1	008 057	798
2	600 969	970	2	920 819	2X2	2	.1X2 ƐX3 47Ɛ	820
3	59X ƐƐ9	9Ɛ4	3	8Ɛ9 537	326	3	Ɛ7X 85Ɛ	865
4	579 205	X37	4	896 211	36X	4	Ɛ55 ƐƐ6	8X8
5	557 38X	X7X	5	872 X63	3Ɛ1	5	Ɛ31 30X	931
6	535 510	Ɛ03	6	84Ɛ 672	436	6	Ɛ08 599	974
7	513 609	Ɛ46	7	828 238	479	7	XX3 825	9Ɛ9
8	4Ɛ1 683	Ɛ8X	8	804 97Ɛ	501	8	X7X X28	X41
9	48Ɛ 6Ɛ5	22 012	9	7X1 47X	546	9	X55 ƐX7	X85
X	469 6X3	056	X	779 Ɛ34	589	X	X31 122	Ɛ09
Ɛ	447 649	099	Ɛ	756 567	611	Ɛ	X08 215	Ɛ51
.0620	425 570	121	.0660	732 Ɛ56	655	.06X0	9X3 284	Ɛ95
1	403 44Ɛ	165	1	70Ɛ 501	698	1	97X 2XƐ	25 019
2	3X1 2X6	1X8	2	6X7 X25	721	2	955 292	061
3	37Ɛ 0ƐX	230	3	684 304	765	3	930 231	0X6
4	358 X8X	274	4	660 75Ɛ	7X8	4	907 147	129
5	336 816	2Ɛ8	5	638 Ɛ73	831	5	8X2 01X	172
6	314 51X	340	6	615 342	874	6	878 X68	1Ɛ5
7	2Ɛ2 19X	383	7	5Ɛ1 68X	8Ɛ9	7	853 873	23X
8	28Ɛ X17	407	8	589 991	940	8	82X 635	282
9	269 610	44Ɛ	9	566 051	985	9	805 373	306
X	247 181	493	X	542 288	X08	X	7X0 069	34Ɛ
Ɛ	224 8XX	516	Ɛ	51X 480	X50	Ɛ	776 91X	392
.0630	202 394	55X	.0670	4Ɛ6 630	X94	.06Ɛ0	751 548	416
1	19Ɛ X36	5X2	1	492 758	Ɛ18	1	728 132	45Ɛ
2	179 454	626	2	46X 840	Ɛ60	2	702 893	4X3
3	156 X2X	66X	3	446 8X0	ƐX4	3	699 3Ɛ0	527
4	134 380	6Ɛ1	4	422 8Ɛ8	24 028	4	673 X85	56Ɛ
5	111 88Ɛ	736	5	3ƐX 890	070	5	64X 516	5Ɛ3
6	0XƐ 155	779	6	396 820	0Ɛ4	6	624 Ɛ23	637
7	088 598	800	7	372 728	138	7	5ƐƐ 4X8	680
8	065 998	845	8	34X 5Ɛ0	180	8	595 X28	704
9	043 153	889	9	326 430	204	9	570 324	748
X	020 486	910	X	302 228	248	X	546 798	790
Ɛ	.1X3 ƐƐ9 776	954	Ɛ	299 ƐX0	290	Ɛ	521 008	814

N	N Cot N	d	N	N Cot N	d	N	N Cot N	d
.0700	.1X2 4Ɛ7 3Ɛ4	25 858	.0740	.1X1 69Ɛ 3X4	27 1XX	.0780	.1X0 825 591	28 749
1	491 758	8X1	1	674 1Ɛ6	233	1	7Ɛ8 X44	792
2	467 X77	925	2	648 Ɛ83	276	2	790 272	816
3	442 152	969	3	621 909	2ƐƐ	3	763 658	85X
4	418 3X5	9Ɛ1	4	5Ɛ6 60X	344	4	736 9ƐX	8X3
5	3Ɛ2 5Ɛ4	X35	5	58Ɛ 286	388	5	70X 117	928
6	388 77Ɛ	X7X	6	563 XƐX	410	6	6X1 3XƐ	970
7	362 901	Ɛ02	7	538 6XX	455	7	674 63Ɛ	9Ɛ5
8	338 9ƐƐ	Ɛ46	8	511 255	499	8	647 846	X3X
9	312 X75	Ɛ8X	9	4X5 978	521	9	61X X08	X82
X	2X8 XX7	26 013	X	47X 457	566	X	5Ɛ1 Ɛ46	Ɛ07
Ɛ	282 X94	056	Ɛ	452 XƐ1	5XX	Ɛ	585 03Ɛ	Ɛ4Ɛ
.0710	258 X3X	09Ɛ	.0750	427 503	633	.0790	558 0Ɛ0	Ɛ95
1	232 95Ɛ	123	1	3ƐƐ X90	677	1	52Ɛ 117	29 018
2	208 838	168	2	394 415	700	2	502 0ƐƐ	062
3	1X2 690	1Ɛ0	3	368 915	744	3	495 059	0X6
4	178 4X0	233	4	341 191	788	4	467 Ɛ73	12X
5	152 269	279	5	315 605	811	5	43X X45	173
6	127 ƐƐ0	300	6	2X9 9Ɛ4	855	6	411 892	1Ɛ8
7	101 8Ɛ0	345	7	282 15Ɛ	89X	7	3X4 696	241
8	097 567	389	8	256 481	923	8	377 455	285
9	071 19X	411	9	22X 75X	966	9	34X 190	30X
X	046 989	455	X	202 9Ɛ4	9Ɛ0	X	320 X82	353
Ɛ	020 534	49X	Ɛ	197 004	X33	Ɛ	2Ɛ3 72Ɛ	307
.0720	.1X1 ƐƐ6 056	522	.0760	16Ɛ 191	X78	.07X0	286 354	420
1	Ɛ8Ɛ 734	566	1	143 315	Ɛ01	1	258 Ɛ34	465
2	Ɛ65 18X	5XƐ	2	117 414	Ɛ45	2	22Ɛ 68Ɛ	4X9
3	Ɛ3X 79Ɛ	633	3	0XƐ 48Ɛ	Ɛ8X	3	202 1X2	532
4	Ɛ14 168	677	4	083 501	28 012	4	194 870	577
5	XX9 6Ɛ1	6ƐƐ	5	057 4XƐ	056	5	167 2Ɛ5	5ƐƐ
6	X82 ƐƐ2	744	6	02Ɛ 455	09Ɛ	6	139 8Ɛ6	644
7	X58 46X	788	7	003 376	124	7	110 272	689
8	X31 8X2	811	8	.1X0 Ɛ97 252	168	8	0X2 7X5	712
9	X07 091	854	9	Ɛ6Ɛ 0X6	1Ɛ1	9	075 093	756
X	9X0 439	899	X	Ɛ42 XƐ5	235	X	047 539	79Ɛ
Ɛ	975 760	922	Ɛ	Ɛ16 880	279	Ɛ	019 95X	824
.0730	94X X3X	965	.0770	XXX 603	303	.07Ɛ0	.19Ɛ ƐƐ0 136	868
1	924 095	9XX	1	X82 300	346	1	Ɛ82 48X	8Ɛ1
2	8Ɛ9 2X7	X33	2	X55 Ɛ76	390	2	Ɛ54 799	936
3	892 474	X76	3	X29 7X6	413	3	Ɛ26 X63	97Ɛ
4	867 5ƐX	XƐƐ	4	X01 393	459	4	XƐ9 0X4	X03
5	840 6ƐƐ	Ɛ44	5	994 Ɛ36	4X1	5	X8Ɛ 2X1	X49
6	815 777	Ɛ88	6	968 655	525	6	X61 454	X91
7	7XX 7XƐ	27 010	7	940 130	56X	7	X33 583	Ɛ15
8	783 79Ɛ	054	8	913 782	5Ɛ2	8	X05 66X	Ɛ5Ɛ
9	758 747	099	9	8X7 190	638	9	997 70Ɛ	ƐX3
X	731 66X	121	X	87X 754	67Ɛ	X	969 728	2X 028
Ɛ	706 549	165	Ɛ	852 095	704	Ɛ	93Ɛ 700	071

N	N Cot N	d	N	N Cot N	d	N	N Cot N	d
.0800	.19Ɛ 911 64Ɛ	2χ 0Ɛ6	.0840	.19χ 95Ɛ 254	2Ɛ 671	.0880	.199 94χ 239	31 037
1	8χ3 555	13χ	1	92Ɛ 7χ3	6Ɛ6	1	919 202	081
2	875 417	183	2	900 0χ9	73Ɛ	2	8χ8 141	105
3	847 254	208	3	890 56χ	784	3	877 038	14Ɛ
4	819 048	251	4	860 9χ6	809	4	845 χχ9	194
5	7χχ 9Ɛ7	296	5	831 199	852	5	814 915	219
6	780 721	31χ	6	801 547	897	6	7χ3 6Ɛ8	262
7	752 403	363	7	791 870	920	7	772 456	2χ8
8	724 060	3χ9	8	761 Ɛ50	965	8	741 16χ	331
9	6Ɛ5 873	430	9	732 1χ7	9χχ	9	70Ɛ χ39	376
χ	687 443	476	χ	702 3Ɛ9	χ33	χ	69χ 683	400
Ɛ	658 Ɛ89	4ƐƐ	Ɛ	692 586	χ78	Ɛ	669 283	445
.0810	62χ 68χ	543	.0850	662 70χ	Ɛ02	.0890	637 χ3χ	48χ
1	600 147	589	1	632 808	Ɛ46	1	606 570	514
2	591 77χ	611	2	602 882	Ɛ8Ɛ	2	595 058	559
3	563 169	656	3	592 8Ɛ3	30 015	3	563 6ƐƐ	5χ2
4	534 713	69Ɛ	4	562 89χ	05χ	4	532 119	627
5	506 034	723	5	532 840	0χ2	5	500 6Ɛ2	671
6	497 511	769	6	502 75χ	128	6	48Ɛ 041	6Ɛ6
7	468 964	7Ɛ1	7	492 632	171	7	459 547	740
8	43χ 173	837	8	462 481	1Ɛ6	8	427 χ07	784
9	40Ɛ 538	87Ɛ	9	432 287	23Ɛ	9	3Ɛ6 243	80Ɛ
χ	3χ0 879	904	χ	402 048	285	χ	384 634	853
Ɛ	371 Ɛ75	949	Ɛ	391 983	309	Ɛ	352 9χ1	899
.0820	343 228	992	.0860	361 676	352	.08χ0	321 104	922
1	314 456	χ17	1	331 324	398	1	2χƐ 3χ2	968
2	2χ5 63Ɛ	χ5Ɛ	2	300 Ɛ48	421	2	279 636	9Ɛ1
3	276 7χ0	χχ5	3	290 727	466	3	247 845	χ36
4	247 8Ɛ7	Ɛ2χ	4	260 281	4χƐ	4	215 χ0Ɛ	χ80
5	218 989	Ɛ72	5	22Ɛ 992	534	5	1χ3 Ɛ4Ɛ	Ɛ05
6	1χ9 χ17	ƐƐ7	6	1ƐƐ 45χ	579	6	172 046	Ɛ4χ
7	17χ χ20	2Ɛ 041	7	18χ χχ1	603	7	140 0Ɛ8	Ɛ94
8	14Ɛ 99Ɛ	085	8	15χ 49χ	648	8	10χ 124	32 019
9	120 916	10χ	9	129 χ52	690	9	098 107	063
χ	0Ɛ1 808	153	χ	0Ɛ9 382	716	χ	066 064	0χ8
Ɛ	082 675	198	Ɛ	088 868	760	Ɛ	033 Ɛ78	132
.0830	053 499	222	.0870	058 108	7χ4	.08Ɛ0	001 χ46	177
1	024 277	266	1	027 524	829	1	.198 Ɛ8Ɛ 88Ɛ	200
2	.19χ ƐƐ5 011	2χχ	2	.199 ƐƐ6 8Ɛ7	873	2	Ɛ59 68Ɛ	246
3	Ɛ85 923	334	3	Ɛ86 044	8Ɛ8	3	Ɛ27 445	28Ɛ
4	Ɛ56 5χƐ	379	4	Ɛ55 348	941	4	χƐ5 176	315
5	Ɛ27 232	402	5	Ɛ24 607	987	5	χ82 χ61	35χ
6	χƐ7 χ30	447	6	χƐ3 840	χ0Ɛ	6	χ50 703	3χ4
7	χ88 5χ5	490	7	χ82 χ31	χ55	7	χ1χ 31Ɛ	429
8	χ59 115	515	8	χ51 Ɛ98	χ9χ	8	9χ7 χƐ2	472
9	χ29 800	55χ	9	χ21 0Ɛχ	Ɛ23	9	975 640	4Ɛ8
χ	9Ɛχ 262	5χ2	χ	9Ɛ0 197	Ɛ69	χ	943 144	542
Ɛ	98χ 880	628	Ɛ	97Ɛ 22χ	ƐƐ1	Ɛ	910 802	586

N	N Cot N	d	N	N Cot N	d	N	N Cot N	d
.0900	.198 89X 238	32 611	.0940	.197 78X X67	33 ƐƐ6	.0980	.196 61Ɛ Ɛ01	35 5Ɛ0
1	867 827	656	1	756 X71	34 03Ɛ	1	5X6 511	635
2	835 191	69Ɛ	2	722 X32	086	2	570 X98	680
3	802 6ƐƐ	725	3	6XX 968	10Ɛ	3	537 418	705
4	78Ɛ Ɛ89	76X	4	676 859	154	4	501 913	750
5	759 41Ɛ	7Ɛ4	5	642 705	19Ɛ	5	488 183	795
6	726 827	83X	6	60X 526	224	6	452 5XX	820
7	6Ɛ3 ƐX9	883	7	596 302	26X	7	418 98X	866
8	681 326	908	8	562 054	2Ɛ4	8	3X3 124	8XƐ
9	64X 61X	952	9	529 960	33X	9	369 435	936
X	617 888	998	X	4Ɛ5 622	383	X	333 6ƐƐ	980
Ɛ	5X4 XƐ0	X21	Ɛ	481 25Ɛ	409	Ɛ	2Ɛ9 93Ɛ	X06
.0910	572 08Ɛ	X66	.0950	448 X52	453	.0990	283 Ɛ35	X50
1	53Ɛ 225	XƐ0	1	414 5ƐƐ	499	1	24X 0X5	X96
2	508 335	Ɛ36	2	3X0 122	523	2	214 20Ɛ	Ɛ20
3	495 3ƐƐ	Ɛ7Ɛ	3	367 7ƐƐ	568	3	19X 2XƐ	Ɛ66
4	462 440	33 005	4	333 253	5Ɛ2	4	164 345	ƐƐ0
5	42Ɛ 437	04Ɛ	5	2ƐX 861	638	5	12X 355	36 036
6	3Ɛ8 3X8	094	6	286 225	682	6	0Ɛ4 31Ɛ	081
7	385 314	119	7	251 763	708	7	07X 25X	106
8	352 1Ɛ7	163	8	219 057	752	8	044 154	151
9	31Ɛ 054	1X9	9	1X4 505	797	9	00X 003	197
X	2X7 X67	233	X	16Ɛ 92X	822	X	.195 Ɛ93 X28	221
Ɛ	274 834	278	Ɛ	137 108	867	Ɛ	Ɛ59 807	267
.0920	241 578	301	.0960	102 461	8Ɛ1	.09X0	Ɛ23 560	2Ɛ1
1	20X 277	347	1	089 770	937	1	XX9 26Ɛ	337
2	196 Ɛ30	391	2	054 X35	980	2	X72 Ɛ34	381
3	163 75Ɛ	416	3	020 075	X07	3	X38 773	408
4	130 345	461	4	.196 ƐX7 26X	X51	4	X02 367	452
5	0Ɛ8 XX4	4X5	5	Ɛ72 419	X96	5	987 Ɛ15	498
6	085 5ƐƐ	530	6	Ɛ39 543	Ɛ20	6	951 639	522
7	052 08Ɛ	575	7	Ɛ04 623	Ɛ67	7	917 117	568
8	01X 716	5ƐX	8	X8Ɛ 678	ƐƐ0	8	8X0 76Ɛ	5Ɛ3
9	.197 ƐX7 118	644	9	X56 688	35 036	9	866 178	638
X	Ɛ73 694	68X	X	X21 652	080	X	82Ɛ 740	683
Ɛ	Ɛ40 006	714	Ɛ	9X8 592	106	Ɛ	7Ɛ5 079	709
.0930	Ɛ08 4Ɛ2	759	.0970	973 488	150	.09Ɛ0	77X 570	753
1	X94 955	7X3	1	93X 338	196	1	743 X19	79X
2	X61 172	829	2	905 162	21Ɛ	2	709 23Ɛ	823
3	X29 545	872	3	88Ɛ Ɛ43	266	3	692 618	86X
4	9Ɛ5 893	8Ɛ8	4	856 899	2Ɛ0	4	657 96X	8Ɛ4
5	981 Ɛ97	942	5	821 5X9	335	5	621 076	93Ɛ
6	94X 255	987	6	7X8 274	380	6	5X6 337	984
7	916 48X	X11	7	772 XƐ4	405	7	56Ɛ 573	X0Ɛ
8	8X2 679	X57	8	739 6XƐ	450	8	534 764	X55
9	86X 822	XX1	9	704 25Ɛ	495	9	4Ɛ9 90Ɛ	X9Ɛ
X	836 941	Ɛ26	X	68X 986	520	X	482 X30	Ɛ26
Ɛ	802 X17	Ɛ70	Ɛ	655 466	565	Ɛ	447 Ɛ06	Ɛ70

N	N Cot N	d	N	N Cot N	d	N	N Cot N	d
.0X00	.195 410 Ɛ56	36 ƐƐ6	.0X40	.194 161 764	38 612	.0X80	.192 X51 679	3X 040
1	395 Ɛ60	37 040	1	125 152	659	1	X13 639	087
2	35X Ɛ20	087	2	0X8 6Ɛ5	6X3	2	995 572	112
3	323 X55	111	3	070 012	72X	3	957 460	159
4	2X8 944	157	4	033 4X4	774	4	919 303	1X4
5	271 7X9	1X2	5	.193 ƐƐ6 930	800	5	89Ɛ 11Ɛ	22X
6	236 607	228	6	Ɛ7X 130	845	6	860 XƐ1	276
7	1ƐƐ 39Ɛ	272	7	Ɛ41 4X7	890	7	822 837	300
8	184 129	2Ɛ8	8	Ɛ04 817	917	8	7X4 537	347
9	148 X31	343	9	X87 Ɛ00	962	9	766 1Ɛ0	392
X	111 6XX	389	X	X4Ɛ 15X	9X8	X	727 X1X	41X
Ɛ	096 321	414	Ɛ	X12 372	X33	Ɛ	6X9 600	464
.0X10	05X Ɛ09	45X	.0X50	995 53Ɛ	X79	.0X90	66Ɛ 158	4XƐ
1	023 66Ɛ	4X4	1	958 682	Ɛ04	1	630 869	535
2	.194 ƐX8 187	52X	2	91Ɛ 77X	Ɛ4Ɛ	2	5Ɛ2 334	581
3	Ɛ70 859	575	3	8X2 82Ɛ	Ɛ95	3	573 973	608
4	Ɛ35 2X4	600	4	865 856	39 020	4	535 367	653
5	XƐ9 8X4	645	5	828 836	066	5	4Ɛ6 914	699
6	X82 25Ɛ	690	6	7XƐ 790	0Ɛ2	6	478 237	725
7	X46 78Ɛ	717	7	772 69X	138	7	439 712	770
8	X0Ɛ 074	761	8	735 562	182	8	3ƐX Ɛ62	7Ɛ6
9	993 513	7X7	9	6Ɛ8 3X0	20X	9	380 368	842
X	957 928	831	X	67Ɛ 192	254	X	341 726	889
Ɛ	920 0Ɛ7	878	Ɛ	641 Ɛ3X	29X	Ɛ	302 X59	913
.0X20	8X4 43Ɛ	903	.0X60	604 860	326	.0XX0	284 146	95Ɛ
1	868 738	949	1	587 536	370	1	245 3X7	9X5
2	830 9XƐ	993	2	54X 186	3Ɛ7	2	206 602	X31
3	7Ɛ5 018	X1X	3	510 98Ɛ	441	3	187 791	X78
4	779 1ƐX	X64	4	493 54X	488	4	148 915	Ɛ02
5	741 356	XXX	5	456 082	513	5	109 X13	Ɛ4X
6	705 468	Ɛ35	6	418 76Ɛ	55X	6	08X X85	Ɛ95
7	689 533	Ɛ80	7	39Ɛ 211	5X5	7	04Ɛ XƐ0	3Ɛ 020
8	651 573	38 006	8	361 828	62Ɛ	8	010 X90	067
9	615 569	050	9	324 1Ɛ9	676	9	.191 Ɛ91 X25	0Ɛ2
X	599 519	097	X	2X6 743	701	X	Ɛ52 933	139
Ɛ	561 442	122	Ɛ	269 042	747	Ɛ	Ɛ13 7Ɛ6	184
.0X30	525 320	167	.0X70	22Ɛ 4Ɛ7	793	.0XƐ0	X94 632	20Ɛ
1	4X9 175	1Ɛ3	1	1Ɛ1 924	819	1	X55 423	256
2	470 Ɛ82	239	2	174 107	864	2	X16 189	2X2
3	434 945	283	3	136 463	8XƐ	3	996 XX7	328
4	3Ɛ8 682	30X	4	0Ɛ8 774	935	4	957 77Ɛ	374
5	380 374	354	5	07X X3Ɛ	980	5	918 407	3ƐƐ
6	344 020	39Ɛ	6	041 07Ɛ	X08	6	899 008	445
7	307 841	426	7	003 273	X52	7	859 783	491
8	28Ɛ 417	470	8	.192 Ɛ85 421	X98	8	81X 2Ɛ2	519
9	252 Ɛ67	4Ɛ6	9	Ɛ47 545	Ɛ24	9	79X 995	563
X	216 671	541	X	Ɛ09 621	Ɛ6Ɛ	X	75Ɛ 432	5XX
Ɛ	19X 130	588	Ɛ	X8Ɛ 672	ƐƐ5	Ɛ	71Ɛ X44	636

N	N Cot N	d	N	N Cot N	d	N	N Cot N	d
.0Ɛ00	.191 6X0 40X	3Ɛ 681	.0Ɛ40	.190 289 6X6	41 114	.0Ɛ80	.18X X14 9Ɛ5	42 77Ɛ
1	660 949	707	1	248 592	160	1	992 236	808
2	621 242	754	2	207 432	1X7	2	94Ɛ 62X	853
3	5X1 6XX	79X	3	186 247	233	3	908 997	89Ɛ
4	561 Ɛ10	825	4	145 014	27X	4	886 0Ɛ8	927
5	522 2X7	871	5	103 956	306	5	843 391	972
6	4X2 636	8Ɛ8	6	082 650	351	6	800 61Ɛ	9ƐƐ
7	462 93X	943	7	041 2ƐƐ	399	7	779 820	X46
8	422 ƐƐ7	98X	8	.18Ɛ ƐƐƐ Ɛ22	425	8	736 996	X93
9	3X3 229	X15	9	Ɛ7X 6Ɛ9	470	9	6Ɛ3 Ɛ03	Ɛ1X
X	363 414	X61	X	Ɛ39 249	4Ɛ7	X	670 ƐX5	Ɛ66
Ɛ	323 573	XX8	Ɛ	XƐ7 952	543	Ɛ	62X 03Ɛ	ƐƐ2
.0Ɛ10	2X3 687	Ɛ33	.0Ɛ50	X76 40Ɛ	58Ɛ	.0Ɛ90	5X7 049	43 03X
1	263 754	Ɛ7Ɛ	1	X34 X40	616	1	564 00Ɛ	085
2	223 795	40 005	2	9Ɛ3 426	662	2	520 Ɛ46	112
3	1X3 790	051	3	971 984	6X9	3	499 X34	15X
4	163 73Ɛ	099	4	930 297	735	4	456 896	1X5
5	123 662	123	5	8XX 762	781	5	413 6Ɛ1	232
6	0X3 53Ɛ	16Ɛ	6	868 ƐX1	808	6	390 47Ɛ	279
7	063 390	1Ɛ6	7	827 395	854	7	349 202	305
8	023 196	241	8	7X5 741	89Ɛ	8	305 XƐ9	351
9	.190 ƐX2 Ɛ55	289	9	763 X62	927	9	282 768	39X
X	Ɛ62 888	314	X	722 137	973	X	23Ɛ 38X	425
Ɛ	Ɛ22 574	35Ɛ	Ɛ	6X0 384	9ƐX	Ɛ	1Ɛ7 Ɛ65	471
.0Ɛ20	XX2 215	3X7	.0Ɛ60	65X 586	X46	.0ƐX0	174 6Ɛ4	4Ɛ9
1	X61 X2X	432	1	618 740	X92	1	131 1Ɛ7	545
2	X21 5Ɛ8	479	2	596 86X	Ɛ19	2	0X9 872	592
3	9X1 13Ɛ	505	3	554 951	Ɛ65	3	066 2X0	619
4	960 836	550	4	512 9X8	ƐƐ0	4	022 883	665
5	920 2X6	597	5	490 9Ɛ8	42 039	5	.189 Ɛ9Ɛ 21X	6Ɛ1
6	89Ɛ 90Ɛ	623	6	44X 97Ɛ	084	6	Ɛ57 729	739
7	85Ɛ 2X8	66X	7	408 8Ɛ7	10Ɛ	7	Ɛ13 ƐƐ0	786
8	81X 83X	6Ɛ5	8	386 7X8	158	8	X90 426	811
9	79X 145	741	9	344 650	1X3	9	X48 815	859
X	759 604	788	X	302 469	22X	X	X04 Ɛ78	8X6
Ɛ	718 X38	814	Ɛ	280 23Ɛ	277	Ɛ	981 292	931
.0Ɛ30	698 224	85Ɛ	.0Ɛ70	239 Ɛ84	302	.0ƐƐ0	939 561	97X
1	657 585	8X6	1	1Ɛ7 882	34X	1	8Ɛ5 7X3	X05
2	616 89Ɛ	932	2	175 534	396	2	871 99X	X52
3	595 Ɛ69	979	3	133 15X	421	3	829 Ɛ48	X9X
4	555 1Ɛ0	X05	4	0Ɛ0 939	469	4	7X6 06X	Ɛ26
5	514 3X7	X50	5	06X 490	4Ɛ5	5	762 144	Ɛ72
6	493 557	X97	6	027 Ɛ97	541	6	71X 192	ƐƐX
7	452 680	Ɛ23	7	.18X ƐX5 656	589	7	696 194	44 046
8	411 759	Ɛ6Ɛ	8	Ɛ63 089	614	8	652 14X	092
9	390 7XX	ƐƐ6	9	Ɛ20 675	660	9	60X 078	11Ɛ
X	34Ɛ 7Ɛ4	41 041	X	X9X 015	6X8	X	585 Ɛ59	166
Ɛ	30X 773	089	Ɛ	X57 529	734	Ɛ	541 9Ɛ3	1Ɛ3

N	N Cot N	d	N	N Cot N	d	N	N Cot N	d
.1000	.189 4Ɛ9 800	44 23Ɛ	.1040	.187 Ɛ3Ɛ 763	45 913	.1080	.186 51χ 29Ɛ	47 401
1	475 581	287	1	χƐ5 χ50	960	1	492 χ9χ	44χ
2	431 2Ɛ6	314	2	χ70 0Ɛ0	9χ8	2	447 650	496
3	3χ8 Ɛχ2	35Ɛ	3	χ26 304	χ35	3	400 176	524
4	364 843	3χ8	4	9χ0 48Ɛ	χ81	4	374 852	570
5	320 457	433	5	956 60χ	Ɛ0χ	5	329 2χ2	5Ɛ9
6	298 024	480	6	910 700	Ɛ56	6	2χ1 8χ5	646
7	253 764	509	7	886 766	Ɛχ3	7	256 25Ɛ	693
8	20Ɛ 257	554	8	840 783	46 030	8	20χ 788	720
9	186 903	5χ1	9	7Ɛ6 753	078	9	183 068	769
χ	142 322	629	χ	770 697	104	χ	137 4ƐƐ	7Ɛ6
Ɛ	0Ɛ9 8Ɛ5	675	Ɛ	726 593	152	Ɛ	0χƐ 905	843
.1010	075 240	701	.1050	6χ0 441	19χ	.1090	064 082	890
1	030 73Ɛ	74χ	1	656 263	226	1	018 3Ɛ2	919
2	.188 Ɛχ7 ƐƐ1	796	2	610 039	273	2	.185 Ɛ90 695	966
3	Ɛ63 417	822	3	585 986	300	3	Ɛ44 92Ɛ	9Ɛ3
4	Ɛ1χ 7Ɛ5	86χ	4	53Ɛ 686	348	4	χƐ8 Ɛ38	χ3Ɛ
5	χ95 Ɛ47	8Ɛ7	5	4Ɛ5 33χ	395	5	χ71 0Ɛ9	χ89
6	χ51 250	943	6	46χ Ɛ65	422	6	χ25 230	Ɛ16
7	χ08 509	98Ɛ	7	424 743	46χ	7	999 316	Ɛ63
8	983 73χ	χ18	8	39χ 295	4Ɛ7	8	951 373	ƐƐ0
9	93χ 922	χ64	9	353 99χ	544	9	905 383	48 039
χ	8Ɛ5 χ7χ	χ20	χ	309 456	590	χ	879 346	086
Ɛ	870 Ɛ8χ	Ɛ39	Ɛ	282 χ86	619	Ɛ	831 280	113
.1020	828 051	Ɛ85	.1060	238 469	666	.10χ0	7χ5 169	160
1	7χ3 088	45 011	1	1Ɛ1 χ03	6Ɛ2	1	759 009	1χχ
2	75χ 077	059	2	167 311	73Ɛ	2	710 χ1Ɛ	236
3	715 01χ	0χ6	3	120 792	788	3	684 7χ5	283
4	68Ɛ Ɛ34	133	4	096 006	815	4	638 522	311
5	646 χ01	17χ	5	04Ɛ 3Ɛ1	861	5	5Ɛ0 211	35χ
6	601 843	207	6	004 750	8χχ	6	563 χ73	3χ6
7	578 638	254	7	.186 Ɛ79 χ62	937	7	517 689	434
8	533 3χ4	2χ0	8	Ɛ33 127	983	8	48Ɛ 255	481
9	4χχ 104	328	9	χχ8 364	χ11	9	442 994	50χ
χ	464 998	375	χ	χ61 553	χ59	χ	3Ɛ6 486	558
Ɛ	41Ɛ 623	401	Ɛ	χ16 6Ɛ6	χχ6	Ɛ	369 Ɛ2χ	5χ4
.1030	396 222	449	.1070	98Ɛ 810	Ɛ32	.10Ɛ0	321 546	632
1	350 995	496	1	944 89χ	Ɛ80	1	294 Ɛ14	67Ɛ
2	307 4ƐƐ	522	2	8Ɛ9 91χ	47 008	2	248 455	708
3	281 Ɛ99	56Ɛ	3	872 912	055	3	1ƐƐ 949	755
4	238 62χ	5Ɛ7	4	827 879	0χ2	4	173 1Ɛ4	7χ2
5	1Ɛ3 033	644	5	7χ0 797	12Ɛ	5	126 612	830
6	169 5χƐ	690	6	755 668	177	6	099 9χ2	879
7	123 Ɛ1Ɛ	719	7	70χ 4Ɛ1	204	7	051 125	906
8	09χ 402	765	8	683 2χ9	252	8	004 41Ɛ	953
9	054 859	7Ɛ2	9	638 057	29χ	9	.184 Ɛ77 688	9χ0
χ	00Ɛ 067	83χ	χ	5Ɛ0 979	327	χ	Ɛ2χ 8χ8	χ2χ
Ɛ	.187 Ɛ85 429	886	Ɛ	565 652	373	Ɛ	χχ1 χ7χ	χ77

N	N Cot N	d	N	N Cot N	d	N	N Cot N	d
.1100	.184 X55 003	48 Ɛ04	1140	.183 327 502	4X 623	.1180	.181 754 Ɛ5Ɛ	50 158
1	X08 0ƐƐ	Ɛ52	1	298 X9Ɛ	670	1	704 X03	1X6
2	97Ɛ 169	Ɛ9Ɛ	2	24X 42Ɛ	6Ɛ9	2	674 819	233
3	932 18X	49 028	3	1ƐƐ 932	748	3	624 5X6	283
4	8X5 162	075	4	171 1X6	795	4	594 323	310
5	858 0X9	103	5	122 611	823	5	544 013	35X
6	80X ƐX6	150	6	093 9XX	870	6	4Ɛ3 875	3X8
7	781 X56	199	7	045 13X	8ƐƐ	7	463 489	437
8	734 879	227	8	.182 ƐƐ6 43Ɛ	948	8	413 052	484
9	6X7 652	274	9	Ɛ67 6Ɛ3	995	9	382 78X	513
X	65X 39X	301	X	Ɛ18 91X	X24	X	332 277	561
Ɛ	611 099	34Ɛ	Ɛ	X89 XƐ6	X71	Ɛ	2X1 916	5XƐ
.1110	583 94X	398	.1150	X3Ɛ 045	XƐƐ	.1190	251 327	63X
1	536 572	425	1	9Ɛ0 146	Ɛ49	1	200 8X9	687
2	4X9 149	473	2	961 1Ɛ9	Ɛ96	2	170 222	716
3	45Ɛ 896	500	3	912 223	4Ɛ 024	3	11Ɛ 708	763
4	412 396	54X	4	883 1ƐƐ	072	4	08X Ɛ65	7Ɛ2
5	384 X48	597	5	834 149	100	5	03X 373	841
6	337 471	624	6	7X5 049	14X	6	.180 ƐX9 732	88X
7	2X9 X49	672	7	755 XƐƐ	197	7	Ɛ58 X64	919
8	260 397	6ƐƐ	8	706 924	226	8	Ɛ08 147	967
9	212 898	748	9	677 6ƐX	273	9	X77 3X0	9Ɛ5
X	185 150	796	X	628 447	301	X	X26 5X7	X43
Ɛ	137 576	824	Ɛ	599 146	34X	Ɛ	995 764	X92
.1120	0X9 952	871	.1160	549 9Ɛ8	399	.11X0	944 892	Ɛ20
1	060 0X1	8ƐX	1	4ƐX 61Ɛ	427	1	8Ɛ3 972	Ɛ6X
2	012 3X3	948	2	46Ɛ 1Ɛ4	474	2	862 X04	ƐƐ8
3	.183 Ɛ84 657	996	3	41Ɛ 940	502	3	811 X08	51 047
4	Ɛ36 881	X23	4	390 43X	551	4	780 981	095
5	XX8 X5X	X70	5	340 XX9	59X	5	72Ɛ 8X8	124
6	X5X ƐXX	XƐX	6	2Ɛ1 50Ɛ	628	6	69X 784	172
7	X11 0Ɛ0	Ɛ47	7	261 XX3	675	7	649 612	200
8	983 165	Ɛ95	8	212 42X	704	8	5Ɛ8 412	24X
9	935 190	4X 023	9	182 926	752	9	567 184	299
X	8X7 169	070	X	133 194	7X0	X	515 XX7	327
Ɛ	859 0Ɛ9	0Ɛ9	Ɛ	0X3 5Ɛ4	829	Ɛ	484 780	375
.1130	80Ɛ 000	147	.1170	053 987	878	.11Ɛ0	433 407	404
1	780 X75	195	1	004 10Ɛ	906	1	3X2 003	453
2	732 8X0	222	2	.181 Ɛ74 405	953	2	350 770	4X0
3	6X4 67X	270	3	Ɛ24 672	9X2	3	2ƐƐ 290	52Ɛ
4	656 40X	2Ɛ9	4	X94 890	X2Ɛ	4	269 961	57X
5	608 111	347	5	X44 X61	X7X	5	218 3X3	608
6	579 986	395	6	9Ɛ4 ƐX3	Ɛ08	6	186 997	656
7	52Ɛ 5Ɛ1	422	7	965 097	Ɛ55	7	135 341	6X5
8	4X1 18Ɛ	470	8	915 142	ƐX4	8	0X3 858	733
9	452 91Ɛ	4Ɛ9	9	885 15X	50 031	9	052 125	782
X	404 422	548	X	835 129	080	X	000 563	810
Ɛ	375 X96	594	Ɛ	7X5 069	10X	Ɛ	.17Ɛ Ɛ6X 953	85Ɛ

N	N Cot N	d	N	N Cot N	d	N	N Cot N	d
.1200	.17Ɛ Ɛ19 0Ɛ4	51 8X9	.1240	.17X 237 277	53 457	.1280	.178 4XX 972	55 022
1	X87 407	937	1	1X3 X20	4X6	1	455 950	072
2	X35 690	986	2	150 536	534	2	400 89X	101
3	9X3 906	X15	3	0Ɛ9 002	584	3	367 799	150
4	951 XƐ1	X63	4	065 63X	613	4	312 649	19Ɛ
5	900 04X	XƐ2	5	012 027	662	5	279 46X	22Ɛ
6	86X 158	Ɛ40	6	.179 Ɛ7X 585	6Ɛ0	6	224 23Ɛ	27Ɛ
7	818 218	Ɛ8Ɛ	7	Ɛ26 X95	740	7	18X Ɛ80	30X
8	786 249	52 019	8	X93 355	78X	8	135 872	359
9	734 230	068	9	X3Ɛ 787	81X	9	0X0 515	3X9
X	6X2 184	0Ɛ6	X	9X7 Ɛ69	869	X	047 128	438
Ɛ	650 08X	145	Ɛ	954 300	8Ɛ7	Ɛ	.177 ƐƐ1 8Ɛ0	488
.1210	5Ɛ9 Ɛ45	194	.1250	900 605	947	.1290	Ɛ58 424	517
1	567 971	222	1	868 87X	996	1	Ɛ02 Ɛ09	567
2	515 74Ɛ	271	2	814 XX4	X25	2	X69 562	5Ɛ6
3	483 49X	300	3	781 07Ɛ	X74	3	X13 Ɛ68	646
4	431 19X	34X	4	729 207	Ɛ02	4	97X 522	695
5	39X X50	398	5	695 305	Ɛ52	5	924 X49	725
6	348 674	428	6	641 373	ƐX2	6	88Ɛ 324	774
7	2Ɛ6 248	476	7	5X9 391	54 030	7	835 770	804
8	263 992	504	8	555 361	07Ɛ	8	79Ɛ Ɛ68	853
9	211 48X	554	9	501 2X2	10X	9	746 315	8X3
X	17X Ɛ36	5X2	X	469 194	15X	X	6Ɛ0 632	933
Ɛ	128 554	630	Ɛ	415 036	1X9	Ɛ	656 8ƐƐ	982
.1220	095 Ɛ24	680	.1260	380 X49	237	.12X0	600 Ɛ39	X11
1	043 464	70X	1	328 812	287	1	567 128	X62
2	.17X ƐƐ0 956	759	2	294 547	316	2	511 286	XƐ1
3	Ɛ5X 1Ɛ9	7X7	3	240 231	366	3	477 395	Ɛ40
4	Ɛ07 612	837	4	1X7 X87	3Ɛ4	4	421 455	Ɛ91
5	X74 997	885	5	153 693	444	5	387 484	56 01Ɛ
6	X22 112	914	6	0ƐƐ 24Ɛ	493	6	331 465	070
7	98Ɛ 3ƐX	962	7	066 978	522	7	297 3Ɛ5	0ƐƐ
8	938 658	9Ɛ2	8	012 456	571	8	241 2Ɛ6	14Ɛ
9	8X5 866	X40	9	.178 Ɛ79 XX5	600	9	1X7 167	19Ɛ
X	852 X26	X8Ɛ	X	Ɛ25 4X5	650	X	150 Ɛ88	22X
Ɛ	7ƐƐ Ɛ57	Ɛ19	Ɛ	X90 X55	69Ɛ	Ɛ	0Ɛ6 95X	27X
.1230	769 03X	Ɛ69	.1270	X38 376	72X	.12Ɛ0	060 6X0	309
1	716 091	ƐƐ7	1	9X3 848	77X	1	006 393	35X
2	683 096	53 046	2	94Ɛ 08X	809	2	.176 Ɛ70 035	3X9
3	630 050	095	3	8Ɛ6 481	858	3	Ɛ15 848	439
4	598 Ɛ77	124	4	861 825	8X7	4	X7Ɛ 40Ɛ	489
5	545 X53	173	5	808 Ɛ3X	937	5	X24 Ɛ42	518
6	4Ɛ2 8X0	202	6	774 203	986	6	98X 626	568
7	45Ɛ 69X	250	7	71Ɛ 439	X15	7	934 07X	5Ɛ8
8	408 44X	29Ɛ	8	686 624	X65	8	899 682	648
9	375 16Ɛ	32Ɛ	9	631 77Ɛ	XƐ3	9	843 036	697
X	321 X40	379	X	598 888	Ɛ44	X	7X8 55Ɛ	728
Ɛ	28X 683	408	Ɛ	543 944	Ɛ92	Ɛ	751 X33	777

N	N Cot N	d	N	N Cot N	d	N	N Cot N	d
.1300	.176 6Ɛ7 278	56 807	.1340	.174 857 X42	58 40X	.1380	.172 950 109	5X 031
1	660 671	857	1	7ƐƐ 634	45Ɛ	1	8ƐƐ 098	083
2	605 X16	8X6	2	763 195	4Ɛ0	2	854 015	113
3	56Ɛ 130	937	3	706 8X5	53Ɛ	3	7Ɛ5 Ɛ02	164
4	514 3Ɛ5	986	4	66X 366	590	4	757 95X	1Ɛ5
5	479 62Ɛ	X17	5	611 996	620	5	6Ɛ9 765	246
6	422 814	X66	6	575 376	671	6	65Ɛ 51Ɛ	296
7	387 96X	XƐ6	7	518 905	701	7	601 245	328
8	330 X74	Ɛ46	8	480 204	752	8	562 Ɛ19	378
9	295 Ɛ2X	Ɛ96	9	423 672	7X2	9	504 761	40X
X	23X Ɛ54	57 026	X	386 X90	832	X	466 353	45X
Ɛ	1X3 Ɛ2X	076	Ɛ	32X 25X	883	Ɛ	407 XƐ5	4XƐ
.1310	148 X74	106	.1350	291 597	913	.1390	369 606	540
1	0Ɛ1 96X	155	1	234 884	963	1	30Ɛ 086	591
2	056 815	1X6	2	197 Ɛ21	924	2	270 6Ɛ5	622
3	.175 ƐƐƐ 62Ɛ	236	3	13Ɛ 129	X45	3	212 093	673
4	Ɛ64 3Ɛ5	285	4	0X2 2X4	X95	4	173 620	704
5	Ɛ09 130	316	5	045 40Ɛ	Ɛ25	5	114 Ɛ18	755
6	X71 X16	366	6	.173 ƐX8 4X6	Ɛ76	6	076 383	7X6
7	X16 670	3Ɛ5	7	Ɛ4Ɛ 530	59 007	7	017 799	837
8	97Ɛ 277	446	8	XƐ2 525	057	8	.171 Ɛ78 Ɛ62	887
9	923 X31	496	9	X55 48X	0X7	9	Ɛ1X 297	919
X	888 557	526	X	9Ɛ8 3X3	138	X	X7Ɛ 57X	96X
Ɛ	831 031	576	Ɛ	95Ɛ 267	189	Ɛ	X20 810	9ƐƐ
.1320	795 677	606	.1360	902 09X	219	.13X0	981 X11	X50
1	73X 071	656	1	864 X81	26X	1	922 Ɛ81	XX2
2	6X2 617	6X6	2	807 813	2ƐX	2	884 09Ɛ	Ɛ32
3	646 Ɛ31	736	3	76X 515	34Ɛ	3	825 169	Ɛ83
4	5XƐ 3Ɛ7	786	4	711 186	3X0	4	786 1X6	5Ɛ 015
5	553 831	817	5	673 9X6	430	5	727 191	065
6	4Ɛ8 016	866	6	616 576	480	6	688 128	0Ɛ7
7	460 370	8Ɛ7	7	579 0Ɛ6	512	7	629 031	147
8	404 675	947	8	51Ɛ 7X4	562	8	589 XX6	199
9	368 92X	997	9	482 242	5Ɛ2	9	52X 909	22X
X	310 Ɛ53	X27	X	424 850	644	X	48Ɛ 69Ɛ	280
Ɛ	275 128	X77	Ɛ	387 208	693	Ɛ	430 41Ɛ	310
.1330	219 271	Ɛ08	.1370	329 735	725	.13Ɛ0	391 10Ɛ	362
1	181 365	Ɛ58	1	290 010	775	1	331 969	3Ɛ2
2	125 409	ƐX8	2	232 457	806	2	292 577	444
3	089 421	58 038	3	194 851	857	3	233 133	496
4	031 3X5	088	4	136 ƐƐ6	8X8	4	193 859	526
5	.174 Ɛ95 319	119	5	099 30X	938	5	134 333	578
6	Ɛ39 200	169	6	03Ɛ 592	989	6	094 977	609
7	XX1 053	1Ɛ9	7	.172 ƐX1 805	X19	7	035 36X	65X
8	X44 X56	24X	8	Ɛ43 9X8	X6Ɛ	8	.170 Ɛ95 910	6XƐ
9	9X8 808	299	9	XX5 Ɛ39	XƐƐ	9	Ɛ36 221	741
X	950 52Ɛ	32X	X	X48 03X	Ɛ50	X	X96 6X0	792
Ɛ	8Ɛ4 201	37Ɛ	Ɛ	9XX 0XX	ƐX1	Ɛ	X36 Ɛ0X	823

N	N Cot N	d	N	N Cot N	d	N	N Cot N	d
.1400	.170 997 2X7	5Ɛ 875	.1440	.16X 974 778	61 518	.1480	.168 8X3 6Ɛ4	63 1X2
1	937 632	906	1	913 260	56Ɛ	1	840 512	235
2	897 928	957	2	871 8Ɛ1	600	2	799 299	287
3	837 Ɛ91	9X9	3	810 2Ɛ1	652	3	736 012	319
4	798 1X4	X3X	4	76X 85Ɛ	6X4	4	692 8Ɛ5	370
5	738 366	X8Ɛ	5	709 177	736	5	62Ɛ 545	402
6	698 497	Ɛ21	6	667 641	788	6	588 143	455
7	638 576	Ɛ72	7	605 X75	819	7	524 8XX	4X7
8	598 604	60 004	8	564 258	870	8	481 403	539
9	538 600	055	9	502 5X8	902	9	419 X86	590
X	498 567	0X6	X	460 8X6	953	X	376 4Ɛ6	623
Ɛ	438 481	138	Ɛ	3ƐX Ɛ53	9X6	Ɛ	312 X93	675
.1410	398 345	189	.1450	359 169	X37	.1490	26Ɛ 41X	707
1	338 178	21Ɛ	1	2Ɛ7 332	X8X	1	207 913	75Ɛ
2	297 Ɛ59	270	2	255 464	Ɛ1Ɛ	2	164 174	7Ɛ0
3	237 8X9	302	3	1Ɛ3 545	Ɛ72	3	100 584	843
4	197 5X7	353	4	151 593	62 003	4	058 941	896
5	137 254	3X5	5	0XƐ 590	056	5	.167 ƐƐ5 067	929
6	096 X6Ɛ	436	6	049 536	0X8	6	Ɛ51 33X	97X
7	036 635	488	7	.169 ƐX7 44X	139	7	XX9 580	X12
8	.16Ɛ Ɛ96 169	519	8	Ɛ45 311	190	8	X45 76X	X64
9	Ɛ35 850	56Ɛ	9	XX3 141	222	9	9X1 906	XƐ7
X	X95 2X1	600	X	X40 Ɛ1Ɛ	273	X	939 X0Ɛ	Ɛ49
Ɛ	X34 8X1	652	Ɛ	99X 868	306	Ɛ	895 X82	ƐX0
.1420	994 24Ɛ	6X3	.1460	938 562	359	.14X0	831 XX2	64 033
1	933 768	735	1	896 205	3XX	1	789 X6Ɛ	086
2	893 033	787	2	833 X17	440	2	725 9X5	118
3	832 468	818	3	791 597	493	3	681 889	16X
4	791 850	86X	4	72Ɛ 104	524	4	619 71Ɛ	202
5	730 ƐX2	8ƐƐ	5	688 7X0	577	5	575 519	254
6	690 2X3	952	6	626 225	609	6	511 285	2X7
7	62Ɛ 551	9X2	7	583 818	65Ɛ	7	468 Ɛ9X	33X
8	58X 76Ɛ	X35	8	521 179	6Ɛ1	8	404 860	390
9	529 936	X86	9	47X 688	744	9	360 490	423
X	488 X70	Ɛ18	X	417 Ɛ44	796	X	2Ɛ8 069	476
Ɛ	427 Ɛ54	Ɛ69	Ɛ	375 36X	828	Ɛ	253 7Ɛ3	509
.1430	386 ƐX7	ƐƐƐ	.1470	312 742	87X	.14Ɛ0	1XƐ 2X6	55Ɛ
1	325 ƐX8	61 051	1	26Ɛ X84	911	1	146 947	5Ɛ3
2	284 Ɛ57	0X3	2	209 173	962	2	0X2 354	645
3	223 X74	134	3	166 411	9Ɛ5	3	039 90Ɛ	698
4	182 940	187	4	103 618	X48	4	.166 Ɛ95 233	72Ɛ
5	121 775	217	5	060 790	X99	5	Ɛ30 704	781
6	080 55X	26X	6	.168 ƐƐ9 8Ɛ3	Ɛ30	6	X87 Ɛ43	815
7	01Ɛ 2Ɛ0	300	7	Ɛ56 983	Ɛ83	7	X23 32X	868
8	.16X Ɛ79 ƐƐ0	351	8	XƐ3 X00	63 014	8	97X 682	8ƐX
9	Ɛ18 85Ɛ	3X3	9	X50 9X8	067	9	915 984	951
X	X77 478	435	X	9X9 941	0ƐX	X	871 033	9X4
Ɛ	X16 043	487	Ɛ	946 843	14Ɛ	Ɛ	808 24Ɛ	X37

N	N Cot N	d	N	N Cot N	d	N	N Cot N	d
.1500	.166 763 414	64 X8Ɛ	.1540	.164 573 225	66 79X	.1580	.162 312 3ƐƐ	68 510
1	6ƐX 545	Ɛ21	1	508 647	831	1	265 XXƐ	565
2	655 624	Ɛ73	2	461 X16	884	2	1Ɛ9 546	5Ɛ9
3	5Ɛ0 671	65 007	3	3Ɛ7 152	918	3	150 Ɛ49	651
4	547 666	05X	4	350 436	96Ɛ	4	0X4 4Ɛ8	6X5
5	4X2 608	0Ɛ1	5	2X5 687	X03	5	037 X13	739
6	439 517	144	6	23X 884	X57	6	.161 Ɛ8Ɛ 296	791
7	394 393	197	7	193 X29	XXX	7	Ɛ22 705	826
8	32Ɛ 1Ɛ8	22X	8	128 Ɛ3Ɛ	Ɛ42	8	X75 X9Ɛ	87X
9	285 Ɛ8X	281	9	081 ƐƐ9	Ɛ95	9	X09 221	912
X	220 909	314	X	017 024	67 029	X	960 50Ɛ	966
Ɛ	177 5Ɛ5	368	Ɛ	.163 Ɛ6Ɛ ƐƐ7	081	Ɛ	8Ɛ3 765	9ƐƐ
.1510	112 249	3ƐX	.1550	Ɛ04 Ɛ36	115	.1590	846 966	X53
1	068 X4Ɛ	451	1	X59 X21	168	1	799 Ɛ13	XX7
2	003 5ƐX	4X5	2	9Ɛ2 875	1ƐƐ	2	731 028	Ɛ3Ɛ
3	.165 Ɛ5X 115	537	3	947 676	254	3	684 0X9	Ɛ94
4	XƐ4 79X	58Ɛ	4	8X0 422	2X7	4	617 115	69 028
5	X4Ɛ 20Ɛ	622	5	835 137	33Ɛ	5	56X 0X9	080
6	9X5 7X9	675	6	789 9Ɛ8	393	6	501 029	115
7	940 134	708	7	722 625	426	7	453 Ɛ14	169
8	896 628	75Ɛ	8	677 1ƐƐ	47X	8	3X6 967	201
9	830 X89	7Ɛ3	9	60Ɛ 941	512	9	339 766	256
X	787 296	846	X	564 42Ɛ	566	X	290 510	2XX
Ɛ	721 650	899	Ɛ	4Ɛ8 X85	5Ɛ9	Ɛ	223 222	343
.1520	677 973	930	.1560	451 488	652	.15X0	175 X9Ɛ	397
1	612 043	983	1	3X5 X36	6X5	1	108 704	42Ɛ
2	568 280	X17	2	33X 351	739	2	05Ɛ 295	484
3	502 465	X6X	3	292 814	791	3	.160 ƐƐ1 X11	518
4	458 5Ɛ7	Ɛ01	4	227 043	824	4	Ɛ44 4Ɛ5	571
5	3Ɛ2 6Ɛ6	Ɛ55	5	17Ɛ 41Ɛ	879	5	X96 Ɛ44	605
6	348 761	ƐX7	6	113 762	910	6	X29 53Ɛ	65X
7	2X2 776	66 040	7	067 X52	965	7	97Ɛ XX1	6Ɛ2
8	238 736	092	8	000 0X9	9Ɛ8	8	912 3XƐ	747
9	192 664	126	9	.162 Ɛ54 2Ɛ1	X50	9	864 864	79Ɛ
X	128 53X	179	X	XX8 461	XX4	X	7Ɛ7 085	834
Ɛ	082 381	210	Ɛ	X40 579	Ɛ38	Ɛ	749 451	889
.1530	018 171	264	.1570	994 641	Ɛ90	.15Ɛ0	69Ɛ 784	921
1	.164 Ɛ71 Ɛ09	2Ɛ7	1	928 671	68 024	1	631 X63	975
2	Ɛ07 812	34Ɛ	2	880 649	078	2	584 0XX	X0X
3	X61 483	3X2	3	814 591	110	3	516 2X0	X63
4	9Ɛ7 0X1	436	4	768 481	164	4	468 439	XƐ7
5	950 867	488	5	700 319	1Ɛ8	5	3ƐX 542	Ɛ50
6	8X6 39Ɛ	521	6	654 121	250	6	350 5Ɛ2	ƐX5
7	83Ɛ X7X	574	7	5X7 X91	2X5	7	2X2 609	6X 039
8	795 506	607	8	53Ɛ 7X8	338	8	234 590	092
9	72X XƐƐ	65Ɛ	9	493 470	390	9	186 4ƐX	127
X	684 460	6Ɛ2	X	427 0X0	424	X	118 393	17Ɛ
Ɛ	619 96X	745	Ɛ	37X 878	479	Ɛ	06X 214	214

.1600 .160 000 000

Logarithms of Numbers

The following table of logarithms of numbers was derived from Professor Peters' tables and from Logarithmetica Britannica. One dozen and seven duodecimal places were calculated.

The table may be used to obtain seven places of a logarithm by direct proportion or nine places by direct proportion after increasing the book difference by $\frac{1 - \text{Interval}}{2}$ of the second difference.

The number corresponding to a given logarithm may be obtained to seven figures by direct proportion or to nine figures by direct proportion after increasing the book difference by $\frac{1 - \text{Interval}}{2}$ of the second difference.

Example:

Find log *3.184 80949(4)*

(a) To seven places by direct proportion

Log	*3.184*	*.563 Ɛ5X 01*	
			165 44
Interval	*.80949*		
Add	*.80949 (16544)*	*104 94*	
Log	*3.184 809(5)*	*.564 062 9(5)*	

(b) To nine places, using second difference

Log	*3.184*	*.563 Ɛ5X 013*		*(5X)*
			165 439	
Add to book diff.	*5X* $\frac{1 - .809}{2}$		*Ɛ*	
Corrected difference			*165 448*	
Multiply by	*.809 494*	*104 946*		
Add to log *3.184*		*.564 062 959*		

Logarithms of Numbers

Example:

Find the number whose log is *.564 062 959*

(a) To seven figures by direct proportion

Log	*3.184*	*.563 Ɛ5X(0)*	
			165(4)
Difference		*104(9)*	
Int. $\frac{1049}{1654}$ =	*.809(4)*		
Number is	*3.184 809(4)*		

(b) To nine figures, using second difference

Log	*3.184*	*.563 Ɛ5X 013*		*(5X)*
			165 439	
Add to book diff. *5X* $\frac{1 - .809}{2}$			*Ɛ*	
Corrected difference			*165 448*	
Int. $\frac{104946}{165448}$ =	*.80949(5)*			
Number is	*3.184 80949*			

It may be noted that nine places of any logarithm may be found by direct proportion without serious error if we use the second half of the table, by means of a factor.

Example:

Find log *3.184 80949(4)*

Mult.by *3*	*9.512 02424(0)*		
Log	*9.512*	*.XX0 023 2X8*	
			61 947
Add	*.02424 (61947)*	*1 254*	
		.XX0 024 540	
Subtract log *3*		*.537 Ɛ81 7X3*	
Log	*3.184 80949(4)*	*.564 062 959*	

Example:

Find the number whose log is *.564 062 959*

Add log *3*		*.537 Ɛ81 7X3*	
		.XX0 024 540	
Log	*9.512*	*.XX0 023 2X8*	
			61 947
Difference		*1 254*	
Int. $\frac{1254}{61947}$ =	*.02424*		
Number is	*9.512 02424*		
Div. by *3*	*3.184 80949*		

Note: On the two pages following are given extended values for numbers up to *100*, and a dozen places for *1.000* to *1.100*, with second differences. This may be used to check the nine place table or to find one dozen places of any logarithm by the use of a factor. For the Everett coefficients, see pages *296-29Ɛ*.

N	Log N	N	Log N	N	Log N
		40	1.684 03X 418 723 938	80	1.X06 059 626 X95 7Ɛ7
		41	1.696 447 589 993 584	81	1.X11 2Ɛ5 Ɛ3Ɛ 12Ɛ 273
2	.342 01Ɛ 20X 371 X7X	42	1.6X8 4Ɛ8 040 4X8 718	82	1.X18 466 798 145 442
3	.537 Ɛ81 7X3 498 284	43	1.6ƐX 227 9X5 5Ɛ2 623	83	1.X23 532 293 2ƐX 71X
4	.684 03X 418 723 938	44	1.70Ɛ 831 64X 17Ɛ 475	84	1.X2X 517 24X 85X 596
5	.793 24X 517 079 42Ɛ	45	1.720 Ɛ26 923 557 XƐ5	85	1.X35 41Ɛ ƐƐX Ɛ43 082
6	.879 ƐX0 9Ɛ1 84X 142	46	1.731 Ɛ24 178 602 689	86	1.X40 246 ƐƐ3 964 4X1
7	.949 223 8X4 XX7 8X2	47	1.742 839 423 603 602	87	1.X46 Ɛ96 5X1 395 25Ɛ
8	.X06 059 626 X95 7Ɛ7	48	1.753 281 30Ɛ 981 499	88	1.X51 850 858 531 334
9	.X73 Ɛ43 386 974 547	49	1.763 645 Ɛ11 8ƐX 196	89	1.X58 433 9X3 441 394
X	.Ɛ15 269 725 42Ɛ 2X9	4X	1.773 760 825 592 535	8X	1.X62 Ɛ45 Ɛ31 909 973
Ɛ	.Ɛ62 5XX Ɛ08 546 193	4Ɛ	1.783 61X 221 839 537	8Ɛ	1.X69 589 130 915 204
10	1.000 000 000 000 000	50	1.793 24X 517 079 42Ɛ	90	1.X73 Ɛ43 386 974 547
11	1.047 7Ɛ3 231 657 739	51	1.7X2 840 X05 0Ɛ2 20X	91	1.X7X 432 5X3 294 072
12	1.08Ɛ 242 XƐ3 259 760	52	1.7Ɛ2 004 321 099 8Ɛ5	92	1.X84 858 631 975 480
13	1.10Ɛ 210 0ƐX 555 6Ɛ2	53	1.801 167 06Ɛ 860 229	93	1.X8X ƐƐƐ 2X9 Ɛ88 Ɛ27
14	1.148 078 835 247 675	54	1.810 0Ɛ7 051 96Ɛ 3Ɛ1	94	1.X95 2X0 51X 133 357
15	1.182 266 202 116 35Ɛ	55	1.81X X41 748 714 Ɛ68	95	1.X9Ɛ 501 99X 53Ɛ 013
16	1.1Ɛ5 Ɛ62 595 126 405	56	1.829 58Ɛ 8ƐX 194 315	96	1.XX5 665 120 070 054
17	1.227 684 32X 421 Ɛ12	57	1.837 Ɛ29 ƐX6 039 50X	97	1.XXƐ 74Ɛ XXƐ 668 972
18	1.257 288 933 7X1 167	58	1.846 2X4 61X 83X 097	98	1.XƐ5 77Ɛ X33 944 3Ɛ3
19	1.285 1X5 488 383 Ɛ66	59	1.854 483 177 X87 807	99	1.XƐƐ 736 5Ɛ8 410 084
1X	1.2Ɛ1 60X 116 8Ɛ8 051	5X	1.862 491 40X 316 Ɛ8Ɛ	9X	1.Ɛ05 639 42Ɛ ƐXƐ 3Ɛ6
1Ɛ	1.318 501 594 5XƐ 543	5Ɛ	1.870 316 348 4XX 555	9Ɛ	1.Ɛ0Ɛ 489 XX7 002 041
20	1.342 01Ɛ 20X 371 X7X	60	1.879 ƐX0 9Ɛ1 84X 142	X0	1.Ɛ15 269 725 42Ɛ 2X9
21	1.366 498 X32 136 859	61	1.887 6Ɛ3 672 X97 835	X1	1.Ɛ1X Ɛ99 X14 X90 366
22	1.389 812 43Ɛ X09 5Ɛ7	62	1.895 058 914 X62 722	X2	1.Ɛ24 860 013 464 088
23	1.3XƐ Ɛ04 Ɛ6X 250 80Ɛ	63	1.8X2 45X 615 612 Ɛ21	X3	1.Ɛ2X 475 530 4Ɛ5 Ɛ4Ɛ
24	1.411 262 101 60Ɛ 61X	64	1.8XƐ 702 746 Ɛ45 84Ɛ	X4	1.Ɛ34 023 52Ɛ 44Ɛ 773
25	1.431 741 617 220 677	65	1.8Ɛ8 812 7Ɛ1 431 X75	X5	1.Ɛ39 727 349 1Ɛ4 088
26	1.451 22Ɛ 308 907 571	66	1.905 794 023 2X5 87Ɛ	X6	1.Ɛ43 186 27X 012 0X7
27	1.46Ɛ ƐX5 112 927 X36	67	1.912 60Ɛ X18 5Ɛ5 61Ɛ	X7	1.Ɛ48 781 573 020 5X1
28	1.48X 097 X43 5Ɛ9 533	68	1.91Ɛ 307 150 304 XX3	X8	1.Ɛ52 116 260 121 26Ɛ
29	1.4X7 570 6XƐ X22 457	69	1.927 X86 751 728 X92	X9	1.Ɛ57 609 730 X98 897
2X	1.504 285 410 488 219	6X	1.934 512 Ɛ57 38Ɛ 745	XX	1.Ɛ60 X60 956 X86 X26
2Ɛ	1.520 472 1ƐƐ Ɛ65 111	6Ɛ	1.940 X30 69X 6Ɛ6 X47	XƐ	1.Ɛ66 254 X4X 595 628
30	1.537 Ɛ81 7X3 498 284	70	1.949 223 8X4 XX7 8X2	Ɛ0	1.Ɛ6Ɛ 5XX Ɛ08 546 193
31	1.553 039 706 62Ɛ 864	71	1.955 4Ɛ4 719 193 78X	Ɛ1	1.Ɛ74 8X8 013 309 7Ɛ4
32	1.569 6X3 538 793 990	72	1.961 667 157 972 492	Ɛ2	1.Ɛ79 Ɛ49 1Ɛ4 3XƐ 388
33	1.583 774 X14 Ɛ33 X01	73	1.969 703 12X 6Ɛ8 93Ɛ	Ɛ3	1.Ɛ83 153 485 30X 03X
34	1.599 2X7 Ɛ41 Ɛ53 025	74	1.975 648 533 41Ɛ 98X	Ɛ4	1.Ɛ88 303 828 ƐXƐ Ɛ56
35	1.5Ɛ2 4Ɛ3 949 019 887	75	1.981 482 646 47X 2Ɛ5	Ɛ5	1.Ɛ91 41Ɛ 014 Ɛ77 685
36	1.607 204 696 735 X24	76	1.989 12Ɛ XƐ0 1X3 834	Ɛ6	1.Ɛ96 4X2 386 239 685
37	1.61Ɛ 647 Ɛ49 600 613	77	1.994 X16 Ɛ16 543 41Ɛ	Ɛ7	1.Ɛ9Ɛ 512 612 36X 94X
38	1.633 629 325 069 Ɛ0Ɛ	78	1.9X0 53Ɛ 9Ɛ1 113 27Ɛ	Ɛ8	1.ƐX4 4Ɛ0 618 688 X49
39	1.647 191 8X1 X31 976	79	1.9X7 Ɛ66 8Ɛ6 204 0ƐX	Ɛ9	1.ƐX9 439 256 X64 691
3X	1.65X 520 7X2 961 401	7X	1.9Ɛ3 496 881 93X 288	ƐX	1.ƐƐ2 335 556 860 413
3Ɛ	1.671 477 673 588 40X	7Ɛ	1.9ƐX 912 845 49Ɛ 341	ƐƐ	1.ƐƐ7 1X2 139 ƐX1 910

N	Log N	d_2 -	N	Log N	d_2 -	N	Log N	d_2 -
1000	000 000 000 000	49Ɛ 495	1040	017 077 Ɛ23 214	46χ 398	1080	031 721 955 2Ɛ8	440 161
1	49Ɛ 244 965	χ 716	1	540 419 627	9 6Ɛ0	1	Ɛ90 4χ5 012	43Ɛ 535
2	979 Ɛχχ Ɛ24	9 961	2	χ04 466 34χ	8 χ07	2	032 43χ 7Ɛ5 3Ɛ3	χ 913
3	001 258 477 4χ2	8 Ɛχ6	3	018 288 046 266	8 123	3	8χ8 686 χ81	χ 0Ɛ1
4	736 466 9χ6	8 236	4	74Ɛ 37χ 05Ɛ	7 441	4	033 156 11χ 45χ	9 492
5	002 013 Ɛ7χ 074	7 483	5	019 012 246 613	6 762	5	603 334 565	8 872
6	4Ɛ1 1Ɛ5 χ7Ɛ	6 718	6	494 868 425	5 χ85	6	χ70 111 9Ɛχ	8 058
7	989 Ɛ57 16χ	5 970	7	956 χ24 372	5 1χχ	7	034 318 673 1Ɛ7	7 442
8	003 266 422 6χ9	5 006	8	01χ 218 737 111	4 514	8	784 799 172	6 829
9	742 415 022	4 265	9	699 Ɛχ5 558	3 843	9	035 030 488 500	6 017
χ	004 019 Ɛ33 2Ɛ2	3 505	χ	Ɛ5χ Ɛ20 160	2 Ɛ71	χ	497 941 833	5 407
Ɛ	4Ɛ5 17χ 079	2 766	Ɛ	01Ɛ 41Ɛ 753 9Ɛ3	2 2χ2	Ɛ	942 981 75Ɛ	4 7Ɛ8
1010	98Ɛ Ɛ32 29χ	1 χ0Ɛ	1050	89Ɛ χ55 364	1 616	1090	036 1χ9 588 χ8Ɛ	3 Ɛ21
1	005 266 414 6Ɛ0	1 077	1	020 15Ɛ 8Ɛ5 2ƐƐ	0 950	1	653 960 20χ	3 3χ5
2	740 425 χ47	0 323	2	61Ɛ 2Ɛ4 506	0 088	2	χƐ9 900 164	2 7χ1
3	006 015 Ɛ66 χ7Ɛ	48Ɛ 593	3	χ9χ 453 645	45Ɛ 405	3	037 363 429 519	1 Ɛ9χ
4	4χƐ 218 520	χ 846	4	021 359 153 37Ɛ	χ 745	4	808 724 8Ɛ4	1 399
5	983 ƐƐƐ 337	9 χƐ8	5	817 5Ɛ4 570	9 χ88	5	038 071 5χχ 8Ɛ2	0 79χ
6	007 258 514 256	9 175	6	022 095 5Ɛ7 895	9 20Ɛ	6	516 044 112	42Ɛ Ɛχ1
7	730 560 000	8 431	7	553 161 9χƐ	8 555	7	97χ 269 551	Ɛ 3χ6
8	008 004 11Ɛ 535	7 6Ɛ0	8	χ10 46Ɛ 570	7 8χ2	8	039 222 063 5χ6	χ 7χƐ
9	497 413 37χ	6 971	9	023 289 321 44Ɛ	7 030	9	685 62χ χ50	9 ƐƐχ
χ	96χ 240 452	6 037	χ	745 938 2Ɛχ	6 380	χ	Ɛ28 788 2Ɛ8	9 407
Ɛ	009 240 7χ3 4χƐ	5 2Ɛχ	Ɛ	024 001 χƐ8 9χ9	5 713	Ɛ	03χ 38Ɛ 4Ɛ8 359	8 816
1020	712 881 24χ	4 58χ	1060	479 823 985	4 χ68	10χ0	831 9ƐƐ 7χ4	8 02χ
1	Ɛχ4 496 61Ɛ	3 855	1	935 0Ɛ5 χƐ5	4 201	1	03Ɛ 093 χ97 001	7 441
2	00χ 475 828 157	2 Ɛ29	2	025 1Ɛ0 133 χ24	3 55Ɛ	2	535 746 Ɛ99	6 856
3	946 6Ɛ6 966	2 1ƐƐ	3	666 91χ 3Ɛ4	2 8Ɛ8	3	996 Ɛ90 31Ɛ	6 073
4	00Ɛ 217 103 376	1 495	4	Ɛ21 072 088	2 05Ɛ	4	040 237 ƐχƐ 5χχ	5 48Ɛ
5	6χ7 24χ 4Ɛ1	0 770	5	026 396 Ɛ73 901	1 400	5	698 7χ5 3χχ	4 8χχ
6	Ɛ76 Ɛ14 χ78	47Ɛ χ4Ɛ	6	850 624 136	0 765	6	Ɛ38 Ɛ76 500	4 111
7	010 446 31Ɛ 5Ɛ4	Ɛ 12Ɛ	7	027 105 843 χ06	44Ɛ Ɛ0Ɛ	7	041 398 Ɛ23 501	3 532
8	915 267 001	χ 411	8	57χ 613 787	Ɛ 27χ	8	838 668 Ɛ90	2 957
9	011 1χ3 934 1Ɛ9	9 6Ɛ7	9	χ32 Ɛ54 28χ	χ 627	9	042 097 98Ɛ 904	2 183
χ	671 Ɛ43 8Ɛχ	8 9χ1	χ	028 2χ7 046 366	9 998	χ	536 890 475	1 5χ9
Ɛ	Ɛ3Ɛ 896 61χ	8 08χ	Ɛ	75χ 8χχ 666	9 14Ɛ	Ɛ	995 36Ɛ 639	0 χ18
1030	012 409 171 270	7 37Ɛ	1070	029 012 105 817	8 504	10Ɛ0	043 233 629 9χ5	0 248
1	896 190 743	6 670	1	485 094 484	7 87χ	1	691 487 Ɛ05	41Ɛ 67χ
2	013 162 935 566	5 963	2	937 817 473	7 038	2	Ɛ2χ Ɛ06 567	χ χƐ1
3	62Ɛ 024 626	5 05χ	3	02χ 1χ9 Ɛ13 426	6 3Ɛ6	3	044 388 126 118	χ 326
4	χƐ6 χ5χ 648	4 357	4	65Ɛ 984 Ɛχ3	5 777	4	824 Ɛ27 563	9 762
5	014 382 420 313	3 655	5	Ɛ11 320 Ɛχ5	4 Ɛ3χ	5	045 081 50Ɛ 248	8 Ɛ9χ
6	849 52χ 545	2 956	6	02Ɛ 382 594 069	4 302	6	519 695 Ɛ53	8 419
7	015 114 185 χ21	2 058	7	833 332 χ2Ɛ	3 689	7	975 444 441	7 85χ
8	59χ 56Ɛ 261	1 362	8	030 0χ3 84χ 124	2 χ55	8	046 210 997 091	7 09Ɛ
9	χ64 4χ3 33Ɛ	0 66χ	9	553 922 584	2 225	9	667 Ɛ12 842	6 523
χ	016 329 Ɛ66 96Ɛ	46Ɛ 976	χ	χ03 574 7ƐƐ	1 5Ɛ5	χ	Ɛ02 833 χ90	5 96χ
Ɛ	7Ɛ3 17χ 625	Ɛ 087	Ɛ	031 272 985 441	0 987	Ɛ	047 359 13Ɛ 370	5 1Ɛ4
						1100	7Ɛ3 231 658	4 643

N	Log N	d	N	Log N	d	N	Log N	d
1000	000 000 000	49Ɛ 245	1040	017 077 Ɛ23	484 4Ɛ7	1080	031 721 955	46X 750
1	49Ɛ 245	49X 966	1	540 41X	048	1	Ɛ90 4X5	310
2	979 ƐXƐ	488	2	X04 466	483 7X0	2	032 43X 7Ɛ5	469 X92
3	001 258 477	499 ƐƐ0	3	018 288 046	334	3	8X8 687	653
4	736 467	713	4	74Ɛ 37X	482 X89	4	033 156 11X	216
5	002 013 Ɛ7X	238	5	019 012 247	621	5	603 334	468 99X
6	4Ɛ1 1Ɛ6	498 961	6	494 868	178	6	X70 112	561
7	989 Ɛ57	488	7	956 X24	481 913	7	034 318 673	126
8	003 266 423	497 ƐƐ2	8	01X 218 737	46X	8	784 799	467 8XƐ
9	742 415	71X	9	699 ƐX5	007	9	035 030 488	476
X	004 019 Ɛ33	247	X	Ɛ5X ƐƐ0	480 764	X	497 942	040
Ɛ	4Ɛ5 17X	496 974	Ɛ	01Ɛ 41Ɛ 754	301	Ɛ	942 982	466 807
1010	98Ɛ Ɛ32	4X3	1050	89Ɛ X55	47Ɛ X60	1090	036 1X9 589	393
1	005 266 415	011	1	020 15Ɛ 8Ɛ5	5ƐƐ	1	653 960	465 Ɛ60
2	740 426	495 741	2	61Ɛ 2Ɛ4	160	2	XƐ9 900	729
3	006 015 Ɛ67	271	3	X9X 454	47X 8ƐƐ	3	037 363 429	2Ɛ8
4	4XƐ 218	494 9X3	4	021 359 153	461	4	808 725	464 X86
5	983 ƐƐƐ	515	5	817 5Ɛ4	004	5	038 071 5XƐ	655
6	007 258 514	048	6	022 095 5Ɛ8	479 766	6	516 044	225
7	730 560	493 77Ɛ	7	553 162	309	7	97X 269	463 9Ɛ6
8	008 004 11Ɛ	2Ɛ4	8	X10 46Ɛ	478 X72	8	039 222 063	588
9	497 413	492 X29	9	023 289 321	617	9	685 62Ɛ	159
X	96X 240	563	X	745 938	181	X	Ɛ28 788	462 930
Ɛ	009 240 7X3	09X	Ɛ	024 001 XƐ9	477 927	Ɛ	03X 38Ɛ 4Ɛ8	504
1020	712 881	491 816	1060	479 824	492	10X0	831 X00	097
1	ƐX4 497	351	1	935 0Ɛ6	03X	1	03Ɛ 093 X97	461 870
2	00X 475 828	490 X8Ɛ	2	025 1Ɛ0 134	476 7X6	2	535 747	445
3	946 6Ɛ7	608	3	666 91X	354	3	996 Ɛ90	01Ɛ
4	00Ɛ 217 103	147	4	Ɛ21 072	475 Ɛ02	4	040 237 ƐXƐ	460 7Ɛ6
5	6X7 24X	48Ɛ 887	5	026 396 Ɛ74	670	5	698 7X5	391
6	Ɛ76 Ɛ15	406	6	850 624	220	6	Ɛ38 Ɛ76	45Ɛ Ɛ69
7	010 446 31Ɛ	48X Ɛ48	7	027 105 844	474 990	7	041 398 Ɛ23	746
8	915 267	689	8	57X 614	540	8	838 669	323
9	011 1X3 934	210	9	X32 Ɛ54	0Ɛ2	9	042 097 990	45X Ɛ00
X	671 Ɛ44	489 953	X	028 2X7 046	473 865	X	536 890	6X0
Ɛ	Ɛ3Ɛ 897	496	Ɛ	75X 8XƐ	417	Ɛ	995 370	27X
1030	012 409 171	020	1070	029 012 106	472 Ɛ8X	10Ɛ0	043 233 62X	459 X5X
1	896 191	488 764	1	485 094	743	1	691 488	63X
2	013 162 935	2Ɛ0	2	937 817	2Ɛ8	2	ƐƐX Ɛ06	220
3	62Ɛ 025	487 X36	3	02X 1X9 Ɛ13	471 X72	3	044 388 126	458 X01
4	XƐ6 X5Ɛ	581	4	65Ɛ 985	628	4	824 Ɛ27	5X4
5	014 382 420	10X	5	Ɛ11 3Ɛ1	1X3	5	045 081 50Ɛ	187
6	849 52X	486 858	6	02Ɛ 382 594	470 95Ɛ	6	519 696	457 96X
7	015 114 186	3X5	7	833 333	517	7	975 444	553
8	59X 56Ɛ	485 Ɛ34	8	030 0X3 84X	094	8	046 210 997	138
9	X64 4X3	684	9	553 922	46Ɛ 853	9	667 Ɛ13	456 921
X	016 329 Ɛ67	214	X	X03 575	410	X	Ɛ02 834	507
Ɛ	7Ɛ3 17Ɛ	484 964	Ɛ	031 272 985	46X Ɛ90	Ɛ	047 359 13Ɛ	0Ɛ3

N	Log N	d	N	Log N	d	N	Log N	d
1100	047 7Ɛ3 232	455 899	1140	061 326 35Ɛ	441 842	1180	076 532 166	42X 532
1	048 048 Ɛ0Ɛ	486	1	767 ƐX1	453	1	960 698	166
2	4X2 395	073	2	ƐX9 434	065	2	077 18X 842	429 99Ɛ
3	937 448	454 860	3	062 42X 499	440 878	3	5Ɛ8 621	615
4	049 190 0X8	449	4	86Ɛ 155	48X	4	X26 036	24Ɛ
5	624 535	039	5	063 0XƐ 623	0X3	5	078 253 285	428 X85
6	X78 572	453 828	6	52Ɛ 706	43Ɛ 8Ɛ6	6	680 14X	701
7	04X 310 19X	417	7	96Ɛ 400	510	7	XX8 84Ɛ	338
8	763 5Ɛ5	009	8	064 1XX 910	125	8	079 314 Ɛ87	427 Ɛ74
9	ƐƐ6 602	452 7Ɛ9	9	629 X35	43X 93Ɛ	9	740 Ɛ3Ɛ	7Ɛ1
X	04Ɛ 449 1ƐƐ	3XƐ	X	X68 774	555	X	Ɛ68 730	42Ɛ
Ɛ	89Ɛ 5XX	451 ƐX1	Ɛ	065 2X7 109	170	Ɛ	07X 393 Ɛ5Ɛ	068
1110	050 131 58Ɛ	795	1150	725 279	439 989	1190	7ƐƐ 007	426 8X6
1	583 164	388	1	Ɛ63 046	5X4	1	07Ɛ 025 8Ɛ1	526
2	X14 530	450 Ɛ80	2	066 3X0 62X	201	2	450 217	165
3	051 265 4Ɛ0	775	3	819 82Ɛ	438 X1Ɛ	3	876 380	425 9X5
4	6Ɛ6 065	36Ɛ	4	067 056 64X	639	4	080 0X0 165	625
5	Ɛ46 414	44Ɛ Ɛ64	5	493 087	257	5	505 78X	266
6	052 396 378	760	6	90Ɛ 322	437 X77	6	92X X34	424 XX8
7	825 Ɛ18	357	7	068 147 199	696	7	081 153 920	72X
8	053 075 273	44X Ɛ52	8	582 873	2Ɛ6	8	578 44X	370
9	504 205	74Ɛ	9	9Ɛ9 Ɛ69	436 Ɛ17	9	9X0 7ƐX	423 Ɛ24
X	952 954	349	X	069 234 X84	739	X	082 204 7Ɛ2	837
Ɛ	054 1X1 0X1	449 Ɛ46	Ɛ	66Ɛ 601	35Ɛ	Ɛ	628 429	480
1120	62Ɛ 027	744	1160	XX5 960	435 Ɛ81	11X0	X4Ɛ 8X9	104
1	X78 76Ɛ	344	1	06X 31Ɛ 921	7X5	1	083 272 9Ɛ1	422 94X
2	055 305 XƐ3	448 Ɛ43	2	755 506	408	2	695 73Ɛ	593
3	752 X36	743	3	Ɛ8X 912	030	3	XƐ8 112	219
4	Ɛ9Ɛ 579	344	4	06Ɛ 403 942	434 855	4	084 31X 32Ɛ	421 X64
5	056 427 901	447 Ɛ46	5	838 597	47X	5	740 193	6Ɛ0
6	873 847	747	6	070 070 X55	0X5	6	Ɛ61 883	338
7	057 0ƐƐ 392	34X	7	4X4 Ɛ3X	433 90Ɛ	7	085 382 ƐƐƐ	420 Ɛ83
8	546 720	446 Ɛ52	8	918 849	535	8	7X3 Ɛ82	811
9	991 672	755	9	071 150 182	162	9	086 004 793	45X
X	058 218 207	359	X	583 324	432 98X	X	425 031	0X8
Ɛ	662 564	445 Ɛ63	Ɛ	9Ɛ6 0Ɛ2	5Ɛ6	Ɛ	845 119	41Ɛ 937
1130	XX8 507	768	1170	072 228 6X8	224	11Ɛ0	087 064 X54	585
1	059 332 073	373	1	65X 910	431 X51	1	484 419	215
2	777 426	444 Ɛ79	2	X90 761	680	2	8X3 632	41X X65
3	05X 000 3X3	784	3	073 302 221	2XƐ	3	088 102 497	6Ɛ5
4	444 Ɛ67	391	4	733 510	430 Ɛ1X	4	520 Ɛ90	347
5	889 338	443 Ɛ99	5	Ɛ64 42X	74X	5	93Ɛ 317	419 Ɛ98
6	05Ɛ 111 315	7X7	6	074 394 Ɛ78	37Ɛ	6	089 159 2Ɛ3	82X
7	554 Ɛ00	3Ɛ4	7	805 337	42Ɛ ƐƐ0	7	576 Ɛ21	480
8	998 2Ɛ4	003	8	075 035 327	822	8	994 3X1	114
9	060 21Ɛ 2Ɛ7	442 811	9	464 Ɛ49	454	9	08X 1Ɛ1 4Ɛ5	418 967
X	661 Ɛ08	421	X	894 3X1	087	X	60X 260	5ƐƐ
Ɛ	XX4 329	032	Ɛ	076 103 468	42X 8ƐX	Ɛ	X26 85Ɛ	254

N	Log N	d	N	Log N	d	N	Log N	d
1200	08Ɛ 242 XƐ3	417 XX9	1240	0X3 686 366	406 078	1280	0Ɛ7 667 742	3Ɛ4 9Ɛ2
1	65X 9X0	743	1	X90 422	405 930	1	X60 534	685
2	X76 523	398	2	0X4 296 152	5X6	2	0Ɛ8 254 ƐƐ9	358
3	090 291 8ƐƐ	034	3	69Ɛ 738	261	3	649 355	031
4	6X8 933	416 88X	4	XX4 999	404 Ɛ16	4	X41 386	3Ɛ3 904
5	Ɛ03 601	526	5	0X5 2X9 8Ɛ3	792	5	0Ɛ9 235 08X	599
6	091 319 Ɛ27	182	6	6Ɛ2 485	449	6	628 667	273
7	734 0X9	415 X1Ɛ	7	XƐ6 912	104	7	X1Ɛ 91X	3Ɛ2 Ɛ47
8	Ɛ49 Ɛ08	678	8	0X6 2ƐX X16	403 982	8	0ƐX 212 865	822
9	092 363 584	315	9	702 798	639	9	605 487	4Ɛ9
X	778 899	414 Ɛ74	X	Ɛ06 215	2Ɛ8	X	9Ɛ7 984	193
Ɛ	Ɛ91 851	812	Ɛ	0X7 309 511	402 Ɛ75	Ɛ	0ƐƐ 1X9 Ɛ57	3Ɛ1 X6X
1210	093 3X6 463	471	1250	710 486	833	1290	59Ɛ X05	746
1	7ƐX 914	111	1	Ɛ13 0Ɛ9	4Ɛ2	1	991 54Ɛ	423
2	094 012 X25	413 972	2	0X8 315 5XƐ	171	2	100 182 972	0ƐƐ
3	426 797	611	3	717 760	401 X30	3	573 X71	3Ɛ0 997
4	83X 1X8	273	4	Ɛ19 590	6Ɛ1	4	964 848	676
5	095 051 45Ɛ	412 Ɛ15	5	0X9 31Ɛ 081	371	5	101 155 302	353
6	464 374	776	6	720 432	032	6	545 655	032
7	876 Ɛ2X	419	7	Ɛ21 464	400 8Ɛ3	7	935 687	3XƐ 910
8	096 089 347	080	8	0XX 322 157	576	8	102 125 397	5Ɛ0
9	49Ɛ 407	411 924	9	722 711	238	9	514 987	28Ɛ
X	8Ɛ1 12Ɛ	588	X	Ɛ22 949	3ƐƐ XƐX	X	904 056	3XX Ɛ6Ɛ
Ɛ	097 102 6Ɛ7	230	Ɛ	0XƐ 322 847	782	Ɛ	103 0Ɛ3 005	850
1220	513 927	410 X96	1260	722 409	445	12X0	4X1 855	530
1	924 801	73Ɛ	1	Ɛ21 852	10X	1	890 185	212
2	098 135 340	3X5	2	0Ɛ0 320 960	3ƐX 993	2	104 07X 397	3X9 XƐ4
3	545 725	04Ɛ	3	71Ɛ 733	657	3	468 28Ɛ	795
4	955 774	40Ɛ 8Ɛ7	4	Ɛ1X 18X	321	4	855 X64	479
5	099 165 46Ɛ	562	5	0Ɛ1 318 4XƐ	3Ɛ9 ƐX7	5	105 043 321	15Ɛ
6	574 X11	20X	6	716 496	871	6	430 480	3X8 X43
7	984 01Ɛ	40X X76	7	Ɛ14 147	539	7	819 303	727
8	09X 192 X95	724	8	0Ɛ2 311 684	203	8	106 005 X2X	40X
9	5X1 5Ɛ9	390	9	70X 887	3Ɛ8 X90	9	3Ɛ2 238	0Ɛ4
X	9XƐ 989	03Ɛ	X	Ɛ07 757	758	X	79X 330	3X7 999
Ɛ	09Ɛ 1Ɛ9 X08	409 8X9	Ɛ	0Ɛ3 304 2Ɛ3	424	Ɛ	Ɛ86 109	682
1230	607 6Ɛ5	558	1270	700 717	0Ɛ2	12Ɛ0	107 371 78Ɛ	368
1	X15 051	207	1	XƐ8 809	3Ɛ7 97Ɛ	1	758 Ɛ37	053
2	0X0 222 258	408 X77	2	0Ɛ4 2Ɛ4 588	649	2	Ɛ43 Ɛ8X	3X6 939
3	62Ɛ 113	728	3	6Ɛ0 015	318	3	108 32X 907	625
4	X37 83Ɛ	398	4	XX7 331	3Ɛ6 ƐX6	4	715 330	310
5	0X1 244 017	049	5	0Ɛ5 2X2 317	876	5	XƐƐ 640	3X5 ƐƐ8
6	650 064	407 900	6	698 Ɛ91	546	6	109 2X5 638	8X5
7	X57 964	571	7	X93 517	216	7	68Ɛ 321	592
8	0X2 263 315	224	8	0Ɛ6 289 731	3Ɛ5 XX7	8	X74 8Ɛ3	27Ɛ
9	66X 539	406 X97	9	683 618	778	9	10X 259 Ɛ72	3X4 Ɛ68
X	X75 414	74Ɛ	X	X79 194	44X	X	642 Ɛ1X	857
Ɛ	0X3 27Ɛ Ɛ63	403	Ɛ	0Ɛ7 272 622	120	Ɛ	X27 775	545

N	Log N	d	N	Log N	d	N	Log N	d
1300	10Ɛ 210 0ƐX	3X4 235	1340	122 55X ƐƐƐ	394 128	1380	135 4Ɛ5 X90	384 640
1	5Ɛ4 333	3X3 Ɛ23	1	933 127	393 X32	1	87X 510	360
2	998 256	814	2	123 106 Ɛ59	739	2	136 042 870	080
3	110 17Ɛ X6X	503	3	49X 696	444	3	406 930	383 9X2
4	563 371	1Ɛ4	4	871 Ɛ1X	150	4	78X 712	703
5	946 565	3X2 XX5	5	124 045 06X	392 X58	5	Ɛ52 215	425
6	111 129 44X	797	6	417 Ɛ06	764	6	137 315 63X	148
7	510 025	488	7	7XX 66X	471	7	698 786	382 X69
8	8Ɛ2 4Ɛ1	17Ɛ	8	Ɛ80 Ɛ1Ɛ	17X	8	X5Ɛ 633	791
9	112 094 670	3X1 X71	9	125 353 099	391 X87	9	138 222 204	4Ɛ4
X	476 521	764	X	724 Ɛ64	796	X	5X4 6Ɛ8	218
Ɛ	858 085	458	Ɛ	XƐ6 73X	4X4	Ɛ	966 914	381 Ɛ3Ɛ
1310	113 039 521	14Ɛ	1350	126 288 022	1Ɛ2	1390	139 128 853	864
1	41X 670	3X0 X44	1	659 214	390 Ɛ02	1	4XX 4Ɛ7	588
2	7ƐƐ 4Ɛ4	739	2	X2X 116	811	2	86Ɛ X83	2Ɛ2
3	ƐX0 031	431	3	127 1ƐX 927	520	3	13X 031 175	017
4	114 380 462	127	4	58Ɛ 247	231	4	3Ɛ2 190	380 941
5	760 589	39Ɛ X21	5	95Ɛ 478	38Ɛ Ɛ42	5	772 Ɛ11	666
6	Ɛ40 3XX	717	6	128 12Ɛ 3ƐX	853	6	Ɛ33 577	392
7	115 31Ɛ Ɛ05	412	7	4ƐƐ 051	563	7	13Ɛ 2Ɛ3 949	0Ɛ8
8	6ƐƐ 317	109	8	88X 5Ɛ4	276	8	673 X45	37Ɛ X23
9	X9X 424	39X X04	9	129 059 86X	38X Ɛ88	9	X33 868	74X
X	116 279 228	700	X	428 836	89X	X	140 1Ɛ3 3Ɛ6	477
Ɛ	657 928	3Ɛ9	Ɛ	7Ɛ7 514	5Ɛ0	Ɛ	572 871	1X3
1320	X36 125	0Ɛ5	1360	Ɛ85 Ɛ04	305	13X0	931 X54	37X Ɛ0Ɛ
1	117 214 21X	399 9Ɛ2	1	12X 354 209	017	1	141 0Ɛ0 963	838
2	5Ɛ2 010	6Ɛ0	2	722 224	389 930	2	46Ɛ 59Ɛ	566
3	98Ɛ 700	3X9	3	XXƐ Ɛ54	644	3	829 Ɛ45	293
4	118 168 XX9	0X8	4	12Ɛ 279 598	358	4	ƐX8 218	001
5	545 Ɛ95	398 9X7	5	646 934	072	5	142 366 219	379 92Ɛ
6	922 980	6X5	6	X13 9X6	388 987	6	723 Ɛ48	65X
7	119 0ƐƐ 465	3X5	7	130 1X0 771	6X1	7	XX1 5X6	389
8	497 84X	0X5	8	569 252	3Ɛ7	8	143 25X 973	0Ɛ9
9	873 933	397 9X5	9	935 649	111	9	617 X70	378 X28
X	11X 04Ɛ 718	6X6	X	131 101 75X	387 X29	X	994 898	758
Ɛ	427 202	3X6	Ɛ	489 587	744	Ɛ	144 151 434	488
1330	802 5X8	0X9	1370	855 10Ɛ	45Ɛ	13Ɛ0	509 900	1Ɛ9
1	Ɛ99 695	396 9XX	1	132 020 56X	177	1	885 XƐ9	377 ƐƐ2
2	11Ɛ 374 483	6Ɛ0	2	3X7 725	386 X94	2	145 041 X28	85Ɛ
3	74X Ɛ73	3Ɛ2	3	772 5Ɛ9	7Ɛ1	3	3Ɛ9 687	592
4	Ɛ25 365	0Ɛ6	4	Ɛ39 1XX	509	4	775 059	303
5	120 2ƐƐ 45Ɛ	395 9Ɛ9	5	133 303 6Ɛ7	227	5	Ɛ30 360	036
6	695 258	701	6	689 922	385 Ɛ45	6	146 2X7 396	376 969
7	X6X 959	405	7	X53 867	863	7	662 143	6X0
8	121 244 162	10X	8	134 219 50X	582	8	X18 823	414
9	619 270	394 X12	9	5X2 X90	2X1	9	147 193 037	147
X	9Ɛ2 082	718	X	968 171	000	X	549 182	375 X7Ɛ
Ɛ	122 186 79X	421	Ɛ	135 131 171	384 91Ɛ	Ɛ	903 041	7Ɛ4

N	Log N	d	N	Log N	d	N	Log N	d
1400	148 078 835	375 529	1440	15X 485 9X6	366 968	1480	170 536 459	358 6ƐƐ
1	432 162	262	1	830 752	6Ɛ6	1	892 Ɛ58	45X
2	7X7 404	374 Ɛ97	2	Ɛ97 248	442	2	171 02Ɛ 3Ɛ6	1ƐƐ
3	Ɛ60 39Ɛ	912	3	15Ɛ 341 68X	190	3	387 5Ɛ5	357 Ɛ5Ɛ
4	149 315 0Ɛ1	647	4	6X7 85X	365 Ɛ1X	4	723 554	8ƐƐ
5	689 738	382	5	X51 778	868	5	X7Ɛ 253	661
6	X41 XƐX	0Ɛ9	6	160 1Ɛ7 424	5Ɛ6	6	172 216 8Ɛ4	402
7	14X 1Ɛ5 ƐƐ7	373 X34	7	560 X1X	346	7	572 0Ɛ6	163
8	569 X2Ɛ	770	8	906 164	094	8	909 259	356 Ɛ06
9	921 59Ɛ	4X7	9	161 06Ɛ 238	364 X24	9	173 064 163	867
X	14Ɛ 094 X86	224	X	414 060	774	X	3ƐX X0X	60Ɛ
Ɛ	448 0XX	372 Ɛ60	Ɛ	778 814	504	Ɛ	755 419	370
1410	7ƐƐ 04X	899	1450	Ɛ21 118	255	1490	XXƐ 789	114
1	Ɛ71 927	617	1	162 285 371	363 ƐX5	1	174 245 8X1	355 X78
2	150 324 342	354	2	629 356	937	2	59Ɛ 759	81Ɛ
3	696 696	091	3	991 091	687	3	935 378	583
4	X48 767	371 X10	4	163 134 758	41X	4	175 08X 93Ɛ	327
5	151 1ƐX 577	74Ɛ	5	497 Ɛ76	16Ɛ	5	424 066	090
6	570 106	489	6	83Ɛ 125	362 Ɛ02	6	779 136	354 X35
7	921 593	209	7	ƐX2 027	854	7	Ɛ11 Ɛ6Ɛ	79X
8	152 092 7X0	370 Ɛ48	8	164 344 87Ɛ	5X8	8	176 266 749	543
9	443 728	888	9	6X7 267	33X	9	5ƐƐ 090	2X9
X	7Ɛ4 3Ɛ4	609	X	X49 5X5	093	X	953 379	053
Ɛ	Ɛ64 X01	348	Ɛ	165 1XƐ 678	361 X26	Ɛ	177 0X7 410	353 9Ɛ9
1420	153 315 149	08X	1460	551 4X2	77X	14X0	43Ɛ 209	764
1	685 217	36Ɛ X0Ɛ	1	8Ɛ3 060	512	1	792 971	50Ɛ
2	X35 026	750	2	166 054 572	268	2	Ɛ26 280	276
3	154 1X4 776	493	3	3Ɛ5 81X	001	3	178 279 536	022
4	554 049	214	4	756 81Ɛ	360 956	4	610 558	352 989
5	903 261	36X Ɛ57	5	XƐ7 575	6Ɛ0	5	963 325	735
6	155 072 1Ɛ8	89X	6	167 258 065	445	6	179 0Ɛ5 X5X	4X2
7	420 X96	620	7	5Ɛ8 4XX	1X0	7	448 340	24X
8	78Ɛ 4Ɛ6	365	8	958 68X	35Ɛ Ɛ37	8	79X 58X	351 ƐƐ8
9	Ɛ39 85Ɛ	0X8	9	168 0Ɛ8 605	892	9	Ɛ30 586	964
X	156 2X7 947	369 X30	X	458 297	629	X	17X 282 32X	712
Ɛ	655 777	775	Ɛ	7Ɛ7 904	385	Ɛ	613 X40	480
1430	X03 330	4ƐX	1470	Ɛ57 089	120	14Ɛ0	965 300	22X
1	157 170 82X	242	1	169 2Ɛ6 1X9	35X X79	1	17Ɛ 0Ɛ6 52X	350 Ɛ98
2	519 X70	368 Ɛ88	2	655 066	815	2	447 506	947
3	886 X38	912	3	9Ɛ3 87Ɛ	572	3	798 251	6Ɛ6
4	158 033 74X	658	4	16X 152 231	30Ɛ	4	Ɛ28 947	465
5	3X0 1X6	3X2	5	4Ɛ0 540	068	5	180 279 1Ɛ0	215
6	748 588	129	6	84X 5X8	359 X06	6	609 405	34Ɛ Ɛ84
7	XƐ4 6Ɛ5	367 X74	7	ƐX8 3Ɛ2	765	7	959 389	935
8	159 260 569	800	8	16Ɛ 345 Ɛ57	502	8	181 0X9 102	6X4
9	608 169	547	9	6X3 459	261	9	438 7X6	456
X	973 6Ɛ4	293	X	X40 6ƐX	000	X	788 040	206
Ɛ	15X 11X 987	01Ɛ	Ɛ	170 199 6ƐX	358 95Ɛ	Ɛ	Ɛ17 246	34X Ɛ78

N	Log N	d	N	Log N	d	N	Log N	d
1500	182 266 202	34X 929	1540	193 86Ɛ X67	341 400	1580	1X4 Ɛ65 140	334 306
1	5Ɛ4 Ɛ2Ɛ	69Ɛ	1	ƐƐ1 267	182	1	1X5 299 446	099
2	943 60X	451	2	194 332 429	340 Ɛ46	2	611 523	333 X70
3	183 091 X5Ɛ	204	3	673 373	90X	3	945 393	845
4	420 063	349 Ɛ76	4	9Ɛ4 081	691	4	1X6 079 018	619
5	76X 019	929	5	195 134 752	455	5	3Ɛ0 635	3Ɛ1
6	XƐ7 946	6X0	6	474 ƐX7	21X	6	723 X26	186
7	184 245 426	453	7	7Ɛ5 205	33Ɛ ƐX2	7	X56 ƐƐ0	332 Ɛ5Ɛ
8	592 879	208	8	Ɛ35 1X7	967	8	1X7 189 Ɛ4Ɛ	933
9	91Ɛ X85	348 Ɛ7Ɛ	9	196 274 Ɛ52	730	9	500 882	70X
X	185 068 X44	934	X	5Ɛ4 682	4Ɛ6	X	833 390	4X3
Ɛ	3Ɛ5 778	6X8	Ɛ	933 Ɛ78	27Ɛ	Ɛ	Ɛ65 873	279
1510	742 264	461	1550	197 073 237	045	1590	1X8 297 Ɛ30	053
1	X8X 705	217	1	3Ɛ2 280	33X X0Ɛ	1	609 Ɛ83	331 X29
2	186 216 920	347 Ɛ8Ɛ	2	731 08Ɛ	795	2	93Ɛ 9Ɛ0	805
3	562 8XƐ	946	3	X6Ɛ 864	561	3	1X9 071 5Ɛ5	59Ɛ
4	8XX 635	6ƐƐ	4	198 1XX 205	327	4	3X2 Ɛ94	376
5	187 036 134	476	5	528 530	0Ɛ2	5	714 34X	152
6	381 5XX	230	6	866 622	339 X7X	6	X45 4X0	330 Ɛ29
7	708 81X	346 ƐX7	7	ƐX4 4X0	845	7	1XX 176 409	905
8	X53 805	963	8	199 322 125	612	8	4X7 112	6X2
9	188 19X 568	719	9	65Ɛ 737	399	9	817 7Ɛ4	479
X	525 085	495	X	998 Ɛ14	167	X	Ɛ48 071	257
Ɛ	86Ɛ 55X	252	Ɛ	19X 116 07Ɛ	338 Ɛ33	Ɛ	1XƐ 278 308	033
1520	ƐƐ5 7Ɛ0	009	1560	452 ƐƐ2	900	15X0	5X8 33Ɛ	32Ɛ X10
1	189 33Ɛ 7Ɛ9	345 986	1	78Ɛ 8Ɛ2	689	1	918 14Ɛ	7XX
2	685 583	742	2	Ɛ08 37Ɛ	457	2	1Ɛ0 047 939	588
3	X0Ɛ 105	500	3	19Ɛ 244 816	224	3	377 305	365
4	18X 154 605	279	4	580 X3X	337 ƐƐ3	4	6X6 66X	143
5	499 882	036	5	8Ɛ8 X31	981	5	X15 7Ɛ1	32X Ɛ22
6	822 8Ɛ8	344 9Ɛ5	6	1X0 034 7Ɛ2	750	6	1Ɛ1 144 713	900
7	Ɛ67 6Ɛ1	772	7	370 342	51X	7	473 413	6X0
8	18Ɛ 2Ɛ0 263	531	8	6X7 860	2X9	8	7X1 XƐ3	47X
9	634 794	2XƐ	9	X22 Ɛ49	079	9	Ɛ10 371	259
X	978 X83	06Ɛ	X	1X1 15X 006	336 X49	X	1Ɛ2 23X 60X	03X
Ɛ	190 100 Ɛ32	343 X29	Ɛ	494 X53	818	Ɛ	568 648	329 X19
1530	444 95Ɛ	7X9	1570	80Ɛ 66Ɛ	5X8	15Ɛ0	896 465	7Ɛ9
1	788 548	569	1	Ɛ46 057	379	1	1Ɛ3 004 062	599
2	Ɛ0Ɛ XƐ5	329	2	1X2 280 414	14X	2	331 63Ɛ	37X
3	191 253 222	0X9	3	5Ɛ6 562	335 Ɛ1X	3	65X 9Ɛ9	15X
4	596 30Ɛ	342 X6X	4	930 480	8XƐ	4	987 Ɛ57	328 Ɛ40
5	919 179	82X	5	1X3 066 16Ɛ	681	5	1Ɛ4 0Ɛ4 X97	921
6	192 05Ɛ 9X7	5Ɛ0	6	39Ɛ 830	452	6	421 7Ɛ8	702
7	3X2 397	371	7	715 082	225	7	74X 2ƐX	4X4
8	724 748	132	8	X4X 2X7	334 ƐƐ6	8	X76 7X2	287
9	X66 87X	341 XƐ5	9	1X4 183 2X1	989	9	1Ɛ5 1X2 X69	068
X	193 1X8 773	877	X	4Ɛ8 06X	760	X	50X Ɛ15	327 X4Ɛ
Ɛ	52X 42X	639	Ɛ	830 80X	532	Ɛ	836 964	831

N	Log N	d	N	Log N	d	N	Log N	d
1600	1Ɛ5 Ɛ62 595	327 615	1640	206 877 840	31Ɛ 101	1680	217 2ƐƐ 728	312 Ɛ61
1	1Ɛ6 289 Ɛχχ	3Ɛ7	1	Ɛ96 941	31χ χƐ2	1	612 689	961
2	5Ɛ5 3χ5	19Ɛ	2	207 2Ɛ5 833	8χ6	2	925 42χ	763
3	920 584	326 Ɛ83	3	614 519	698	3	218 037 Ɛ91	564
4	1Ɛ7 047 547	966	4	932 ƐƐ5	48Ɛ	4	34χ 535	365
5	372 2Ɛ1	74Ɛ	5	208 051 484	282	5	660 89χ	167
6	698 χ40	533	6	36Ɛ 746	076	6	972 χ45	311 Ɛ68
7	χ03 373	318	7	689 800	319 χ69	7	219 084 9Ɛ1	96Ɛ
8	1Ɛ8 129 68Ɛ	100	8	9χ7 669	862	8	396 760	771
9	453 78Ɛ	325 χχ6	9	209 105 30Ɛ	655	9	6χ8 311	574
χ	779 675	88χ	χ	422 964	449	χ	9Ɛ9 885	377
Ɛ	χχ3 343	675	Ɛ	740 1Ɛ1	243	Ɛ	21χ 10Ɛ 040	179
1610	1Ɛ9 208 9Ɛ8	45χ	1650	χ59 434	037	1690	420 1Ɛ9	310 Ɛ80
1	532 256	244	1	20χ 176 46Ɛ	318 χƐ2	1	731 179	984
2	857 49χ	02χ	2	493 29χ	826	2	χ41 Ɛ41	788
3	Ɛ80 508	324 χ15	3	7χƐ Ɛ04	61χ	3	21Ɛ 152 709	58Ɛ
4	1Ɛχ 2χ5 321	800	4	Ɛ08 522	414	4	463 098	394
5	609 Ɛ21	5χ6	5	20Ɛ 224 936	20χ	5	773 470	197
6	932 507	392	6	540 Ɛ44	004	6	χ83 647	30Ɛ Ɛχ0
7	1ƐƐ 056 899	179	7	858 Ɛ48	317 9ƐƐ	7	220 193 627	9χ5
8	37χ χ56	323 Ɛ65	8	Ɛ74 947	7Ɛ5	8	4χ3 410	7χ9
9	6χ2 9ƐƐ	951	9	210 290 540	5Ɛ0	9	7Ɛ2 ƐƐ9	5Ɛ3
χ	χ06 750	738	χ	5χ7 Ɛ30	3χ6	χ	Ɛ02 5Ɛ0	3Ɛ7
Ɛ	200 12χ 288	526	Ɛ	903 316	1χ2	Ɛ	221 211 9χ7	202
1620	451 7Ɛ2	311	1660	211 01χ 4Ɛ8	316 Ɛ9χ	16χ0	520 Ɛχ9	007
1	774 Ɛ03	0ƐƐ	1	335 496	995	1	82Ɛ Ɛ24	30χ χ10
2	χ98 002	322 χχ7	2	650 26Ɛ	790	2	Ɛ3χ χ04	817
3	201 1Ɛχ χχ9	895	3	966 χ3Ɛ	589	3	222 249 61Ɛ	622
4	521 782	682	4	212 081 408	385	4	558 041	427
5	844 244	471	5	397 791	182	5	866 468	233
6	Ɛ66 6Ɛ5	25χ	6	6Ɛ1 953	315 Ɛ7Ɛ	6	Ɛ74 69Ɛ	039
7	202 288 953	048	7	χ07 912	977	7	223 282 718	309 χ45
8	5χχ 99Ɛ	321 χ36	8	213 121 689	774	8	590 561	84Ɛ
9	910 815	826	9	437 241	572	9	89χ 1Ɛ0	658
χ	203 032 43Ɛ	614	χ	750 7Ɛ3	370	χ	Ɛχ7 848	463
Ɛ	353 χ53	403	Ɛ	χ65 Ɛ63	169	Ɛ	224 2Ɛ5 0χƐ	26Ɛ
1630	675 256	1Ɛ3	1670	214 17Ɛ 110	314 Ɛ68	16Ɛ0	602 35χ	077
1	996 449	320 Ɛχ2	1	494 078	965	1	90Ɛ 415	308 χ84
2	204 0Ɛ7 42Ɛ	992	2	7χ8 χ21	764	2	225 018 299	890
3	418 201	782	3	Ɛ01 585	563	3	324 Ɛ69	699
4	738 983	573	4	215 215 Ɛ28	362	4	631 646	4χ6
5	χ59 336	362	5	52χ 28χ	160	5	939 Ɛ30	2Ɛ3
6	205 179 698	154	6	842 42χ	313 Ɛ60	6	226 046 223	101
7	499 830	31Ɛ Ɛ44	7	Ɛ56 38χ	960	7	352 324	307 Ɛ0χ
8	7Ɛ9 774	936	8	216 26χ 12χ	760	8	65χ 232	918
9	Ɛ19 4χχ	727	9	581 88χ	55Ɛ	9	965 Ɛ4χ	726
χ	206 239 015	519	χ	895 229	35Ɛ	χ	227 071 674	534
Ɛ	558 532	30χ	Ɛ	Ɛχ8 588	160	Ɛ	378 Ɛχ8	342

N	Log N	d	N	Log N	d	N	Log N	d
1700	227 684 32X	307 151	1740	237 79Ɛ 042	2ƐƐ 671	1780	247 658 63X	2Ɛ4 2X0
1	98Ɛ 47Ɛ	306 Ɛ60	1	X9X 6Ɛ3	489	1	950 91X	105
2	228 096 41Ɛ	96Ɛ	2	238 199 Ɛ80	2X5	2	248 044 X23	2Ɛ3 Ɛ2Ɛ
3	3X1 18X	77Ɛ	3	499 265	103	3	338 952	954
4	6X7 949	589	4	798 368	2ƐX Ɛ1Ɛ	4	630 6X6	77X
5	9Ɛ2 316	399	5	X97 287	938	5	924 264	5X4
6	229 0Ɛ8 6Ɛ3	1XX	6	239 196 003	755	6	249 017 848	40X
7	402 8X1	305 ƐƐ9	7	494 758	573	7	30Ɛ 056	234
8	708 89X	X09	8	793 10Ɛ	391	8	602 28X	05Ɛ
9	X12 6X7	81X	9	X91 4X0	1XX	9	8Ɛ5 329	2Ɛ2 X86
X	22X 118 305	62X	X	23X 18Ɛ 68X	008	X	ƐX8 1Ɛ3	8Ɛ1
Ɛ	421 933	43Ɛ	Ɛ	489 696	2Ɛ9 X27	Ɛ	24X 29X XX4	718
1710	727 172	250	1750	787 501	844	1790	591 600	543
1	X30 402	062	1	X85 145	664	1	883 Ɛ43	36Ɛ
2	22Ɛ 135 464	304 X73	2	23Ɛ 182 7X9	482	2	Ɛ76 2Ɛ2	196
3	43X 317	884	3	480 06Ɛ	2X1	3	24Ɛ 268 488	002
4	742 Ɛ9Ɛ	697	4	779 350	101	4	55X 48X	2Ɛ1 X2X
5	X47 676	4X8	5	X76 451	2Ɛ8 Ɛ1Ɛ	5	850 2Ɛ8	856
6	230 14Ɛ Ɛ62	2ƐƐ	6	240 173 370	93Ɛ	6	Ɛ41 Ɛ52	683
7	454 261	111	7	470 0XƐ	75Ɛ	7	250 233 615	4XƐ
8	758 372	303 Ɛ23	8	768 84X	57Ɛ	8	524 Ɛ04	318
9	X60 295	937	9	X65 209	39Ɛ	9	816 220	144
X	231 164 010	749	X	241 161 5X8	1ƐƐ	X	Ɛ07 364	2Ɛ0 Ɛ72
Ɛ	467 759	561	Ɛ	459 7X7	020	Ɛ	251 1Ɛ8 316	99Ɛ
1720	76Ɛ 0ƐX	374	1760	755 807	2Ɛ7 X40	17X0	4X9 0Ɛ5	809
1	X72 472	188	1	X51 647	861	1	799 902	636
2	232 175 63X	302 Ɛ9Ɛ	2	242 149 2X8	682	2	X8X 338	464
3	478 619	9Ɛ4	3	444 96X	4X4	3	252 17X 7X0	292
4	77Ɛ 411	807	4	740 252	304	4	46X X72	100
5	X82 018	621	5	X37 556	127	5	75X Ɛ72	2XƐ Ɛ2X
6	233 184 639	434	6	243 132 681	2Ɛ6 Ɛ48	6	X4X XX0	959
7	486 X71	24X	7	429 609	96X	7	253 13X 839	787
8	789 0ƐƐ	062	8	724 377	790	8	42X 404	5Ɛ7
9	X8Ɛ 161	301 X78	9	X1X Ɛ47	5Ɛ3	9	719 9ƐƐ	425
X	234 191 019	891	X	244 115 53X	415	X	X09 224	255
Ɛ	492 8XX	6X7	Ɛ	40Ɛ 953	238	Ɛ	254 0Ɛ8 479	084
1730	794 395	500	1770	705 Ɛ8Ɛ	05X	17Ɛ0	3X7 541	2XX XƐ3
1	X95 895	317	1	X00 029	2Ɛ5 X82	1	696 434	923
2	235 196 Ɛ20	130	2	245 0Ɛ5 XXƐ	8X5	2	985 157	753
3	498 120	300 Ɛ47	3	3XƐ 794	708	3	255 073 8XX	584
4	799 067	961	4	6X5 2X0	531	4	362 272	3Ɛ3
5	X99 X08	779	5	99X 811	353	5	650 665	224
6	236 19X 585	593	6	246 093 Ɛ64	178	6	93X 889	055
7	49X Ɛ58	3XX	7	389 120	2Ɛ4 ƐX0	7	256 028 922	2X9 X85
8	79Ɛ 346	206	8	682 100	X05	8	316 7X7	8Ɛ6
9	X9Ɛ 550	021	9	976 Ɛ05	829	9	604 4X1	728
X	237 19Ɛ 571	2ƐƐ X38	X	247 06Ɛ 732	652	X	8Ɛ2 009	558
Ɛ	49Ɛ 3X9	855	Ɛ	364 184	476	Ɛ	Ɛ9Ɛ 565	38Ɛ

N	Log N	d	N	Log N	d	N	Log N	d
1800	257 288 934	2X9 200	1840	266 87Ɛ 222	2X2 3Ɛ4	1880	276 042 73X	297 866
1	575 Ɛ34	031	1	Ɛ61 616	233	1	31X 3X4	6Ɛ0
2	862 Ɛ65	2X8 X64	2	267 243 849	070	2	5Ɛ5 X94	535
3	Ɛ4Ɛ X09	896	3	525 8Ɛ9	2X1 XXƐ	3	891 409	380
4	258 238 6X3	708	4	807 7X8	929	4	Ɛ68 789	206
5	525 1XƐ	53Ɛ	5	XX9 515	768	5	277 243 993	050
6	811 72X	371	6	268 18Ɛ 081	5X7	6	51X X23	296 X97
7	XƐ9 X9Ɛ	1X5	7	470 668	425	7	7Ɛ5 8ƐX	921
8	259 1X6 084	017	8	751 X91	265	8	X90 61Ɛ	768
9	492 09Ɛ	2X7 X4Ɛ	9	X33 136	0X4	9	278 167 187	5Ɛ3
X	779 Ɛ2X	882	X	269 114 21X	2X0 Ɛ24	X	441 77X	43X
Ɛ	X65 7Ɛ0	6Ɛ5	Ɛ	3Ɛ5 142	963	Ɛ	717 ƐƐ8	286
1810	25X 151 2X5	529	1850	695 XX5	7X3	1890	9Ɛ2 282	111
1	438 812	361	1	976 688	623	1	279 088 393	295 Ɛ58
2	723 Ɛ73	196	2	26X 057 0XƐ	462	2	362 32Ɛ	9X5
3	X0Ɛ 149	009	3	337 551	2X4	3	638 114	830
4	25Ɛ 026 156	2X6 X42	4	617 835	123	4	911 944	678
5	3X0 Ɛ98	877	5	8Ɛ7 958	29Ɛ Ɛ64	5	ƐX7 400	504
6	687 853	6XƐ	6	Ɛ97 900	9X5	6	27X 280 904	351
7	972 342	524	7	26Ɛ 277 6X5	826	7	556 055	199
8	260 058 866	359	8	557 30Ɛ	667	8	82Ɛ 232	026
9	343 003	193	9	836 976	4X8	9	Ɛ04 258	294 X73
X	629 196	008	X	Ɛ16 262	32X	X	27Ɛ 199 10Ɛ	900
Ɛ	913 1X2	2X5 X41	Ɛ	270 1Ɛ5 590	16Ɛ	Ɛ	471 X0Ɛ	748
1820	ƐƐ9 023	878	1860	494 73Ɛ	29X Ɛ21	18X0	746 557	597
1	261 2X2 89Ɛ	6Ɛ1	1	773 730	X32	1	X1X Ɛ32	423
2	588 390	527	2	X52 562	875	2	280 0Ɛ3 355	271
3	871 8Ɛ7	362	3	271 131 217	6Ɛ7	3	387 606	0ƐƐ
4	Ɛ57 059	198	4	40Ɛ 912	539	4	65Ɛ 705	293 Ɛ49
5	262 240 235	013	5	6XX 24Ɛ	380	5	933 652	997
6	525 248	2X4 X49	6	988 60Ɛ	202	6	281 007 429	825
7	80X 095	885	7	272 066 811	046	7	29Ɛ 052	673
8	XƐ2 95X	700	8	344 857	299 X88	8	572 705	502
9	263 197 45X	537	9	622 723	910	9	846 007	351
X	47Ɛ 995	372	X	900 433	753	X	Ɛ19 358	19Ɛ
Ɛ	764 147	1XX	Ɛ	Ɛ99 Ɛ86	596	Ɛ	282 1Ɛ0 537	02Ɛ
1830	X48 335	026	1870	273 277 560	41X	18Ɛ0	483 566	292 X79
1	264 130 35Ɛ	2X3 X62	1	554 97X	262	1	756 423	909
2	414 201	89X	2	832 020	0X5	2	X29 130	758
3	6Ɛ7 X9Ɛ	716	3	Ɛ0Ɛ 105	298 Ɛ2X	3	283 0ƐƐ 888	5X8
4	99Ɛ 5Ɛ5	553	4	274 1X8 033	972	4	392 274	437
5	265 082 Ɛ48	38Ɛ	5	484 9X5	7Ɛ7	5	664 6XƐ	287
6	366 317	208	6	761 5X0	63Ɛ	6	936 976	118
7	649 523	045	7	X3X 01Ɛ	484	7	284 008 X92	291 Ɛ67
8	930 568	2X2 X82	8	275 116 4X3	309	8	29X X39	9Ɛ8
9	266 013 42X	900	9	3Ɛ2 7Ɛ0	152	9	570 835	849
X	2Ɛ6 12X	739	X	68X 942	297 Ɛ97	X	842 482	699
Ɛ	598 867	577	Ɛ	966 919	X21	Ɛ	Ɛ13 Ɛ5Ɛ	529

N	Log N	d	N	Log N	d	N	Log N	d
1900	285 1X5 488	291 37Ɛ	1940	294 135 46X	287 122	1980	2X2 X7Ɛ Ɛ65	281 0ƐX
1	476 847	210	1	400 590	286 Ɛ79	1	2X3 141 063	280 Ɛ60
2	747 X57	061	2	687 549	X16	2	402 003	X04
3	X18 XƐ8	290 XƐ2	3	952 363	872	3	682 X07	866
4	286 0X9 9XX	944	4	295 019 015	70X	4	943 671	70X
5	37X 732	796	5	2X3 723	567	5	2X4 004 17Ɛ	571
6	64Ɛ 308	627	6	56X 08X	404	6	284 730	415
7	91Ɛ 933	47X	7	834 492	261	7	544 Ɛ45	278
8	ƐƐ0 1Ɛ1	30Ɛ	8	XƐX 733	0ƐX	8	805 201	121
9	287 280 500	162	9	296 184 831	285 Ɛ58	9	X85 322	27Ɛ Ɛ84
X	550 662	28Ɛ ƐƐ4	X	44X 789	9Ɛ5	X	2X5 145 2X6	X28
Ɛ	820 656	X47	Ɛ	714 582	852	Ɛ	405 112	890
1910	XƐ0 4X1	899	1950	99X 214	6Ɛ0	1990	684 9X2	735
1	288 180 17X	731	1	297 063 904	54X	1	944 517	599
2	44Ɛ 8XƐ	583	2	329 252	3X8	2	2X6 003 XƐ4	441
3	71Ɛ 272	417	3	5Ɛ2 63X	245	3	283 335	2X7
4	9XX 689	26X	4	877 883	0X5	4	542 620	14Ɛ
5	289 079 937	101	5	Ɛ40 968	284 Ɛ42	5	801 76Ɛ	27X ƐƐ4
6	348 X38	28X Ɛ55	6	298 205 8XX	9X1	6	X80 763	X59
7	617 991	9X9	7	48X 68Ɛ	840	7	2X7 13Ɛ 600	903
8	8X6 77X	841	8	753 30Ɛ	69X	8	3ƐX 303	768
9	Ɛ75 3ƐƐ	694	9	X17 9X9	53X	9	678 X6Ɛ	612
X	28X 243 X93	529	X	299 0X0 327	398	X	937 481	477
Ɛ	512 400	381	Ɛ	364 703	238	Ɛ	ƐƐ5 938	321
1920	7X0 781	216	1960	628 93Ɛ	097	19X0	2X8 274 059	187
1	X6X 997	06X	1	8Ɛ0 X16	283 Ɛ37	1	532 224	031
2	28Ɛ 138 X45	289 Ɛ04	2	Ɛ74 951	996	2	7Ɛ0 255	279 X97
3	406 949	958	3	29X 238 727	836	3	X6X 130	941
4	694 6X5	7Ɛ1	4	500 361	697	4	2X9 127 X71	7X9
5	962 296	646	5	783 X38	536	5	3X5 65X	652
6	290 02Ɛ 920	4X0	6	X47 372	396	6	663 0Ɛ0	4Ɛ9
7	2Ɛ9 200	335	7	29Ɛ 10X 748	237	7	920 5X9	365
8	586 535	18Ɛ	8	391 983	097	8	Ɛ99 952	20Ɛ
9	853 704	025	9	654 X5X	282 Ɛ38	9	2XX 256 Ɛ61	076
X	Ɛ20 729	288 X7Ɛ	X	917 996	998	X	514 017	278 Ɛ22
Ɛ	291 1X9 5X8	915	Ɛ	Ɛ9X 772	839	Ɛ	790 Ɛ39	989
1930	476 301	76Ɛ	1970	2X0 261 3XƐ	69Ɛ	19Ɛ0	X49 906	834
1	742 X70	605	1	523 X8X	540	1	2XƐ 106 53X	6X1
2	X0Ɛ 475	460	2	7X6 40X	3X1	2	383 01Ɛ	548
3	292 097 915	2Ɛ7	3	X68 7XƐ	242	3	63Ɛ 567	3Ɛ3
4	364 010	151	4	2X1 12X X31	0X4	4	8Ɛ7 95X	260
5	630 161	287 ƐX9	5	3Ɛ0 Ɛ15	281 Ɛ46	5	Ɛ73 ƐƐX	109
6	8Ɛ8 14X	X43	6	672 X5Ɛ	9X7	6	2Ɛ0 230 107	277 Ɛ74
7	Ɛ83 Ɛ91	89Ɛ	7	934 846	84X	7	4X8 07Ɛ	X21
8	293 24Ɛ 870	736	8	ƐƐ6 494	6Ɛ0	8	763 XX0	889
9	517 3X6	592	9	2X2 277 Ɛ84	552	9	X1Ɛ 769	737
X	7X2 978	429	X	539 516	3Ɛ4	X	2Ɛ1 097 2X4	5X3
Ɛ	X6X 1X5	285	Ɛ	7ƐX 90X	257	Ɛ	352 887	450

N	Log N	d	N	Log N	d	N	Log N	d
1X00	2Ɛ1 60X 117	277 2Ɛ9	1X40	2ƐƐ Ɛ68 403	271 709	1X80	30X 322 X37	268 11X
1	885 414	166	1	300 219 Ɛ10	581	1	58X Ɛ55	267 Ɛ96
2	Ɛ40 57X	014	2	48Ɛ 491	434	2	836 Ɛ2Ɛ	X54
3	2Ɛ2 1Ɛ7 592	276 X81	3	740 905	2X8	3	XX2 983	911
4	472 453	92Ɛ	4	9Ɛ1 ƐƐ1	160	4	30Ɛ 14X 694	78Ɛ
5	729 182	799	5	301 063 151	013	5	3Ɛ6 263	649
6	9X3 95Ɛ	646	6	314 164	270 X88	6	661 8Ɛ0	506
7	2Ɛ3 05X 3X5	4Ɛ5	7	585 030	93Ɛ	7	909 1Ɛ6	385
8	314 89X	362	8	835 96Ɛ	7Ɛ4	8	Ɛ74 57Ɛ	242
9	58Ɛ 040	211	9	XX6 563	668	9	310 21Ɛ 801	101
X	845 251	080	X	302 157 00Ɛ	521	X	486 902	266 Ɛ7Ɛ
Ɛ	XƐƐ 311	275 ƐƐX	Ɛ	407 530	395	Ɛ	731 881	X39
1X10	2Ɛ4 175 23Ɛ	998	1X50	677 905	24X	1X90	998 6ƐX	8Ɛ8
1	42Ɛ 017	847	1	927 Ɛ53	103	1	311 043 3Ɛ6	776
2	6X4 862	6Ɛ7	2	Ɛ98 056	26Ɛ Ɛ78	2	2X9 Ɛ70	635
3	95X 359	565	3	303 248 012	X30	3	554 5X5	4Ɛ4
4	2Ɛ5 013 902	414	4	4Ɛ7 X42	8X7	4	7ƐX X99	373
5	289 116	284	5	767 729	75Ɛ	5	X65 250	232
6	542 39X	133	6	X17 288	615	6	312 10Ɛ 482	0Ɛ2
7	7Ɛ7 511	274 ƐX3	7	304 086 8X1	48X	7	375 574	265 Ɛ71
8	X70 4Ɛ4	X53	8	336 16Ɛ	345	8	61Ɛ 525	X30
9	2Ɛ6 125 347	902	9	5X5 4Ɛ4	1ƐX	9	885 355	8Ɛ0
X	39X 049	772	X	854 6Ɛ2	074	X	Ɛ2Ɛ 045	76Ɛ
Ɛ	652 7ƐƐ	623	Ɛ	Ɛ03 766	26X Ɛ2X	Ɛ	313 194 7Ɛ4	62Ɛ
1X20	907 222	492	1X60	305 172 694	9X4	1XX0	43X 223	4XƐ
1	Ɛ7Ɛ 6Ɛ4	343	1	421 478	85X	1	6X3 712	370
2	2Ɛ7 233 X37	1Ɛ3	2	690 116	715	2	948 X82	22Ɛ
3	4X8 02X	064	3	93X 82Ɛ	590	3	ƐƐ2 0Ɛ1	0Ɛ0
4	760 092	273 Ɛ15	4	ƐX9 1ƐƐ	446	4	314 257 1X1	264 Ɛ70
5	X13 ƐX7	985	5	306 257 645	301	5	500 151	X31
6	2Ɛ8 087 970	837	6	505 946	178	6	764 Ɛ82	8Ɛ1
7	33Ɛ 5X7	6X7	7	773 Ɛ02	033	7	X09 873	772
8	5Ɛ3 092	559	8	X21 Ɛ35	269 XXX	8	315 072 425	633
9	866 62Ɛ	40X	9	307 08Ɛ X23	966	9	316 X58	4Ɛ3
X	Ɛ19 X39	280	X	339 789	821	X	57Ɛ 34Ɛ	375
Ɛ	2Ɛ9 191 0Ɛ9	131	Ɛ	5X7 3XX	698	Ɛ	823 704	237
1X30	444 22X	272 ƐX3	1X70	854 X86	554	1XƐ0	X87 93Ɛ	0Ɛ7
1	6Ɛ7 211	X54	1	Ɛ02 41X	410	1	316 12Ɛ X36	263 Ɛ79
2	96X 065	907	2	308 16Ɛ 82X	288	2	393 9Ɛ3	X3X
3	2ƐX 020 970	779	3	418 X26	144	3	637 831	900
4	293 529	62Ɛ	4	686 03X	000	4	89Ɛ 531	782
5	545 Ɛ58	4X2	5	933 03X	268 X78	5	Ɛ43 0Ɛ3	644
6	7Ɛ8 43X	353	6	Ɛ9Ɛ X26	935	6	317 1X6 737	506
7	X6X 791	207	7	309 248 82Ɛ	7Ɛ1	7	44X 041	388
8	2ƐƐ 120 998	079	8	4Ɛ5 420	669	8	6Ɛ1 409	24X
9	392 X55	271 Ɛ30	9	761 X89	527	9	954 657	111
X	644 985	9X3	X	X0X 3Ɛ4	3X3	X	ƐƐ7 768	262 Ɛ93
Ɛ	8Ɛ6 768	857	Ɛ	30X 076 797	260	Ɛ	318 25X 73Ɛ	X55

N	Log N	d	N	Log N	d	N	Log N	d
1Ɛ00	318 501 594	262 919	1Ɛ40	326 50Ɛ 827	259 6Ɛ7	1Ɛ80	334 354 765	254 665
1	764 2Ɛ1	79Ɛ	1	769 322	582	1	5X9 20X	537
2	X06 X90	662	2	X06 8X4	44Ɛ	2	841 745	407
3	319 069 532	525	3	327 064 133	318	3	X95 Ɛ50	29X
4	30Ɛ X57	3X9	4	301 44Ɛ	1X4	4	335 12X 22X	16Ɛ
5	572 244	26Ɛ	5	55X 633	071	5	382 399	041
6	814 4Ɛ3	133	6	7Ɛ7 6X4	258 Ɛ39	6	616 41X	253 Ɛ12
7	X76 626	261 ƐƐ7	7	X54 621	X06	7	86X 330	9X5
8	31X 118 621	X7X	8	328 0Ɛ1 427	893	8	Ɛ02 115	877
9	37X 49Ɛ	941	9	34X 0ƐX	761	9	336 155 990	748
X	620 220	806	X	5X6 85Ɛ	629	X	3X9 518	61Ɛ
Ɛ	881 X26	68X	Ɛ	843 288	4Ɛ7	Ɛ	640 Ɛ37	4Ɛ2
1Ɛ10	Ɛ23 4Ɛ4	551	1Ɛ50	X9Ɛ 783	384	1Ɛ90	894 429	384
1	31Ɛ 184 X45	416	1	329 137 Ɛ47	251	1	Ɛ27 7Ɛ1	256
2	426 25Ɛ	29X	2	394 198	11Ɛ	2	337 17X X47	129
3	687 539	163	3	630 2Ɛ7	257 ƐX9	3	411 Ɛ74	000
4	928 6X0	027	4	888 2X4	X77	4	664 Ɛ74	252 X93
5	Ɛ89 707	260 XƐ0	5	Ɛ24 15Ɛ	944	5	8Ɛ7 X47	966
6	320 22X 5Ɛ7	974	6	32X 17Ɛ XX3	813	6	Ɛ4X 7Ɛ1	839
7	48Ɛ 36Ɛ	83X	7	417 6Ɛ6	6X1	7	338 1X1 42X	710
8	72Ɛ ƐX9	702	8	673 197	56Ɛ	8	433 Ɛ3X	5X3
9	990 6XƐ	587	9	90X 746	439	9	686 521	477
X	321 031 076	451	X	Ɛ65 Ɛ83	308	X	918 998	34X
Ɛ	291 507	316	Ɛ	32Ɛ 201 28Ɛ	196	Ɛ	Ɛ6Ɛ 126	222
1Ɛ20	531 821	19Ɛ	1Ɛ60	458 465	065	1ƐX0	339 201 348	0Ɛ6
1	791 X00	065	1	6Ɛ3 50X	256 Ɛ34	1	453 442	251 Ɛ89
2	X31 X65	25Ɛ Ɛ2X	2	94X 442	X03	2	6X5 40Ɛ	X62
3	322 091 993	9Ɛ4	3	ƐX5 245	891	3	937 271	935
4	331 787	87X	4	330 23Ɛ Ɛ16	761	4	Ɛ88 ƐX6	80X
5	591 445	745	5	496 677	630	5	33X 21X 7Ɛ4	6X1
6	830 Ɛ8X	60X	6	731 0X7	500	6	470 295	576
7	X90 598	494	7	987 5X7	38X	7	701 84Ɛ	44Ɛ
8	323 12Ɛ X70	35Ɛ	8	331 021 975	25Ɛ	8	953 09X	323
9	38Ɛ 20Ɛ	225	9	278 014	129	9	ƐX4 401	1Ɛ7
X	62X 434	0XƐ	X	512 141	255 ƐƐX	X	33Ɛ 235 5Ɛ8	091
Ɛ	889 523	25X Ɛ77	Ɛ	768 13Ɛ	X8X	Ɛ	486 689	250 Ɛ65
1Ɛ30	Ɛ28 49X	X41	1Ɛ70	X02 009	959	1ƐƐ0	717 632	X3X
1	324 187 31Ɛ	907	1	332 057 966	829	1	968 470	913
2	426 026	793	2	2Ɛ1 593	6ƐX	2	ƐƐ9 183	7X9
3	684 7Ɛ9	65X	3	547 091	58X	3	340 249 970	681
4	923 257	525	4	7X0 65Ɛ	45X	4	49X 431	557
5	Ɛ81 780	3Ɛ1	5	X35 XƐ9	32Ɛ	5	72X 988	430
6	325 21Ɛ Ɛ71	278	6	333 08Ɛ 228	200	6	97Ɛ 1Ɛ8	306
7	47X 229	143	7	324 428	090	7	341 00Ɛ 502	1X0
8	718 370	00Ɛ	8	579 4Ɛ8	254 Ɛ61	8	25Ɛ 6X2	075
9	976 37Ɛ	259 X97	9	812 459	X31	9	4XƐ 757	24Ɛ Ɛ4Ɛ
X	326 014 256	962	X	X67 28X	903	X	73Ɛ 6X6	X25
Ɛ	271 ƐƐ8	82Ɛ	Ɛ	334 0ƐƐ Ɛ91	794	Ɛ	98Ɛ 50Ɛ	8ƐƐ

N	Log N	d	N	Log N	d	N	Log N	d
2000	342 01Ɛ 20X	24Ɛ 796	2040	34Ɛ 731 X8Ɛ	246 X7X	2080	359 097 131	242 308
1	26X 9X4	66Ɛ	1	978 949	958	1	319 439	1XƐ
2	4ƐX 453	546	2	350 003 6X5	837	2	55Ɛ 628	092
3	749 999	420	3	24X 320	716	3	7X1 6ƐX	241 Ɛ77
4	999 1Ɛ9	2Ɛ7	4	494 X36	5Ɛ6	4	X23 675	X5X
5	343 028 4Ɛ4	192	5	71Ɛ 430	495	5	35X 065 513	942
6	277 686	068	6	965 905	375	6	2X7 255	825
7	506 732	24X Ɛ43	7	ƐƐ0 07X	254	7	528 X7X	70X
8	755 675	X1X	8	351 236 312	133	8	76X 588	5Ɛ2
9	9X4 493	8Ɛ5	9	480 445	014	9	9XƐ Ɛ7X	497
X	344 033 188	791	X	706 459	245 XƐ3	X	35Ɛ 031 455	37Ɛ
Ɛ	281 959	667	Ɛ	950 350	993	Ɛ	272 814	263
2010	510 404	543	2050	Ɛ96 123	873	2090	4Ɛ3 X77	147
1	75X 947	41X	1	352 21Ɛ 996	754	1	735 002	031
2	9X9 165	2Ɛ6	2	465 52X	633	2	976 033	240 Ɛ15
3	345 037 45Ɛ	192	3	6XX Ɛ61	514	3	ƐƐ6 Ɛ48	9Ɛ9
4	285 631	069	4	934 475	3Ɛ5	4	360 237 945	8X3
5	513 69X	249 Ɛ45	5	Ɛ79 86X	294	5	478 628	788
6	761 623	X21	6	353 202 Ɛ42	176	6	6Ɛ9 1Ɛ4	671
7	9XƐ 444	8ƐX	7	448 0Ɛ8	056	7	939 865	555
8	346 039 142	795	8	691 152	244 Ɛ37	8	Ɛ7X 1ƐX	440
9	286 917	671	9	916 089	X18	9	361 1ƐX 63X	324
X	514 388	54X	X	Ɛ5X XX5	8Ɛ9	X	43X 962	20X
Ɛ	761 916	427	Ɛ	354 1X3 7X2	79X	Ɛ	67X Ɛ70	0Ɛ4
2020	9XƐ 141	302	2060	428 380	67Ɛ	20X0	8ƐƐ 064	23Ɛ Ɛ99
1	347 038 443	1X0	1	670 X3Ɛ	560	1	Ɛ3Ɛ 041	X83
2	285 623	078	2	8Ɛ5 39Ɛ	442	2	362 17X Ɛ04	968
3	512 69Ɛ	248 Ɛ55	3	Ɛ39 821	323	3	3ƐX 870	853
4	75Ɛ 634	X32	4	355 181 Ɛ44	204	4	63X 503	738
5	9X8 466	90Ɛ	5	406 148	0X7	5	87X 03Ɛ	623
6	348 035 175	7X8	6	64X 233	243 Ɛ88	6	XƐ9 662	509
7	281 961	686	7	892 1ƐƐ	X6X	7	363 138 Ɛ6Ɛ	3Ɛ3
8	50X 427	562	8	Ɛ16 069	950	8	378 362	299
9	756 989	441	9	356 159 9Ɛ9	832	9	5Ɛ7 63Ɛ	184
X	9X3 20X	319	X	3X1 62Ɛ	714	X	836 803	06X
Ɛ	349 02Ɛ 527	1Ɛ8	Ɛ	625 143	5Ɛ6	Ɛ	X75 871	23X Ɛ55
2030	277 723	094	2070	868 739	498	20Ɛ0	364 0Ɛ4 806	X40
1	503 7Ɛ7	247 Ɛ73	1	XƐ0 015	37Ɛ	1	333 646	926
2	74Ɛ 76X	X51	2	357 133 394	262	2	572 370	811
3	997 5ƐƐ	92Ɛ	3	376 636	144	3	7Ɛ0 Ɛ81	6Ɛ9
4	34X 023 32X	809	4	5Ɛ9 77X	026	4	X2Ɛ 67X	5X3
5	26X Ɛ37	6X7	5	840 7X4	242 Ɛ0X	5	365 06X 061	48Ɛ
6	4Ɛ6 622	585	6	X83 6Ɛ2	9Ɛ0	6	2X8 530	375
7	741 ƐX7	464	7	358 106 4X2	893	7	526 8X5	262
8	989 44Ɛ	342	8	349 175	776	8	764 Ɛ47	148
9	34Ɛ 014 791	221	9	58Ɛ 92Ɛ	65X	9	9X3 093	034
X	25Ɛ 9Ɛ2	0ƐƐ	X	812 389	540	X	366 021 107	239 Ɛ20
Ɛ	4X6 XƐ1	246 Ɛ9X	Ɛ	X54 909	424	Ɛ	25Ɛ 027	X07

N	Log N	d	N	Log N	d	N	Log N	d
2100	366 498 X32	239 8Ɛ3	2140	373 740 Ɛ64	235 42Ɛ	2180	380 851 00X	231 0Ɛ2
1	716 725	79Ɛ	1	976 393	320	1	X82 100	230 ƐX5
2	954 304	687	2	ƐXƐ 6Ɛ3	210	2	381 0Ɛ3 0X5	X9X
3	Ɛ91 98Ɛ	573	3	374 224 903	101	3	323 Ɛ83	992
4	367 20Ɛ 342	45Ɛ	4	459 X04	234 ƐƐ0	4	554 955	887
5	448 7X1	348	5	692 9Ɛ4	XX1	5	785 620	77Ɛ
6	685 Ɛ29	233	6	907 895	992	6	9Ɛ6 19Ɛ	673
7	903 160	120	7	Ɛ40 667	882	7	382 026 852	568
8	Ɛ40 280	009	8	375 175 329	772	8	257 1ƐX	460
9	368 179 289	238 XƐ5	9	3X9 X9Ɛ	664	9	487 65X	356
X	3Ɛ6 182	9X2	X	622 543	554	X	6Ɛ7 9Ɛ4	24X
Ɛ	632 Ɛ64	88X	Ɛ	856 X97	445	Ɛ	928 042	143
2110	86Ɛ 832	778	2150	X8Ɛ 320	336	2190	Ɛ58 185	038
1	XX8 3XX	664	1	376 103 656	227	1	383 188 201	22Ɛ Ɛ31
2	369 124 X52	551	2	337 881	119	2	3Ɛ8 132	X26
3	361 3X3	43Ɛ	3	56Ɛ 99X	009	3	627 Ɛ58	91Ɛ
4	599 822	328	4	7X3 9X7	233 XƐƐ	4	857 877	815
5	815 Ɛ4X	215	5	X17 8X6	9Ɛ1	5	X87 490	70X
6	X52 163	102	6	377 04Ɛ 697	8X2	6	384 0Ɛ6 Ɛ9X	604
7	36X 08X 265	237 ƐƐ0	7	283 379	793	7	326 5X2	4Ɛ9
8	306 255	X99	8	4Ɛ6 Ɛ50	685	8	555 X9Ɛ	3Ɛ2
9	542 132	987	9	72X 615	577	9	785 291	2X9
X	779 XƐ9	875	X	961 Ɛ90	469	X	9Ɛ4 57X	1X2
Ɛ	9Ɛ5 772	762	Ɛ	Ɛ95 439	35X	Ɛ	385 023 760	098
2120	36Ɛ 031 314	650	2160	378 208 797	251	21X0	252 838	22X Ɛ92
1	268 964	53Ɛ	1	43Ɛ X28	142	1	481 80X	X88
2	4X4 2X3	428	2	672 Ɛ6X	035	2	6Ɛ0 696	982
3	71Ɛ 70Ɛ	317	3	8X5 ƐX3	232 Ɛ27	3	91Ɛ 458	879
4	956 X26	205	4	Ɛ18 Ɛ0X	X1X	4	Ɛ4X 115	772
5	Ɛ92 02Ɛ	0Ɛ3	5	379 14Ɛ 928	910	5	386 178 887	669
6	370 209 122	236 ƐX1	6	382 638	802	6	3X7 334	564
7	444 103	X90	7	5Ɛ5 23X	6Ɛ5	7	615 898	45X
8	67X Ɛ93	97Ɛ	8	827 933	5X8	8	844 136	354
9	8Ɛ5 952	869	9	X5X 31Ɛ	49X	9	X72 48X	24Ɛ
X	Ɛ30 5ƐƐ	758	X	37X 090 7Ɛ9	391	X	387 0X0 719	146
Ɛ	371 167 157	647	Ɛ	302 Ɛ8X	284	Ɛ	30X 863	041
2130	3X1 7X2	536	2170	535 252	178	21Ɛ0	538 8X4	229 Ɛ38
1	618 118	425	1	767 40X	06X	1	766 820	X33
2	852 541	314	2	999 478	231 Ɛ61	2	994 653	929
3	X88 855	203	3	37Ɛ 00Ɛ 419	X55	3	388 002 380	825
4	372 102 X58	0Ɛ3	4	241 272	948	4	22Ɛ ƐX5	721
5	338 Ɛ4Ɛ	235 ƐX2	5	472 ƐƐX	83Ɛ	5	459 706	617
6	572 Ɛ31	X91	6	6X4 839	733	6	687 121	513
7	7X8 X02	981	7	916 370	627	7	8Ɛ4 634	40X
8	X22 783	870	8	Ɛ47 997	51X	8	Ɛ21 X42	306
9	373 058 433	761	9	380 179 2Ɛ5	412	9	389 14Ɛ 148	202
X	291 Ɛ94	650	X	3XX 707	305	X	378 34X	0Ɛ9
Ɛ	507 624	540	Ɛ	61Ɛ X10	1ƐX	Ɛ	5X5 447	228 ƐƐ5

N	Log N	d	N	Log N	d	N	Log N	d
2200	389 812 440	228 χƐ1	2240	396 64χ 235	224 χ22	2280	3χ3 345 569	220 χ7Ɛ
1	χ3Ɛ 331	9χ9	1	873 057	923	1	566 428	983
2	38χ 068 11χ	8χ4	2	χ97 97χ	821	2	787 1χƐ	886
3	294 χ02	7χ1	3	397 100 59Ɛ	722	3	9χ7 χ75	789
4	501 5χ3	69χ	4	325 101	622	4	3χ4 008 642	691
5	72χ 081	595	5	549 723	521	5	229 113	594
6	956 656	492	6	772 044	422	6	449 6χ7	498
7	Ɛ82 Ɛ28	38χ	7	996 466	321	7	669 Ɛ83	3χ0
8	38Ɛ 1χƐ 2Ɛ6	286	8	ƐƐχ 787	222	8	88χ 363	2χ3
9	417 580	184	9	398 222 9χ9	122	9	χχχ 646	1χ8
χ	643 744	080	χ	446 Ɛ0Ɛ	023	χ	3χ5 10χ 832	0χƐ
Ɛ	86Ɛ 804	227 Ɛ78	Ɛ	66χ Ɛ32	223 Ɛ23	Ɛ	32χ 921	21Ɛ ƐƐ3
2210	χ97 780	χ76	2250	892 χ55	χ23	2290	54χ 914	χƐ7
1	390 103 636	972	1	χƐ6 878	924	1	76χ 80Ɛ	χ00
2	32Ɛ 3χ8	86Ɛ	2	399 11χ 5χ0	825	2	98χ 60Ɛ	903
3	557 057	769	3	342 205	725	3	Ɛχχ 312	808
4	782 804	665	4	565 92χ	627	4	3χ6 209 Ɛ1χ	710
5	9χχ 269	563	5	789 355	527	5	429 62χ	615
6	391 015 810	460	6	9Ɛ0 880	428	6	649 043	519
7	241 070	359	7	39χ 014 0χ8	329	7	868 560	422
8	468 409	257	8	237 415	22χ	8	χ87 982	326
9	693 664	154	9	45χ 643	130	9	3χ7 0χ7 0χ8	22Ɛ
χ	8Ɛχ 7Ɛ8	052	χ	681 773	030	χ	306 317	134
Ɛ	Ɛ25 84χ	226 Ɛ50	Ɛ	8χ4 7χ3	222 Ɛ32	Ɛ	525 44Ɛ	039
2220	392 150 79χ	χ49	2260	Ɛ07 715	χ34	22χ0	744 488	21χ Ɛ41
1	377 627	947	1	39Ɛ 12χ 549	934	1	963 409	χ47
2	5χ2 372	845	2	351 281	837	2	Ɛ82 254	950
3	808 ƐƐ7	743	3	573 χƐ8	738	3	3χ8 1χ0 Ɛχ4	854
4	χ33 73χ	641	4	796 634	63χ	4	3ƐƐ 838	75χ
5	393 05χ 17Ɛ	53Ɛ	5	9Ɛ9 072	53Ɛ	5	61χ 396	664
6	284 6Ɛχ	43χ	6	3χ0 01Ɛ 5Ɛ1	441	6	838 χ3χ	568
7	4χχ Ɛ38	337	7	241 χ32	344	7	χ57 3χ6	472
8	715 273	237	8	464 176	245	8	3χ9 075 858	378
9	93Ɛ 4χχ	134	9	686 3ƐƐ	147	9	294 014	281
χ	Ɛ65 622	033	χ	8χ8 546	04χ	χ	4Ɛ2 295	187
Ɛ	394 18Ɛ 655	225 Ɛ32	Ɛ	Ɛ0χ 594	221 Ɛ50	Ɛ	710 460	090
2230	3Ɛ5 587	χ30	2270	3χ1 130 524	χ52	22Ɛ0	92χ 530	219 Ɛ97
1	61Ɛ 3Ɛ7	92Ɛ	1	352 376	954	1	Ɛ48 507	χχ0
2	845 126	82χ	2	574 10χ	857	2	3χχ 166 3χ7	9χ6
3	χ6χ 954	729	3	795 965	759	3	384 191	8Ɛ0
4	395 094 481	628	4	9Ɛ7 502	660	4	5χ1 χ81	7Ɛ6
5	2Ɛ9 χχ9	526	5	3χ2 018 Ɛ62	563	5	7ƐƐ 677	701
6	523 413	426	6	23χ 505	465	6	χ19 178	606
7	748 839	326	7	45Ɛ 96χ	368	7	3χƐ 036 782	511
8	971 Ɛ63	224	8	681 116	270	8	254 093	417
9	Ɛ97 187	124	9	8χ2 386	172	9	471 4χχ	322
χ	396 200 2χƐ	023	χ	Ɛ03 538	075	χ	68χ 810	228
Ɛ	425 312	224 Ɛ23	Ɛ	3χ3 124 5Ɛ1	220 Ɛ78	Ɛ	8χ7 χ38	132

N	Log N	d	N	Log N	d	N	Log N	d
2300	3XƐ Ɛ04 Ɛ6X	219 039	2340	3Ɛ8 551 374	215 312	2380	404 X6X XƐ7	211 6Ɛ8
1	3Ɛ0 121 ƐX7	218 Ɛ44	1	766 686	220	1	405 080 5Ɛ3	608
2	33X Ɛ2Ɛ	X4Ɛ	2	97Ɛ 8X6	12X	2	291 ƐƐƐ	51X
3	557 97X	956	3	Ɛ94 X14	038	3	4X3 519	430
4	774 714	860	4	3Ɛ9 1X9 X50	214 Ɛ47	4	6Ɛ4 949	341
5	991 374	768	5	402 997	X54	5	906 08X	252
6	ƐX9 Ɛ20	672	6	617 82Ɛ	964	6	Ɛ17 320	164
7	3Ɛ1 206 592	57X	7	830 593	871	7	406 128 484	075
8	422 Ɛ50	485	8	X45 244	780	8	339 539	210 Ɛ88
9	63Ɛ 415	390	9	3ƐX 059 X04	68Ɛ	9	54X 505	X99
X	857 7X5	298	X	272 493	599	X	75Ɛ 3X2	9XƐ
Ɛ	X73 X81	1X3	Ɛ	486 X70	4X8	Ɛ	970 191	900
2310	3Ɛ2 090 064	0XX	2350	69Ɛ 358	3Ɛ7	2390	Ɛ80 X91	813
1	2X8 152	217 Ɛ26	1	8Ɛ3 753	306	1	407 191 6X4	725
2	504 148	Ɛ02	2	Ɛ07 X59	215	2	3X2 209	637
3	720 04X	X09	3	3ƐƐ 120 072	123	3	5Ɛ2 844	549
4	937 X57	915	4	334 195	033	4	803 191	45Ɛ
5	Ɛ53 770	821	5	548 208	213 Ɛ41	5	X13 630	371
6	3Ɛ3 16Ɛ 391	729	6	760 149	X51	6	408 023 9X1	284
7	386 XƐX	634	7	973 Ɛ9X	961	7	234 065	196
8	5X2 532	541	8	Ɛ87 93Ɛ	86Ɛ	8	444 23Ɛ	0X9
9	7Ɛ9 X73	449	9	400 19Ɛ 5XX	77Ɛ	9	654 328	000
X	X15 300	355	X	3Ɛ3 169	68X	X	864 328	20Ɛ Ɛ11
Ɛ	3Ɛ4 030 655	261	Ɛ	606 837	59X	Ɛ	X74 239	X25
2320	247 8Ɛ6	16X	2360	81X 215	4XX	23X0	409 084 062	937
1	462 X64	076	1	X31 703	3Ɛ9	1	293 999	84X
2	679 Ɛ1X	216 Ɛ82	2	401 044 Ɛ00	309	2	4X3 627	761
3	894 XX0	X8Ɛ	3	258 209	218	3	6Ɛ3 188	674
4	XXƐ 96Ɛ	998	4	46Ɛ 425	129	4	902 840	587
5	3Ɛ5 106 747	8X4	5	682 552	038	5	Ɛ12 207	49X
6	321 42Ɛ	7Ɛ1	6	895 58X	212 Ɛ48	6	40X 121 6X5	3Ɛ1
7	538 020	6ƐX	7	XX8 516	X59	7	330 X96	305
8	752 71X	607	8	402 0ƐƐ 373	968	8	540 19Ɛ	217
9	969 125	513	9	312 11Ɛ	879	9	74Ɛ 3Ɛ6	12Ɛ
X	Ɛ83 638	421	X	524 998	789	X	95X 525	042
Ɛ	3Ɛ6 199 X59	32X	Ɛ	737 565	699	Ɛ	Ɛ69 567	20X Ɛ56
2330	3Ɛ4 187	236	2370	94X 042	5XX	23Ɛ0	40Ɛ 178 501	X69
1	60X 401	145	1	Ɛ60 630	4ƐX	1	387 36X	981
2	824 546	051	2	403 172 Ɛ2X	40Ɛ	2	596 12Ɛ	894
3	X3X 597	215 Ɛ5Ɛ	3	385 339	31Ɛ	3	7X4 X03	7X9
4	3Ɛ7 054 536	X68	4	597 658	230	4	9Ɛ3 5Ɛ0	700
5	26X 3X2	975	5	7X9 888	141	5	410 002 0Ɛ0	613
6	484 157	883	6	9ƐƐ X09	051	6	210 703	528
7	699 X1X	791	7	404 011 X5X	211 Ɛ62	7	41Ɛ 02Ɛ	43Ɛ
8	8Ɛ3 5XƐ	69Ɛ	8	223 X00	X74	8	629 46X	354
9	Ɛ09 08X	5X8	9	435 874	984	9	837 802	268
X	3Ɛ8 122 676	4Ɛ6	X	647 638	895	X	X45 X6X	17Ɛ
Ɛ	337 Ɛ70	404	Ɛ	859 311	7X6	Ɛ	411 054 029	095

N	Log N	d	N	Log N	d	N	Log N	d
2400	411 262 102	209 ƐX8	2440	419 532 Ɛ36	206 59Ɛ	2480	425 6X5 574	203 08Ɛ
1	470 0XX	Ɛ00	1	739 515	4Ɛ6	1	8X8 643	202 ƐX9
2	679 ƐXX	X15	2	943 X0Ɛ	412	2	XXƐ 630	Ɛ07
3	887 X03	92X	3	Ɛ4X 221	329	3	426 0Ɛ2 537	X26
4	X95 731	842	4	41X 154 54X	245	4	2Ɛ5 361	943
5	412 0X3 373	757	5	35X 793	160	5	4Ɛ8 0X4	863
6	2Ɛ0 Ɛ0X	66Ɛ	6	564 933	078	6	6ƐX 947	780
7	4ƐX 579	584	7	76X 9XƐ	205 Ɛ94	7	901 507	6X0
8	707 Ɛ41	499	8	974 983	XXƐ	8	Ɛ03 ƐX7	5ƐX
9	915 41X	3Ɛ1	9	Ɛ7X 872	X07	9	427 106 5X5	518
X	Ɛ22 80Ɛ	307	X	41Ɛ 184 679	923	X	308 Ɛ01	438
Ɛ	413 12Ɛ Ɛ16	21Ɛ	Ɛ	38X 3X0	83Ɛ	Ɛ	50Ɛ 339	356
2410	339 135	135	2450	594 01Ɛ	757	2490	711 693	275
1	546 26X	049	1	799 776	673	1	913 948	194
2	753 2Ɛ7	208 Ɛ63	2	9X3 229	58Ɛ	2	Ɛ15 Ɛ20	0Ɛ3
3	960 25X	X78	3	ƐX8 7Ɛ8	4X8	3	428 118 013	012
4	Ɛ69 116	991	4	420 1Ɛ2 0X4	403	4	31X 025	201 Ɛ31
5	414 175 XX7	8X7	5	3Ɛ7 4X7	320	5	51Ɛ Ɛ56	X50
6	382 792	800	6	600 807	238	6	721 9X6	96Ɛ
7	58Ɛ 392	716	7	805 X43	155	7	923 755	88Ɛ
8	797 XX8	62Ɛ	8	X0X Ɛ98	071	8	Ɛ25 424	7XX
9	9X4 517	544	9	421 014 049	204 Ɛ89	9	429 127 012	709
X	Ɛ20 X5Ɛ	45X	X	219 016	XX7	X	328 71Ɛ	629
Ɛ	415 1Ɛ9 2Ɛ9	374	Ɛ	421 Ɛ01	X02	Ɛ	52X 148	548
2420	405 671	28X	2460	626 903	920	24X0	72Ɛ 694	468
1	611 93Ɛ	1X4	1	82Ɛ 623	838	1	930 Ɛ40	387
2	819 Ɛ23	0Ɛ9	2	X34 25Ɛ	756	2	Ɛ32 307	2X7
3	X26 020	014	3	422 038 9Ɛ5	672	3	42X 133 5Ɛ2	207
4	416 032 034	207 Ɛ29	4	241 467	58Ɛ	4	334 7Ɛ9	126
5	239 Ɛ61	X44	5	445 X36	4X8	5	535 923	047
6	445 9X5	95X	6	64X 322	405	6	736 96X	200 Ɛ66
7	651 743	874	7	852 727	322	7	937 914	X86
8	859 3Ɛ7	78X	8	X56 X49	240	8	Ɛ38 79X	9X7
9	X64 Ɛ85	6X4	9	423 05Ɛ 089	158	9	42Ɛ 139 585	906
X	417 070 669	5ƐƐ	X	263 225	076	X	33X 28Ɛ	826
Ɛ	278 068	516	Ɛ	467 29Ɛ	203 Ɛ94	Ɛ	53X XƐ5	747
2430	483 582	430	2470	66Ɛ 273	XƐ1	24Ɛ0	73Ɛ 640	667
1	68X 9Ɛ2	346	1	873 164	X0X	1	940 0X7	587
2	896 138	262	2	X76 Ɛ72	928	2	Ɛ40 672	4X8
3	XX1 39X	178	3	424 07X 89X	845	3	430 140 Ɛ5X	408
4	418 0X8 556	092	4	282 523	763	4	341 366	328
5	2Ɛ3 628	206 ƐXX	5	486 086	681	5	541 692	249
6	4ƐX 616	Ɛ04	6	689 747	59Ɛ	6	741 91Ɛ	16X
7	705 51X	X1Ɛ	7	891 126	4Ɛ9	7	941 X89	08X
8	910 339	937	8	X94 623	416	8	Ɛ41 Ɛ57	1ƐƐ ƐXƐ
9	Ɛ17 074	851	9	425 097 X39	334	9	431 141 Ɛ46	Ɛ0Ɛ
X	419 121 905	769	X	29Ɛ 171	253	X	341 X55	X31
Ɛ	328 472	684	Ɛ	4X2 404	170	Ɛ	541 886	951

N	Log N	d	N	Log N	d	N	Log N	d
2500	431 741 617	1ƐƐ 872	2540	439 686 950	1Ɛ8 545	2580	445 500 ᘔ63	1Ɛ5 303
1	941 289	794	1	883 295	469	1	6Ɛ6 166	22ᘔ
2	Ɛ40 ᘔ61	6Ɛ4	2	ᘔ7Ɛ 742	391	2	8ᘔƐ 394	153
3	432 140 555	615	3	43ᘔ 077 Ɛ13	2Ɛ4	3	ᘔᘔ4 527	07ᘔ
4	33Ɛ Ɛ6ᘔ	537	4	274 207	218	4	446 099 5ᘔ5	1Ɛ4 Ɛᘔ5
5	53Ɛ 4ᘔ5	458	5	470 423	141	5	292 58ᘔ	Ɛ0Ɛ
6	73ᘔ 941	379	6	668 564	064	6	487 499	ᘔ36
7	93ᘔ 0Ɛᘔ	29ᘔ	7	864 608	1Ɛ7 Ɛ88	7	680 313	960
8	Ɛ39 398	200	8	ᘔ60 594	ᘔƐ0	8	875 073	887
9	433 138 598	121	9	43Ɛ 058 484	ᘔ14	9	ᘔ69 93ᘔ	7Ɛ1
ᘔ	337 6Ɛ9	043	ᘔ	254 298	939	ᘔ	447 062 52Ɛ	718
Ɛ	536 740	1Ɛᘔ Ɛ64	Ɛ	450 015	861	Ɛ	257 047	643
2510	735 6ᘔ4	ᘔ86	2550	647 876	785	2590	44Ɛ 68ᘔ	56ᘔ
1	934 56ᘔ	9ᘔ8	1	843 43Ɛ	6ᘔ9	1	644 038	495
2	Ɛ33 356	909	2	ᘔ3ᘔ Ɛ28	612	2	838 511	400
3	434 132 063	82Ɛ	3	440 036 53ᘔ	536	3	ᘔ30 911	327
4	330 892	751	4	231 ᘔ74	45ᘔ	4	448 025 038	252
5	52Ɛ 423	673	5	429 312	384	5	219 28ᘔ	179
6	729 ᘔ96	594	6	624 696	2ᘔ7	6	411 447	0ᘔ4
7	928 46ᘔ	4Ɛ7	7	81Ɛ 981	211	7	605 52Ɛ	00Ɛ
8	Ɛ26 965	419	8	ᘔ16 Ɛ92	135	8	7Ɛ9 53ᘔ	1Ɛ3 Ɛ37
9	435 125 182	33Ɛ	9	441 012 107	05ᘔ	9	9Ɛ1 475	ᘔ62
ᘔ	323 501	261	ᘔ	209 165	1Ɛ6 Ɛ83	ᘔ	Ɛᘔ5 317	98ᘔ
Ɛ	521 762	183	Ɛ	404 128	ᘔᘔ7	Ɛ	449 199 0ᘔ5	8Ɛ1
2520	71Ɛ 925	0ᘔ6	2560	5ƐƐ 013	ᘔ11	25ᘔ0	390 999	821
1	919 ᘔ0Ɛ	008	1	7Ɛ5 ᘔ24	936	1	584 5Ɛᘔ	748
2	Ɛ17 ᘔ17	1Ɛ9 Ɛ2ᘔ	2	9Ɛ0 75ᘔ	85ᘔ	2	778 146	673
3	436 115 945	ᘔ51	3	Ɛᘔ7 3Ɛ8	784	3	96Ɛ 7Ɛ9	59Ɛ
4	313 796	973	4	442 1ᘔ1 Ɛ80	6ᘔ9	4	Ɛ63 198	507
5	511 549	896	5	398 669	612	5	44ᘔ 156 6ᘔ3	433
6	70Ɛ 223	7Ɛ9	6	593 07Ɛ	537	6	349 Ɛ16	35ᘔ
7	908 ᘔ20	71Ɛ	7	789 5Ɛ6	461	7	541 274	286
8	Ɛ06 53Ɛ	642	8	983 ᘔ57	386	8	734 53ᘔ	1Ɛ2
9	437 103 Ɛ81	565	9	Ɛ7ᘔ 221	2ᘔƐ	9	927 730	11ᘔ
ᘔ	301 526	487	ᘔ	443 174 510	215	ᘔ	Ɛ1ᘔ 84ᘔ	047
Ɛ	4Ɛᘔ 9Ɛ1	3ᘔƐ	Ɛ	36ᘔ 725	13ᘔ	Ɛ	44Ɛ 111 895	1Ɛ2 Ɛ72
2530	6Ɛ8 1ᘔ0	311	2570	564 863	064	25Ɛ0	304 847	ᘔ9ᘔ
1	8Ɛ5 4Ɛ1	235	1	75ᘔ 907	1Ɛ5 Ɛ8ᘔ	1	4Ɛ7 725	ᘔ07
2	ᘔƐ2 726	157	2	954 895	ᘔƐ3	2	6ᘔᘔ 530	932
3	438 0ᘔƐ 881	07Ɛ	3	Ɛ4ᘔ 788	ᘔ19	3	8ᘔ1 262	85Ɛ
4	2ᘔ8 940	1Ɛ8 Ɛᘔ2	4	444 144 5ᘔ5	943	4	ᘔ93 Ɛ01	787
5	4ᘔ5 922	Ɛ05	5	33ᘔ 328	869	5	450 086 688	6Ɛ4
6	6ᘔ2 827	ᘔ28	6	533 Ɛ95	793	6	279 180	620
7	89Ɛ 653	950	7	729 768	6Ɛ8	7	46Ɛ 7ᘔ0	549
8	ᘔ98 3ᘔ3	873	8	923 264	623	8	662 129	475
9	439 095 056	796	9	Ɛ18 887	548	9	854 5ᘔ2	3ᘔ1
ᘔ	291 830	6Ɛᘔ	ᘔ	445 112 213	473	ᘔ	ᘔ46 983	30Ɛ
Ɛ	48ᘔ 32ᘔ	622	Ɛ	307 686	399	Ɛ	451 039 092	237

N	Log N	d	N	Log N	d	N	Log N	d
2600	451 22Ɛ 309	1Ɛ2 163	2640	458 X55 333	1XƐ 0X3	2680	464 57X 20X	1X8 0Ɛ9
1	421 470	091	1	459 044 416	012	1	766 307	02X
2	613 541	1Ɛ1 ƐƐ9	2	233 428	1XX Ɛ42	2	952 335	1X7 Ɛ60
3	805 53X	Ɛ27	3	422 36X	X70	3	Ɛ3X 295	X92
4	9Ɛ7 465	X53	4	611 21X	9X1	4	465 126 167	X04
5	ƐX9 2Ɛ8	980	5	7ƐƐ ƐƐƐ	90Ɛ	5	311 Ɛ6Ɛ	935
6	452 19Ɛ 078	8X9	6	9XX 90X	83Ɛ	6	4Ɛ9 8X4	867
7	390 965	816	7	Ɛ99 549	76Ɛ	7	6X5 54Ɛ	799
8	582 57Ɛ	744	8	45X 188 0Ɛ8	69X	8	891 128	70Ɛ
9	774 103	671	9	376 796	609	9	X78 837	641
X	965 774	599	X	565 1X3	53X	X	466 064 278	573
Ɛ	Ɛ57 151	508	Ɛ	753 721	469	Ɛ	24Ɛ 82Ɛ	4X5
2610	453 148 659	434	2650	941 Ɛ8X	399	2690	437 114	417
1	339 X91	362	1	Ɛ30 367	308	1	622 52Ɛ	349
2	52Ɛ 233	290	2	45Ɛ 11X 673	239	2	809 878	27Ɛ
3	720 503	1Ɛ9	3	308 8Ɛ0	168	3	9Ɛ4 Ɛ37	1Ɛ2
4	911 700	126	4	4Ɛ6 X58	099	4	ƐX0 129	124
5	Ɛ02 826	054	5	6X4 Ɛ35	008	5	467 187 251	056
6	454 0Ɛ3 87X	1Ɛ0 Ɛ82	6	892 Ɛ41	1X9 Ɛ39	6	372 2X7	1X6 Ɛ89
7	2X4 840	XXƐ	7	X80 X7X	X68	7	559 274	XƐƐ
8	495 72Ɛ	X1X	8	460 06X 926	999	8	744 173	X31
9	686 549	947	9	258 703	909	9	92X ƐX4	964
X	877 294	874	X	446 410	839	X	Ɛ15 948	897
Ɛ	X67 Ɛ48	7X3	Ɛ	634 049	76X	Ɛ	468 100 623	809
2620	455 058 72Ɛ	711	2660	821 7Ɛ7	69X	26X0	2X7 230	740
1	249 240	63Ɛ	1	X0Ɛ 295	60X	1	491 970	672
2	439 87Ɛ	569	2	ƐƐ8 8X3	53Ɛ	2	678 422	5X6
3	62X 228	497	3	461 1X6 222	46Ɛ	3	862 X08	518
4	81X 703	405	4	393 691	3X0	4	X49 324	44Ɛ
5	X0X Ɛ08	333	5	580 X71	310	5	469 033 773	382
6	ƐƐƐ 23Ɛ	262	6	76X 181	241	6	219 Ɛ35	2Ɛ5
7	456 1XƐ 4X1	18Ɛ	7	957 402	172	7	404 22X	228
8	39Ɛ 670	0ƐƐ	8	Ɛ44 574	0X2	8	5XX 456	15Ɛ
9	58Ɛ 76Ɛ	028	9	462 131 656	013	9	794 5Ɛ5	092
X	77Ɛ 797	1XƐ Ɛ58	X	31X 669	1X8 Ɛ45	X	97X 687	005
Ɛ	96Ɛ 733	X85	Ɛ	507 5Ɛ2	X75	Ɛ	Ɛ64 690	1X5 Ɛ38
2630	Ɛ5Ɛ 5Ɛ8	9Ɛ5	2670	6Ɛ4 467	9X6	26Ɛ0	46X 14X 608	X70
1	457 14Ɛ 3Ɛ1	922	1	8X1 251	916	1	334 478	9X3
2	33Ɛ 113	852	2	X89 Ɛ67	848	2	51X 25Ɛ	916
3	52X 965	780	3	463 076 7Ɛ3	779	3	703 Ɛ75	84X
4	71X 525	6XƐ	4	263 370	6XƐ	4	8X9 803	781
5	90X 014	61X	5	44Ɛ X5Ɛ	61Ɛ	5	X93 384	6Ɛ4
6	XƐ9 632	549	6	638 47X	551	6	46Ɛ 078 X78	628
7	458 0X8 Ɛ7Ɛ	477	7	824 X0Ɛ	481	7	262 4X4	560
8	298 436	3X7	8	X11 290	3Ɛ4	8	447 X44	493
9	487 821	316	9	ƐƐ9 684	324	9	631 317	407
X	676 Ɛ37	244	X	464 1X5 9X8	256	X	816 722	33X
Ɛ	866 17Ɛ	174	Ɛ	392 042	188	Ɛ	9ƐƐ X60	273

N	Log N	d	N	Log N	d	N	Log N	d
2700	46Ɛ ƐX5 113	1X5 1X6	2740	477 515 09X	1X2 363	2780	482 951 062	19Ɛ 5X8
1	470 18X 2Ɛ9	11X	1	6Ɛ7 441	299	1	Ɛ30 64X	523
2	373 417	052	2	899 71X	213	2	483 10Ɛ Ɛ71	460
3	558 469	1X4 Ɛ85	3	X7Ɛ 931	149	3	2XƐ 411	399
4	741 432	XƐX	4	478 061 X7X	083	4	48X 7XX	314
5	926 330	X32	5	243 Ɛ41	1X1 ƐƐX	5	669 Ɛ02	251
6	Ɛ0Ɛ 162	966	6	425 Ɛ3Ɛ	Ɛ33	6	849 153	189
7	471 0Ɛ3 Ɛ08	89X	7	607 X72	X6X	7	X28 320	106
8	298 7X6	812	8	7X9 920	9X5	8	484 007 426	042
9	481 3Ɛ8	747	9	98Ɛ 705	91Ɛ	9	1X6 468	19X Ɛ7Ɛ
X	665 Ɛ43	67X	X	Ɛ71 424	855	X	385 427	XƐ7
Ɛ	84X 601	5Ɛ3	Ɛ	479 153 079	790	Ɛ	564 322	X34
2710	X32 ƐƐ4	527	2750	334 849	706	2790	743 156	971
1	472 017 51Ɛ	460	1	516 353	641	1	921 Ɛ07	8X9
2	1ƐƐ 97Ɛ	394	2	6Ɛ7 994	578	2	Ɛ00 7Ɛ4	827
3	3X4 153	309	3	899 350	4Ɛ2	3	485 09Ɛ 41Ɛ	762
4	588 460	241	4	X7X 842	429	4	279 Ɛ81	6X0
5	770 6X1	176	5	47X 060 06Ɛ	363	5	458 661	619
6	954 857	0XƐ	6	241 412	29Ɛ	6	637 07X	555
7	Ɛ38 946	023	7	422 6Ɛ1	215	7	815 613	493
8	473 120 969	1X3 Ɛ57	8	603 906	151	8	9Ɛ3 XX6	40Ɛ
9	304 904	X91	9	7X4 X57	087	9	Ɛ92 2Ɛ5	349
X	4X8 795	X06	X	985 Ɛ22	002	X	486 170 642	286
Ɛ	690 59Ɛ	93X	Ɛ	Ɛ66 Ɛ24	1X0 Ɛ39	Ɛ	34X 908	202
2720	874 319	873	2760	47Ɛ 147 X61	X75	27X0	528 Ɛ0X	140
1	X57 Ɛ90	7X8	1	328 916	9XƐ	1	707 04X	07X
2	474 03Ɛ 778	721	2	509 705	927	2	8X5 108	199 ƐƐ6
3	223 299	657	3	6XX 430	862	3	X83 102	Ɛ34
4	406 934	58Ɛ	4	88Ɛ 092	799	4	487 061 036	X71
5	5XX 303	504	5	X6Ɛ 86Ɛ	714	5	23X XX7	9XƐ
6	791 807	43X	6	480 050 383	650	6	418 896	928
7	975 045	373	7	230 X13	587	7	5Ɛ6 602	865
8	Ɛ58 3Ɛ8	2X8	8	411 39X	503	8	794 267	7X3
9	475 13Ɛ 6X4	221	9	5Ɛ1 8X1	43X	9	971 X4X	721
X	322 905	157	X	792 11Ɛ	375	X	Ɛ4Ɛ 56Ɛ	65X
Ɛ	505 X60	091	Ɛ	972 494	2Ɛ2	Ɛ	488 129 009	598
2730	6X8 Ɛ31	005	2770	Ɛ52 786	228	27Ɛ0	306 5X5	515
1	88Ɛ Ɛ36	1X2 Ɛ3Ɛ	1	481 132 9Ɛ2	165	1	4X3 XƐX	454
2	X72 X75	X75	2	312 Ɛ57	0X0	2	681 352	391
3	476 055 92X	9XƐ	3	4Ɛ3 037	018	3	85X 723	30X
4	238 719	924	4	693 053	19Ɛ Ɛ54	4	X37 X31	249
5	41Ɛ 441	859	5	872 ƐX7	X8Ɛ	5	489 015 07X	187
6	602 09X	794	6	X52 X76	X07	6	1Ɛ2 245	105
7	7X4 872	709	7	482 032 881	944	7	38Ɛ 34X	042
8	987 37Ɛ	643	8	212 605	87Ɛ	8	568 390	198 Ɛ81
9	Ɛ69 X02	579	9	3Ɛ2 284	7Ɛ7	9	745 351	XƐƐ
X	477 150 37Ɛ	4Ɛ3	X	591 X7Ɛ	734	X	922 250	X38
Ɛ	332 872	428	Ɛ	771 5Ɛ3	66Ɛ	Ɛ	XƐƐ 088	977

N	Log N	d	N	Log N	d	N	Log N	d
2800	48X 097 X43	198 8Ɛ6	2840	495 334 358	196 084	2880	4X0 4X4 ƐƐ5	193 513
1	274 739	833	1	50X 420	005	1	678 508	455
2	451 370	772	2	6X4 425	195 Ɛ46	2	84Ɛ 961	397
3	629 Ɛ22	6Ɛ0	3	87X 36Ɛ	X85	3	X23 138	31X
4	806 612	62Ɛ	4	X54 234	X06	4	ƐƐ6 456	260
5	9X3 041	569	5	496 02X 03X	947	5	4X1 189 6Ɛ6	1X2
6	Ɛ7Ɛ 5XX	4X7	6	203 985	886	6	360 898	125
7	48Ɛ 157 X95	426	7	399 64Ɛ	808	7	533 X01	067
8	334 2ƐƐ	364	8	573 257	748	8	706 X68	192 ƐXX
9	510 663	2X3	9	748 9X3	688	9	899 X56	Ɛ30
X	6X8 946	222	X	922 46Ɛ	609	X	X70 986	X73
Ɛ	884 Ɛ68	160	Ɛ	XƐ7 X78	54X	Ɛ	4X2 043 839	9Ɛ5
2810	X61 108	09Ɛ	2850	497 091 406	48Ɛ	2890	216 632	938
1	490 039 1X7	01X	1	266 895	40Ɛ	1	3X9 36X	87X
2	215 205	197 Ɛ59	2	440 0X4	350	2	580 028	802
3	3Ɛ1 162	X97	3	615 434	291	3	752 82X	744
4	589 039	X17	4	7XX 705	211	4	925 372	687
5	764 X54	955	5	983 916	153	5	XƐ7 X39	60X
6	940 7X9	894	6	Ɛ58 X69	094	6	4X3 08X 447	550
7	Ɛ18 481	814	7	498 131 Ɛ41	014	7	260 997	494
8	491 0Ɛ4 095	752	8	306 Ɛ55	194 Ɛ56	8	433 26Ɛ	416
9	28Ɛ 827	691	9	49Ɛ XXƐ	X97	9	605 685	35X
X	467 2Ɛ8	611	X	674 986	X17	X	797 X23	2X0
Ɛ	642 909	550	Ɛ	849 7X1	959	Ɛ	96X 103	224
2820	81X 259	48X	2860	X22 53X	89X	28X0	Ɛ40 327	166
1	9Ɛ5 727	40Ɛ	1	ƐƐ7 218	820	1	4X4 112 491	0XX
2	Ɛ90 Ɛ36	349	2	499 18Ɛ X38	760	2	2X4 57Ɛ	031
3	492 168 283	289	3	364 598	6X2	3	476 5Ɛ0	191 Ɛ75
4	343 550	208	4	539 07X	624	4	648 565	XƐ7
5	51X 758	148	5	711 6X2	565	5	81X 460	X3Ɛ
6	6Ɛ5 8X4	087	6	8X6 047	4X6	6	9Ɛ0 29Ɛ	982
7	890 96Ɛ	007	7	X7X 531	427	7	Ɛ82 061	906
8	X67 976	196 Ɛ46	8	49X 052 958	36X	8	4X5 153 967	849
9	493 042 900	X86	9	227 106	2XX	9	325 5Ɛ4	790
X	219 786	X05	X	3ƐƐ 3Ɛ4	231	X	4Ɛ7 184	714
Ɛ	3Ɛ4 58Ɛ	945	Ɛ	593 625	172	Ɛ	688 898	658
2830	58Ɛ 314	885	2870	767 797	0Ɛ3	28Ɛ0	85X 334	59Ɛ
1	765 Ɛ99	805	1	93Ɛ 88X	036	1	X2Ɛ 913	522
2	940 7X2	744	2	Ɛ13 904	193 Ɛ77	2	4X6 001 235	467
3	Ɛ17 326	684	3	49Ɛ 0X7 87Ɛ	XƐ9	3	192 6X0	3XX
4	494 0Ɛ1 9XX	605	4	27Ɛ 778	X3X	4	363 X8X	331
5	288 3Ɛ3	544	5	453 5Ɛ6	981	5	535 1ƐƐ	276
6	462 937	484	6	627 377	903	6	706 475	1Ɛ9
7	639 1ƐƐ	404	7	7ƐƐ 07X	844	7	897 672	142
8	813 603	344	8	992 902	787	8	X68 7Ɛ4	085
9	9X9 947	284	9	Ɛ66 489	708	9	4X7 039 879	009
X	Ɛ84 00Ɛ	204	X	4X0 139 Ɛ95	64Ɛ	X	20X 886	190 Ɛ51
Ɛ	495 15X 213	145	Ɛ	311 624	591	Ɛ	39Ɛ 817	X95

N	Log N	d	N	Log N	d	N	Log N	d
2900	4X7 570 6Ɛ0	190 X19	2940	4Ɛ2 555 667	18X 399	2980	4Ɛ9 45X 418	187 X0X
1	741 509	961	1	723 X44	322	1	626 226	956
2	912 26X	8X5	2	8Ɛ2 166	268	2	7Ɛ1 Ɛ80	8X1
3	XX2 Ɛ53	82X	3	X80 412	1Ɛ2	3	979 861	829
4	4X8 073 781	771	4	4Ɛ3 04X 604	139	4	Ɛ45 48X	775
5	244 332	6Ɛ6	5	218 741	082	5	4ƐX 111 043	701
6	414 X28	63X	6	3X6 803	008	6	298 744	649
7	5X5 466	583	7	574 80Ɛ	189 Ɛ53	7	464 191	595
8	775 X29	507	8	742 762	X99	8	62Ɛ 766	521
9	946 334	44Ɛ	9	910 63Ɛ	X22	9	7Ɛ7 087	468
X	Ɛ16 783	394	X	X9X 461	96X	X	982 533	3Ɛ5
Ɛ	4X9 0X6 Ɛ57	318	Ɛ	4Ɛ4 068 20Ɛ	8Ɛ3	Ɛ	Ɛ49 928	341
2910	277 273	260	2950	235 Ɛ02	83X	2990	4ƐƐ 115 069	288
1	447 513	1X6	1	403 740	784	1	2X0 335	215
2	617 6Ɛ9	129	2	591 304	70Ɛ	2	467 54X	161
3	7X7 826	073	3	75X X13	655	3	632 6XƐ	0XX
4	977 899	18Ɛ ƐƐ7	4	928 468	59Ɛ	4	7Ɛ9 799	035
5	Ɛ47 894	Ɛ40	5	XƐ5 X47	526	5	984 812	186 Ɛ82
6	4XX 117 814	X84	6	4Ɛ5 083 371	471	6	Ɛ4Ɛ 794	Ɛ0X
7	2X7 698	X09	7	250 822	3Ɛ7	7	500 116 6X2	X57
8	477 4X5	952	8	41X 019	341	8	2X1 539	9X2
9	647 237	897	9	5X7 35X	289	9	468 31Ɛ	930
X	816 Ɛ12	820	X	774 627	213	X	633 04Ɛ	877
Ɛ	9X6 732	765	Ɛ	941 83X	15X	Ɛ	7Ɛ9 906	804
2920	Ɛ76 297	6XX	2960	Ɛ0X 998	0X4	29X0	984 50X	751
1	4XƐ 145 985	633	1	4Ɛ6 097 X80	030	1	Ɛ4Ɛ 05Ɛ	699
2	315 3Ɛ8	577	2	264 XƐ0	188 Ɛ76	2	501 115 738	626
3	4X4 973	501	3	431 X66	Ɛ01	3	2X0 162	573
4	674 274	446	4	5ƐX 967	X48	4	466 715	4ƐƐ
5	843 6ƐX	38Ɛ	5	787 7Ɛ3	993	5	631 014	447
6	X12 X89	315	6	954 586	91X	6	7Ɛ7 45Ɛ	395
7	ƐX2 1X2	259	7	Ɛ21 2X4	865	7	981 834	321
8	4Ɛ0 171 43Ɛ	1X3	8	4Ɛ7 0X9 Ɛ49	7Ɛ0	8	Ɛ47 Ɛ55	26X
9	340 622	128	9	276 739	737	9	502 112 203	1Ɛ7
X	50Ɛ 74X	072	X	443 274	683	X	298 3ƐX	144
Ɛ	69X 800	18X ƐƐ7	Ɛ	60Ɛ 937	609	Ɛ	462 542	091
2930	869 7Ɛ7	Ɛ40	2970	798 344	555	29Ɛ0	628 613	01X
1	X38 737	X86	1	964 899	4X0	1	7Ɛ2 631	185 Ɛ66
2	4Ɛ1 007 601	X0Ɛ	2	Ɛ31 179	427	2	978 597	XƐ4
3	196 410	955	3	4Ɛ8 0Ɛ9 5X4	373	3	Ɛ42 48Ɛ	X41
4	365 165	89X	4	285 957	2ƐX	4	503 108 310	98X
5	533 X43	824	5	452 055	245	5	292 09X	917
6	702 667	76X	6	61X 29X	191	6	457 9Ɛ5	864
7	891 215	6Ɛ3	7	7X6 46Ɛ	118	7	621 659	7Ɛ1
8	X5Ɛ 908	639	8	972 587	064	8	7X7 24X	73Ɛ
9	4Ɛ2 02X 345	583	9	Ɛ3X 62Ɛ	187 ƐXƐ	9	970 989	688
X	1Ɛ8 908	509	X	4Ɛ9 106 61X	Ɛ37	X	Ɛ36 455	615
Ɛ	387 215	452	Ɛ	292 555	X83	Ɛ	504 0ƐƐ X6X	562

N	Log N	d	N	Log N	d	N	Log N	d
2X00	504 285 410	185 4Ɛ0	2X40	50Ɛ 014 9ƐX	183 03Ɛ	2X80	515 88Ɛ 075	180 836
1	44X 900	43X	1	197 X39	182 Ɛ8X	1	X4Ɛ 8XƐ	786
2	614 13X	386	2	35X X07	Ɛ1X	2	516 010 475	717
3	799 504	315	3	521 925	X68	3	190 Ɛ90	668
4	962 819	261	4	6X4 791	9Ɛ8	4	351 638	5Ɛ8
5	Ɛ27 X7X	1Ɛ0	5	867 589	947	5	512 034	54X
6	505 0Ɛ1 06X	138	6	X2X 314	896	6	692 582	49X
7	276 1X6	087	7	ƐƐ0 ƐXX	825	7	852 X60	42Ɛ
8	43Ɛ 271	014	8	510 173 813	775	8	X13 28Ɛ	380
9	604 285	184 Ɛ62	9	336 388	704	9	Ɛ93 64Ɛ	311
X	789 227	XƐ0	X	4Ɛ8 X90	654	X	517 153 960	263
Ɛ	952 117	X39	Ɛ	67Ɛ 524	5X3	Ɛ	314 003	1Ɛ3
2X10	Ɛ16 Ɛ54	987	2X50	841 Ɛ07	532	2X90	494 1Ɛ6	144
1	506 09Ɛ 91Ɛ	915	1	X04 439	482	1	654 33X	095
2	264 634	863	2	Ɛ86 8ƐƐ	411	2	814 413	027
3	429 297	7Ɛ1	3	511 149 110	361	3	994 43X	17Ɛ Ɛ77
4	5Ɛ1 X88	73X	4	30Ɛ 471	2Ɛ1	4	Ɛ54 3Ɛ5	Ɛ09
5	776 606	689	5	491 762	240	5	518 114 302	X5X
6	93Ɛ 093	617	6	653 9X2	190	6	294 160	9Ɛ0
7	Ɛ03 6XX	564	7	815 Ɛ72	120	7	453 Ɛ50	941
8	507 088 052	4Ɛ3	8	998 092	06Ɛ	8	613 891	892
9	250 545	441	9	Ɛ5X 141	181 ƐƐƐ	9	793 563	823
X	414 986	38Ɛ	X	512 120 140	Ɛ4Ɛ	X	953 186	775
Ɛ	599 155	319	Ɛ	2X2 08Ɛ	X9Ɛ	Ɛ	Ɛ12 93Ɛ	706
2X20	761 472	268	2X60	463 Ɛ6X	X2X	2XX0	519 092 445	658
1	925 71X	1Ɛ6	1	625 998	97Ɛ	1	251 XX1	5X9
2	XX9 914	144	2	7X7 757	90X	2	411 48X	53Ɛ
3	508 071 X58	092	3	969 465	85X	3	590 X09	490
4	235 Ɛ2X	021	4	Ɛ2Ɛ 103	7XƐ	4	750 299	422
5	3Ɛ9 Ɛ4Ɛ	183 Ɛ6Ɛ	5	513 0Ɛ0 8Ɛ2	73X	5	90Ɛ 6ƐƐ	374
6	581 XƐX	XƐ9	6	272 430	68Ɛ	6	X8X X73	305
7	745 9Ɛ7	X48	7	433 XƐƐ	61X	7	51X 04X 178	257
8	909 843	997	8	5Ɛ5 519	56Ɛ	8	209 413	1X9
9	X91 61X	925	9	776 X88	4ƐƐ	9	388 600	13X
X	509 055 343	873	X	938 387	44Ɛ	X	547 73X	090
Ɛ	218 ƐƐ6	802	Ɛ	XƐ9 816	3X0	Ɛ	706 80X	022
2X30	3X0 7Ɛ8	751	2X70	514 07X ƐƐ6	32Ɛ	2XƐ0	885 830	17X Ɛ74
1	564 349	6X0	1	240 325	280	1	X44 7X4	Ɛ06
2	727 X29	62X	2	401 5X5	211	2	51Ɛ 003 6XX	X58
3	8XƐ 457	579	3	582 7Ɛ6	160	3	182 546	9XX
4	X72 X14	507	4	743 956	0Ɛ1	4	341 334	93Ɛ
5	50X 036 31Ɛ	457	5	904 X47	042	5	500 073	892
6	1Ɛ9 776	3X5	6	X85 X89	180 Ɛ92	6	67X 945	824
7	380 Ɛ5Ɛ	335	7	515 046 X5Ɛ	Ɛ22	7	839 569	776
8	544 294	283	8	207 981	X73	8	9Ɛ8 123	708
9	707 557	212	9	388 834	X04	9	Ɛ76 82Ɛ	65X
X	88X 769	161	X	549 638	954	X	520 135 289	5Ɛ0
Ɛ	X51 90X	0Ɛ0	Ɛ	70X 390	8X5	Ɛ	2Ɛ3 879	543

N	Log N	d	N	Log N	d	N	Log N	d
2Ɛ00	520 472 200	17χ 495	2Ɛ40	526 Ɛ84 34χ	178 197	2Ɛ80	531 607 549	175 Ɛ3χ
1	630 695	427	1	527 140 525	12Ɛ	1	781 487	χ93
2	7χχ Ɛ00	379	2	2Ɛ8 654	083	2	937 35χ	χ28
3	969 279	310	3	474 717	016	3	χƐ1 186	982
4	Ɛ27 589	262	4	630 731	177 Ɛ6χ	4	532 066 Ɛ48	917
5	521 0χ5 82Ɛ	1Ɛ5	5	7χ8 69Ɛ	Ɛ03	5	220 863	870
6	263 χ24	147	6	964 5χ2	χ56	6	396 513	806
7	421 Ɛ6Ɛ	09χ	7	Ɛ20 438	9χχ	7	550 119	75Ɛ
8	5χ0 049	030	8	528 098 226	943	8	705 878	6Ɛ5
9	75χ 079	179 Ɛ82	9	253 Ɛ69	896	9	87Ɛ 371	64Ɛ
χ	918 03Ɛ	Ɛ16	χ	40Ɛ 843	82Ɛ	χ	χ34 χ00	5χ4
Ɛ	χ95 Ɛ55	χ67	Ɛ	587 472	782	Ɛ	Ɛχχ 3χ4	539
2Ɛ10	522 053 χ00	9ƐƐ	2Ɛ50	743 034	717	2Ɛ90	533 163 921	494
1	211 7ƐƐ	951	1	8Ɛχ 74Ɛ	66Ɛ	1	319 1Ɛ5	429
2	38Ɛ 550	8χ4	2	χ76 1Ɛχ	603	2	492 622	382
3	549 234	836	3	529 031 801	558	3	647 9χ4	319
4	706 χ6χ	78χ	4	1χ9 159	4Ɛ0	4	801 101	272
5	884 638	720	5	364 649	444	5	976 373	208
6	χ42 158	673	6	51Ɛ χ91	398	6	Ɛ2Ɛ 57Ɛ	162
7	ƐƐƐ 80Ɛ	606	7	697 269	331	7	534 0χ4 721	0Ɛ8
8	523 179 215	558	8	852 59χ	285	8	259 819	051
9	336 771	4Ɛ0	9	χ09 863	21χ	9	412 86χ	174 Ɛχ8
χ	4Ɛ4 061	443	χ	Ɛ84 χ81	172	χ	587 856	Ɛ41
Ɛ	671 4χ4	395	Ɛ	52χ 140 033	107	Ɛ	740 797	χ98
2Ɛ20	82χ 879	329	2Ɛ60	2Ɛ7 13χ	05Ɛ	2Ɛχ0	8Ɛ5 673	χ31
1	9χ7 Ɛχ6	280	1	472 199	176 Ɛ24	1	χ6χ 4χ4	988
2	Ɛ65 266	213	2	629 191	Ɛ49	2	535 023 270	921
3	524 122 479	165	3	7χ4 11χ	χχ1	3	197 Ɛ91	878
4	29Ɛ 622	0Ɛχ	4	95χ ƐƐƐ	χ36	4	350 849	812
5	458 720	050	5	Ɛ15 χ35	98χ	5	505 45Ɛ	768
6	615 770	178 Ɛχ3	6	52Ɛ 090 803	923	6	67χ 007	702
7	792 753	Ɛ37	7	247 526	878	7	832 709	659
8	94Ɛ 68χ	χ8χ	8	402 1χ2	811	8	9χ7 166	5Ɛ2
9	Ɛ08 558	χ21	9	578 9Ɛ3	765	9	Ɛ5Ɛ 758	549
χ	525 085 379	975	χ	733 558	6ƐƐ	χ	536 114 0χ5	4χ4
Ɛ	242 132	908	Ɛ	8χχ 057	653	Ɛ	288 589	439
2Ɛ30	3Ɛχ χ3χ	860	2Ɛ70	χ64 6χχ	5χ8	2ƐƐ0	440 χ06	394
1	577 69χ	7Ɛ3	1	530 01Ɛ 096	541	1	5Ɛ5 19χ	32Ɛ
2	734 291	746	2	195 617	496	2	769 509	284
3	8Ɛ0 χ17	69χ	3	34Ɛ χƐ1	430	3	921 791	220
4	χ69 4Ɛ5	631	4	506 321	384	4	χ95 9Ɛ1	175
5	526 025 Ɛ26	586	5	680 6χ5	319	5	537 049 Ɛ66	111
6	1χ2 4Ɛ0	518	6	836 χ02	272	6	202 077	067
7	35χ χ08	470	7	9Ɛ1 074	208	7	376 122	001
8	517 278	404	8	Ɛ67 280	160	8	52χ 123	173 Ɛ58
9	693 680	358	9	531 121 420	0Ɛ6	9	6χ2 07Ɛ	χƐ3
χ	84Ɛ χ18	2χƐ	χ	297 516	04Ɛ	χ	855 Ɛ72	χ49
Ɛ	χ08 107	243	Ɛ	451 565	175 Ɛχ4	Ɛ	χ09 9ƐƐ	9χ4

N	Log N	d	N	Log N	d	N	Log N	d
3000	537 Ɛ81 7X3	173 93Ɛ	3040	542 470 X00	171 799	3080	548 896 X4X	16Ɛ 692
1	538 135 522	896	1	622 599	735	1	X46 520	62Ɛ
2	2X9 1Ɛ8	830	2	794 112	691	2	ƐƐ5 Ɛ4Ɛ	589
3	460 X28	787	3	945 7X3	629	3	549 165 518	526
4	614 5Ɛ3	722	4	XƐ7 210	586	4	314 X42	484
5	788 115	679	5	543 068 796	522	5	484 306	421
6	93Ɛ 792	614	6	21X 0Ɛ8	47X	6	633 727	37Ɛ
7	XƐ3 1X6	56Ɛ	7	38Ɛ 576	416	7	7X2 XX6	319
8	539 066 755	506	8	540 990	373	8	952 203	277
9	21X 05Ɛ	461	9	6Ɛ2 143	310	9	Ɛ01 47X	214
X	391 500	3Ɛ7	X	863 453	268	X	54X 070 692	173
Ɛ	544 8Ɛ7	353	Ɛ	X14 6ƐƐ	204	Ɛ	21Ɛ 845	110
3010	6Ɛ8 04X	2XX	3050	Ɛ85 903	161	3090	38X 955	06X
1	86Ɛ 338	245	1	544 136 X64	0Ɛ9	1	539 X03	007
2	X22 581	1X0	2	2X7 Ɛ61	056	2	6X8 X0X	16X Ɛ66
3	Ɛ95 761	138	3	458 ƐƐ7	170 ƐƐ2	3	857 974	Ɛ04
4	53X 148 899	092	4	609 ƐX9	Ɛ4Ɛ	4	X06 878	X61
5	2ƐƐ 96Ɛ	02X	5	77X Ɛ38	XX8	5	Ɛ75 719	X00
6	472 999	172 Ɛ85	6	92Ɛ X24	X44	6	54Ɛ 124 519	959
7	625 962	Ɛ21	7	XX0 868	9X1	7	293 276	8Ɛ8
8	798 883	X78	8	545 051 649	93X	8	441 Ɛ72	856
9	94Ɛ 73Ɛ	X13	9	202 387	896	9	5Ɛ0 808	7Ɛ4
X	Ɛ02 552	96X	X	373 061	834	X	75Ɛ 400	752
Ɛ	53Ɛ 075 300	906	Ɛ	523 895	790	Ɛ	909 Ɛ52	6Ɛ0
3020	228 006	861	3060	694 465	728	30X0	X78 642	64X
1	39X 867	7Ɛ9	1	844 Ɛ91	686	1	550 027 090	5X9
2	551 464	754	2	9Ɛ5 657	623	2	195 679	547
3	703 ƐƐ8	6Ɛ0	3	Ɛ66 07X	57Ɛ	3	344 004	4X5
4	876 6X8	648	4	546 116 639	519	4	4Ɛ2 4X9	443
5	X29 134	5X3	5	286 Ɛ56	476	5	660 930	3X2
6	Ɛ9Ɛ 717	53X	6	437 410	412	6	80Ɛ 112	340
7	540 152 055	497	7	5X7 822	370	7	979 452	29X
8	304 530	431	8	757 Ɛ92	308	8	Ɛ27 730	239
9	476 961	38X	9	908 29X	266	9	551 095 969	198
X	629 12Ɛ	325	X	X78 544	203	X	243 Ɛ45	135
Ɛ	79Ɛ 454	282	Ɛ	547 028 747	160	Ɛ	3Ɛ2 07X	095
3030	951 716	219	3070	198 8X7	0Ɛ9	30Ɛ0	560 153	032
1	Ɛ03 933	174	1	348 9X4	056	1	70X 185	169 Ɛ92
2	541 075 XX7	111	2	4Ɛ8 X3X	16Ɛ ƐƐ4	2	878 157	Ɛ30
3	227 ƐƐ8	068	3	668 X32	Ɛ51	3	X26 087	X8X
4	39X 064	005	4	818 983	XXX	4	Ɛ93 Ɛ55	X29
5	550 069	171 Ɛ60	5	988 871	X47	5	552 141 982	988
6	702 009	XƐ9	6	Ɛ38 6Ɛ8	9X5	6	2XƐ 74X	927
7	873 Ɛ06	X54	7	548 0X8 4X1	942	7	459 475	885
8	X25 95X	9Ɛ0	8	258 223	8X0	8	607 13X	824
9	Ɛ97 74X	949	9	407 Ɛ03	839	9	774 962	783
X	542 149 497	8X4	X	577 740	796	X	922 525	721
Ɛ	2ƐƐ 17Ɛ	841	Ɛ	727 316	734	Ɛ	X90 046	681

N	Log N	d	N	Log N	d	N	Log N	d
3100	553 039 707	169 61Ɛ	3140	559 31X 937	167 600	3180	563 540 1Ɛ7	165 633
1	1X7 126	57X	1	486 337	560	1	6X5 82X	594
2	354 6X4	519	2	631 897	501	2	84Ɛ 202	536
3	502 001	478	3	799 198	461	3	9Ɛ4 738	497
4	66Ɛ 479	417	4	944 639	401	4	Ɛ5X 013	438
5	818 894	376	5	XXƐ X3X	361	5	564 103 44Ɛ	39Ɛ
6	986 04X	315	6	55X 057 19Ɛ	302	6	268 82X	340
7	Ɛ33 363	274	7	202 4X1	262	7	411 Ɛ6X	2X1
8	554 0X0 617	213	8	369 743	202	8	577 24Ɛ	243
9	249 82X	172	9	514 945	163	9	720 492	1X5
X	3Ɛ6 9X0	111	X	67Ɛ XX8	103	X	885 677	146
Ɛ	563 XƐ1	070	Ɛ	826 ƐXƐ	064	Ɛ	X2X 801	0X8
3110	710 Ɛ61	010	3150	992 053	004	3190	Ɛ93 8X9	04X
1	879 Ɛ71	168 Ɛ6Ɛ	1	Ɛ39 057	166 Ɛ65	1	565 138 937	164 ƐXƐ
2	X26 Ɛ20	Ɛ0X	2	55Ɛ 0X4 000	Ɛ05	2	2X1 926	Ɛ52
3	Ɛ93 X2X	X69	3	24X Ɛ05	X65	3	446 878	XƐ3
4	555 140 897	X09	4	3Ɛ5 96X	X07	4	5XƐ 76Ɛ	X55
5	2X9 6X4	968	5	560 775	967	5	754 604	9Ɛ7
6	456 450	907	6	707 520	907	6	8Ɛ9 3ƐƐ	959
7	603 157	867	7	872 227	868	7	X62 158	8ƐX
8	76Ɛ X02	806	8	X18 X93	809	8	566 006 X56	861
9	918 608	765	9	Ɛ83 6X0	76X	9	16Ɛ 6Ɛ7	802
X	X85 171	705	X	560 12X 24X	70X	X	314 2Ɛ9	765
Ɛ	556 031 876	664	Ɛ	294 958	66Ɛ	Ɛ	478 X62	706
3120	19X 31X	604	3160	43Ɛ 407	610	31X0	621 568	669
1	346 922	564	1	5X5 X17	571	1	786 015	60Ɛ
2	4Ɛ3 286	503	2	750 388	511	2	92X 624	570
3	65Ɛ 789	462	3	8Ɛ6 899	473	3	X92 Ɛ94	513
4	808 02Ɛ	403	4	X61 150	413	4	567 037 4X7	475
5	974 432	362	5	561 007 563	374	5	19Ɛ 960	417
6	Ɛ20 794	301	6	171 917	315	6	344 177	37X
7	557 088 X95	261	7	318 030	277	7	4X8 535	31Ɛ
8	235 136	201	8	482 2X7	217	8	650 854	282
9	3X1 337	161	9	628 502	178	9	7Ɛ4 Ɛ16	224
X	549 498	100	X	792 67X	119	X	959 13X	187
Ɛ	6Ɛ5 598	061	Ɛ	938 797	07X	Ɛ	Ɛ01 305	129
3130	861 639	000	3170	XX2 855	020	31Ɛ0	568 065 432	08Ɛ
1	X09 639	167 Ɛ60	1	562 048 875	165 Ɛ80	1	209 501	031
2	Ɛ75 599	Ɛ00	2	1Ɛ2 835	Ɛ22	2	371 532	163 Ɛ94
3	558 121 499	X5Ɛ	3	358 757	X83	3	515 506	Ɛ36
4	289 338	X00	4	502 61X	X24	4	679 440	X99
5	435 138	960	5	668 442	986	5	821 319	X3Ɛ
6	5X0 X98	8ƐƐ	6	812 208	926	6	985 158	9X2
7	748 797	860	7	977 Ɛ32	888	7	Ɛ28 Ɛ3X	944
8	8Ɛ4 437	800	8	Ɛ21 7ƐX	829	8	569 090 882	8X7
9	X60 037	760	9	563 087 427	78Ɛ	9	234 569	849
X	559 007 797	700	X	230 ƐƐ6	730	X	398 1Ɛ6	7Ɛ0
Ɛ	173 297	660	Ɛ	396 726	691	Ɛ	53Ɛ 9X6	753

N	Log N	d	N	Log N	d	N	Log N	d
3200	569 6χ3 539	163 6Ɛ5	3240	573 78χ 308	161 806	3280	579 7Ɛχ 250	15Ɛ 964
1	847 032	658	1	92Ɛ Ɛ12	76χ	1	959 Ɛ24	909
2	9χχ 68χ	5Ɛχ	2	χ91 680	712	2	χƐ9 901	872
3	Ɛ52 088	562	3	574 033 192	676	3	57χ 059 573	817
4	56χ 0Ɛ5 62χ	504	4	194 848	61χ	4	1Ɛ9 18χ	780
5	258 Ɛ32	467	5	336 266	581	5	358 94χ	726
6	400 399	409	6	497 827	526	6	4Ɛ8 474	68χ
7	563 7χ6	371	7	639 151	48χ	7	657 Ɛ42	634
8	706 Ɛ57	313	8	79χ 61Ɛ	432	8	7Ɛ7 576	599
9	86χ 26χ	277	9	93Ɛ χ51	396	9	956 Ɛ53	542
χ	χ11 525	219	χ	χχ1 227	33χ	χ	χƐ6 495	4χ8
Ɛ	Ɛ74 742	180	Ɛ	575 042 565	2χ2	Ɛ	57Ɛ 055 981	450
3210	56Ɛ 117 902	123	3250	1χ3 847	246	3290	1Ɛ5 211	3Ɛ6
1	27χ χ25	086	1	344 χ91	1χƐ	1	354 607	360
2	421 χχƐ	029	2	4χ6 080	152	2	4Ɛ3 967	304
3	584 Ɛ18	162 Ɛ90	3	647 212	0Ɛ7	3	653 06Ɛ	26χ
4	727 χχ8	Ɛ33	4	7χ8 309	05Ɛ	4	7Ɛ2 319	214
5	88χ χ1Ɛ	χ96	5	949 368	004	5	951 531	179
6	χ31 8Ɛ5	χ3χ	6	χχχ 370	160 Ɛ67	6	χƐ0 6χχ	122
7	Ɛ94 733	9χ0	7	576 04Ɛ 317	Ɛ10	7	580 04Ɛ 810	088
8	570 137 513	944	8	1Ɛ0 227	χ75	8	1χχ 898	031
9	29χ 257	8χ6	9	351 0χ0	χ18	9	349 909	15χ Ɛ97
χ	440 Ɛ41	84χ	χ	4Ɛ1 χ28	982	χ	4χ8 8χ4	Ɛ41
Ɛ	5χ3 78Ɛ	7Ɛ2	Ɛ	652 87χ	925	Ɛ	647 825	χχ6
3220	746 381	754	3260	7Ɛ3 5χ3	88χ	32χ0	7χ6 70Ɛ	χ4Ɛ
1	8χ8 Ɛ15	6Ɛ8	1	954 271	832	1	945 55χ	9Ɛ6
2	χ4Ɛ 611	65Ɛ	2	χƐ4 χχ3	797	2	χχ4 354	95Ɛ
3	ƐƐ2 070	602	3	577 055 67χ	740	3	581 043 0Ɛ3	904
4	571 154 672	566	4	1Ɛ6 1Ɛχ	6χ4	4	1χ1 9Ɛ7	86χ
5	2Ɛ7 018	509	5	356 8χ2	648	5	340 665	814
6	459 525	471	6	4Ɛ7 32χ	5Ɛ2	6	49Ɛ 279	77χ
7	5ƐƐ 996	414	7	657 920	555	7	639 χ37	724
8	762 1χχ	377	8	7Ɛ8 275	4ƐƐ	8	798 55Ɛ	689
9	904 565	31Ɛ	9	958 774	463	9	937 028	633
χ	χ66 884	282	χ	χƐ9 017	407	χ	χ95 65Ɛ	599
Ɛ	572 008 Ɛ46	226	Ɛ	578 059 422	371	Ɛ	582 034 038	542
3230	16Ɛ 170	18χ	3270	1Ɛ9 793	315	32Ɛ0	192 57χ	4χ9
1	311 33χ	131	1	359 χχ8	27χ	1	330 χ67	453
2	473 46Ɛ	095	2	4Ɛχ 166	223	2	48Ɛ 2Ɛχ	3Ɛ8
3	615 544	038	3	65χ 389	187	3	629 6Ɛ6	363
4	777 580	161 Ɛχ0	4	7Ɛχ 554	131	4	787 χ59	308
5	919 560	Ɛ44	5	95χ 685	095	5	926 165	272
6	χ7Ɛ 4χ4	χχ7	6	χƐχ 75χ	03χ	6	χ84 417	219
7	573 021 38Ɛ	χ4Ɛ	7	579 05χ 798	15Ɛ Ɛχ3	7	583 022 634	182
8	183 21χ	9Ɛ3	8	1Ɛχ 77Ɛ	Ɛ48	8	180 7Ɛ6	129
9	325 011	956	9	35χ 707	χƐ1	9	31χ 923	092
χ	486 967	8ƐƐ	χ	4Ɛχ 5Ɛ8	χ56	χ	478 9Ɛ5	039
Ɛ	628 666	862	Ɛ	65χ 452	9Ɛχ	Ɛ	616 χ32	159 Ɛχ3

N	Log N	d
3300	583 774 χ15	159 Ɛ49
1	912 962	χƐ3
2	χ70 855	χ5χ
3	584 00χ 6Ɛ3	χ03
4	168 4Ɛ6	96χ
5	306 264	914
6	463 Ɛ78	87Ɛ
7	601 837	825
8	75Ɛ 460	78Ɛ
9	8Ɛ9 02Ɛ	736
χ	χ56 765	6χ0
Ɛ	ƐƐ4 245	646
3310	585 151 88Ɛ	5Ɛ1
1	2χƐ 280	557
2	448 817	502
3	5χ6 119	468
4	743 585	413
5	8χ0 998	379
6	χ3χ 155	324
7	Ɛ97 479	28Ɛ
8	586 134 748	235
9	291 981	1χ0
χ	42χ Ɛ61	147
Ɛ	588 0χ8	0Ɛ1
3320	725 199	058
1	882 235	003
2	χ1Ɛ 238	158 Ɛ69
3	Ɛ78 1χ5	Ɛ14
4	587 115 0Ɛ9	χ7Ɛ
5	271 Ɛ78	χ26
6	40χ 9χ2	991
7	567 773	938
8	704 4χƐ	8χ2
9	861 191	84χ
χ	9Ɛ9 χ1Ɛ	7Ɛ4
Ɛ	Ɛ56 613	760
3330	588 0Ɛ3 173	706
1	24Ɛ 879	672
2	3χ8 32Ɛ	618
3	544 947	584
4	6χ1 30Ɛ	52χ
5	839 839	496
6	996 113	441
7	Ɛ32 554	3χ8
8	589 08χ 940	353
9	227 093	2ƐƐ
χ	383 392	266
Ɛ	51Ɛ 638	211

N	Log N	d
3340	589 677 849	158 178
1	813 χ05	123
2	96Ɛ Ɛ28	08Ɛ
3	Ɛ07 ƐƐ7	036
4	58χ 064 031	157 Ɛχ2
5	200 013	Ɛ49
6	357 Ɛ60	χƐ4
7	4Ɛ3 χ54	χ60
8	64Ɛ 8Ɛ4	χ07
9	7χ7 6ƐƐ	973
χ	943 472	91χ
Ɛ	χ9Ɛ 190	886
3350	58Ɛ 036 χ56	831
1	192 687	799
2	32χ 264	745
3	485 9χ9	6Ɛ0
4	621 499	657
5	778 Ɛ34	604
6	914 538	56Ɛ
7	χ6Ɛ χχ7	517
8	590 007 402	482
9	162 884	42χ
χ	2Ɛχ 0Ɛ2	396
Ɛ	455 488	342
3360	5Ɛ0 80χ	2χχ
1	747 χƐ8	255
2	8χ3 151	202
3	χ3χ 353	169
4	Ɛ95 500	115
5	591 130 615	081
6	287 696	029
7	422 703	156 Ɛ95
8	579 698	Ɛ41
9	714 619	χχ9
χ	86Ɛ 506	χ55
Ɛ	χ06 35Ɛ	χ01
3370	Ɛ61 160	96χ
1	592 0Ɛ7 Ɛ0χ	915
2	252 823	882
3	3χ9 4χ5	829
4	544 112	796
5	69χ 8χ8	742
6	835 42χ	6χχ
7	98Ɛ Ɛ18	657
8	Ɛ26 573	602
9	593 080 Ɛ75	570
χ	217 525	517
Ɛ	371 χ40	484

N	Log N	d
3380	593 508 304	156 430
1	662 734	398
2	7Ɛ8 Ɛ10	345
3	953 255	2Ɛ1
4	χχ9 546	25χ
5	594 043 7χ4	206
6	199 9χχ	173
7	333 Ɛ61	11Ɛ
8	48χ 080	088
9	624 148	034
χ	77χ 180	155 Ɛχ1
Ɛ	914 161	Ɛ49
3390	χ6χ 0χχ	χƐ6
1	595 003 Ɛχ4	χ63
2	159 χ47	χ0Ɛ
3	2Ɛ3 856	979
4	449 613	924
5	5χ3 337	892
6	739 009	83χ
7	892 847	7χ7
8	χ28 432	754
9	Ɛ81 Ɛ86	701
χ	596 117 687	669
Ɛ	271 134	617
33χ0	406 74Ɛ	583
1	560 112	530
2	6Ɛ5 642	499
3	84χ Ɛ1Ɛ	447
4	9χ4 366	3Ɛ3
5	Ɛ39 759	360
6	597 092 χƐ9	309
7	228 206	276
8	381 480	223
9	516 6χ3	190
χ	66Ɛ 873	13χ
Ɛ	804 9Ɛ1	0χ6
33Ɛ0	959 χ97	054
1	χƐ2 ƐƐ2	001
2	598 047 Ɛ30	154 Ɛ6χ
3	1χ0 χ9χ	Ɛ17
4	335 9Ɛ5	χ85
5	48χ 87χ	χ32
6	623 6Ɛ0	99Ɛ
7	778 48Ɛ	948
8	911 217	8Ɛ6
9	χ65 Ɛ11	863
χ	ƐƐχ 774	810
Ɛ	599 153 384	77χ

N	Log N	d	N	Log N	d	N	Log N	d
3400	599 2X7 Ɛ42	154 727	3440	5X3 018 231	152 X65	3480	5X8 89X 430	151 222
1	440 669	695	1	16Ɛ 096	X13	1	X2Ɛ 652	192
2	595 142	642	2	301 XX9	981	2	Ɛ80 824	142
3	729 784	5Ɛ0	3	454 86X	930	3	5X9 111 966	0Ɛ1
4	882 174	559	4	5X7 59X	89Ɛ	4	262 X57	060
5	X16 711	506	5	73X 279	849	5	3Ɛ3 XƐ7	010
6	Ɛ6Ɛ 017	474	6	890 Ɛ06	7Ɛ7	6	544 Ɛ07	150 Ɛ80
7	59X 103 48Ɛ	422	7	X23 701	766	7	695 X87	Ɛ2Ɛ
8	257 8Ɛ1	38Ɛ	8	Ɛ76 267	715	8	826 9Ɛ6	X9Ɛ
9	3Ɛ0 080	339	9	5X4 108 980	683	9	977 895	X4Ɛ
X	544 3Ɛ9	2X7	X	25Ɛ 443	632	X	Ɛ08 724	9ƐX
Ɛ	698 6X4	254	Ɛ	3Ɛ1 X75	5X1	Ɛ	5XX 059 522	969
3410	830 938	202	3450	544 456	550	3490	1XX 28Ɛ	91X
1	984 Ɛ3X	170	1	696 9X6	4ƐX	1	33X ƐX9	889
2	Ɛ19 0XX	119	2	829 2X4	469	2	48Ɛ 876	839
3	59Ɛ 071 207	087	3	97Ɛ 751	417	3	620 4Ɛ3	7X9
4	205 292	035	4	Ɛ11 Ɛ68	387	4	771 0X0	758
5	359 307	153 ƐX2	5	5X5 064 333	335	5	901 838	709
6	4Ɛ1 2X9	Ɛ51	6	1Ɛ6 668	2X4	6	X52 345	678
7	645 23X	XƐX	7	348 950	253	7	ƐX2 X01	628
8	799 138	X68	8	49X ƐX3	202	8	5XƐ 133 429	597
9	930 ƐX4	X16	9	631 1X5	170	9	283 X04	548
X	X84 9ƐX	984	X	783 355	120	X	414 350	4Ɛ8
Ɛ	5X0 018 782	931	Ɛ	915 475	08X	Ɛ	564 848	467
3420	170 4Ɛ3	8X0	3460	X67 543	03X	34X0	6Ɛ5 0Ɛ3	418
1	304 193	84X	1	ƐƐ9 581	151 ƐX8	1	845 50Ɛ	387
2	457 X21	7Ɛ7	2	5X6 14Ɛ 569	Ɛ58	2	995 896	337
3	5XƐ 618	766	3	2X1 505	Ɛ06	3	Ɛ26 011	2X8
4	743 182	713	4	433 40Ɛ	X75	4	5Ɛ0 076 2Ɛ9	257
5	896 895	682	5	585 284	X25	5	206 554	208
6	X2X 357	630	6	717 0X9	993	6	356 760	177
7	Ɛ81 987	599	7	868 X80	943	7	4X6 917	128
8	5X1 115 364	548	8	9ƐX 803	8Ɛ2	8	636 X43	098
9	268 8Ɛ0	4Ɛ6	9	Ɛ50 4Ɛ5	861	9	786 Ɛ1Ɛ	047
X	400 1X6	464	X	5X7 0X2 156	810	X	916 Ɛ66	14Ɛ Ɛ Ɛ8
Ɛ	553 64X	413	Ɛ	233 966	77Ɛ	Ɛ	X66 Ɛ62	Ɛ69
3430	6X6 X61	380	3470	385 525	72Ɛ	34Ɛ0	ƐƐ6 Ɛ0Ɛ	Ɛ18
1	83X 221	32Ɛ	1	517 054	699	1	5Ɛ1 146 X27	X89
2	991 550	299	2	668 731	649	2	296 8Ɛ4	X38
3	Ɛ24 829	247	3	7ƐX 17X	5Ɛ8	3	426 730	9X9
4	5X2 077 X74	1Ɛ6	4	94Ɛ 776	568	4	576 519	95X
5	20Ɛ 06X	163	5	XX1 122	517	5	706 277	909
6	362 211	113	6	5X8 032 639	486	6	855 Ɛ84	87X
7	4Ɛ5 324	080	7	183 Ɛ03	435	7	9X5 842	82X
8	648 3X4	02Ɛ	8	315 338	3X5	8	Ɛ35 470	79Ɛ
9	79Ɛ 413	152 Ɛ99	9	466 721	354	9	5Ɛ2 085 04Ɛ	74Ɛ
X	932 3Ɛ0	Ɛ47	X	5Ɛ7 X75	304	X	214 79X	6ƐƐ
Ɛ	X85 337	XƐ6	Ɛ	749 179	273	Ɛ	364 299	670

N	Log N	d	N	Log N	d	N	Log N	d
3500	5Ɛ2 4Ɛ3 949	14Ɛ 620	3540	5Ɛ8 061 948	149 X58	3580	601 765 766	148 312
1	643 369	591	1	1XƐ 7X4	X0X	1	8Ɛ1 X78	284
2	792 93X	541	2	339 5Ɛ2	97Ɛ	2	X3X 140	236
3	922 27Ɛ	4Ɛ2	3	487 371	931	3	Ɛ86 376	1X9
4	X71 771	462	4	615 0X2	8X2	4	602 112 563	160
5	5Ɛ3 001 013	412	5	762 984	854	5	25X 703	112
6	150 425	383	6	8Ɛ0 618	805	6	3X6 815	084
7	29Ɛ 7X8	334	7	X3X 221	776	7	532 899	036
8	42X Ɛ20	2X5	8	Ɛ87 997	728	8	67X 913	147 ƐXX
9	57X 205	254	9	5Ɛ9 115 503	69X	9	806 901	Ɛ5Ɛ
X	709 459	206	X	262 ƐX1	64Ɛ	X	952 860	Ɛ12
Ɛ	858 663	176	Ɛ	3Ɛ0 630	601	Ɛ	X9X 772	X85
3510	9X7 819	127	3550	53X 031	573	3590	603 026 637	X37
1	Ɛ36 944	098	1	687 5X4	524	1	172 472	9XX
2	5Ɛ4 085 X20	048	2	814 Ɛ08	496	2	2ƐX 260	961
3	214 X68	14X ƐƐ9	3	962 3X2	447	3	446 001	913
4	363 X65	Ɛ6X	4	XXƐ 829	3ƐX	4	591 914	885
5	4Ɛ2 X13	Ɛ1X	5	5ƐX 039 027	36X	5	719 599	838
6	641 931	X90	6	186 395	321	6	865 215	7XƐ
7	790 801	X40	7	313 6Ɛ6	293	7	9Ɛ0 X04	762
8	91Ɛ 641	9Ɛ1	8	460 989	244	8	Ɛ38 566	714
9	X6X 432	962	9	5XX 011	1Ɛ6	9	604 084 07X	687
X	ƐƐ9 194	913	X	737 207	168	X	20Ɛ 745	63X
Ɛ	5Ɛ5 147 XX7	883	Ɛ	884 373	119	Ɛ	357 183	5Ɛ1
3520	296 76X	835	3560	X11 490	090	35X0	4X2 774	563
1	425 3X3	7X5	1	Ɛ5X 560	041	1	62X 117	516
2	573 Ɛ88	757	2	5ƐƐ 0X7 5X1	148 ƐƐ3	2	775 631	489
3	702 723	707	3	234 594	Ɛ66	3	900 XƐX	440
4	851 22X	678	4	381 53X	Ɛ17	4	X48 33X	3Ɛ3
5	99Ɛ 8X6	62X	5	50X 455	X89	5	Ɛ93 731	365
6	Ɛ2X 314	59X	6	657 322	X3Ɛ	6	605 11X X96	319
7	5Ɛ6 078 8Ɛ2	550	7	7X4 161	9Ɛ1	7	266 1Ɛ3	28Ɛ
8	207 242	500	8	930 Ɛ52	963	8	3Ɛ1 482	242
9	355 742	472	9	X79 8Ɛ5	915	9	538 704	1Ɛ5
X	4X3 ƐƐ4	422	X	600 006 60X	887	X	683 8Ɛ9	169
Ɛ	632 416	394	Ɛ	153 295	83X	Ɛ	80X X66	11Ɛ
3530	780 7XX	345	3570	29Ɛ Ɛ13	7XƐ	35Ɛ0	955 Ɛ85	092
1	90X Ɛ33	2Ɛ6	1	428 702	761	1	XX1 057	045
2	X59 229	268	2	575 263	714	2	606 028 0X0	146 ƐƐ8
3	ƐX7 495	218	3	701 977	686	3	173 098	Ɛ70
4	5Ɛ7 135 6Ɛ1	18X	4	84X 441	637	4	2ƐX 048	Ɛ22
5	283 87Ɛ	13Ɛ	5	996 X78	5XX	5	444 Ɛ6X	X96
6	411 9ƐX	0Ɛ1	6	Ɛ23 466	561	6	58Ɛ X44	X48
7	55Ɛ XXƐ	061	7	601 06Ɛ X07	512	7	716 890	X00
8	6X9 Ɛ50	013	8	1Ɛ8 319	485	8	861 690	973
9	837 Ɛ63	149 Ɛ84	9	344 7X2	437	9	9X8 443	926
X	985 Ɛ27	Ɛ36	X	491 019	3X9	X	Ɛ33 169	899
Ɛ	Ɛ13 X61	XX7	Ɛ	619 406	360	Ɛ	607 079 X46	851

N	Log N	d	N	Log N	d	N	Log N	d
3600	607 204 697	146 803	3640	610 7ƐƐ 990	145 130	3680	616 154 679	143 694
1	34Ɛ 29X	777	1	944 Ɛ00	0X5	1	298 151	649
2	495 X55	72Ɛ	2	X89 ƐX5	05X	2	41Ɛ 79X	602
3	620 584	6X1	3	611 013 043	011	3	563 1X0	577
4	767 065	655	4	158 054	144 Ɛ85	4	6X6 757	530
5	8Ɛ1 6ƐX	608	5	2X1 019	Ɛ3X	5	82X 087	4X6
6	X38 106	580	6	425 Ɛ57	XƐ2	6	971 571	45X
7	Ɛ82 686	532	7	56X X49	X66	7	XƐ4 X0Ɛ	414
8	608 108 Ɛ28	4X7	8	6Ɛ3 8Ɛ3	X1X	8	617 038 223	388
9	253 4X3	459	9	838 711	993	9	17Ɛ 5XƐ	342
X	399 940	411	X	981 4X4	947	X	302 931	2Ɛ7
Ɛ	524 151	385	Ɛ	Ɛ06 22Ɛ	900	Ɛ	446 028	271
3610	66X 516	338	3650	612 04X Ɛ2Ɛ	873	3690	589 299	225
1	7Ɛ4 852	2XƐ	1	193 7X2	828	1	710 502	19Ɛ
2	93X Ɛ41	263	2	318 40X	7X1	2	853 6X1	153
3	X85 1X4	217	3	460 ƐXƐ	755	3	996 834	10X
4	609 00Ɛ 3ƐƐ	18X	4	5X5 744	709	4	Ɛ19 942	082
5	155 589	141	5	72X 251	682	5	618 060 X04	038
6	29Ɛ 70X	0Ɛ5	6	872 913	636	6	1X3 X40	142 ƐƐ1
7	425 803	069	7	9Ɛ7 349	5XX	7	326 X31	Ɛ66
8	56Ɛ 870	020	8	Ɛ3Ɛ 937	563	8	469 997	Ɛ20
9	6Ɛ5 890	145 Ɛ94	9	613 084 29X	518	9	5Ɛ0 8Ɛ7	X95
X	83Ɛ 864	Ɛ48	X	208 7Ɛ6	490	X	733 790	X4X
Ɛ	985 7Ɛ0	XƐƐ	Ɛ	351 086	445	Ɛ	876 61X	X04
3620	Ɛ0Ɛ 6XƐ	X73	3660	495 50Ɛ	3Ɛ9	36X0	9Ɛ9 422	979
1	60X 055 562	X27	1	619 908	372	1	Ɛ40 19Ɛ	933
2	19Ɛ 389	99X	2	762 07X	326	2	619 082 Ɛ12	8X8
3	325 167	952	3	8X6 3X4	29Ɛ	3	205 7ƐX	862
4	46X X29	906	4	X2X 683	254	4	348 460	817
5	5Ɛ4 803	87X	5	Ɛ72 917	208	5	48Ɛ 077	791
6	73X 481	831	6	614 0Ɛ6 Ɛ23	181	6	611 848	746
7	884 0Ɛ2	7X5	7	23Ɛ 0X4	136	7	754 392	700
8	X09 897	759	8	383 21X	0XX	8	896 X92	675
9	Ɛ53 434	711	9	507 308	063	9	X19 547	62Ɛ
X	60Ɛ 098 Ɛ45	685	X	64Ɛ 36Ɛ	018	X	Ɛ5Ɛ Ɛ76	5X4
Ɛ	222 60X	638	Ɛ	793 387	143 Ɛ91	Ɛ	61X 0X2 55X	55X
3630	368 046	5Ɛ1	3670	917 358	Ɛ45	36Ɛ0	224 XƐ8	514
1	4Ɛ1 637	564	1	X5Ɛ 2X1	XƐX	1	367 410	489
2	636 Ɛ9Ɛ	519	2	ƐX3 19Ɛ	X73	2	4X9 899	443
3	780 428	490	3	615 127 052	X28	3	630 120	3Ɛ9
4	905 988	445	4	26X X7X	9X1	4	772 519	373
5	X4Ɛ 211	3Ɛ8	5	3Ɛ2 85Ɛ	955	5	8Ɛ4 890	328
6	Ɛ94 609	370	6	536 5Ɛ4	90Ɛ	6	X36 Ɛ28	2X2
7	610 119 979	325	7	67X 303	883	7	Ɛ79 29X	257
8	263 0X2	298	8	801 Ɛ86	838	8	61Ɛ 0ƐƐ 535	212
9	3X8 37X	250	9	945 802	7Ɛ1	9	241 747	187
X	531 60X	205	X	X89 3Ɛ3	767	X	383 912	141
Ɛ	676 813	179	Ɛ	616 010 Ɛ5X	71Ɛ	Ɛ	505 X53	0Ɛ7

N	Log N	d	N	Log N	d	N	Log N	d
3700	61Ɛ 647 Ɛ4X	142 070	3740	624 X9Ɛ 173	140 682	3780	62X 293 267	13Ɛ 106
1	789 ƐƐX	027	1	625 01Ɛ 835	638	1	412 371	081
2	910 025	141 ƐX0	2	160 271	5Ɛ3	2	551 432	039
3	X52 005	Ɛ56	3	2X0 864	56X	3	690 46Ɛ	13X ƐƐ4
4	Ɛ93 Ɛ5Ɛ	Ɛ11	4	421 212	524	4	80Ɛ 463	Ɛ70
5	620 115 X70	X86	5	561 736	49Ɛ	5	94X 413	Ɛ27
6	257 936	X40	6	6X2 015	456	6	X89 33X	XX3
7	399 776	9Ɛ6	7	822 46Ɛ	411	7	62Ɛ 008 221	X5Ɛ
8	51Ɛ 570	970	8	962 880	387	8	147 080	X16
9	661 320	926	9	XX3 047	343	9	285 X96	992
X	7X3 046	8X0	X	626 023 38X	2Ɛ9	X	404 868	949
Ɛ	924 926	856	Ɛ	163 687	274	Ɛ	543 5Ɛ5	905
3710	X66 580	810	3750	2X3 93Ɛ	22Ɛ	3790	682 2ƐX	881
1	ƐX8 190	786	1	423 Ɛ6X	1X5	1	800 Ɛ7Ɛ	839
2	621 129 956	741	2	564 153	161	2	93Ɛ 7Ɛ8	7Ɛ4
3	26Ɛ 497	6Ɛ6	3	6X4 2Ɛ4	118	3	X7X 3Ɛ0	770
4	3Ɛ0 Ɛ91	670	4	824 410	092	4	ƐƐ8 Ɛ60	728
5	532 641	627	5	964 4X2	04X	5	630 137 688	6X3
6	674 068	5X1	6	XX4 530	004	6	276 16Ɛ	65Ɛ
7	7Ɛ5 649	557	7	627 024 534	13Ɛ Ɛ80	7	3Ɛ4 80X	618
8	936 ƐX4	511	8	164 4Ɛ4	Ɛ36	8	533 226	592
9	X78 4Ɛ5	487	9	2X4 42X	XƐ2	9	671 7Ɛ8	54Ɛ
X	ƐƐ9 980	442	X	424 320	X69	X	7Ɛ0 147	507
Ɛ	622 13Ɛ 202	3Ɛ8	Ɛ	564 189	X23	Ɛ	92X 652	482
3720	280 5ƐX	372	3760	6X3 Ɛ20	99Ɛ	37X0	X68 Ɛ14	43X
1	401 970	328	1	823 98Ɛ	956	1	ƐX7 352	3Ɛ7
2	543 098	2X3	2	963 725	911	2	631 125 749	372
3	684 37Ɛ	259	3	XX3 436	888	3	263 XƐƐ	32X
4	805 618	213	4	628 023 102	843	4	3X2 229	2X6
5	946 82Ɛ	18X	5	162 945	7ƐƐ	5	520 513	262
6	X87 9Ɛ9	144	6	2X2 544	775	6	65X 775	21X
7	623 008 Ɛ41	0ƐX	7	422 0Ɛ9	731	7	798 993	196
8	14X 03Ɛ	075	8	561 82X	6X8	8	916 Ɛ69	152
9	28Ɛ 0Ɛ4	02Ɛ	9	6X1 316	663	9	X55 0ƐƐ	10X
X	410 123	140 ƐX6	X	820 979	61Ɛ	X	Ɛ93 209	086
Ɛ	551 109	Ɛ60	Ɛ	960 398	595	Ɛ	632 111 293	042
3730	692 069	Ɛ17	3770	X9Ɛ 971	551	37Ɛ0	24Ɛ 315	139 ƐƐX
1	812 Ɛ84	X91	1	629 01Ɛ 302	509	1	389 313	Ɛ76
2	953 X55	X47	2	15X 80Ɛ	483	2	507 289	Ɛ33
3	X94 8X0	X02	3	29X 092	43Ɛ	3	645 200	XXX
4	624 015 6X2	979	4	419 511	3Ɛ7	4	783 0XX	X67
5	156 45Ɛ	933	5	558 908	371	5	900 Ɛ55	X23
6	297 192	8XX	6	698 079	329	6	X3X 978	99Ɛ
7	417 X80	864	7	817 3X6	2X5	7	Ɛ78 757	957
8	558 724	81Ɛ	8	956 68Ɛ	260	8	633 0Ɛ6 4Ɛ2	913
9	699 343	795	9	X95 92Ɛ	217	9	234 205	890
X	819 Ɛ18	751	X	62X 014 Ɛ46	193	X	371 X95	848
Ɛ	95X 669	706	Ɛ	154 119	14X	Ɛ	4XƐ 721	804

N	Log N	d	N	Log N	d	N	Log N	d
3800	633 629 325	139 780	3840	638 926 430	138 269	3880	641 Ɛ87 611	136 986
1	766 XX5	739	1	X62 699	225	1	642 102 397	943
2	8X4 622	6Ɛ5	2	Ɛ9X 902	1X3	2	239 11X	902
3	X22 117	672	3	639 116 XX5	160	3	373 X20	87Ɛ
4	Ɛ5Ɛ 789	629	4	253 045	119	4	4XX 69Ɛ	839
5	634 099 1Ɛ6	5X6	5	38Ɛ 162	097	5	625 318	7Ɛ7
6	216 7X0	563	6	507 239	053	6	75Ɛ Ɛ13	775
7	354 143	51Ɛ	7	643 290	010	7	896 688	733
8	491 662	497	8	77Ɛ 2X0	137 Ɛ8X	8	X11 1ƐƐ	6Ɛ1
9	60X Ɛ39	453	9	8Ɛ7 26X	Ɛ47	9	Ɛ47 8Ɛ0	66Ɛ
X	748 390	410	X	X33 1Ɛ5	Ɛ04	X	643 082 35Ɛ	629
Ɛ	885 7X0	389	Ɛ	Ɛ6Ɛ 0Ɛ9	X82	Ɛ	1Ɛ8 988	5X6
3810	X02 Ɛ69	345	3850	63X 0X6 Ɛ7Ɛ	X3X	3890	333 372	565
1	Ɛ40 2Ɛ2	301	1	222 9Ɛ9	9Ɛ8	1	469 917	523
2	635 079 5Ɛ3	27X	2	35X 7Ɛ5	975	2	5X4 23X	4X1
3	1Ɛ6 871	237	3	496 56X	933	3	71X 71Ɛ	45Ɛ
4	333 XX8	1Ɛ3	4	612 2X1	8XƐ	4	854 Ɛ7X	418
5	471 09Ɛ	170	5	749 Ɛ90	869	5	98Ɛ 396	397
6	5XX 24Ɛ	128	6	885 839	827	6	Ɛ05 771	355
7	727 377	0X5	7	X01 464	7X3	7	644 03Ɛ Ɛ06	313
8	864 460	061	8	Ɛ39 047	761	8	176 219	292
9	9X1 501	01X	9	63Ɛ 074 7X8	71Ɛ	9	2Ɛ0 4XƐ	24Ɛ
X	Ɛ1X 51Ɛ	138 Ɛ97	X	1Ɛ0 307	698	X	426 73X	20X
Ɛ	636 057 4Ɛ6	Ɛ53	Ɛ	327 9X3	655	Ɛ	560 948	187
3820	194 449	Ɛ10	3860	463 438	613	38X0	696 Ɛ13	146
1	311 359	X88	1	59X X4Ɛ	590	1	811 059	104
2	44X 225	X46	2	716 41Ɛ	54X	2	947 161	083
3	587 06Ɛ	X02	3	851 969	507	3	X81 224	040
4	703 X71	97X	4	989 274	484	4	ƐƐ7 264	135 ƐƐƐ
5	840 82Ɛ	938	5	Ɛ04 738	442	5	645 131 263	Ɛ79
6	979 567	8Ɛ4	6	640 03Ɛ Ɛ7X	400	6	267 220	Ɛ37
7	XƐ6 25Ɛ	871	7	177 37X	379	7	3X1 157	XƐ6
8	637 032 Ɛ10	82X	8	2Ɛ2 737	337	8	517 051	X74
9	16Ɛ 73X	7X7	9	429 X72	2Ɛ4	9	650 Ɛ05	X32
X	2X8 325	763	X	565 166	272	X	786 937	9Ɛ0
Ɛ	424 X88	720	Ɛ	6X0 418	230	Ɛ	900 727	96Ɛ
3830	561 5X8	69X	3870	817 648	1X9	38Ɛ0	X36 496	92X
1	69X 086	656	1	952 835	167	1	Ɛ70 204	8X7
2	816 720	613	2	X89 9X0	124	2	646 0X5 XXƐ	866
3	953 133	590	3	641 004 Ɛ04	0X2	3	212 755	825
4	X8Ɛ 703	548	4	13Ɛ ƐX6	060	4	355 37X	7X3
5	638 008 04Ɛ	506	5	277 046	01X	5	48X Ɛ61	761
6	144 555	483	6	3Ɛ2 064	136 Ɛ97	6	604 702	720
7	280 X18	43Ɛ	7	529 03Ɛ	Ɛ55	7	73X 222	69X
8	3Ɛ9 257	3Ɛ9	8	663 Ɛ94	Ɛ12	8	873 900	659
9	535 654	376	9	79X XX6	X91	9	9X9 359	617
X	671 X0X	332	X	915 977	X4X	X	Ɛ22 974	596
Ɛ	7XX 140	2Ɛ0	Ɛ	X50 805	X08	Ɛ	647 058 34X	554

N	Log N	d	N	Log N	d	N	Log N	d
3900	647 191 8X2	135 513	3940	650 342 046	134 08Ɛ	3980	655 459 432	132 875
1	307 1Ɛ5	491	1	476 115	04X	1	590 0X7	836
2	440 686	450	2	5XX 163	00X	2	702 921	7Ɛ5
3	575 Ɛ16	40Ɛ	3	722 171	133 Ɛ89	3	835 516	776
4	6XƐ 325	389	4	856 13X	Ɛ48	4	968 090	736
5	824 6Ɛ2	348	5	98X 086	Ɛ07	5	X9X 806	6Ɛ5
6	959 X3X	306	6	Ɛ01 Ɛ91	X87	6	656 011 2ƐƐ	676
7	X93 144	285	7	651 035 X58	X47	7	143 975	636
8	648 008 409	244	8	169 8X3	X06	8	276 3XƐ	5Ɛ6
9	141 651	202	9	2X1 6X9	985	9	3X8 9X5	576
X	276 853	182	X	415 472	944	X	51Ɛ 35Ɛ	537
Ɛ	3XƐ X15	140	Ɛ	549 1Ɛ6	904	Ɛ	651 896	4Ɛ6
3910	524 Ɛ55	0ƐX	3950	680 XƐX	884	3990	784 190	476
1	65X 053	07X	1	7Ɛ4 782	843	1	8Ɛ6 646	437
2	793 111	038	2	928 405	802	2	X28 X81	3Ɛ7
3	908 149	134 ƐƐ7	3	X60 007	782	3	Ɛ5Ɛ 278	377
4	X41 144	Ɛ75	4	Ɛ93 789	742	4	657 091 633	337
5	Ɛ76 0Ɛ9	Ɛ35	5	652 107 30Ɛ	700	5	203 96X	2Ɛ8
6	649 0XƐ 032	XƐ3	6	23X X0Ɛ	681	6	336 066	278
7	223 Ɛ25	X72	7	372 490	640	7	468 322	238
8	358 997	X31	8	4X5 Ɛ10	600	8	59X 55X	1Ɛ8
9	491 808	9Ɛ0	9	619 510	57Ɛ	9	710 756	179
X	606 5Ɛ8	96Ɛ	X	750 X8Ɛ	53Ɛ	X	842 913	139
Ɛ	73Ɛ 367	92X	Ɛ	884 40X	4ƐX	Ɛ	974 X50	0Ɛ9
3920	874 095	8X8	3960	9Ɛ7 908	47X	39X0	XX6 Ɛ49	079
1	9X8 981	868	1	ƐƐƐ 186	43X	1	658 019 006	03X
2	Ɛ21 629	826	2	653 062 604	3Ɛ9	2	14Ɛ 044	131 ƐƐƐ
3	64X 056 253	7X6	3	195 X01	379	3	281 043	Ɛ7X
4	18X X39	764	4	309 17X	339	4	3Ɛ3 001	Ɛ3Ɛ
5	303 5X1	723	5	440 4Ɛ7	2Ɛ9	5	524 Ɛ40	Ɛ00
6	438 104	6X3	6	573 7Ɛ4	278	6	656 X40	X80
7	570 7X7	661	7	6X6 X70	238	7	788 900	X40
8	6X5 248	621	8	81X 0X8	1Ɛ7	8	8ƐX 740	X01
9	819 869	59Ɛ	9	951 2X3	178	9	X30 541	981
X	952 248	55Ɛ	X	X84 45Ɛ	137	X	Ɛ62 302	941
Ɛ	X86 7X7	519	Ɛ	ƐƐ7 596	0Ɛ7	Ɛ	659 094 043	903
3930	ƐƐƐ 104	499	3970	654 12X 691	077	39Ɛ0	205 946	882
1	64Ɛ 133 5X1	458	1	261 748	036	1	337 608	843
2	267 X39	417	2	394 782	132 ƐƐ7	2	469 24Ɛ	804
3	3X0 254	396	3	507 779	Ɛ76	3	59X X53	784
4	514 62X	355	4	63X 733	Ɛ36	4	710 617	745
5	648 983	315	5	771 669	XƐ6	5	842 160	706
6	781 098	293	6	8X4 563	X76	6	973 866	686
7	8Ɛ5 36Ɛ	253	7	X17 419	X36	7	XX5 330	646
8	X29 602	212	8	Ɛ4X 253	9Ɛ6	8	65X 016 976	607
9	Ɛ61 814	191	9	655 081 049	975	9	148 381	588
X	650 095 9X5	151	X	1Ɛ3 X02	936	X	279 949	549
Ɛ	209 Ɛ36	110	Ɛ	326 738	8Ɛ6	Ɛ	3XƐ 296	509

N	Log N	d	N	Log N	d	N	Log N	d
3X00	65X 520 7X3	131 48X	3X40	663 550 X2Ɛ	130 10Ɛ	3X80	668 52X X35	12X 978
1	652 071	44X	1	680 Ɛ3X	090	1	659 7Ɛ1	93Ɛ
2	783 4ƐƐ	40Ɛ	2	7Ɛ1 00X	052	2	788 530	900
3	8Ɛ4 90X	390	3	921 060	013	3	8Ɛ7 230	883
4	X26 09X	351	4	X51 073	12Ɛ Ɛ95	4	X25 XƐ3	844
5	Ɛ57 42Ɛ	311	5	Ɛ81 048	Ɛ55	5	Ɛ54 737	807
6	65Ɛ 088 740	293	6	664 0Ɛ0 ƐX1	Ɛ18	6	669 083 342	788
7	1Ɛ9 X13	253	7	220 XƐ9	X99	7	1Ɛ1 Ɛ0X	74Ɛ
8	32Ɛ 066	213	8	350 996	X5X	8	320 659	711
9	460 279	195	9	480 834	X20	9	44Ɛ 16X	693
X	591 452	155	X	5Ɛ0 654	9X1	X	579 841	656
Ɛ	702 5X7	116	Ɛ	720 435	963	Ɛ	6X8 297	617
3X10	833 701	097	3X50	850 198	924	3X90	816 8Ɛ2	59X
1	964 798	058	1	97Ɛ Ɛ00	8X6	1	945 290	55Ɛ
2	X95 834	019	2	XXƐ 7X6	867	2	X73 82Ɛ	522
3	660 006 851	130 Ɛ9X	3	665 01Ɛ 451	829	3	ƐX2 151	4X5
4	137 82Ɛ	Ɛ5X	4	14Ɛ 07X	7XƐ	4	66X 110 636	466
5	268 789	Ɛ20	5	27X 869	770	5	23X XX0	429
6	399 6X9	XX0	6	3XX 419	732	6	369 309	3XƐ
7	50X 589	X62	7	519 Ɛ4Ɛ	6Ɛ3	7	497 6Ɛ8	371
8	63Ɛ 42Ɛ	X22	8	649 642	675	8	605 X69	333
9	770 251	9X3	9	779 0Ɛ7	637	9	734 1X0	2Ɛ6
X	8X1 034	965	X	8X8 732	5Ɛ8	X	862 496	278
Ɛ	X11 999	925	Ɛ	X18 12X	57X	Ɛ	990 752	23Ɛ
3X20	Ɛ42 702	8X6	3X60	Ɛ47 6X8	540	3XX0	XƐX 991	201
1	661 073 3X8	868	1	666 077 028	501	1	66Ɛ 028 Ɛ92	183
2	1X4 054	828	2	1X6 529	483	2	157 155	146
3	314 880	7XX	3	315 9Ɛ0	445	3	285 29Ɛ	108
4	445 46X	76X	4	445 235	406	4	3Ɛ3 3X7	08X
5	576 018	730	5	574 63Ɛ	389	5	521 475	051
6	6X6 748	6Ɛ0	6	6X3 X08	34X	6	64Ɛ 506	013
7	817 238	672	7	813 156	30Ɛ	7	779 519	129 Ɛ95
8	947 8XX	633	8	942 465	292	8	8X7 4Ɛ2	Ɛ59
9	X78 321	5Ɛ4	9	X71 737	254	9	X15 44Ɛ	Ɛ1X
X	ƐX8 915	576	X	ƐX0 98Ɛ	215	X	Ɛ43 369	XX1
Ɛ	662 119 28Ɛ	536	Ɛ	667 10Ɛ ƐX4	197	Ɛ	670 071 24X	X64
3X30	249 805	4Ɛ8	3X70	23Ɛ 17Ɛ	159	3XƐ0	19Ɛ 0Ɛ2	X26
1	37X 101	478	1	36X 318	11Ɛ	1	308 Ɛ18	9X8
2	4XX 579	43Ɛ	2	499 437	0X1	2	436 904	96Ɛ
3	61X 9Ɛ8	3ƐƐ	3	608 518	062	3	564 673	932
4	74Ɛ 1Ɛ7	380	4	737 57X	025	4	692 3X5	8Ɛ4
5	87Ɛ 577	342	5	866 5X3	12X ƐX6	5	800 099	877
6	9XƐ 8Ɛ9	303	6	995 589	Ɛ69	6	929 954	839
7	Ɛ20 000	284	7	Ɛ04 536	Ɛ2X	7	X57 591	800
8	663 050 284	246	8	668 033 464	XƐ0	8	Ɛ85 191	783
9	180 50X	207	9	162 354	X73	9	671 0Ɛ2 954	745
X	2Ɛ0 715	188	X	291 207	X34	X	220 499	708
Ɛ	420 8X1	14X	Ɛ	400 03Ɛ	9Ɛ6	Ɛ	349 ƐX5	68X

N	Log N	d	N	Log N	d	N	Log N	d
3Ɛ00	671 477 673	129 652	3Ɛ40	676 373 973	128 351	3Ɛ80	67Ɛ 220 557	127 076
1	5X5 105	614	1	4X0 104	314	1	347 611	03Ɛ
2	712 719	596	2	608 418	298	2	472 650	003
3	840 0Ɛ3	559	3	734 6Ɛ4	25Ɛ	3	599 653	126 Ɛ87
4	969 650	520	4	860 953	222	4	704 61X	Ɛ4X
5	X96 Ɛ70	4X3	5	988 Ɛ75	1X6	5	82Ɛ 568	Ɛ13
6	672 004 453	465	6	XƐ5 15Ɛ	169	6	956 47Ɛ	X97
7	131 8Ɛ8	429	7	677 021 308	130	7	X81 356	X5X
8	25Ɛ 125	3XƐ	8	149 438	0Ɛ4	8	ƐX8 1Ɛ4	X23
9	388 514	371	9	275 530	077	9	680 113 017	9X7
X	4Ɛ5 885	335	X	3X1 5X7	03Ɛ	X	239 X02	96Ɛ
Ɛ	622 ƐƐX	2Ɛ7	Ɛ	509 626	002	Ɛ	364 771	933
3Ɛ10	750 2Ɛ5	27Ɛ	3Ɛ50	635 628	127 Ɛ86	3Ɛ90	48Ɛ 4X4	8Ɛ7
1	879 574	241	1	761 5Ɛ2	Ɛ49	1	5Ɛ6 19Ɛ	87Ɛ
2	9X6 7Ɛ5	204	2	889 53Ɛ	Ɛ10	2	720 X5X	843
3	Ɛ13 9Ɛ9	187	3	9Ɛ5 44Ɛ	X94	3	847 6X1	807
4	673 040 Ɛ84	149	4	Ɛ21 323	X58	4	972 2X8	78Ɛ
5	16X 111	111	5	678 049 17Ɛ	X1Ɛ	5	X98 X77	754
6	297 222	093	6	174 Ɛ9X	9X2	6	681 003 60Ɛ	718
7	404 2Ɛ5	057	7	2X0 980	967	7	12X 127	6X0
8	531 350	019	8	408 727	929	8	254 807	664
9	65X 369	128 ƐX0	9	534 454	8Ɛ2	9	37Ɛ 26Ɛ	628
X	787 349	Ɛ64	X	660 146	875	X	4X5 897	5Ɛ1
Ɛ	8Ɛ4 2Ɛ1	Ɛ26	Ɛ	787 9ƐƐ	838	Ɛ	610 288	574
3Ɛ20	X21 217	XX9	3Ɛ60	8Ɛ3 637	800	3ƐX0	736 840	539
1	Ɛ4X 104	X70	1	X1Ɛ 237	784	1	861 179	501
2	674 076 Ɛ74	X34	2	Ɛ46 9ƐƐ	747	2	987 67X	486
3	1X3 9X8	9Ɛ6	3	679 072 546	70Ɛ	3	XƐ1 Ɛ44	44X
4	310 7X2	979	4	19X 055	693	4	682 018 392	412
5	439 55Ɛ	940	5	305 728	657	5	142 7X4	396
6	566 29Ɛ	904	6	431 183	61X	6	268 Ɛ7X	35X
7	692 ƐX3	886	7	558 7X1	5X2	7	393 318	323
8	7ƐƐ 869	84X	8	684 183	565	8	4Ɛ9 63Ɛ	2X8
9	928 4Ɛ7	811	9	7XƐ 728	529	9	623 927	26Ɛ
X	X55 108	794	X	917 055	4Ɛ1	X	749 Ɛ96	234
Ɛ	Ɛ81 8X0	757	Ɛ	X42 546	475	Ɛ	874 20X	1Ɛ9
3Ɛ30	675 0XX 437	71X	3Ɛ70	Ɛ69 9ƐƐ	439	3ƐƐ0	99X 407	180
1	216 Ɛ55	6X1	1	67X 095 238	400	1	Ɛ04 587	145
2	343 636	664	2	200 638	384	2	683 02X 710	10X
3	470 09X	628	3	327 X00	348	3	154 81X	092
4	598 706	5XƐ	4	453 148	310	4	27X 8Ɛ0	056
5	705 0Ɛ5	572	5	57X 458	294	5	3X4 946	01Ɛ
6	831 667	535	6	6X5 730	257	6	50X 965	125 ƐX4
7	959 ƐX0	4Ɛ9	7	810 987	21Ɛ	7	634 949	Ɛ67
8	X86 499	47Ɛ	8	937 ƐX6	1X4	8	75X 8Ɛ4	Ɛ31
9	ƐƐ2 958	443	9	X63 18X	167	9	884 825	XƐ4
X	676 11Ɛ 19Ɛ	407	X	Ɛ8X 335	12Ɛ	X	9XX 719	X7X
Ɛ	247 5X6	389	Ɛ	67Ɛ 0Ɛ5 464	0Ɛ3	Ɛ	Ɛ14 597	X42

N	Log N	d	N	Log N	d	N	Log N	d
4000	684 03X 419	125 X06	4040	688 X0X 34Ɛ	124 77Ɛ	4080	691 751 09X	123 558
1	164 223	98Ɛ	1	Ɛ32 Ɛ0X	744	1	874 636	521
2	289 ƐƐ2	953	2	689 057 652	709	2	997 Ɛ57	4X7
3	3Ɛ3 945	918	3	180 15Ɛ	692	3	XƐƐ 442	471
4	519 661	8X1	4	2X4 831	658	4	692 022 8Ɛ3	437
5	643 342	865	5	409 289	620	5	146 12X	400
6	768 ƐX7	82X	6	531 8X9	5X6	6	269 52X	387
7	892 815	7Ɛ3	7	656 293	56Ɛ	7	390 8Ɛ5	350
8	9Ɛ8 408	777	8	77X 842	535	8	4Ɛ4 045	316
9	Ɛ21 Ɛ83	73Ɛ	9	8X3 177	4Ɛ9	9	617 35Ɛ	29Ɛ
X	685 047 702	705	X	X07 674	483	X	73X 63X	266
Ɛ	171 207	689	Ɛ	Ɛ2Ɛ Ɛ37	448	Ɛ	861 8X4	22Ɛ
4010	296 894	652	4050	68X 054 383	412	4090	984 Ɛ13	1Ɛ6
1	400 326	616	1	178 795	397	1	XX8 109	17Ɛ
2	525 940	59Ɛ	2	2X0 Ɛ70	360	2	693 00Ɛ 288	145
3	64Ɛ 31Ɛ	564	3	405 310	325	3	132 411	10Ɛ
4	774 883	529	4	529 635	2XƐ	4	255 520	095
5	89X 1Ɛ0	4Ɛ2	5	651 924	274	5	378 5Ɛ5	05Ɛ
6	X03 6X2	476	6	775 Ɛ98	239	6	49Ɛ 654	024
7	Ɛ28 Ɛ58	43Ɛ	7	89X 215	203	7	602 678	122 ƐXƐ
8	686 052 397	403	8	X02 418	188	8	725 667	Ɛ75
9	177 79X	389	9	Ɛ26 5X4	152	9	848 620	Ɛ3X
X	2X0 Ɛ67	351	X	68Ɛ 04X 736	116	X	96Ɛ 55X	Ɛ05
Ɛ	406 2Ɛ8	316	Ɛ	172 850	0X1	Ɛ	X92 463	X8X
4020	52Ɛ 612	2X0	4060	296 931	066	40X0	ƐƐ5 331	X55
1	654 8Ɛ2	263	1	3ƐX 997	02Ɛ	1	694 118 186	X1Ɛ
2	779 Ɛ55	229	2	522 X06	123 ƐƐ4	2	23X ƐX5	9X4
3	8X3 182	1Ɛ2	3	646 9ƐX	Ɛ7Ɛ	3	361 989	96Ɛ
4	X08 374	176	4	76X 979	Ɛ43	4	484 738	935
5	Ɛ31 52X	140	5	892 900	Ɛ09	5	5X7 471	8ƐƐ
6	687 056 66X	104	6	9Ɛ6 809	X93	6	70X 170	885
7	17Ɛ 772	089	7	Ɛ1X 6X0	X58	7	830 X35	84Ɛ
8	2X4 83Ɛ	052	8	690 042 538	X22	8	953 684	815
9	409 891	017	9	166 35X	9X7	9	X76 299	79Ɛ
X	532 8X8	124 ƐX1	X	28X 145	971	X	Ɛ98 X78	765
Ɛ	657 889	Ɛ65	Ɛ	3Ɛ1 XƐ6	936	Ɛ	695 0ƐƐ 621	730
4030	780 832	Ɛ2X	4070	515 830	900	40Ɛ0	222 151	6Ɛ5
1	8X5 760	XƐ3	1	639 530	885	1	344 846	680
2	X0X 653	X78	2	761 1Ɛ5	84Ɛ	2	467 306	646
3	Ɛ33 50Ɛ	X41	3	884 X44	815	3	589 950	610
4	688 058 350	X06	4	9X8 659	79X	4	6Ɛ0 360	597
5	181 156	98Ɛ	5	Ɛ10 237	764	5	812 937	560
6	2X5 Ɛ25	954	6	691 033 99Ɛ	72X	6	935 297	527
7	40X 879	91X	7	157 509	6Ɛ3	7	X57 802	4Ɛ1
8	533 597	8X2	8	27Ɛ 000	679	8	Ɛ7X 0Ɛ3	477
9	658 279	868	9	3X2 679	643	9	696 0X0 56X	442
X	780 Ɛ25	830	X	506 100	608	X	202 9Ɛ0	408
Ɛ	8X5 755	7Ɛ6	Ɛ	629 708	592	Ɛ	325 1Ɛ8	392

N	Log N	d	N	Log N	d	N	Log N	d
4100	696 447 58X	122 358	4140	69Ɛ 0Ɛ6 340	121 180	4180	6X3 91X 272	120 007
1	569 926	323	1	217 500	147	1	X3X 279	11Ɛ Ɛ92
2	690 049	2X9	2	338 647	112	2	Ɛ5X 24Ɛ	Ɛ5X
3	7Ɛ2 336	273	3	459 759	099	3	6X4 07X 1X9	Ɛ25
4	914 5X9	23X	4	57X 836	064	4	19X 112	X20
5	X36 827	204	5	69Ɛ 89X	02Ɛ	5	2ƐX 002	X78
6	Ɛ58 X2Ɛ	18X	6	800 909	120 ƐƐ5	6	419 X7X	X44
7	697 07X ƐƐ9	155	7	921 902	Ɛ81	7	539 902	X0Ɛ
8	1X1 152	11Ɛ	8	X42 883	Ɛ47	8	659 711	997
9	303 271	0X6	9	Ɛ63 80X	Ɛ13	9	779 4X8	962
X	425 357	070	X	6X0 084 721	X99	X	899 24X	929
Ɛ	547 407	036	Ɛ	1X5 5ƐX	X65	Ɛ	9Ɛ8 Ɛ77	8Ɛ5
4110	669 441	001	4150	306 463	X2Ɛ	4190	Ɛ18 870	881
1	78Ɛ 442	121 Ɛ87	1	427 292	9Ɛ7	1	6X5 038 531	848
2	8Ɛ1 409	Ɛ52	2	548 089	981	2	158 179	814
3	X13 35Ɛ	Ɛ18	3	668 X4X	949	3	277 991	79Ɛ
4	Ɛ35 277	XX3	4	789 797	913	4	397 570	767
5	698 057 15X	X69	5	8XX 4XX	89Ɛ	5	4Ɛ7 117	732
6	179 007	X34	6	X0Ɛ 189	865	6	616 849	6ƐX
7	29X X3Ɛ	9ƐX	7	Ɛ2Ɛ X32	831	7	736 347	686
8	400 839	985	8	6X1 050 663	7Ɛ8	8	855 X11	651
9	522 602	94Ɛ	9	171 25Ɛ	783	9	975 462	619
X	644 351	916	X	291 X22	74X	X	X94 X7Ɛ	5X5
Ɛ	766 067	8X0	Ɛ	3Ɛ2 570	715	Ɛ	ƐƐ4 464	570
4120	887 947	867	4160	513 085	6X0	41X0	6X6 113 X14	538
1	9X9 5Ɛ2	832	1	633 765	668	1	233 350	504
2	Ɛ0Ɛ 224	7Ɛ8	2	754 211	632	2	352 854	48Ɛ
3	699 030 X20	782	3	874 843	5ƐX	3	472 123	457
4	152 5X2	74X	4	995 241	585	4	591 57X	423
5	274 130	714	5	XƐ5 806	550	5	6Ɛ0 9X1	3XƐ
6	395 844	69X	6	6X2 016 156	517	6	810 190	376
7	4Ɛ7 322	666	7	136 671	4X3	7	92Ɛ 546	342
8	618 988	630	8	256 Ɛ54	469	8	X4X 888	30X
9	73X 3Ɛ8	5Ɛ6	9	377 401	435	9	Ɛ69 Ɛ96	295
X	85Ɛ 9Ɛ2	582	X	497 836	401	X	6X7 089 26Ɛ	262
Ɛ	981 374	548	Ɛ	5Ɛ8 037	387	Ɛ	1X8 511	229
4130	XX2 900	513	4170	718 402	353	41Ɛ0	307 73X	1Ɛ5
1	69X 004 213	499	1	838 755	31X	1	426 933	181
2	125 6Ɛ0	464	2	958 X73	2X5	2	545 XƐ4	148
3	246 Ɛ54	42Ɛ	3	X79 158	271	3	665 040	115
4	368 383	3Ɛ6	4	Ɛ99 409	238	4	784 155	0X0
5	489 779	381	5	6X3 0Ɛ9 645	203	5	8X3 235	068
6	5XX Ɛ3X	347	6	219 848	18X	6	X02 2X1	034
7	710 285	312	7	339 X16	156	7	Ɛ21 315	000
8	831 597	299	8	459 Ɛ70	122	8	6X8 040 315	11X Ɛ88
9	952 874	264	9	57X 092	0X8	9	15Ɛ 2X1	Ɛ54
X	X73 Ɛ18	22X	X	69X 17X	074	X	27X 235	Ɛ20
Ɛ	Ɛ95 146	1Ɛ6	Ɛ	7ƐX 232	040	Ɛ	399 155	XX7

N	Log N	d	N	Log N	d	N	Log N	d
4200	6Ⅹ8 4Ɛ8 040	11Ⅹ Ⅹ74	4240	6Ɛ1 050 522	119 942	4280	6Ɛ5 760 172	118 831
1	616 ⅩƐ4	Ⅹ40	1	16Ⅹ 264	90Ɛ	1	878 9Ⅹ3	7ƐƐ
2	735 934	Ⅹ07	2	287 Ɛ73	897	2	995 5Ⅹ2	787
3	854 73Ɛ	994	3	3Ⅹ5 84Ⅹ	863	3	ⅩƐ2 169	755
4	973 513	95Ɛ	4	503 4Ɛ1	830	4	6Ɛ6 00Ⅹ 902	721
5	Ⅹ92 272	927	5	621 121	7Ɛ8	5	127 423	6ⅩƐ
6	ƐƐ0 Ɛ99	8Ɛ4	6	73Ⅹ 919	785	6	243 Ɛ12	677
7	6Ⅹ9 10Ɛ 891	87Ɛ	7	858 4Ⅹ2	752	7	360 589	645
8	22Ⅹ 550	848	8	976 034	71Ⅹ	8	479 012	612
9	349 198	814	9	Ⅹ93 752	6Ⅹ7	9	595 624	59Ɛ
Ⅹ	467 9Ɛ0	79Ɛ	Ⅹ	ƐƐ1 239	673	Ⅹ	6Ɛ2 003	567
Ɛ	586 58Ɛ	768	Ɛ	6Ɛ2 10Ⅹ 8Ɛ0	640	Ɛ	80Ⅹ 56Ⅹ	535
4210	6Ⅹ5 137	734	4250	228 330	608	4290	926 ⅩⅩ3	503
1	803 86Ɛ	700	1	345 938	596	1	Ⅹ43 3Ⅹ6	48Ɛ
2	922 36Ɛ	688	2	463 312	561	2	Ɛ5Ɛ 875	458
3	Ⅹ40 Ⅹ37	654	3	580 873	52Ɛ	3	6Ɛ7 078 111	426
4	Ɛ5Ɛ 48Ɛ	620	4	69Ⅹ 1Ⅹ2	4Ɛ7	4	194 537	3Ɛ3
5	6ⅩⅩ 079 ⅩⅩƐ	5Ⅹ8	5	7Ɛ7 699	483	5	2Ɛ0 92Ⅹ	380
6	198 497	575	6	914 Ɛ60	451	6	409 0ⅩⅩ	349
7	2Ɛ6 Ⅹ50	540	7	Ⅹ32 3Ɛ1	419	7	525 437	316
8	415 390	509	8	Ɛ4Ɛ 80Ⅹ	3Ⅹ5	8	641 751	2Ⅹ4
9	533 899	495	9	6Ɛ3 068 ƐƐ3	373	9	759 Ⅹ35	270
Ⅹ	652 172	461	Ⅹ	186 366	33Ɛ	Ⅹ	876 0Ⅹ5	23Ⅹ
Ɛ	770 613	42Ⅹ	Ɛ	2Ⅹ3 6Ⅹ5	308	Ɛ	992 323	207
4220	88Ⅹ Ⅹ41	3Ɛ5	4260	400 9Ɛ1	294	42Ⅹ0	ⅩⅩⅩ 52Ⅹ	195
1	9Ⅹ9 236	382	1	51Ⅹ 085	262	1	6Ɛ8 006 703	162
2	Ɛ07 5Ɛ8	34Ⅹ	2	637 327	22Ⅹ	2	122 865	12Ɛ
3	6ⅩƐ 025 946	316	3	754 555	1Ɛ6	3	23Ⅹ 994	0Ɛ8
4	144 060	2Ⅹ3	4	871 74Ɛ	184	4	356 Ⅹ90	085
5	262 343	26Ɛ	5	98Ⅹ 913	150	5	472 Ɛ55	053
6	380 5Ɛ2	237	6	ⅩⅩ7 Ⅹ63	11Ⅹ	6	58Ⅹ ƐⅩ8	020
7	49Ⅹ 829	203	7	6Ɛ4 004 Ɛ81	0Ⅹ6	7	6Ⅹ7 008	117 ƐⅩⅩ
8	5Ɛ8 Ⅹ30	190	8	122 067	073	8	802 Ɛ26	Ɛ77
9	717 000	158	9	23Ɛ 11Ⅹ	03Ɛ	9	91Ⅹ Ɛ71	Ɛ44
Ⅹ	835 158	124	Ⅹ	358 159	009	Ⅹ	Ⅹ36 ⅩƐ5	Ɛ11
Ɛ	953 280	0Ɛ1	Ɛ	475 166	118 Ɛ95	Ɛ	Ɛ52 Ⅹ06	Ⅹ9Ɛ
4230	Ⅹ71 371	079	4270	592 13Ɛ	Ɛ62	42Ɛ0	6Ɛ9 06Ⅹ 8Ⅹ5	Ⅹ68
1	Ɛ8Ɛ 42Ⅹ	045	1	6ⅩƐ 0Ⅹ1	Ɛ2Ɛ	1	186 751	Ⅹ36
2	6Ɛ0 0Ⅹ9 473	012	2	808 010	ⅩƐ8	2	2Ⅹ2 587	Ⅹ03
3	207 485	119 Ɛ9Ⅹ	3	924 Ɛ08	Ⅹ85	3	3ƐⅩ 38Ⅹ	990
4	325 463	Ɛ66	4	Ⅹ41 991	Ⅹ52	4	516 15Ⅹ	95Ⅹ
5	443 409	Ɛ33	5	Ɛ5Ⅹ 823	Ⅹ1Ɛ	5	631 ⅩƐ8	927
6	561 340	ⅩƐƐ	6	6Ɛ5 077 642	9Ⅹ7	6	749 823	8Ɛ5
7	67Ɛ 23Ɛ	Ⅹ88	7	194 429	975	7	865 518	882
8	799 107	Ⅹ54	8	2Ɛ1 1Ⅹ2	941	8	981 19Ⅹ	850
9	8Ɛ6 Ɛ5Ɛ	Ⅹ21	9	409 Ɛ23	90Ɛ	9	Ⅹ98 Ⅹ2Ⅹ	819
Ⅹ	Ⅹ14 980	9Ⅹ9	Ⅹ	526 832	897	Ⅹ	ƐƐ4 647	7Ⅹ6
Ɛ	Ɛ32 769	975	Ɛ	643 509	865	Ɛ	6ƐⅩ 110 231	774

N	Log N	d	N	Log N	d	N	Log N	d
4300	6ƐX 227 9X5	117 742	4340	702 870 218	116 672	4380	707 271 X46	115 602
1	343 527	70Ɛ	1	986 88X	640	1	387 448	590
2	45Ɛ 036	699	2	XX1 30X	60X	2	4X0 X18	55Ɛ
3	576 713	666	3	ƐƐ7 918	598	3	5Ɛ6 377	52X
4	692 179	633	4	703 112 2Ɛ4	566	4	70Ɛ 8X5	4Ɛ7
5	7X9 7Ɛ0	602	5	228 85X	533	5	825 1X0	487
6	905 1Ɛ2	58X	6	343 191	502	6	93X 667	455
7	X20 780	559	7	459 693	491	7	X53 Ɛ00	423
8	Ɛ38 119	526	8	573 Ɛ64	45X	8	Ɛ69 323	3Ɛ2
9	6ƐƐ 053 643	4Ɛ3	9	68X 402	428	9	708 082 715	381
X	16X Ɛ36	481	X	7X4 82X	3Ɛ6	X	197 X96	34Ɛ
Ɛ	286 3Ɛ7	44Ɛ	Ɛ	8ƐƐ 024	385	Ɛ	2Ɛ1 225	31X
4310	3X1 846	418	4350	X15 3X9	352	4390	406 543	2X8
1	4Ɛ9 062	3X6	1	Ɛ2Ɛ 73Ɛ	321	1	51Ɛ 82Ɛ	277
2	614 448	374	2	704 045 X60	2XƐ	2	634 XX6	246
3	72Ɛ 800	341	3	160 14Ɛ	279	3	74X 130	214
4	846 Ɛ41	30Ɛ	4	276 408	247	4	863 344	1X3
5	962 250	299	5	390 653	216	5	978 527	172
6	X79 529	266	6	4X6 869	1X3	6	X91 699	140
7	Ɛ94 793	234	7	600 X50	172	7	ƐX6 819	10Ɛ
8	700 0XƐ X07	202	8	717 002	140	8	709 0ƐƐ 928	099
9	207 009	190	9	831 142	10X	9	214 X05	069
X	322 199	159	X	947 250	098	X	329 X72	037
Ɛ	439 336	127	Ɛ	X61 328	067	Ɛ	442 XX9	006
4320	554 461	0Ɛ4	4360	Ɛ77 393	035	43X0	557 XƐ3	114 Ɛ94
1	66Ɛ 555	083	1	705 091 408	003	1	670 X87	Ɛ63
2	786 618	050	2	1X7 40Ɛ	115 Ɛ91	2	785 X2X	Ɛ32
3	8X1 668	01X	3	301 3X0	Ɛ60	3	89X 960	Ɛ01
4	9Ɛ8 686	116 ƐX8	4	417 340	Ɛ2X	4	9Ɛ3 861	X8Ɛ
5	Ɛ13 672	Ɛ75	5	531 26X	XƐ8	5	Ɛ08 730	X5Ɛ
6	701 02X 627	Ɛ44	6	647 166	X87	6	70X 021 58Ɛ	X29
7	145 56Ɛ	Ɛ11	7	761 031	X55	7	136 3Ɛ8	9Ɛ8
8	260 480	X9Ɛ	8	876 X86	X23	8	24Ɛ 1Ɛ4	986
9	377 35Ɛ	X69	9	990 8X9	9Ɛ1	9	363 Ɛ7X	956
X	492 208	X37	X	XX6 69X	980	X	478 914	924
Ɛ	5X9 043	X04	Ɛ	706 000 45X	94X	Ɛ	591 638	8Ɛ3
4330	703 X47	993	4370	116 1X8	919	43Ɛ0	6X6 32Ɛ	882
1	81X 81X	960	1	22Ɛ Ɛ05	8X7	1	7ƐX ƐƐ1	851
2	935 57X	92Ɛ	2	345 7Ɛ0	875	2	913 842	820
3	X50 2X9	8Ɛ8	3	45Ɛ 465	844	3	X28 462	7XX
4	Ɛ66 ƐX5	886	4	575 0X9	812	4	Ɛ41 050	77X
5	702 081 86Ɛ	854	5	68X 8ƐƐ	7X1	5	70Ɛ 055 80X	748
6	198 503	822	6	7X4 4X0	76Ɛ	6	16X 356	718
7	2Ɛ3 125	7Ɛ0	7	8ƐX 04Ɛ	739	7	282 X72	6X6
8	409 915	77X	8	X13 788	708	8	397 558	675
9	524 493	748	9	Ɛ29 294	696	9	4Ɛ0 011	644
X	63Ɛ 01Ɛ	715	X	707 042 96X	665	X	604 655	613
Ɛ	755 734	6X4	Ɛ	158 413	633	Ɛ	719 068	5X2

N	Log N	d	N	Log N	d	N	Log N	d
4400	70Ɛ 831 64χ	114 571	4440	714 16Ɛ 9χ8	113 53Ɛ	4480	718 669 443	112 528
1	945 ƐƐƐ	540	1	283 327	50χ	1	77Ɛ 96Ɛ	4Ɛ7
2	χ5χ 53Ɛ	50Ɛ	2	396 835	49χ	2	892 266	487
3	Ɛ72 χ4χ	49χ	3	4χχ 113	469	3	9χ4 731	457
4	710 087 328	469	4	601 580	439	4	χƐ6 Ɛ88	427
5	19Ɛ 795	438	5	714 9Ɛ9	408	5	719 009 3Ɛ3	3Ɛ7
6	2Ɛ4 011	407	6	828 205	398	6	11Ɛ 7χχ	387
7	408 418	396	7	93Ɛ 5χ1	367	7	231 Ɛ75	356
8	520 7Ɛ2	365	8	χ52 948	337	8	344 30Ɛ	327
9	634 Ɛ57	334	9	Ɛ66 083	306	9	456 636	2Ɛ7
χ	749 28Ɛ	303	χ	715 079 389	296	χ	568 931	287
Ɛ	861 592	292	Ɛ	190 663	266	Ɛ	67χ ƐƐ8	256
4410	975 864	262	4450	2χ3 909	235	4490	791 252	227
1	χ89 Ɛ06	230	1	3Ɛ6 Ɛ42	204	1	8χ3 479	1Ɛ7
2	Ɛχ2 136	1ƐƐ	2	50χ 146	194	2	9Ɛ5 674	187
3	711 0Ɛ6 335	18Ɛ	3	621 31χ	164	3	Ɛ07 83Ɛ	157
4	20χ 504	15χ	4	734 482	133	4	71χ 019 996	127
5	322 662	129	5	847 5Ɛ5	103	5	12Ɛ Ɛ01	0Ɛ7
6	436 78Ɛ	0Ɛ8	6	95χ 6Ɛ8	092	6	241 ƐƐ8	087
7	54χ 887	087	7	χ71 78χ	062	7	354 083	057
8	662 952	056	8	Ɛ84 830	032	8	466 11χ	027
9	776 9χ8	026	9	716 097 862	001	9	578 145	111 ƐƐ7
χ	88χ χ12	113 ƐƐ5	χ	1χχ 863	112 Ɛ91	χ	68χ 140	Ɛ88
Ɛ	9χ2 χ07	Ɛ84	Ɛ	301 834	Ɛ61	Ɛ	7χ0 108	Ɛ57
4420	χƐ6 98Ɛ	Ɛ53	4460	414 795	Ɛ30	44χ0	8Ɛ2 063	Ɛ28
1	712 00χ 922	Ɛ22	1	527 705	Ɛ00	1	χ03 Ɛ8Ɛ	χƐ8
2	122 844	χƐ2	2	63χ 605	χ90	2	Ɛ15 χ87	χ88
3	236 736	χ80	3	751 495	χ5Ɛ	3	71Ɛ 027 953	χ58
4	34χ 5Ɛ6	χ50	4	864 334	χ30	4	139 7χƐ	χ28
5	462 446	χ20	5	977 164	9Ɛχ	5	24Ɛ 617	9Ɛ8
6	576 266	9χχ	6	χ89 Ɛ62	98Ɛ	6	361 413	989
7	68χ 054	97χ	7	Ɛχ0 931	95χ	7	473 1χ0	959
8	7χ1 χ12	949	8	717 0Ɛ3 68Ɛ	92χ	8	584 Ɛ39	929
9	8Ɛ5 75Ɛ	919	9	206 3Ɛ9	8Ɛχ	9	696 866	8Ɛ9
χ	χ09 478	8χ7	χ	319 0Ɛ7	889	χ	7χ8 563	889
Ɛ	Ɛ21 163	877	Ɛ	42Ɛ 984	85χ	Ɛ	8Ɛχ 230	85χ
4430	713 034 χ1χ	847	4470	542 622	829	44Ɛ0	χ0Ɛ χ8χ	82χ
1	148 665	815	1	655 24Ɛ	7Ɛ9	1	Ɛ21 6Ɛ8	7Ɛχ
2	260 27χ	7χ5	2	767 χ48	788	2	720 033 2Ɛ6	78Ɛ
3	373 χ63	774	3	87χ 614	759	3	144 χ85	75χ
4	487 617	744	4	991 171	728	4	256 623	72Ɛ
5	59Ɛ 15Ɛ	713	5	χχ3 899	6Ɛ8	5	368 152	6ƐƐ
6	6Ɛ2 872	6χ3	6	ƐƐ6 395	688	6	479 851	690
7	806 355	672	7	718 108 χ61	658	7	58Ɛ 321	660
8	919 χ07	641	8	21Ɛ 4Ɛ9	628	8	6χ0 981	630
9	χ31 448	610	9	331 Ɛ25	5Ɛ8	9	7Ɛ2 3Ɛ1	600
χ	Ɛ44 χ58	5χ0	χ	444 521	587	χ	903 9Ɛ1	591
Ɛ	714 058 438	570	Ɛ	556 χχ8	557	Ɛ	χ15 382	561

N	Log N	d	N	Log N	d	N	Log N	d
4500	720 ε26 923	111 532	4540	725 364 777	110 555	4580	729 763 696	10ε 596
1	721 038 255	502	1	475 110	527	1	873 070	568
2	149 757	492	2	585 637	4ε6	2	982 618	538
3	25ε 029	463	3	695 ε31	488	3	χ91 ε54	50χ
4	370 490	433	4	7χ6 3ε9	459	4	εχ1 462	49ε
5	481 903	403	5	8ε6 856	429	5	72χ 0ε0 941	471
6	593 106	394	6	χ07 083	3εχ	6	200 1ε2	442
7	6χ4 49χ	364	7	ε17 481	38ε	7	30ε 634	413
8	7ε5 842	335	8	726 027 850	360	8	41χ χ47	3χ4
9	906 ε77	305	9	137 εε0	331	9	52χ 22ε	376
χ	χ18 280	295	χ	248 321	302	χ	639 5χ5	347
ε	ε29 555	266	ε	358 623	293	ε	748 930	318
4510	722 03χ 7εε	237	4550	468 8ε6	263	4590	858 048	2χχ
1	14ε χ36	207	1	578 ε59	235	1	967 336	27ε
2	261 041	197	2	689 192	205	2	χ76 5ε5	250
3	372 218	168	3	799 397	196	3	ε85 845	222
4	483 384	138	4	8χ9 571	168	4	72ε 094 χ67	1ε3
5	594 500	109	5	9ε9 719	138	5	1χ4 05χ	184
6	6χ5 609	09χ	6	ε09 855	109	6	2ε3 222	156
7	7ε6 6χ7	06χ	7	727 019 962	09χ	7	402 378	127
8	907 755	03χ	8	129 χ40	06ε	8	511 4χ3	0ε9
9	χ18 793	00ε	9	239 χχε	040	9	620 5χ0	08χ
χ	ε29 7χ2	110 εχ0	χ	349 ε2ε	011	χ	72ε 66χ	060
ε	723 03χ 782	ε70	ε	459 ε40	10ε εχ2	ε	83χ 70χ	031
4520	14ε 732	ε41	4560	569 ε22	ε74	45χ0	949 73ε	002
1	260 673	ε11	1	679 χ96	ε44	1	χ58 741	10χ ε94
2	371 584	χχ2	2	789 χ1χ	ε15	2	ε67 715	ε65
3	482 466	χ72	3	899 933	χχ6	3	730 076 67χ	ε37
4	593 318	χ43	4	9χ9 819	χ77	4	185 5ε5	ε08
5	6χ4 15ε	χ14	5	χε9 694	χ49	5	294 501	χ9χ
6	7ε4 ε73	9χ5	6	728 009 521	χ19	6	3χ3 39ε	χ70
7	905 958	975	7	119 33χ	9χε	7	4ε2 24ε	χ40
8	χ16 711	945	8	229 129	97ε	8	601 08ε	χ13
9	ε27 456	917	9	338 χχ8	951	9	70ε χχ2	9χ4
χ	724 038 171	8χ7	χ	448 839	921	χ	81χ 886	975
ε	148 χ58	877	ε	558 55χ	8ε3	ε	929 63ε	947
4530	259 713	849	4570	668 251	884	45ε0	χ38 386	918
1	36χ 360	819	1	777 ε15	855	1	ε47 0χ2	8χχ
2	47χ ε79	7χ9	2	887 76χ	827	2	731 055 990	880
3	58ε 766	77ε	3	997 395	7ε7	3	164 650	851
4	6χ0 325	74ε	4	χχ6 ε90	789	4	273 2χ1	823
5	7ε0 χ74	720	5	εε6 759	759	5	381 ε04	7ε4
6	901 594	6ε0	6	729 106 2ε6	72ε	6	490 6ε8	786
7	χ12 084	682	7	215 χ25	701	7	59ε 282	758
8	ε22 746	652	8	325 526	691	8	6χ9 χ1χ	729
9	725 033 198	623	9	434 εε7	662	9	7ε8 547	6εε
χ	143 7εε	5ε4	χ	544 659	634	χ	907 046	690
ε	254 1ε3	584	ε	654 091	605	ε	χ15 716	663

N	Log N	d	N	Log N	d	N	Log N	d
4600	731 Ɛ24 179	10χ 633	4640	736 266 Ɛ05	109 6χ9	4680	73χ 570 582	108 780
1	732 032 7Ɛ0	606	1	374 5Ɛ2	680	1	679 142	752
2	141 1Ɛ6	597	2	482 072	652	2	785 894	725
3	24Ɛ 791	569	3	58Ɛ 704	624	3	892 3Ɛ9	6Ɛ7
4	35χ 13χ	53χ	4	699 128	5Ɛ6	4	99χ χƐ4	68χ
5	468 678	511	5	7χ6 722	589	5	χχ7 582	660
6	576 Ɛ89	4χ1	6	8Ɛ4 0χƐ	55χ	6	ƐƐ4 022	633
7	685 46χ	474	7	χ01 649	531	7	73Ɛ 100 655	605
8	793 922	445	8	Ɛ0χ Ɛ7χ	502	8	209 05χ	598
9	8χ2 167	418	9	737 018 480	495	9	315 636	56Ɛ
χ	9Ɛ0 583	3χ9	χ	125 955	467	χ	421 Ɛχ5	541
Ɛ	χƐχ 970	37χ	Ɛ	233 200	43χ	Ɛ	52χ 526	514
4610	733 009 12χ	351	4650	340 63χ	40Ɛ	4690	636 χ3χ	4χ6
1	117 47Ɛ	322	1	449 χ49	3χ2	1	743 324	479
2	225 7χ1	2Ɛ4	2	557 22Ɛ	373	2	84Ɛ 7χ1	44Ɛ
3	333 χ95	285	3	664 5χ2	346	3	958 030	422
4	442 15χ	258	4	771 928	319	4	χ64 452	3Ɛ5
5	550 3Ɛ6	229	5	87Ɛ 045	2χχ	5	Ɛ70 847	388
6	65χ 623	1ƐƐ	6	988 333	281	6	740 079 013	35χ
7	768 822	192	7	χ95 5Ɛ4	253	7	185 371	330
8	876 9Ɛ4	162	8	Ɛχ2 847	225	8	291 6χ1	304
9	984 Ɛ56	135	9	738 0χƐ χ70	1Ɛ7	9	399 9χ5	296
χ	χ93 08Ɛ	107	χ	1Ɛ9 067	18χ	χ	4χ6 07Ɛ	268
Ɛ	Ɛχ1 196	098	Ɛ	306 235	160	Ɛ	5Ɛ2 327	240
4620	734 0χƐ 272	06χ	4660	413 395	132	46χ0	6Ɛχ 567	212
1	1Ɛ9 320	040	1	520 507	105	1	806 779	1χ5
2	307 360	012	2	629 610	097	2	912 962	177
3	415 372	109 Ɛχ4	3	736 6χ7	069	3	χ1χ Ɛ19	14χ
4	523 356	Ɛ76	4	843 754	03Ɛ	4	Ɛ27 067	121
5	631 310	Ɛ48	5	950 793	012	5	741 033 188	0Ɛ4
6	73Ɛ 258	Ɛ1χ	6	χ59 7χ5	108 Ɛχ4	6	13Ɛ 280	086
7	849 176	χχƐ	7	Ɛ66 789	Ɛ77	7	247 346	059
8	957 065	χ82	8	739 073 744	Ɛ49	8	353 3χ3	030
9	χ64 Ɛ27	χ53	9	180 691	Ɛ1Ɛ	9	45Ɛ 413	003
χ	Ɛ72 97χ	χ26	χ	289 5Ɛ0	χƐ2	χ	567 416	107 Ɛ96
Ɛ	735 080 7χ4	9Ɛ7	Ɛ	396 4χ2	χ84	Ɛ	673 3Ɛ0	Ɛ68
4630	18χ 59Ɛ	989	4670	4χ3 366	χ56	46Ɛ0	77Ɛ 358	Ɛ3Ɛ
1	298 368	960	1	5Ɛ0 200	χ29	1	887 297	Ɛ12
2	3χ6 108	931	2	6Ɛ9 029	9ƐƐ	2	993 1χ9	χχ4
3	4Ɛ3 χ39	904	3	805 χ28	991	3	χ9Ɛ 091	χ78
4	601 741	895	4	912 7Ɛ9	964	4	Ɛχ6 Ɛ49	χ4χ
5	70Ɛ 416	867	5	χ1Ɛ 561	937	5	742 0Ɛ2 997	χ21
6	819 081	83χ	6	Ɛ28 298	909	6	1Ɛχ 7Ɛ8	9Ɛ4
7	926 8ƐƐ	80Ɛ	7	73χ 034 Ɛχ5	89Ɛ	7	306 5Ɛ0	987
8	χ34 50χ	7χ2	8	141 884	872	8	412 377	95χ
9	Ɛ42 0Ɛ0	773	9	24χ 536	844	9	51χ 115	931
χ	736 04Ɛ 863	746	χ	357 17χ	817	χ	625 χ46	903
Ɛ	159 3χ9	718	Ɛ	463 995	7χ9	Ɛ	731 749	897

N	Log N	d	N	Log N	d	N	Log N	d
4700	742 839 424	107 869	4740	746 X8X 105	106 973	4780	74Ɛ 0X3 270	105 X92
1	945 091	840	1	Ɛ94 X78	945	1	1X9 142	X66
2	X50 911	813	2	747 09Ɛ 801	919	2	2Ɛ2 ƐX8	X39
3	Ɛ58 524	7X6	3	1X6 51X	8Ɛ0	3	3Ɛ8 X25	X11
4	743 064 10X	779	4	2Ɛ1 20X	883	4	502 836	9X4
5	16Ɛ 887	750	5	3Ɛ7 X91	857	5	608 61X	979
6	277 417	723	6	502 728	82X	6	712 397	950
7	382 Ɛ3X	6Ɛ6	7	609 356	801	7	818 127	924
8	48X 634	688	8	713 Ɛ57	795	8	921 X4Ɛ	8Ɛ7
9	596 100	660	9	81X 730	768	9	X27 746	890
X	6X1 760	633	X	925 298	73Ɛ	X	Ɛ31 416	863
Ɛ	7X9 193	605	Ɛ	X2Ɛ X17	713	Ɛ	750 037 079	837
4710	8Ɛ4 798	599	4750	Ɛ36 52X	6X7	4790	140 8Ɛ4	80X
1	X00 175	570	1	748 041 015	679	1	246 502	7X3
2	Ɛ07 725	542	2	147 692	651	2	350 0X5	776
3	744 013 067	516	3	252 123	625	3	455 85Ɛ	74X
4	11X 581	4X9	4	358 748	5Ɛ8	4	55Ɛ 3X9	722
5	225 X6X	480	5	463 144	58Ɛ	5	664 Ɛ0Ɛ	6Ɛ6
6	331 32X	453	6	569 713	563	6	76X 605	689
7	438 781	425	7	674 076	536	7	874 092	661
8	543 ƐX6	3Ɛ9	8	77X 5Ɛ0	50X	8	979 733	636
9	64Ɛ 3X3	390	9	884 XƐX	4X1	9	X83 169	609
X	756 773	364	X	98Ɛ 39Ɛ	475	X	Ɛ88 776	5X1
Ɛ	861 Ɛ17	336	Ɛ	X95 854	448	Ɛ	751 092 157	574
4720	969 251	309	4760	ƐX0 0X0	41Ɛ	47X0	197 70Ɛ	549
1	X74 55X	2X0	1	749 0X6 4ƐƐ	3Ɛ3	1	2X1 058	521
2	Ɛ7Ɛ 83X	274	2	1Ɛ0 8Ɛ2	387	2	3X6 579	4Ɛ4
3	745 086 XƐ2	247	3	2Ɛ7 079	35X	3	4XƐ X71	488
4	192 139	219	4	401 417	332	4	5Ɛ5 339	461
5	299 356	1Ɛ1	5	507 749	305	5	6ƐX 79X	434
6	3X4 547	184	6	611 X52	299	6	804 012	408
7	4XƐ 70Ɛ	158	7	718 12Ɛ	270	7	909 41X	3X0
8	5Ɛ6 867	12X	8	822 39Ɛ	244	8	X12 7ƐX	374
9	701 995	101	9	928 623	217	9	Ɛ17 Ɛ72	348
X	808 X96	095	X	X32 83X	1XƐ	X	752 021 2ƐX	320
Ɛ	913 Ɛ6Ɛ	068	Ɛ	Ɛ38 X29	183	Ɛ	126 61X	2Ɛ4
4730	X1Ɛ 017	03Ɛ	4770	74X 042 ƐƐ0	156	47Ɛ0	22Ɛ 912	287
1	Ɛ26 056	012	1	149 146	12X	1	334 Ɛ99	260
2	746 031 068	106 ƐX6	2	253 274	101	2	43X 239	234
3	138 052	Ɛ79	3	359 375	095	3	543 471	208
4	243 00Ɛ	Ɛ50	4	463 44X	068	4	648 679	19Ɛ
5	349 Ɛ5Ɛ	Ɛ23	5	569 4Ɛ6	041	5	751 858	174
6	454 X82	XƐ6	6	673 537	013	6	856 X10	148
7	55Ɛ 978	X8X	7	779 54X	105 ƐX8	7	95Ɛ Ɛ58	120
8	666 846	X61	8	883 536	Ɛ7Ɛ	8	X65 078	0Ɛ4
9	771 6X7	X34	9	989 4Ɛ5	Ɛ53	9	Ɛ6X 170	088
X	878 51Ɛ	X08	X	X93 448	Ɛ26	X	753 073 238	060
Ɛ	983 327	99X	Ɛ	Ɛ99 372	XƐX	Ɛ	178 298	034

N	Log N	d	N	Log N	d	N	Log N	d
4800	753 281 310	105 008	4840	757 424 880	104 158	4880	75Ɛ 552 144	103 303
1	386 318	104 Ɛχ0	1	528 χ18	131	1	655 447	298
2	48Ɛ 2Ɛ8	Ɛ74	2	630 Ɛ49	106	2	758 723	271
3	594 270	Ɛ49	3	735 053	09χ	3	85Ɛ 994	245
4	699 1Ɛ9	Ɛ20	4	839 131	073	4	963 019	21Ɛ
5	7χ2 119	χƐ5	5	941 1χ4	047	5	χ66 238	1Ɛ3
6	8χ7 012	χ88	6	χ45 22Ɛ	01Ɛ	6	Ɛ69 42Ɛ	188
7	9χƐ χ9χ	χ61	7	Ɛ49 24χ	103 ƐƐ4	7	760 070 5Ɛ7	161
8	χƐ4 93Ɛ	χ35	8	758 051 242	Ɛ89	8	173 758	136
9	ƐƐ9 774	χ09	9	155 20Ɛ	Ɛ61	9	276 892	10Ɛ
χ	754 102 581	9χ2	χ	259 170	Ɛ35	χ	379 9χ1	0χ4
Ɛ	207 363	975	Ɛ	361 0χ5	Ɛ0χ	Ɛ	480 χ85	078
4810	310 118	949	4850	464 ƐƐ3	χχ3	4890	583 Ɛ41	052
1	414 χ65	922	1	568 χ96	χ77	1	686 Ɛ93	026
2	519 787	8Ɛ6	2	670 951	χ50	2	789 ƐƐ9	000
3	622 481	88χ	3	774 7χ1	χ24	3	890 ƐƐ9	102 Ɛ94
4	727 14Ɛ	862	4	878 605	9Ɛ9	4	993 Ɛ91	Ɛ69
5	82Ɛ 9Ɛ1	837	5	980 402	991	5	χ96 Ɛ3χ	Ɛ42
6	934 628	80Ɛ	6	χ84 193	966	6	Ɛ99 χ80	Ɛ17
7	χ39 237	7χ3	7	Ɛ87 Ɛ39	93Ɛ	7	761 0χ0 997	χƐ1
8	Ɛ41 χ1χ	777	8	759 08Ɛ 878	913	8	1χ3 888	χ85
9	755 046 595	74Ɛ	9	193 58Ɛ	8χ8	9	2χ6 751	χ5χ
χ	14Ɛ 124	724	χ	297 277	880	χ	3χ9 5χƐ	χ33
Ɛ	253 848	6Ɛ8	Ɛ	39χ Ɛ37	855	Ɛ	4Ɛ0 422	χ08
4820	358 344	690	4860	4χ2 790	82χ	48χ0	5Ɛ3 22χ	9χ0
1	460 χ14	664	1	5χ6 3Ɛχ	802	1	6Ɛ6 00χ	976
2	565 478	639	2	6χχ 000	797	2	7Ɛ8 984	94Ɛ
3	669 χƐ5	611	3	7Ɛ1 797	770	3	8ƐƐ 713	924
4	772 506	5χ5	4	8Ɛ5 347	744	4	χ02 437	8Ɛχ
5	876 χχƐ	579	5	9Ɛ8 χ8Ɛ	719	5	Ɛ05 135	892
6	97Ɛ 468	552	6	Ɛ00 5χ8	6Ɛ2	6	762 007 χ07	867
7	χ83 9Ɛχ	526	7	75χ 004 09χ	686	7	10χ 672	840
8	Ɛ88 324	4ƐƐ	8	107 764	65Ɛ	8	211 2Ɛ2	815
9	756 090 823	493	9	20Ɛ 203	633	9	313 Ɛ07	7χχ
χ	195 0Ɛ6	467	χ	312 836	609	χ	416 6Ɛ5	784
Ɛ	299 561	43Ɛ	Ɛ	416 243	5χ1	Ɛ	519 279	758
4830	3χ1 9χ0	414	4870	519 824	576	48Ɛ0	61Ɛ χ15	732
1	4χ6 1Ɛ4	3χ8	1	621 19χ	54χ	1	722 547	706
2	5χχ 5χ0	381	2	724 728	524	2	825 051	6χ0
3	6Ɛ2 961	355	3	828 050	4Ɛ8	3	927 731	675
4	7Ɛ7 0Ɛ6	329	4	92Ɛ 548	491	4	χ2χ 1χ6	64χ
5	8ƐƐ 423	302	5	χ32 χ19	465	5	Ɛ30 834	623
6	χ03 725	296	6	Ɛ36 282	43Ɛ	6	763 033 257	5Ɛ8
7	Ɛ07 9ƐƐ	26χ	7	75Ɛ 039 701	413	7	135 853	592
8	757 010 069	243	8	140 Ɛ14	3χ8	8	238 225	566
9	114 2Ɛ0	218	9	244 300	380	9	33χ 78Ɛ	540
χ	218 508	1χƐ	χ	347 680	356	χ	441 10Ɛ	515
Ɛ	320 6Ɛ7	185	Ɛ	44χ χ16	32χ	Ɛ	543 624	4χχ

N	Log N	d	N	Log N	d	N	Log N	d
4900	763 645 Ɛ12	102 483	4940	767 704 783	101 658	7980	76Ɛ 74X 8X2	100 847
1	748 395	458	1	806 21Ɛ	632	1	84Ɛ 529	821
2	84X 831	432	2	907 851	608	2	950 14X	7Ɛ7
3	951 063	407	3	X09 259	5X1	3	X50 945	790
4	X53 46X	3X0	4	Ɛ0X 83X	577	4	Ɛ51 515	767
5	Ɛ55 84X	375	5	768 010 1Ɛ5	550	5	770 052 080	740
6	764 058 003	34X	6	111 745	526	6	152 800	717
7	15X 351	324	7	213 06Ɛ	500	7	253 317	6Ɛ0
8	260 675	2Ɛ9	8	314 56Ɛ	495	8	353 X07	687
9	362 972	292	9	415 X44	46Ɛ	9	454 492	660
X	465 044	267	X	517 2Ɛ3	444	X	554 Ɛ32	636
Ɛ	567 2XƐ	241	Ɛ	618 737	41X	Ɛ	655 568	610
4910	669 530	216	4950	719 Ɛ55	3Ɛ4	4990	755 Ɛ78	5X6
1	76Ɛ 746	1XƐ	1	81Ɛ 349	389	1	856 562	580
2	871 935	185	2	920 716	363	2	956 Ɛ22	557
3	973 XƐX	159	3	X21 X79	338	3	X57 479	530
4	X76 057	133	4	Ɛ23 1Ɛ5	312	4	Ɛ57 9X9	506
5	Ɛ78 18X	109	5	769 024 507	2X8	5	771 058 2Ɛ3	4X0
6	765 07X 297	0X2	6	125 7Ɛ3	282	6	158 793	476
7	180 379	077	7	226 X75	257	7	259 049	450
8	282 434	050	8	328 110	231	8	359 499	426
9	384 484	026	9	429 341	206	9	459 903	401
X	486 4XX	101 ƐƐƐ	X	52X 547	1X0	X	55X 104	396
Ɛ	588 4X9	Ɛ94	Ɛ	62Ɛ 727	176	Ɛ	65X 49X	370
4920	68X 481	Ɛ6X	4960	730 8X1	150	49X0	75X 84X	347
1	790 42Ɛ	Ɛ43	1	831 X31	125	1	85X Ɛ95	320
2	892 372	Ɛ18	2	932 Ɛ56	0ƐƐ	2	95Ɛ 2Ɛ5	2Ɛ7
3	994 28X	XƐ2	3	X34 055	095	3	X5Ɛ 5Ɛ0	290
4	X96 180	X87	4	Ɛ35 12X	06Ɛ	4	Ɛ5Ɛ 880	267
5	Ɛ98 047	X61	5	76X 036 199	044	5	772 05Ɛ Ɛ27	241
6	766 099 XX8	X36	6	137 221	01X	6	160 168	217
7	19Ɛ 922	X10	7	238 23Ɛ	100 ƐƐ4	7	260 383	1Ɛ1
8	2X1 732	9X4	8	339 233	Ɛ8X	8	360 574	187
9	3X3 516	97Ɛ	9	43X 201	Ɛ63	9	460 73Ɛ	161
X	4X5 295	953	X	53Ɛ 164	Ɛ39	X	560 8X0	138
Ɛ	5X7 028	92X	Ɛ	640 0X1	Ɛ13	Ɛ	660 X18	111
4930	6X8 956	902	4970	740 ƐƐ4	XX9	49Ɛ0	760 Ɛ29	0X8
1	7XX 658	898	1	841 XX1	X82	1	861 015	082
2	8Ɛ0 334	872	2	942 963	X59	2	961 097	058
3	9Ɛ1 ƐX6	847	3	X43 800	X32	3	X61 133	032
4	XƐ3 831	820	4	Ɛ44 632	X08	4	Ɛ61 165	008
5	ƐƐ5 451	7Ɛ6	5	76Ɛ 045 43X	9X2	5	773 061 171	ƐƐ ƐX3
6	767 0Ɛ7 047	790	6	146 220	978	6	161 154	Ɛ79
7	1Ɛ8 817	765	7	246 Ɛ98	951	7	261 111	Ɛ53
8	2ƐX 380	73X	8	347 929	928	8	361 064	Ɛ29
9	3ƐƐ XƐX	714	9	448 655	901	9	460 Ɛ91	Ɛ03
X	501 612	6XX	X	549 356	897	X	560 X94	X9X
Ɛ	603 100	683	Ɛ	64X 031	871	Ɛ	660 972	X73

N	Log N	d	N	Log N	d	N	Log N	d
4X00	773 760 825	ƐƐ X4Ɛ	4X40	777 73X Ɛ34	ƐƐ 065	4X80	77Ɛ 6X5 Ɛ5X	ƐX 295
1	860 674	X24	1	839 Ɛ99	040	1	7X4 233	270
2	960 498	9ƐX	2	939 019	017	2	8X2 4X3	247
3	X60 296	995	3	X38 034	ƐX ƐƐ1	3	9X0 72X	222
4	Ɛ60 06Ɛ	96Ɛ	4	Ɛ37 025	Ɛ88	4	X9X 950	1Ɛ9
5	774 05Ɛ X1X	945	5	778 035 ƐƐ1	Ɛ63	5	Ɛ98 Ɛ49	194
6	15Ɛ 763	920	6	134 Ɛ54	Ɛ39	6	780 097 121	16Ɛ
7	25Ɛ 483	8Ɛ6	7	233 X91	Ɛ13	7	195 290	145
8	35Ɛ 179	890	8	332 9X4	XXƐ	8	293 415	121
9	45X X49	866	9	431 893	X85	9	391 536	0Ɛ8
X	55X 6Ɛ3	841	X	530 758	X5Ɛ	X	48Ɛ 632	092
Ɛ	65X 334	817	Ɛ	62Ɛ 5Ɛ7	X37	Ɛ	589 704	06X
4X10	759 Ɛ4Ɛ	7Ɛ1	4X50	72X 432	X11	4X90	687 772	044
1	859 740	788	1	829 243	9X7	1	785 7Ɛ6	020
2	959 308	762	2	928 02X	982	2	883 816	Ɛ9 ƐƐ7
3	X58 X6X	739	3	X26 9Ɛ0	959	3	981 811	Ɛ91
4	Ɛ58 5X7	712	4	Ɛ25 749	934	4	X7Ɛ 7X2	Ɛ69
5	775 058 0Ɛ9	6X9	5	779 024 481	90X	5	Ɛ79 74Ɛ	Ɛ43
6	157 7X6	684	6	123 18Ɛ	8X5	6	781 077 692	Ɛ1Ɛ
7	257 26X	65X	7	221 X74	880	7	175 5Ɛ1	XƐ6
8	356 908	634	8	320 734	856	8	273 4X7	X90
9	456 340	60X	9	41Ɛ 38X	832	9	371 377	X68
X	555 94X	5X5	X	51X 000	807	X	46Ɛ 223	X43
Ɛ	655 333	580	Ɛ	618 807	7X3	Ɛ	569 066	X1X
4X20	754 8Ɛ3	555	4X60	717 3XX	779	4XX0	666 X84	9Ɛ5
1	854 248	530	1	815 Ɛ67	754	1	764 879	990
2	953 778	507	2	914 6ƐƐ	72Ɛ	2	862 649	967
3	X53 083	4X1	3	X13 22X	706	3	960 3Ɛ4	942
4	Ɛ52 564	477	4	Ɛ11 934	6X0	4	X5X 136	919
5	776 051 X1Ɛ	452	5	77X 010 414	677	5	Ɛ57 X53	8Ɛ5
6	151 271	429	6	10X X8Ɛ	652	6	782 055 748	88Ɛ
7	250 69X	402	7	209 521	629	7	153 417	867
8	34Ɛ XX0	399	8	307 Ɛ4X	604	8	251 082	842
9	44Ɛ 279	374	9	406 552	59X	9	34X 904	819
X	54X 631	34X	X	504 Ɛ30	575	X	448 521	7Ɛ4
Ɛ	649 97Ɛ	325	Ɛ	603 4X5	550	Ɛ	546 115	78Ɛ
4X30	749 0X4	2ƐƐ	4X70	701 X35	527	4XƐ0	643 8X4	766
1	848 3X3	296	1	800 360	501	1	741 44X	742
2	947 679	270	2	8ƐX 861	499	2	83X Ɛ90	718
3	X46 929	246	3	9Ɛ9 13X	473	3	938 6X8	6Ɛ4
4	Ɛ45 Ɛ73	222	4	XƐ7 5Ɛ1	44X	4	X36 1X0	68Ɛ
5	777 045 195	1Ɛ7	5	ƐƐ5 X3Ɛ	425	5	Ɛ33 86Ɛ	666
6	144 390	192	6	77Ɛ 0Ɛ4 264	400	6	783 031 315	642
7	243 562	169	7	1Ɛ2 664	397	7	12X 957	618
8	342 70Ɛ	143	8	2Ɛ0 X3Ɛ	371	8	228 373	5Ɛ4
9	441 852	11X	9	3XƐ 1Ɛ0	349	9	325 967	58Ɛ
X	540 970	0Ɛ5	X	4X9 539	323	X	423 336	566
Ɛ	63Ɛ X65	08Ɛ	Ɛ	5X7 860	2ƐX	Ɛ	520 8X0	542

N	Log N	d	N	Log N	d	N	Log N	d
4Ɛ00	783 61X 222	Ɛ9 518	4Ɛ40	787 520 071	Ɛ8 774	4Ɛ80	78Ɛ 3XƐ ƐX8	Ɛ7 X22
1	717 73X	4Ɛ4	1	618 825	74Ɛ	1	4X7 X0X	9ƐX
2	815 032	48Ɛ	2	715 374	727	2	5X3 808	996
3	912 501	467	3	811 X9Ɛ	703	3	69Ɛ 5X2	972
4	X0Ɛ 968	442	4	90X 5X2	69X	4	797 354	94X
5	Ɛ09 1XX	418	5	X07 080	676	5	893 0X2	925
6	784 006 606	3Ɛ5	6	Ɛ03 736	651	6	98X X07	902
7	103 9ƐƐ	38Ɛ	7	788 000 187	629	7	X86 709	89X
8	201 18X	367	8	0Ɛ8 7Ɛ4	604	8	Ɛ82 3X7	875
9	2ƐX 535	342	9	1Ɛ5 1Ɛ8	5X0	9	790 07X 060	851
X	3Ɛ7 877	319	X	2Ɛ1 798	578	X	175 8Ɛ1	82X
Ɛ	4Ɛ4 Ɛ94	2Ɛ5	Ɛ	3XX 154	553	Ɛ	271 51Ɛ	805
4Ɛ10	5Ɛ2 289	290	4Ɛ50	4X6 6X7	52Ɛ	4Ɛ90	369 124	7X1
1	6XƐ 559	267	1	5X3 016	507	1	464 905	779
2	7X8 804	243	2	69Ɛ 521	4X2	2	560 482	755
3	8X5 X47	21X	3	797 X03	47X	3	658 017	732
4	9X3 065	1Ɛ5	4	894 281	456	4	753 749	709
5	XX0 25X	191	5	990 717	431	5	84Ɛ 256	6X5
6	Ɛ99 42Ɛ	168	6	X88 Ɛ48	409	6	946 93Ɛ	681
7	785 096 597	143	7	Ɛ85 355	3X4	7	X42 400	659
8	193 71X	11Ɛ	8	789 081 739	381	8	Ɛ39 X59	635
9	290 839	0Ɛ6	9	179 XƐX	358	9	791 035 492	611
X	389 933	092	X	276 256	333	X	130 XX3	5X9
Ɛ	486 X05	069	Ɛ	372 589	310	Ɛ	228 490	585
4Ɛ20	583 X72	044	4Ɛ60	46X 899	2X7	4ƐX0	323 X55	561
1	680 XƐ6	020	1	566 Ɛ84	283	1	41Ɛ 3Ɛ6	539
2	779 Ɛ16	Ɛ8 ƐƐ7	2	663 247	25X	2	516 933	516
3	876 Ɛ11	Ɛ92	3	75Ɛ 4X5	236	3	612 249	4Ɛ1
4	973 XX3	Ɛ6X	4	857 71Ɛ	213	4	709 73X	489
5	X70 X51	Ɛ46	5	953 932	1X9	5	805 007	466
6	Ɛ69 997	Ɛ21	6	X4Ɛ Ɛ1Ɛ	186	6	900 471	441
7	786 066 8Ɛ8	XƐ8	7	Ɛ48 0X5	161	7	9Ɛ7 8Ɛ2	419
8	163 7Ɛ4	X93	8	78X 044 246	139	8	XƐ3 10Ɛ	3Ɛ6
9	260 687	X70	9	140 383	115	9	ƐXX 505	392
X	359 537	X46	X	238 498	0Ɛ1	X	792 0X5 897	36X
Ɛ	456 381	X22	Ɛ	334 589	088	Ɛ	1X1 045	345
4Ɛ30	553 1X3	9ƐX	4Ɛ70	430 655	064	4ƐƐ0	298 38X	322
1	64Ɛ ƐX1	995	1	528 6Ɛ9	040	1	393 6Ɛ0	2ƐX
2	748 976	970	2	624 739	018	2	48X 9XX	297
3	845 726	948	3	720 755	Ɛ7 ƐƐ4	3	586 085	272
4	942 472	924	4	818 749	Ɛ8Ɛ	4	681 337	24X
5	X3Ɛ 196	8ƐƐ	5	914 718	Ɛ67	5	778 585	227
6	Ɛ37 X95	897	6	X10 683	Ɛ43	6	873 7Ɛ0	203
7	787 034 770	872	7	Ɛ08 606	Ɛ1Ɛ	7	96X 9Ɛ3	19Ɛ
8	131 422	849	8	78Ɛ 004 525	XƐ7	8	X65 Ɛ92	177
9	22X 06Ɛ	825	9	100 420	X93	9	Ɛ61 149	153
X	326 894	801	X	1Ɛ8 2Ɛ3	X6X	X	793 058 2X0	12Ɛ
Ɛ	423 495	798	Ɛ	2Ɛ4 161	X47	Ɛ	153 40Ɛ	108

N	Log N	d	N	Log N	d	N	Log N	d
5000	793 24X 517	Ɛ7 0X4	5040	797 077 93X	Ɛ6 378	5080	79X X74 541	Ɛ5 663
1	345 5ƐƐ	080	1	172 0Ɛ6	354	1	Ɛ69 ƐX4	640
2	440 67Ɛ	058	2	268 44X	331	2	79Ɛ 063 624	619
3	537 717	034	3	362 77Ɛ	30X	3	159 041	5Ɛ5
4	632 74Ɛ	011	4	458 X89	2X6	4	252 636	593
5	729 760	Ɛ6 ƐX9	5	553 173	283	5	348 009	56Ɛ
6	824 749	Ɛ85	6	649 436	25Ɛ	6	441 578	548
7	91Ɛ 712	Ɛ61	7	743 695	238	7	536 Ɛ04	525
8	X16 673	Ɛ39	8	839 911	214	8	630 429	501
9	Ɛ11 5Ɛ0	Ɛ16	9	933 Ɛ25	1Ɛ1	9	725 92X	49Ɛ
X	794 008 506	XƐ2	X	X2X 116	189	X	81Ɛ 209	477
Ɛ	103 3Ɛ8	X8X	Ɛ	Ɛ24 2X3	166	Ɛ	914 684	454
5010	1ƐX 286	X67	5050	798 01X 449	143	5090	X09 Ɛ18	431
1	2Ɛ5 131	X42	1	114 590	11Ɛ	1	Ɛ03 349	40X
2	3XƐ Ɛ73	X1Ɛ	2	20X 6XƐ	0Ɛ8	2	ƐƐ8 757	3X7
3	4X6 992	9Ɛ8	3	304 7X7	094	3	7X0 0Ɛ1 Ɛ42	384
4	5X1 78X	993	4	3ƐX 87Ɛ	071	4	1X7 306	361
5	698 561	970	5	4Ɛ4 930	049	5	2X0 667	339
6	793 311	948	6	5XX 979	026	6	395 9X4	316
7	88X 059	925	7	6X4 9X3	003	7	48Ɛ 0ƐX	2Ɛ4
8	984 982	901	8	79X 9X6	Ɛ5 Ɛ9Ɛ	8	584 3Ɛ2	290
9	X7Ɛ 683	899	9	894 985	Ɛ78	9	679 682	269
X	Ɛ76 360	875	X	98X 941	Ɛ54	X	772 92Ɛ	246
Ɛ	795 071 015	852	Ɛ	X84 895	Ɛ32	Ɛ	867 Ɛ75	223
5020	167 867	82X	5060	Ɛ7X 807	Ɛ09	50X0	961 198	200
1	262 495	807	1	799 074 714	XX7	1	X56 398	199
2	359 0X0	7X2	2	16X 5ƐƐ	X83	2	Ɛ4Ɛ 575	176
3	453 882	780	3	264 482	X60	3	7X1 044 72Ɛ	153
4	54X 442	757	4	35X 322	X38	4	139 882	130
5	644 Ɛ99	734	5	454 15X	X15	5	232 9Ɛ2	108
6	73Ɛ 711	710	6	549 Ɛ73	9Ɛ2	6	327 XƐX	0X6
7	836 221	6X9	7	643 965	98X	7	420 ƐX4	083
8	930 90X	685	8	739 733	968	8	516 067	05Ɛ
9	X27 393	661	9	833 49Ɛ	944	9	60Ɛ 106	039
X	Ɛ21 X34	63X	X	929 223	920	X	704 143	016
Ɛ	796 018 472	616	Ɛ	X22 Ɛ43	8Ɛ9	Ɛ	7Ɛ9 159	Ɛ4 ƐƐ3
5030	112 X88	5Ɛ3	5070	Ɛ18 840	896	50Ɛ0	8Ɛ2 150	Ɛ8Ɛ
1	209 47Ɛ	58Ɛ	1	79X 012 516	873	1	9X7 11Ɛ	Ɛ69
2	303 X4X	568	2	108 189	84Ɛ	2	XX0 088	Ɛ46
3	3ƐX 3Ɛ6	544	3	201 X18	829	3	Ɛ95 012	Ɛ23
4	4Ɛ4 93X	520	4	2Ɛ7 645	805	4	7X2 089 Ɛ35	Ɛ00
5	5XƐ 25X	4Ɛ9	5	3Ɛ1 24X	7X1	5	182 X35	X98
6	6X5 757	495	6	4X6 X2Ɛ	77Ɛ	6	277 911	X76
7	7X0 030	472	7	5X0 5XX	757	7	370 787	X53
8	896 4X2	44X	8	696 145	734	8	465 61X	X30
9	990 930	427	9	78Ɛ 879	711	9	55X 44X	X0X
X	X87 157	403	X	885 38X	6X9	X	653 258	9X6
Ɛ	Ɛ81 55X	3X0	Ɛ	97X X77	686	Ɛ	748 042	983

N	Log N	d	N	Log N	d	N	Log N	d
5100	7X2 840 X05	Ɛ4 960	5140	7X6 599 418	Ɛ4 070	5180	7XX 306 43X	Ɛ3 391
1	935 765	93X	1	691 488	049	1	3Ɛ9 80Ɛ	36Ɛ
2	X2X 4X3	917	2	785 515	027	2	4Ɛ0 Ɛ7X	349
3	Ɛ23 1ƐX	8Ɛ3	3	879 540	004	3	5X4 307	326
4	7X3 017 XƐ1	891	4	971 544	Ɛ3 ƐX1	4	697 631	304
5	110 782	86X	5	X65 525	Ɛ7Ɛ	5	78X 935	2X1
6	205 430	847	6	Ɛ59 4X4	Ɛ58	6	882 016	27Ɛ
7	2ƐX 077	824	7	7X7 051 440	Ɛ36	7	975 295	259
8	3Ɛ2 89Ɛ	801	8	145 376	Ɛ13	8	X68 532	237
9	4X7 4X0	79Ɛ	9	239 289	XƐ0	9	Ɛ5Ɛ 769	214
X	5X0 07Ɛ	778	X	331 179	X8X	X	7XƐ 052 981	1Ɛ2
Ɛ	694 837	754	Ɛ	425 047	X67	Ɛ	145 Ɛ73	190
5110	789 38Ɛ	732	5150	518 XƐ2	X45	5190	239 143	16X
1	881 Ɛ01	70Ɛ	1	610 937	X23	1	330 2Ɛ1	147
2	976 610	6X9	2	704 75X	9ƐƐ	2	423 438	125
3	X6Ɛ 0Ɛ9	685	3	7Ɛ8 559	99X	3	516 561	103
4	Ɛ63 782	663	4	8Ɛ0 337	976	4	609 664	0X1
5	7X4 058 225	640	5	9X4 0Ɛ1	955	5	700 745	07X
6	150 865	619	6	X97 X46	931	6	7Ɛ3 803	058
7	245 282	5Ɛ6	7	Ɛ8Ɛ 777	90Ɛ	7	8X6 85Ɛ	036
8	339 878	593	8	7X8 083 486	8X9	8	999 895	014
9	432 24Ɛ	571	9	177 173	886	9	X90 8X9	Ɛ2 ƐƐ1
X	526 800	54X	X	26X X39	864	X	Ɛ83 89X	Ɛ90
Ɛ	61Ɛ 14X	527	Ɛ	362 6X1	841	Ɛ	7Ɛ0 076 86X	Ɛ69
5120	713 675	504	5160	456 322	81Ɛ	51X0	169 817	Ɛ47
1	807 Ɛ79	4X2	1	549 Ɛ41	7Ɛ8	1	260 762	Ɛ24
2	900 45Ɛ	47Ɛ	2	641 739	796	2	353 686	Ɛ03
3	9Ɛ4 91X	458	3	735 313	773	3	446 589	XX0
4	XX9 176	435	4	828 X86	751	4	539 469	X7X
5	ƐX1 5XƐ	413	5	920 617	72Ɛ	5	630 327	X58
6	7X5 095 X02	3Ɛ0	6	X14 146	708	6	723 183	X36
7	18X 1Ɛ2	389	7	Ɛ07 852	6X5	7	815 ƐƐ9	X14
8	282 57Ɛ	366	8	ƐƐƐ 337	683	8	908 X11	9Ɛ2
9	376 925	344	9	7X9 0Ɛ2 9ƐX	661	9	9ƐƐ 803	98Ɛ
X	46Ɛ 069	321	X	1X6 45Ɛ	63X	X	XƐ2 592	969
Ɛ	563 38X	2ƐX	Ɛ	299 X99	618	Ɛ	ƐX5 33Ɛ	948
5130	657 688	298	5170	391 4Ɛ5	5Ɛ6	51Ɛ0	7Ɛ1 098 087	925
1	74Ɛ 964	275	1	484 XXƐ	593	1	18X 9Ɛ0	903
2	844 019	252	2	578 482	571	2	281 6Ɛ3	8X0
3	938 26Ɛ	230	3	66Ɛ X33	54X	3	374 393	87Ɛ
4	X30 49Ɛ	209	4	763 381	528	4	467 052	859
5	Ɛ24 6X8	1X6	5	856 8X9	505	5	559 8XƐ	836
6	7X6 018 892	184	6	94X 1Ɛ2	4X4	6	650 525	815
7	110 X56	161	7	X41 696	480	7	743 13X	7Ɛ2
8	204 ƐƐ7	13X	8	Ɛ34 Ɛ56	45Ɛ	8	835 930	791
9	2Ɛ9 135	118	9	7XX 028 3Ɛ5	438	9	928 501	76X
X	3Ɛ1 251	0Ɛ5	X	11Ɛ 831	416	X	X1Ɛ 06Ɛ	748
Ɛ	4X5 346	092	Ɛ	213 047	3Ɛ3	Ɛ	Ɛ11 7Ɛ7	726

N	Log N	d	N	Log N	d	N	Log N	d
5200	7Ɛ2 004 321	Ɛ2 704	5240	7Ɛ5 893 527	Ɛ1 X49	5280	7Ɛ9 534 2X9	Ɛ1 1X2
1	0Ɛ6 X25	6X2	1	985 374	X26	1	625 48Ɛ	180
2	1X9 507	680	2	X77 19X	X05	2	716 64Ɛ	160
3	29Ɛ Ɛ87	65X	3	Ɛ68 ƐX3	9X4	3	807 7XƐ	139
4	392 625	638	4	7Ɛ6 05X 987	981	4	8Ɛ8 928	118
5	485 061	616	5	150 748	960	5	9X9 X44	0Ɛ7
6	577 677	5Ɛ4	6	242 4X8	93X	6	X9X Ɛ3Ɛ	095
7	66X 06Ɛ	592	7	334 226	918	7	Ɛ90 014	074
8	760 641	570	8	425 Ɛ42	8Ɛ6	8	7ƐX 081 088	053
9	852 ƐƐ1	54X	9	517 838	895	9	172 11Ɛ	030
X	945 53Ɛ	527	X	609 511	873	X	263 14Ɛ	010
Ɛ	X37 X66	506	Ɛ	6ƐƐ 184	852	Ɛ	354 15Ɛ	Ɛ0 ƐXX
5210	Ɛ2X 370	4X4	5250	7Ɛ0 X16	82Ɛ	5290	445 149	Ɛ88
1	7Ɛ3 020 854	482	1	8X2 645	80X	1	536 115	Ɛ68
2	113 116	460	2	994 253	7X9	2	627 081	Ɛ45
3	205 576	43X	3	X85 X40	786	3	718 006	Ɛ25
4	2Ɛ7 9Ɛ4	418	4	Ɛ77 606	765	4	808 Ɛ2Ɛ	Ɛ03
5	3XX 210	3Ɛ6	5	7Ɛ7 069 16Ɛ	743	5	8Ɛ9 X32	XX1
6	4X0 606	395	6	15X 8Ɛ2	722	6	9XX 913	X80
7	592 99Ɛ	372	7	250 414	700	7	X9Ɛ 793	X5Ɛ
8	685 151	350	8	341 Ɛ14	69X	8	Ɛ90 632	X39
9	777 4X1	32X	9	433 5Ɛ2	679	9	7ƐƐ 081 46Ɛ	X18
X	869 80Ɛ	309	X	525 06Ɛ	657	X	172 287	9Ɛ7
Ɛ	95Ɛ Ɛ18	2X6	Ɛ	616 706	635	Ɛ	263 082	995
5220	X52 202	285	5260	708 13Ɛ	614	52X0	353 X57	974
1	Ɛ44 487	263	1	7Ɛ9 753	5Ɛ2	1	444 80Ɛ	952
2	7Ɛ4 036 72X	241	2	8XƐ 145	590	2	535 561	931
3	128 96Ɛ	21Ɛ	3	9X0 715	56Ɛ	3	626 292	910
4	21X Ɛ8X	1Ɛ9	4	X92 084	549	4	716 ƐX2	8XƐ
5	311 187	197	5	Ɛ83 611	528	5	807 891	889
6	403 362	175	6	7Ɛ8 074 Ɛ39	506	6	8Ɛ8 55X	868
7	4Ɛ5 517	153	7	166 443	4X4	7	9X9 206	846
8	5X7 66X	132	8	257 927	483	8	X99 X50	825
9	699 7X0	110	9	349 1XX	461	9	Ɛ8X 675	804
X	78Ɛ 8Ɛ0	0X9	X	43X 64Ɛ	440	X	800 07Ɛ 279	7X3
Ɛ	881 999	088	Ɛ	52Ɛ X8Ɛ	41X	Ɛ	16Ɛ X60	781
5230	973 X65	067	5270	621 2X9	3Ɛ8	52Ɛ0	260 621	760
1	X65 Ɛ10	044	1	712 6X5	397	1	351 181	73X
2	Ɛ57 Ɛ54	022	2	803 X80	375	2	441 8ƐƐ	71X
3	7Ɛ5 049 Ɛ76	001	3	8Ɛ5 235	354	3	532 419	6Ɛ8
4	13Ɛ Ɛ77	Ɛ1 Ɛ9Ɛ	4	9X6 589	332	4	622 Ɛ15	696
5	231 Ɛ56	Ɛ79	5	X97 8ƐƐ	311	5	713 5XƐ	676
6	323 Ɛ13	Ɛ57	6	Ɛ89 010	2XƐ	6	804 065	654
7	415 X6X	Ɛ35	7	7Ɛ9 07X 2ƐƐ	28X	7	8Ɛ4 6Ɛ9	633
8	507 9X3	Ɛ14	8	16Ɛ 589	268	8	9X5 130	612
9	5Ɛ9 8Ɛ7	XƐ2	9	260 835	247	9	X95 742	5Ɛ0
X	6XƐ 7X9	X90	X	351 X80	225	X	Ɛ86 132	590
Ɛ	7X1 679	X6X	Ɛ	443 0X5	204	Ɛ	801 076 702	56X

N	Log N	d	N	Log N	d	N	Log N	d
5300	801 167 070	Ɛ0 548	5340	804 970 270	χƐ 905	5380	808 548 119	χƐ 090
1	257 5Ɛ8	528	1	χ5Ɛ Ɛ75	8χ3	1	637 1χ9	070
2	347 Ɛ24	506	2	Ɛ4Ɛ 858	882	2	726 259	04Ɛ
3	438 42χ	4χ6	3	805 03Ɛ 51χ	862	3	815 2χ8	02χ
4	528 914	483	4	12Ɛ 180	840	4	904 316	00χ
5	619 197	463	5	21χ χ00	820	5	9Ɛ3 324	χχ Ɛχ8
6	709 63χ	442	6	30χ 620	7Ɛχ	6	χχ2 310	Ɛ89
7	7Ɛ9 χ80	420	7	3Ɛχ 21χ	79χ	7	Ɛ91 299	Ɛ67
8	8χχ 2χ0	3ƐƐ	8	4χ9 9Ɛ8	779	8	809 080 244	Ɛ47
9	99χ 69Ɛ	39χ	9	599 575	757	9	16Ɛ 18Ɛ	Ɛ26
χ	χ8χ χ79	379	χ	689 110	737	χ	25χ 0Ɛ5	Ɛ06
Ɛ	Ɛ7Ɛ 236	358	Ɛ	778 847	716	Ɛ	348 ƐƐƐ	χχ5
5310	802 06Ɛ 592	336	5350	868 361	6Ɛ5	5390	437 χχ4	χ84
1	15Ɛ 908	315	1	957 χ56	695	1	526 968	χ64
2	250 021	2Ɛ5	2	χ47 52Ɛ	673	2	615 810	χ43
3	340 316	293	3	Ɛ36 Ɛχ2	652	3	704 653	χ22
4	430 5χ9	271	4	806 026 634	632	4	7Ɛ3 475	χ02
5	520 85χ	251	5	116 066	611	5	8χ2 277	9χ1
6	610 χχƐ	230	6	205 677	5χƐ	6	991 058	981
7	701 11Ɛ	20χ	7	2Ɛ5 066	58Ɛ	7	χ7Ɛ χ19	960
8	7Ɛ1 329	1χχ	8	3χ4 635	56Ɛ	8	Ɛ6χ 779	93Ɛ
9	8χ1 517	188	9	493 Ɛχ4	549	9	80χ 059 4Ɛ8	91Ɛ
χ	991 6χ3	167	χ	583 531	528	χ	148 217	8Ɛχ
Ɛ	χ81 84χ	146	Ɛ	672 χ59	508	Ɛ	236 Ɛ15	89χ
5320	Ɛ71 994	125	5360	762 365	4χ7	53χ0	325 7Ɛ3	879
1	803 061 χƐ9	104	1	851 850	485	1	414 470	859
2	152 001	0χ2	2	941 115	466	2	503 109	837
3	242 0χ3	082	3	χ30 57Ɛ	444	3	5Ɛ1 944	818
4	332 165	061	4	Ɛ1Ɛ χ03	423	4	6χ0 560	7Ɛ7
5	422 206	03Ɛ	5	807 00Ɛ 226	403	5	78Ɛ 157	796
6	512 245	01Ɛ	6	0Ɛχ 629	3χ2	6	879 931	776
7	602 264	χƐ ƐƐ9	7	1χ9 χ0Ɛ	381	7	968 4χ7	755
8	6Ɛ2 261	Ɛ99	8	299 190	360	8	χ57 040	734
9	7χ2 23χ	Ɛ77	9	388 530	340	9	Ɛ45 774	715
χ	892 1Ɛ5	Ɛ56	χ	477 870	31χ	χ	80Ɛ 034 289	6Ɛ3
Ɛ	982 14Ɛ	Ɛ35	Ɛ	566 Ɛ8χ	2Ɛχ	Ɛ	122 980	693
5330	χ72 084	Ɛ15	5370	656 2Ɛ8	299	53Ɛ0	211 453	673
1	Ɛ61 Ɛ99	χƐ3	1	745 565	279	1	2ƐƐ Ɛ06	652
2	804 051 χ90	χ92	2	834 822	257	2	3χχ 558	631
3	141 962	χ71	3	923 χ79	237	3	498 Ɛ89	611
4	231 813	χ50	4	χ13 0Ɛ4	216	4	587 59χ	5Ɛ1
5	321 663	χ2Ɛ	5	Ɛ02 30χ	1Ɛ6	5	675 Ɛ8Ɛ	590
6	411 492	χ0χ	6	ƐƐ1 504	194	6	764 55Ɛ	570
7	501 2χ0	9χχ	7	808 0χ0 698	174	7	852 Ɛ0Ɛ	54Ɛ
8	5Ɛ1 08χ	988	8	18Ɛ 850	153	8	941 45χ	52Ɛ
9	6χ0 χ56	967	9	27χ 9χ3	133	9	χ2Ɛ 989	50χ
χ	790 801	946	χ	369 Ɛ16	112	χ	Ɛ1χ 297	4χχ
Ɛ	880 547	925	Ɛ	459 028	0Ɛ1	Ɛ	810 008 785	489

N	Log N	d	N	Log N	d	N	Log N	d
5400	810 0Ɛ7 052	XX 469	5440	813 839 467	X9 855	5480	817 353 566	X9 052
1	1X5 4ƐƐ	448	1	927 100	836	1	440 5Ɛ8	033
2	293 947	428	2	X14 936	815	2	529 62Ɛ	012
3	382 173	408	3	Ɛ02 54Ɛ	7Ɛ5	3	616 641	X8 ƐƐ3
4	470 57Ɛ	3X7	4	ƐƐ0 144	795	4	703 634	Ɛ92
5	55X 966	386	5	814 099 919	774	5	7Ɛ0 606	Ɛ73
6	649 130	367	6	187 491	755	6	899 579	Ɛ53
7	737 497	345	7	275 026	734	7	986 510	Ɛ33
8	825 820	326	8	362 75X	715	8	X73 443	Ɛ12
9	913 Ɛ46	305	9	450 273	6Ɛ4	9	Ɛ60 355	XƐ3
X	X02 24Ɛ	2X5	X	539 967	693	X	818 049 248	X94
Ɛ	XƐ0 534	284	Ɛ	627 43X	674	Ɛ	136 120	X73
5410	Ɛ9X 7Ɛ8	264	5450	714 XƐ2	654	5490	222 Ɛ93	X53
1	811 088 X60	243	1	802 546	633	1	30Ɛ X26	X34
2	177 0X3	223	2	8XƐ Ɛ79	614	2	3Ɛ8 85X	X13
3	265 306	203	3	999 591	5Ɛ3	3	4X5 671	9Ɛ4
4	353 509	1X3	4	X86 Ɛ84	593	4	592 465	994
5	441 6Ɛ0	182	5	Ɛ74 557	573	5	67Ɛ 239	974
6	52Ɛ 872	161	6	815 061 Ɛ0X	553	6	767 ƐƐ1	954
7	619 X13	142	7	14Ɛ 461	533	7	854 945	934
8	707 Ɛ55	121	8	238 994	513	8	941 679	915
9	7Ɛ6 076	100	9	326 2X7	4Ɛ2	9	X2X 392	8Ɛ5
X	8X4 176	0X1	X	413 799	493	X	Ɛ17 087	894
Ɛ	992 257	080	Ɛ	501 070	473	Ɛ	819 003 95Ɛ	875
5420	X80 317	05Ɛ	5460	5XX 523	452	54X0	0Ɛ0 614	856
1	Ɛ6X 376	040	1	697 975	432	1	199 26X	835
2	812 058 3Ɛ6	01Ɛ	2	785 1X7	413	2	285 XX3	815
3	146 415	X9 ƐƐƐ	3	872 5ƐX	3Ɛ2	3	372 6Ɛ8	7Ɛ6
4	234 414	Ɛ9X	4	95Ɛ 9Ɛ0	392	4	45Ɛ 2Ɛ2	796
5	322 3Ɛ2	Ɛ7X	5	X49 182	372	5	547 X88	776
6	410 370	Ɛ5X	6	Ɛ36 534	353	6	634 642	756
7	4ƐX 30X	Ɛ3X	7	816 023 887	332	7	721 198	737
8	5X8 248	Ɛ19	8	110 ƐƐ9	312	8	809 913	717
9	696 165	XƐ9	9	1ƐX 30Ɛ	2Ɛ2	9	8Ɛ6 42X	6Ɛ7
X	784 062	X99	X	2X7 601	292	X	9X2 Ɛ25	697
Ɛ	871 Ɛ3Ɛ	X78	Ɛ	394 893	272	Ɛ	X8Ɛ 600	677
5430	95Ɛ 9Ɛ7	X59	5470	481 Ɛ45	252	54Ɛ0	Ɛ78 077	658
1	X49 854	X38	1	56Ɛ 197	232	1	81X 064 713	638
2	Ɛ37 690	X17	2	658 409	212	2	151 14Ɛ	618
3	813 025 4X7	9Ɛ8	3	745 61Ɛ	1Ɛ2	3	239 767	5Ɛ9
4	113 2X3	997	4	832 811	192	4	326 164	598
5	201 07X	977	5	91Ɛ 9X3	172	5	412 740	579
6	2XX X35	957	6	X08 Ɛ55	152	6	4ƐƐ 0Ɛ9	559
7	398 790	937	7	XƐ6 0X7	132	7	5X7 656	53X
8	486 507	916	8	ƐX3 219	112	8	693 Ɛ94	51X
9	574 221	8Ɛ6	9	817 090 32Ɛ	0Ɛ3	9	780 4Ɛ2	4ƐX
X	661 Ɛ17	896	X	179 422	092	X	868 9Ɛ0	49X
Ɛ	74Ɛ 7Ɛ1	876	Ɛ	266 4Ɛ4	072	Ɛ	955 28X	47Ɛ

N	Log N	d	N	Log N	d	N	Log N	d
5500	81X X41 749	X8 45Ɛ	5540	822 504 203	X7 877	5580	825 Ɛ5Ɛ 535	X7 0X3
1	Ɛ29 ƐX8	43Ɛ	1	5XƐ X7X	858	1	826 046 618	084
2	81Ɛ 016 427	41Ɛ	2	697 716	838	2	131 6X0	064
3	102 846	400	3	783 352	819	3	218 744	046
4	1XƐ 046	3X0	4	86X Ɛ6Ɛ	7Ɛ9	4	303 78X	026
5	297 426	381	5	956 768	79X	5	3XX 7Ɛ4	007
6	383 7X7	361	6	X42 346	77Ɛ	6	495 7ƐƐ	X6 ƐX7
7	46Ɛ Ɛ48	341	7	Ɛ29 Ɛ05	75Ɛ	7	580 7X6	Ɛ89
8	558 289	321	8	823 015 664	740	8	667 773	Ɛ69
9	644 5XX	302	9	101 1X4	720	9	752 720	Ɛ4X
X	730 8Ɛ0	2X2	X	1X8 904	701	X	839 66X	Ɛ2Ɛ
Ɛ	818 Ɛ92	283	Ɛ	294 405	6X1	Ɛ	924 599	Ɛ10
5510	905 255	263	5550	37Ɛ XX6	682	5590	X0Ɛ 4X9	XƐ1
1	9Ɛ1 4Ɛ8	243	1	467 568	663	1	XƐ6 39X	X91
2	X99 73Ɛ	224	2	553 00Ɛ	643	2	ƐX1 26Ɛ	X73
3	Ɛ85 963	204	3	63X 652	624	3	827 088 122	X53
4	820 071 Ɛ67	1X4	4	726 076	605	4	172 Ɛ75	X34
5	15X 14Ɛ	185	5	811 67Ɛ	5X5	5	259 9X9	X15
6	246 314	165	6	8Ɛ9 064	586	6	344 802	9Ɛ6
7	332 479	146	7	9X4 62X	566	7	42Ɛ 5Ɛ8	996
8	41X 603	126	8	X8Ɛ Ɛ94	547	8	516 392	978
9	506 729	106	9	Ɛ77 51Ɛ	528	9	601 14X	958
X	5Ɛ2 833	0X7	X	824 062 X47	508	X	6X7 XX6	93X
Ɛ	69X 91X	087	Ɛ	14X 353	4X9	Ɛ	792 824	91X
5520	786 9X5	067	5560	235 840	48X	55X0	879 542	8ƐƐ
1	872 X50	049	1	321 10X	46X	1	964 241	8X0
2	95X X99	028	2	408 578	44Ɛ	2	X4X Ɛ21	881
3	X46 Ɛ05	009	3	4Ɛ3 X07	430	3	Ɛ35 7X2	862
4	Ɛ32 Ɛ12	X7 ƐX9	4	59Ɛ 237	410	4	828 020 444	842
5	821 01X XƐƐ	Ɛ8X	5	686 647	3Ɛ1	5	107 086	824
6	106 X89	Ɛ6X	6	771 X38	392	6	1Ɛ1 8XX	805
7	1Ɛ2 X37	Ɛ4Ɛ	7	859 20X	372	7	298 4Ɛ3	7X5
8	29X 986	Ɛ2Ɛ	8	944 580	353	8	383 098	786
9	386 8Ɛ5	Ɛ10	9	X2Ɛ 913	334	9	469 862	768
X	472 805	XƐ0	X	Ɛ17 047	315	X	554 40X	748
Ɛ	55X 6Ɛ5	X90	Ɛ	825 002 360	2Ɛ5	Ɛ	63X Ɛ56	729
5530	646 585	X71	5570	0X9 655	296	55Ɛ0	725 683	70Ɛ
1	732 436	X52	1	194 92Ɛ	277	1	810 192	6XƐ
2	81X 288	X32	2	27Ɛ ƐX6	257	2	8Ɛ6 881	690
3	906 0ƐX	X12	3	367 241	238	3	9X1 351	671
4	9Ɛ1 Ɛ10	9Ɛ3	4	452 479	219	4	X87 X02	652
5	X99 903	994	5	539 696	1ƐX	5	Ɛ72 454	633
6	Ɛ85 697	974	6	624 894	19X	6	829 058 X87	614
7	822 071 44Ɛ	955	7	70Ɛ X72	17Ɛ	7	143 49Ɛ	5Ɛ5
8	159 1X4	935	8	7Ɛ7 031	160	8	229 X94	596
9	244 Ɛ19	915	9	8X2 191	140	9	314 46X	577
X	330 832	8Ɛ6	X	989 311	122	X	3ƐX X25	558
Ɛ	418 528	897	Ɛ	X74 433	102	Ɛ	4X5 381	539

N	Log N	d	N	Log N	d	N	Log N	d
5600	829 58Ɛ 8ƐX	X6 51X	5640	830 Ɛ95 4X5	X5 965	5680	834 574 876	X5 1Ɛ9
1	676 218	4ƐƐ	1	831 07Ɛ 24X	945	1	659 X73	19Ɛ
2	760 717	4X0	2	164 Ɛ93	927	2	743 052	180
3	846 ƐƐ7	481	3	24X 8ƐX	908	3	828 212	162
4	931 478	462	4	334 606	8X9	4	911 374	144
5	X17 91X	444	5	41X 2Ɛ3	88Ɛ	5	9Ɛ6 4Ɛ8	124
6	Ɛ02 162	424	6	503 Ɛ82	86Ɛ	6	X9Ɛ 620	107
7	ƐX8 586	405	7	5X9 831	851	7	Ɛ84 727	0X8
8	82X 092 98Ɛ	3X6	8	693 482	833	8	835 069 813	089
9	179 175	388	9	779 0Ɛ5	813	9	152 8X0	06Ɛ
X	263 541	368	X	862 908	7Ɛ5	X	237 94Ɛ	050
Ɛ	349 8X9	34X	Ɛ	948 501	797	Ɛ	320 99Ɛ	032
5610	434 037	32X	5650	X32 098	777	5690	405 X11	014
1	51X 365	310	1	Ɛ17 853	759	1	4XX X25	X4 ƐƐ5
2	604 675	2Ɛ0	2	832 001 3Ɛ0	73X	2	593 X1X	Ɛ96
3	6XX 965	292	3	0X6 Ɛ2X	720	3	678 9Ɛ4	Ɛ78
4	795 037	273	4	190 64X	700	4	761 970	Ɛ5X
5	87Ɛ 2XX	254	5	276 14X	6X2	5	846 90X	Ɛ3Ɛ
6	965 542	235	6	35Ɛ 830	684	6	92Ɛ 849	Ɛ21
7	X4Ɛ 777	216	7	445 2Ɛ4	665	7	X14 76X	Ɛ02
8	Ɛ35 991	1Ɛ8	8	52X 959	646	8	XƐ9 670	XX4
9	82Ɛ 01Ɛ Ɛ89	198	9	614 3X3	627	9	ƐX2 554	X85
X	106 165	179	X	6Ɛ9 X0X	609	X	836 087 419	X67
Ɛ	1Ɛ0 322	15Ɛ	Ɛ	7X3 417	5XX	Ɛ	170 284	X48
5620	296 481	140	5660	888 X05	58Ɛ	56X0	255 110	X2Ɛ
1	380 601	121	1	972 394	571	1	339 Ɛ3Ɛ	X0Ɛ
2	466 722	102	2	X57 945	552	2	422 94X	9Ɛ1
3	550 824	0X3	3	Ɛ41 297	534	3	507 73Ɛ	993
4	636 907	084	4	833 026 80Ɛ	515	4	5Ɛ0 512	975
5	720 98Ɛ	066	5	110 124	4Ɛ6	5	695 287	956
6	806 X35	046	6	1Ɛ5 61X	498	6	77X 021	938
7	8Ɛ0 X7Ɛ	028	7	29X X26	479	7	862 959	919
8	996 XX7	009	8	384 373	45Ɛ	8	947 676	8ƐƐ
9	X80 XƐ4	X5 ƐXX	9	469 812	440	9	X30 375	8X0
X	Ɛ66 XX2	Ɛ8Ɛ	X	553 052	421	X	Ɛ15 055	883
Ɛ	830 050 X71	Ɛ71	Ɛ	638 473	403	Ɛ	ƐƐ9 918	863
5630	136 X22	Ɛ52	5670	721 876	3X4	56Ɛ0	837 0X2 57Ɛ	846
1	220 974	Ɛ32	1	807 05X	385	1	187 205	827
2	306 8X6	Ɛ14	2	8Ɛ0 423	367	2	26Ɛ X30	809
3	3Ɛ0 7ƐX	XƐ6	3	995 78X	349	3	354 639	7XX
4	496 6Ɛ4	X96	4	X7X Ɛ17	329	4	439 227	790
5	580 58X	X78	5	Ɛ64 244	310	5	521 9Ɛ7	772
6	666 446	X59	6	834 049 554	2Ɛ0	6	606 569	753
7	750 2X3	X3X	7	132 844	292	7	6XƐ 100	735
8	836 121	X1Ɛ	8	217 Ɛ16	274	8	793 835	717
9	91Ɛ Ɛ40	X01	9	301 18X	255	9	878 350	6Ɛ8
X	X05 941	9X1	X	3X6 423	237	X	960 X48	69X
Ɛ	XXƐ 722	983	Ɛ	48Ɛ 65X	218	Ɛ	X45 526	680

N	Log N	d	N	Log N	d	N	Log N	d
5700	837 Ɛ29 ƐX6	X4 661	5740	83Ɛ 479 626	X3 Ɛ14	5780	842 9X3 719	X3 395
1	838 012 647	644	1	561 53X	XƐ6	1	X86 XƐ2	377
2	0Ɛ7 08Ɛ	624	2	645 434	X98	2	Ɛ6X 269	35X
3	19Ɛ 6Ɛ3	607	3	729 310	X7X	3	843 051 607	340
4	284 0ƐX	5X8	4	811 18X	X60	4	134 947	321
5	368 6X6	58X	5	8Ɛ5 02X	X41	5	218 068	304
6	451 074	570	6	998 X6Ɛ	X24	6	2ƐƐ 370	2X7
7	535 624	551	7	X80 893	X06	7	3X2 657	288
8	619 Ɛ75	534	8	Ɛ64 699	9X7	8	485 923	26X
9	702 4X9	514	9	840 048 484	98X	9	568 Ɛ91	251
X	7X6 X01	4Ɛ7	X	130 252	962	X	650 222	233
Ɛ	88Ɛ 2Ɛ8	498	Ɛ	214 001	952	Ɛ	733 455	215
5710	973 794	47Ɛ	5750	2Ɛ7 953	933	5790	816 66X	1Ɛ7
1	X58 053	45Ɛ	1	39Ɛ 686	916	1	8Ɛ9 865	199
2	Ɛ40 4Ɛ2	442	2	483 3X0	8Ɛ7	2	9X0 X42	180
3	839 024 934	423	3	567 097	899	3	X84 002	162
4	109 157	406	4	64X 974	880	4	Ɛ67 164	144
5	1Ɛ1 561	3X7	5	732 634	861	5	844 04X 2X8	126
6	295 948	388	6	816 295	843	6	131 412	108
7	37X 114	36Ɛ	7	8Ɛ9 Ɛ18	826	7	214 51X	0XƐ
8	462 483	350	8	9X1 742	807	8	2Ɛ7 609	091
9	546 813	332	9	X85 349	7X9	9	39X 69X	073
X	62X Ɛ45	314	X	Ɛ68 Ɛ36	790	X	481 751	055
Ɛ	713 259	2Ɛ6	Ɛ	841 050 706	771	Ɛ	564 7X6	037
5720	7Ɛ7 553	297	5760	134 277	753	57X0	647 821	01X
1	89Ɛ 82X	279	1	217 X0X	736	1	72X 83Ɛ	000
2	983 XX7	25Ɛ	2	2ƐƐ 544	717	2	811 83Ɛ	X2 ƐX2
3	X68 146	241	3	3X3 05Ɛ	6ƐX	3	8Ɛ4 821	Ɛ85
4	Ɛ50 387	223	4	486 759	69Ɛ	4	997 7X6	Ɛ66
5	83X 034 5XX	205	5	56X 238	682	5	X7X 750	Ɛ49
6	118 7Ɛ3	1X6	6	651 8ƐX	663	6	Ɛ61 699	Ɛ30
7	200 999	188	7	735 361	646	7	845 044 609	Ɛ11
8	2X4 Ɛ65	16X	8	818 9X7	628	8	127 51X	XƐ4
9	389 113	150	9	900 413	60X	9	20X 412	X96
X	471 263	132	X	9X3 X21	5XƐ	X	2Ɛ1 2X8	X78
Ɛ	555 395	113	Ɛ	X87 410	592	Ɛ	394 164	X5Ɛ
5730	639 4X8	0Ɛ6	5770	Ɛ6X 9X2	574	57Ɛ0	477 003	X41
1	721 5X2	097	1	842 052 356	556	1	559 X44	X23
2	805 679	079	2	135 8Ɛ0	539	2	640 867	X06
3	8X9 736	05Ɛ	3	219 229	51X	3	723 671	9X8
4	991 795	041	4	300 747	500	4	806 459	98X
5	X75 816	023	5	3X4 047	4X3	5	8X9 227	970
6	Ɛ59 839	005	6	487 52X	484	6	98Ɛ Ɛ97	953
7	83Ɛ 041 842	X3 ƐX6	7	56X 9Ɛ2	467	7	X72 92X	935
8	125 828	Ɛ89	8	652 259	449	8	Ɛ55 663	917
9	209 7Ɛ5	Ɛ6X	9	735 6X6	42Ɛ	9	846 038 37X	8ƐX
X	2Ɛ1 763	Ɛ51	X	818 Ɛ15	411	X	11Ɛ 078	8X0
Ɛ	395 6Ɛ4	Ɛ32	Ɛ	900 326	3Ɛ3	Ɛ	201 958	883

N	Log N	d	N	Log N	d	N	Log N	d
5800	846 2χ4 61Ɛ	χ2 864	5840	849 780 681	χ2 142	5880	851 034 008	χ1 62χ
1	387 283	848	1	862 803	125	1	115 636	611
2	469 Ɛ0Ɛ	829	2	944 928	108	2	1Ɛ7 047	5Ɛ4
3	550 738	810	3	χ26 χ34	0χχ	3	298 63Ɛ	597
4	633 348	7Ɛ2	4	Ɛ08 Ɛ22	091	4	37χ 016	579
5	715 Ɛ3χ	795	5	Ɛχχ ƐƐ3	073	5	45Ɛ 593	560
6	7Ɛ8 713	777	6	84χ 091 066	056	6	540 Ɛ33	543
7	89Ɛ 28χ	759	7	173 100	038	7	622 476	525
8	981 χ27	73Ɛ	8	255 138	01Ɛ	8	703 99Ɛ	509
9	χ64 566	723	9	337 157	002	9	7χ5 2χ8	4χƐ
χ	Ɛ47 089	704	χ	419 159	χ1 Ɛχ4	χ	886 797	492
Ɛ	847 029 791	6χ7	Ɛ	4ƐƐ 141	Ɛ87	Ɛ	968 069	475
5810	110 278	689	5850	5χ1 108	Ɛ69	5890	χ49 522	458
1	1Ɛ2 945	670	1	683 075	Ɛ50	1	Ɛ2χ 97χ	43χ
2	295 3Ɛ5	652	2	765 005	Ɛ33	2	852 010 1Ɛ8	421
3	377 χ47	634	3	846 Ɛ38	Ɛ15	3	0Ɛ1 619	405
4	45χ 47Ɛ	617	4	928 χ51	χƐ8	4	192 χ22	3χ7
5	540 χ96	5Ɛ9	5	χ0χ 949	χ9Ɛ	5	274 209	389
6	623 493	5χ0	6	χƐ0 828	χ81	6	355 596	371
7	705 χ73	582	7	Ɛ92 6χ9	χ64	7	436 947	353
8	7χ8 435	565	8	84Ɛ 074 551	χ46	8	518 09χ	337
9	88χ 99χ	547	9	156 397	χ29	9	5Ɛ9 415	319
χ	971 325	529	χ	238 204	χ10	χ	69χ 732	300
Ɛ	χ53 852	510	Ɛ	31χ 014	9Ɛ3	Ɛ	77Ɛ χ32	2χ3
5820	Ɛ36 162	4Ɛ3	5860	3ƐƐ χ07	995	58χ0	861 115	286
1	848 018 655	494	1	4χ1 7χ0	977	1	942 39Ɛ	268
2	0Ɛχ Ɛ29	478	2	583 557	95Ɛ	2	χ23 647	250
3	1χ1 3χ5	459	3	665 2Ɛ6	941	3	Ɛ04 897	232
4	283 842	440	4	747 037	924	4	Ɛχ5 Ɛ09	215
5	366 082	423	5	828 95Ɛ	906	5	853 087 122	1Ɛ9
6	448 4χ5	405	6	90χ 665	8χ9	6	168 31Ɛ	19Ɛ
7	52χ 8χχ	3χ8	7	9Ɛ0 352	890	7	249 4Ɛχ	182
8	611 096	38χ	8	χ92 022	873	8	32χ 680	164
9	6Ɛ3 464	371	9	Ɛ73 895	855	9	40Ɛ 824	148
χ	795 815	353	χ	850 055 52χ	838	χ	4Ɛ0 970	12Ɛ
Ɛ	877 Ɛ68	335	Ɛ	137 166	81χ	Ɛ	591 χ9Ɛ	111
5830	95χ 2χ1	318	5870	218 984	802	58Ɛ0	672 ƐƐ0	0Ɛ5
1	χ40 5Ɛ9	2ƐƐ	1	2Ɛχ 586	7χ4	1	754 0χ5	097
2	Ɛ22 8Ɛ8	2χ1	2	3χ0 16χ	786	2	835 180	07Ɛ
3	849 004 Ɛ99	284	3	481 934	76χ	3	916 23Ɛ	061
4	0χ7 261	266	4	563 4χ2	750	4	9Ɛ7 2χ0	044
5	189 507	248	5	645 032	733	5	χ98 324	027
6	26Ɛ 753	230	6	726 765	716	6	Ɛ79 34Ɛ	00χ
7	351 983	211	7	808 27Ɛ	6Ɛ8	7	854 05χ 359	χ0 ƐƐ1
8	433 Ɛ94	1Ɛ5	8	8χ9 977	69Ɛ	8	13Ɛ 34χ	Ɛ94
9	516 189	196	9	98Ɛ 456	682	9	220 322	Ɛ77
χ	5Ɛ8 363	17χ	χ	χ70 Ɛ18	665	χ	301 299	Ɛ5χ
Ɛ	69χ 521	160	Ɛ	Ɛ52 581	647	Ɛ	3χ2 237	Ɛ41

N	Log N	d	N	Log N	d	N	Log N	d
5900	854 483 178	X0 Ɛ24	5940	857 8XX 283	X0 428	5980	85Ɛ 0Ɛ1 653	9Ɛ 939
1	564 0X0	Ɛ06	1	98X 6XƐ	40X	1	191 390	91Ɛ
2	644 ƐX6	XXX	2	X6X XƐ9	3Ɛ1	2	271 0XƐ	903
3	725 X94	X91	3	Ɛ4Ɛ 2XX	395	3	350 9Ɛ2	8X6
4	806 965	X74	4	858 02Ɛ 683	378	4	430 698	88X
5	8X7 819	X56	5	10Ɛ X3Ɛ	35Ɛ	5	510 366	871
6	988 673	X3X	6	1Ɛ0 19X	342	6	5Ɛ0 017	855
7	X69 4Ɛ1	X21	7	290 520	326	7	68Ɛ 870	837
8	Ɛ4X 312	X03	8	370 846	309	8	76Ɛ 4X7	820
9	855 02Ɛ 115	9X7	9	450 Ɛ53	2XƐ	9	84Ɛ 107	802
X	10Ɛ Ɛ00	98X	X	531 242	294	X	92X 909	7X6
Ɛ	1Ɛ0 88X	971	Ɛ	611 516	276	Ɛ	X0X 4Ɛ3	78X
5910	291 63Ɛ	953	5950	6Ɛ1 790	259	5990	XXX 081	771
1	372 392	937	1	791 X29	241	1	Ɛ89 832	754
2	453 109	91X	2	872 06X	224	2	860 069 386	738
3	533 X27	901	3	952 292	207	3	148 Ɛ02	71Ɛ
4	614 728	8X4	4	X32 499	1XƐ	4	228 621	703
5	6Ɛ5 410	887	5	Ɛ12 688	192	5	308 124	6X6
6	796 097	869	6	ƐƐ2 85X	175	6	3X7 80X	689
7	876 944	851	7	859 092 X13	158	7	487 297	671
8	957 595	834	8	172 Ɛ6Ɛ	13Ɛ	8	566 948	655
9	X38 209	818	9	253 0XX	123	9	646 3X1	638
X	Ɛ18 X25	7ƐX	X	333 211	106	X	725 X19	61Ɛ
Ɛ	ƐƐ9 623	7X1	Ɛ	413 317	0X9	Ɛ	805 438	603
5920	856 09X 204	784	5960	4Ɛ3 404	090	59X0	8X4 X3Ɛ	5X6
1	17X 988	768	1	593 494	074	1	984 425	58X
2	25Ɛ 534	74X	2	673 548	057	2	X63 9Ɛ3	571
3	340 082	732	3	753 5X3	03Ɛ	3	Ɛ43 364	554
4	420 7Ɛ4	714	4	833 622	021	4	861 022 8Ɛ8	539
5	501 308	6Ɛ8	5	913 643	005	5	102 235	51Ɛ
6	5X1 X04	69Ɛ	6	9Ɛ3 648	9Ɛ ƐX8	6	1X1 754	503
7	682 4X3	681	7	X93 634	Ɛ90	7	281 057	4X7
8	762 Ɛ64	665	8	Ɛ73 604	Ɛ73	8	360 542	48X
9	843 609	649	9	85X 053 577	Ɛ56	9	43Ɛ X10	472
X	924 056	62Ɛ	X	133 511	Ɛ39	X	51Ɛ 282	455
Ɛ	X04 685	612	Ɛ	213 44X	Ɛ21	Ɛ	5ƐX 717	438
5930	XX5 097	5Ɛ6	5970	2Ɛ3 36Ɛ	Ɛ04	59Ɛ0	699 Ɛ53	420
1	Ɛ85 691	598	1	393 273	XX7	1	779 373	404
2	857 066 069	580	2	473 15X	X8Ɛ	2	858 777	3X7
3	146 629	563	3	553 029	X72	3	937 Ɛ62	38Ɛ
4	226 Ɛ90	546	4	632 X9Ɛ	X55	4	X17 331	372
5	307 516	529	5	712 934	X39	5	XƐ6 6X3	356
6	3X7 X43	510	6	7Ɛ2 771	X20	6	Ɛ95 X39	339
7	488 353	4Ɛ3	7	892 591	X03	7	862 075 176	321
8	568 846	497	8	972 394	9X7	8	154 497	305
9	649 121	479	9	X52 17Ɛ	98X	9	233 7X0	2X8
X	729 59X	461	X	Ɛ31 Ɛ49	972	X	312 X88	28Ɛ
Ɛ	809 X3Ɛ	444	Ɛ	85Ɛ 011 8ƐƐ	954	Ɛ	3Ɛ2 157	273

N	Log N	d	N	Log N	d	N	Log N	d
5X00	862 491 40X	9Σ 257	5X40	865 849 X88	9X 782	5X80	868 ΣX3 559	9X 0Σ7
1	570 665	23X	1	928 64X	766	1	869 081 654	0X0
2	64Σ 8X3	222	2	X07 1Σ4	74X	2	15Σ 734	083
3	72X Σ05	205	3	XX5 942	732	3	239 7Σ7	067
4	80X 10X	1X9	4	Σ84 474	716	4	317 862	050
5	8X9 2Σ7	191	5	866 062 Σ8X	6Σ9	5	3Σ5 8Σ2	033
6	988 488	174	6	141 687	6X1	6	493 925	017
7	X67 640	158	7	220 168	685	7	571 940	99 ΣΣΣ
8	Σ46 798	13Σ	8	2ΣX 831	668	8	64Σ 93Σ	ΣX3
9	863 025 917	123	9	399 299	651	9	729 922	Σ88
X	104 X3X	106	X	477 92X	634	X	807 8XX	Σ6Σ
Σ	1X3 Σ44	0XX	Σ	556 362	618	Σ	8X5 859	Σ53
5X10	283 032	092	5X50	634 97X	600	5X90	983 7Σ0	Σ37
1	362 104	075	1	713 37X	5X4	1	X61 727	Σ1Σ
2	441 179	059	2	7Σ1 962	587	2	Σ3Σ 646	Σ03
3	520 216	041	3	890 329	56Σ	3	86X 019 549	XX8
4	5ΣΣ 257	024	4	96X 898	554	4	0Σ7 435	X8Σ
5	69X 27Σ	008	5	X49 230	536	5	195 304	X73
6	779 287	9X ΣΣ0	6	Σ27 766	51Σ	6	273 177	X57
7	858 277	Σ93	7	867 006 085	503	7	351 012	X3Σ
8	937 24X	Σ76	8	0X4 588	4X6	8	42X X51	X24
9	X16 204	Σ5Σ	9	182 X72	48X	9	508 875	X07
X	XΣ5 163	Σ42	X	261 340	473	X	5X6 680	9XΣ
Σ	Σ94 0X5	Σ26	Σ	33Σ 7Σ3	456	Σ	684 46Σ	994
5X20	864 073 00Σ	Σ09	5X60	41X 049	439	5XX0	762 243	977
1	151 Σ18	XΣ1	1	4Σ8 486	422	1	83Σ ΣΣX	95Σ
2	230 X09	X95	2	596 8X8	406	2	919 959	944
3	30Σ 8X2	X78	3	675 0Σ2	3X9	3	9Σ7 6X1	927
4	3XX 75X	X60	4	753 49Σ	391	4	X95 408	910
5	489 5ΣX	X44	5	831 870	375	5	Σ73 118	8Σ4
6	568 442	X27	6	910 025	359	6	86Σ 050 X10	897
7	647 269	X10	7	9XX 382	341	7	12X 6X7	880
8	726 079	9Σ2	8	X88 703	325	8	208 367	864
9	804 X6Σ	997	9	Σ66 X28	309	9	2X6 00Σ	848
X	8X3 846	97X	X	868 045 135	2Σ0	X	383 857	830
Σ	982 604	962	Σ	123 425	295	Σ	461 487	814
5X30	X61 366	946	5X70	201 6ΣX	278	5XΣ0	53Σ 09Σ	7Σ8
1	Σ40 0Σ0	929	1	29Σ 976	260	1	618 897	7X1
2	865 01X X19	911	2	37X 016	245	2	6Σ6 478	784
3	0Σ9 72X	8Σ5	3	458 25Σ	228	3	794 040	768
4	198 423	898	4	536 487	210	4	871 7X8	751
5	277 0ΣΣ	881	5	614 697	1Σ4	5	94Σ 339	735
6	355 980	864	6	6Σ2 88Σ	197	6	X28 X72	719
7	434 624	847	7	790 X66	180	7	Σ06 58Σ	700
8	513 26Σ	830	8	86Σ 026	164	8	ΣX4 08Σ	6X6
9	5Σ1 X9Σ	813	9	949 18X	148	9	870 081 775	689
X	690 6Σ2	7Σ7	X	X27 316	12Σ	X	15Σ 242	671
Σ	76Σ 2X9	79Σ	Σ	Σ05 445	114	Σ	238 8Σ3	655

N	Log N	d	N	Log N	d	N	Log N	d
5Ɛ00	870 316 348	99 63X	5Ɛ40	873 626 758	98 Ɛ88	5Ɛ80	876 914 881	98 525
1	3Ɛ3 986	622	1	703 724	Ɛ71	1	9Ɛ1 1X6	509
2	491 3X8	606	2	7X0 695	Ɛ55	2	X89 6Ɛ3	4Ɛ1
3	56X 9Ɛ2	5XX	3	879 62X	Ɛ3X	3	Ɛ65 ƐX4	496
4	648 3X0	592	4	956 568	Ɛ22	4	877 042 47X	47Ɛ
5	725 972	576	5	X33 48X	Ɛ06	5	11X 939	463
6	803 328	55X	6	Ɛ10 394	XXƐ	6	1Ɛ7 1X0	447
7	8X0 886	543	7	ƐX9 283	X93	7	293 627	430
8	97X 209	527	8	874 086 156	X77	8	36Ɛ X57	415
9	X57 734	50Ɛ	9	163 011	X60	9	448 270	3Ɛ9
X	Ɛ35 043	4Ɛ3	X	23Ɛ X71	X44	X	524 669	3X2
Ɛ	871 012 536	497	Ɛ	318 8Ɛ5	X28	Ɛ	600 X4Ɛ	386
5Ɛ10	0XƐ X11	480	5Ɛ50	3Ɛ5 721	X11	5Ɛ90	699 215	36Ɛ
1	189 291	463	1	492 532	9Ɛ5	1	775 584	354
2	266 734	448	2	56Ɛ 327	99X	2	851 918	337
3	343 Ɛ80	430	3	648 105	982	3	92X 053	321
4	421 3Ɛ0	415	4	724 X87	966	4	X06 374	305
5	4ƐX 805	3Ɛ8	5	801 831	94X	5	XX2 679	2XX
6	598 001	3X1	6	89X 57Ɛ	934	6	Ɛ7X 967	292
7	675 3X2	385	7	977 2Ɛ3	917	7	878 057 039	277
8	752 767	369	8	X54 00X	900	8	133 2Ɛ4	25Ɛ
9	82Ɛ Ɛ14	351	9	Ɛ30 90X	8X4	9	20Ɛ 553	244
X	909 265	336	X	875 009 5Ɛ2	889	X	2X7 797	228
Ɛ	9X6 59Ɛ	319	Ɛ	0X6 27Ɛ	871	Ɛ	383 X03	211
5Ɛ20	X83 8Ɛ8	302	5Ɛ60	182 Ɛ30	855	5ƐX0	460 014	1Ɛ6
1	Ɛ60 ƐƐX	2X6	1	25Ɛ 785	83X	1	538 20X	19X
2	872 03X 2X4	28Ɛ	2	338 403	822	2	614 3X8	183
3	117 573	273	3	415 025	807	3	6Ɛ0 56Ɛ	168
4	1Ɛ4 826	257	4	4Ɛ1 830	7XƐ	4	788 717	150
5	291 X81	23Ɛ	5	58X 41Ɛ	794	5	864 867	135
6	36Ɛ 100	223	6	666 ƐƐ3	778	6	940 9X0	119
7	448 323	208	7	743 76Ɛ	760	7	X18 XƐ9	102
8	525 52Ɛ	1Ɛ0	8	820 30Ɛ	745	8	XƐ4 ƐƐƐ	0X7
9	602 71Ɛ	194	9	8Ɛ8 X54	729	9	Ɛ91 0X6	08Ɛ
X	69Ɛ 8Ɛ3	178	X	995 581	712	X	879 069 175	074
Ɛ	778 X6Ɛ	161	Ɛ	X72 093	6Ɛ6	Ɛ	145 229	058
5Ɛ30	856 010	145	5Ɛ70	Ɛ4X 789	69Ɛ	5ƐƐ0	221 285	041
1	933 155	12X	1	876 027 268	683	1	2Ɛ9 306	026
2	X10 283	111	2	103 92Ɛ	668	2	395 330	00X
3	XX9 394	0Ɛ6	3	1X0 397	650	3	471 33X	97 ƐƐ3
4	Ɛ86 48X	09X	4	278 X27	635	4	549 331	Ɛ98
5	873 063 568	083	5	355 460	619	5	625 309	Ɛ81
6	140 62Ɛ	066	6	431 X79	601	6	701 28X	Ɛ65
7	219 695	04Ɛ	7	50X 47X	5X6	7	799 233	Ɛ49
8	2Ɛ6 724	034	8	5X6 X64	58Ɛ	8	875 180	Ɛ33
9	393 758	017	9	683 433	573	9	951 0Ɛ3	Ɛ17
X	470 773	000	X	75Ɛ 9X6	557	X	X29 00X	XƐƐ
Ɛ	549 773	98 ƐX5	Ɛ	838 341	540	Ɛ	Ɛ04 Ɛ09	XX5

N	Log N	d	N	Log N	d	N	Log N	d
6000	879 ƐX0 9Ɛ2	97 X89	6040	881 247 214	97 43Ɛ	6080	884 490 00X	96 9Ɛ8
1	87X 078 87Ɛ	X72	1	322 653	423	1	566 X06	9X1
2	154 731	X56	2	3Ɛ9 X76	408	2	641 7X7	986
3	230 587	X3Ɛ	3	495 282	3Ɛ0	3	718 571	96Ɛ
4	308 406	X24	4	570 672	396	4	7Ɛ3 320	954
5	3X4 22X	X08	5	647 X48	37Ɛ	5	88X 074	939
6	480 036	9Ɛ2	6	723 207	363	6	964 9Ɛ1	922
7	557 X28	996	7	7ƐX 56X	349	7	X3Ɛ 713	907
8	633 802	97X	8	895 8Ɛ7	331	8	Ɛ16 41X	8Ɛ1
9	70Ɛ 580	964	9	971 028	316	9	ƐƐ1 10Ɛ	895
X	7X7 324	948	X	X48 342	2ƐƐ	X	885 087 9X4	87X
Ɛ	883 070	931	Ɛ	Ɛ23 641	2X4	Ɛ	162 662	864
6010	95X 9X1	915	6050	ƐƐX 925	289	6090	239 306	848
1	X36 6Ɛ6	8ƐƐ	1	882 095 ƐƐ2	272	1	313 Ɛ52	832
2	Ɛ12 3Ɛ5	8X3	2	171 264	256	2	3XX 784	817
3	ƐXX 098	887	3	248 4ƐX	240	3	485 39Ɛ	800
4	87Ɛ 085 963	871	4	323 73X	224	4	55Ɛ Ɛ9Ɛ	7X5
5	161 614	855	5	3ƐX 962	20X	5	636 784	78X
6	239 269	83X	6	495 Ɛ70	1Ɛ2	6	711 352	773
7	314 XX7	823	7	571 162	197	7	7X7 Ɛ05	758
8	3Ɛ0 70X	807	8	648 339	181	8	882 661	741
9	488 315	7Ɛ1	9	723 4ƐX	165	9	959 1X2	727
X	563 Ɛ06	795	X	7ƐX 663	14X	X	X33 909	70Ɛ
Ɛ	63Ɛ 69Ɛ	77X	Ɛ	895 7Ɛ1	133	Ɛ	Ɛ0X 418	6Ɛ5
6020	717 259	762	6060	970 924	118	60X0	ƐX4 Ɛ11	69X
1	7Ɛ2 9ƐƐ	747	1	X47 X40	101	1	886 07Ɛ 5XƐ	683
2	88X 546	731	2	Ɛ22 Ɛ41	0X6	2	156 072	668
3	966 077	715	3	ƐƐX 027	08Ɛ	3	230 71X	651
4	X41 790	6Ɛ9	4	883 095 0Ɛ6	073	4	307 16Ɛ	637
5	Ɛ19 289	6X3	5	170 169	059	5	3X1 7X6	61Ɛ
6	ƐƐ4 970	687	6	247 206	042	6	478 205	605
7	880 090 437	670	7	322 248	027	7	552 80X	5X9
8	167 XX7	655	8	3Ɛ9 273	010	8	629 1Ɛ7	593
9	243 540	63X	9	494 283	96 ƐƐ4	9	703 78X	578
X	31X Ɛ7X	622	X	56Ɛ 277	Ɛ9X	X	79X 146	562
Ɛ	3Ɛ6 5X0	608	Ɛ	646 255	Ɛ83	Ɛ	874 6X8	546
6030	491 ƐX8	5Ɛ0	6070	721 218	Ɛ67	60Ɛ0	94Ɛ 032	530
1	569 598	595	1	7Ɛ8 183	Ɛ51	1	X25 562	514
2	644 Ɛ71	579	2	893 114	Ɛ36	2	XƐƐ X76	4ƐX
3	720 52X	563	3	96X 04X	Ɛ1X	3	Ɛ96 374	4X3
4	7Ɛ7 X91	548	4	X44 Ɛ68	Ɛ04	4	887 070 857	489
5	893 419	530	5	Ɛ1Ɛ X70	XX9	5	147 124	471
6	96X 949	515	6	ƐƐ6 959	X91	6	221 595	457
7	X46 262	4ƐX	7	884 091 82X	X77	7	2Ɛ7 X30	440
8	Ɛ21 760	4X3	8	168 6X5	X60	8	392 270	425
9	ƐƐ9 043	487	9	243 545	X45	9	468 695	40X
X	881 094 50X	471	X	31X 38X	X29	X	542 XX3	3Ɛ3
Ɛ	16Ɛ 97Ɛ	455	Ɛ	3Ɛ5 1Ɛ7	X13	Ɛ	619 296	399

N	Log N	d	N	Log N	d	N	Log N	d
6100	887 6Ɛ3 673	96 382	6140	88χ 8Ɛ6 059	95 954	6180	891 χ97 850	95 333
1	789 χ35	367	1	98Ɛ 9Ɛ1	939	1	Ɛ70 Ɛ83	318
2	864 1χ0	350	2	χ65 72χ	923	2	892 046 29Ɛ	301
3	93χ 530	336	3	Ɛ3Ɛ 451	908	3	11Ɛ 5χ0	2χ7
4	χ14 866	31χ	4	88Ɛ 015 159	8Ɛ2	4	1Ɛ4 887	291
5	χχχ Ɛ84	304	5	0χχ χ4Ɛ	897	5	289 Ɛ58	276
6	Ɛ85 288	2χ9	6	184 726	880	6	363 212	260
7	888 05Ɛ 575	293	7	25χ 3χ6	866	7	438 472	245
8	135 848	277	8	334 050	84Ɛ	8	511 6Ɛ7	22Ɛ
9	20Ɛ Ɛ03	261	9	409 89Ɛ	835	9	5χ6 926	214
χ	2χ6 164	246	χ	4χ3 514	81χ	χ	67Ɛ Ɛ3χ	1Ɛχ
Ɛ	380 3χχ	230	Ɛ	579 132	803	Ɛ	755 138	1χ4
6110	456 61χ	214	6150	652 935	7χ9	6190	82χ 320	189
1	530 832	1Ɛχ	1	728 522	793	1	903 4χ9	173
2	606 χ30	1χ3	2	802 0Ɛ5	777	2	998 660	159
3	6χ1 013	189	3	897 870	762	3	χ71 7Ɛ9	142
4	777 1χ0	172	4	971 412	746	4	Ɛ46 93Ɛ	127
5	851 352	156	5	χ46 Ɛ58	730	5	893 01Ɛ χ66	112
6	927 4χ8	141	6	Ɛ20 688	716	6	0Ɛ4 Ɛ78	0Ɛ6
7	χ01 629	125	7	ƐƐ6 1χ2	6ƐƐ	7	18χ 072	0χ1
8	χ97 752	10Ɛ	8	890 08Ɛ 8χ1	6χ4	8	263 153	086
9	Ɛ71 861	0Ɛ4	9	165 385	68χ	9	338 219	070
χ	889 047 955	099	χ	23χ χ53	673	χ	411 289	055
Ɛ	121 χ32	083	Ɛ	314 506	659	Ɛ	4χ6 322	03Ɛ
6120	1Ɛ7 χƐ5	068	6160	3χ9 Ɛ63	642	61χ0	57Ɛ 361	024
1	291 Ɛ61	051	1	483 5χ5	628	1	654 385	00Ɛ
2	367 ƐƐ2	037	2	559 011	611	2	729 394	94 ƐƐ4
3	442 029	020	3	632 622	5Ɛ7	3	802 388	Ɛ99
4	518 049	005	4	708 019	5χ0	4	897 365	Ɛ83
5	5Ɛ2 052	95 Ɛχχ	5	7χ1 5Ɛ9	585	5	970 328	Ɛ69
6	688 040	Ɛ94	6	876 Ɛ82	56Ɛ	6	χ45 295	Ɛ52
7	762 014	Ɛ79	7	950 531	555	7	Ɛ1χ 227	Ɛ39
8	837 Ɛ91	Ɛ62	8	χ25 χ86	53χ	8	ƐƐ3 164	Ɛ21
9	911 Ɛ33	Ɛ48	9	χƐƐ 404	524	9	894 088 085	Ɛ08
χ	9χ7 χ7Ɛ	Ɛ31	χ	Ɛ94 928	509	χ	160 Ɛ91	χƐ1
Ɛ	χ81 9Ɛ0	Ɛ17	Ɛ	891 06χ 235	4Ɛ2	Ɛ	235 χ82	χ96
6130	Ɛ57 907	χƐƐ	6170	143 727	498	61Ɛ0	30χ 958	χ81
1	88χ 031 806	χχ5	1	219 003	482	1	3χ3 819	χ66
2	107 6χƐ	χ8Ɛ	2	2Ɛ2 485	467	2	478 683	χ50
3	1χ1 57χ	χ74	3	387 930	450	3	551 513	χ35
4	277 432	χ59	4	461 180	437	4	626 348	χ1Ɛ
5	351 28Ɛ	χ42	5	536 5Ɛ7	41Ɛ	5	6ƐƐ 167	χ05
6	427 111	χ28	6	60Ɛ χ16	405	6	793 Ɛ70	9χƐ
7	500 Ɛ39	χ11	7	6χ5 21Ɛ	3χƐ	7	868 95Ɛ	994
8	596 94χ	9Ɛ7	8	77χ 60χ	394	8	941 733	97χ
9	670 745	9χ0	9	853 9χ2	37χ	9	χ16 4Ɛ1	964
χ	746 525	985	χ	929 160	363	χ	χχƐ 255	949
Ɛ	820 2χχ	96Ɛ	Ɛ	χ02 503	349	Ɛ	Ɛ83 Ɛχ2	933

N	Log N	d	N	Log N	d	N	Log N	d
6200	895 058 915	94 919	6240	898 1Ɛ9 529	94 30Ɛ	6280	89Ɛ 339 Ɛ45	93 909
1	131 632	902	1	291 838	2Ɛ5	1	411 852	8Ɛ3
2	206 334	8X8	2	365 Ɛ31	29X	2	4X5 545	899
3	29Ɛ 020	892	3	43X 20Ɛ	285	3	579 222	884
4	373 8Ɛ2	878	4	512 494	26Ɛ	4	650 XX6	869
5	448 56X	861	5	5X6 743	254	5	724 753	853
6	521 20Ɛ	847	6	67X 997	23Ɛ	6	7Ɛ8 3X6	83X
7	5Ɛ5 X56	831	7	753 016	224	7	890 024	823
8	68X 687	817	8	827 23X	20X	8	963 847	809
9	763 2X2	800	9	8ƐƐ 448	1Ɛ4	9	X37 454	7Ɛ4
X	837 XX2	7X6	X	993 640	19X	X	Ɛ0Ɛ 048	79X
Ɛ	910 688	790	Ɛ	X67 81X	184	Ɛ	ƐX2 826	783
6210	9X5 258	776	6250	Ɛ3Ɛ 9X2	16X	6290	8X0 076 3X9	76X
1	X79 X12	75Ɛ	1	899 013 Ɛ50	153	1	149 Ɛ57	754
2	Ɛ52 571	745	2	0X8 0X3	13X	2	221 6XƐ	73X
3	896 027 0Ɛ6	72Ɛ	3	180 221	124	3	2Ɛ5 229	724
4	0ƐƐ 825	715	4	254 345	109	4	388 951	70X
5	194 33X	6ƐX	5	328 452	0Ɛ4	5	460 45Ɛ	6Ɛ5
6	268 X38	6X4	6	400 546	099	6	533 Ɛ54	69X
7	341 520	68X	7	494 623	083	7	607 632	684
8	415 ƐXX	674	8	568 6X6	069	8	69Ɛ 0Ɛ6	66Ɛ
9	4XX 662	659	9	640 753	054	9	772 765	655
X	583 0ƐƐ	644	X	714 7X7	039	X	846 1ƐX	63X
Ɛ	657 743	629	Ɛ	7X8 824	023	Ɛ	919 838	625
6220	730 170	613	6260	880 847	009	62X0	9Ɛ1 261	60Ɛ
1	804 783	5Ɛ8	1	954 854	93 ƐƐ3	1	X84 870	5Ɛ5
2	899 17Ɛ	5X3	2	X28 847	Ɛ99	2	Ɛ58 265	5X0
3	971 762	588	3	Ɛ00 824	Ɛ83	3	8X1 02Ɛ 845	585
4	X46 12X	572	4	Ɛ94 7X7	Ɛ69	4	103 20X	56Ɛ
5	Ɛ1X 6X0	558	5	89X 068 754	Ɛ53	5	196 779	556
6	ƐƐ3 038	542	6	140 6X7	Ɛ39	6	26X 113	540
7	897 087 57X	528	7	214 624	Ɛ23	7	341 653	526
8	15Ɛ XX6	511	8	2X8 547	Ɛ09	8	414 Ɛ79	510
9	234 3Ɛ7	4Ɛ7	9	380 454	XƐ2	9	4X8 489	4Ɛ6
X	308 8Ɛ2	4X1	X	454 346	X99	X	57Ɛ 983	4X0
Ɛ	3X1 193	487	Ɛ	528 223	X83	Ɛ	653 263	487
6230	475 65X	471	6270	600 0X6	X69	62Ɛ0	726 72X	471
1	549 Ɛ0Ɛ	456	1	693 Ɛ53	X53	1	7Ɛ9 Ɛ9Ɛ	456
2	622 365	441	2	767 9X6	X39	2	891 435	441
3	6Ɛ6 7X6	426	3	83Ɛ 823	X22	3	964 876	428
4	78Ɛ 010	410	4	913 645	X09	4	X38 0X2	411
5	863 420	3Ɛ6	5	9X7 452	9Ɛ3	5	Ɛ0Ɛ 4Ɛ3	3Ɛ8
6	937 816	3X0	6	X7Ɛ 245	999	6	ƐX2 8XƐ	3X1
7	X0Ɛ ƐƐ6	385	7	Ɛ53 022	983	7	8X2 076 090	388
8	XX4 37Ɛ	370	8	89Ɛ 026 9X5	969	8	149 458	372
9	Ɛ78 72Ɛ	355	9	0ƐX 752	953	9	220 80X	358
X	898 050 X84	340	X	192 4X5	939	X	2Ɛ3 Ɛ66	343
Ɛ	125 204	325	Ɛ	266 222	923	Ɛ	387 2X9	329

N	Log N	d	N	Log N	d	N	Log N	d
6300	8X2 45X 616	93 312	6340	8X5 55Ɛ 405	92 925	6380	8X8 640 777	92 341
1	531 928	2Ɛ9	1	632 12X	90X	1	712 XƐ8	327
2	605 025	2X4	2	704 X38	8Ɛ5	2	7X5 223	312
3	698 309	289	3	797 731	89Ɛ	3	877 535	2Ɛ9
4	76Ɛ 596	274	4	86X 410	886	4	949 832	2X3
5	842 84X	25X	5	941 096	870	5	X1Ɛ Ɛ15	28X
6	915 XX8	244	6	X13 946	856	6	XƐ2 1X3	274
7	9X9 130	22X	7	XX6 5X0	841	7	Ɛ84 457	25Ɛ
8	X80 35X	215	8	Ɛ79 221	827	8	8X9 056 6Ɛ6	245
9	Ɛ53 573	1ƐX	9	8X6 04Ɛ X48	812	9	128 93Ɛ	230
X	8X3 026 771	1X5	X	122 65X	7Ɛ8	X	1ƐX Ɛ6Ɛ	216
Ɛ	0Ɛ9 956	190	Ɛ	1Ɛ5 256	7X2	Ɛ	291 185	201
6310	190 Ɛ26	175	6350	287 X38	789	6390	363 386	1X7
1	264 09Ɛ	160	1	35X 605	773	1	435 571	192
2	337 23Ɛ	146	2	431 178	759	2	507 743	179
3	40X 385	130	3	503 915	744	3	599 900	163
4	4X1 4Ɛ5	116	4	596 459	72Ɛ	4	66Ɛ X63	149
5	574 60Ɛ	101	5	668 Ɛ88	714	5	741 Ɛ20	135
6	647 710	0X7	6	73Ɛ 6X0	6ƐƐ	6	814 125	11X
7	71X 7Ɛ7	091	7	812 19Ɛ	6X6	7	8X6 243	106
8	7Ɛ1 888	078	8	8X4 885	690	8	978 349	0Ɛ0
9	884 944	061	9	977 355	676	9	X4X 439	096
X	957 9X5	048	X	X49 X0Ɛ	661	X	Ɛ20 513	081
Ɛ	X2X X31	033	Ɛ	Ɛ20 470	647	Ɛ	ƐƐ2 594	068
6320	Ɛ01 X64	018	6360	ƐƐ2 XƐ7	632	63X0	8XX 084 640	052
1	Ɛ94 X80	003	1	8X7 085 529	618	1	156 692	039
2	8X4 067 X83	92 ƐX9	2	157 Ɛ45	603	2	228 70Ɛ	023
3	13X X70	Ɛ94	3	22X 548	5X9	3	2ƐX 732	00X
4	211 X44	Ɛ79	4	300 Ɛ35	593	4	390 740	91 ƐƐ5
5	2X4 X01	Ɛ64	5	393 508	57X	5	462 735	Ɛ9Ɛ
6	377 965	Ɛ4Ɛ	6	465 X86	564	6	534 714	Ɛ86
7	44X 8Ɛ4	Ɛ34	7	538 42X	54Ɛ	7	606 69X	Ɛ70
8	521 828	Ɛ1Ɛ	8	60X 979	536	8	698 64X	Ɛ58
9	5Ɛ4 747	Ɛ05	9	6X1 2Ɛ3	51Ɛ	9	76X 5X6	Ɛ41
X	687 650	XƐ0	X	773 812	506	X	840 527	Ɛ28
Ɛ	75X 540	X96	Ɛ	846 118	4Ɛ1	Ɛ	912 453	Ɛ13
6330	831 416	X80	6370	918 609	497	63Ɛ0	9X4 366	XƐX
1	904 296	X66	1	9XX XX4	482	1	X76 264	XX4
2	997 140	X51	2	X81 366	468	2	Ɛ48 148	X8Ɛ
3	X69 Ɛ91	X37	3	Ɛ53 812	452	3	8XƐ 01X 017	X75
4	Ɛ40 X08	X22	4	8X8 026 064	43X	4	0XƐ X90	X60
5	8X5 013 82X	X08	5	0Ɛ8 4X2	423	5	181 930	X47
6	0X6 636	9Ɛ2	6	18X 905	40X	6	253 777	X31
7	179 428	998	7	261 113	3Ɛ5	7	325 5X8	X18
8	250 204	983	8	333 508	39Ɛ	8	3Ɛ7 404	X03
9	322 Ɛ87	969	9	405 8X7	385	9	489 207	9X9
X	3Ɛ5 934	954	X	498 070	370	X	55X Ɛ24	994
Ɛ	488 688	939	Ɛ	56X 420	357	Ɛ	630 988	97Ɛ

N	Log N	d	N	Log N	d	N	Log N	d
6400	8XƐ 702 747	91 965	6440	8Ɛ2 765 58Ɛ	91 395	6480	8Ɛ5 7X9 516	90 X10
1	794 4Ɛ0	950	1	836 964	37Ɛ	1	87X 326	9Ɛ7
2	866 240	937	2	908 123	367	2	94Ɛ 121	9X1
3	937 Ɛ77	921	3	999 48X	351	3	X1Ɛ Ɛ02	989
4	X09 898	908	4	X6X 81Ɛ	338	4	XƐ0 88Ɛ	973
5	X9Ɛ 5X4	8Ɛ3	5	Ɛ3Ɛ Ɛ57	323	5	Ɛ81 642	95X
6	Ɛ71 297	899	6	8Ɛ3 011 27X	30X	6	8Ɛ6 052 3X0	946
7	8Ɛ0 042 Ɛ74	884	7	0X2 588	2Ɛ5	7	123 126	930
8	114 838	86Ɛ	8	173 881	29Ɛ	8	1Ɛ3 X56	918
9	1X6 4X7	855	9	244 Ɛ60	286	9	284 772	902
X	278 140	840	X	316 226	271	X	355 474	8X9
Ɛ	349 980	827	Ɛ	3X7 497	258	Ɛ	426 161	895
6410	41Ɛ 5X7	812	6450	478 733	243	6490	4Ɛ6 X36	87Ɛ
1	4Ɛ1 1Ɛ9	7Ɛ8	1	549 976	22X	1	587 6Ɛ5	867
2	582 9Ɛ5	7X3	2	61X ƐX4	214	2	658 360	851
3	654 598	789	3	6Ɛ0 1Ɛ8	200	3	728 ƐƐ1	838
4	726 165	775	4	781 3Ɛ8	1X6	4	7Ɛ9 829	824
5	7Ɛ7 91X	75Ɛ	5	852 5X2	191	5	88X 451	80X
6	889 479	745	6	923 773	178	6	95Ɛ 05Ɛ	7Ɛ6
7	95Ɛ 002	731	7	9Ɛ4 92Ɛ	163	7	X2Ɛ 855	7X0
8	X30 733	717	8	X85 X92	14X	8	Ɛ00 435	788
9	Ɛ02 24X	702	9	Ɛ57 020	135	9	Ɛ91 001	772
X	Ɛ93 950	6X9	X	8Ɛ4 028 155	11Ɛ	X	8Ɛ7 061 773	75X
Ɛ	8Ɛ1 065 439	693	Ɛ	0Ɛ9 274	107	Ɛ	132 311	744
6420	136 Ɛ10	67X	6460	18X 37Ɛ	0Ɛ1	64X0	202 X55	730
1	208 58X	665	1	25Ɛ 470	098	1	293 585	716
2	29X 033	650	2	330 548	083	2	364 09Ɛ	702
3	36Ɛ 683	636	3	401 60Ɛ	06X	3	434 7X1	6X9
4	441 0Ɛ9	621	4	492 679	055	4	505 28X	694
5	512 71X	608	5	563 712	040	5	595 962	67Ɛ
6	5X4 126	5Ɛ3	6	634 752	027	6	666 421	665
7	675 719	599	7	705 779	011	7	736 X86	651
8	747 0Ɛ6	584	8	796 78X	90 ƐƐ9	8	807 517	638
9	818 67X	56Ɛ	9	867 787	ƐX3	9	897 Ɛ53	624
X	8XX 029	556	X	938 76X	Ɛ8Ɛ	X	968 577	60X
Ɛ	97Ɛ 583	541	Ɛ	X09 739	Ɛ75	Ɛ	X38 Ɛ85	5Ɛ5
6430	X50 Ɛ04	527	6470	X9X 6Ɛ2	Ɛ60	64Ɛ0	Ɛ09 57X	5X0
1	Ɛ22 42Ɛ	512	1	Ɛ6Ɛ 652	Ɛ47	1	Ɛ99 Ɛ5X	588
2	ƐƐ3 941	4Ɛ9	2	8Ɛ5 040 599	Ɛ32	2	8Ɛ8 06X 526	572
3	8Ɛ2 085 23X	4X3	3	111 50Ɛ	Ɛ19	3	13X X98	55X
4	156 721	48Ɛ	4	1X2 428	Ɛ04	4	20Ɛ 436	544
5	227 ƐƐ0	475	5	273 330	XXƐ	5	29Ɛ 97X	530
6	2Ɛ9 465	460	6	344 21Ɛ	X96	6	370 2XX	517
7	38X 905	447	7	415 0Ɛ5	X81	7	440 805	502
8	460 150	431	8	4X5 Ɛ76	X67	8	511 107	4X9
9	531 581	419	9	576 X21	X53	9	5X1 5Ɛ4	494
X	602 99X	403	X	647 874	X3X	X	671 X88	47Ɛ
Ɛ	694 1X1	3XX	Ɛ	718 6Ɛ2	X24	Ɛ	742 347	466

N	Log N	d	N	Log N	d	N	Log N	d
6500	8Ɛ8 812 7Ɛ1	90 452	6540	8ƐƐ 819 45Ɛ	8Ɛ Χ9Χ	6580	902 805 919	8Ɛ 532
1	8Χ3 043	438	1	8Χ9 339	Χ86	1	895 24Ɛ	51Χ
2	973 47Ɛ	424	2	979 203	Χ70	2	964 769	505
3	Χ43 8Χ3	40Ɛ	3	Χ49 073	Χ58	3	Χ34 072	4Ɛ0
4	Ɛ14 0Ɛ2	3Ɛ6	4	Ɛ18 Ɛ0Ɛ	Χ44	4	Ɛ03 562	498
5	ƐΧ4 4Χ8	3Χ1	5	ƐΧ8 953	Χ2Χ	5	Ɛ92 Χ3Χ	483
6	8Ɛ9 074 889	388	6	900 078 781	Χ16	6	903 062 301	46Χ
7	145 055	373	7	148 597	Χ02	7	131 76Ɛ	456
8	215 408	35Ɛ	8	218 399	9Χ8	8	201 005	442
9	2Χ5 767	345	9	2Χ8 185	994	9	290 447	429
Χ	375 ΧƐ0	331	Χ	377 Ɛ59	97Ɛ	Χ	35Ɛ 874	414
Ɛ	446 221	318	Ɛ	447 918	966	Ɛ	42Ɛ 088	400
6510	516 539	303	6550	517 682	952	6590	4ƐΧ 488	3Χ7
1	5Χ6 840	2ΧΧ	1	5Χ7 414	939	1	589 873	392
2	676 Ɛ2Χ	295	2	677 151	924	2	659 045	37Χ
3	747 203	281	3	746 Χ75	90Ɛ	3	728 403	366
4	817 484	267	4	816 784	8Ɛ7	4	7Ɛ7 769	351
5	8Χ7 72Ɛ	253	5	8Χ6 47Ɛ	8Χ2	5	886 ΧƐΧ	338
6	977 982	23Χ	6	976 161	88Χ	6	956 236	324
7	Χ48 000	225	7	Χ45 Χ2Ɛ	874	7	Χ25 55Χ	30Ɛ
8	Ɛ18 225	210	8	Ɛ15 6Χ3	860	8	ΧƐ4 869	2Ɛ7
9	ƐΧ8 435	1Ɛ8	9	ƐΧ5 343	848	9	Ɛ83 Ɛ64	2Χ2
Χ	8ƐΧ 078 631	1Χ2	Χ	901 074 Ɛ8Ɛ	833	Χ	904 053 246	28Χ
Ɛ	148 813	18Χ	Ɛ	144 802	81Χ	Ɛ	122 514	275
6520	218 9Χ1	175	6560	214 420	805	65Χ0	1Ɛ1 789	260
1	2Χ8 Ɛ56	160	1	2Χ4 025	7Ɛ1	1	280 Χ29	248
2	379 0Ɛ6	148	2	373 816	798	2	350 075	234
3	449 242	132	3	443 3Ɛ2	783	3	41Ɛ 2Χ9	21Ɛ
4	519 374	11Χ	4	512 Ɛ75	76Ɛ	4	4ΧΧ 508	206
5	5Χ9 492	105	5	5Χ2 724	756	5	579 712	1Ɛ2
6	679 597	0Ɛ0	6	672 27Χ	741	6	648 904	19Χ
7	749 687	098	7	741 9ƐƐ	729	7	717 ΧΧ2	185
8	819 763	082	8	811 528	714	8	7Χ7 067	170
9	8Χ9 825	06Χ	9	8Χ1 040	6ƐƐ	9	876 217	158
Χ	979 893	055	Χ	970 73Ɛ	6Χ7	Χ	945 373	144
Ɛ	Χ49 928	040	Ɛ	Χ40 226	692	Ɛ	Χ14 4Ɛ7	12Ɛ
6530	Ɛ19 968	028	6570	Ɛ0Ɛ 8Ɛ8	67Χ	65Ɛ0	ΧΧ3 626	116
1	ƐΧ9 994	012	1	Ɛ9Ɛ 376	665	1	Ɛ72 740	102
2	8ƐƐ 079 9Χ6	8Ɛ ƐƐΧ	2	902 06Χ Χ1Ɛ	650	2	905 041 842	0Χ9
3	149 9Χ4	ƐΧ5	3	13Χ 46Ɛ	637	3	110 92Ɛ	095
4	219 989	Ɛ91	4	209 ΧΧ6	623	4	19Ɛ Χ04	081
5	2Χ9 95Χ	Ɛ77	5	299 509	60Ɛ	5	26Χ Χ85	068
6	379 915	Ɛ63	6	368 Ɛ18	5Ɛ6	6	339 Ɛ31	054
7	449 878	Ɛ4Χ	7	438 512	5Χ1	7	408 Ɛ85	03Ɛ
8	519 806	Ɛ35	8	507 ΧƐ3	588	8	498 004	026
9	5Χ9 73Ɛ	Ɛ21	9	597 47Ɛ	574	9	567 02Χ	012
Χ	679 660	Ɛ08	Χ	666 Χ33	55Ɛ	Χ	636 040	8Χ ƐƐΧ
Ɛ	749 568	ΧƐ3	Ɛ	736 392	547	Ɛ	705 03Χ	ƐΧ5

N	Log N	d	N	Log N	d	N	Log N	d
6600	905 794 023	8χ Ɛ91	6640	908 744 3χ7	8χ 636	6680	90Ɛ 696 χ57	8χ 0χ6
1	862 ƐƐ4	Ɛ78	1	812 χ21	622	1	764 Ɛ41	092
2	931 Ɛ70	Ɛ64	2	8χ1 443	60χ	2	833 013	07χ
3	χ00 Ɛ14	Ɛ50	3	96Ɛ χ51	5Ɛ5	3	901 091	066
4	χ8Ɛ χ64	Ɛ36	4	χ3χ 446	5χ1	4	98Ɛ 137	051
5	Ɛ5χ 99χ	Ɛ23	5	Ɛ08 χ27	588	5	χ59 188	039
6	906 029 901	Ɛ0χ	6	Ɛ97 3Ɛ3	575	6	Ɛ27 205	026
7	0Ɛ8 80Ɛ	χƐ6	7	909 065 968	560	7	ƐƐ5 22Ɛ	011
8	187 705	χχ1	8	134 308	547	8	910 083 240	89 ƐƐ9
9	256 5χ6	χ89	9	202 853	534	9	151 239	Ɛχ4
χ	325 473	χ74	χ	291 187	51Ɛ	χ	21Ɛ 221	Ɛ91
Ɛ	3Ɛ4 327	χ60	Ɛ	35Ɛ 6χ6	507	Ɛ	2χ9 1Ɛ2	Ɛ78
6610	483 187	χ47	6650	429 ƐƐ1	4Ɛ2	6690	377 16χ	Ɛ64
1	552 012	χ33	1	4Ɛ8 4χ3	49χ	1	445 112	Ɛ51
2	620 χ45	χ1Ɛ	2	586 981	486	2	513 063	Ɛ37
3	6χƐ 864	χ06	3	655 247	472	3	5χ0 Ɛ9χ	Ɛ24
4	77χ 66χ	9Ɛ2	4	723 6Ɛ9	459	4	66χ Ɛ02	Ɛ10
5	849 460	999	5	7Ɛ1 Ɛ56	446	5	738 χ12	χƐ8
6	918 239	985	6	880 3χ0	431	6	806 90χ	χχ3
7	9χ7 002	971	7	94χ 811	418	7	894 7Ɛ1	χ8Ɛ
8	χ75 973	958	8	χ19 029	405	8	962 680	χ77
9	Ɛ44 70Ɛ	944	9	χχ7 432	3Ɛ0	9	χ30 537	χ63
χ	907 013 453	92Ɛ	χ	Ɛ75 822	397	χ	χƐχ 39χ	χ4Ɛ
Ɛ	0χ2 182	917	Ɛ	90χ 043 ƐƐ9	384	Ɛ	Ɛ88 229	χ37
6620	170 χ99	903	6660	112 381	36Ɛ	66χ0	911 056 064	χ23
1	23Ɛ 7χ0	8χχ	1	1χ0 730	358	1	123 χ87	χ0Ɛ
2	30χ 48χ	896	2	26χ χ88	342	2	1Ɛ1 896	9Ɛ6
3	399 164	881	3	339 20χ	32Ɛ	3	27Ɛ 690	9χ2
4	467 χ25	869	4	407 539	316	4	349 472	98Ɛ
5	536 692	855	5	495 853	302	5	417 241	976
6	605 327	840	6	563 Ɛ55	2χχ	6	4χ4 Ɛ27	962
7	693 Ɛ67	828	7	632 243	296	7	572 959	94χ
8	762 793	814	8	700 519	281	8	640 6χ7	936
9	831 3χ7	7ƐƐ	9	78χ 79χ	26χ	9	70χ 421	922
χ	8ƐƐ Ɛχ6	7χ7	χ	858 χ48	255	χ	798 143	909
Ɛ	98χ 791	793	Ɛ	927 0χ1	241	Ɛ	865 χ50	8Ɛ6
6630	χ59 364	77χ	6670	9Ɛ5 322	228	66Ɛ0	933 746	8χ2
1	Ɛ27 Ɛ22	766	1	χ83 54χ	214	1	χ01 428	889
2	ƐƐ6 688	751	2	Ɛ51 762	201	2	χ8Ɛ 0Ɛ5	876
3	908 085 219	739	3	90Ɛ 01Ɛ 963	1χ8	3	Ɛ58 96Ɛ	861
4	153 956	725	4	0χ9 Ɛ4Ɛ	193	4	912 026 610	849
5	222 47Ɛ	710	5	178 122	180	5	0Ɛ4 259	835
6	2Ɛ0 Ɛ8Ɛ	6Ɛ9	6	246 2χ2	167	6	181 χ92	822
7	37Ɛ 688	6χ3	7	314 449	153	7	24Ɛ 6Ɛ4	809
8	44χ 16Ɛ	690	8	3χ2 5χ0	13Ɛ	8	319 301	7Ɛ5
9	518 83Ɛ	677	9	470 71Ɛ	127	9	3χ6 χƐ6	7χ1
χ	5χ7 2Ɛ6	663	χ	53χ 846	113	χ	474 697	789
Ɛ	675 959	64χ	Ɛ	608 959	0Ɛχ	Ɛ	542 264	774

N	Log N	d	N	Log N	d	N	Log N	d
6700	912 60Ɛ X18	89 761	6740	915 527 512	89 222	6780	918 425 959	88 8XX
1	699 579	749	1	5Ɛ4 734	20X	1	4Ɛ2 647	895
2	767 106	735	2	681 942	1Ɛ6	2	57Ɛ 320	882
3	834 83Ɛ	721	3	74X Ɛ38	1X2	3	647 ƐX2	86Ɛ
4	902 360	708	4	818 11X	18Ɛ	4	714 851	856
5	98Ɛ X68	6Ɛ5	5	8X5 2X9	176	5	7X1 4X7	843
6	X59 561	6X1	6	972 463	163	6	86X 12X	82Ɛ
7	Ɛ27 042	688	7	X3Ɛ 606	14X	7	936 959	817
8	ƐƐ4 70X	675	8	Ɛ08 754	137	8	X03 574	803
9	913 082 183	660	9	Ɛ95 88Ɛ	123	9	X90 177	7Ɛ0
X	14Ɛ 823	649	X	916 062 9Ɛ2	10Ɛ	X	Ɛ58 967	798
Ɛ	219 270	634	Ɛ	12Ɛ Ɛ01	0Ɛ7	Ɛ	919 025 543	784
6710	2X6 8X4	621	6750	1Ɛ8 ƐƐ8	0X4	6790	0Ɛ2 107	770
1	374 305	608	1	286 0X0	08Ɛ	1	17X 877	759
2	441 911	5Ɛ5	2	353 16Ɛ	078	2	247 414	745
3	50Ɛ 306	5X0	3	420 227	063	3	313 Ɛ59	731
4	598 8X6	589	4	4X9 28X	050	4	3X0 68X	71X
5	666 273	574	5	576 31X	038	5	469 1X8	705
6	733 827	561	6	643 356	024	6	535 8Ɛ1	6Ɛ2
7	801 188	549	7	710 37X	010	7	602 3X3	69Ɛ
8	88X 715	534	8	799 38X	88 ƐƐ9	8	68X X82	686
9	958 049	521	9	866 387	ƐX4	9	757 548	673
X	X25 56X	508	X	933 36Ɛ	Ɛ91	X	823 ƐƐƐ	65Ɛ
Ɛ	XƐ2 X76	4Ɛ5	Ɛ	X00 340	Ɛ79	Ɛ	8Ɛ0 65X	648
6720	Ɛ80 36Ɛ	4X0	6760	X89 2Ɛ9	Ɛ65	67X0	979 0X6	633
1	914 049 84Ɛ	489	1	Ɛ56 262	Ɛ51	1	X45 719	620
2	117 118	475	2	917 023 1Ɛ3	Ɛ39	2	Ɛ12 139	609
3	1X4 591	460	3	0Ɛ0 130	Ɛ25	3	Ɛ9X 746	5Ɛ4
4	271 X31	449	4	179 055	Ɛ12	4	91X 067 13X	5X1
5	33Ɛ 27X	435	5	245 Ɛ67	XƐX	5	133 71Ɛ	589
6	408 6Ɛ3	421	6	312 X65	XX6	6	200 0X8	576
7	495 Ɛ14	408	7	39Ɛ 94Ɛ	X92	7	288 662	562
8	563 320	3Ɛ5	8	468 821	X7X	8	355 004	54X
9	630 715	3X1	9	535 69Ɛ	X67	9	421 552	536
X	6Ɛ9 XƐ6	389	X	602 546	X52	X	4X9 X88	523
Ɛ	787 283	375	Ɛ	68Ɛ 398	X3Ɛ	Ɛ	576 3XƐ	50Ɛ
6730	854 638	361	6770	758 217	X27	67Ɛ0	642 8ƐX	4Ɛ7
1	921 999	34X	1	825 042	X14	1	70Ɛ 1Ɛ5	4X4
2	9XƐ 127	335	2	8Ɛ1 X56	9ƐƐ	2	797 699	490
3	X78 460	321	3	97X 855	9X8	3	863 Ɛ69	478
4	Ɛ45 781	309	4	X47 641	993	4	930 425	465
5	915 012 X8X	2Ɛ6	5	Ɛ14 414	980	5	9Ɛ8 88X	451
6	0X0 184	2X1	6	ƐX1 194	969	6	X85 11Ɛ	439
7	169 465	28X	7	918 069 Ɛ41	954	7	Ɛ51 558	426
8	236 733	275	8	136 895	941	8	91Ɛ 019 982	412
9	303 9X8	262	9	203 616	929	9	0X6 194	3ƐX
X	391 04X	24X	X	290 343	915	X	172 592	3X7
Ɛ	45X 298	236	Ɛ	359 058	901	Ɛ	23X 979	393

N	Log N	d	N	Log N	d	N	Log N	d
6800	91Ɛ 307 150	88 380	6840	922 18Ɛ 702	87 χ57	6880	925 037 440	87 53χ
1	393 510	367	1	257 559	χ44	1	102 97χ	526
2	45Ɛ 877	355	2	323 3χ1	χ31	2	18χ 2χ4	513
3	528 010	340	3	3χƐ 212	χ19	3	255 7Ɛ7	500
4	5Ɛ4 350	329	4	477 02Ɛ	χ05	4	321 0Ɛ7	4χ9
5	680 679	315	5	542 χ34	9Ɛ2	5	3χ8 5χ4	495
6	748 992	302	6	60χ 826	99Ɛ	6	473 χ79	481
7	815 094	2χχ	7	696 605	987	7	53Ɛ 33χ	46χ
8	8χ1 382	296	8	762 390	974	8	606 7χ8	457
9	969 658	283	9	82χ 144	960	9	692 043	444
χ	χ35 91Ɛ	26Ɛ	χ	8Ɛ5 χχ4	948	χ	759 487	430
Ɛ	Ɛ01 Ɛ8χ	258	Ɛ	981 830	935	Ɛ	824 8Ɛ7	419
6810	Ɛ8χ 226	243	6850	χ49 565	922	6890	8Ɛ0 114	405
1	920 056 469	231	1	Ɛ15 287	90χ	1	977 519	3Ɛ2
2	122 69χ	218	2	Ɛχ0 Ɛ95	8Ɛ7	2	χ42 90Ɛ	39Ɛ
3	1χχ 8Ɛ6	205	3	923 068 890	8χ3	3	Ɛ0χ 0χχ	388
4	276 χƐƐ	1Ɛ2	4	134 573	88Ɛ	4	Ɛ95 476	374
5	343 0Ɛ1	19χ	5	200 242	879	5	926 060 82χ	360
6	40Ɛ 28Ɛ	186	6	287 χƐƐ	864	6	127 Ɛ8χ	34χ
7	497 455	173	7	353 763	852	7	1Ɛ3 318	336
8	563 608	15Ɛ	8	41Ɛ 3Ɛ5	839	8	27χ 652	322
9	62Ɛ 767	147	9	4χ7 032	827	9	345 974	310
χ	6Ɛ7 8Ɛ2	134	χ	572 859	813	χ	411 084	2Ɛ8
Ɛ	783 χ26	120	Ɛ	63χ 470	7ƐƐ	Ɛ	498 380	2χ4
6820	84Ɛ Ɛ46	109	6860	706 06Ɛ	7χ8	68χ0	563 664	292
1	918 053	0Ɛ5	1	791 857	795	1	62χ 936	27χ
2	9χ4 148	0χ2	2	859 430	781	2	6Ɛ5 ƐƐ4	267
3	χ70 22χ	08χ	3	924 Ɛ21	769	3	781 25Ɛ	253
4	Ɛ38 2Ɛ8	076	4	9Ɛ0 75χ	757	4	848 4Ɛ2	240
5	921 004 372	063	5	χ78 2Ɛ5	742	5	913 732	229
6	090 415	04Ɛ	6	Ɛ43 χ37	730	6	99χ 95Ɛ	215
7	158 464	038	7	924 00Ɛ 567	717	7	χ65 Ɛ74	203
8	224 4χ0	024	8	097 082	705	8	Ɛ31 177	1χχ
9	2Ɛ0 504	011	9	162 787	6Ɛ1	9	ƐƐ8 365	198
χ	378 515	87 ƐƐ9	χ	22χ 278	69χ	χ	927 083 541	184
Ɛ	444 512	Ɛχ6	Ɛ	2Ɛ5 956	686	Ɛ	14χ 705	171
6830	510 4Ɛ8	Ɛ92	6870	381 420	672	68Ɛ0	215 876	15χ
1	598 48χ	Ɛ7χ	1	448 χ92	660	1	2χ0 χ14	146
2	664 448	Ɛ67	2	514 532	648	2	367 Ɛ5χ	133
3	730 3Ɛ3	Ɛ53	3	59Ɛ Ɛ7χ	634	3	433 091	120
4	7Ɛ8 346	Ɛ40	4	667 5Ɛ2	621	4	4Ɛχ 1Ɛ1	109
5	884 286	Ɛ28	5	733 013	60χ	5	585 2Ɛχ	0Ɛ5
6	950 1Ɛ2	Ɛ15	6	7Ɛχ 621	5Ɛ6	6	650 3Ɛ3	0χ2
7	χ18 107	Ɛ01	7	886 017	5χ3	7	717 495	08Ɛ
8	χχ4 008	χχχ	8	951 5Ɛχ	590	8	7χ2 564	077
9	Ɛ6Ɛ χƐ6	χ96	9	χ18 Ɛ8χ	578	9	869 61Ɛ	064
χ	922 037 990	χ83	χ	χχ4 546	564	χ	934 683	051
Ɛ	103 853	χ6Ɛ	Ɛ	Ɛ6Ɛ χχχ	552	Ɛ	9ƐƐ 714	03χ

N	Log N	d	N	Log N	d	N	Log N	d
6900	927 χ86 752	87 026	6940	92χ 8Ɛ9 63χ	86 719	6980	931 714 301	86 216
1	Ɛ51 778	013	1	984 157	706	1	79χ 517	202
2	928 018 78Ɛ	000	2	χ4χ 861	6Ɛ2	2	864 719	1χƐ
3	0χ3 78Ɛ	86 Ɛχ8	3	Ɛ15 353	6χ0	3	92χ 908	198
4	16χ 777	Ɛ96	4	Ɛ9Ɛ χ33	688	4	9Ɛ4 χχ4	186
5	235 751	Ɛ82	5	92Ɛ 066 4ƐƐ	675	5	χ7Ɛ 06χ	172
6	300 713	Ɛ6Ɛ	6	130 Ɛ74	662	6	Ɛ45 220	15Ɛ
7	387 682	Ɛ57	7	1Ɛ7 616	64Ɛ	7	932 00Ɛ 37Ɛ	148
8	452 619	Ɛ45	8	282 065	638	8	095 507	135
9	519 562	Ɛ31	9	348 6χ1	625	9	15Ɛ 640	123
χ	5χ4 493	Ɛ1χ	χ	413 106	611	χ	225 763	10Ɛ
Ɛ	66Ɛ 3Ɛ1	Ɛ06	Ɛ	499 717	5ƐƐ	Ɛ	2χƐ 872	0Ɛ8
6910	736 2Ɛ7	χƐ4	6950	564 116	5χ7	6990	375 96χ	0χ5
1	801 1χƐ	χχ0	1	62χ 701	594	1	43Ɛ χ53	093
2	888 08Ɛ	χ89	2	6Ɛ5 095	581	2	505 Ɛ26	07Ɛ
3	952 Ɛ58	χ75	3	77Ɛ 656	56Ɛ	3	58Ɛ Ɛχ5	068
4	χ19 χ11	χ63	4	846 005	556	4	656 051	056
5	χχ4 874	χ4Ɛ	5	910 55Ɛ	544	5	720 0χ7	042
6	Ɛ6Ɛ 703	χ38	6	996 χχ3	531	6	7χ6 129	02Ɛ
7	929 036 53Ɛ	χ25	7	χ61 414	51χ	7	870 158	019
8	101 364	χ12	8	Ɛ27 932	506	8	936 175	005
9	188 176	9Ɛχ	9	ƐƐ2 238	4Ɛ4	9	χ00 17χ	85 ƐƐ3
χ	252 Ɛ74	9χ7	χ	930 078 730	4χ0	χ	χ86 171	Ɛ9Ɛ
Ɛ	319 95Ɛ	995	Ɛ	143 010	48χ	Ɛ	Ɛ50 150	Ɛ89
6920	3χ4 734	980	6960	209 49χ	476	69χ0	933 016 119	Ɛ76
1	46Ɛ 4Ɛ4	96χ	1	293 954	463	1	0χ0 093	Ɛ62
2	536 262	956	2	35χ 1Ɛ7	450	2	166 035	Ɛ50
3	600 ƐƐ8	944	3	424 647	439	3	22Ɛ Ɛ85	Ɛ39
4	687 940	930	4	4χχ χ84	426	4	2Ɛ5 Ɛ02	Ɛ26
5	752 670	919	5	575 2χχ	413	5	37Ɛ χ28	Ɛ13
6	819 389	905	6	63Ɛ 701	400	6	445 93Ɛ	Ɛ00
7	8χ4 092	8Ɛ3	7	705 Ɛ01	3χ9	7	50Ɛ 83Ɛ	χχ9
8	96χ 985	89Ɛ	8	790 2χχ	396	8	595 728	χ96
9	χ35 664	888	9	856 684	383	9	65Ɛ 602	χ83
χ	Ɛ00 330	875	χ	920 χ47	36Ɛ	χ	725 485	χ70
Ɛ	Ɛ86 Ɛχ5	862	Ɛ	9χ7 1Ɛ6	359	Ɛ	7χƐ 335	χ5χ
6930	92χ 051 847	84Ɛ	6970	χ71 553	345	69Ɛ0	875 193	χ46
1	118 496	837	1	Ɛ37 898	333	1	93Ɛ 019	χ33
2	1χ3 111	824	2	931 002 00Ɛ	31Ɛ	2	χ04 χ50	χ21
3	269 935	812	3	088 32χ	309	3	χ8χ 871	χ0χ
4	334 547	7Ɛχ	4	152 637	2Ɛ5	4	Ɛ54 67Ɛ	9Ɛ6
5	3ƐƐ 145	7χ6	5	218 930	2χ3	5	934 01χ 475	9χ4
6	485 92Ɛ	794	6	2χ3 013	28Ɛ	6	0χ4 259	991
7	550 503	781	7	369 2χ2	278	7	16χ 02χ	97χ
8	617 084	769	8	433 55χ	266	8	233 9χ8	967
9	6χ1 831	756	9	4Ɛ9 804	252	9	2Ɛ9 753	955
χ	768 387	743	χ	583 χ56	23Ɛ	χ	383 4χ8	941
Ɛ	832 Ɛ0χ	730	Ɛ	64χ 095	228	Ɛ	449 229	92χ

N	Log N	d	N	Log N	d	N	Log N	d
6χ00	934 512 Ɛ57	85 918	6χ40	937 2Ɛ5 978	85 424	6χ80	93χ 080 Ɛ56	84 Ɛ36
1	598 873	904	1	37Ɛ 1χ0	411	1	145 χ90	Ɛ23
2	662 577	8Ɛ2	2	444 5Ɛ1	3Ɛχ	2	20χ 9Ɛ3	Ɛ10
3	728 269	89Ɛ	3	509 9χƐ	3χ7	3	293 903	χƐ9
4	7Ɛ1 Ɛ48	888	4	593 196	395	4	358 800	χχ7
5	877 814	875	5	658 56Ɛ	382	5	421 6χ7	χ95
6	941 489	862	6	721 931	36Ɛ	6	4χ6 580	χ81
7	χ07 12Ɛ	850	7	7χ7 0χ0	358	7	56Ɛ 441	χ6Ɛ
8	χ90 97Ɛ	838	8	870 438	346	8	634 2Ɛ0	χ59
9	Ɛ56 5Ɛ7	826	9	935 782	333	9	6Ɛ9 149	χ45
χ	935 020 221	813	χ	9Ɛχ χƐ5	320	χ	781 Ɛ92	χ33
Ɛ	0χ5 χ34	800	Ɛ	χ84 215	309	Ɛ	846 χ05	χ21
6χ10	16Ɛ 634	7χ9	6χ50	Ɛ49 522	2Ɛ7	6χ90	90Ɛ 826	χ0χ
1	235 221	796	1	938 012 819	2χ3	1	994 634	9Ɛ7
2	2Ɛχ 9Ɛ7	783	2	097 Ɛ00	291	2	χ59 42Ɛ	9χ5
3	384 57χ	770	3	161 191	27Ɛ	3	Ɛ22 214	992
4	44χ 12χ	75χ	4	226 450	267	4	Ɛχ6 Ɛχ6	97Ɛ
5	513 888	747	5	2χƐ 6Ɛ7	255	5	93Ɛ 06Ɛ 965	969
6	599 413	734	6	374 950	243	6	134 712	956
7	662 Ɛ47	721	7	439 Ɛ93	22Ɛ	7	1Ɛ9 468	943
8	728 668	70χ	8	503 202	219	8	282 1χƐ	931
9	7Ɛ2 176	6Ɛ7	9	588 41Ɛ	206	9	346 Ɛ20	91Ɛ
χ	877 871	6χ5	χ	651 625	1Ɛ3	χ	40Ɛ 83Ɛ	907
Ɛ	941 356	692	Ɛ	716 818	1χ1	Ɛ	494 546	8Ɛ6
6χ20	χ06 χ28	67χ	6χ60	79Ɛ 9Ɛ9	189	6χχ0	559 240	8χ2
1	χ90 4χ6	668	1	864 Ɛ86	178	1	621 Ɛ22	890
2	Ɛ55 Ɛ52	656	2	92χ 142	164	2	6χ6 7Ɛ2	87χ
3	936 01Ɛ 5χ8	642	3	9Ɛ3 2χ6	152	3	76Ɛ 470	866
4	0χ5 02χ	630	4	χ78 438	13Ɛ	4	834 116	855
5	16χ 65χ	618	5	Ɛ41 577	128	5	8Ɛ8 96Ɛ	841
6	234 076	606	6	939 006 6χ3	116	6	981 5Ɛ0	82Ɛ
7	2Ɛ9 680	5Ɛ3	7	08Ɛ 7Ɛ9	103	7	χ46 21Ɛ	819
8	383 073	5χ1	8	154 900	0Ɛ0	8	Ɛ0χ χ38	806
9	448 654	589	9	219 9Ɛ0	09χ	9	Ɛ93 642	7Ɛ3
χ	512 021	577	χ	2χ2 χ8χ	086	χ	940 058 235	7χ1
Ɛ	597 598	564	Ɛ	367 Ɛ54	075	Ɛ	120 χ16	78χ
6χ30	660 Ɛ40	551	6χ70	431 009	061	6χƐ0	1χ5 5χ4	777
1	726 491	53χ	1	4Ɛ6 06χ	04Ɛ	1	26χ 15Ɛ	765
2	7χƐ χ0Ɛ	528	2	57Ɛ 0Ɛ9	038	2	332 904	753
3	875 337	514	3	644 135	026	3	3Ɛ7 457	740
4	93χ 84Ɛ	502	4	709 15Ɛ	012	4	47Ɛ Ɛ97	729
5	χ04 151	4χƐ	5	792 171	000	5	544 704	717
6	χ89 640	499	6	857 171	84 Ɛχχ	6	609 21Ɛ	704
7	Ɛ52 Ɛ19	485	7	920 15Ɛ	Ɛ97	7	691 923	6Ɛ2
8	937 018 3χ2	473	8	9χ5 136	Ɛ84	8	756 415	69Ɛ
9	0χ1 855	460	9	χ6χ 0Ɛχ	Ɛ71	9	81χ χƐ4	689
χ	167 0Ɛ5	449	χ	Ɛ33 06Ɛ	Ɛ5Ɛ	χ	8χ3 581	676
Ɛ	230 542	436	Ɛ	ƐƐ8 00χ	Ɛ48	Ɛ	968 037	664

N	Log N	d	N	Log N	d	N	Log N	d
6Ɛ00	940 χ30 69Ɛ	84 651	6Ɛ40	943 784 974	84 172	6Ɛ80	946 501 982	83 899
1	χƐ5 130	63χ	1	848 Ɛ26	160	1	585 65Ɛ	886
2	Ɛ79 76χ	628	2	911 086	149	2	649 325	875
3	941 042 196	615	3	995 213	137	3	710 Ɛ9χ	862
4	106 7χƐ	603	4	χ59 34χ	125	4	794 840	84Ɛ
5	18Ɛ 1Ɛ2	5Ɛ1	5	Ɛ21 473	112	5	858 48Ɛ	83χ
6	253 7χ3	59χ	6	Ɛχ5 585	0ƐƐ	6	920 109	827
7	318 181	587	7	944 069 684	0χχ	7	9χ3 934	814
8	3χ0 748	575	8	131 772	097	8	χ67 548	803
9	465 101	562	9	1Ɛ5 849	084	9	ƐƐƐ 14Ɛ	7Ɛ0
χ	529 663	550	χ	279 911	072	χ	ƐƐ2 93Ɛ	79χ
Ɛ	5Ɛ1 ƐƐ3	539	Ɛ	341 983	060	Ɛ	947 076 519	787
6Ɛ10	676 530	527	6Ɛ50	405 χ23	049	6Ɛ90	13χ 0χ4	776
1	73χ χ57	514	1	489 χ70	037	1	201 85χ	763
2	803 36Ɛ	502	2	551 χχ7	025	2	285 401	751
3	887 871	4χƐ	3	615 Ɛ10	012	3	348 Ɛ52	73χ
4	950 160	499	4	699 Ɛ22	000	4	410 690	728
5	χ14 639	486	5	761 Ɛ22	83 Ɛχ9	5	494 1Ɛ8	716
6	χ98 Ɛ03	474	6	825 Ɛ0Ɛ	Ɛ97	6	557 912	704
7	Ɛ61 377	462	7	8χ9 χχ6	Ɛ85	7	61Ɛ 416	6Ɛ2
8	942 025 819	44χ	8	971 χ6Ɛ	Ɛ72	8	6χ2 Ɛ08	69Ɛ
9	0χχ 067	439	9	χ35 χ21	Ɛ60	9	766 5χ7	689
χ	172 4χ4	426	χ	χƐ9 981	Ɛ49	χ	82χ 074	677
Ɛ	236 90χ	413	Ɛ	Ɛ81 90χ	Ɛ37	Ɛ	8Ɛ1 72Ɛ	664
6Ɛ20	2ƐƐ 121	401	6Ɛ60	945 045 845	Ɛ25	6Ɛχ0	975 193	652
1	383 522	3χχ	1	109 76χ	Ɛ13	1	χ38 825	640
2	447 910	398	2	191 681	Ɛ00	2	Ɛ00 265	62χ
3	510 0χ8	386	3	255 581	χχ9	3	Ɛ83 893	617
4	594 472	373	4	319 46χ	χ98	4	948 047 2χχ	606
5	658 825	360	5	3χ1 346	χ85	5	10χ 8Ɛ4	5Ɛ3
6	720 Ɛ85	34χ	6	465 20Ɛ	χ73	6	192 2χ7	5χ0
7	7χ5 313	338	7	529 082	χ60	7	255 887	58Ɛ
8	869 64Ɛ	325	8	5Ɛ0 Ɛ22	χ4χ	8	319 256	578
9	931 974	313	9	674 970	χ38	9	3χ0 812	566
χ	9Ɛ6 087	300	χ	738 7χ8	χ25	χ	464 178	554
Ɛ	χ7χ 387	2χχ	Ɛ	800 611	χ13	Ɛ	527 710	542
6Ɛ30	Ɛ42 675	297	6Ɛ70	884 424	χ00	6ƐƐ0	5χƐ 052	52Ɛ
1	943 006 950	285	1	948 224	9χƐ	1	672 581	519
2	08Ɛ 015	272	2	χ10 013	998	2	735 χ9χ	507
3	153 287	261	3	χ93 9χƐ	985	3	7Ɛ9 3χ5	4Ɛ5
4	217 528	249	4	Ɛ57 774	974	4	880 89χ	4χ3
5	29Ɛ 775	237	5	946 01Ɛ 528	961	5	944 181	490
6	363 9Ɛ0	225	6	0χ3 289	94χ	6	χ07 651	47χ
7	428 015	212	7	167 017	939	7	χ8χ Ɛ0Ɛ	468
8	4Ɛ0 227	200	8	22χ 954	926	8	Ɛ52 377	456
9	574 427	1χ9	9	2Ɛ2 67χ	914	9	949 015 811	443
χ	638 614	197	χ	376 392	901	χ	099 054	432
Ɛ	700 7χƐ	185	Ɛ	43χ 093	8χƐ	Ɛ	160 486	41Ɛ

N	Log N	d	N	Log N	d	N	Log N	d
7000	949 223 8X5	83 409	7040	94Ɛ Ɛ2X 8ƐX	82 Ɛ42	7080	952 81X Ɛ9X	82 681
1	2X7 0Ɛ2	3Ɛ7	1	ƐƐ1 840	Ɛ30	1	8X1 65Ɛ	670
2	36X 4X9	3X4	2	950 074 770	Ɛ1Ɛ	2	964 10Ɛ	659
3	431 891	393	3	137 68Ɛ	Ɛ08	3	X26 768	648
4	4Ɛ5 064	380	4	1ƐX 597	XƐ6	4	XX9 1Ɛ4	635
5	578 424	36X	5	281 491	XX4	5	Ɛ6Ɛ 829	624
6	63Ɛ 792	358	6	344 375	X92	6	953 032 251	611
7	702 Ɛ2X	345	7	407 247	X80	7	0Ɛ4 862	600
8	786 273	334	8	48X 107	X6X	8	177 262	5XX
9	849 5X7	321	9	550 Ɛ75	X58	9	239 850	598
X	910 908	30Ɛ	X	613 X11	X46	X	300 228	585
Ɛ	994 017	2Ɛ9	Ɛ	696 857	X34	Ɛ	382 7Ɛ1	574
7010	X57 314	2X7	7050	759 68Ɛ	X22	7090	445 165	562
1	Ɛ1X 5ƐƐ	295	1	820 4Ɛ1	X0Ɛ	1	507 707	550
2	ƐX1 894	282	2	8X3 300	9ƐX	2	58X 057	53X
3	94X 064 Ɛ56	271	3	966 0ƐX	9X8	3	650 595	528
4	128 207	25X	4	X28 XX6	995	4	712 Ɛ01	517
5	1XƐ 465	248	5	XXƐ 87Ɛ	984	5	795 418	504
6	272 6Ɛ1	236	6	Ɛ72 643	971	6	857 920	4Ɛ2
7	335 927	224	7	951 035 3Ɛ4	95Ɛ	7	91X 212	4X1
8	3Ɛ8 Ɛ4Ɛ	211	8	0Ɛ8 153	94X	8	9X0 6Ɛ3	48X
9	480 160	200	9	17X XX1	937	9	X62 Ɛ81	479
X	543 360	1X9	X	241 818	925	X	Ɛ25 43X	466
Ɛ	606 549	197	Ɛ	304 541	914	Ɛ	ƐX7 8X4	455
7020	689 724	185	7060	387 255	901	70X0	954 06X 139	443
1	750 8X9	173	1	449 Ɛ56	8XƐ	1	130 580	431
2	813 X60	161	2	510 845	89X	2	1Ɛ2 9Ɛ1	41Ɛ
3	897 001	14Ɛ	3	593 523	887	3	275 210	409
4	95X 150	138	4	656 1XX	875	4	337 619	3Ɛ7
5	X21 288	127	5	718 X63	863	5	3Ɛ9 X14	3X5
6	XX4 3Ɛ3	114	6	79Ɛ 706	851	6	480 1Ɛ9	393
7	Ɛ67 507	102	7	862 357	83Ɛ	7	542 590	382
8	94Ɛ 02X 609	0Ɛ0	8	924 Ɛ96	82X	8	604 952	370
9	0Ɛ1 6Ɛ9	09X	9	9X7 804	817	9	687 102	359
X	174 797	088	X	X6X 41Ɛ	805	X	749 45Ɛ	348
Ɛ	237 863	076	Ɛ	Ɛ31 024	7Ɛ3	Ɛ	80Ɛ 7X7	336
7030	2ƐX 919	063	7070	ƐƐ3 817	7X1	70Ɛ0	891 Ɛ21	324
1	381 980	052	1	952 076 3Ɛ8	78Ɛ	1	954 245	312
2	444 X12	03Ɛ	2	138 Ɛ87	77X	2	X16 557	300
3	507 X51	029	3	1ƐƐ 745	767	3	X98 857	2XƐ
4	58X X7X	018	4	282 2Ɛ0	755	4	Ɛ5X Ɛ46	298
5	651 X96	005	5	344 X45	743	5	955 021 222	287
6	714 X9Ɛ	82 ƐƐ3	6	407 588	731	6	0X3 4X9	274
7	797 X92	ƐX1	7	48X 0Ɛ9	720	7	165 761	263
8	85X X73	Ɛ8Ɛ	8	550 819	709	8	227 X04	251
9	921 X42	Ɛ78	9	613 326	6Ɛ7	9	2XX 055	23Ɛ
X	9X4 9ƐX	Ɛ67	X	695 X21	6X6	X	370 294	22X
Ɛ	X67 965	Ɛ55	Ɛ	758 507	693	Ɛ	432 502	217

N	Log N	d	N	Log N	d	N	Log N	d
7100	955 4Ɛ4 719	82 206	7140	958 173 887	81 953	7180	95X X18 631	81 4X5
1	576 923	1Ɛ3	1	235 61X	941	1	X99 Ɛ16	494
2	638 Ɛ16	1X2	2	2Ɛ7 35Ɛ	930	2	Ɛ5Ɛ 3XX	482
3	6ƐƐ 0Ɛ8	190	3	379 08Ɛ	919	3	95Ɛ 020 870	471
4	781 288	17X	4	43X 9X8	908	4	0X2 121	45X
5	843 446	169	5	500 6Ɛ4	8Ɛ6	5	163 57Ɛ	44X
6	905 5Ɛ3	156	6	582 3XX	8X5	6	224 X09	437
7	987 749	145	7	644 093	893	7	2X6 244	426
8	X49 892	132	8	705 966	881	8	367 66X	415
9	Ɛ0Ɛ X04	121	9	787 627	86Ɛ	9	428 X83	402
X	Ɛ91 Ɛ25	10Ɛ	X	849 296	859	X	4XX 285	3Ɛ2
Ɛ	956 054 034	0ƐX	Ɛ	90X Ɛ33	848	Ɛ	56Ɛ 677	39Ɛ
7110	116 132	0X7	7150	990 77Ɛ	836	7190	630 X56	38X
1	198 219	096	1	X52 3Ɛ5	825	1	6Ɛ2 224	378
2	25X 2Ɛ3	083	2	Ɛ14 01X	812	2	773 5X0	367
3	320 376	072	3	Ɛ95 830	801	3	834 947	355
4	3X2 428	060	4	959 057 431	7XƐ	4	8Ɛ6 0X0	343
5	464 488	04Ɛ	5	119 020	79X	5	977 423	332
6	526 517	038	6	19X 7ƐX	788	6	X38 755	321
7	5X8 553	027	7	260 386	776	7	XƐ9 X76	30X
8	66X 57X	015	8	321 Ɛ40	764	8	Ɛ7Ɛ 184	2Ɛ9
9	730 593	003	9	3X3 6X4	753	9	960 040 481	2X8
X	7Ɛ2 596	81 ƐƐ1	X	465 237	741	X	101 769	295
Ɛ	874 587	Ɛ9Ɛ	Ɛ	526 978	72Ɛ	Ɛ	182 X42	285
7120	936 566	Ɛ8X	7160	5X8 4X7	719	71X0	244 107	272
1	9Ɛ8 534	Ɛ77	1	66X 004	708	1	305 379	261
2	X7X 4XƐ	Ɛ66	2	72Ɛ 710	6Ɛ6	2	386 61X	250
3	Ɛ40 455	Ɛ55	3	7Ɛ1 206	6X5	3	447 86X	23X
4	957 002 3XX	Ɛ42	4	872 8XƐ	693	4	508 XX8	228
5	084 330	Ɛ31	5	934 382	681	5	58X 114	217
6	146 261	Ɛ1X	6	9Ɛ5 X43	66Ɛ	6	64Ɛ 32Ɛ	205
7	208 17Ɛ	Ɛ09	7	X77 4Ɛ2	65X	7	710 534	1Ɛ3
8	28X 088	XƐ8	8	Ɛ38 Ɛ50	648	8	791 727	1X2
9	34Ɛ Ɛ84	XX5	9	ƐƐX 598	636	9	852 909	191
X	411 X69	X94	X	95X 080 012	625	X	913 X9X	17Ɛ
Ɛ	493 941	X82	Ɛ	141 637	613	Ɛ	995 059	169
7130	555 803	X70	7170	203 04X	601	71Ɛ0	X56 206	158
1	617 673	X5X	1	284 64Ɛ	5Ɛ0	1	Ɛ17 362	146
2	699 511	X49	2	346 03Ɛ	59X	2	Ɛ98 4X8	134
3	75Ɛ 35X	X36	3	407 619	588	3	961 059 620	123
4	821 194	X25	4	488 ƐX5	577	4	11X 743	112
5	8X2 ƐƐ9	X14	5	54X 560	565	5	19Ɛ 855	100
6	964 X11	X01	6	60Ɛ Ɛ05	553	6	260 955	0XX
7	X26 812	9Ɛ0	7	691 458	542	7	321 X43	099
8	XX8 602	99X	8	752 99X	530	8	3X2 Ɛ20	087
9	Ɛ6X 3X0	988	9	814 30X	51Ɛ	9	463 ƐX7	076
X	958 030 168	976	X	895 829	508	X	525 061	064
Ɛ	0Ɛ1 Ɛ22	965	Ɛ	957 135	4Ɛ8	Ɛ	5X6 105	053

N	Log N	d	N	Log N	d	N	Log N	d
7200	961 667 158	81 041	7240	964 29Ɛ 808	80 7X2	7280	966 XƐX 382	80 347
1	728 199	02Ɛ	1	360 3XX	790	1	Ɛ7X 709	336
2	7X9 208	01X	2	420 Ɛ7X	77Ɛ	2	967 03X X43	325
3	86X 226	009	3	4X1 739	76X	3	0ƐƐ 168	313
4	92Ɛ 233	80 ƐƐ7	4	562 2X7	758	4	17Ɛ 47Ɛ	303
5	9Ɛ0 22X	ƐX5	5	622 X43	746	5	23Ɛ 782	2Ɛ0
6	X71 213	Ɛ94	6	6X3 589	735	6	2ƐƐ X72	2X0
7	Ɛ32 1X7	Ɛ83	7	764 102	724	7	380 152	28X
8	ƐƐ3 16X	Ɛ70	8	824 826	713	8	440 420	279
9	962 074 11X	Ɛ60	9	8X5 339	701	9	500 699	267
X	135 07X	Ɛ4X	X	965 X3X	6XƐ	X	580 944	257
Ɛ	1Ɛ6 008	Ɛ38	Ɛ	X26 529	69X	Ɛ	640 Ɛ9Ɛ	244
7210	276 Ɛ44	Ɛ27	7250	XX7 007	689	7290	701 223	234
1	337 X6Ɛ	Ɛ15	1	Ɛ67 694	677	1	781 457	222
2	3Ɛ8 984	Ɛ04	2	965 028 14Ɛ	666	2	841 679	211
3	479 888	XƐ2	3	0X8 7Ɛ5	655	3	901 88X	200
4	53X 77X	XX1	4	169 24X	643	4	981 X8X	1XX
5	5ƐƐ 65Ɛ	X8Ɛ	5	229 891	631	5	X42 078	19X
6	680 52X	X7X	6	2XX 302	621	6	Ɛ02 256	187
7	741 3X8	X68	7	36X 923	60Ɛ	7	Ɛ82 421	177
8	802 254	X57	8	42Ɛ 332	5Ɛ9	8	968 042 598	165
9	883 0XƐ	X45	9	4XƐ 92Ɛ	5X8	9	102 741	154
X	943 Ɛ34	X34	X	570 317	597	X	182 895	143
Ɛ	X04 968	X22	Ɛ	630 8Ɛ2	585	Ɛ	242 X18	131
7220	X85 78X	X11	7260	6Ɛ1 277	574	72X0	302 Ɛ49	120
1	Ɛ46 59Ɛ	9ƐƐ	1	771 82Ɛ	563	1	383 069	10Ɛ
2	963 007 39X	9XX	2	832 192	551	2	443 178	0Ɛ9
3	088 188	999	3	8Ɛ2 723	540	3	503 275	0X9
4	148 Ɛ65	986	4	973 063	52X	4	583 362	097
5	209 92Ɛ	976	5	X33 591	519	5	643 439	085
6	28X 6X5	964	6	XƐ3 XXX	508	6	703 502	075
7	34Ɛ 449	952	7	Ɛ74 3Ɛ6	4Ɛ7	7	783 577	063
8	410 19Ɛ	941	8	966 034 8Ɛ1	4X5	8	843 61X	052
9	490 Ɛ20	930	9	0Ɛ5 196	493	9	903 670	041
X	551 850	91X	X	175 669	482	X	983 6Ɛ1	02Ɛ
Ɛ	612 56X	908	Ɛ	235 Ɛ2Ɛ	471	Ɛ	X43 720	01X
7230	693 276	8Ɛ7	7270	2Ɛ6 3X0	460	72Ɛ0	Ɛ03 73X	009
1	753 Ɛ71	8X6	1	376 840	44X	1	Ɛ83 747	7Ɛ ƐƐ8
2	814 857	894	2	437 08X	439	2	969 043 743	ƐX6
3	895 52Ɛ	883	3	4Ɛ7 507	427	3	103 729	Ɛ95
4	956 1Ɛ2	871	4	577 932	416	4	183 702	Ɛ84
5	X16 X63	860	5	638 148	405	5	243 686	Ɛ73
6	X97 703	84Ɛ	6	6Ɛ8 551	3Ɛ4	6	303 639	Ɛ61
7	Ɛ58 352	839	7	778 945	3X2	7	383 59X	Ɛ50
8	964 018 Ɛ8Ɛ	827	8	839 127	391	8	443 52X	Ɛ3Ɛ
9	099 7Ɛ6	816	9	8Ɛ9 4Ɛ8	37Ɛ	9	503 469	Ɛ2X
X	15X 410	805	X	979 877	36X	X	583 397	Ɛ18
Ɛ	21Ɛ 015	7Ɛ3	Ɛ	X3X 025	359	Ɛ	643 2Ɛ3	Ɛ08

N	Log N	d	N	Log N	d	N	Log N	d
7300	969 703 1ƐƐ	7Ɛ XƐ6	7340	970 2Ɛ2 475	7Ɛ 66X	7380	972 X88 122	7Ɛ 226
1	783 0Ɛ5	XX4	1	371 Ɛ23	658	1	Ɛ47 348	215
2	842 Ɛ99	X94	2	431 57Ɛ	647	2	973 006 561	203
3	902 X71	X82	3	4Ɛ1 006	636	3	085 764	1Ɛ3
4	982 933	X71	4	570 640	625	4	144 957	1X2
5	X42 7X4	X60	5	630 065	614	5	203 Ɛ39	190
6	Ɛ02 644	X4Ɛ	6	6XƐ 679	603	6	283 109	180
7	Ɛ82 493	X39	7	76Ɛ 080	5Ɛ1	7	342 289	16X
8	96X 042 310	X28	8	82X 671	5X1	8	401 437	15X
9	102 138	X17	9	8XX 052	58Ɛ	9	480 595	148
X	181 Ɛ53	X06	X	969 621	57X	X	53Ɛ 721	138
Ɛ	241 959	9Ɛ5	Ɛ	X28 Ɛ9Ɛ	56X	Ɛ	5ƐX 859	126
7310	301 752	9X3	7350	XX8 549	558	7390	679 983	116
1	381 535	992	1	Ɛ67 XX5	547	1	738 X99	104
2	441 307	981	2	971 027 430	535	2	7Ɛ7 ƐX1	0Ɛ4
3	501 088	970	3	0X6 965	525	3	877 095	0X2
4	580 X38	95Ɛ	4	166 28X	514	4	936 177	092
5	640 797	949	5	225 7X2	502	5	9Ɛ5 249	080
6	700 524	938	6	2X5 0X4	4Ɛ2	6	X74 309	070
7	780 260	927	7	364 596	4X0	7	Ɛ33 379	05X
8	83Ɛ Ɛ87	916	8	423 X76	48Ɛ	8	ƐƐ2 417	04X
9	8ƐƐ 8X1	905	9	4X3 345	47Ɛ	9	974 071 465	038
X	97Ɛ 5X6	8Ɛ3	X	562 804	469	X	130 4X1	028
Ɛ	X3Ɛ 299	8X3	Ɛ	622 071	458	Ɛ	1XƐ 509	016
7320	XƐX 280	891	7360	6X1 509	447	73X0	26X 523	006
1	Ɛ7X 851	880	1	760 954	436	1	329 529	7X ƐƐ4
2	96Ɛ 03X 511	86X	2	820 18X	424	2	3X8 521	ƐX4
3	0ƐX 17Ɛ	85X	3	89Ɛ 5Ɛ2	414	3	467 505	Ɛ93
4	179 X19	848	4	95X X06	403	4	526 498	Ɛ81
5	239 665	838	5	X1X 209	3Ɛ1	5	5X5 459	Ɛ71
6	2Ɛ9 2X1	826	6	X99 5ƐX	3X1	6	664 40X	Ɛ60
7	378 Ɛ07	815	7	Ɛ58 99Ɛ	38Ɛ	7	723 36X	Ɛ4Ɛ
8	438 720	803	8	972 018 16X	37Ɛ	8	7X2 2Ɛ9	Ɛ39
9	4Ɛ8 323	7Ɛ3	9	097 529	369	9	861 236	Ɛ29
X	577 Ɛ16	7X1	X	156 896	358	X	920 163	Ɛ18
Ɛ	637 6Ɛ7	791	Ɛ	216 032	347	Ɛ	99Ɛ 07Ɛ	Ɛ07
7330	6Ɛ7 288	77Ɛ	7370	295 379	337	73Ɛ0	X59 Ɛ86	XƐ6
1	776 X47	76X	1	354 6Ɛ4	325	1	Ɛ18 X80	XX5
2	836 5Ɛ5	759	2	413 X19	314	2	Ɛ97 965	X94
3	8Ɛ6 152	747	3	493 131	303	3	975 056 839	X83
4	975 899	737	4	552 434	2Ɛ2	4	115 700	X72
5	X35 414	725	5	611 726	2X1	5	194 572	X62
6	XƐ4 Ɛ39	714	6	690 X07	290	6	253 414	X50
7	Ɛ74 651	703	7	750 097	27X	7	312 264	X3Ɛ
8	970 034 154	6Ɛ2	8	80Ɛ 355	26X	8	391 0X3	X2Ɛ
9	0Ɛ3 846	6X1	9	88X 603	259	9	44Ɛ Ɛ12	X19
X	173 327	690	X	949 860	248	X	50X 92Ɛ	X09
Ɛ	232 9Ɛ7	67X	Ɛ	X08 XX8	236	Ɛ	589 738	9Ɛ7

N	Log N	d	N	Log N	d	N	Log N	d
7400	975 648 533	7X 9X7	7440	978 1Ɛ3 657	7X 570	7480	97X 945 63X	7X 13Ɛ
1	707 31X	996	1	272 007	560	1	X03 779	12X
2	786 0Ɛ4	985	2	330 567	54Ɛ	2	X81 8X7	119
3	844 X79	973	3	3XX XƐ6	53X	3	Ɛ3Ɛ X04	109
4	903 830	963	4	469 434	529	4	ƐƐ9 Ɛ11	0Ɛ7
5	982 593	953	5	527 961	518	5	97Ɛ 078 008	0X8
6	X41 326	941	6	5X6 279	507	6	136 0Ɛ4	096
7	Ɛ00 067	930	7	664 784	4Ɛ7	7	1Ɛ4 18X	086
8	Ɛ7X 997	91Ɛ	8	723 07Ɛ	4X6	8	272 254	074
9	976 039 6Ɛ6	90Ɛ	9	7X1 565	495	9	330 308	065
X	0Ɛ8 405	8Ɛ9	X	85Ɛ X3X	484	X	3XX 371	053
Ɛ	177 102	8X9	Ɛ	91X 302	473	Ɛ	468 404	043
7410	235 9XƐ	897	7450	998 775	463	7490	526 447	032
1	2Ɛ4 686	887	1	X57 018	451	1	5X4 479	021
2	373 351	876	2	Ɛ15 469	441	2	662 49X	011
3	432 007	865	3	Ɛ93 8XX	431	3	720 4XƐ	000
4	4Ɛ0 870	854	4	979 052 11Ɛ	41Ɛ	4	79X 4XƐ	79 ƐXƐ
5	56Ɛ 504	843	5	110 53X	40X	5	858 49X	Ɛ9X
6	62X 147	832	6	18X 948	3ƐX	6	916 478	Ɛ8X
7	6X8 979	822	7	249 146	3X9	7	994 446	Ɛ79
8	767 59Ɛ	810	8	307 533	398	8	X52 403	Ɛ69
9	826 1XƐ	800	9	385 90Ɛ	387	9	Ɛ10 370	Ɛ58
X	8X4 9XƐ	7XX	X	444 096	377	X	Ɛ8X 308	Ɛ47
Ɛ	963 599	79X	Ɛ	502 451	366	Ɛ	980 048 253	Ɛ36
7420	X22 177	789	7460	580 7Ɛ7	355	74X0	106 189	Ɛ25
1	XX0 944	778	1	63X Ɛ50	344	1	184 0Ɛ2	Ɛ15
2	Ɛ5Ɛ 500	767	2	6Ɛ9 294	333	2	242 007	Ɛ05
3	977 01X 067	757	3	777 607	323	3	2ƐƐ Ɛ10	XƐ3
4	098 802	745	4	835 92X	312	4	379 X03	XX3
5	157 347	735	5	8Ɛ4 040	301	5	437 8X6	X92
6	215 X80	723	6	972 341	2Ɛ0	6	4Ɛ5 778	X82
7	294 5X3	713	7	X30 631	2X0	7	573 63X	X71
8	353 0Ɛ6	702	8	XXX 911	28Ɛ	8	631 4XƐ	X60
9	411 7Ɛ8	6Ɛ1	9	Ɛ68 ƐX0	27X	9	6XƐ 34Ɛ	X50
X	490 2X9	6X1	X	97X 027 25X	269	X	769 19Ɛ	X3X
Ɛ	54X 98X	68Ɛ	Ɛ	0X5 507	258	Ɛ	827 019	X2Ɛ
7430	609 459	67X	7470	163 763	248	74Ɛ0	8X4 X48	X19
1	687 Ɛ17	66X	1	221 9XƐ	237	1	962 865	X09
2	746 585	659	2	2X0 026	226	2	X20 672	9Ɛ8
3	805 022	648	3	35X 250	216	3	X9X 46X	9X8
4	883 66X	637	4	418 466	204	4	Ɛ58 256	997
5	942 0X5	626	5	496 66X	1Ɛ4	5	981 016 031	986
6	X00 70Ɛ	616	6	554 862	1X3	6	093 9Ɛ7	975
7	X7Ɛ 125	604	7	612 X45	193	7	151 770	965
8	Ɛ39 729	5Ɛ4	8	691 018	182	8	20Ɛ 515	954
9	ƐƐ8 121	5X3	9	74Ɛ 19X	170	9	289 269	944
X	978 076 704	592	X	809 34X	161	X	346 ƐƐ1	933
Ɛ	135 096	581	Ɛ	887 4XƐ	14Ɛ	Ɛ	404 924	922

N	Log N	d	N	Log N	d	N	Log N	d
7500	981 482 646	79 912	7540	983 Ɛχ6 81Ɛ	79 4χ9	7580	986 6Ɛ6 122	79 089
1	540 358	901	1	984 064 108	499	1	773 1χƐ	079
2	5Ɛχ 059	8Ɛ1	2	121 5χ5	488	2	830 268	068
3	677 94χ	89Ɛ	3	19χ χ71	478	3	8χ9 314	058
4	735 629	88Ɛ	4	258 329	467	4	966 370	047
5	7Ɛ3 2Ɛ8	87Ɛ	5	315 794	456	5	χ23 3Ɛ7	037
6	870 Ɛ77	86χ	6	393 02χ	446	6	χχ0 432	026
7	92χ 825	859	7	450 474	435	7	Ɛ59 458	016
8	9χ8 482	849	8	509 8χ9	425	8	987 016 472	006
9	χ66 10Ɛ	838	9	587 112	415	9	093 478	78 ƐƐ5
χ	Ɛ23 947	827	χ	644 527	403	χ	150 471	Ɛχ5
Ɛ	Ɛχ1 572	817	Ɛ	701 92χ	3Ɛ4	Ɛ	209 456	Ɛ94
7510	982 05Ɛ 189	806	7550	77Ɛ 122	3χ3	7590	286 42χ	Ɛ84
1	118 993	7Ɛ5	1	838 505	392	1	343 3Ɛ2	Ɛ73
2	196 588	7χ5	2	8Ɛ5 897	381	2	400 365	Ɛ63
3	254 171	795	3	973 058	372	3	479 308	Ɛ53
4	311 946	783	4	χ30 40χ	360	4	536 25Ɛ	Ɛ42
5	38Ɛ 509	773	5	χχ9 76χ	350	5	5Ɛ3 1χ1	Ɛ32
6	449 080	763	6	Ɛ66 χƐχ	340	6	670 113	Ɛ21
7	506 823	752	7	985 024 23χ	32Ɛ	7	729 034	Ɛ11
8	584 375	741	8	0χ1 569	31Ɛ	8	7χ5 Ɛ45	Ɛ01
9	641 χƐ6	731	9	15χ 888	30χ	9	862 χ46	χƐ0
χ	6ƐƐ 627	720	χ	217 Ɛ96	2Ɛχ	χ	91Ɛ 936	χ9Ɛ
Ɛ	779 147	70Ɛ	Ɛ	295 294	2χ9	Ɛ	998 815	χ90
7520	836 856	6ƐƐ	7560	352 581	298	75χ0	χ55 6χ5	χ7χ
1	8Ɛ4 355	6χχ	1	40Ɛ 859	288	1	Ɛ12 563	χ6Ɛ
2	971 χ43	69χ	2	488 Ɛ25	278	2	Ɛ8Ɛ 412	χ5χ
3	χ2Ɛ 521	689	3	546 1χ1	267	3	988 048 270	χ49
4	χχ8 Ɛχχ	679	4	603 448	257	4	105 0Ɛ9	χ3χ
5	Ɛ66 667	667	5	680 6χ3	246	5	181 Ɛ37	χ28
6	983 024 112	658	6	739 929	236	6	23χ 963	χ19
7	0χ1 76χ	647	7	7Ɛ6 Ɛ63	225	7	2Ɛ7 780	χ08
8	15Ɛ 1Ɛ5	636	8	874 188	214	8	374 588	9Ɛ8
9	218 82Ɛ	625	9	931 3χ0	205	9	431 384	9χ7
χ	296 254	615	χ	9χχ 5χ5	1Ɛ3	χ	4χχ 16Ɛ	997
Ɛ	353 869	605	Ɛ	χ67 798	1χ4	Ɛ	566 Ɛ46	986
7530	411 272	5Ɛ4	7570	Ɛ24 980	192	75Ɛ0	623 910	976
1	48χ 866	5χ3	1	Ɛχ1 Ɛ52	183	1	6χ0 686	966
2	548 249	593	2	986 05Ɛ 115	171	2	759 430	955
3	605 820	582	3	118 286	162	3	816 185	945
4	683 1χ2	572	4	195 428	151	4	892 Ɛ0χ	935
5	740 754	561	5	252 579	140	5	94Ɛ 843	924
6	7Ɛχ 0Ɛ5	550	6	30Ɛ 6Ɛ9	130	6	χ08 567	914
7	877 645	540	7	388 829	11Ɛ	7	χ85 27Ɛ	903
8	934 Ɛ85	52Ɛ	8	445 948	10Ɛ	8	Ɛ41 Ɛ82	8Ɛ3
9	9Ɛ2 4Ɛ4	51Ɛ	9	502 χ57	0ƐƐ	9	ƐƐχ 875	8χ3
χ	χ6Ɛ χ13	50χ	χ	57Ɛ Ɛ56	0χχ	χ	989 077 558	892
Ɛ	Ɛ29 321	4Ɛχ	Ɛ	639 044	09χ	Ɛ	134 22χ	882

N	Log N	d	N	Log N	d	N	Log N	d
7600	989 1Ɛ0 XƐ0	78 872	7640	98Ɛ 893 2X3	78 45X	7680	992 361 254	78 04Ɛ
1	269 762	861	1	94Ɛ 741	44Ɛ	1	419 2X3	040
2	326 403	851	2	X07 Ɛ90	439	2	495 323	02Ɛ
3	3X3 054	840	3	X84 409	42X	3	551 352	01Ɛ
4	45Ɛ 894	831	4	Ɛ40 837	419	4	609 371	00Ɛ
5	518 505	81Ɛ	5	ƐƐ9 054	40X	5	685 380	77 ƐƐƐ
6	595 124	810	6	990 075 462	3Ɛ8	6	741 37Ɛ	ƐXX
7	651 934	7ƐƐ	7	131 85X	3X9	7	7Ɛ9 369	Ɛ9Ɛ
8	70X 533	7XƐ	8	1XX 047	398	8	875 348	Ɛ8X
9	787 122	79X	9	266 423	388	9	931 316	Ɛ7X
X	843 900	78X	X	322 7XƐ	378	X	9X9 294	Ɛ6X
Ɛ	900 48X	77X	Ɛ	39X Ɛ67	368	Ɛ	X65 242	Ɛ5X
7610	979 048	769	7650	457 313	357	7690	Ɛ21 1X0	Ɛ49
1	X35 7Ɛ5	759	1	513 66X	347	1	Ɛ99 129	Ɛ3X
2	XƐ2 352	749	2	58Ɛ 9Ɛ5	337	2	993 055 067	Ɛ29
3	Ɛ6X X9Ɛ	739	3	648 130	327	3	110 Ɛ94	Ɛ19
4	98X 027 618	728	4	704 457	316	4	188 XƐ1	Ɛ09
5	0X4 144	717	5	780 771	306	5	244 9ƐX	XƐ9
6	160 85Ɛ	708	6	838 X77	2Ɛ6	6	300 8Ɛ7	XX8
7	219 367	6Ɛ7	7	8Ɛ5 171	2X5	7	378 7X3	X99
8	295 X62	6X7	8	971 456	296	8	434 680	X88
9	352 549	696	9	X29 730	285	9	4Ɛ0 548	X79
X	40Ɛ 023	686	X	XX5 9Ɛ5	275	X	568 405	X68
Ɛ	487 6X9	676	Ɛ	Ɛ62 06X	265	Ɛ	624 271	X58
7620	544 163	665	7660	991 01X 313	254	76X0	6X0 109	X47
1	600 808	655	1	096 567	244	1	757 Ɛ54	X38
2	679 261	645	2	152 7XƐ	234	2	813 990	X28
3	735 8X6	635	3	20X X23	224	3	88Ɛ 7Ɛ8	X17
4	7Ɛ2 31Ɛ	624	4	287 047	214	4	947 613	X07
5	86X 943	614	5	343 25Ɛ	203	5	X03 41X	9Ɛ7
6	927 357	604	6	3ƐƐ 462	1Ɛ3	6	X7Ɛ 215	9X7
7	9X3 95Ɛ	5Ɛ3	7	477 655	1X3	7	Ɛ37 000	997
8	X60 352	5X3	8	533 838	193	8	ƐƐ2 997	987
9	Ɛ18 935	593	9	5XƐ X0Ɛ	183	9	994 06X 762	977
X	Ɛ95 308	582	X	667 Ɛ92	172	X	126 519	966
Ɛ	98Ɛ 051 88X	572	Ɛ	724 144	162	Ɛ	1X2 283	957
7630	10X 240	562	7670	7X0 2X6	152	76Ɛ0	25X 01X	946
1	186 7X2	551	1	858 438	142	1	315 964	936
2	243 133	542	2	914 57X	131	2	391 69X	926
3	2ƐƐ 675	531	3	990 6XƐ	121	3	449 404	916
4	377 ƐX6	520	4	X48 810	111	4	505 11X	906
5	434 506	511	5	Ɛ04 921	101	5	580 X24	8Ɛ6
6	4Ɛ0 X17	500	6	Ɛ80 X22	0Ɛ1	6	638 71X	8X6
7	569 317	4Ɛ0	7	992 038 Ɛ13	0X1	7	6Ɛ4 404	895
8	625 807	49Ɛ	8	0Ɛ4 ƐƐ4	090	8	770 099	886
9	6X2 0X6	48Ɛ	9	171 084	080	9	827 963	875
X	75X 575	47Ɛ	X	229 144	070	X	8X3 618	865
Ɛ	816 X34	46Ɛ	Ɛ	2X5 1Ɛ4	060	Ɛ	95Ɛ 281	855

N	Log N	d	N	Log N	d	N	Log N	d
7700	994 X16 Ɛ16	77 846	7740	997 478 640	77 443	7780	999 Ɛ06 157	77 045
1	X92 760	835	1	533 X83	432	1	Ɛ81 1X0	035
2	Ɛ4X 395	824	2	5XƐ 2Ɛ5	423	2	99X 038 215	025
3	995 005 ƐƐ9	815	3	666 718	413	3	0Ɛ3 23X	015
4	081 812	805	4	721 Ɛ2Ɛ	403	4	16X 253	005
5	139 417	7Ɛ5	5	799 332	3Ɛ3	5	225 258	76 ƐƐ5
6	1Ɛ5 010	7X4	6	854 725	3X3	6	2X0 251	ƐX5
7	270 7Ɛ4	795	7	90Ɛ Ɛ08	392	7	357 236	Ɛ96
8	328 389	784	8	987 29X	383	8	412 210	Ɛ85
9	3X3 Ɛ51	774	9	X42 661	373	9	489 195	Ɛ76
X	45Ɛ 705	765	X	XƐ9 X14	363	X	544 14Ɛ	Ɛ65
Ɛ	517 26X	754	Ɛ	Ɛ75 177	353	Ɛ	5ƐƐ 0Ɛ4	Ɛ56
7710	592 X02	744	7750	998 030 50X	343	7790	676 04X	Ɛ46
1	64X 546	734	1	0X7 851	333	1	730 Ɛ94	Ɛ36
2	706 07X	724	2	162 Ɛ84	323	2	7X7 Ɛ0X	Ɛ26
3	781 7X2	714	3	21X 2X7	312	3	862 X34	Ɛ16
4	839 2Ɛ6	704	4	295 5Ɛ9	303	4	919 94X	Ɛ06
5	8Ɛ4 9ƐX	6Ɛ4	5	350 900	2Ɛ3	5	994 854	XƐ7
6	970 4Ɛ2	6X3	6	407 ƐƐ3	2X3	6	X4Ɛ 74Ɛ	XX6
7	X27 Ɛ95	694	7	483 296	294	7	Ɛ06 635	X97
8	XX3 669	684	8	53X 56X	283	8	Ɛ81 510	X87
9	Ɛ5Ɛ 131	673	9	5Ɛ5 831	273	9	99Ɛ 038 397	X77
X	996 016 7X4	664	X	670 XX4	263	X	0Ɛ3 252	X67
Ɛ	092 248	653	Ɛ	728 147	253	Ɛ	16X 0Ɛ9	X57
7720	149 89Ɛ	643	7760	7X3 39X	243	77X0	224 Ɛ54	X47
1	205 322	634	1	85X 621	234	1	29Ɛ 99Ɛ	X37
2	280 956	623	2	915 855	223	2	356 816	X28
3	338 379	613	3	990 X78	213	3	411 642	X18
4	3Ɛ3 990	604	4	X48 08Ɛ	204	4	488 45X	X07
5	46Ɛ 394	5Ɛ3	5	Ɛ03 293	1Ɛ3	5	543 265	9Ɛ8
6	526 987	5X3	6	Ɛ7X 486	1X4	6	5ƐX 061	9X8
7	5X2 36X	593	7	999 035 66X	193	7	674 X49	999
8	659 941	583	8	0Ɛ0 841	184	8	72Ɛ 826	988
9	715 304	573	9	167 X05	174	9	7X6 5Ɛ2	978
X	790 877	563	X	222 Ɛ79	163	X	861 36X	969
Ɛ	848 21X	553	Ɛ	29X 120	154	Ɛ	918 117	959
7730	903 771	543	7770	355 274	144	77Ɛ0	992 X74	949
1	97Ɛ 0Ɛ4	533	1	410 3Ɛ8	134	1	X49 801	939
2	X36 627	523	2	487 530	124	2	Ɛ04 53X	929
3	XƐ1 Ɛ4X	513	3	542 654	114	3	Ɛ7Ɛ 267	919
4	Ɛ69 461	503	4	5Ɛ9 768	104	4	9X0 035 Ɛ84	90X
5	997 024 964	4Ɛ3	5	674 870	0Ɛ4	5	0Ɛ0 892	8ƐX
6	0X0 257	4X3	6	72Ɛ 964	0X5	6	167 590	8X9
7	157 73X	493	7	7X6 X49	094	7	222 279	89X
8	213 011	482	8	861 Ɛ21	084	8	298 Ɛ57	88Ɛ
9	28X 493	473	9	918 ƐX5	075	9	353 826	87X
X	345 946	463	X	994 05X	065	X	40X 4X4	86X
Ɛ	401 1X9	453	Ɛ	X4Ɛ 103	054	Ɛ	485 152	85Ɛ

N	Log N	d	N	Log N	d	N	Log N	d
7800	9X0 53Ɛ 9Ɛ1	76 84Ɛ	7840	9X2 Ɛ61 910	76 459	7880	9X5 570 039	76 070
1	5Ɛ6 640	83Ɛ	1	9X3 018 169	44X	1	626 0X9	05Ɛ
2	671 27Ɛ	82Ɛ	2	092 5Ɛ7	439	2	6X0 148	050
3	727 XXX	81Ɛ	3	148 X34	42X	3	756 198	040
4	7X2 709	810	4	203 262	41X	4	810 218	031
5	859 319	800	5	279 680	40X	5	886 249	021
6	913 Ɛ19	7Ɛ0	6	333 X8X	3ƐƐ	6	940 26X	012
7	98X 709	7X0	7	3XX 289	3XƐ	7	9Ɛ6 280	001
8	X45 2X9	790	8	464 678	39Ɛ	8	X70 281	75 ƐƐ2
9	XƐƐ X79	780	9	51X X57	38Ɛ	9	Ɛ26 273	ƐX3
X	Ɛ76 639	771	X	595 226	380	X	ƐX0 256	Ɛ93
Ɛ	9X1 031 1XX	761	Ɛ	64Ɛ 5X6	370	Ɛ	9X6 056 229	Ɛ83
7810	0X7 94Ɛ	751	7850	705 956	360	7890	110 1Ɛ0	Ɛ73
1	162 4X0	741	1	780 0Ɛ6	351	1	186 163	Ɛ64
2	219 021	731	2	836 447	340	2	240 107	Ɛ54
3	293 752	722	3	8Ɛ0 787	332	3	2Ɛ6 05Ɛ	Ɛ45
4	34X 274	712	4	966 XƐ9	321	4	36Ɛ ƐX4	Ɛ35
5	404 986	702	5	X21 21X	312	5	425 Ɛ19	Ɛ25
6	47Ɛ 488	6Ɛ2	6	X97 530	301	6	49Ɛ X42	Ɛ16
7	535 Ɛ7X	6X2	7	Ɛ51 831	2Ɛ3	7	555 958	Ɛ06
8	5Ɛ0 660	693	8	9X4 007 Ɛ24	2X2	8	60Ɛ 862	XƐ7
9	667 133	682	9	082 206	293	9	685 759	XX6
X	721 7Ɛ5	673	X	138 499	283	X	73Ɛ 643	X98
Ɛ	798 268	664	Ɛ	1Ɛ2 760	273	Ɛ	7Ɛ5 51Ɛ	X87
7820	852 910	653	7860	268 X13	264	78X0	86Ɛ 3X6	X78
1	909 363	644	1	323 077	254	1	925 262	X68
2	983 9X7	634	2	399 30Ɛ	244	2	99Ɛ 10X	X59
3	X3X 41Ɛ	624	3	453 553	235	3	X54 Ɛ67	X49
4	XƐ4 X43	614	4	509 788	225	4	Ɛ0X 9Ɛ4	X3X
5	Ɛ6Ɛ 457	604	5	583 9Ɛ1	215	5	Ɛ84 832	X2X
6	9X2 025 X5Ɛ	5Ɛ5	6	63X 006	205	6	9X7 03X 660	X1X
7	0X0 454	5X5	7	6Ɛ4 20Ɛ	1Ɛ6	7	0Ɛ4 47X	X0Ɛ
8	156 X39	595	8	76X 405	1X6	8	16X 289	9ƐƐ
9	211 412	586	9	824 5XƐ	197	9	224 088	9XƐ
X	287 998	575	X	89X 786	186	X	299 X77	9X0
Ɛ	342 351	566	Ɛ	954 950	177	Ɛ	353 857	990
7830	3Ɛ8 8Ɛ7	556	7870	X0X Ɛ07	168	78Ɛ0	409 627	981
1	473 251	547	1	X85 073	157	1	483 3X8	971
2	529 798	536	2	Ɛ3Ɛ 20X	148	2	539 159	961
3	5X4 112	527	3	ƐƐ5 356	139	3	5Ɛ2 XƐX	952
4	65X 639	517	4	9X5 06Ɛ 493	128	4	668 850	943
5	714 Ɛ54	507	5	125 5ƐƐ	119	5	722 593	932
6	78Ɛ 45Ɛ	4Ɛ8	6	19Ɛ 718	10X	6	798 305	923
7	845 957	4X8	7	255 826	0Ɛ9	7	852 028	914
8	900 243	498	8	30Ɛ 923	0XX	8	907 940	904
9	976 71Ɛ	488	9	385 X11	09Ɛ	9	981 644	8Ɛ4
X	X30 ƐX7	479	X	43Ɛ X20	08X	X	X37 338	8X5
Ɛ	XX7 464	468	Ɛ	4Ɛ5 Ɛ7X	07Ɛ	Ɛ	XƐ1 021	895

N	Log N	d	N	Log N	d	N	Log N	d
7900	9χ7 Ɛ66 8Ɛ6	75 886	7940	9χχ 54χ 043	75 4χ4	7980	9Ɛ0 Ɛ19 Ɛ9Ɛ	75 106
1	9χ8 020 580	876	1	603 527	495	1	Ɛ93 0χ5	0Ɛ7
2	096 236	866	2	678 χ00	485	2	9Ɛ1 048 1χ0	0χ7
3	14Ɛ χχ0	857	3	732 285	475	3	101 287	098
4	205 737	847	4	7χ7 73χ	466	4	176 363	089
5	27Ɛ 382	838	5	860 Ɛχ4	456	5	22Ɛ 430	079
6	334 ƐƐχ	828	6	916 43χ	447	6	2χ4 4χ9	06χ
7	3χχ 826	819	7	98Ɛ 885	438	7	359 557	05χ
8	464 443	809	8	χ45 101	428	8	412 5Ɛ5	04Ɛ
9	51χ 050	7Ɛχ	9	χƐχ 529	418	9	487 644	03Ɛ
χ	593 84χ	7χχ	χ	Ɛ73 945	409	χ	540 683	030
Ɛ	649 438	79χ	Ɛ	9χƐ 029 152	3Ɛχ	Ɛ	5Ɛ5 6Ɛ3	021
7910	703 016	78Ɛ	7950	0χ2 550	3χχ	7990	66χ 714	011
1	778 7χ5	77Ɛ	1	157 93χ	39Ɛ	1	723 725	002
2	832 364	770	2	211 119	38Ɛ	2	798 727	74 ƐƐ3
3	8χ7 Ɛ14	760	3	286 4χ8	380	3	851 71χ	Ɛχ3
4	961 674	750	4	33Ɛ 868	370	4	906 701	Ɛ94
5	χ17 204	741	5	3Ɛ5 018	361	5	97Ɛ 695	Ɛ84
6	χ90 945	732	6	46χ 379	351	6	χ34 659	Ɛ75
7	Ɛ46 477	722	7	523 70χ	342	7	χχ9 612	Ɛ65
8	ƐƐƐ Ɛ99	712	8	598 χ50	332	8	Ɛ62 577	Ɛ57
9	9χ9 075 6χƐ	703	9	652 182	323	9	9Ɛ2 017 512	Ɛ46
χ	12Ɛ 1Ɛ2	6Ɛ4	χ	707 4χ5	313	χ	090 458	Ɛ38
Ɛ	1χ4 8χ6	6χ3	Ɛ	780 7Ɛ8	304	Ɛ	145 394	Ɛ28
7920	25χ 389	695	7960	835 Ɛ00	2Ɛ5	79χ0	1Ɛχ 300	Ɛ19
1	313 χ62	684	1	8χƐ 1Ɛ5	2χ5	1	273 219	Ɛ09
2	389 526	676	2	964 49χ	295	2	328 126	χƐχ
3	442 Ɛχ0	665	3	χ19 773	287	3	3χ1 024	χχƐ
4	4Ɛ8 645	656	4	χ92 χ3χ	276	4	455 Ɛ13	χ9Ɛ
5	572 09Ɛ	647	5	Ɛ48 0Ɛ4	268	5	50χ 9Ɛ2	χ90
6	627 726	637	6	9Ɛ0 001 360	257	6	583 882	χ80
7	6χ1 161	628	7	076 5Ɛ7	249	7	638 742	χ71
8	756 789	618	8	12Ɛ 844	239	8	6Ɛ1 5Ɛ3	χ62
9	810 1χ5	608	9	1χ4 χ81	229	9	766 455	χ53
χ	885 7Ɛ1	5Ɛ9	χ	25χ 0χχ	21χ	χ	81Ɛ 2χ8	χ43
Ɛ	93Ɛ 1χχ	5χχ	Ɛ	313 308	20Ɛ	Ɛ	894 12Ɛ	χ33
7930	9Ɛ4 798	59χ	7970	388 517	1ƐƐ	79Ɛ0	948 Ɛ62	χ25
1	χ6χ 176	58χ	1	441 716	1Ɛ0	1	χ01 987	χ15
2	Ɛ23 744	57Ɛ	2	4Ɛ6 906	1χ0	2	χ76 7χ0	χ05
3	Ɛ99 103	56Ɛ	3	56Ɛ χχ6	191	3	Ɛ2Ɛ 5χ5	9Ɛ7
4	9χχ 052 672	560	4	625 077	182	4	Ɛχ4 3χ0	9χ7
5	108 012	551	5	69χ 239	172	5	9Ɛ3 059 187	997
6	181 563	541	6	753 3χƐ	162	6	111 Ɛ62	988
7	236 χχ4	531	7	808 551	154	7	186 92χ	979
8	2Ɛ0 415	522	8	881 6χ5	143	8	23Ɛ 6χ7	96χ
9	365 937	512	9	936 828	135	9	2Ɛ4 455	95χ
χ	41Ɛ 249	503	χ	9χƐ 961	125	χ	369 1Ɛ3	94Ɛ
Ɛ	494 750	4Ɛ3	Ɛ	χ64 χ86	115	Ɛ	421 Ɛ42	940

N	Log N	d	N	Log N	d	N	Log N	d
7X00	9Ɛ3 496 882	74 930	7X40	9Ɛ5 X40 425	74 55X	7X80	9Ɛ8 392 Ɛ82	74 190
1	54Ɛ 5Ɛ2	921	1	XƐ4 983	54Ɛ	1	447 152	181
2	604 313	912	2	Ɛ69 312	540	2	4ƐƐ 313	171
3	679 025	902	3	9Ɛ6 021 852	531	3	573 484	163
4	731 927	8Ɛ3	4	096 183	521	4	627 627	153
5	7X6 61X	8X3	5	14X 6X4	512	5	69Ɛ 77X	144
6	85Ɛ 301	895	6	202 ƐƐ6	503	6	753 902	135
7	913 Ɛ96	885	7	277 4Ɛ9	4Ɛ3	7	807 X37	126
8	988 85Ɛ	875	8	32Ɛ 9Ɛ0	4X4	8	87Ɛ Ɛ61	117
9	X41 514	867	9	3X4 294	495	9	934 078	107
X	XƐ6 17Ɛ	857	X	458 769	486	X	9X8 183	0Ɛ9
Ɛ	Ɛ6X X16	847	Ɛ	511 033	477	Ɛ	X60 280	0X9
7X10	9Ɛ4 023 661	839	7X50	585 4XX	467	7X90	Ɛ14 369	09X
1	098 29X	829	1	639 955	458	1	Ɛ88 447	08Ɛ
2	150 Ɛ07	81X	2	6Ɛ2 1Ɛ1	449	2	9Ɛ9 040 516	080
3	205 725	80X	3	766 63X	43X	3	0Ɛ4 596	070
4	27X 333	7ƐƐ	4	81X X78	42X	4	168 646	062
5	332 Ɛ32	7Ɛ0	5	893 2X6	41Ɛ	5	220 6X8	052
6	3X7 722	7X1	6	947 705	410	6	294 73X	043
7	460 303	791	7	9ƐƐ Ɛ15	401	7	348 781	034
8	514 X94	782	8	X74 316	3Ɛ2	8	400 7Ɛ5	025
9	589 656	772	9	Ɛ28 708	3X2	9	474 81X	016
X	642 208	764	X	ƐX0 XXX	393	X	528 834	007
Ɛ	6Ɛ6 970	754	Ɛ	9Ɛ7 055 281	384	Ɛ	5X0 83Ɛ	73 ƐƐ7
7X20	76Ɛ 504	745	7X60	109 645	374	7XX0	654 836	ƐX9
1	824 049	735	1	181 9Ɛ9	366	1	708 823	Ɛ99
2	898 782	726	2	236 163	356	2	780 800	Ɛ8X
3	951 2X8	717	3	2XX 4Ɛ9	347	3	834 78X	Ɛ7Ɛ
4	X05 X03	708	4	362 844	338	4	8X8 749	Ɛ70
5	X7X 50Ɛ	6Ɛ8	5	416 Ɛ80	329	5	960 6Ɛ9	Ɛ60
6	Ɛ33 007	6X9	6	48Ɛ 2X9	319	6	X14 659	Ɛ52
7	ƐX7 6Ɛ4	69X	7	543 606	30X	7	X88 5XƐ	Ɛ42
8	9Ɛ5 060 192	68X	8	5Ɛ7 914	2ƐƐ	8	Ɛ40 531	Ɛ34
9	114 860	680	9	670 013	2Ɛ0	9	ƐƐ4 465	Ɛ24
X	189 320	66Ɛ	X	724 303	2X1	X	9ƐX 068 389	Ɛ15
Ɛ	241 98Ɛ	661	Ɛ	798 5X4	291	Ɛ	120 2X2	Ɛ06
7X30	2Ɛ6 430	652	7X70	850 875	282	7XƐ0	194 1X8	XƐ7
1	36X X82	642	1	904 Ɛ37	273	1	248 0X3	XX8
2	423 504	632	2	979 1XX	264	2	2ƐƐ Ɛ8Ɛ	X98
3	497 Ɛ36	624	3	X31 452	255	3	373 X67	X8X
4	550 55X	614	4	XX5 6X7	245	4	427 935	X7X
5	604 Ɛ72	605	5	Ɛ59 930	237	5	49Ɛ 7Ɛ3	X70
6	679 577	5Ɛ6	6	9Ɛ8 011 Ɛ67	227	6	553 663	X60
7	731 Ɛ71	5X7	7	086 192	218	7	607 Ɛ03	X51
8	7X6 558	597	8	13X 3XX	208	8	67Ɛ 354	X42
9	85X Ɛ33	588	9	1Ɛ2 5Ɛ6	1ƐX	9	733 196	X33
X	913 4ƐƐ	579	X	266 7Ɛ4	1XX	X	7X7 009	X24
Ɛ	987 X78	569	Ɛ	31X 9X2	1X0	Ɛ	85X X31	X14

N	Log N	d	N	Log N	d	N	Log N	d
7Ɛ00	9ƐХ 912 845	73 Х06	7Ɛ40	Х01 23Ɛ 765	73 643	7Ɛ80	Х03 755 Х4Ɛ	73 283
1	986 64Ɛ	9Ɛ7	1	2Ɛ3 1Х8	634	1	809 112	275
2	Х3Х 446	9Х7	2	366 820	625	2	880 387	267
3	ХƐ2 231	998	3	41Х 245	616	3	933 632	257
4	Ɛ66 009	98Х	4	491 85Ɛ	606	4	9Х6 889	248
5	9ƐƐ 019 997	97Х	5	545 265	5Ɛ8	5	Х59 Ɛ15	239
6	091 755	96Ɛ	6	5Ɛ8 861	5Х9	6	Ɛ11 152	22Х
7	145 504	960	7	670 24Х	59Х	7	Ɛ84 380	220
8	1Ɛ9 264	951	8	723 828	58Ɛ	8	Х04 037 5Х0	210
9	270 ƐƐ5	942	9	797 1Ɛ7	580	9	0ХХ 7Ɛ0	202
Х	324 937	932	Х	84Х 777	570	Х	161 9Ɛ2	1Ɛ2
Ɛ	398 669	924	Ɛ	902 127	562	Ɛ	214 ƐХ4	1Х4
7Ɛ10	450 391	915	7Ɛ50	975 689	553	7Ɛ90	288 188	195
1	504 0Х6	905	1	Х29 020	544	1	33Ɛ 361	186
2	577 9ХƐ	8Ɛ6	2	ХХ0 564	535	2	3Ɛ2 527	177
3	62Ɛ 6Х5	8Х8	3	Ɛ53 Х99	526	3	465 6Х2	168
4	6Х3 391	898	4	Х02 007 403	517	4	518 84Х	159
5	757 069	889	5	07Х 91Х	507	5	58Ɛ 9Х7	14Х
6	80Х 936	87Ɛ	6	132 225	4Ɛ9	6	642 Ɛ35	13Ɛ
7	882 5Ɛ5	86Ɛ	7	1Х5 722	4ХХ	7	6Ɛ6 074	131
8	936 264	860	8	259 010	49Ɛ	8	769 1Х5	121
9	9Х9 Ɛ04	851	9	310 4ХƐ	490	9	820 306	113
Х	Х61 755	842	Х	383 97Ɛ	481	Х	893 419	103
Ɛ	Ɛ15 397	832	Ɛ	437 240	472	Ɛ	946 520	0Ɛ5
7Ɛ20	Ɛ89 009	824	7Ɛ60	4ХХ 6Ɛ2	463	7ƐХ0	9Ɛ9 615	0Х6
1	Х00 040 831	815	1	561 Ɛ55	454	1	Х70 6ƐƐ	097
2	0Ɛ4 446	806	2	615 3Х9	445	2	Ɛ23 796	088
3	168 050	7Ɛ6	3	688 832	436	3	Ɛ96 862	079
4	21Ɛ 846	7Х8	4	740 068	427	4	Х05 049 91Ɛ	06Х
5	293 432	799	5	7Ɛ3 493	418	5	100 989	05Ɛ
6	347 00Ɛ	789	6	866 8ХƐ	409	6	173 Х28	051
7	3ƐХ 798	77Х	7	91Х 0Ɛ8	3ƐХ	7	226 Х79	041
8	472 356	770	8	991 4Ɛ6	3Ɛ0	8	299 ХƐХ	033
9	525 Ɛ06	760	9	Х44 8Х6	3Х0	9	350 Ɛ31	024
Х	599 666	752	Х	ХƐ8 086	391	Х	403 Ɛ55	015
Ɛ	651 1Ɛ8	742	Ɛ	Ɛ6Ɛ 457	382	Ɛ	476 Ɛ6Х	006
7Ɛ30	704 93Х	733	7Ɛ70	Х03 022 819	374	7ƐƐ0	529 Ɛ74	72 ƐƐ7
1	778 471	724	1	095 Ɛ91	364	1	5Х0 Ɛ6Ɛ	ƐХ8
2	82Ɛ Ɛ95	716	2	149 335	355	2	653 Ɛ57	Ɛ99
3	8Х3 6ХƐ	706	3	200 68Х	347	3	706 Ɛ34	Ɛ8Ɛ
4	957 1Ɛ5	6Ɛ7	4	273 Х15	337	4	779 Ɛ03	Ɛ7Ɛ
5	Х0Х 8Ɛ0	6Х8	5	327 150	329	5	830 Х82	Ɛ71
6	Х82 398	699	6	39Х 479	31Х	6	8Х3 Х33	Ɛ62
7	Ɛ35 Х75	68Х	7	451 797	30Х	7	956 995	Ɛ53
8	ƐХ9 543	67Ɛ	8	504 ХХ5	300	8	Х09 928	Ɛ44
9	Х01 061 002	670	9	578 1Х5	2Ɛ1	9	Х80 870	Ɛ35
Х	114 672	661	Х	62Ɛ 496	2Х2	Х	Ɛ33 7Х5	Ɛ26
Ɛ	188 113	652	Ɛ	6Х2 778	293	Ɛ	ƐХ6 70Ɛ	Ɛ18

N	Log N	d	N	Log N	d	N	Log N	d
8000	χ06 059 627	72 Ɛ09	8040	χ08 54χ 821	72 755	8080	χ0χ χ29 559	72 3χ5
1	110 534	χƐ9	1	601 376	746	1	χ9Ɛ 942	396
2	183 431	χχƐ	2	673 Ɛ00	737	2	Ɛ52 118	387
3	236 320	χχ0	3	726 637	729	3	χ0Ɛ 004 4χ3	379
4	2χ9 200	χ91	4	799 164	719	4	076 860	36χ
5	360 091	χ83	5	84Ɛ 881	70Ɛ	5	129 00χ	35Ɛ
6	412 Ɛ54	χ73	6	902 390	701	6	19Ɛ 369	351
7	485 χ07	χ65	7	974 χ91	6Ɛ1	7	251 6Ɛχ	341
8	538 870	χ55	8	χ27 582	6χ3	8	303 χ3Ɛ	334
9	5χƐ 705	χ47	9	χ9χ 065	694	9	376 173	324
χ	662 550	χ38	χ	Ɛ50 739	685	χ	428 497	316
Ɛ	715 388	χ2χ	Ɛ	χ09 003 202	676	Ɛ	49χ 7Ɛ1	307
8010	788 1Ɛ6	χ1χ	8050	075 878	667	8090	550 χƐ8	2Ɛ8
1	83Ɛ 014	χ0Ɛ	1	128 323	659	1	603 1Ɛ4	2χχ
2	8Ɛ1 χ23	χ01	2	19χ 980	64χ	2	675 4χ2	29Ɛ
3	964 824	9Ɛ2	3	251 40χ	63Ɛ	3	727 781	290
4	χ17 616	9χ3	4	303 χ49	631	4	799 χ51	281
5	χ8χ 3Ɛ9	994	5	376 47χ	622	5	850 112	273
6	Ɛ41 191	985	6	428 χχ0	613	6	902 385	264
7	ƐƐ3 Ɛ56	977	7	49Ɛ 4Ɛ3	604	7	974 629	256
8	χ07 066 911	967	8	551 χƐ7	5Ɛ5	8	χ26 883	247
9	119 678	959	9	604 4Ɛ0	5χ7	9	χ98 Ɛ0χ	238
χ	190 415	94χ	χ	676 χ97	598	χ	Ɛ4Ɛ 146	229
Ɛ	243 163	93Ɛ	Ɛ	729 473	589	Ɛ	χ10 001 373	21Ɛ
8020	2Ɛ5 χχ2	931	8060	79Ɛ χ40	57χ	80χ0	073 592	210
1	368 813	921	1	852 3Ɛχ	570	1	125 7χ2	201
2	41Ɛ 534	913	2	904 96χ	561	2	197 9χ3	1Ɛ3
3	492 247	904	3	977 30Ɛ	552	3	249 Ɛ96	1χ4
4	544 Ɛ4Ɛ	8Ɛ5	4	χ29 861	543	4	300 17χ	195
5	5Ɛ7 844	8χ6	5	χχ0 1χ4	535	5	372 353	187
6	66χ 52χ	897	6	Ɛ52 719	526	6	424 51χ	178
7	721 205	889	7	χ0χ 005 043	517	7	496 696	169
8	793 χ92	879	8	077 55χ	509	8	548 843	15Ɛ
9	846 74Ɛ	86Ɛ	9	129 χ67	4Ɛ9	9	5Ɛχ 9χ2	150
χ	8Ɛ9 3Ɛχ	861	χ	1χ0 364	4χƐ	χ	670 Ɛ32	141
Ɛ	970 05Ɛ	851	Ɛ	252 853	4χ0	Ɛ	723 073	133
8030	χ22 8Ɛ0	842	8070	305 133	492	80Ɛ0	795 1χ6	124
1	χ95 532	834	1	377 605	483	1	847 30χ	115
2	Ɛ48 166	825	2	429 χ88	474	2	8Ɛ9 423	107
3	ƐƐχ 98Ɛ	816	3	4χ0 340	465	3	96Ɛ 52χ	0Ɛ8
4	χ08 071 5χ5	807	4	552 7χ5	457	4	χ21 626	0χχ
5	124 1Ɛ0	7Ɛ9	5	605 040	447	5	χ93 714	09χ
6	196 9χ9	7χ9	6	677 487	439	6	Ɛ45 7Ɛ2	090
7	249 596	79Ɛ	7	729 904	42Ɛ	7	ƐƐ7 882	082
8	300 175	790	8	7χ0 133	41Ɛ	8	χ11 069 944	073
9	372 945	782	9	852 552	411	9	11Ɛ 9Ɛ7	064
χ	425 507	772	χ	904 963	403	χ	191 χ5Ɛ	055
Ɛ	498 079	764	Ɛ	977 166	3Ɛ3	Ɛ	243 χƐ4	047

N	Log N	d	N	Log N	d	N	Log N	d
8100	χ11 2Ɛ5 Ɛ3Ɛ	72 038	8140	χ13 770 2χ8	71 893	8180	χ16 014 540	71 531
1	367 Ɛ77	02χ	1	821 Ɛ7Ɛ	885	1	085 χ71	523
2	419 Ɛχ5	01Ɛ	2	893 844	876	2	137 394	515
3	490 004	010	3	945 4Ɛχ	867	3	1χ8 8χ9	506
4	542 014	002	4	9Ɛ7 165	859	4	25χ 1Ɛ3	4Ɛ8
5	5Ɛ4 016	71 ƐƐ3	5	χ68 χ02	84χ	5	30Ɛ 6χƐ	4χ9
6	666 009	Ɛχ4	6	Ɛ1χ 650	840	6	380 Ɛ98	49χ
7	717 ƐƐ1	Ɛ96	7	Ɛ90 290	831	7	432 476	490
8	789 Ɛ87	Ɛ87	8	χ14 041 Ɛ01	823	8	4χ3 946	482
9	83Ɛ Ɛ52	Ɛ79	9	0Ɛ3 724	814	9	555 208	473
χ	8Ɛ1 Ɛ0Ɛ	Ɛ69	χ	165 338	806	χ	606 67Ɛ	465
Ɛ	963 χ78	Ɛ60	Ɛ	216 Ɛ42	7Ɛ7	Ɛ	677 Ɛ24	456
8110	χ15 χ18	Ɛ50	8150	288 739	7χ8	8190	729 37χ	448
1	χ87 968	Ɛ42	1	33χ 325	79χ	1	79χ 806	439
2	Ɛ39 8χχ	Ɛ34	2	3χƐ Ɛ03	78Ɛ	2	850 043	42Ɛ
3	ƐχƐ 822	Ɛ24	3	461 692	781	3	901 472	420
4	χ12 061 746	Ɛ16	4	513 253	772	4	972 892	412
5	113 660	Ɛ08	5	584 χ05	764	5	χ24 0χ4	403
6	185 568	χƐ9	6	636 569	755	6	χ95 4χ7	3Ɛ5
7	237 465	χχχ	7	6χ8 102	747	7	Ɛ46 8χ0	3χ6
8	2χ9 353	χχ0	8	759 849	738	8	ƐƐ8 086	398
9	35Ɛ 233	χ91	9	80Ɛ 385	729	9	χ17 069 462	38χ
χ	411 104	χ82	χ	880 χƐ2	71Ɛ	χ	11χ 830	37Ɛ
Ɛ	482 Ɛ86	χ74	Ɛ	932 611	711	Ɛ	18Ɛ ƐχƐ	370
8120	534 χ3χ	χ65	8160	9χ4 122	702	81χ0	241 35Ɛ	362
1	5χ6 8χ3	χ57	1	χ55 824	6Ɛ3	1	2Ɛ2 701	354
2	658 73χ	χ48	2	Ɛ07 317	6χ5	2	363 χ55	345
3	70χ 586	χ3χ	3	Ɛ78 χ00	696	3	415 19χ	337
4	780 404	χ2χ	4	χ15 02χ 496	688	4	486 515	328
5	832 232	χ21	5	09Ɛ Ɛ62	679	5	537 841	319
6	8χ4 053	χ11	6	151 61Ɛ	66Ɛ	6	5χ8 Ɛ5χ	310
7	955 χ64	χ03	7	203 08χ	660	7	65χ 26χ	301
8	χ07 867	9Ɛ5	8	274 72χ	652	8	70Ɛ 56Ɛ	2Ɛ2
9	χ79 660	9χ6	9	326 180	643	9	780 861	2χ4
χ	ƐƐƐ 446	997	χ	397 803	635	χ	831 Ɛ45	296
Ɛ	Ɛχ1 221	988	Ɛ	449 238	626	Ɛ	8χ3 21Ɛ	287
8130	χ13 052 Ɛχ9	97Ɛ	8170	4Ɛχ 862	618	81Ɛ0	954 4χ6	278
1	104 968	96Ɛ	1	570 27χ	609	1	χ05 762	26χ
2	176 717	961	2	621 887	5Ɛχ	2	χ76 χ10	260
3	228 478	952	3	693 285	5Ɛ0	3	Ɛ28 070	251
4	29χ 20χ	944	4	744 875	5χ2	4	Ɛ99 301	243
5	34Ɛ Ɛ52	935	5	7Ɛ6 257	593	5	χ18 04χ 544	235
6	401 887	927	6	867 82χ	585	6	0ƐƐ 779	226
7	473 5Ɛ2	918	7	919 1Ɛ3	576	7	170 9χ3	217
8	525 30χ	909	8	98χ 769	567	8	221 ƐƐχ	209
9	597 017	8ƐƐ	9	χ40 114	559	9	293 207	1ƐƐ
χ	648 916	8Ɛ0	χ	χƐ1 671	54Ɛ	χ	344 406	1Ɛ0
Ɛ	6Ɛχ 606	8χ2	Ɛ	Ɛ63 000	540	Ɛ	3Ɛ5 5Ɛ6	1χ2

N	Log N	d	N	Log N	d	N	Log N	d
8200	X18 466 798	71 194	8240	X1X 8X6 Ɛ55	70 X39	8280	X21 115 54X	70 6X5
1	517 970	184	1	957 992	X2X	1	186 033	697
2	588 Ɛ34	177	2	X08 800	X20	2	236 70X	689
3	63X 0XƐ	168	3	X79 620	X12	3	2X7 197	67X
4	6XƐ 257	15X	4	Ɛ2X 432	X03	4	357 855	671
5	760 3Ɛ5	14Ɛ	5	Ɛ9Ɛ 235	9Ɛ5	5	408 306	662
6	811 544	141	6	X1Ɛ 050 02X	9X7	6	478 968	653
7	882 685	133	7	100 X15	998	7	529 3ƐƐ	645
8	933 7Ɛ8	124	8	171 7Ɛ1	98X	8	599 X44	637
9	9X4 920	115	9	222 57Ɛ	97Ɛ	9	64X 47Ɛ	629
X	X55 X35	107	X	293 33X	971	X	6ƐX XX8	61Ɛ
Ɛ	Ɛ06 Ɛ40	0Ɛ9	Ɛ	344 0XƐ	963	Ɛ	76Ɛ 507	610
8210	Ɛ78 039	0XƐ	8250	3Ɛ4 X52	955	8290	81Ɛ Ɛ17	602
1	X19 029 128	0X0	1	465 7X7	946	1	890 519	5Ɛ4
2	09X 208	091	2	516 531	938	2	940 Ɛ11	5X5
3	14Ɛ 299	083	3	587 269	929	3	9Ɛ1 4Ɛ6	597
4	200 360	075	4	637 Ɛ96	91Ɛ	4	X61 X91	589
5	271 415	067	5	6X8 8Ɛ5	911	5	Ɛ12 45X	57Ɛ
6	322 480	057	6	759 606	903	6	Ɛ82 X19	570
7	393 517	04X	7	80X 309	8Ɛ4	7	X22 033 389	562
8	444 565	03Ɛ	8	87Ɛ 001	8X6	8	0X3 92Ɛ	554
9	4Ɛ5 5X4	031	9	92Ɛ 8X7	897	9	154 283	546
X	566 615	022	X	9X0 582	889	X	204 809	537
Ɛ	617 637	014	Ɛ	X51 24Ɛ	87Ɛ	Ɛ	275 144	529
8220	688 64Ɛ	006	8260	Ɛ01 Ɛ0X	871	82X0	325 671	51Ɛ
1	739 655	70 ƐƐ7	1	Ɛ72 77Ɛ	862	1	395 Ɛ90	511
2	7XX 650	ƐX9	2	X20 023 421	854	2	446 4X1	502
3	85Ɛ 639	Ɛ9Ɛ	3	094 075	845	3	4Ɛ6 9X3	4Ɛ4
4	910 618	Ɛ90	4	144 8ƐX	838	4	567 297	4X6
5	981 5X8	Ɛ81	5	1Ɛ5 536	829	5	617 781	497
6	X32 569	Ɛ74	6	266 163	81X	6	688 058	48X
7	XX3 521	Ɛ64	7	316 981	811	7	738 526	47Ɛ
8	Ɛ54 485	Ɛ57	8	387 592	802	8	7X8 9X5	471
9	X1X 005 420	Ɛ48	9	438 194	7Ɛ3	9	859 256	462
X	076 368	Ɛ3X	X	4X8 987	7X6	X	909 6Ɛ8	455
Ɛ	127 2X6	Ɛ2Ɛ	Ɛ	559 571	797	Ɛ	979 Ɛ51	446
8230	198 215	Ɛ21	8270	60X 148	789	82Ɛ0	X2X 397	438
1	249 136	Ɛ13	1	67X 915	77X	1	X9X 813	42X
2	2ƐX 049	Ɛ04	2	72Ɛ 493	771	2	Ɛ4Ɛ 041	41Ɛ
3	36X Ɛ51	XƐ6	3	7X0 044	761	3	ƐƐƐ 460	411
4	41Ɛ X47	XX8	4	850 7X5	754	4	X23 06Ɛ 871	403
5	490 933	X99	5	901 339	745	5	120 074	3Ɛ5
6	541 810	X8Ɛ	6	971 X82	737	6	190 469	3X7
7	5Ɛ2 69Ɛ	X80	7	X22 5Ɛ9	729	7	240 854	398
8	663 55Ɛ	X72	8	X93 126	71Ɛ	8	2Ɛ1 030	38X
9	714 411	X64	9	Ɛ43 845	710	9	361 3ƐX	380
X	785 275	X55	X	ƐƐ4 355	702	X	411 77X	372
Ɛ	836 10X	X47	Ɛ	X21 064 X57	6Ɛ3	Ɛ	481 Ɛ30	363

N	Log N	d	N	Log N	d	N	Log N	d
8300	X23 532 293	70 355	8340	X25 939 480	70 009	8380	X28 133 023	6Ɛ 883
1	5X2 628	348	1	9X9 489	6Ɛ ƐƐX	1	1X2 8X6	875
2	652 974	338	2	X59 487	ƐƐ0	2	252 55Ɛ	866
3	703 0Ɛ0	32Ɛ	3	Ɛ09 477	ƐX2	3	302 205	859
4	773 41Ɛ	320	4	Ɛ79 459	Ɛ94	4	371 X62	84Ɛ
5	823 73Ɛ	312	5	X26 029 431	Ɛ86	5	421 6Ɛ1	841
6	893 X51	304	6	099 3Ɛ7	Ɛ78	6	491 332	832
7	944 155	2Ɛ6	7	149 373	Ɛ69	7	540 Ɛ64	825
8	9Ɛ4 44Ɛ	2X8	8	1Ɛ9 320	Ɛ60	8	5Ɛ0 789	816
9	X64 737	299	9	269 280	Ɛ51	9	660 3X3	809
X	Ɛ14 X14	28Ɛ	X	319 211	Ɛ43	X	70Ɛ ƐƐ0	7ƐX
Ɛ	Ɛ85 0X3	281	Ɛ	389 154	Ɛ35	Ɛ	77Ɛ 7XX	7Ɛ0
8310	X24 035 364	273	8350	439 089	Ɛ27	8390	82Ɛ 39X	7X2
1	0X5 617	264	1	4X8 ƐƐ4	Ɛ18	1	89X Ɛ80	794
2	155 87Ɛ	257	2	558 Ɛ10	Ɛ0Ɛ	2	94X 754	786
3	205 Ɛ16	248	3	608 X1Ɛ	Ɛ00	3	9ƐX 31X	778
4	276 162	23X	4	678 91Ɛ	XƐ3	4	X69 X96	76X
5	326 3X0	230	5	728 812	XX4	5	Ɛ19 644	760
6	396 610	221	6	798 6Ɛ6	X96	6	Ɛ89 1X4	752
7	446 831	214	7	848 590	X88	7	X29 038 936	744
8	4Ɛ6 X45	205	8	8Ɛ8 458	X7X	8	0X8 47X	735
9	567 04X	1Ɛ7	9	968 316	X6Ɛ	9	157 ƐƐ3	728
X	617 245	1X9	X	X18 185	X62	X	207 71Ɛ	71X
Ɛ	687 432	19X	Ɛ	X88 027	X53	Ɛ	277 239	70Ɛ
8320	737 610	191	8360	Ɛ37 X7X	X46	83X0	326 948	702
1	7X7 7X1	182	1	ƐX7 904	X37	1	396 44X	6Ɛ3
2	857 963	174	2	X27 057 73Ɛ	X29	2	445 Ɛ41	6X6
3	907 Ɛ17	166	3	107 568	X1Ɛ	3	4Ɛ5 627	697
4	978 081	158	4	177 387	X11	4	565 102	689
5	X28 219	149	5	227 198	X03	5	614 78Ɛ	680
6	X98 366	140	6	296 Ɛ9Ɛ	9Ɛ5	6	684 24Ɛ	671
7	Ɛ48 4X6	131	7	346 994	9X6	7	733 900	663
8	ƐƐ8 617	123	8	3Ɛ6 77X	999	8	7X3 363	655
9	X25 068 73X	115	9	466 557	98X	9	852 9Ɛ8	647
X	118 853	107	X	516 325	980	X	902 443	63X
Ɛ	188 95X	0Ɛ8	Ɛ	586 0X5	973	Ɛ	971 X81	62Ɛ
8330	238 X56	0XƐ	8370	635 X58	964	83Ɛ0	X21 4Ɛ0	621
1	2X8 Ɛ45	0X0	1	6X5 800	956	1	X90 Ɛ11	613
2	359 025	092	2	755 556	948	2	Ɛ40 524	605
3	409 0Ɛ7	084	3	805 2X2	939	3	ƐXƐ Ɛ29	5Ɛ7
4	479 17Ɛ	075	4	875 01Ɛ	930	4	X2X 05Ɛ 524	5X9
5	529 234	068	5	924 94Ɛ	922	5	10X Ɛ11	59Ɛ
6	599 2X0	059	6	994 671	913	6	17X 4Ɛ0	590
7	649 339	050	7	X44 384	906	7	229 X80	583
8	6Ɛ9 389	041	8	XƐ4 08X	8Ɛ7	8	299 443	575
9	769 40X	033	9	Ɛ63 985	8X9	9	348 9Ɛ8	567
X	819 441	025	X	X28 013 672	8X0	X	3Ɛ8 363	559
Ɛ	889 466	016	Ɛ	083 352	891	Ɛ	467 900	54Ɛ

N	Log N	d	N	Log N	d	N	Log N	d
8400	X2X 517 24Ɛ	6Ɛ 541	8440	X30 8XX 04Ɛ	6Ɛ 202	8480	X33 06Ɛ 731	6X X85
1	586 790	532	1	959 251	1Ɛ4	1	11X 5Ɛ6	X79
2	636 102	525	2	X08 445	1X5	2	189 473	X6X
3	6X5 627	517	3	X77 62X	198	3	238 321	X60
4	754 Ɛ42	509	4	Ɛ26 806	18X	4	2X7 181	X52
5	804 44Ɛ	4ƐX	5	Ɛ95 994	180	5	356 013	X45
6	873 949	4Ɛ1	6	X31 044 Ɛ54	173	6	404 X58	X37
7	923 23X	4X3	7	0Ɛ4 107	164	7	473 893	X28
8	992 721	495	8	163 26Ɛ	156	8	522 6ƐƐ	X1Ɛ
9	X41 ƐƐ6	486	9	212 405	148	9	591 51X	X11
X	XƐ1 480	479	X	281 551	13Ɛ	X	640 32Ɛ	X03
Ɛ	Ɛ60 939	46Ɛ	Ɛ	330 690	130	Ɛ	6XƐ 132	9Ɛ6
8410	X2Ɛ 010 1X8	460	8450	39Ɛ 800	123	8490	759 Ɛ28	9X7
1	07Ɛ 648	453	1	44X 923	114	1	808 913	99X
2	12X X9Ɛ	445	2	4Ɛ9 X37	107	2	877 6Ɛ1	98Ɛ
3	19X 324	437	3	568 Ɛ42	0Ɛ9	3	926 480	982
4	249 75Ɛ	429	4	618 03Ɛ	0XX	4	995 242	974
5	2Ɛ8 Ɛ88	41X	5	687 129	0X1	5	X43 ƐƐ6	966
6	368 3X6	411	6	736 20X	093	6	XƐ2 960	959
7	417 7Ɛ7	403	7	7X5 2X1	085	7	Ɛ61 6Ɛ9	94X
8	486 ƐƐX	3Ɛ5	8	854 366	077	8	X34 010 447	941
9	536 3Ɛ3	3X7	9	903 421	069	9	07Ɛ 188	932
X	5X5 79X	398	X	972 48X	060	X	129 XƐX	925
Ɛ	654 Ɛ76	38Ɛ	Ɛ	X21 52X	051	Ɛ	198 823	917
8420	704 345	381	8460	X90 57Ɛ	044	84X0	247 53X	909
1	773 706	373	1	Ɛ3Ɛ 603	035	1	2Ɛ6 247	900
2	822 X79	365	2	ƐXX 638	028	2	364 Ɛ47	8Ɛ1
3	892 222	357	3	X32 059 664	019	3	413 838	8X4
4	941 579	349	4	108 681	010	4	482 520	896
5	9Ɛ0 906	33Ɛ	5	177 691	002	5	531 1Ɛ6	888
6	X60 045	331	6	226 693	6X ƐƐ4	6	59Ɛ X82	87X
7	Ɛ0Ɛ 376	323	7	295 687	ƐX6	7	64X 740	870
8	Ɛ7X 699	315	8	344 671	Ɛ98	8	6Ɛ9 3Ɛ0	862
9	X30 029 9Ɛ2	307	9	3Ɛ3 649	Ɛ8Ɛ	9	768 052	855
X	099 0Ɛ9	2Ɛ9	X	462 618	Ɛ80	X	816 8X7	847
Ɛ	148 3Ɛ6	2Ɛ0	Ɛ	511 598	Ɛ73	Ɛ	885 532	839
8430	1Ɛ7 6X6	2X1	8470	580 54Ɛ	Ɛ64	84Ɛ0	934 16Ɛ	82Ɛ
1	266 987	293	1	62Ɛ 4Ɛ3	Ɛ57	1	9X2 99X	821
2	316 05X	285	2	69X 44X	Ɛ49	2	X51 5ƐƐ	813
3	385 323	278	3	749 397	Ɛ3X	3	Ɛ00 212	806
4	434 59Ɛ	269	4	7Ɛ8 315	Ɛ31	4	Ɛ6X X18	7Ɛ8
5	4X3 848	25Ɛ	5	867 246	Ɛ24	5	X35 019 614	7XX
6	552 XX7	252	6	916 16X	Ɛ15	6	088 202	7X0
7	602 139	243	7	985 083	Ɛ07	7	136 9X2	792
8	671 380	236	8	X33 Ɛ8X	XƐX	8	1X5 574	784
9	720 5Ɛ6	228	9	XX2 X88	XXƐ	9	254 138	777
X	78Ɛ 822	219	X	Ɛ51 977	XX2	X	302 8Ɛ3	769
Ɛ	83X X3Ɛ	210	Ɛ	X33 000 859	X94	Ɛ	371 460	75Ɛ

N	Log N	d	N	Log N	d	N	Log N	d
8500	χ35 41Ɛ ƐƐƐ	6χ 751	8540	χ37 77Ɛ 380	6χ 420	8580	χ39 Ɛ09 739	6χ 0Ɛ1
1	48χ 750	744	1	829 7χ0	412	1	Ɛ77 82χ	0χ3
2	539 294	735	2	897 ƐƐ2	404	2	χ3χ 025 911	096
3	5χ7 χ09	728	3	946 3Ɛ6	3Ɛ6	3	093 9χ7	088
4	656 535	71χ	4	9Ɛ4 7Ɛ0	3χ9	4	141 χ73	07χ
5	705 053	710	5	χ62 Ɛ99	39χ	5	1χƐ Ɛ31	071
6	773 763	702	6	Ɛ11 377	392	6	259 Ɛχ2	063
7	822 265	6Ɛ5	7	Ɛ7Ɛ 749	383	7	308 045	055
8	890 95χ	6χ6	8	χ38 029 Ɛ10	376	8	376 09χ	048
9	93Ɛ 444	699	9	098 286	367	9	424 126	03χ
χ	9χ9 Ɛ21	68Ɛ	χ	146 631	35Ɛ	χ	492 164	030
Ɛ	χ58 5Ɛ0	682	Ɛ	1Ɛ4 990	350	Ɛ	540 194	022
8510	Ɛ07 072	673	8550	263 120	343	8590	5χχ 1Ɛ6	015
1	Ɛ75 725	666	1	311 463	335	1	658 20Ɛ	008
2	χ36 024 18Ɛ	658	2	37Ɛ 798	327	2	706 217	69 .ƐƐ9
3	092 827	64χ	3	429 Ɛ03	319	3	774 214	ƐƐ0
4	141 275	640	4	498 220	310	4	822 204	Ɛχ2
5	1χƐ 8Ɛ5	633	5	546 530	302	5	890 1χ6	Ɛ95
6	25χ 328	625	6	5Ɛ4 832	2Ɛ4	6	93χ 17Ɛ	Ɛ87
7	308 951	617	7	662 Ɛ26	2χ7	7	9χ8 146	Ɛ79
8	377 368	609	8	711 211	299	8	χ56 103	Ɛ70
9	425 975	5ƐƐ	9	77Ɛ 4χχ	28Ɛ	9	Ɛ04 073	Ɛ61
χ	494 374	5Ɛ2	χ	829 779	281	χ	Ɛ72 014	Ɛ55
Ɛ	542 966	5χ3	Ɛ	897 χ3χ	274	Ɛ	χ3Ɛ 01Ɛ Ɛ69	Ɛ46
8520	5Ɛ1 349	596	8560	946 0Ɛ2	266	85χ0	089 χƐ3	Ɛ39
1	65Ɛ 923	589	1	9Ɛ4 358	258	1	137 χ30	Ɛ30
2	70χ 2Ɛ0	57χ	2	χ62 5Ɛ4	24χ	2	1χ5 960	Ɛ21
3	778 86χ	571	3	Ɛ10 842	241	3	253 881	Ɛ14
4	827 21Ɛ	563	4	Ɛ7χ χ83	233	4	301 795	Ɛ06
5	895 782	555	5	χ39 029 0Ɛ6	226	5	36Ɛ 69Ɛ	χƐ9
6	944 117	547	6	097 320	217	6	419 598	χχƐ
7	9Ɛ2 662	53χ	7	145 537	20χ	7	487 487	χχ2
8	χ60 Ɛχ0	52Ɛ	8	1Ɛ3 745	201	8	535 369	χ93
9	Ɛ0Ɛ 50Ɛ	522	9	261 946	1Ɛ2	9	5χ3 240	χ86
χ	Ɛ79 χ31	515	χ	30Ɛ Ɛ38	1χ5	χ	651 106	χ79
Ɛ	χ37 028 346	506	Ɛ	37χ 121	197	Ɛ	6Ɛχ Ɛ83	χ6Ɛ
8530	096 850	4Ɛ9	8570	428 2Ɛ8	189	85Ɛ0	768 χ32	χ61
1	145 149	4χƐ	1	496 485	180	1	816 893	χ53
2	1Ɛ3 638	4χ1	2	544 645	172	2	884 726	χ46
3	261 Ɛ19	493	3	5Ɛ2 7Ɛ7	164	3	932 570	χ39
4	310 3Ɛ0	486	4	660 95Ɛ	157	4	9χ0 3χ9	χ2χ
5	37χ 876	478	5	70χ χ26	149	5	χ4χ 217	χ21
6	429 132	46χ	6	779 043	13Ɛ	6	χƐ8 038	χ13
7	497 5χ0	460	7	827 182	132	7	Ɛ65 χ4Ɛ	χ06
8	545 χ40	453	8	895 2Ɛ4	123	8	χ40 013 855	9Ɛ8
9	5Ɛ4 293	445	9	943 417	117	9	081 651	9χƐ
χ	662 718	437	χ	9Ɛ1 532	108	χ	12Ɛ 440	9χ1
Ɛ	710 Ɛ53	429	Ɛ	χ5Ɛ 63χ	0ƐƐ	Ɛ	199 221	993

N	Log N	d	N	Log N	d	N	Log N	d
8600	X40 246 ƐƐ4	69 985	8640	X42 573 66Ɛ	69 661	8680	X44 88Ɛ 427	69 33Ɛ
1	2Ɛ4 979	978	1	621 110	654	1	938 766	332
2	362 735	96Ɛ	2	68X 764	646	2	9X5 X98	325
3	410 4X4	960	3	738 1XX	638	3	X53 201	317
4	47X 244	953	4	7X5 826	62Ɛ	4	Ɛ00 518	30X
5	527 Ɛ97	946	5	853 255	621	5	Ɛ69 826	300
6	595 921	938	6	900 876	614	6	X45 016 Ɛ26	2Ɛ3
7	643 659	92X	7	96X 28X	606	7	084 219	2X5
8	6Ɛ1 387	921	8	X17 894	5Ɛ9	8	131 502	298
9	75Ɛ 0X8	913	9	X85 291	5XƐ	9	19X 79X	28X
X	808 9ƐƐ	905	X	Ɛ32 880	5X2	X	247 X68	281
Ɛ	876 704	8Ɛ8	Ɛ	ƐX0 262	594	Ɛ	2Ɛ5 129	273
8610	924 400	8XX	8650	X43 049 836	586	8690	362 3X0	266
1	992 0XX	8X1	1	0Ɛ7 200	579	1	40Ɛ 646	258
2	X3Ɛ 98Ɛ	893	2	164 779	570	2	478 8X2	24Ɛ
3	XX9 662	885	3	212 129	561	3	525 Ɛ31	241
4	Ɛ57 327	878	4	27Ɛ 68X	555	4	593 172	234
5	X41 004 ƐX3	86X	5	329 023	546	5	640 3X6	226
6	072 851	861	6	396 569	53X	6	6X9 610	219
7	120 4Ɛ2	852	7	443 XX7	52Ɛ	7	756 829	20Ɛ
8	18X 144	846	8	4Ɛ1 416	523	8	803 X38	202
9	237 98X	838	9	55X 939	514	9	871 03X	1Ɛ5
X	2X5 606	82X	X	608 251	507	X	91X 233	1X7
Ɛ	353 234	820	Ɛ	675 758	4ƐX	Ɛ	987 41X	199
8620	400 X54	813	8660	723 056	4Ɛ0	86X0	X34 5Ɛ7	190
1	46X 667	806	1	790 546	4X2	1	XX1 787	183
2	518 271	7Ɛ7	2	839 X28	495	2	Ɛ4X 94X	175
3	585 X68	7XƐ	3	8X7 301	488	3	ƐƐ7 Ɛ03	167
4	633 657	7X0	4	954 789	47X	4	X46 065 06X	15Ɛ
5	6X1 237	793	5	X02 047	470	5	112 209	150
6	74X X0X	786	6	X6Ɛ 4Ɛ7	463	6	17Ɛ 359	144
7	7Ɛ8 594	778	7	Ɛ18 95X	455	7	228 4X1	135
8	866 150	76X	8	Ɛ86 1Ɛ3	448	8	295 616	129
9	913 8ƐX	761	9	X44 033 63Ɛ	43X	9	342 743	11Ɛ
X	981 45Ɛ	753	X	0X0 X79	431	X	3XƐ 862	111
Ɛ	X2X ƐƐ2	745	Ɛ	14X 2XX	423	Ɛ	458 973	104
8630	X98 737	738	8670	1Ɛ7 711	416	86Ɛ0	505 X77	0Ɛ6
1	Ɛ46 273	72Ɛ	1	264 Ɛ27	408	1	572 Ɛ71	0X9
2	ƐƐ3 9X2	720	2	312 333	3ƐƐ	2	620 05X	0X0
3	X42 061 502	714	3	37Ɛ 732	3Ɛ1	3	689 13X	092
4	10Ɛ 016	705	4	428 Ɛ23	3X4	4	736 210	085
5	178 71Ɛ	6Ɛ8	5	496 307	396	5	7X3 295	077
6	226 217	6XƐ	6	543 6X1	389	6	850 350	06X
7	293 906	6X1	7	5Ɛ0 X6X	37Ɛ	7	8Ɛ9 3ƐX	060
8	341 3X7	693	8	65X 229	372	8	966 45X	053
9	3XX X7X	686	9	707 59Ɛ	364	9	X13 4Ɛ1	046
X	458 544	678	X	774 943	356	X	X80 537	038
Ɛ	506 000	66Ɛ	Ɛ	822 099	34X	Ɛ	Ɛ29 573	02X

N	Log N	d	N	Log N	d	N	Log N	d
8700	X46 Ɛ96 5X1	69 021	8740	X49 291 055	68 905	8780	X4Ɛ 577 101	68 5Ɛ1
1	X47 043 602	014	1	339 95X	8Ɛ8	1	623 6Ɛ2	5X3
2	0Ɛ0 616	006	2	3X6 656	8XƐ	2	690 095	597
3	159 620	68 ƐƐ9	3	453 345	8X2	3	738 670	589
4	206 619	ƐƐ0	4	500 027	894	4	7X5 039	57Ɛ
5	273 609	ƐX2	5	568 8ƐƐ	887	5	851 5Ɛ8	573
6	320 5XƐ	Ɛ94	6	615 586	879	6	8Ɛ9 Ɛ6Ɛ	565
7	389 583	Ɛ87	7	682 243	870	7	966 514	557
8	436 54X	Ɛ7X	8	72X XƐ3	862	8	X12 X6Ɛ	54Ɛ
9	4X3 508	Ɛ70	9	797 755	856	9	X7Ɛ 3ƐX	541
X	550 478	Ɛ63	X	844 3XƐ	847	X	Ɛ27 93Ɛ	534
Ɛ	5Ɛ9 41Ɛ	Ɛ55	Ɛ	8Ɛ1 036	83Ɛ	Ɛ	Ɛ94 273	526
8710	666 374	Ɛ48	8750	959 875	831	8790	X50 040 799	519
1	713 300	Ɛ3Ɛ	1	X06 4X6	824	1	0X9 0Ɛ6	510
2	780 23Ɛ	Ɛ31	2	X73 10X	816	2	155 606	503
3	829 170	Ɛ24	3	Ɛ1Ɛ 924	809	3	201 Ɛ09	4Ɛ5
4	896 094	Ɛ16	4	Ɛ88 531	800	4	26X 402	4X8
5	942 ƐXX	Ɛ09	5	X4X 035 131	7Ɛ2	5	316 8XX	49Ɛ
6	9XƐ XƐ7	Ɛ00	6	0X1 923	7X5	6	383 189	491
7	X58 9Ɛ7	XƐ2	7	14X 508	798	7	42Ɛ 65X	484
8	Ɛ05 8X9	XX4	8	1Ɛ7 0X4	78X	8	497 Ɛ22	477
9	Ɛ72 791	X97	9	263 872	781	9	544 399	469
X	X48 01Ɛ 668	X8X	X	310 433	774	X	5Ɛ0 846	461
Ɛ	088 536	X81	Ɛ	378 ƐX7	766	Ɛ	659 0X7	453
8720	135 3Ɛ7	X73	8760	425 751	759	87X0	705 53X	445
1	1X2 26X	X65	1	492 2XX	74Ɛ	1	771 983	439
2	24Ɛ 113	X58	2	53X X39	743	2	81X 200	42Ɛ
3	2Ɛ7 Ɛ6Ɛ	X4Ɛ	3	5X7 580	734	3	886 62Ɛ	421
4	364 9ƐX	X42	4	654 0Ɛ4	728	4	932 X50	415
5	411 840	X34	5	700 820	71X	5	99Ɛ 265	407
6	47X 674	X26	6	769 33X	711	6	X47 670	3ƐX
7	527 49X	X19	7	815 X4Ɛ	703	7	XƐ3 X6X	3Ɛ1
8	594 2Ɛ7	X10	8	882 552	6Ɛ6	8	Ɛ60 25Ɛ	3X3
9	641 107	X02	9	92Ɛ 048	6X9	9	X51 008 642	396
X	6X9 Ɛ09	9Ɛ5	X	997 735	6X0	X	074 X18	389
Ɛ	756 902	9X8	Ɛ	X44 215	692	Ɛ	121 1X5	380
8730	803 6XX	99X	8770	XƐ0 8X7	685	87Ɛ0	189 565	372
1	870 488	991	1	Ɛ59 370	677	1	235 917	365
2	919 259	983	2	X4Ɛ 005 X27	66X	2	2X2 080	358
3	986 020	976	3	072 495	661	3	34X 418	34X
4	X32 996	969	4	11X Ɛ36	654	4	3Ɛ6 766	341
5	X9Ɛ 743	95Ɛ	5	187 58X	646	5	462 XX7	334
6	Ɛ48 4X2	952	6	234 014	639	6	50Ɛ 21Ɛ	327
7	ƐƐ5 234	945	7	2X0 651	62Ɛ	7	577 546	319
8	X49 061 Ɛ79	937	8	349 080	622	8	623 863	311
9	10X 8Ɛ4	929	9	3Ɛ5 6X2	615	9	68Ɛ Ɛ74	302
X	177 621	921	X	462 0Ɛ7	608	X	738 276	2Ɛ6
Ɛ	224 342	913	Ɛ	50X 703	5ƐX	Ɛ	7X4 570	2X8

N	Log N	d	N	Log N	d	N	Log N	d
8800	χ51 850 858	68 2χ0	8840	χ53 Ɛ15 Ɛ99	67 Ɛ90	8880	χ56 18χ Ɛ26	67 884
1	8Ɛ8 Ɛ38	291	1	Ɛ81 Ɛ69	Ɛ83	1	236 87χ	877
2	965 209	285	2	χ54 029 Ɛ30	Ɛ76	2	2χ2 535	86χ
3	χ11 492	277	3	095 χχ6	Ɛ68	3	34χ 1χ3	861
4	χ79 749	26χ	4	141 χ52	Ɛ60	4	3Ɛ5 χ44	853
5	Ɛ25 9Ɛ7	261	5	1χ9 9Ɛ2	Ɛ52	5	461 697	846
6	Ɛ92 058	254	6	255 944	Ɛ45	6	509 321	83χ
7	χ52 03χ 2Ɛ0	246	7	301 889	Ɛ38	7	574 25Ɛ	830
8	0χ6 536	239	8	369 805	Ɛ2χ	8	620 78Ɛ	823
9	152 773	230	9	415 733	Ɛ22	9	688 3Ɛ2	815
χ	1Ɛχ 9χ3	223	χ	481 655	Ɛ14	χ	734 007	809
Ɛ	267 006	215	Ɛ	529 569	Ɛ07	Ɛ	79Ɛ 814	800
8810	313 21Ɛ	208	8850	595 474	χƐχ	8890	847 414	7Ɛ2
1	37Ɛ 427	1ƐƐ	1	641 372	χƐ1	1	8Ɛ3 006	7χ5
2	427 626	1Ɛ2	2	6χ9 263	χχ3	2	95χ 7χƐ	799
3	493 818	1χ4	3	755 146	χ96	3	χ06 388	78Ɛ
4	53Ɛ χ00	197	4	801 020	χ89	4	χ71 Ɛ57	782
5	5χ7 Ɛ97	18χ	5	868 χχ9	χ80	5	Ɛ19 719	774
6	654 165	181	6	914 969	χ73	6	Ɛ85 291	768
7	700 326	173	7	980 820	χ66	7	χ57 030 χ39	75Ɛ
8	768 499	166	8	χ28 686	χ58	8	098 598	751
9	814 643	159	9	χ94 522	χ4Ɛ	9	144 129	745
χ	880 7χ0	150	χ	Ɛ40 371	χ43	χ	1χƐ 872	737
Ɛ	928 930	143	Ɛ	Ɛχ8 1Ɛ4	χ34	Ɛ	257 3χ9	72χ
8820	994 χ73	135	8860	χ55 054 028	χ28	88χ0	302 Ɛ17	721
1	χ40 Ɛχ8	128	1	0ƐƐ χ54	χ1Ɛ	1	36χ 638	714
2	χχ9 114	11Ɛ	2	167 873	χ11	2	416 150	707
3	Ɛ55 233	111	3	213 684	χ04	3	481 857	6Ɛ9
4	χ53 001 344	105	4	27Ɛ 488	9Ɛ8	4	529 354	6Ɛ1
5	069 449	0Ɛ7	5	327 284	9χ9	5	594 χ45	6χ3
6	115 544	0χχ	6	393 071	9χ1	6	640 528	697
7	181 632	0χ0	7	43χ χ52	994	7	6χ8 003	689
8	229 712	094	8	4χ6 826	986	8	753 690	680
9	295 7χ6	086	9	552 5Ɛ0	979	9	7ƐƐ 150	673
χ	341 870	079	χ	5Ɛχ 369	971	χ	866 803	666
Ɛ	3χ9 929	070	Ɛ	666 11χ	963	Ɛ	912 269	659
8830	455 999	063	8870	711 χ81	955	88Ɛ0	979 906	650
1	501 χ40	055	1	779 816	949	1	χ25 356	643
2	569 χ95	048	2	825 563	93Ɛ	2	χ90 999	635
3	615 Ɛ21	03Ɛ	3	891 2χ2	933	3	Ɛ38 412	629
4	681 Ɛ60	032	4	939 015	925	4	Ɛχ3 χ3Ɛ	61Ɛ
5	729 Ɛ92	025	5	9χ4 93χ	918	5	χ58 04Ɛ 45χ	612
6	795 ƐƐ7	017	6	χ50 656	90Ɛ	6	0Ɛ6 χ70	606
7	842 012	00χ	7	χƐ8 365	902	7	162 476	5Ɛ8
8	8χχ 020	001	8	Ɛ64 067	8Ɛ4	8	209 χ72	5χƐ
9	956 021	67 ƐƐ4	9	χ56 00Ɛ 95Ɛ	8χ8	9	275 461	5χ2
χ	χ02 015	Ɛχ7	χ	077 647	89χ	χ	320 χ43	595
Ɛ	χ6χ 000	Ɛ99	Ɛ	123 325	891	Ɛ	388 418	587

N	Log N	d	N	Log N	d	N	Log N	d
8900	X58 433 9X3	67 57Ɛ	8940	X5X 688 652	67 278	8980	X60 911 271	66 Ɛ79
1	49Ɛ 362	572	1	733 90X	26Ɛ	1	978 22X	Ɛ6Ɛ
2	546 914	564	2	79X Ɛ79	262	2	X23 199	Ɛ63
3	5Ɛ2 278	558	3	846 21Ɛ	255	3	X8X 140	Ɛ55
4	659 814	54X	4	8Ɛ1 474	248	4	Ɛ35 095	Ɛ48
5	705 162	541	5	958 700	23Ɛ	5	ƐX0 021	Ɛ40
6	770 6X3	535	6	X03 93Ɛ	232	6	X61 046 Ɛ61	Ɛ32
7	818 018	527	7	X6X Ɛ71	225	7	0Ɛ1 X93	Ɛ26
8	883 543	51X	8	Ɛ16 196	218	8	158 9Ɛ9	Ɛ19
9	92X X61	511	9	Ɛ81 3Ɛ2	20Ɛ	9	203 916	Ɛ0Ɛ
X	996 372	504	X	X5Ɛ 028 601	202	X	26X 825	Ɛ03
Ɛ	X41 876	4Ɛ7	Ɛ	093 803	1Ɛ5	Ɛ	315 728	XƐ6
8910	XX9 171	4X9	8950	13X 9Ɛ8	1X8	8990	380 622	XX8
1	Ɛ54 65X	4X1	1	1X5 ƐX4	19Ɛ	1	427 50X	XX0
2	ƐƐƐ Ɛ3Ɛ	494	2	251 183	192	2	492 3XX	X93
3	X59 067 413	486	3	2Ɛ8 355	185	3	539 281	X86
4	112 899	47X	4	363 51X	178	4	5X4 147	X79
5	17X 157	470	5	40X 696	16X	5	64Ɛ 004	X70
6	225 607	464	6	475 844	162	6	6Ɛ5 X74	X63
7	290 X6Ɛ	456	7	520 9X6	155	7	760 917	X56
8	338 305	44X	8	587 Ɛ3Ɛ	148	8	807 771	X4X
9	3X3 753	440	9	633 087	13Ɛ	9	872 5ƐƐ	X40
X	44X Ɛ93	433	X	69X 206	132	X	919 43Ɛ	X33
Ɛ	4Ɛ6 406	426	Ɛ	745 338	125	Ɛ	984 272	X26
8920	561 830	419	8960	7Ɛ0 461	118	89X0	X2Ɛ 098	X1X
1	609 049	410	1	857 579	10X	1	X95 XƐ6	X10
2	674 459	403	2	902 687	102	2	Ɛ40 906	X04
3	71Ɛ 860	3Ɛ6	3	969 789	0Ɛ5	3	ƐX7 70X	9Ɛ6
4	787 056	3X9	4	X14 882	0X8	4	X62 052 504	9XX
5	832 443	3X0	5	X7Ɛ 96X	09Ɛ	5	0Ɛ9 2Ɛ2	9X1
6	899 823	393	6	Ɛ26 X49	092	6	164 093	994
7	944 ƐƐ6	385	7	Ɛ91 Ɛ1Ɛ	085	7	20X X67	987
8	9Ɛ0 37Ɛ	379	8	X60 038 ƐX4	078	8	275 832	97X
9	X57 738	370	9	0X4 060	06Ɛ	9	320 5Ɛ0	971
X	Ɛ02 XX8	362	X	14Ɛ 10Ɛ	062	X	387 361	964
Ɛ	Ɛ6X 24X	356	Ɛ	1Ɛ6 171	055	Ɛ	432 105	957
8930	X5X 015 5X4	348	8970	261 206	048	89Ɛ0	498 X60	94X
1	080 930	340	1	308 252	03Ɛ	1	543 7XX	941
2	128 070	332	2	373 291	032	2	5XX 52Ɛ	935
3	193 3X2	326	3	41X 303	025	3	655 264	927
4	23X 708	318	4	485 328	018	4	6ƐƐ Ɛ8Ɛ	91Ɛ
5	2X5 X24	30Ɛ	5	530 344	00Ɛ	5	766 8XX	911
6	351 133	303	6	597 353	002	6	811 5ƐƐ	905
7	3Ɛ8 436	2Ɛ5	7	642 355	66 ƐƐ6	7	878 304	8Ɛ8
8	463 72Ɛ	2X8	8	6X9 34Ɛ	ƐX8	8	923 000	8XƐ
9	50X X17	29Ɛ	9	754 337	Ɛ9Ɛ	9	989 8XƐ	8X2
X	576 0Ɛ6	293	X	7ƐƐ 316	Ɛ92	X	X34 591	895
Ɛ	621 389	285	Ɛ	866 2X8	Ɛ85	Ɛ	X9Ɛ 266	888

N	Log N	d	N	Log N	d	N	Log N	d
8X00	X62 Ɛ45 Ɛ32	66 87Ɛ	8X40	X65 16X 940	66 585	8X80	X67 383 985	66 291
1	ƐƐ0 7Ɛ1	872	1	215 305	578	1	42X 056	285
2	X63 057 463	866	2	27Ɛ 881	56Ɛ	2	494 31Ɛ	277
3	102 109	858	3	326 230	562	3	53X 596	26Ɛ
4	168 965	850	4	390 792	556	4	5X4 845	262
5	213 5Ɛ5	842	5	437 128	548	5	64X XX7	255
6	27X 237	836	6	4X1 674	540	6	6Ɛ5 140	248
7	324 X71	829	7	547 ƐƐ4	533	7	75Ɛ 388	23Ɛ
8	38Ɛ 69X	820	8	5Ɛ2 527	526	8	805 607	233
9	436 2ƐX	813	9	658 X51	519	9	86Ɛ 83X	226
X	4X0 Ɛ11	806	X	703 36X	510	X	915 X64	219
Ɛ	547 717	7Ɛ9	Ɛ	769 87X	504	Ɛ	980 081	210
8X10	5Ɛ2 314	7Ɛ1	8X50	814 182	4Ɛ6	8X90	X26 291	204
1	658 Ɛ05	7X3	1	87X 678	4XX	1	X90 495	1Ɛ7
2	703 6X8	797	2	924 Ɛ66	4X1	2	Ɛ36 690	1XX
3	76X 283	789	3	98Ɛ 447	494	3	ƐX0 87X	1X1
4	814 X50	781	4	X35 91Ɛ	487	4	X68 046 X5Ɛ	194
5	87Ɛ 611	774	5	XX0 1X6	47Ɛ	5	0Ɛ1 033	188
6	926 185	767	6	Ɛ46 665	471	6	157 1ƐƐ	17Ɛ
7	990 930	75X	7	ƐƐ0 Ɛ16	465	7	201 37X	172
8	X37 48X	751	8	X66 057 37Ɛ	458	8	267 530	165
9	XX2 01Ɛ	745	9	101 817	44Ɛ	9	311 695	158
X	Ɛ48 764	737	X	168 066	442	X	377 831	150
Ɛ	ƐƐ3 29Ɛ	72Ɛ	Ɛ	212 4X8	436	Ɛ	421 981	143
8X20	X64 059 X0X	721	8X60	278 922	428	8XX0	487 Ɛ04	136
1	104 52Ɛ	715	1	323 14X	420	1	532 03X	129
2	16Ɛ 044	708	2	389 56X	413	2	598 167	121
3	215 750	6ƐƐ	3	433 981	406	3	642 288	114
4	280 24Ɛ	6Ɛ2	4	49X 187	3Ɛ9	4	6X8 3X0	107
5	326 941	6X5	5	544 584	3Ɛ1	5	752 4X7	0ƐX
6	391 426	699	6	5XX 975	3X3	6	7Ɛ8 5X5	0Ɛ2
7	437 Ɛ03	68Ɛ	7	655 158	397	7	862 697	0X5
8	4X2 592	683	8	6ƐƐ 533	38X	8	908 780	098
9	549 055	676	9	765 901	381	9	972 858	08Ɛ
X	5Ɛ3 70Ɛ	669	X	810 082	375	X	X18 927	082
Ɛ	65X 178	660	Ɛ	876 437	367	Ɛ	X82 9X9	076
8X30	704 818	653	8X70	920 7X2	35Ɛ	8XƐ0	Ɛ28 X63	069
1	76Ɛ 26Ɛ	646	1	986 Ɛ41	352	1	Ɛ92 Ɛ10	060
2	815 8Ɛ5	639	2	X31 293	345	2	X69 038 Ɛ70	054
3	880 332	631	3	X97 618	338	3	0X3 004	046
4	926 963	624	4	Ɛ41 954	330	4	149 04X	03X
5	991 387	616	5	ƐX8 084	322	5	1Ɛ3 088	031
6	X37 9X1	60X	6	X67 052 3X6	316	6	259 0Ɛ9	025
7	XX2 3XƐ	601	7	0Ɛ8 700	309	7	303 122	018
8	Ɛ48 9Ɛ0	5Ɛ5	8	162 X09	301	8	369 13X	00X
9	ƐƐ3 3X5	5X7	9	209 10X	2Ɛ3	9	413 148	003
X	X65 059 990	59Ɛ	X	273 401	2X7	X	479 14Ɛ	65 ƐƐ5
Ɛ	104 36Ɛ	591	Ɛ	319 6X8	299	Ɛ	523 144	ƐX9

N	Log N	d	N	Log N	d	N	Log N	d
8Ɛ00	χ69 589 131	65 Ɛχ0	8Ɛ40	χ6Ɛ 782 8χ4	65 8Ɛ2	8Ɛ80	χ71 968 949	65 606
1	633 111	Ɛ93	1	828 596	8χ4	1	χ12 353	5Ɛ8
2	699 0χ4	Ɛ86	2	892 27χ	899	2	χ77 94Ɛ	5Ɛ1
3	743 06χ	Ɛ7χ	3	937 Ɛ57	88Ɛ	3	Ɛ21 340	5χ3
4	7χ9 028	Ɛ71	4	9χ1 826	883	4	Ɛ86 923	597
5	852 Ɛ99	Ɛ64	5	χ47 4χ9	876	5	χ72 030 2Ɛχ	58Ɛ
6	8Ɛ8 Ɛ41	Ɛ58	6	χƐ1 163	869	6	095 889	581
7	962 χ99	Ɛ4χ	7	Ɛ56 χ10	860	7	13Ɛ 24χ	575
8	χ08 χ27	Ɛ42	8	χ70 000 670	854	8	1χ4 803	569
9	χ72 969	Ɛ36	9	066 304	848	9	24χ 170	560
χ	Ɛ18 8χ3	Ɛ28	χ	10Ɛ Ɛ50	83χ	χ	2Ɛ3 710	553
Ɛ	Ɛ82 80Ɛ	Ɛ20	Ɛ	175 78χ	832	Ɛ	359 063	547
8Ɛ10	χ6χ 028 72Ɛ	Ɛ13	8Ɛ50	21Ɛ 400	825	8Ɛ90	402 5χχ	53χ
1	092 642	Ɛ06	1	285 025	819	1	467 Ɛ28	531
2	138 548	χƐχ	2	32χ 842	810	2	511 459	525
3	1χ2 446	χƐ1	3	394 452	803	3	576 982	518
4	248 337	χχ4	4	43χ 055	7Ɛ6	4	620 29χ	50Ɛ
5	2Ɛ2 21Ɛ	χ97	5	4χ3 84Ɛ	7χχ	5	685 7χ9	503
6	358 0Ɛ6	χ8Ɛ	6	549 439	7χ1	6	72Ɛ 0Ɛ0	4Ɛ6
7	401 Ɛ85	χ82	7	5Ɛ3 01χ	795	7	794 5χ6	4χχ
8	467 χ47	χ75	8	658 7Ɛ3	788	8	839 χ94	4χ1
9	511 900	χ69	9	702 37Ɛ	77Ɛ	9	8χ3 375	494
χ	577 769	χ60	χ	767 Ɛ3χ	772	χ	948 849	488
Ɛ	621 609	χ53	Ɛ	811 6Ɛ0	766	Ɛ	9Ɛ2 115	47Ɛ
8Ɛ20	687 460	χ46	8Ɛ60	877 256	759	8Ɛχ0	χ57 594	473
1	731 2χ6	χ3χ	1	920 9Ɛ3	751	1	Ɛ00 χ47	466
2	797 124	χ31	2	986 544	744	2	Ɛ66 2Ɛ1	459
3	840 Ɛ55	χ24	3	χ30 088	737	3	χ73 00Ɛ 74χ	451
4	8χ6 979	χ17	4	χ95 803	72χ	4	074 Ɛ9Ɛ	444
5	950 794	χ0Ɛ	5	Ɛ3Ɛ 331	722	5	11χ 423	437
6	9Ɛ6 5χ3	χ02	6	Ɛχ4 χ53	715	6	183 85χ	42Ɛ
7	χ60 3χ5	9Ɛ5	7	χ71 04χ 568	709	7	229 089	422
8	Ɛ06 19χ	9χ9	8	0Ɛ4 075	700	8	292 4χƐ	416
9	Ɛ6Ɛ Ɛ87	9χ0	9	159 775	6Ɛ3	9	337 905	409
χ	χ6Ɛ 015 967	993	χ	203 268	6χ7	χ	3χ1 112	401
Ɛ	07Ɛ 73χ	987	Ɛ	268 953	69χ	Ɛ	446 513	3Ɛ4
8Ɛ30	125 505	97χ	8Ɛ70	312 431	691	8ƐƐ0	4χƐ 907	3χ7
1	18Ɛ 283	971	1	377 Ɛ02	684	1	555 0Ɛ2	39Ɛ
2	235 034	964	2	421 586	678	2	5Ɛχ 491	392
3	29χ 998	958	3	487 042	670	3	663 863	385
4	344 734	94Ɛ	4	530 6Ɛ2	662	4	709 028	379
5	3χχ 483	942	5	596 154	656	5	772 3χ5	370
6	454 205	936	6	63Ɛ 7χχ	64χ	6	817 755	364
7	4Ɛ9 Ɛ3Ɛ	929	7	6χ5 238	641	7	880 χƐ9	357
8	563 868	920	8	74χ 879	634	8	926 254	34Ɛ
9	609 588	913	9	7Ɛ4 2Ɛ1	627	9	98Ɛ 5χ3	342
χ	673 29Ɛ	907	χ	859 918	61Ɛ	χ	χ34 925	335
Ɛ	718 Ɛχ6	8Ɛχ	Ɛ	903 337	612	Ɛ	χ9χ 05χ	329

N	Log N	d	N	Log N	d	N	Log N	d
9000	Ӿ73 Ɛ43 387	65 320	9040	Ӿ76 10Ӿ 480	65 03Ӿ	9080	Ӿ78 286 113	64 959
1	ƐӾ8 6Ӿ7	314	1	173 4ƐӾ	031	1	32Ӿ Ӿ70	951
2	Ӿ74 051 9ƐƐ	307	2	218 52Ɛ	024	2	393 801	944
3	0Ɛ7 106	2ƐӾ	3	281 553	018	3	438 545	938
4	160 404	2Ɛ2	4	326 56Ɛ	00Ɛ	4	4Ӿ1 281	92Ɛ
5	205 6Ɛ6	2Ӿ5	5	38Ɛ 57Ӿ	003	5	545 Ɛ20	923
6	26Ӿ 99Ɛ	299	6	434 581	64 ƐƐ6	6	5ӾӾ 913	916
7	314 078	290	7	499 577	ƐӾӾ	7	653 629	90Ӿ
8	379 348	284	8	542 565	ƐӾ1	8	6Ɛ8 337	901
9	422 610	277	9	5Ӿ7 546	Ɛ94	9	761 038	8Ɛ5
Ӿ	487 887	26Ӿ	Ӿ	650 51Ӿ	Ɛ89	Ӿ	805 931	8Ӿ8
Ɛ	530 Ɛ35	262	Ɛ	6Ɛ5 4Ӿ7	Ɛ7Ɛ	Ɛ	86Ӿ 619	8Ӿ0
9010	596 197	255	9050	75Ӿ 466	Ɛ73	9090	913 2Ɛ9	893
1	63Ɛ 430	249	1	803 419	Ɛ67	1	977 Ɛ90	887
2	6Ӿ4 679	240	2	868 384	Ɛ5Ӿ	2	Ӿ20 857	87Ɛ
3	749 8Ɛ9	233	3	911 322	Ɛ51	3	Ӿ85 516	872
4	7Ɛ2 Ɛ30	227	4	976 273	Ɛ46	4	Ɛ2Ӿ 188	866
5	858 157	21Ɛ	5	Ӿ1Ɛ 1Ɛ9	Ɛ38	5	Ɛ92 Ӿ32	859
6	901 376	212	6	Ӿ84 135	Ɛ30	6	Ӿ79 037 68Ɛ	850
7	966 588	205	7	Ɛ29 065	Ɛ24	7	0Ӿ0 31Ɛ	845
8	Ӿ0Ɛ 791	1Ɛ9	8	Ɛ91 Ɛ89	Ɛ16	8	144 Ɛ64	837
9	Ӿ74 98Ӿ	1Ɛ0	9	Ӿ77 036 ӾӾ3	Ɛ0Ɛ	9	1Ӿ9 79Ɛ	830
Ӿ	Ɛ19 Ɛ7Ӿ	1Ӿ3	Ӿ	09Ɛ 9Ɛ2	Ɛ02	Ӿ	252 40Ɛ	823
Ɛ	Ɛ83 161	197	Ɛ	144 8Ɛ4	ӾƐ5	Ɛ	2Ɛ7 032	816
9020	Ӿ75 028 338	18Ɛ	9060	1Ӿ9 7Ӿ9	ӾӾ9	90Ӿ0	35Ɛ 848	80Ӿ
1	091 507	182	1	252 696	ӾӾ1	1	404 456	801
2	136 689	175	2	2Ɛ7 577	Ӿ94	2	469 057	7Ɛ5
3	19Ɛ 842	169	3	360 44Ɛ	Ӿ87	3	511 850	7Ӿ9
4	244 9ӾƐ	160	4	405 316	Ӿ7Ɛ	4	576 439	7Ӿ0
5	2Ӿ9 Ɛ4Ɛ	154	5	46Ӿ 195	Ӿ73	5	61Ɛ 019	794
6	353 0Ӿ3	147	6	513 048	Ӿ65	6	683 7Ɛ1	787
7	3Ɛ8 22Ӿ	13Ɛ	7	577 Ӿ21	Ӿ5Ӿ	7	728 378	77Ɛ
8	461 369	132	8	620 94Ɛ	Ӿ51	8	790 Ɛ37	772
9	506 49Ɛ	125	9	685 7Ӿ0	Ӿ44	9	835 6Ӿ9	766
Ӿ	56Ɛ 604	119	Ӿ	72Ӿ 624	Ӿ38	Ӿ	89Ӿ 253	759
Ɛ	614 721	111	Ɛ	793 460	Ӿ30	Ɛ	942 9Ɛ0	751
9030	679 832	103	9070	838 290	Ӿ23	90Ɛ0	9Ӿ7 541	745
1	722 935	0Ɛ8	1	8Ӿ1 0Ɛ3	Ӿ16	1	Ӿ50 086	738
2	787 Ӿ31	0ӾƐ	2	945 Ɛ09	Ӿ0Ӿ	2	ӾƐ4 802	730
3	830 Ɛ20	0Ӿ2	3	9ӾӾ 917	Ӿ02	3	Ɛ59 332	723
4	896 002	095	4	Ӿ53 719	9Ɛ5	4	Ӿ7Ӿ 001 Ӿ55	717
5	93Ɛ 097	08Ӿ	5	ӾƐ8 512	9Ӿ8	5	066 570	70Ӿ
6	9Ӿ4 165	080	6	Ɛ61 2ƐӾ	9Ӿ0	6	10Ɛ 07Ӿ	702
7	Ӿ49 225	074	7	Ӿ78 006 09Ӿ	994	7	173 780	6Ɛ6
8	ӾƐ2 299	068	8	06Ӿ Ӿ72	987	8	218 276	6Ӿ9
9	Ɛ57 345	05Ɛ	9	113 839	97Ӿ	9	280 963	6Ӿ0
Ӿ	Ӿ76 000 3Ӿ4	052	Ӿ	178 5Ɛ7	972	Ӿ	325 443	694
Ɛ	065 436	046	Ɛ	221 369	966	Ɛ	389 Ɛ17	688

N	Log N	d	N	Log N	d	N	Log N	d
9100	X7X 432 5X3	64 680	9140	X80 58Ɛ 791	64 3X4	9180	X82 719 775	64 10Ɛ
1	497 063	673	1	633 Ɛ75	397	1	781 884	103
2	53Ɛ 716	666	2	698 350	390	2	825 987	0Ɛ7
3	5X4 180	65X	3	740 720	382	3	889 X82	0XX
4	648 81X	652	4	7X4 XX2	377	4	931 Ɛ70	0X2
5	6Ɛ1 270	645	5	849 259	36X	5	996 052	095
6	755 8Ɛ5	639	6	8Ɛ1 607	362	6	X3X 127	08X
7	7ƐX 332	630	7	955 969	355	7	XX2 1Ɛ5	081
8	862 962	624	8	9ƐX 102	349	8	Ɛ46 276	074
9	907 386	618	9	X62 44Ɛ	341	9	ƐXX 32X	068
X	96Ɛ 9X2	60Ɛ	X	Ɛ06 790	335	X	X83 052 396	060
Ɛ	X14 3Ɛ1	602	Ɛ	Ɛ6X Ɛ05	327	Ɛ	0Ɛ6 436	054
9110	X78 9Ɛ3	5Ɛ7	9150	X81 013 230	320	9190	15X 48X	047
1	Ɛ21 3XX	5XX	1	077 550	313	1	202 515	040
2	Ɛ85 998	5X1	2	11Ɛ 863	307	2	266 555	032
3	X7Ɛ 02X 379	595	3	183 Ɛ6X	2ƐƐ	3	30X 587	027
4	092 952	589	4	228 269	2Ɛ2	4	372 5Ɛ2	01X
5	137 31Ɛ	580	5	290 55Ɛ	2X6	5	416 610	012
6	19Ɛ 89Ɛ	574	6	334 845	299	6	47X 622	005
7	244 253	567	7	398 Ɛ22	291	7	522 627	63 ƐƐ9
8	2X8 7ƐX	55Ɛ	8	441 1Ɛ3	285	8	586 624	ƐƐ1
9	351 159	553	9	4X5 478	278	9	62X 615	ƐX5
X	3Ɛ5 6Ɛ0	546	X	549 734	270	X	692 5ƐX	Ɛ98
Ɛ	45X 036	53X	Ɛ	5Ɛ1 9X4	264	Ɛ	736 596	Ɛ90
9120	502 574	531	9160	656 048	257	91X0	79X 566	Ɛ84
1	566 XX5	525	1	6ƐX 2X3	24Ɛ	1	842 52X	Ɛ77
2	60Ɛ 40X	519	2	762 532	243	2	8X6 4X5	Ɛ6Ɛ
3	673 927	510	3	806 775	236	3	94X 454	Ɛ63
4	718 237	504	4	86X 9XƐ	22X	4	9Ɛ2 3Ɛ7	Ɛ56
5	780 73Ɛ	4Ɛ7	5	913 019	222	5	X56 351	Ɛ4Ɛ
6	825 036	4XƐ	6	977 23Ɛ	215	6	XƐX 2X0	Ɛ42
7	889 525	4X3	7	X1Ɛ 454	209	7	Ɛ62 222	Ɛ35
8	931 X08	496	8	X83 661	200	8	X84 006 157	Ɛ2X
9	996 2X2	48X	9	Ɛ27 861	1Ɛ5	9	06X 085	Ɛ21
X	X3X 770	481	X	Ɛ8Ɛ X56	1X7	X	111 ƐX6	Ɛ14
Ɛ	XX3 031	475	Ɛ	X82 034 041	1X0	Ɛ	175 XƐX	Ɛ09
9130	Ɛ47 4X6	469	9170	098 221	193	91Ɛ0	219 X07	Ɛ00
1	ƐXƐ 953	460	1	140 3Ɛ4	187	1	281 907	XƐ4
2	X80 054 1Ɛ3	454	2	1X4 57Ɛ	17X	2	325 7ƐƐ	XX7
3	0Ɛ8 647	447	3	248 739	173	3	389 6X6	XX0
4	160 X92	440	4	2Ɛ0 8Ɛ0	165	4	431 586	X93
5	205 312	432	5	354 X55	15X	5	495 459	X86
6	269 744	427	6	3Ɛ8 ƐƐ3	151	6	539 323	X7Ɛ
7	311 Ɛ6Ɛ	41X	7	461 144	145	7	5X1 1X2	X72
8	376 389	411	8	505 289	138	8	645 054	X66
9	41X 79X	405	9	569 405	131	9	6X8 XƐX	X59
X	482 ƐX3	3Ɛ9	X	611 536	123	X	750 957	X52
Ɛ	527 3X0	3Ɛ1	Ɛ	675 659	118	Ɛ	7Ɛ4 7X9	X45

N	Log N	d	N	Log N	d	N	Log N	d
9200	↊84 858 632	63 ↊39	9240	↊86 988 45↋	63 769	9280	↊88 ↊↊9 314	63 49↋
1	900 46↋	↊30	1	↊30 008	760	1	↋50 7↋3	493
2	964 29↋	↊24	2	↊93 768	755	2	↋↋4 086	487
3	↊08 103	↊18	3	↋37 301	748	3	↊89 057 551	47↊
4	↊6↋ ↋1↋	↊10	4	↋9↊ ↊49	740	4	0↋↊ ↊0↋	473
5	↋13 92↋	↊03	5	↊87 042 589	733	5	162 282	466
6	↋77 732	9↋7	6	0↊6 100	728	6	205 728	45↊
7	↊85 01↋ 529	9↊↋	7	149 828	71↋	7	268 ↋86	452
8	083 318	9↊3	8	1↋1 347	713	8	310 418	446
9	127 0↋↋	996	9	254 ↊5↊	707	9	373 862	439
↊	18↊ ↊95	98↊	↊	2↋8 565	6↋↊	↊	417 09↋	432
↋	232 863	982	↋	360 063	6↋3	↋	47↊ 511	425
9210	296 625	976	9250	403 756	6↊6	9290	521 936	419
1	33↊ 39↋	969	1	467 240	69↊	1	585 153	411
2	3↊2 148	961	2	50↊ 91↊	691	2	628 564	405
3	445 ↊↊9	955	3	572 3↊↋	686	3	68↋ 969	3↋8
4	4↊9 842	948	4	615 ↊75	679	4	733 165	3↋1
5	551 58↊	941	5	679 532	671	5	796 556	3↊4
6	5↋5 30↋	934	6	720 ↋↊3	665	6	839 93↊	398
7	659 043	927	7	784 648	659	7	8↊1 116	390
8	700 96↊	920	8	828 0↊5	650	8	944 4↊6	384
9	764 68↊	913	9	88↋ 735	644	9	9↊7 86↊	378
↊	808 3↊1	907	↊	933 179	638	↊	↊4↋ 026	36↋
↋	870 0↊8	8↋↋	↋	996 7↋5	630	↋	↊↋2 395	364
9220	913 9↊7	8↋2	9260	↊3↊ 225	624	92↊0	↋55 739	357
1	977 699	8↊6	1	↊↊1 849	617	1	↋↋8 ↊94	34↋
2	↊1↋ 383	89↊	2	↋45 264	610	2	↊8↊ 060 223	343
3	↊83 061	892	3	↋↊8 874	603	3	103 566	337
4	↋26 933	886	4	↊88 050 277	5↋7	4	166 8↊1	32↊
5	↋8↊ 5↋9	879	5	0↋3 872	5↊↊	5	20↊ 00↋	323
6	↊86 032 276	871	6	157 260	5↊3	6	271 332	316
7	095 ↋27	864	7	1↋↊ 843	596	7	314 648	30↊
8	139 78↋	859	8	262 219	58↊	8	377 956	302
9	1↊1 428	850	9	305 7↊7	582	9	41↋ 058	2↋6
↊	245 078	844	↊	369 169	576	↊	482 352	2↊↊
↋	2↊8 900	838	↋	410 723	569	↋	525 640	2↊1
9230	350 538	830	9270	474 090	561	92↋0	588 921	296
1	3↋4 168	823	1	517 631	556	1	62↋ ↋↋7	289
2	457 98↋	817	2	57↊ ↋87	549	2	693 284	281
3	4↋↋ 5↊6	80↋	3	622 514	540	3	736 545	275
4	563 1↋5	802	4	685 ↊54	535	4	799 7↋↊	269
5	606 9↋7	7↋7	5	729 389	528	5	840 ↊67	261
6	66↊ 5↋2	7↊↊	6	790 8↋5	520	6	8↊4 108	255
7	712 1↊0	7↊2	7	834 215	514	7	947 361	248
8	775 982	795	8	897 729	508	8	9↊↊ 5↊9	241
9	819 557	78↊	9	93↋ 035	500	9	↊51 82↊	234
↊	881 125	781	↊	9↊2 535	4↋3	↊	↊↋4 ↊62	228
↋	924 8↊6	775	↋	↊45 ↊28	4↊8	↋	↋58 08↊	220

N	Log N	d	N	Log N	d	N	Log N	d
9300	X8X ƐƐƐ 2XX	63 214	9340	X91 102 47Ɛ	62 Ɛ4Ɛ	9380	X93 1Ɛ6 91X	62 888
1	X8Ɛ 062 502	208	1	165 40X	Ɛ42	1	259 5X6	880
2	105 70X	1ƐƐ	2	208 350	Ɛ37	2	300 266	875
3	168 909	1Ɛ4	3	26Ɛ 287	Ɛ2Ɛ	3	362 Ɛ1Ɛ	868
4	20Ɛ Ɛ01	1X7	4	312 1Ɛ6	Ɛ23	4	405 787	860
5	273 0X8	19Ɛ	5	375 119	Ɛ16	5	468 427	854
6	316 287	193	6	418 033	Ɛ0Ɛ	6	50Ɛ 07Ɛ	849
7	379 45X	187	7	47X Ɛ42	Ɛ02	7	571 908	840
8	420 625	17Ɛ	8	521 X44	XƐ6	8	614 548	834
9	483 7X4	173	9	584 93X	XXƐ	9	677 180	828
X	526 957	167	X	627 629	XX2	X	719 9X8	820
Ɛ	589 Ɛ02	15X	Ɛ	68X 70Ɛ	X96	Ɛ	780 608	814
9310	631 060	153	9350	731 5X5	X8X	9390	823 220	808
1	694 1Ɛ3	146	1	794 473	X82	1	885 X28	800
2	737 339	13X	2	837 335	X76	2	928 628	7Ɛ4
3	79X 477	132	3	89X 1XƐ	X6X	3	98Ɛ 220	7X8
4	841 5X9	126	4	941 059	X62	4	X31 X08	7X0
5	8X4 713	11X	5	9X3 XƐƐ	X56	5	X94 5X8	794
6	947 831	112	6	X46 955	X49	6	Ɛ37 180	788
7	9XX 943	105	7	XX9 7X2	X42	7	Ɛ99 948	780
8	X51 X48	0ƐX	8	Ɛ50 624	X35	8	X94 040 508	774
9	XƐ4 Ɛ46	0Ɛ1	9	ƐƐ3 459	X2X	9	0X3 080	768
X	Ɛ58 037	0X6	X	X92 056 287	X21	X	145 828	760
Ɛ	ƐƐƐ 121	099	Ɛ	0Ɛ9 0X8	X16	Ɛ	1X8 388	754
9320	X90 062 1ƐX	091	9360	15Ɛ Ɛ02	X09	93X0	24X Ɛ20	748
1	105 28Ɛ	085	1	202 90Ɛ	X02	1	2Ɛ1 668	740
2	168 354	079	2	265 711	9Ɛ5	2	354 1X8	734
3	20Ɛ 411	071	3	308 506	9X9	3	3Ɛ6 920	727
4	272 482	065	4	36Ɛ 2Ɛ3	9X1	4	459 447	720
5	315 527	058	5	412 094	995	5	4ƐƐ Ɛ67	714
6	378 583	051	6	474 X69	989	6	562 67Ɛ	708
7	41Ɛ 614	044	7	517 836	981	7	605 187	700
8	482 658	038	8	57X 5Ɛ7	975	8	667 887	6Ɛ4
9	525 694	031	9	621 370	969	9	70X 37Ɛ	6X8
X	588 705	024	X	684 119	961	X	770 X67	6X0
Ɛ	62Ɛ 729	018	Ɛ	726 X7X	955	Ɛ	813 547	694
9330	692 745	010	9370	789 813	949	93Ɛ0	876 01Ɛ	687
1	735 755	004	1	830 560	940	1	918 6X6	680
2	798 759	62 ƐƐ7	2	893 2X0	935	2	97Ɛ 166	674
3	83Ɛ 754	ƐƐ0	3	936 015	929	3	X21 81X	668
4	8X2 744	ƐX4	4	998 942	920	4	X84 286	660
5	945 728	Ɛ97	5	X3Ɛ 662	915	5	Ɛ26 926	654
6	9X8 703	Ɛ90	6	XX2 377	908	6	Ɛ89 37X	648
7	X4Ɛ 693	Ɛ83	7	Ɛ45 083	901	7	X95 02Ɛ X06	640
8	XƐ2 656	Ɛ77	8	ƐX7 984	8Ɛ4	8	092 446	634
9	Ɛ55 611	Ɛ6Ɛ	9	X93 04X 678	8X9	9	134 X7X	628
X	ƐƐ8 580	Ɛ64	X	0Ɛ1 365	8X0	X	197 4X6	620
Ɛ	X91 05Ɛ 524	Ɛ57	Ɛ	154 045	895	Ɛ	239 Ɛ06	614

N	Log N	d	N	Log N	d	N	Log N	d
9400	χ95 2χ0 51χ	62 608	9440	χ97 377 552	62 34χ	9480	χ99 443 χ8χ	62 092
1	342 Ɛ26	600	1	419 8χ0	342	1	4χ5 Ɛ60	087
2	3χ5 526	5Ɛ4	2	480 022	336	2	548 027	07χ
3	447 Ɛ1χ	5χ8	3	522 358	32χ	3	5χχ 0χ5	073
4	4χχ 506	5χ1	4	584 686	323	4	650 158	066
5	550 χχ7	594	5	626 9χ9	316	5	6Ɛ2 202	05Ɛ
6	5Ɛ3 47Ɛ	588	6	689 103	30χ	6	754 261	053
7	655 χ47	580	7	72Ɛ 411	303	7	7Ɛ6 2Ɛ4	047
8	6Ɛ8 407	574	8	791 714	2Ɛ7	8	858 33Ɛ	040
9	75χ 97Ɛ	569	9	833 χ0Ɛ	2χχ	9	8Ɛχ 37Ɛ	033
χ	801 328	560	χ	896 0Ɛ9	2χ3	χ	960 3Ɛ2	027
Ɛ	863 888	554	Ɛ	938 3χ0	297	Ɛ	χ02 419	020
9410	906 220	548	9450	99χ 677	28Ɛ	9490	χ64 439	014
1	968 768	541	1	χ40 946	283	1	Ɛ06 451	007
2	χ0Ɛ 0χ9	534	2	χχ3 009	277	2	Ɛ68 458	000
3	χ71 621	529	3	Ɛ45 284	26Ɛ	3	χ9χ 00χ 458	61 ƐƐ4
4	Ɛ13 Ɛ4χ	520	4	Ɛχ7 533	263	4	070 450	Ɛχ9
5	Ɛ76 46χ	515	5	χ98 049 796	257	5	112 439	Ɛχ0
6	χ96 018 983	508	6	0χƐ χ31	250	6	174 419	Ɛ94
7	07Ɛ 28Ɛ	501	7	152 081	243	7	216 3Ɛ1	Ɛ89
8	121 790	4Ɛ4	8	1Ɛ4 304	238	8	278 37χ	Ɛ81
9	184 084	4χ9	9	256 540	22Ɛ	9	31χ 33Ɛ	Ɛ74
χ	226 571	4χ1	χ	2Ɛ8 76Ɛ	224	χ	380 2Ɛ3	Ɛ69
Ɛ	288 χ52	494	Ɛ	35χ 993	218	Ɛ	422 260	Ɛ61
9420	32Ɛ 326	489	9460	400 ƐχƐ	20Ɛ	94χ0	484 201	Ɛ56
1	391 7Ɛ3	481	1	463 1Ɛχ	204	1	526 157	Ɛ49
2	434 074	475	2	505 402	1Ɛ8	2	588 0χ4	Ɛ42
3	496 529	469	3	567 5Ɛχ	1Ɛ1	3	62χ 026	Ɛ35
4	538 996	460	4	609 7χƐ	1χ4	4	68Ɛ Ɛ5Ɛ	Ɛ2χ
5	59Ɛ 236	455	5	66Ɛ 993	198	5	731 χ89	Ɛ22
6	641 68Ɛ	449	6	711 Ɛ6Ɛ	191	6	793 9χƐ	Ɛ16
7	6χ3 Ɛ18	441	7	774 140	184	7	835 905	Ɛ0χ
8	746 359	436	8	816 304	179	8	897 813	Ɛ03
9	7χ8 793	429	9	878 481	170	9	939 716	χƐ6
χ	84Ɛ 000	421	χ	91χ 631	165	χ	99Ɛ 610	χχƐ
Ɛ	8Ɛ1 421	415	Ɛ	980 796	159	Ɛ	χ41 4ƐƐ	χχ2
9430	953 836	40χ	9470	χ22 933	151	94Ɛ0	χχ3 3χ1	χ97
1	9Ɛ6 044	401	1	χ84 χ84	145	1	Ɛ45 278	χ8Ɛ
2	χ58 445	3Ɛ5	2	Ɛ27 009	139	2	Ɛχ7 147	χ84
3	χƐχ 83χ	3χχ	3	Ɛ89 146	132	3	χ9Ɛ 049 00Ɛ	χ77
4	Ɛ61 028	3χ1	4	χ99 02Ɛ 278	125	4	0χχ χ86	χ70
5	χ97 003 409	396	5	091 3χ1	11χ	5	150 936	χ63
6	065 7χ3	38χ	6	133 4ƐƐ	111	6	1Ɛ2 799	χ58
7	107 Ɛ71	381	7	195 610	106	7	254 635	χ50
8	16χ 332	376	8	237 716	0Ɛχ	8	2Ɛ6 485	χ44
9	210 6χ8	36χ	9	299 814	0Ɛ2	9	358 309	χ38
χ	272 χ56	362	χ	33Ɛ 906	0χ6	χ	3Ɛχ 145	χ31
Ɛ	315 1Ɛ8	356	Ɛ	3χ1 9Ɛ0	09χ	Ɛ	45Ɛ Ɛ76	χ24

N	Log N	d	N	Log N	d	N	Log N	d
9500	χ9Ɛ 501 99χ	61 χ19	9540	χχ1 571 352	61 766	9580	χχ3 612 438	61 4Ɛ4
1	563 7Ɛ7	χ11	1	612 χƐ8	759	1	673 930	4χ9
2	605 608	χ05	2	674 655	752	2	715 219	4χ1
3	667 411	9Ɛ9	3	716 1χ7	746	3	776 6Ɛχ	495
4	709 20χ	9Ɛ2	4	777 931	73Ɛ	4	817 Ɛ93	489
5	76Ɛ 000	9χ5	5	819 470	732	5	879 460	482
6	810 9χ5	99χ	6	87χ Ɛχ2	727	6	91χ 922	476
7	872 783	992	7	920 709	71Ɛ	7	980 198	46χ
8	914 555	986	8	982 228	713	8	χ21 646	462
9	976 31Ɛ	97χ	9	χ23 93Ɛ	707	9	χ82 χχ8	457
χ	χ18 099	973	χ	χ85 446	700	χ	Ɛ24 343	44Ɛ
Ɛ	χ79 χ50	966	Ɛ	Ɛ26 Ɛ46	6Ɛ4	Ɛ	Ɛ85 792	443
9510	Ɛ1Ɛ 7Ɛ6	95Ɛ	9550	Ɛ88 63χ	6χ8	9590	χχ4 027 015	437
1	Ɛ81 555	953	1	χχ2 02χ 126	6χ0	1	088 450	430
2	χχ0 023 2χ8	947	2	08Ɛ 806	694	2	129 880	424
3	085 033	93Ɛ	3	131 29χ	689	3	18Ɛ 0χ4	418
4	126 972	934	4	192 967	681	4	230 500	411
5	188 6χ6	927	5	234 428	675	5	291 911	404
6	22χ 411	920	6	295 χχ1	669	6	333 115	3Ɛ9
7	290 131	914	7	337 54χ	662	7	394 512	3Ɛ2
8	331 χ45	908	8	398 ƐƐ0	655	8	435 904	3χ5
9	393 751	900	9	43χ 645	64χ	9	497 0χ9	39χ
χ	435 451	8Ɛ5	χ	4χ0 093	642	χ	538 487	392
Ɛ	497 146	8χ8	Ɛ	541 715	637	Ɛ	599 859	387
9520	538 χ32	8χ1	9560	5χ3 150	62χ	95χ0	63Ɛ 024	37χ
1	59χ 713	895	1	644 77χ	623	1	6χ0 3χ2	373
2	640 3χ8	889	2	6χ6 1χ1	617	2	741 755	367
3	6χ2 075	882	3	747 7Ɛ8	610	3	7χ2 Ɛ00	360
4	743 937	875	4	7χ9 208	603	4	844 260	353
5	7χ5 5Ɛ0	86χ	5	84χ 80Ɛ	5Ɛ8	5	8χ5 5Ɛ3	348
6	847 25χ	862	6	8Ɛ0 207	5Ɛ0	6	946 93Ɛ	341
7	8χ8 Ɛ00	856	7	951 7Ɛ7	5χ4	7	9χ8 080	334
8	94χ 756	84χ	8	9Ɛ3 19Ɛ	599	8	χ49 3Ɛ4	329
9	9Ɛ0 3χ4	843	9	χ54 778	591	9	χχχ 721	321
χ	χ52 027	837	χ	χƐ6 149	584	χ	Ɛ4Ɛ χ42	316
Ɛ	χƐ3 862	82χ	Ɛ	Ɛ57 711	57χ	Ɛ	ƐƐ1 158	309
9530	Ɛ55 490	824	9570	ƐƐ9 08Ɛ	571	95Ɛ0	χχ5 052 465	302
1	ƐƐ7 0Ɛ4	817	1	χχ3 05χ 640	566	1	0Ɛ3 767	2Ɛ7
2	χχ1 058 90Ɛ	80Ɛ	2	0ƐƐ Ɛχ6	55χ	2	154 χ62	2χχ
3	0Ɛχ 51χ	804	3	161 544	552	3	1Ɛ6 150	2χ3
4	160 122	7Ɛ8	4	202 χ96	546	4	257 433	297
5	201 91χ	7Ɛ0	5	264 420	53Ɛ	5	2Ɛ8 70χ	290
6	263 50χ	7χ4	6	305 95Ɛ	533	6	359 99χ	283
7	305 0Ɛ2	799	7	367 292	527	7	3ƐƐ 061	278
8	366 88Ɛ	790	8	408 7Ɛ9	51Ɛ	8	460 319	270
9	408 45Ɛ	785	9	46χ 118	514	9	501 589	265
χ	46χ 024	779	χ	50Ɛ 630	508	χ	562 832	259
Ɛ	50Ɛ 7χ1	771	Ɛ	570 Ɛ38	500	Ɛ	603 χ8Ɛ	251

N	Log N	d	N	Log N	d	N	Log N	d
9600	XX5 665 120	61 245	9640	XX7 6X9 68Ɛ	60 Ɛ99	9680	XX9 723 991	60 932
1	706 365	23X	1	74X 668	Ɛ91	1	784 703	927
2	767 5X3	232	2	7XƐ 639	Ɛ85	2	825 42X	91X
3	808 815	227	3	850 602	Ɛ7X	3	886 148	914
4	869 X40	21X	4	8Ɛ1 580	Ɛ72	4	926 X60	907
5	90Ɛ 05X	213	5	952 532	Ɛ67	5	987 767	900
6	970 271	207	6	9Ɛ3 499	Ɛ5X	6	X28 467	8Ɛ5
7	X11 478	200	7	X54 437	Ɛ53	7	X89 160	8X9
8	X72 678	1Ɛ4	8	XƐ5 38X	Ɛ48	8	Ɛ29 X49	8X1
9	Ɛ13 870	1X8	9	Ɛ56 316	Ɛ40	9	Ɛ8X 72X	895
X	Ɛ74 X58	1X0	X	ƐƐ7 256	Ɛ34	X	XXX 02Ɛ 403	88X
Ɛ	XX6 016 038	195	Ɛ	XX8 058 18X	Ɛ28	Ɛ	090 091	883
9610	077 211	189	9650	0Ɛ9 0Ɛ6	Ɛ21	9690	130 954	876
1	118 39X	182	1	15X 017	Ɛ15	1	191 60X	870
2	179 560	175	2	1ƐX Ɛ30	Ɛ0X	2	232 27X	863
3	21X 715	16X	3	25Ɛ X3X	Ɛ02	3	292 Ɛ21	858
4	27Ɛ 883	163	4	300 940	XƐ6	4	333 779	851
5	320 X26	156	5	361 836	XXƐ	5	394 40X	844
6	381 Ɛ80	14Ɛ	6	402 725	XX3	6	435 052	839
7	423 10Ɛ	143	7	463 608	X97	7	495 88Ɛ	832
8	484 252	138	8	504 4X3	X90	8	536 501	826
9	525 38X	130	9	565 373	X84	9	597 127	81X
X	586 4ƐX	124	X	606 237	X78	X	637 945	813
Ɛ	627 622	118	Ɛ	667 0Ɛ3	X71	Ɛ	698 558	807
9620	688 73X	111	9660	707 Ɛ64	X65	96X0	739 163	800
1	729 84Ɛ	105	1	768 X09	X5X	1	799 963	7Ɛ4
2	78X 954	0ƐX	2	809 867	X51	2	83X 557	7X8
3	82Ɛ X52	0Ɛ1	3	86X 6Ɛ8	X47	3	89Ɛ 143	7X1
4	890 Ɛ43	0X7	4	90Ɛ 543	X3X	4	93Ɛ 924	795
5	932 02X	09X	5	970 381	X33	5	9X0 4Ɛ9	78X
6	993 108	093	6	X11 1Ɛ4	X27	6	X41 087	782
7	X34 19Ɛ	087	7	X72 01Ɛ	X20	7	XX1 849	776
8	X95 266	07Ɛ	8	Ɛ12 X3Ɛ	X14	8	Ɛ42 403	76Ɛ
9	Ɛ36 325	074	9	Ɛ73 853	X09	9	ƐX2 Ɛ72	764
X	Ɛ97 399	068	X	XX9 014 660	X00	X	XXƐ 043 716	757
Ɛ	XX7 038 445	060	Ɛ	075 460	9Ɛ6	Ɛ	0X4 271	750
9630	099 4X5	055	9670	116 256	9X9	96Ɛ0	144 X01	745
1	13X 53X	049	1	177 043	9X2	1	1X5 546	739
2	19Ɛ 587	041	2	217 X25	996	2	246 083	731
3	240 608	036	3	278 7ƐƐ	98Ɛ	3	2X6 7Ɛ4	726
4	2X1 642	02X	4	319 58X	983	4	347 31X	71X
5	342 670	022	5	37X 351	977	5	3X7 X38	713
6	3X3 692	017	6	41Ɛ 108	970	6	448 54Ɛ	707
7	444 6X9	00Ɛ	7	47Ɛ X78	964	7	4X9 056	6ƐƐ
8	4X5 6Ɛ8	003	8	520 820	959	8	549 755	6Ɛ4
9	546 6ƐƐ	60 ƐƐ8	9	581 579	951	9	5XX 249	6X9
X	5X7 6Ɛ7	ƐƐ0	X	622 30X	945	X	64X 936	6X0
Ɛ	648 6X7	ƐX4	Ɛ	683 053	93X	Ɛ	6XƐ 416	696

N	Log N	d	N	Log N	d	N	Log N	d
9700	χχƐ 74Ɛ χƐ0	60 689	9740	χƐ1 769 χƐ1	60 427	9780	χƐ3 779 χ59	60 187
1	7Ɛ0 579	682	1	80χ 318	41Ɛ	1	81χ 024	17Ɛ
2	851 03Ɛ	677	2	86χ 737	415	2	87χ 1χ3	174
3	8Ɛ1 6Ɛ6	66Ɛ	3	90χ Ɛ50	408	3	91χ 357	169
4	952 165	663	4	96Ɛ 358	401	4	97χ 504	161
5	9Ɛ2 808	658	5	χ0Ɛ 759	3Ɛ6	5	χ1χ 665	155
6	χ53 264	650	6	χ6Ɛ Ɛ53	3χχ	6	χ7χ 7Ɛχ	14χ
7	χƐ3 8Ɛ4	644	7	Ɛ10 341	3χ3	7	Ɛ1χ 948	143
8	Ɛ54 338	63χ	8	Ɛ70 724	397	8	Ɛ7χ χ8Ɛ	137
9	ƐƐ4 976	631	9	χƐ2 010 χƐƐ	38Ɛ	9	χƐ4 01Ɛ 006	12Ɛ
χ	χƐ0 055 3χ7	626	χ	071 28χ	384	χ	07Ɛ 135	125
Ɛ	0Ɛ5 χ11	61χ	Ɛ	111 652	379	Ɛ	11Ɛ 25χ	118
9710	156 42Ɛ	613	9750	171 χ0Ɛ	371	9790	17Ɛ 376	111
1	1Ɛ6 χ42	607	1	212 180	365	1	21Ɛ 487	106
2	257 449	600	2	272 525	35χ	2	27Ɛ 591	0Ɛχ
3	2Ɛ7 χ49	5Ɛ4	3	312 883	353	3	31Ɛ 68Ɛ	0Ɛ3
4	358 441	5χ9	4	373 016	346	4	37Ɛ 782	0χ8
5	3Ɛ8 χ2χ	5χ1	5	413 360	340	5	41Ɛ 86χ	09Ɛ
6	459 40Ɛ	595	6	473 6χ0	334	6	47Ɛ 949	095
7	4Ɛ9 9χ4	58χ	7	513 χ14	328	7	51Ɛ χ22	089
8	55χ 372	583	8	574 140	321	8	57Ɛ χχƐ	081
9	5Ɛχ 935	576	9	614 461	315	9	61Ɛ Ɛ70	076
χ	65Ɛ 2χƐ	570	χ	674 776	30χ	χ	680 026	06Ɛ
Ɛ	6ƐƐ 85Ɛ	563	Ɛ	714 χ84	302	Ɛ	720 095	063
9720	760 202	559	9760	775 186	2Ɛ7	97χ0	780 138	057
1	800 75Ɛ	550	1	815 481	2Ɛ0	1	820 193	050
2	861 0χƐ	545	2	875 771	2χ3	2	880 223	045
3	901 634	53χ	3	915 χ54	299	3	920 268	039
4	961 Ɛ72	532	4	976 131	291	4	980 2χ5	032
5	χ02 4χ4	526	5	χ16 402	285	5	χ20 317	026
6	χ62 χ0χ	51Ɛ	6	χ76 687	27χ	6	χ80 341	01Ɛ
7	Ɛ03 329	513	7	Ɛ16 945	272	7	Ɛ20 360	013
8	Ɛ63 840	508	8	Ɛ76 ƐƐ7	267	8	Ɛ80 373	008
9	χƐ1 004 148	500	9	χƐ3 017 262	25Ɛ	9	χƐ5 020 37Ɛ	001
χ	064 648	4Ɛ5	χ	077 501	254	χ	080 380	5Ɛ ƐƐ5
Ɛ	104 Ɛ41	4χ9	Ɛ	117 755	248	Ɛ	120 375	Ɛχ9
9730	165 42χ	4χ2	9770	177 9χ1	241	97Ɛ0	180 362	Ɛχ2
1	205 910	496	1	218 022	235	1	220 344	Ɛ97
2	266 1χ6	48Ɛ	2	278 257	22χ	2	280 31Ɛ	Ɛ8Ɛ
3	306 675	483	3	318 485	223	3	320 2χχ	Ɛ84
4	366 Ɛ38	477	4	378 6χ8	216	4	380 272	Ɛ78
5	407 3Ɛ3	470	5	418 902	210	5	420 22χ	Ɛ71
6	467 863	464	6	478 Ɛ12	204	6	480 19Ɛ	Ɛ65
7	508 107	459	7	519 116	1Ɛ8	7	520 144	Ɛ5χ
8	568 564	452	8	579 312	1Ɛ1	8	580 0χ2	Ɛ53
9	608 9Ɛ6	445	9	619 503	1χ5	9	620 035	Ɛ47
χ	669 23Ɛ	43Ɛ	χ	679 6χ8	19χ	χ	67Ɛ Ɛ80	Ɛ40
Ɛ	709 67χ	433	Ɛ	719 886	193	Ɛ	71Ɛ Ɛ00	Ɛ34

N	Log N	d	N	Log N	d	N	Log N	d
9800	χƐ5 77Ɛ χ34	5Ɛ Ɛ29	9840	χƐ7 773 Ɛ01	5Ɛ 890	9880	χƐ9 75χ 142	5Ɛ 636
1	81Ɛ 961	Ɛ21	1	813 791	886	1	7Ɛ9 778	62Ɛ
2	87Ɛ 882	Ɛ16	2	873 457	879	2	859 1χ7	624
3	91Ɛ 798	Ɛ0χ	3	913 114	873	3	8Ɛ8 80Ɛ	619
4	97Ɛ 6χ6	Ɛ03	4	972 987	867	4	958 228	611
5	χ1Ɛ 5χ9	χƐ8	5	χ12 632	85Ɛ	5	9Ɛ7 839	605
6	χ7Ɛ 4χ5	χƐ0	6	χ72 291	854	6	χ57 242	5ƐƐ
7	Ɛ1Ɛ 395	χχ4	7	Ɛ11 Ɛ25	849	7	χƐ6 841	5Ɛ3
8	Ɛ7Ɛ 279	χ9χ	8	Ɛ71 772	842	8	Ɛ56 234	5χ7
9	χƐ6 01Ɛ 157	χ91	9	χƐ8 011 3Ɛ4	836	9	ƐƐ5 81Ɛ	5χ0
χ	07Ɛ 028	χ87	χ	071 02χ	82χ	χ	χƐχ 055 1ƐƐ	595
Ɛ	11χ χƐ3	χ7Ɛ	Ɛ	110 858	824	Ɛ	0Ɛ4 794	58χ
9810	17χ 972	χ73	9850	170 480	817	9890	154 162	582
1	21χ 825	χ68	1	210 097	811	1	1Ɛ3 724	577
2	27χ 691	χ61	2	26Ɛ 8χ8	805	2	253 09Ɛ	56Ɛ
3	31χ 532	χ55	3	30Ɛ 4Ɛ1	7Ɛχ	3	2Ɛ2 64χ	565
4	37χ 387	χ4χ	4	36Ɛ 0χƐ	7Ɛ2	4	351 ƐƐ3	559
5	41χ 215	χ42	5	40χ 8χ1	7χ7	5	3Ɛ1 550	551
6	47χ 057	χ37	6	46χ 488	79Ɛ	6	450 χχ1	546
7	519 χ92	χ30	7	50χ 067	794	7	4Ɛ0 427	53Ɛ
8	579 902	χ24	8	569 83Ɛ	789	8	54Ɛ 966	533
9	619 726	χ18	9	609 408	782	9	5χƐ 299	529
χ	679 542	χ12	χ	668 Ɛ8χ	776	χ	64χ 806	520
Ɛ	719 354	χ05	Ɛ	708 744	76χ	Ɛ	6χχ 126	516
9820	779 159	9ƐƐ	9860	768 2Ɛ2	764	98χ0	749 640	50χ
1	818 Ɛ58	9Ɛ3	1	807 χ56	757	1	7χ8 Ɛ4χ	503
2	878 94Ɛ	9χ7	2	867 5Ɛ1	751	2	848 451	4Ɛ7
3	918 736	9χ0	3	907 142	745	3	8χ7 948	4Ɛ0
4	978 516	995	4	966 887	73χ	4	947 238	4χ5
5	χ18 2χƐ	989	5	χ06 405	732	5	9χ6 721	49χ
6	χ78 078	982	6	χ65 Ɛ37	727	6	χ45 ƐƐƐ	492
7	Ɛ17 χ3χ	977	7	Ɛ05 662	720	7	χχ5 491	487
8	Ɛ77 7Ɛ5	96Ɛ	8	Ɛ65 182	714	8	Ɛ44 958	47Ɛ
9	χƐ7 017 564	964	9	χƐ9 004 896	709	9	Ɛχ4 217	474
χ	077 308	958	χ	064 3χ3	701	χ	χƐƐ 043 68Ɛ	469
Ɛ	117 064	951	Ɛ	103 χχ4	6Ɛ7	Ɛ	0χ2 Ɛ38	462
9830	176 9Ɛ5	945	9870	163 59Ɛ	6χχ	98Ɛ0	142 39χ	456
1	216 73χ	93χ	1	203 089	6χ4	1	1χ1 834	44Ɛ
2	276 478	933	2	262 771	698	2	241 083	443
3	316 1χƐ	927	3	302 249	690	3	2χ0 506	438
4	375 Ɛ16	920	4	361 919	686	4	33Ɛ 942	431
5	415 836	914	5	401 3χ3	67χ	5	39Ɛ 173	426
6	475 54χ	909	6	460 χ61	672	6	43χ 599	41χ
7	515 257	902	7	500 513	668	7	499 9Ɛ7	413
8	574 Ɛ59	8Ɛ6	8	55Ɛ Ɛ7Ɛ	65Ɛ	8	539 20χ	407
9	614 853	8χχ	9	5ƐƐ 61χ	655	9	598 615	401
χ	674 541	8χ4	χ	65Ɛ 073	649	χ	637 χ16	3Ɛ5
Ɛ	714 225	898	Ɛ	6Ɛχ 700	642	Ɛ	697 20Ɛ	3χ9

N	Log N	d	N	Log N	d	N	Log N	d
9900	XƐƐ 736 5Ɛ8	5Ɛ 3X3	9940	Ɛ01 705 169	5Ɛ 150	9980	Ɛ03 686 092	5X Ɛ00
1	795 99Ɛ	397	1	764 2Ɛ9	145	1	724 Ɛ92	XƐ5
2	835 176	38Ɛ	2	803 442	139	2	783 X87	XXX
3	894 545	385	3	862 57Ɛ	133	3	822 975	XX2
4	933 90X	379	4	901 6Ɛ2	127	4	881 857	X97
5	993 087	372	5	960 819	120	5	920 732	X90
6	X32 439	366	6	9ƐƐ 939	114	6	97Ɛ 602	X85
7	X91 7X3	35Ɛ	7	X5X X51	10X	7	X1X 487	X79
8	Ɛ30 Ɛ42	354	8	XƐ9 Ɛ5Ɛ	102	8	X79 344	X73
9	Ɛ90 296	349	9	Ɛ59 061	0Ɛ7	9	Ɛ18 1Ɛ7	X67
X	Ɛ00 02Ɛ 623	341	X	ƐƐ8 158	0XƐ	X	Ɛ77 062	X60
Ɛ	08X 964	336	Ɛ	Ɛ02 057 247	0X4	Ɛ	Ɛ04 015 Ɛ02	X54
9910	12X 09X	32X	9950	0Ɛ6 32Ɛ	099	9990	074 956	X4X
1	189 408	324	1	155 408	092	1	113 7X4	X42
2	228 730	318	2	1Ɛ4 49X	087	2	172 626	X37
3	287 X48	310	3	253 565	07Ɛ	3	211 461	X2Ɛ
4	327 158	306	4	2Ɛ2 624	074	4	270 290	X25
5	386 462	2ƐX	5	351 698	068	5	30Ɛ 0Ɛ5	X19
6	425 760	2Ɛ3	6	3Ɛ0 744	062	6	369 Ɛ12	X12
7	484 X53	2X7	7	44Ɛ 7X6	056	7	408 924	X07
8	524 13X	2X0	8	4XX 840	04Ɛ	8	467 72Ɛ	X00
9	583 41X	295	9	549 88Ɛ	044	9	506 52Ɛ	9Ɛ4
X	622 6Ɛ3	28X	X	5X8 913	038	X	565 323	9X9
Ɛ	681 981	282	Ɛ	647 94Ɛ	031	Ɛ	604 110	9X2
9920	721 043	277	9960	6X6 980	026	99X0	662 XƐ2	997
1	780 2ƐX	270	1	745 9X6	01Ɛ	1	701 889	98Ɛ
2	81Ɛ 56X	264	2	7X4 X05	013	2	760 658	985
3	87X 812	25X	3	843 X18	008	3	7ƐƐ 421	979
4	919 X70	251	4	8X2 X24	001	4	85X 19X	972
5	979 101	247	5	941 X25	5X ƐƐ6	5	8Ɛ8 Ɛ50	967
6	X18 348	23Ɛ	6	9X0 X1Ɛ	ƐXX	6	957 8Ɛ7	95Ɛ
7	X77 587	234	7	X3Ɛ X09	ƐX3	7	9Ɛ6 656	954
8	Ɛ16 7ƐƐ	229	8	X9X 9Ɛ0	Ɛ98	8	X55 3XX	94X
9	Ɛ75 X28	221	9	Ɛ39 988	Ɛ91	9	XƐ4 138	941
X	Ɛ01 015 049	216	X	Ɛ98 959	Ɛ85	X	Ɛ52 X79	937
Ɛ	074 263	20Ɛ	Ɛ	Ɛ03 037 922	Ɛ7Ɛ	Ɛ	ƐƐ1 7Ɛ4	930
9930	113 472	204	9970	096 8X1	Ɛ73	99Ɛ0	Ɛ05 050 524	924
1	172 676	1Ɛ8	1	135 854	Ɛ67	1	0XƐ 248	919
2	211 872	1Ɛ1	2	194 7ƐƐ	Ɛ61	2	149 Ɛ65	912
3	270 X63	1X6	3	233 760	Ɛ55	3	1X8 877	907
4	310 049	19X	4	292 6Ɛ5	Ɛ4X	4	247 582	8ƐƐ
5	36Ɛ 227	193	5	331 643	Ɛ43	5	2X6 281	8Ɛ4
6	40X 3ƐX	188	6	390 586	Ɛ37	6	344 Ɛ75	8X9
7	469 586	181	7	42Ɛ 501	Ɛ30	7	3X3 862	8X2
8	508 747	175	8	48X 431	Ɛ25	8	442 544	897
9	567 900	16X	9	529 356	Ɛ1X	9	4X1 21Ɛ	890
X	606 X6X	163	X	588 274	Ɛ13	X	53Ɛ XXƐ	884
Ɛ	666 011	158	Ɛ	627 187	Ɛ07	Ɛ	59X 773	879

N	Log N	d	N	Log N	d	N	Log N	d
9X00	Ɛ05 639 430	5X 872	9X40	Ɛ07 5X3 080	5X 626	9X80	Ɛ09 53Ɛ 280	5X 39Ɛ
1	698 0X2	867	1	641 6X6	61X	1	599 65Ɛ	394
2	736 949	85Ɛ	2	6X0 104	614	2	637 X33	38X
3	795 5X8	855	3	73X 718	608	3	696 201	382
4	834 241	849	4	799 124	601	4	734 583	377
5	892 X8X	842	5	837 725	5Ɛ6	5	792 93X	370
6	931 710	837	6	896 11Ɛ	5XƐ	6	831 0XX	364
7	990 347	82Ɛ	7	934 70X	5X4	7	88Ɛ 452	35X
8	X2X Ɛ76	825	8	993 0Ɛ2	598	8	929 7Ɛ0	353
9	X89 79Ɛ	819	9	X31 68X	592	9	987 Ɛ43	347
X	Ɛ28 3Ɛ8	812	X	X90 060	586	X	X26 28X	341
Ɛ	Ɛ87 00X	807	Ɛ	Ɛ2X 626	57Ɛ	Ɛ	X84 60Ɛ	335
9X10	Ɛ06 025 815	7ƐƐ	9X50	Ɛ88 ƐX5	574	9X90	Ɛ22 944	32X
1	084 414	7Ɛ5	1	Ɛ08 027 559	569	1	Ɛ81 072	323
2	123 009	7X9	2	085 Ɛ06	561	2	Ɛ0X 01Ɛ 395	318
3	181 7Ɛ6	7X2	3	124 467	557	3	079 6Ɛ1	311
4	220 398	797	4	182 X02	54Ɛ	4	117 X02	306
5	27X Ɛ73	790	5	221 351	545	5	176 108	2ƐX
6	319 743	785	6	27Ɛ 896	539	6	214 406	2Ɛ4
7	378 308	779	7	31X 213	532	7	272 6ƐX	2X9
8	416 X85	773	8	378 745	527	8	310 9X7	2X1
9	475 638	767	9	417 070	520	9	36Ɛ 088	296
X	514 1X3	760	X	475 590	514	X	409 362	28Ɛ
Ɛ	572 943	754	Ɛ	513 XX4	50X	Ɛ	467 631	285
9X20	611 497	74X	9X60	572 3Ɛ2	502	9XX0	505 8Ɛ6	279
1	670 025	742	1	610 8Ɛ4	4Ɛ7	1	563 Ɛ73	272
2	70X 767	738	2	66Ɛ 1XƐ	4Ɛ0	2	602 225	266
3	769 2X3	730	3	709 69Ɛ	4X5	3	660 48Ɛ	260
4	807 X13	725	4	767 Ɛ84	49X	4	6ƐX 72Ɛ	255
5	866 538	719	5	806 462	493	5	758 984	249
6	905 055	713	6	864 935	487	6	7Ɛ7 011	243
7	963 768	707	7	903 200	481	7	855 254	237
8	X02 273	701	8	961 681	475	8	8Ɛ3 48Ɛ	231
9	X60 974	6Ɛ5	9	9ƐƐ Ɛ36	46X	9	951 700	225
X	XƐƐ 469	6XX	X	X5X 3X4	463	X	9XƐ 925	21X
Ɛ	Ɛ59 Ɛ57	6X2	Ɛ	XƐ8 847	458	Ɛ	X49 Ɛ43	213
9X30	ƐƐ8 639	698	9X70	Ɛ57 0X3	451	9XƐ0	XX8 156	208
1	Ɛ07 057 115	690	1	ƐƐ5 534	446	1	Ɛ46 362	201
2	0Ɛ5 7X5	686	2	Ɛ09 053 97X	43X	2	ƐX4 563	1Ɛ6
3	154 26Ɛ	67X	3	0Ɛ2 1Ɛ8	434	3	Ɛ0Ɛ 042 759	1XƐ
4	1Ɛ2 929	673	4	150 630	428	4	0X0 948	1X3
5	251 3X0	668	5	1XX X58	422	5	13X Ɛ2Ɛ	199
6	2XƐ X48	660	6	249 27X	416	6	199 108	191
7	34X 4X8	656	7	2X7 694	40Ɛ	7	237 299	187
8	3X8 Ɛ42	64X	8	345 XX3	404	8	295 464	17Ɛ
9	447 590	643	9	3X4 2X7	3Ɛ8	9	333 623	175
X	4X6 013	638	X	442 6X3	3Ɛ2	X	391 798	169
Ɛ	544 64Ɛ	631	Ɛ	4X0 X95	3X7	Ɛ	42Ɛ 945	162

N	Log N	d	N	Log N	d	N	Log N	d
9Ɛ00	Ɛ0Ɛ 489 χχ7	5χ 157	9Ɛ40	Ɛ11 40Ɛ 1Ɛ6	59 Ɛ15	9Ɛ80	Ɛ13 343 063	59 894
1	528 042	150	1	469 10Ɛ	Ɛ09	1	3χ0 937	88χ
2	586 192	145	2	507 018	Ɛ03	2	43χ 605	882
3	624 317	13χ	3	564 Ɛ1Ɛ	χƐ7	3	498 287	877
4	682 455	133	4	602 χ16	χƐ1	4	535 Ɛ42	870
5	720 588	127	5	660 907	χχ5	5	593 7Ɛ2	865
6	77χ 6Ɛ3	121	6	6Ɛχ 7Ɛ0	χ9Ɛ	6	631 457	85χ
7	818 814	116	7	758 68Ɛ	χ93	7	68Ɛ 0Ɛ5	853
8	876 92χ	10χ	8	7Ɛ6 562	χ89	8	728 948	848
9	914 χ38	104	9	854 42Ɛ	χ81	9	786 594	841
χ	972 Ɛ40	0Ɛ8	χ	8Ɛ2 2Ɛ0	χ76	χ	824 215	837
Ɛ	χ11 038	0Ɛ2	Ɛ	950 166	χ70	Ɛ	881 χ50	82Ɛ
9Ɛ10	χ6Ɛ 12χ	0χ6	9Ɛ50	9χχ 016	χ64	9Ɛ90	91Ɛ 67Ɛ	824
1	Ɛ09 214	09Ɛ	1	χ47 χ7χ	χ59	1	979 2χ3	819
2	Ɛ67 2Ɛ3	094	2	χχ5 917	χ53	2	χ16 Ɛ00	812
3	Ɛ10 005 387	089	3	Ɛ43 76χ	χ47	3	χ74 712	808
4	063 454	082	4	Ɛχ1 5Ɛ5	χ40	4	Ɛ12 31χ	800
5	101 516	077	5	Ɛ12 03Ɛ 435	χ35	5	Ɛ6Ɛ Ɛ1χ	7Ɛ5
6	15Ɛ 591	070	6	099 26χ	χ2χ	6	Ɛ14 009 713	7χƐ
7	1Ɛ9 641	065	7	137 098	χ24	7	067 302	7χ3
8	257 6χ6	05χ	8	194 Ɛ00	χ18	8	104 χχ5	798
9	2Ɛ5 744	053	9	232 918	χ11	9	162 681	792
χ	353 797	048	χ	290 729	χ06	χ	200 253	786
Ɛ	3Ɛ1 823	040	Ɛ	32χ 533	9ƐƐ	Ɛ	259 χ19	780
9Ɛ20	44Ɛ 863	036	9Ɛ60	388 332	9Ɛ4	9Ɛχ0	2Ɛ7 599	774
1	4χ9 899	02Ɛ	1	426 126	9χ9	1	355 151	76χ
2	547 908	023	2	483 Ɛ13	9χ3	2	3Ɛ2 8ƐƐ	762
3	5χ5 92Ɛ	019	3	521 8Ɛ6	997	3	450 461	758
4	643 948	011	4	57Ɛ 691	990	4	4χ9 ƐƐ9	750
5	6χ1 959	006	5	619 461	985	5	547 749	746
6	73Ɛ 963	000	6	677 226	97χ	6	5χ5 293	73Ɛ
7	799 963	59 ƐƐ4	7	714 Ɛχ4	973	7	642 χ12	733
8	837 957	Ɛχ9	8	772 957	968	8	6χ0 545	729
9	895 944	Ɛχ2	9	810 703	961	9	73χ 072	722
χ	933 926	Ɛ98	χ	86χ 464	956	χ	797 794	717
Ɛ	991 902	Ɛ90	Ɛ	908 1Ɛχ	94Ɛ	Ɛ	835 2χƐ	70Ɛ
9Ɛ30	χ2Ɛ 892	Ɛ85	9Ɛ70	965 Ɛ49	944	9ƐƐ0	892 9Ɛχ	705
1	χ89 857	Ɛ7χ	1	χ03 891	939	1	930 503	6Ɛχ
2	Ɛ27 815	Ɛ73	2	χ61 60χ	932	2	98χ 001	6Ɛ3
3	Ɛ85 788	Ɛ68	3	χƐƐ 340	927	3	χ27 6Ɛ4	6χ8
4	Ɛ11 023 734	Ɛ61	4	Ɛ59 067	920	4	χ85 1χ0	6χ1
5	081 695	Ɛ55	5	ƐƐ6 987	915	5	Ɛ22 881	696
6	11Ɛ 62χ	Ɛ4Ɛ	6	Ɛ13 054 6χ0	90χ	6	Ɛ80 357	68Ɛ
7	179 579	Ɛ44	7	0Ɛ2 3χχ	903	7	Ɛ15 019 χ26	684
8	217 501	Ɛ39	8	150 0Ɛ1	8Ɛ8	8	077 4χχ	67χ
9	275 43χ	Ɛ32	9	1χ9 9χ9	8Ɛ1	9	114 Ɛ68	672
χ	313 370	Ɛ26	χ	247 69χ	8χ6	χ	172 61χ	667
Ɛ	371 296	Ɛ20	Ɛ	2χ5 384	89Ɛ	Ɛ	210 085	660

N	Log N	d	N	Log N	d	N	Log N	d
X000	Ɛ15 269 725	59 656	X040	Ɛ17 186 X75	59 419	X080	Ɛ19 096 Ɛ48	59 1X1
1	307 17Ɛ	64X	1	224 292	411	1	134 129	197
2	364 809	644	2	281 6X3	407	2	191 304	190
3	402 251	638	3	31X XXX	400	3	22X 494	185
4	45Ɛ 889	632	4	378 2XX	3Ɛ5	4	287 659	17X
5	4Ɛ9 2ƐƐ	626	5	415 6X3	3XX	5	324 817	173
6	556 925	620	6	472 X91	3X3	6	381 98X	168
7	5Ɛ4 345	615	7	510 274	398	7	41X Ɛ36	161
8	651 95X	609	8	569 650	391	8	478 097	157
9	6XƐ 367	603	9	606 X21	386	9	515 232	150
X	748 96X	5Ɛ8	X	664 1X7	380	X	572 382	144
Ɛ	7X6 366	5Ɛ1	Ɛ	701 567	374	Ɛ	60Ɛ 506	13X
X010	843 957	5X6	X050	75X 91Ɛ	36X	X090	668 644	133
1	8X1 341	59Ɛ	1	7Ɛ8 089	363	1	705 777	128
2	93X 920	594	2	855 430	357	2	762 8X3	122
3	998 2Ɛ4	589	3	8Ɛ2 787	351	3	7ƐƐ X05	116
4	X35 881	582	4	94Ɛ Ɛ18	346	4	858 Ɛ1Ɛ	110
5	X93 243	578	5	9X9 262	33Ɛ	5	8Ɛ6 02Ɛ	104
6	Ɛ30 7ƐƐ	570	6	X46 5X1	334	6	953 133	0ƐX
7	Ɛ8X 16Ɛ	565	7	XX3 915	32X	7	9Ɛ0 231	0Ɛ3
8	Ɛ16 027 714	55Ɛ	8	Ɛ41 043	322	8	X49 324	0X8
9	085 073	553	9	Ɛ9X 365	317	9	XX6 410	0X2
X	122 606	549	X	Ɛ18 037 680	311	X	Ɛ43 4Ɛ2	096
Ɛ	17Ɛ Ɛ53	542	Ɛ	094 991	306	Ɛ	ƐX0 588	090
X020	219 495	536	X060	132 097	2ƐƐ	X0X0	Ɛ1X 039 658	084
1	276 X0Ɛ	530	1	18Ɛ 396	2Ɛ3	1	096 720	07X
2	314 33Ɛ	525	2	228 689	2X9	2	133 79X	073
3	371 864	51X	3	285 976	2X2	3	190 851	068
4	40Ɛ 182	513	4	323 058	298	4	229 8Ɛ9	061
5	468 695	508	5	380 334	290	5	286 95X	057
6	505 ƐX1	501	6	419 604	285	6	323 9Ɛ5	04Ɛ
7	563 4X2	4Ɛ6	7	476 889	27Ɛ	7	380 X44	045
8	600 998	4XƐ	8	513 Ɛ48	274	8	419 X89	03X
9	65X 287	4X5	9	571 200	268	9	476 Ɛ07	033
X	6Ɛ7 770	499	X	60X 468	262	X	513 Ɛ3X	028
Ɛ	755 049	493	Ɛ	667 70X	257	Ɛ	570 Ɛ66	021
X030	7Ɛ2 520	487	X070	704 965	250	X0Ɛ0	609 Ɛ87	017
1	84Ɛ 9X7	481	1	761 ƐƐ5	245	1	666 ƐX2	00Ɛ
2	8X9 268	475	2	7ƐƐ 23X	23Ɛ	2	703 Ɛ Ɛ1	005
3	946 721	46Ɛ	3	858 479	233	3	760 ƐƐ6	58 ƐƐX
4	9X3 Ɛ90	464	4	8Ɛ5 6Ɛ0	229	4	7Ɛ9 ƐƐ4	ƐƐ3
5	X41 434	459	5	952 919	221	5	856 ƐX7	ƐX8
6	X9X 891	452	6	9XƐ Ɛ3X	217	6	8Ɛ3 Ɛ93	ƐX2
7	Ɛ38 123	447	7	X49 155	210	7	950 Ɛ75	Ɛ96
8	Ɛ95 56X	440	8	XX6 365	205	8	9X9 Ɛ4Ɛ	Ɛ90
9	Ɛ17 032 9XX	436	9	Ɛ43 56X	1ƐX	9	X46 Ɛ1Ɛ	Ɛ85
X	090 224	42X	X	ƐX0 768	1Ɛ3	X	XX3 XX4	Ɛ7X
Ɛ	129 652	423	Ɛ	Ɛ19 039 95Ɛ	1X9	Ɛ	Ɛ40 X62	Ɛ73

N	Log N	d	N	Log N	d	N	Log N	d
X100	£1X £99 X15	58 £68	X140	£20 X93 750	58 935	X180	£22 980 3X7	58 703
1	£1£ 036 981	£62	1	£30 485	92X	1	X18 XXX	6£9
2	093 923	£56	2	£89 1£3	923	2	X75 5X7	6£1
3	130 879	£50	3	£21 025 £16	919	3	£12 098	6X7
4	189 809	£45	4	082 833	911	4	£6X 783	6X1
5	226 752	£3X	5	11£ 544	907	5	£23 007 264	695
6	283 690	£34	6	178 24£	900	6	063 939	68£
7	320 604	£28	7	214 £4£	8£6	7	100 408	684
8	379 530	£22	8	271 845	8XX	8	158 X90	679
9	416 452	£16	9	30X 533	8X4	9	1£5 549	673
X	473 368	£10	X	367 217	899	X	252 000	668
£	510 278	£06	£	403 X£4	892	£	2XX 668	661
X110	569 182	X£X	X150	460 786	888	X190	347 109	656
1	606 080	X£3	1	4£9 452	880	1	3X3 763	64£
2	662 £73	XX9	2	556 112	876	2	440 1£2	645
3	6££ X60	XX2	3	5£2 988	86£	3	498 837	63X
4	758 942	X97	4	64£ 637	864	4	535 275	633
5	7£5 819	X90	5	6X8 29£	85X	5	591 8X8	629
6	852 6X9	X85	6	744 £39	852	6	62X 315	621
7	8X£ 572	X7£	7	7X1 78£	848	7	686 936	617
8	948 431	X73	8	83X 417	841	8	723 351	611
9	9X5 2X4	X69	9	897 058	836	9	77£ 962	605
X	X42 151	X62	X	933 892	830	X	818 367	5££
£	X9X £23	X58	£	990 502	825	£	874 966	5£4
X120	£37 X4£	X50	X160	X29 127	81X	X1X0	911 35X	5X9
1	£94 89£	X46	1	X85 945	813	1	969 947	5X3
2	£20 031 725	X3X	2	£22 558	808	2	X06 32X	597
3	08X 563	X34	3	£7£ 164	802	3	X62 905	591
4	127 397	X29	4	£22 017 966	7£7	4	X££ 296	587
5	184 204	X23	5	074 561	7£0	5	£57 861	57£
6	221 027	X17	6	111 151	7X5	6	££4 220	575
7	279 X42	X11	7	169 936	79X	7	£24 050 795	56X
8	316 853	X06	8	206 514	794	8	0X9 143	563
9	373 659	9££	9	263 0X8	789	9	145 6X6	559
X	410 458	9£4	X	2££ 875	782	X	1X2 043	552
£	469 250	9XX	£	358 437	777	£	23X 595	547
X130	506 03X	9X2	X170	3£4 ££2	771	X1£0	296 £20	540
1	562 X20	998	1	451 763	766	1	333 460	536
2	5££ 7£8	991	2	4XX 309	75£	2	38£ 996	52£
3	658 589	986	3	546 X68	754	3	428 305	524
4	6£5 353	980	4	5X3 600	74X	4	484 829	519
5	752 113	974	5	640 14X	742	5	521 146	513
6	7XX X87	96X	6	698 890	738	6	579 659	508
7	847 835	963	7	735 408	731	7	615 £65	501
8	8X4 598	958	8	791 £39	727	8	672 466	4£6
9	941 334	951	9	82X 664	720	9	70X 960	4£0
X	99X 085	947	X	887 184	714	X	767 250	4X5
£	X36 X10	940	£	923 898	70£	£	803 735	49X

N	Log N	d
X200	Ɛ24 860 013	58 494
1	8Ɛ8 4X7	489
2	954 974	482
3	9Ɛ1 236	477
4	X49 6Ɛ1	471
5	XX5 Ɛ62	466
6	Ɛ42 408	45Ɛ
7	Ɛ9X 867	455
8	Ɛ25 037 100	449
9	093 549	443
X	12Ɛ 990	439
Ɛ	188 209	431
X210	224 63X	427
1	280 X65	420
2	319 285	416
3	375 69Ɛ	40X
4	411 XX9	404
5	46X 2Ɛ1	3ƐX
6	506 6XƐ	3Ɛ2
7	562 XX1	3X8
8	5ƐƐ 289	3X1
9	657 66X	397
X	6Ɛ3 X45	390
Ɛ	750 215	385
X220	7X8 59X	37X
1	844 958	374
2	8X1 110	368
3	939 478	363
4	995 81Ɛ	357
5	X31 Ɛ76	351
6	X8X 307	346
7	Ɛ26 651	33Ɛ
8	Ɛ82 990	335
9	Ɛ26 01Ɛ 105	32X
X	077 433	323
Ɛ	113 756	319
X230	16Ɛ X73	312
1	208 185	307
2	264 490	300
3	300 790	2Ɛ6
4	358 X86	2XƐ
5	3Ɛ5 175	2X5
6	451 45X	299
7	4X9 737	293
8	545 X0X	288
9	5X2 096	282
X	63X 358	277
Ɛ	696 613	270

N	Log N	d
X240	Ɛ26 732 883	58 266
1	78X Ɛ29	25Ɛ
2	827 188	254
3	883 420	249
4	91Ɛ 669	243
5	977 8Ɛ0	238
6	X13 Ɛ28	231
7	X70 159	227
8	Ɛ08 384	220
9	Ɛ64 5X4	215
X	Ɛ27 000 7Ɛ9	20Ɛ
Ɛ	058 X08	204
X250	0Ɛ5 010	1Ɛ9
1	151 209	1Ɛ3
2	1X9 400	1X8
3	245 5X8	1X1
4	2X1 789	197
5	339 964	18Ɛ
6	395 Ɛ33	186
7	432 0Ɛ9	17X
8	48X 277	174
9	526 42Ɛ	169
X	582 598	163
Ɛ	61X 73Ɛ	158
X260	676 897	151
1	712 X28	146
2	76X Ɛ72	140
3	807 0Ɛ2	135
4	863 227	12Ɛ
5	8ƐƐ 356	123
6	957 479	11X
7	9Ɛ3 597	112
8	X4Ɛ 6X9	108
9	XX7 7Ɛ5	101
X	Ɛ43 8Ɛ6	0Ɛ6
Ɛ	Ɛ9Ɛ 9Ɛ0	0Ɛ0
X270	Ɛ28 037 XX0	0X5
1	093 Ɛ85	09Ɛ
2	130 064	094
3	188 138	089
4	224 205	082
5	280 287	078
6	318 343	071
7	374 3Ɛ4	067
8	410 45Ɛ	060
9	468 4ƐƐ	055
X	504 554	04X
Ɛ	560 5X2	044

N	Log N	d
X280	Ɛ28 5Ɛ8 626	58 03X
1	654 664	032
2	6Ɛ0 696	028
3	748 702	021
4	7X4 723	017
5	840 73X	010
6	898 74X	005
7	934 753	57 ƐƐƐ
8	990 752	ƐƐ4
9	X28 746	ƐX9
X	X84 733	ƐX3
Ɛ	Ɛ20 716	Ɛ98
X290	Ɛ78 6Ɛ2	Ɛ91
1	Ɛ29 014 683	Ɛ87
2	070 64X	Ɛ80
3	108 60X	Ɛ76
4	164 584	Ɛ6Ɛ
5	200 533	Ɛ64
6	258 497	Ɛ5X
7	2Ɛ4 435	Ɛ52
8	350 387	Ɛ49
9	3X8 314	Ɛ41
X	444 255	Ɛ37
Ɛ	4X0 190	Ɛ31
X2X0	538 101	Ɛ26
1	594 027	Ɛ1Ɛ
2	62Ɛ Ɛ46	Ɛ14
3	687 X5X	Ɛ0X
4	723 968	Ɛ03
5	77Ɛ 86Ɛ	XƐ9
6	817 768	XƐ2
7	873 65X	XX7
8	90Ɛ 545	XX1
9	967 426	X96
X	X03 300	X8Ɛ
Ɛ	X5Ɛ 18Ɛ	X85
X2Ɛ0	XƐ7 054	X7X
1	Ɛ52 Ɛ12	X73
2	ƐXX 985	X69
3	Ɛ2X 046 832	X63
4	0X2 695	X57
5	13X 530	X51
6	196 381	X47
7	232 208	X40
8	28X 048	X35
9	325 X81	X2X
X	381 8XƐ	X24
Ɛ	419 713	X19

N	Log N	d	N	Log N	d	N	Log N	d
X300	Ɛ2X 475 530	57 X13	X340	Ɛ30 325 649	57 7X9	X380	Ɛ32 188 X25	57 587
1	511 343	X08	1	381 236	7X4	1	224 3Ɛ0	580
2	569 14Ɛ	X02	2	418 X1X	798	2	27Ɛ 970	575
3	604 Ɛ51	9Ɛ6	3	474 5Ɛ6	792	3	317 325	570
4	660 947	9Ɛ1	4	510 188	788	4	372 895	564
5	6Ɛ8 738	9X5	5	567 954	781	5	40X 239	55X
6	754 521	99Ɛ	6	603 515	776	6	465 797	554
7	7Ɛ0 300	995	7	65Ɛ 08Ɛ	770	7	501 12Ɛ	548
8	848 095	989	8	6Ɛ6 83Ɛ	765	8	558 677	543
9	8X3 X62	983	9	752 3X4	75Ɛ	9	5Ɛ3 ƐƐX	538
X	93Ɛ 825	979	X	7X9 Ɛ43	754	X	64Ɛ 536	531
Ɛ	997 5X2	972	Ɛ	845 697	749	Ɛ	6X6 X67	527
X310	X33 354	967	X350	8X1 224	743	X390	742 392	520
1	X8Ɛ 0ƐƐ	961	1	938 967	739	1	799 8Ɛ2	516
2	Ɛ26 X60	956	2	994 4X4	731	2	835 208	50Ɛ
3	Ɛ82 7Ɛ6	94Ɛ	3	X30 015	728	3	890 717	504
4	Ɛ2Ɛ 01X 545	945	4	X87 741	720	4	928 01Ɛ	4ƐX
5	076 28X	93Ɛ	5	Ɛ23 261	716	5	983 519	4Ɛ4
6	112 009	933	6	Ɛ7X 977	710	6	X1X X11	4X9
7	169 940	929	7	Ɛ31 016 487	705	7	X76 2ƐX	4X2
8	205 669	923	8	071 Ɛ90	6ƐX	8	Ɛ11 7X0	498
9	261 390	918	9	109 68X	6Ɛ4	9	Ɛ69 078	492
X	2Ɛ9 0X8	911	X	165 182	6X9	X	Ɛ33 004 54X	487
Ɛ	354 9Ɛ9	907	Ɛ	200 86Ɛ	6X3	Ɛ	05Ɛ X15	480
X320	3Ɛ0 704	900	X360	258 352	698	X3X0	0Ɛ7 295	476
1	448 404	8Ɛ5	1	2Ɛ3 X2X	691	1	152 74Ɛ	46Ɛ
2	4X4 0Ɛ9	8XƐ	2	34Ɛ 4ƐƐ	687	2	1X9 ƐƐX	465
3	53Ɛ 9X8	8X4	3	3X6 Ɛ86	680	3	245 463	45X
4	597 690	89X	4	442 646	676	4	2X0 901	454
5	633 36X	893	5	49X 100	670	5	338 155	449
6	68Ɛ 041	888	6	535 770	664	6	393 5X2	442
7	726 909	882	7	591 214	65X	7	42X X24	438
8	782 58Ɛ	877	8	628 872	654	8	486 260	432
9	81X 246	871	9	684 306	649	9	521 692	427
X	875 XƐ7	866	X	71Ɛ 953	642	X	578 XƐ9	421
Ɛ	911 761	860	Ɛ	777 395	638	Ɛ	614 31X	416
X330	969 401	855	X370	812 X11	632	X3Ɛ0	66Ɛ 734	40Ɛ
1	X05 056	84X	1	86X 443	626	1	706 Ɛ43	405
2	X60 8X4	844	2	905 X69	621	2	762 348	3ƐƐ
3	XƐ8 528	839	3	961 48X	615	3	7Ɛ9 747	3Ɛ3
4	Ɛ54 165	832	4	9Ɛ8 XX3	610	4	854 Ɛ3X	3XX
5	ƐXƐ 997	828	5	X54 4Ɛ3	604	5	8Ɛ0 328	3X3
6	Ɛ30 047 603	822	6	XXƐ XƐ7	5ƐX	6	947 70Ɛ	398
7	0X3 225	816	7	Ɛ47 4Ɛ5	5Ɛ4	7	9X2 XX7	392
8	13X X3Ɛ	810	8	ƐX2 XX9	5X9	8	X3X 279	387
9	196 64Ɛ	806	9	Ɛ32 03X 496	5X2	9	X95 644	381
X	232 255	7ƐƐ	X	095 X78	598	X	Ɛ30 X05	377
Ɛ	289 X54	7Ɛ5	Ɛ	131 454	591	Ɛ	Ɛ88 180	36Ɛ

N	Log N	d	N	Log N	d	N	Log N	d
X400	Ɛ34 023 52Ɛ	57 366	X440	Ɛ35 X71 411	57 145	X480	Ɛ37 8Ɛ2 735	56 Ɛ28
1	07X 895	35X	1	Ɛ08 556	13Ɛ	1	949 661	Ɛ21
2	116 033	355	2	Ɛ63 695	135	2	9X4 582	Ɛ17
3	171 388	349	3	ƐƐX 80X	12X	3	X3Ɛ 499	Ɛ10
4	208 715	344	4	Ɛ36 055 938	124	4	X96 3X9	Ɛ05
5	263 X59	338	5	0Ɛ0 X60	119	5	Ɛ31 2Ɛ2	Ɛ00
6	2ƐƐ 195	333	6	147 Ɛ79	113	6	Ɛ88 1Ɛ2	XƐ4
7	356 508	327	7	1X3 090	108	7	Ɛ38 023 0X6	XXƐ
8	3Ɛ1 833	322	8	23X 198	102	8	079 Ɛ95	XX4
9	448 Ɛ55	316	9	295 29X	0Ɛ7	9	114 X79	X99
X	4X4 26Ɛ	311	X	330 395	0Ɛ1	X	16Ɛ 956	X93
Ɛ	53Ɛ 580	305	Ɛ	387 486	0X6	Ɛ	206 829	X89
X410	596 885	2ƐƐ	X450	422 570	0X0	X490	261 6Ɛ6	X82
1	631 Ɛ84	2Ɛ5	1	479 650	095	1	2Ɛ8 578	X78
2	689 279	2XX	2	514 725	08Ɛ	2	353 434	X71
3	724 567	2X4	3	56Ɛ 7Ɛ4	085	3	3XX 2X5	X67
4	77Ɛ 84Ɛ	299	4	606 879	07X	4	445 150	X61
5	816 Ɛ28	293	5	661 937	073	5	49Ɛ ƐƐ1	X56
6	872 1ƐƐ	288	6	6Ɛ8 9XX	069	6	536 X47	X4Ɛ
7	909 487	282	7	753 X57	063	7	591 896	X46
8	964 749	277	8	7XX XƐX	058	8	628 720	X3X
9	9ƐƐ X04	271	9	845 Ɛ56	052	9	683 55X	X35
X	X57 075	266	X	8X0 ƐX8	047	X	71X 393	X29
Ɛ	XƐ2 31Ɛ	260	Ɛ	938 033	041	Ɛ	775 200	X24
X420	Ɛ49 57Ɛ	255	X460	993 074	036	X4X0	810 024	X19
1	ƐX4 814	24Ɛ	1	X2X 0XX	030	1	866 X41	X13
2	Ɛ35 03Ɛ X63	244	2	X85 11X	025	2	901 854	X08
3	097 0X7	23X	3	Ɛ20 143	01Ɛ	3	958 660	X02
4	132 325	233	4	Ɛ77 162	015	4	9Ɛ3 462	9Ɛ7
5	189 558	229	5	Ɛ37 012 177	00X	5	X4X 259	9Ɛ1
6	224 785	222	6	069 185	003	6	XX5 04X	9X6
7	27Ɛ 9X7	218	7	104 188	56 ƐƐ9	7	Ɛ3Ɛ X34	9X0
8	317 003	211	8	15Ɛ 185	ƐƐ3	8	Ɛ96 814	996
9	372 214	207	9	1Ɛ6 178	ƐX8	9	Ɛ39 031 5XX	98Ɛ
X	409 41Ɛ	200	X	251 164	ƐX2	X	088 379	985
Ɛ	464 61Ɛ	1Ɛ6	Ɛ	2X8 146	Ɛ97	Ɛ	123 142	97Ɛ
X430	4ƐƐ 815	1XƐ	X470	343 121	Ɛ91	X4Ɛ0	179 Ɛ01	974
1	556 X04	1X5	1	39X 0Ɛ2	Ɛ86	1	214 875	969
2	5Ɛ1 ƐX9	19X	2	435 078	Ɛ80	2	26Ɛ 622	963
3	649 187	194	3	490 038	Ɛ76	3	306 385	959
4	6X4 35Ɛ	18X	4	526 ƐƐ2	Ɛ6Ɛ	4	361 122	952
5	73Ɛ 529	182	5	581 Ɛ61	Ɛ64	5	3Ɛ7 X74	948
6	796 6XƐ	179	6	618 Ɛ05	Ɛ5X	6	452 800	942
7	831 868	172	7	673 X63	Ɛ54	7	4X9 542	937
8	888 X1X	167	8	70X 9Ɛ7	Ɛ49	8	544 279	931
9	923 Ɛ85	161	9	765 944	Ɛ43	9	59X ƐXX	926
X	97Ɛ 126	157	X	800 887	Ɛ39	X	635 914	920
Ɛ	X16 281	150	Ɛ	857 804	Ɛ31	Ɛ	690 634	915

N	Log N	d	N	Log N	d	N	Log N	d
χ500	Ɛ39 727 349	56 90Ɛ	χ540	Ɛ3Ɛ 553 4Ɛ7	56 6Ɛ4	χ580	Ɛ41 373 065	56 49Ɛ
1	782 058	905	1	5χ9 ƐχƐ	6χχ	1	409 544	495
2	818 961	8Ɛχ	2	644 699	6χ4	2	463 χ19	48Ɛ
3	873 65Ɛ	8Ɛ4	3	69Ɛ 181	699	3	4Ɛχ 2χ8	484
4	90χ 353	8χ9	4	735 85χ	692	4	554 770	479
5	965 040	8χ3	5	790 330	689	5	5χƐ 029	474
6	9ƐƐ 923	899	6	826 9Ɛ9	682	6	645 4χ1	469
7	χ56 600	892	7	881 47Ɛ	678	7	69Ɛ 94χ	463
8	χƐ1 292	888	8	917 Ɛ37	671	8	736 1Ɛ1	458
9	Ɛ47 Ɛ5χ	881	9	972 5χ8	667	9	790 649	452
χ	Ɛχ2 81Ɛ	877	χ	χ09 053	660	χ	826 χ9Ɛ	448
Ɛ	Ɛ3χ 039 496	871	Ɛ	χ63 6Ɛ3	656	Ɛ	881 327	441
χ510	094 147	866	χ550	χƐχ 149	650	χ590	917 768	437
1	12χ 9Ɛ1	860	1	Ɛ54 799	646	1	971 Ɛχ3	431
2	185 651	855	2	ƐχƐ 223	63Ɛ	2	χ08 414	426
3	220 2χ6	84Ɛ	3	Ɛ40 045 862	635	3	χ62 83χ	420
4	276 Ɛ35	845	4	0χ0 297	62χ	4	χƐ9 05χ	416
5	311 77χ	83χ	5	136 905	624	5	Ɛ53 474	40Ɛ
6	368 3Ɛ8	834	6	191 329	619	6	Ɛχ9 883	406
7	403 030	829	7	227 946	614	7	Ɛ42 044 089	3Ɛχ
8	459 859	823	8	282 35χ	609	8	09χ 487	3Ɛ5
9	4Ɛ4 480	819	9	318 967	602	9	134 880	3χχ
χ	54Ɛ 099	812	χ	373 369	5Ɛ8	χ	18Ɛ 06χ	3χ4
Ɛ	5χ5 8χƐ	808	Ɛ	409 965	5Ɛ2	Ɛ	225 452	399
χ520	640 4Ɛ7	801	χ560	464 357	5χ8	χ5χ0	27Ɛ 82Ɛ	393
1	697 0Ɛ8	7Ɛ7	1	4Ɛχ 943	5χ1	1	316 002	389
2	731 8Ɛ3	7Ɛ1	2	555 324	597	2	370 38Ɛ	382
3	788 4χ4	7χ6	3	5χƐ 8ƐƐ	590	3	406 751	379
4	823 08χ	7χ0	4	646 28Ɛ	586	4	460 Ɛ0χ	371
5	879 86χ	796	5	6χ0 855	580	5	4Ɛ7 27Ɛ	368
6	914 444	78Ɛ	6	737 215	575	6	551 627	361
7	96Ɛ 013	785	7	791 78χ	56Ɛ	7	5χ7 988	357
8	χ05 798	77χ	8	828 139	565	8	642 123	351
9	χ60 356	774	9	882 6χ2	55χ	9	698 474	346
χ	χƐ6 Ɛ0χ	769	χ	919 040	554	χ	732 7Ɛχ	340
Ɛ	Ɛ51 677	764	Ɛ	973 594	549	Ɛ	788 Ɛ3χ	335
χ530	Ɛχ8 21Ɛ	758	χ570	χ09 Ɛ21	544	χ5Ɛ0	823 273	330
1	Ɛ3Ɛ 042 977	753	1	χ64 465	539	1	879 5χ3	325
2	099 50χ	748	2	χƐχ 9χ2	532	2	913 908	31χ
3	134 056	741	3	Ɛ55 314	528	3	96χ 026	315
4	18χ 797	738	4	ƐχƐ 840	522	4	χ04 33Ɛ	30χ
5	225 313	731	5	Ɛ41 046 162	518	5	χ5χ 649	303
6	27Ɛ χ44	726	6	0χ0 67χ	511	6	χƐ4 950	2Ɛχ
7	316 56χ	720	7	136 Ɛ8Ɛ	507	7	Ɛ4Ɛ 04χ	2Ɛ3
8	371 08χ	716	8	191 496	500	8	Ɛχ5 341	2χ9
9	407 7χ4	70Ɛ	9	227 996	4Ɛ6	9	Ɛ43 03Ɛ 62χ	2χ2
χ	462 2Ɛ3	705	χ	282 290	4Ɛ0	χ	095 910	298
Ɛ	4Ɛ8 9Ɛ8	6ƐƐ	Ɛ	318 780	4χ5	Ɛ	12Ɛ Ɛχ8	292

N	Log N	d	N	Log N	d	N	Log N	d
X600	Ɛ43 186 27X	56 288	X640	Ɛ44 Ɛ90 ƐX2	56 076	X680	Ɛ46 98Ɛ 47Ɛ	55 X65
1	220 546	281	1	Ɛ45 027 058	06Ɛ	1	X25 324	X5Ɛ
2	276 807	277	2	081 107	065	2	X7Ɛ 183	X55
3	310 X82	270	3	117 170	05Ɛ	3	Ɛ15 018	X4X
4	367 132	267	4	171 20Ɛ	055	4	Ɛ6X X66	X44
5	401 399	260	5	207 264	04X	5	Ɛ47 004 8XX	X3Ɛ
6	457 639	255	6	261 2Ɛ2	044	6	05X 729	X33
7	4Ɛ1 892	250	7	2Ɛ7 336	039	7	0Ɛ4 560	X2X
8	547 Ɛ22	245	8	351 373	034	8	14X 38X	X23
9	5X2 167	23Ɛ	9	3X7 3X7	029	9	1X4 1Ɛ1	X19
X	638 3X6	234	X	441 414	023	X	23X 00X	X13
Ɛ	692 61X	22X	Ɛ	497 437	019	Ɛ	293 X21	X09
X610	728 848	224	X650	531 454	012	X690	329 82X	X02
1	782 X70	21X	1	587 466	008	1	383 630	9Ɛ8
2	819 08X	213	2	621 472	002	2	419 428	9Ɛ2
3	873 2X1	209	3	677 474	55 ƐƐ7	3	473 21X	9X8
4	909 4XX	203	4	711 46Ɛ	ƐƐ2	4	509 006	9X2
5	963 6Ɛ1	1Ɛ8	5	767 461	ƐX7	5	562 9X8	997
6	9Ɛ9 8X9	1Ɛ3	6	801 448	ƐX1	6	5Ɛ8 783	991
7	X53 XX0	1X7	7	857 429	Ɛ96	7	652 554	987
8	XXX 087	1X2	8	8Ɛ1 403	Ɛ90	8	6X8 31Ɛ	980
9	Ɛ44 269	197	9	947 393	Ɛ86	9	742 09Ɛ	977
X	Ɛ9X 444	191	X	9X1 359	Ɛ80	X	797 X56	970
Ɛ	Ɛ44 034 615	187	Ɛ	X37 319	Ɛ76	Ɛ	831 806	966
X620	08X 7X0	180	X660	X91 293	Ɛ6Ɛ	X6X0	887 570	95Ɛ
1	124 960	176	1	Ɛ27 242	Ɛ65	1	921 30Ɛ	956
2	17X Ɛ16	170	2	Ɛ81 1X7	Ɛ5Ɛ	2	977 065	94Ɛ
3	215 086	166	3	Ɛ46 017 146	Ɛ54	3	X10 9Ɛ4	945
4	26Ɛ 230	15Ɛ	4	071 09X	Ɛ4X	4	X66 739	93Ɛ
5	305 38Ɛ	155	5	107 028	Ɛ44	5	Ɛ00 478	934
6	35Ɛ 524	14X	6	160 Ɛ70	Ɛ3X	6	Ɛ56 1Ɛ0	92Ɛ
7	3Ɛ5 672	145	7	1Ɛ6 XXX	Ɛ33	7	ƐXƐ Ɛ1Ɛ	924
8	44Ɛ 7Ɛ7	13X	8	250 X21	Ɛ2X	8	Ɛ48 045 843	91X
9	4X5 935	134	9	2X6 94Ɛ	Ɛ22	9	09Ɛ 561	913
X	53Ɛ X69	129	X	340 871	Ɛ19	X	135 274	90X
Ɛ	595 Ɛ96	123	Ɛ	396 78X	Ɛ13	Ɛ	18X Ɛ82	903
X630	630 0Ɛ9	119	X670	430 6X1	Ɛ08	X6Ɛ0	224 885	8Ɛ9
1	686 216	113	1	486 5X9	Ɛ02	1	27X 582	8Ɛ3
2	720 329	108	2	520 4XƐ	XƐ7	2	314 275	8X8
3	776 435	102	3	576 3X6	XƐ2	3	369 Ɛ61	8X3
4	810 537	0Ɛ8	4	610 298	XX7	4	403 844	898
5	866 633	0Ɛ2	5	666 183	XX1	5	459 520	892
6	900 725	0X7	6	700 064	X97	6	4Ɛ3 1Ɛ2	888
7	956 810	0X1	7	755 Ɛ3Ɛ	X90	7	548 X7X	881
8	9Ɛ0 8Ɛ1	097	8	7XƐ X0Ɛ	X86	8	5X2 73Ɛ	877
9	X46 988	090	9	845 895	X80	9	638 3Ɛ6	872
X	XX0 X58	086	X	89Ɛ 755	X76	X	692 068	866
Ɛ	Ɛ36 Ɛ22	080	Ɛ	935 60Ɛ	X70	Ɛ	727 912	861

N	Log N	d	N	Log N	d	N	Log N	d
X700	Ɛ48 781 573	55 857	X740	Ɛ4X 567 327	55 649	X780	Ɛ50 344 X01	55 442
1	817 20X	850	1	600 974	643	1	39X 243	437
2	870 X5X	846	2	656 3Ɛ7	639	2	433 67X	432
3	906 6X4	840	3	6XƐ X34	633	3	488 XƐ0	427
4	960 324	835	4	745 467	629	4	522 317	421
5	9Ɛ5 Ɛ59	830	5	79X X94	622	5	577 738	417
6	X4Ɛ 789	825	6	834 4Ɛ6	618	6	610 Ɛ53	411
7	XX5 3Ɛ2	81Ɛ	7	889 Ɛ12	612	7	666 364	406
8	Ɛ3Ɛ 011	815	8	923 524	608	8	6ƐƐ 76X	401
9	Ɛ94 826	80Ɛ	9	978 Ɛ30	602	9	754 Ɛ6Ɛ	3Ɛ6
X	Ɛ49 02X 435	804	X	X12 532	5Ɛ7	X	7XX 365	3Ɛ0
Ɛ	084 039	7ƐX	Ɛ	X67 Ɛ29	5Ɛ2	Ɛ	843 755	3X6
X710	119 837	7Ɛ4	X750	Ɛ01 51Ɛ	5X7	X790	898 Ɛ3Ɛ	3X0
1	173 42Ɛ	7XX	1	Ɛ56 Ɛ06	5X1	1	932 31Ɛ	396
2	209 019	7X4	2	ƐƐ0 4X7	597	2	987 6Ɛ5	390
3	262 801	799	3	Ɛ4Ɛ 045 X82	591	3	X20 X85	385
4	2Ɛ8 39X	793	4	09Ɛ 453	586	4	X76 24X	37Ɛ
5	351 Ɛ71	789	5	134 X19	580	5	Ɛ0Ɛ 609	376
6	3X7 73X	783	6	18X 399	577	6	Ɛ64 983	36Ɛ
7	441 301	779	7	223 954	570	7	ƐƐX 132	365
8	496 X7X	772	8	279 304	566	8	Ɛ51 053 497	35Ɛ
9	530 630	769	9	312 86X	55Ɛ	9	0X8 836	354
X	586 199	762	X	368 209	556	X	141 Ɛ8X	34Ɛ
Ɛ	61Ɛ 93Ɛ	757	Ɛ	401 763	54Ɛ	Ɛ	197 319	345
X720	675 496	752	X760	457 0Ɛ2	545	X7X0	230 662	33X
1	70Ɛ 028	748	1	4Ɛ0 637	540	1	285 9X0	334
2	764 774	741	2	545 Ɛ77	534	2	31Ɛ 114	32X
3	7ƐX 2Ɛ5	737	3	59Ɛ 4XƐ	52Ɛ	3	374 442	324
4	853 X30	731	4	634 X1X	525	4	409 766	31X
5	8X9 561	727	5	68X 343	51X	5	462 X84	314
6	943 088	720	6	723 861	515	6	4Ɛ8 198	309
7	998 7X8	716	7	779 176	50X	7	551 4X5	304
8	X32 302	711	8	812 684	504	8	5X6 7X9	2Ɛ9
9	X87 X13	706	9	867 Ɛ88	4ƐX	9	63Ɛ XX6	2Ɛ3
X	Ɛ21 519	6ƐƐ	X	901 486	4Ɛ3	X	695 199	2X9
Ɛ	Ɛ77 018	6Ɛ6	Ɛ	956 979	4XX	Ɛ	72X 486	2X3
X730	Ɛ4X 010 712	6XƐ	X770	9Ɛ0 267	4X3	X7Ɛ0	783 769	299
1	066 201	6X6	1	X45 74X	499	1	818 X46	293
2	0ƐƐ 8X7	69Ɛ	2	X9Ɛ 027	493	2	872 119	289
3	155 386	695	3	Ɛ34 4ƐX	489	3	907 3X6	282
4	1XX X5Ɛ	68X	4	Ɛ89 987	483	4	960 668	279
5	244 529	685	5	Ɛ50 023 24X	479	5	9Ɛ5 925	272
6	299 ƐƐ2	67X	6	078 707	472	6	X4X Ɛ97	268
7	333 670	674	7	111 Ɛ79	468	7	XX4 243	262
8	389 124	66X	8	167 425	463	8	Ɛ39 4X5	258
9	422 792	664	9	200 888	458	9	Ɛ92 741	252
X	478 236	65X	X	256 124	452	X	Ɛ52 027 993	248
Ɛ	511 894	653	Ɛ	2XƐ 576	447	Ɛ	081 01Ɛ	241

N	Log N	d	N	Log N	d	N	Log N	d
Χ800	Ɛ52 116 260	55 238	Χ840	Ɛ53 Χ9Ɛ 525	55 033	Χ880	Ɛ55 858 675	54 Χ30
1	16Ɛ 498	231	1	Ɛ34 558	029	1	8Ɛ1 4Χ5	Χ26
2	204 709	227	2	Ɛ89 585	022	2	946 30Ɛ	Χ1Ɛ
3	259 934	221	3	Ɛ54 022 5Χ7	019	3	99Ɛ 12Χ	Χ16
4	2Ɛ2 Ɛ55	217	4	077 604	013	4	Χ33 Ɛ44	Χ10
5	348 170	211	5	110 617	008	5	Χ88 954	Χ05
6	3Χ1 381	207	6	165 623	003	6	Ɛ21 759	Χ00
7	436 588	201	7	1ƐΧ 626	54 ƐƐ8	7	Ɛ76 559	9Ɛ5
8	48Ɛ 789	1Ɛ6	8	253 622	ƐƐ2	8	Ɛ56 00Ɛ 352	9Ɛ0
9	524 983	1Ɛ1	9	2Χ8 614	ƐΧ8	9	064 142	9Χ5
Χ	579 Ɛ74	1Χ6	Χ	341 600	ƐΧ2	Χ	0Ɛ8 Ɛ27	99Ɛ
Ɛ	613 15Χ	1Χ1	Ɛ	396 5Χ2	Ɛ99	Ɛ	151 906	996
Χ810	668 33Ɛ	196	Χ850	42Ɛ 57Ɛ	Ɛ91	Χ890	1Χ6 6Χ0	98Ɛ
1	701 515	190	1	484 550	Ɛ88	1	23Ɛ 46Ɛ	985
2	756 6Χ5	186	2	519 518	Ɛ82	2	294 234	97Ɛ
3	7ΧƐ 86Ɛ	180	3	572 49Χ	Ɛ78	3	328 ƐƐ3	976
4	844 Χ2Ɛ	176	4	607 456	Ɛ72	4	381 969	96Ɛ
5	899 ƐΧ5	16Ɛ	5	660 408	Ɛ67	5	416 718	965
6	933 154	166	6	6Ɛ5 373	Ɛ62	6	46Ɛ 481	95Ɛ
7	988 2ƐΧ	15Ɛ	7	74Χ 315	Ɛ57	7	504 220	955
8	Χ21 459	156	8	7Χ3 270	Ɛ52	8	558 Ɛ75	94Ɛ
9	Χ76 5Ɛ3	14Ɛ	9	838 202	Ɛ47	9	5Ɛ1 904	945
Χ	Ɛ0Ɛ 742	145	Χ	891 149	Ɛ41	Χ	646 649	93Ɛ
Ɛ	Ɛ64 887	13Ɛ	Ɛ	926 08Χ	Ɛ38	Ɛ	69Ɛ 388	935
Χ820	ƐƐ9 Χ06	135	Χ860	97Ɛ 006	Ɛ31	Χ8Χ0	734 101	92Χ
1	Ɛ53 052 Ɛ3Ɛ	12Ɛ	1	Χ13 Ɛ37	Ɛ27	1	788 Χ2Ɛ	925
2	0Χ8 06Χ	125	2	Χ68 Χ62	Ɛ21	2	821 754	91Ɛ
3	141 193	11Ɛ	3	Ɛ01 983	Ɛ17	3	876 473	915
4	196 2Ɛ2	114	4	Ɛ56 89Χ	Ɛ11	4	90Ɛ 188	90Χ
5	22Ɛ 406	10Ɛ	5	ƐΧƐ 7ΧƐ	Ɛ07	5	963 Χ96	905
6	284 515	104	6	Ɛ55 044 6Ɛ6	Ɛ00	6	9Ɛ8 79Ɛ	8ƐƐ
7	319 619	0ƐƐ	7	099 5Ɛ6	ΧƐ7	7	Χ51 49Χ	8Ɛ4
8	372 718	0Ɛ4	8	132 4Ɛ1	ΧƐ1	8	ΧΧ6 192	8ΧƐ
9	407 810	0ΧΧ	9	187 3Χ2	ΧΧ6	9	Ɛ3Χ Χ81	8Χ4
Χ	460 8ƐΧ	0Χ4	Χ	220 288	ΧΧ1	Χ	Ɛ93 765	89Ɛ
Ɛ	4Ɛ5 9Χ2	09Χ	Ɛ	275 169	Χ96	Ɛ	Ɛ57 028 444	895
Χ830	54Χ Χ80	094	Χ870	30Χ 043	Χ91	Χ8Ɛ0	081 119	88Χ
1	5Χ3 Ɛ54	08Χ	1	362 Ɛ14	Χ86	1	115 9Χ7	884
2	639 022	083	2	3Ɛ7 99Χ	Χ81	2	16Χ 66Ɛ	87Ɛ
3	692 0Χ5	07Χ	3	450 85Ɛ	Χ76	3	203 32Χ	874
4	727 163	074	4	4Χ5 715	Χ70	4	257 ƐΧ2	86Ɛ
5	780 217	069	5	53Χ 585	Χ66	5	2Ɛ0 851	864
6	815 284	063	6	593 42Ɛ	Χ60	6	345 4Ɛ5	85Χ
7	86Χ 327	05Χ	7	628 28Ɛ	Χ56	7	39Χ 153	855
8	903 385	053	8	681 125	Χ50	8	432 9Χ8	84Χ
9	958 418	049	9	715 Ɛ75	Χ46	9	487 636	844
Χ	9Ɛ1 465	043	Χ	76Χ 9ƐƐ	Χ40	Χ	520 27Χ	83Ɛ
Ɛ	Χ46 4Χ8	039	Ɛ	803 83Ɛ	Χ36	Ɛ	574 ΧƐ9	834

N	Log N	d	N	Log N	d	N	Log N	d
ᘔ900	Ɛ57 609 731	54 82ᘔ	ᘔ940	Ɛ59 372 774	54 62ᘔ	ᘔ980	Ɛ5Ɛ 10Ɛ 823	54 42Ɛ
1	662 35Ɛ	824	1	407 1ᘔ2	625	1	164 052	426
2	6Ɛ6 Ɛ83	81Ɛ	2	45Ɛ 807	61ᘔ	2	1Ɛ8 478	41Ɛ
3	74Ɛ 7ᘔ2	814	3	4Ɛ4 225	614	3	250 897	416
4	7ᘔ4 3Ɛ6	80ᘔ	4	548 839	60ᘔ	4	2ᘔ5 0Ɛ1	410
5	839 004	804	5	5ᘔ1 247	604	5	339 501	406
6	891 808	7Ɛᘔ	6	635 84Ɛ	5ƐƐ	6	391 907	400
7	926 406	7Ɛ4	7	68ᘔ 24ᘔ	5Ɛ4	7	426 107	3Ɛ5
8	97ᘔ ƐƐᘔ	7ᘔᘔ	8	722 842	5ᘔᘔ	8	47ᘔ 500	3Ɛ0
9	ᘔ13 7ᘔ8	7ᘔ5	9	777 230	5ᘔ5	9	512 8Ɛ0	3ᘔ6
ᘔ	ᘔ68 391	79ᘔ	ᘔ	80Ɛ 815	59ᘔ	ᘔ	567 096	3ᘔ0
Ɛ	Ɛ00 Ɛ6Ɛ	794	Ɛ	864 1Ɛ3	594	Ɛ	5ƐƐ 476	396
ᘔ910	Ɛ55 743	78ᘔ	ᘔ950	8Ɛ8 787	58Ɛ	ᘔ990	653 850	391
1	Ɛᘔᘔ 311	784	1	951 156	584	1	6ᘔ8 021	386
2	Ɛ58 042 ᘔ95	77ᘔ	2	9ᘔ5 71ᘔ	57ᘔ	2	740 3ᘔ7	380
3	097 653	774	3	ᘔ3ᘔ 098	575	3	794 767	376
4	130 207	76ᘔ	4	ᘔ92 651	56ᘔ	4	828 Ɛ21	371
5	184 975	764	5	Ɛ26 ƐƐƐ	565	5	881 292	366
6	219 519	75ᘔ	6	Ɛ7Ɛ 564	55ᘔ	6	915 638	361
7	272 077	754	7	Ɛ5ᘔ 013 Ɛ02	555	7	969 999	356
8	306 80Ɛ	74ᘔ	8	068 457	54ᘔ	8	ᘔ02 133	351
9	35Ɛ 359	744	9	100 9ᘔ5	545	9	ᘔ56 484	346
ᘔ	3Ɛ3 ᘔᘔ1	73ᘔ	ᘔ	155 32ᘔ	53Ɛ	ᘔ	ᘔᘔᘔ 80ᘔ	341
Ɛ	448 61Ɛ	734	Ɛ	1ᘔ9 869	534	Ɛ	Ɛ42 Ɛ4Ɛ	337
ᘔ920	4ᘔ1 153	72ᘔ	ᘔ960	242 1ᘔ1	52Ɛ	ᘔ9ᘔ0	Ɛ97 286	330
1	535 881	724	1	296 710	525	1	Ɛ60 02Ɛ 5Ɛ6	327
2	58ᘔ 3ᘔ5	71ᘔ	2	32Ɛ 035	51ᘔ	2	083 921	321
3	622 Ɛ03	714	3	383 553	515	3	118 042	317
4	677 617	70ᘔ	4	417 ᘔ68	50Ɛ	4	170 359	311
5	710 125	704	5	470 377	505	5	204 66ᘔ	307
6	764 829	6Ɛᘔ	6	504 880	4ƐƐ	6	258 975	302
7	7Ɛ9 327	6Ɛ4	7	559 17Ɛ	4Ɛ4	7	2Ɛ1 077	2Ɛ7
8	851 ᘔ1Ɛ	6ᘔᘔ	8	5Ɛ1 673	4ᘔƐ	8	345 372	2Ɛ1
9	8ᘔ6 509	6ᘔ4	9	645 Ɛ62	4ᘔ5	9	399 663	2ᘔ8
ᘔ	93ᘔ ƐƐ1	69ᘔ	ᘔ	69ᘔ 447	49Ɛ	ᘔ	431 94Ɛ	2ᘔ1
Ɛ	993 68Ɛ	694	Ɛ	732 926	495	Ɛ	486 030	297
ᘔ930	ᘔ28 163	68ᘔ	ᘔ970	787 1ƐƐ	48Ɛ	ᘔ9Ɛ0	51ᘔ 307	292
1	ᘔ80 831	684	1	81Ɛ 68ᘔ	485	1	572 599	288
2	Ɛ15 2Ɛ5	67ᘔ	2	873 Ɛ53	480	2	606 865	281
3	Ɛ69 973	675	3	908 413	475	3	65ᘔ Ɛ26	278
4	Ɛ59 002 428	66ᘔ	4	960 888	46Ɛ	4	6Ɛ3 1ᘔ2	272
5	056 ᘔ96	664	5	9Ɛ5 137	465	5	747 454	268
6	0ᘔƐ 53ᘔ	65ᘔ	6	ᘔ49 5ᘔ0	460	6	79Ɛ 700	262
7	143 Ɛ98	654	7	ᘔᘔ1 ᘔ40	455	7	833 962	258
8	198 630	64ᘔ	8	Ɛ36 295	44Ɛ	8	887 ƐƐᘔ	252
9	231 07ᘔ	644	9	Ɛ8ᘔ 724	446	9	920 250	248
ᘔ	285 702	63ᘔ	ᘔ	Ɛ5Ɛ 022 Ɛ6ᘔ	43Ɛ	ᘔ	974 498	243
Ɛ	31ᘔ 140	634	Ɛ	077 3ᘔ9	436	Ɛ	ᘔ08 71Ɛ	238

N	Log N	d	N	Log N	d	N	Log N	d
χχ00	Ɛ60 χ60 957	54 232	χχ40	Ɛ62 7χ5 ƐƐ3	54 037	χχ80	Ɛ64 523 411	53 χ41
1	χƐ4 Ɛ89	229	1	83χ 02χ	031	1	577 252	χ37
2	Ɛ49 1Ɛ6	222	2	892 05Ɛ	027	2	60Ɛ 089	χ30
3	Ɛχ1 418	219	3	926 086	021	3	662 χƐ9	χ27
4	Ɛ61 035 635	213	4	97χ 0χ7	017	4	6Ɛ6 924	χ21
5	089 848	209	5	χ12 102	011	5	74χ 745	χ18
6	121 χ55	202	6	χ66 113	008	6	7χ2 561	χ11
7	176 057	1Ɛ9	7	χƐχ 11Ɛ	001	7	836 372	χ07
8	20χ 254	1Ɛ3	8	Ɛ52 120	53 ƐƐ8	8	88χ 179	χ02
9	262 447	1χχ	9	Ɛχ6 118	ƐƐ2	9	921 Ɛ7Ɛ	9Ɛ8
χ	2Ɛ6 635	1χ3	χ	Ɛ63 03χ 10χ	Ɛχ7	χ	975 977	9Ɛ2
Ɛ	34χ 818	199	Ɛ	092 0Ɛ5	Ɛχ2	Ɛ	χ09 769	9χ8
χχ10	3χ2 9Ɛ5	193	χχ50	126 097	Ɛ98	χχ90	χ61 555	9χ2
1	436 Ɛ88	18χ	1	17χ 073	Ɛ93	1	χƐ5 337	998
2	48Ɛ 156	183	2	212 046	Ɛ88	2	Ɛ49 113	993
3	523 319	17χ	3	266 012	Ɛ82	3	Ɛχ0 χχ6	988
4	577 497	174	4	2Ɛ9 Ɛ94	Ɛ79	4	Ɛ65 034 872	983
5	60Ɛ 64Ɛ	16χ	5	351 Ɛ51	Ɛ72	5	088 635	979
6	663 7Ɛ9	163	6	3χ5 Ɛ03	Ɛ69	6	120 3Ɛ2	973
7	6Ɛ7 960	15χ	7	439 χ70	Ɛ63	7	174 165	969
8	74Ɛ χƐχ	154	8	491 χ13	Ɛ59	8	207 Ɛ12	964
9	7χ4 052	14Ɛ	9	525 970	Ɛ53	9	25Ɛ 876	959
χ	838 1χ1	144	χ	579 903	Ɛ49	χ	2Ɛ3 613	954
Ɛ	890 325	13χ	Ɛ	611 850	Ɛ44	Ɛ	347 367	94χ
χχ20	924 463	135	χχ60	665 794	Ɛ39	χχχ0	39Ɛ 0Ɛ5	944
1	978 598	12χ	1	6Ɛ9 711	Ɛ34	1	432 χ39	93χ
2	χ10 706	125	2	751 645	Ɛ29	2	486 777	934
3	χ64 82Ɛ	11χ	3	7χ5 572	Ɛ24	3	51χ 4χƐ	92χ
4	χƐ8 949	115	4	839 496	Ɛ1χ	4	572 219	925
5	Ɛ50 χ62	10Ɛ	5	891 3Ɛ4	Ɛ14	5	605 Ɛ42	91Ɛ
6	Ɛχ4 Ɛ71	105	6	925 308	Ɛ0χ	6	659 861	915
7	Ɛ62 039 076	0ƐƐ	7	979 216	Ɛ05	7	6Ɛ1 576	90Ɛ
8	091 175	0Ɛ5	8	χ11 11Ɛ	χƐχ	8	745 285	905
9	125 26χ	0χƐ	9	χ65 019	χƐ5	9	798 Ɛ8χ	8ƐƐ
χ	179 359	0χ6	χ	χƐ8 Ɛ12	χχχ	χ	830 889	8Ɛ6
Ɛ	211 443	09Ɛ	Ɛ	Ɛ50 χ00	χχ5	Ɛ	884 583	8χƐ
χχ30	265 522	096	χχ70	Ɛχ4 8χ5	χ9Ɛ	χχƐ0	918 272	8χ6
1	2Ɛ9 5Ɛ8	08Ɛ	1	Ɛ64 038 784	χ95	1	96Ɛ Ɛ58	8χ0
2	351 687	086	2	090 659	χ90	2	χ03 838	896
3	3χ5 751	080	3	124 529	χ85	3	χ57 512	890
4	439 811	076	4	178 3Ɛ2	χ7Ɛ	4	χχƐ 1χ2	887
5	491 887	070	5	210 271	χ76	5	Ɛ42 χ69	880
6	525 937	066	6	264 127	χ70	6	Ɛ96 729	877
7	579 9χ1	060	7	2Ɛ7 Ɛ97	χ66	7	Ɛ66 02χ 3χ4	871
8	611 χ41	057	8	34Ɛ χ41	χ60	8	082 055	867
9	665 χ98	050	9	3χ3 8χ1	χ56	9	115 900	861
χ	6Ɛ9 Ɛ28	047	χ	437 737	χ50	χ	169 561	858
Ɛ	751 Ɛ73	040	Ɛ	48Ɛ 587	χ46	Ɛ	201 1Ɛ9	851

N	Log N	d	N	Log N	d	N	Log N	d
XƐ00	Ɛ66 254 X4X	53 848	XƐ40	Ɛ67 Ɛ7X 743	53 655	XƐ80	Ɛ69 898 750	53 463
1	2X8 696	842	1	Ɛ68 012 198	64X	1	92Ɛ ƐƐ3	458
2	340 318	838	2	065 826	645	2	983 44Ɛ	453
3	393 Ɛ54	832	3	0Ɛ9 26Ɛ	63Ɛ	3	X16 8X2	449
4	427 786	829	4	150 8XX	635	4	X6X 12Ɛ	444
5	47Ɛ 3Ɛ3	822	5	1X4 323	630	5	Ɛ01 573	439
6	513 015	819	6	237 953	625	6	Ɛ54 9Ɛ0	434
7	566 832	813	7	28Ɛ 378	620	7	ƐX8 224	42X
8	5ƐX 445	809	8	322 998	616	8	Ɛ6X 03Ɛ 652	424
9	652 052	803	9	376 3Ɛ2	610	9	092 X76	41Ɛ
X	6X5 855	7ƐX	X	409 X02	606	X	126 295	414
Ɛ	739 453	7Ɛ3	Ɛ	461 408	601	Ɛ	179 6X9	40Ɛ
XƐ10	791 046	7XX	XƐ50	4Ɛ4 X09	5Ɛ7	XƐ90	210 XƐ8	405
1	824 834	7X4	1	548 404	5Ɛ1	1	264 301	400
2	878 418	79X	2	59Ɛ 9Ɛ5	5X7	2	2Ɛ7 701	3Ɛ5
3	90Ɛ ƐƐ6	795	3	633 3X0	5X1	3	34X XƐ6	3Ɛ0
4	963 78Ɛ	78X	4	686 981	598	4	3X2 2X6	3X6
5	9Ɛ7 359	785	5	71X 359	592	5	435 690	3X1
6	X4X Ɛ22	77X	6	771 92Ɛ	588	6	488 X71	396
7	XX2 6X0	775	7	805 2Ɛ7	582	7	520 247	391
8	Ɛ36 255	770	8	858 879	578	8	573 618	387
9	Ɛ89 X05	765	9	8Ɛ0 235	573	9	606 9X3	381
X	Ɛ67 021 56X	75Ɛ	X	943 7X8	569	X	65X 164	378
Ɛ	075 109	756	Ɛ	997 155	563	Ɛ	6Ɛ1 520	372
XƐ20	108 863	750	XƐ60	X2X 6Ɛ8	559	XƐX0	744 892	368
1	160 3Ɛ3	746	1	X82 055	553	1	798 03X	362
2	1Ɛ3 Ɛ39	740	2	Ɛ15 5X8	54X	2	82Ɛ 3X0	358
3	247 679	737	3	Ɛ68 Ɛ36	544	3	882 738	353
4	29Ɛ 1Ɛ4	730	4	Ɛ69 000 47X	53X	4	915 X8Ɛ	349
5	332 924	727	5	053 9Ɛ8	534	5	969 218	343
6	386 44Ɛ	721	6	0X7 330	52Ɛ	6	X00 55Ɛ	33X
7	419 Ɛ70	717	7	13X 85Ɛ	524	7	X53 899	333
8	471 687	712	8	192 183	51Ɛ	8	XX7 010	32X
9	505 199	707	9	225 6X2	515	9	Ɛ3X 33X	324
X	558 8X4	702	X	278 ƐƐ7	510	X	Ɛ91 662	31Ɛ
Ɛ	5Ɛ0 3X6	6Ɛ8	Ɛ	310 507	505	Ɛ	Ɛ6Ɛ 024 981	314
XƐ30	643 XX2	6Ɛ2	XƐ70	363 X10	500	XƐƐ0	078 095	30Ɛ
1	697 594	6X8	1	3Ɛ7 310	4Ɛ6	1	10Ɛ 3X4	305
2	72Ɛ 080	6X3	2	44X 806	4Ɛ0	2	162 6X9	300
3	782 763	698	3	4X2 0Ɛ6	4X7	3	1Ɛ5 9X9	2Ɛ5
4	816 23Ɛ	693	4	535 5X1	4X0	4	249 0X2	2Ɛ0
5	869 912	689	5	588 X81	497	5	2X0 392	2X6
6	901 39Ɛ	683	6	620 358	491	6	333 678	2X1
7	954 X62	67X	7	673 829	488	7	386 959	296
8	9X8 520	673	8	707 0Ɛ5	481	8	41X 033	291
9	X3Ɛ Ɛ93	66X	9	75X 576	478	9	471 304	287
X	X93 641	664	X	7Ɛ1 X32	472	X	504 58Ɛ	282
Ɛ	Ɛ27 0X5	65X	Ɛ	845 2X4	468	Ɛ	557 851	277

N	Log N	d	N	Log N	d	N	Log N	d
Ɛ000	Ɛ6Ɛ 5χχ Ɛ08	53 272	Ɛ040	Ɛ71 2Ɛ5 68Ɛ	53 083	Ɛ080	Ɛ72 Ɛ24 6Ɛ4	52 χ95
1	642 17χ	268	1	348 752	079	1	Ɛ73 047 589	χ8Ɛ
2	695 426	263	2	39Ɛ 80Ɛ	073	2	09χ 458	χ85
3	728 689	259	3	432 882	06χ	3	131 321	χ80
4	77Ɛ 926	252	4	485 930	064	4	184 1χ1	χ77
5	812 Ɛ78	24χ	5	518 994	05χ	5	217 058	χ70
6	866 206	243	6	56Ɛ χ32	054	6	269 Ɛ08	χ67
7	8Ɛ9 449	23χ	7	602 χ86	04Ɛ	7	300 973	χ61
8	950 687	234	8	655 Ɛ15	045	8	353 814	χ58
9	9χ3 8ƐƐ	22χ	9	6χ8 Ɛ5χ	040	9	3χ6 670	χ51
χ	χ36 Ɛ29	224	χ	73Ɛ Ɛ9χ	035	χ	439 501	χ48
Ɛ	χ8χ 151	21Ɛ	Ɛ	793 013	030	Ɛ	490 349	χ43
Ɛ010	Ɛ21 370	215	Ɛ050	826 043	026	Ɛ090	523 190	χ39
1	Ɛ74 585	20Ɛ	1	879 069	021	1	576 009	χ33
2	Ɛ70 007 794	206	2	910 08χ	016	2	608 χ40	χ29
3	05χ 99χ	1ƐƐ	3	963 0χ4	011	3	65Ɛ 869	χ24
4	0Ɛ1 Ɛ99	1Ɛ6	4	9Ɛ6 0Ɛ5	008	4	6ƐƐ 691	χ1χ
5	145 193	1Ɛ1	5	χ49 101	001	5	745 4χƐ	χ14
6	198 384	1χ6	6	χχ0 102	52 ƐƐ8	6	798 303	χ0Ɛ
7	22Ɛ 56χ	1χ1	7	Ɛ33 0Ɛχ	ƐƐ2	7	82Ɛ 112	χ05
8	282 74Ɛ	197	8	Ɛ86 0Ɛ0	Ɛχ9	8	881 Ɛ17	9ƐƐ
9	315 926	191	9	Ɛ72 019 099	Ɛχ3	9	914 916	9Ɛ6
χ	368 χƐ7	188	χ	070 080	Ɛ99	χ	967 710	9Ɛ0
Ɛ	400 083	182	Ɛ	103 059	Ɛ93	Ɛ	9Ɛχ 500	9χ6
Ɛ020	453 245	178	Ɛ060	156 030	Ɛ8χ	Ɛ0χ0	χ51 2χ6	9χ1
1	4χ6 401	172	1	1χ8 ƐƐχ	Ɛ84	1	χχ4 087	996
2	539 573	169	2	23Ɛ Ɛ82	Ɛ7χ	2	Ɛ36 χ61	992
3	590 720	163	3	292 Ɛ40	Ɛ75	3	Ɛ89 833	987
4	623 883	159	4	325 χƐ5	Ɛ6Ɛ	4	Ɛ74 020 5Ɛχ	982
5	676 χ20	154	5	378 χ64	Ɛ65	5	073 380	978
6	709 Ɛ74	14χ	6	40Ɛ χ09	Ɛ5Ɛ	6	106 138	973
7	761 102	144	7	462 968	Ɛ56	7	158 χχƐ	969
8	7Ɛ4 246	13χ	8	4Ɛ5 902	Ɛ50	8	1χƐ 858	963
9	847 384	134	9	548 852	Ɛ46	9	242 5ƐƐ	95χ
χ	89χ 4Ɛ8	12Ɛ	χ	59Ɛ 798	Ɛ41	χ	295 359	953
Ɛ	931 627	125	Ɛ	632 719	Ɛ37	Ɛ	328 0Ɛ0	94Ɛ
Ɛ030	984 750	120	Ɛ070	685 654	Ɛ31	Ɛ0Ɛ0	37χ χ3Ɛ	944
1	χ17 870	115	1	718 585	Ɛ28	1	411 783	93Ɛ
2	χ6χ 985	110	2	76Ɛ 4Ɛ1	Ɛ22	2	464 502	935
3	Ɛ01 χ95	107	3	802 413	Ɛ18	3	4Ɛ7 237	930
4	Ɛ54 Ɛχ0	100	4	855 32Ɛ	Ɛ13	4	549 Ɛ67	926
5	Ɛχ8 0χ0	0Ɛ7	5	8χ8 242	Ɛ08	5	5χ0 891	920
6	Ɛ71 03Ɛ 197	0Ɛ1	6	93Ɛ 14χ	Ɛ03	6	633 5Ɛ1	916
7	092 288	0χ7	7	992 051	χƐχ	7	686 307	911
8	125 373	0χ2	8	χ24 Ɛ4Ɛ	χƐ4	8	719 018	908
9	178 455	098	9	χ77 χ43	χχχ	9	76Ɛ 924	901
χ	20Ɛ 531	092	χ	Ɛ0χ 931	χχ4	χ	802 625	8Ɛ8
Ɛ	262 603	088	Ɛ	Ɛ61 815	χ9Ɛ	Ɛ	855 321	8Ɛ2

N	Log N	d	N	Log N	d	N	Log N	d
Ɛ100	Ɛ74 8X8 013	52 8X9	Ɛ140	Ɛ76 593 X84	52 701	Ɛ180	Ɛ78 274 31Ɛ	52 518
1	93X 900	8X3	1	626 585	6Ɛ8	1	306 837	512
2	991 5X3	899	2	679 081	6Ɛ3	2	359 149	508
3	X24 280	894	3	70Ɛ 774	6X8	3	3XƐ 655	504
4	X76 Ɛ54	88X	4	762 260	6X3	4	441 Ɛ59	4Ɛ9
5	Ɛ09 822	884	5	7Ɛ4 943	69X	5	494 456	4Ɛ4
6	Ɛ60 4X6	87X	6	847 421	693	6	526 94X	4XX
7	ƐƐ3 164	875	7	899 XƐ4	68Ɛ	7	579 238	4X5
8	Ɛ75 045 X19	870	8	930 583	684	8	60Ɛ 721	49Ɛ
9	098 689	865	9	983 047	67Ɛ	9	662 000	495
X	12Ɛ 332	860	X	X15 706	675	X	6Ɛ4 495	490
Ɛ	181 Ɛ92	857	Ɛ	X68 17Ɛ	670	Ɛ	746 965	486
Ɛ110	214 829	850	Ɛ150	XƐX 82Ɛ	666	Ɛ190	799 22Ɛ	481
1	267 479	847	1	Ɛ51 295	660	1	82Ɛ 6Ɛ0	477
2	2ƐX 104	842	2	ƐX3 935	657	2	881 Ɛ67	471
3	350 946	837	3	Ɛ77 036 390	651	3	914 418	468
4	3X3 581	833	4	088 X21	647	4	966 884	462
5	436 1Ɛ4	828	5	11Ɛ 468	642	5	9Ɛ9 126	459
6	488 X20	823	6	171 XXX	639	6	X4Ɛ 583	453
7	51Ɛ 643	819	7	204 527	632	7	XX1 X16	44X
8	572 260	813	8	256 Ɛ59	629	8	Ɛ34 264	444
9	604 X73	80X	9	2X9 586	624	9	Ɛ86 6X8	43X
X	657 681	804	X	33Ɛ ƐXX	619	X	Ɛ79 018 Ɛ26	435
Ɛ	6XX 285	7ƐƐ	Ɛ	392 607	614	Ɛ	06Ɛ 35Ɛ	42Ɛ
Ɛ120	740 X84	7Ɛ5	Ɛ160	425 01Ɛ	60Ɛ	Ɛ1X0	101 78X	425
1	793 679	7XƐ	1	477 62X	605	1	153 ƐƐ3	420
2	826 268	7X6	2	50X 033	5ƐƐ	2	1X6 413	416
3	878 X52	7X0	3	560 632	5Ɛ6	3	238 829	411
4	90Ɛ 632	796	4	5Ɛ3 028	5Ɛ0	4	28Ɛ 03X	407
5	962 208	790	5	645 618	5X6	5	321 445	402
6	9Ɛ4 998	788	6	698 002	5X1	6	373 847	3Ɛ8
7	X47 564	781	7	72X 5X3	597	7	406 043	3Ɛ2
8	X9X 125	778	8	780 Ɛ7X	592	8	458 435	3X9
9	Ɛ30 8X1	772	9	813 550	588	9	4XX 822	3X3
X	Ɛ83 453	768	X	865 Ɛ18	582	X	541 005	39X
Ɛ	Ɛ76 015 ƐƐƐ	763	Ɛ	8Ɛ8 49X	579	Ɛ	593 3X3	394
Ɛ130	068 762	759	Ɛ170	94X X57	573	Ɛ1Ɛ0	625 777	38X
1	0ƐƐ 2ƐƐ	754	1	9X1 40X	56X	1	677 Ɛ45	385
2	151 X53	74X	2	X33 978	564	2	70X 30X	380
3	1X4 5X1	744	3	X86 320	55X	3	760 68X	375
4	237 125	73X	4	Ɛ18 87X	555	4	7Ɛ2 X43	371
5	289 863	735	5	Ɛ6Ɛ 213	54Ɛ	5	845 1Ɛ4	366
6	320 398	730	6	Ɛ78 001 762	545	6	897 55X	361
7	372 Ɛ08	725	7	054 0X7	540	7	929 8ƐƐ	358
8	405 631	720	8	0X6 627	537	8	980 057	351
9	458 151	717	9	138 Ɛ62	530	9	X12 3X8	349
X	4XX 868	711	X	18Ɛ 492	527	X	X64 735	342
Ɛ	541 379	707	Ɛ	221 9Ɛ9	522	Ɛ	XƐ6 X77	339

N	Log N	d	N	Log N	d	N	Log N	d
Ɛ200	Ɛ79 Ɛ49 1Ɛ4	52 334	Ɛ240	Ɛ7Ɛ 816 761	52 150	Ɛ280	Ɛ81 498 834	51 Ɛ6Ɛ
1	Ɛ9Ɛ 528	32χ	1	868 8Ɛ1	147	1	52χ 7χ3	Ɛ65
2	Ɛ7χ 031 856	324	2	8Ɛχ χ38	142	2	580 748	Ɛ60
3	083 Ɛ7χ	31Ɛ	3	950 Ɛ7χ	138	3	612 6χ8	Ɛ56
4	116 299	315	4	9χ3 0Ɛ6	132	4	664 642	Ɛ51
5	168 5Ɛ2	310	5	χ35 228	129	5	6Ɛ6 593	Ɛ47
6	1Ɛχ 902	306	6	χ87 355	123	6	748 51χ	Ɛ42
7	251 008	300	7	Ɛ19 478	11χ	7	79χ 460	Ɛ38
8	2χ3 308	2Ɛ7	8	Ɛ6Ɛ 596	114	8	830 398	Ɛ33
9	335 603	2Ɛ2	9	Ɛ80 001 6χχ	10χ	9	882 30Ɛ	Ɛ29
χ	387 8Ɛ5	2χ7	χ	053 7Ɛ8	105	χ	914 238	Ɛ24
Ɛ	419 Ɛχ0	2χ3	Ɛ	0χ5 901	100	Ɛ	966 160	Ɛ1χ
Ɛ210	470 283	298	Ɛ250	137 χ01	0Ɛ6	Ɛ290	9Ɛ8 07χ	Ɛ14
1	502 55Ɛ	293	1	189 χƐ7	0Ɛ0	1	χ49 Ɛ92	Ɛ0Ɛ
2	554 832	28χ	2	21Ɛ Ɛχ7	0χ7	2	χ9Ɛ χχ1	Ɛ06
3	5χ6 Ɛ00	284	3	272 092	0χ1	3	Ɛ31 9χ7	Ɛ00
4	639 184	27χ	4	304 173	098	4	Ɛ83 8χ7	χƐ7
5	68Ɛ 442	275	5	356 24Ɛ	092	5	Ɛ82 015 7χ2	χƐ1
6	721 6Ɛ7	26Ɛ	6	3χ8 321	089	6	067 693	χχ7
7	773 966	266	7	43χ 3χχ	083	7	0Ɛ9 57χ	χχ2
8	806 010	260	8	490 471	07χ	8	14Ɛ 460	χ99
9	858 270	256	9	522 52Ɛ	074	9	1χ1 339	χ93
χ	8χχ 506	251	χ	574 5χ3	06Ɛ	χ	233 210	χ89
Ɛ	940 757	248	Ɛ	606 652	065	Ɛ	285 099	χ84
Ɛ220	992 9χ3	242	Ɛ260	658 6Ɛ7	05Ɛ	Ɛ2χ0	316 Ɛ61	χ7χ
1	χ25 025	238	1	6χχ 756	056	1	368 χ1Ɛ	χ75
2	χ77 261	233	2	740 7Ɛ0	051	2	3Ɛχ 894	χ70
3	Ɛ09 494	229	3	792 841	047	3	450 744	χ66
4	Ɛ5Ɛ 701	223	4	824 888	041	4	4χ2 5χχ	χ60
5	ƐƐ1 924	21χ	5	876 909	038	5	534 44χ	χ57
6	Ɛ7Ɛ 043 Ɛ42	215	6	908 945	032	6	586 2χ5	χ52
7	096 157	20Ɛ	7	95χ 977	029	7	618 137	χ48
8	128 366	205	8	9Ɛ0 9χ4	023	8	669 Ɛ83	χ42
9	17χ 56Ɛ	200	9	χ42 χ07	01χ	9	6ƐƐ χ05	χ39
χ	210 76Ɛ	1Ɛ6	χ	χ94 χ25	014	χ	751 842	χ33
Ɛ	262 965	1Ɛ1	Ɛ	Ɛ26 χ39	00χ	Ɛ	7χ3 675	χ2χ
Ɛ230	2Ɛ4 Ɛ56	1χ7	Ɛ270	Ɛ78 χ47	006	Ɛ2Ɛ0	835 4χ3	χ25
1	347 141	1χ2	1	Ɛ81 00χ χ51	51 ƐƐƐ	1	887 308	χ1Ɛ
2	399 323	198	2	060 χ50	ƐƐ6	2	919 127	χ15
3	42Ɛ 4ƐƐ	192	3	0Ɛ2 χ46	ƐƐ1	3	96χ Ɛ40	χ10
4	481 691	189	4	144 χ37	Ɛχ7	4	χ00 950	χ06
5	513 85χ	183	5	196 χ22	Ɛχ1	5	χ52 756	χ01
6	565 χ21	17χ	6	228 χ03	Ɛ98	6	χχ4 557	9Ɛ8
7	5Ɛ7 Ɛ9Ɛ	174	7	27χ 99Ɛ	Ɛ93	7	Ɛ36 353	9Ɛ2
8	64χ 153	16Ɛ	8	310 972	Ɛ89	8	Ɛ88 145	9χ8
9	6χ0 302	165	9	362 93Ɛ	Ɛ83	9	Ɛ83 019 Ɛ31	9χ3
χ	732 467	160	χ	3Ɛ4 902	Ɛ7χ	χ	06Ɛ 914	999
Ɛ	784 607	156	Ɛ	446 880	Ɛ74	Ɛ	101 6Ɛ1	994

N	Log N	d	N	Log N	d	N	Log N	d
Ɛ300	Ɛ83 153 485	51 98Ɛ	Ɛ340	Ɛ84 X02 927	51 7XƐ	Ɛ380	Ɛ86 666 X30	51 611
1	1X5 254	985	1	X54 516	7X6	1	6Ɛ8 441	608
2	237 019	97Ɛ	2	XX6 100	7X1	2	749 X49	603
3	288 998	976	3	Ɛ37 8X1	797	3	79Ɛ 450	5Ɛ9
4	31X 752	971	4	Ɛ89 478	791	4	830 X49	5Ɛ4
5	370 503	967	5	Ɛ85 01Ɛ 049	788	5	882 441	5XƐ
6	402 26X	961	6	070 815	783	6	913 X30	5X5
7	454 00Ɛ	958	7	102 398	779	7	965 415	59Ɛ
8	4X5 967	952	8	153 Ɛ55	774	8	9Ɛ6 9Ɛ4	596
9	537 6Ɛ9	94X	9	1X5 709	76X	9	X48 38X	591
X	589 447	943	X	237 277	764	X	X99 95Ɛ	587
Ɛ	61Ɛ 18X	93X	Ɛ	288 X1Ɛ	760	Ɛ	Ɛ2Ɛ 326	582
Ɛ310	670 Ɛ08	935	Ɛ350	31X 57Ɛ	756	Ɛ390	Ɛ80 8X8	578
1	702 841	92Ɛ	1	370 115	750	1	Ɛ87 012 264	573
2	754 570	925	2	401 865	747	2	063 817	569
3	7X6 295	920	3	453 3Ɛ0	741	3	0Ɛ5 184	565
4	837 ƐƐ5	917	4	4X4 Ɛ31	738	4	146 729	55X
5	889 910	911	5	536 669	733	5	198 087	555
6	91Ɛ 621	908	6	588 1X0	729	6	229 620	550
7	971 329	902	7	619 909	723	7	27X Ɛ70	546
8	X03 02Ɛ	8Ɛ9	8	66Ɛ 430	71X	8	310 4Ɛ6	541
9	X54 928	8Ɛ3	9	700 Ɛ4X	715	9	361 X37	538
X	XX6 61Ɛ	8X9	X	752 663	70Ɛ	X	3Ɛ3 373	532
Ɛ	Ɛ38 308	8X5	Ɛ	7X4 172	706	Ɛ	444 8X5	528
Ɛ320	Ɛ89 ƐƐ1	89X	Ɛ360	835 878	700	Ɛ3X0	496 211	524
1	Ɛ84 01Ɛ 88Ɛ	896	1	887 378	6Ɛ7	1	527 735	519
2	071 565	88Ɛ	2	918 X73	6Ɛ2	2	579 052	515
3	103 234	887	3	96X 565	6X8	3	60X 567	50Ɛ
4	154 XƐƐ	881	4	X00 051	6X2	4	65Ɛ X76	505
5	1X6 780	877	5	X51 733	699	5	6Ɛ1 37Ɛ	500
6	238 437	872	6	XX3 210	694	6	742 87Ɛ	4Ɛ7
7	28X 0X9	868	7	Ɛ34 8X4	68X	7	794 176	4Ɛ1
8	31Ɛ 955	863	8	Ɛ86 372	685	8	825 667	4X8
9	371 5Ɛ8	85X	9	Ɛ86 017 X37	67Ɛ	9	876 Ɛ53	4X2
X	403 256	853	X	069 4Ɛ6	676	X	908 435	499
Ɛ	454 XX9	84Ɛ	Ɛ	0ƐX Ɛ70	670	Ɛ	959 912	493
Ɛ330	4X6 738	845	Ɛ370	150 620	667	Ɛ3Ɛ0	9XƐ 1X5	48Ɛ
1	538 381	840	1	1X2 087	661	1	X40 674	484
2	58X 001	836	2	233 728	658	2	X91 Ɛ38	47Ɛ
3	61Ɛ 837	830	3	285 184	653	3	Ɛ23 3Ɛ7	476
4	671 467	827	4	316 817	649	4	Ɛ74 871	471
5	703 092	822	5	368 264	644	5	Ɛ88 006 122	467
6	754 8Ɛ4	818	6	3Ɛ9 8X8	63X	6	057 589	461
7	7X6 510	813	7	44Ɛ 326	635	7	0X8 X2X	458
8	838 123	809	8	4X0 95Ɛ	62Ɛ	8	13X 286	453
9	889 930	804	9	532 38X	626	9	18Ɛ 719	44X
X	91Ɛ 534	7ƐX	X	583 9Ɛ4	621	X	220 Ɛ67	443
Ɛ	971 132	7Ɛ5	Ɛ	615 415	617	Ɛ	272 3XX	43Ɛ

N	Log N	d	N	Log N	d	N	Log N	d
Ɛ400	Ɛ88 303 829	51 435	Ɛ440	Ɛ89 Ɛ55 370	51 25χ	Ɛ480	Ɛ8Ɛ 79Ɛ 88Ɛ	51 084
1	355 062	430	1	Ɛχ6 60χ	255	1	830 953	07χ
2	3χ6 492	426	2	Ɛ8χ 037 863	24Ɛ	2	881 χ11	076
3	437 8Ɛ8	421	3	088 χƐ2	246	3	912 χ87	06Ɛ
4	489 119	417	4	11χ 138	240	4	963 Ɛ36	067
5	51χ 534	412	5	16Ɛ 378	237	5	9Ɛ4 Ɛχ1	061
6	56Ɛ 946	409	6	200 5Ɛ3	231	6	χ46 042	058
7	601 153	403	7	251 824	229	7	χ97 09χ	052
8	652 556	3Ɛχ	8	2χ2 χ51	222	8	Ɛ28 130	049
9	6χ3 954	3Ɛ4	9	334 073	21χ	9	Ɛ79 179	044
χ	735 148	3χƐ	χ	385 291	214	χ	Ɛ90 00χ 201	03χ
Ɛ	786 537	3χ6	Ɛ	416 4χ5	20χ	Ɛ	05Ɛ 23Ɛ	035
Ɛ410	817 921	3χ0	Ɛ450	467 6Ɛ3	206	Ɛ490	0Ɛ0 274	030
1	869 101	397	1	4Ɛ8 8Ɛ9	200	1	141 2χ4	026
2	8Ɛχ 498	391	2	549 χƐ9	1Ɛ6	2	192 30χ	021
3	94Ɛ 869	388	3	59Ɛ 0Ɛ3	1Ɛ1	3	223 32Ɛ	017
4	9χ1 035	383	4	630 2χ4	1χ8	4	274 346	013
5	χ32 3Ɛ8	379	5	681 490	1χ2	5	305 359	009
6	χ83 775	374	6	712 672	199	6	356 366	003
7	Ɛ14 Ɛ29	36χ	7	763 84Ɛ	194	7	3χ7 369	50 ƐƐχ
8	Ɛ66 297	365	8	7Ɛ4 χ23	18χ	8	438 367	ƐƐ5
9	ƐƐ7 640	35Ɛ	9	845 ƐƐ1	185	9	489 360	ƐχƐ
χ	Ɛ89 048 99Ɛ	356	χ	897 176	17Ɛ	χ	51χ 34Ɛ	Ɛχ7
Ɛ	09χ 135	351	Ɛ	928 335	177	Ɛ	56Ɛ 336	Ɛχ0
Ɛ420	12Ɛ 486	347	Ɛ460	979 4Ɛ0	170	Ɛ4χ0	600 316	Ɛ98
1	180 811	342	1	χ0χ 660	168	1	651 2Ɛ2	Ɛ92
2	211 Ɛ53	339	2	χ5Ɛ 808	162	2	6χ2 284	Ɛ88
3	263 290	333	3	χƐ0 96χ	158	3	733 250	Ɛ84
4	2Ɛ4 603	32χ	4	Ɛ41 Ɛ06	153	4	784 214	Ɛ7χ
5	345 931	324	5	Ɛ93 059	14χ	5	815 192	Ɛ74
6	397 055	31Ɛ	6	Ɛ8Ɛ 024 1χ7	145	6	866 146	Ɛ70
7	428 374	316	7	075 330	13Ɛ	7	8Ɛ7 0Ɛ6	Ɛ66
8	479 68χ	310	8	106 46Ɛ	136	8	948 060	Ɛ60
9	50χ 99χ	306	9	157 5χ5	130	9	999 000	Ɛ58
χ	560 0χ4	302	χ	1χ8 715	127	χ	χ29 Ɛ58	Ɛ52
Ɛ	5Ɛ1 3χ6	2Ɛ8	Ɛ	239 840	122	Ɛ	χ7χ χχχ	Ɛ48
Ɛ430	642 6χ2	2Ɛ2	Ɛ470	28χ 962	118	Ɛ4Ɛ0	Ɛ0Ɛ χ36	Ɛ43
1	693 994	2χ9	1	31Ɛ χ7χ	113	1	Ɛ60 979	Ɛ3χ
2	725 081	2χ4	2	370 Ɛ91	109	2	ƐƐ1 8Ɛ7	Ɛ35
3	776 365	29Ɛ	3	402 09χ	105	3	Ɛ91 042 830	Ɛ2Ɛ
4	807 644	295	4	453 1χ3	0Ɛχ	4	093 75Ɛ	Ɛ26
5	858 919	28Ɛ	5	4χ4 2χ1	0Ɛ6	5	124 685	Ɛ21
6	8χ9 Ɛχ8	286	6	535 397	0Ɛ0	6	175 5χ6	Ɛ17
7	93Ɛ 272	281	7	586 487	0χ7	7	206 501	Ɛ12
8	990 533	278	8	617 572	0χ1	8	257 413	Ɛ08
9	χ21 7χƐ	272	9	668 653	098	9	2χ8 31Ɛ	Ɛ04
χ	χ72 χ61	268	χ	6Ɛ9 72Ɛ	093	χ	339 223	χƐ9
Ɛ	Ɛ04 109	263	Ɛ	74χ 802	089	Ɛ	38χ 120	χƐ5

N	Log N	d	N	Log N	d	N	Log N	d
Ɛ500	Ɛ91 41Ɛ 015	50 χχƐ	Ɛ540	Ɛ93 053 217	50 917	Ɛ580	Ɛ94 880 323	50 746
1	46Ɛ Ɛ04	χχ6	1	0χ3 Ɛ32	913	1	910 χ69	740
2	500 9χχ	χχ1	2	134 845	909	2	961 5χ9	737
3	551 88Ɛ	χ97	3	185 552	904	3	9Ɛ2 124	732
4	5χ2 766	χ92	4	216 256	8Ɛχ	4	χ42 856	728
5	633 638	χ88	5	266 Ɛ54	8Ɛ5	5	χ93 382	723
6	684 504	χ83	6	2Ɛ7 849	8Ɛ0	6	Ɛ23 χχ5	71χ
7	715 387	χ7χ	7	348 539	8χ7	7	Ɛ74 603	715
8	766 245	χ75	8	399 224	8χ1	8	Ɛ95 005 118	70Ɛ
9	7Ɛ7 0Ɛχ	χ6Ɛ	9	429 Ɛ05	898	9	055 827	706
χ	847 Ɛ69	χ66	χ	47χ 7χ1	893	χ	0χ6 331	700
Ɛ	898 χ13	χ60	Ɛ	50Ɛ 474	889	Ɛ	136 χ31	6Ɛ8
Ɛ510	929 873	χ58	Ɛ550	560 141	884	Ɛ590	187 529	6Ɛ2
1	97χ 70Ɛ	χ52	1	5Ɛ0 χ05	87Ɛ	1	218 01Ɛ	6χ9
2	χ0Ɛ 561	χ48	2	641 684	876	2	268 708	6χ4
3	χ60 3χ9	χ43	3	692 33χ	870	3	2Ɛ9 1Ɛ0	69χ
4	χƐ1 230	χ3χ	4	722 Ɛχχ	867	4	349 88χ	695
5	Ɛ42 06χ	χ35	5	773 855	861	5	39χ 363	690
6	Ɛ92 χχ3	χ2Ɛ	6	804 4Ɛ6	858	6	42χ χ33	686
7	Ɛ92 023 912	χ26	7	855 152	853	7	47Ɛ 4Ɛ9	682
8	074 738	χ21	8	8χ5 9χ5	84χ	8	50Ɛ Ɛ7Ɛ	677
9	105 559	χ17	9	936 633	844	9	560 636	673
χ	156 374	χ12	χ	987 277	83Ɛ	χ	5Ɛ1 0χ9	66χ
Ɛ	1χ7 186	χ09	Ɛ	χ17 χƐ6	836	Ɛ	641 757	664
Ɛ520	237 Ɛ93	χ03	Ɛ560	χ68 730	831	Ɛ5χ0	692 1ƐƐ	65Ɛ
1	288 996	9Ɛχ	1	χƐ9 361	827	1	722 85χ	655
2	319 794	9Ɛ5	2	Ɛ49 Ɛ88	822	2	773 2Ɛ3	651
3	36χ 589	9χƐ	3	Ɛ9χ 7χχ	818	3	803 944	647
4	3Ɛ2 378	9χ6	4	Ɛ94 02Ɛ 406	814	4	854 38Ɛ	641
5	450 162	9χ1	5	080 01χ	80χ	5	8χ4 χ10	639
6	4χ0 Ɛ43	997	6	110 828	804	6	935 449	633
7	531 91χ	992	7	161 430	800	7	985 χ80	62χ
8	582 6Ɛ0	989	8	1Ɛ2 030	7Ɛ6	8	χ16 4χχ	625
9	613 479	983	9	242 826	7Ɛ1	9	χ66 Ɛ13	61Ɛ
χ	664 240	97χ	χ	293 417	7χ7	χ	χƐ7 532	617
Ɛ	6Ɛ4 ƐƐχ	975	Ɛ	324 002	7χ3	Ɛ	Ɛ47 Ɛ49	611
Ɛ530	745 973	970	Ɛ570	374 7χ5	799	Ɛ5Ɛ0	Ɛ98 55χ	607
1	796 723	966	1	405 382	793	1	Ɛ96 028 Ɛ65	603
2	827 489	961	2	455 Ɛ55	78Ɛ	2	079 568	5Ɛ9
3	878 22χ	957	3	4χ6 724	785	3	109 Ɛ65	5Ɛ4
4	908 Ɛ85	953	4	537 2χ9	780	4	15χ 559	5χχ
5	959 918	949	5	587 χ69	776	5	1χχ Ɛ47	5χ6
6	9χχ 665	943	6	618 623	771	6	23Ɛ 531	5χ0
7	χ3Ɛ 3χ8	93χ	7	669 194	768	7	28Ɛ Ɛ11	596
8	χ90 126	935	8	6Ɛ9 940	763	8	320 4χ7	592
9	Ɛ20 χ5Ɛ	930	9	74χ 4χ3	759	9	370 χ79	588
χ	Ɛ71 78Ɛ	926	χ	79Ɛ 040	754	χ	401 445	583
Ɛ	Ɛ93 002 4Ɛ5	922	Ɛ	82Ɛ 794	74Ɛ	Ɛ	451 χ08	57χ

N	Log N	d	N	Log N	d	N	Log N	d
Ɛ600	Ɛ96 4X2 386	50 575	Ɛ640	Ɛ98 0Ɛ9 412	50 3X5	Ɛ680	Ɛ99 909 492	50 216
1	532 93Ɛ	56Ɛ	1	149 7Ɛ7	3X0	1	959 6X8	211
2	583 2XX	566	2	199 Ɛ97	396	2	9X9 8Ɛ9	208
3	613 854	561	3	22X 371	391	3	X39 Ɛ05	202
4	664 1Ɛ5	557	4	27X 742	388	4	X8X 107	1ƐX
5	6Ɛ4 750	553	5	30X Ɛ0X	382	5	Ɛ1X 305	1Ɛ4
6	745 0X3	549	6	35Ɛ 290	37X	6	Ɛ6X 4Ɛ9	1XƐ
7	795 630	543	7	3XƐ 64X	374	7	ƐƐX 6X8	1X5
8	825 Ɛ73	53Ɛ	8	43Ɛ X02	36Ɛ	8	Ɛ9X 04X 891	1X1
9	876 4Ɛ2	535	9	490 171	365	9	09X X72	197
X	906 X27	530	X	520 516	361	X	12Ɛ 049	192
Ɛ	957 357	527	Ɛ	570 877	357	Ɛ	17Ɛ 21Ɛ	189
Ɛ610	9X7 882	521	Ɛ650	601 012	352	Ɛ690	20Ɛ 3X8	184
1	X38 1X3	518	1	651 364	349	1	25Ɛ 570	17Ɛ
2	X88 6ƐƐ	513	2	6X1 6Ɛ1	343	2	2XƐ 72Ɛ	175
3	Ɛ19 012	50X	3	731 X34	33Ɛ	3	33Ɛ 8X4	170
4	Ɛ69 520	505	4	782 173	335	4	38Ɛ X54	167
5	ƐƐ9 X25	4ƐƐ	5	812 4X8	330	5	41Ɛ ƐƐƐ	162
6	Ɛ97 04X 324	4Ɛ6	6	862 818	326	6	470 161	158
7	09X 81X	4Ɛ0	7	8Ɛ2 Ɛ42	322	7	500 2Ɛ9	154
8	12Ɛ 10X	4X8	8	943 264	318	8	550 451	14X
9	17Ɛ 5Ɛ6	4X2	9	993 580	313	9	5X0 59Ɛ	145
X	20Ɛ X98	499	X	X23 893	30X	X	630 724	140
Ɛ	260 375	494	Ɛ	X73 ƐX1	304	Ɛ	680 864	136
Ɛ620	2Ɛ0 849	48X	Ɛ660	Ɛ04 2X5	300	Ɛ6X0	710 99X	132
1	341 117	486	1	Ɛ54 5X5	2Ɛ6	1	760 Ɛ10	128
2	391 5X1	480	2	ƐX4 89Ɛ	2Ɛ1	2	7Ɛ1 038	123
3	421 X61	476	3	Ɛ99 034 Ɛ90	2X7	3	841 15Ɛ	11X
4	472 317	472	4	085 277	2X3	4	891 279	114
5	502 789	468	5	115 55X	299	5	921 391	10Ɛ
6	553 035	463	6	165 837	294	6	971 4X0	107
7	5X3 498	45X	7	1Ɛ5 Ɛ0Ɛ	28Ɛ	7	X01 5X7	101
8	633 936	455	8	246 19X	285	8	X51 6X8	0Ɛ8
9	684 18Ɛ	44Ɛ	9	296 463	281	9	XX1 7X4	0Ɛ2
X	714 61X	446	X	326 724	277	X	Ɛ31 896	0XX
Ɛ	764 X64	441	Ɛ	376 99Ɛ	272	Ɛ	Ɛ81 984	0X4
Ɛ630	7Ɛ5 2X5	437	Ɛ670	407 051	269	Ɛ6Ɛ0	Ɛ9Ɛ 011 X68	09Ɛ
1	845 720	433	1	457 2ƐX	263	1	061 Ɛ47	096
2	895 Ɛ53	429	2	4X7 561	25X	2	0Ɛ2 021	090
3	926 380	424	3	537 7ƐƐ	256	3	142 0Ɛ1	088
4	976 7X4	41X	4	587 X55	24Ɛ	4	192 179	082
5	X07 002	416	5	618 0X4	247	5	222 23Ɛ	079
6	X57 418	410	6	668 32Ɛ	242	6	272 2Ɛ8	074
7	XX7 828	407	7	6Ɛ8 571	238	7	302 370	06Ɛ
8	Ɛ38 033	402	8	748 7X9	233	8	352 41Ɛ	066
9	Ɛ88 435	3Ɛ8	9	798 X20	22X	9	3X2 485	060
X	Ɛ98 018 831	3Ɛ3	X	829 04X	224	X	432 525	057
Ɛ	069 024	3XX	Ɛ	879 272	220	Ɛ	482 580	052

N	Log N	d	N	Log N	d	N	Log N	d
Ɛ700	Ɛ9Ɛ 512 612	50 049	Ɛ740	ƐX1 110 862	4Ɛ X80	Ɛ780	ƐX2 904 049	4Ɛ 8Ɛ6
1	562 65Ɛ	044	1	160 722	X78	1	953 943	8Ɛ0
2	5Ɛ2 6X3	03X	2	1Ɛ0 59X	X72	2	9X3 633	8X8
3	642 721	036	3	240 450	X69	3	X33 31Ɛ	8X2
4	692 757	030	4	290 2Ɛ9	X64	4	X83 001	899
5	722 787	027	5	320 161	X5Ɛ	5	Ɛ12 89X	894
6	772 7Ɛ2	021	6	370 000	X56	6	Ɛ62 572	88Ɛ
7	802 813	019	7	3ƐƐ X56	X51	7	ƐƐ2 241	886
8	852 830	013	8	44Ɛ 8X7	X47	8	ƐX3 041 Ɛ07	880
9	8X2 843	00Ɛ	9	49Ɛ 732	X42	9	091 787	878
X	932 852	005	X	52Ɛ 574	X39	X	121 443	872
Ɛ	982 857	4Ɛ ƐƐƐ	Ɛ	57Ɛ 3Ɛ1	X34	Ɛ	171 0Ɛ5	869
Ɛ710	X12 856	ƐƐ7	Ɛ750	60Ɛ 225	X2Ɛ	Ɛ790	200 962	865
1	X62 851	ƐƐ2	1	65Ɛ 054	X26	1	250 607	85Ɛ
2	XƐ2 843	ƐX8	2	6XX X7X	X20	2	2X0 266	855
3	Ɛ42 82Ɛ	ƐX3	3	73X 89X	X18	3	32Ɛ XƐƐ	851
4	Ɛ92 812	Ɛ9X	4	78X 6Ɛ6	X12	4	37Ɛ 750	848
5	ƐX0 022 7Ɛ0	Ɛ95	5	81X 508	X09	5	40Ɛ 398	842
6	072 785	Ɛ8Ɛ	6	86X 315	X04	6	45Ɛ 01X	83X
7	102 754	Ɛ87	7	8ƐX 119	9ƐƐ	7	4XX 858	834
8	152 71Ɛ	Ɛ81	8	949 Ɛ18	9Ɛ5	8	53X 490	82Ɛ
9	1X2 6X0	Ɛ78	9	999 911	9Ɛ1	9	58X 0ƐƐ	826
X	232 658	Ɛ73	X	X29 702	9X7	X	619 925	821
Ɛ	282 60Ɛ	Ɛ6X	Ɛ	X79 4X9	9X2	Ɛ	669 546	818
Ɛ720	312 579	Ɛ65	Ɛ760	Ɛ09 28Ɛ	999	Ɛ7X0	6Ɛ9 162	812
1	362 522	Ɛ5Ɛ	1	Ɛ59 068	994	1	748 974	80X
2	3Ɛ2 481	Ɛ56	2	ƐX8 X40	98Ɛ	2	798 582	804
3	442 417	Ɛ51	3	ƐX2 038 80Ɛ	986	3	828 186	7ƐƐ
4	492 368	Ɛ48	4	088 595	980	4	877 985	7Ɛ7
5	522 2Ɛ4	Ɛ43	5	118 355	977	5	907 580	7Ɛ1
6	572 237	Ɛ3X	6	168 110	972	6	957 171	7X8
7	602 175	Ɛ34	7	1Ɛ7 X82	969	7	9X6 959	7X2
8	652 0X9	Ɛ2Ɛ	8	247 82Ɛ	964	8	X36 53Ɛ	79X
9	6X2 018	Ɛ27	9	297 593	95Ɛ	9	X86 119	795
X	731 Ɛ43	Ɛ20	X	327 332	956	X	Ɛ15 8Ɛ2	78Ɛ
Ɛ	781 X63	Ɛ18	Ɛ	377 088	950	Ɛ	Ɛ65 481	786
Ɛ730	811 97Ɛ	Ɛ13	Ɛ770	406 X18	947	Ɛ7Ɛ0	ƐƐ5 047	782
1	861 892	Ɛ09	1	456 763	943	1	ƐX4 044 809	778
2	8Ɛ1 79Ɛ	Ɛ05	2	4X6 4X6	939	2	094 385	773
3	941 6X4	XƐƐ	3	536 223	934	3	123 Ɛ38	76X
4	991 5X3	XƐ6	4	585 Ɛ57	92X	4	173 6X6	764
5	X21 499	XƐ0	5	615 885	926	5	203 24X	760
6	X71 389	XX8	6	665 5XƐ	920	6	252 9XX	757
7	Ɛ01 275	XX2	7	6Ɛ5 30Ɛ	918	7	2X2 545	751
8	Ɛ51 157	X9X	8	745 027	912	8	332 096	748
9	ƐX1 035	X94	9	794 939	909	9	381 822	743
X	ƐX1 030 Ɛ09	X8Ɛ	X	824 646	904	X	411 365	73Ɛ
Ɛ	080 998	X86	Ɛ	874 34X	8ƐƐ	Ɛ	460 XX4	735

N	Log N	d	N	Log N	d	N	Log N	d
Ɛ800	ƐX4 4Ɛ0 619	4Ɛ 72Ɛ	Ɛ840	ƐX6 092 219	4Ɛ 567	Ɛ880	ƐX7 869 096	4Ɛ 3X4
1	540 148	727	1	121 784	562	1	8Ɛ8 47X	39X
2	58Ɛ 873	722	2	171 126	559	2	947 858	396
3	61Ɛ 395	718	3	200 683	554	3	997 032	391
4	66X XƐ1	714	4	250 017	54Ɛ	4	X26 403	387
5	6ƐX 605	70X	5	29Ɛ 566	546	5	X75 78X	383
6	74X 113	705	6	32X XƐ0	541	6	Ɛ04 Ɛ51	379
7	799 818	701	7	37X 431	538	7	Ɛ54 30X	374
8	829 319	6Ɛ7	8	409 969	532	8	ƐX3 682	370
9	878 X14	6Ɛ2	9	459 29Ɛ	52X	9	ƐX8 032 X32	366
X	908 506	6X8	X	4X8 809	524	X	082 198	361
Ɛ	957 ƐƐ2	6X4	Ɛ	538 131	51Ɛ	Ɛ	111 539	358
Ɛ810	9X7 696	69Ɛ	Ɛ850	587 650	517	Ɛ890	160 895	353
1	X37 175	695	1	616 Ɛ67	511	1	1Ɛ0 028	34X
2	X86 84X	691	2	666 478	508	2	23Ɛ 376	345
3	Ɛ16 31Ɛ	687	3	6Ɛ5 984	503	3	28X 6ƐƐ	340
4	Ɛ65 9X6	682	4	745 287	4ƐX	4	319 X3Ɛ	337
5	ƐƐ5 468	679	5	794 785	4Ɛ5	5	369 176	332
6	ƐX5 044 Ɛ25	674	6	824 07X	4Ɛ0	6	3Ɛ8 4X8	328
7	094 599	66Ɛ	7	873 56X	4X6	7	447 814	324
8	124 048	666	8	902 X54	4X2	8	496 Ɛ38	31Ɛ
9	173 6Ɛ2	661	9	952 336	498	9	526 257	315
X	203 153	657	X	9X1 812	494	X	575 570	311
Ɛ	252 7XX	653	Ɛ	X31 0X6	48X	Ɛ	604 881	307
Ɛ820	2X2 241	649	Ɛ860	X80 574	486	Ɛ8X0	653 Ɛ88	303
1	331 88X	644	1	Ɛ0Ɛ X3X	480	1	6X3 28Ɛ	2Ɛ9
2	381 312	640	2	Ɛ5Ɛ 2ƐX	477	2	732 588	2Ɛ5
3	410 952	636	3	ƐXX 775	472	3	781 881	2XƐ
4	460 388	631	4	ƐX7 03X 027	469	4	810 Ɛ70	2X6
5	4XƐ 9Ɛ9	628	5	089 494	464	5	860 256	2X1
6	53Ɛ 425	623	6	118 938	45Ɛ	6	8XƐ 537	299
7	58X X48	619	7	168 197	456	7	93X 814	293
8	61X 465	615	8	1Ɛ7 631	451	8	989 XX7	28X
9	669 X7X	60Ɛ	9	246 X82	448	9	X19 175	285
X	6Ɛ9 489	607	X	296 30X	442	X	X68 43X	280
Ɛ	748 X94	601	Ɛ	325 750	43X	Ɛ	XƐ7 6ƐX	277
Ɛ830	798 495	5Ɛ9	Ɛ870	374 Ɛ8X	434	Ɛ8Ɛ0	Ɛ46 975	272
1	827 X92	5Ɛ3	1	404 402	430	1	Ɛ96 027	268
2	877 485	5XX	2	453 832	426	2	ƐX9 025 293	264
3	906 X73	5X5	3	4X3 058	422	3	074 537	25Ɛ
4	956 458	5X0	4	532 47X	418	4	103 796	256
5	9X5 X38	597	5	581 896	413	5	152 X30	251
6	X35 413	591	6	611 0X9	40X	6	1X2 081	247
7	X84 9X4	589	7	660 4Ɛ7	405	7	231 308	243
8	Ɛ14 371	584	8	6XƐ 900	400	8	280 54Ɛ	239
9	Ɛ63 935	57X	9	73Ɛ 100	3Ɛ7	9	30Ɛ 788	235
X	ƐƐ3 2Ɛ3	576	X	78X 4Ɛ7	3Ɛ2	X	35X X01	22Ɛ
Ɛ	ƐX6 042 869	570	Ɛ	819 8X9	3X9	Ɛ	3XX 030	227

N	Log N	d	N	Log N	d	N	Log N	d
Ɛ900	Ɛχ9 439 257	4Ɛ 221	Ɛ940	ƐχƐ 002 767	4Ɛ 060	Ɛ980	ƐƐ0 781 451	4χ χχ0
1	488 478	219	1	051 807	057	1	810 331	χ97
2	517 695	213	2	0χ0 862	053	2	85Ɛ 208	χ92
3	566 8χ8	20χ	3	12Ɛ 8Ɛ5	049	3	8χχ 09χ	χ8χ
4	5Ɛ5 χƐ6	206	4	17χ 942	044	4	938 Ɛ68	χ84
5	645 100	200	5	209 986	03Ɛ	5	987 χ30	χ7Ɛ
6	694 300	1Ɛ7	6	258 χ05	036	6	χ16 8χƐ	χ76
7	723 4Ɛ7	1Ɛ2	7	2χ7 χ3Ɛ	032	7	χ65 765	χ72
8	772 6χ9	1χ9	8	336 χ71	028	8	χƐ4 617	χ68
9	801 896	1χ5	9	385 χ99	023	9	Ɛ43 483	χ63
χ	850 χ7Ɛ	19Ɛ	χ	414 Ɛ00	01χ	χ	Ɛ92 326	χ5Ɛ
Ɛ	8χ0 05χ	196	Ɛ	463 Ɛ1χ	015	Ɛ	ƐƐ1 021 185	χ55
Ɛ910	92Ɛ 234	191	Ɛ950	4Ɛ2 Ɛ33	010	Ɛ990	070 01χ	χ50
1	97χ 405	188	1	541 Ɛ43	007	1	0Ɛχ χ6χ	χ48
2	χ09 591	183	2	590 Ɛ4χ	002	2	149 8Ɛ6	χ42
3	χ58 754	17χ	3	61Ɛ Ɛ50	4χ ƐƐχ	3	198 738	χ39
4	χχ7 912	175	4	66χ Ɛ4χ	ƐƐ4	4	227 575	χ35
5	Ɛ36 χ87	16Ɛ	5	6Ɛ9 Ɛ42	ƐχƐ	5	276 3χχ	χ2Ɛ
6	Ɛ86 036	167	6	748 Ɛ31	Ɛχ6	6	305 219	χ27
7	Ɛχχ 015 1χ1	162	7	797 Ɛ17	Ɛχ1	7	354 044	χ21
8	064 343	159	8	826 χƐ8	Ɛ98	8	3χ2 χ65	χ19
9	0Ɛ3 4χ0	154	9	875 χ94	Ɛ93	9	431 882	χ13
χ	142 634	14χ	χ	904 χ67	Ɛ8χ	χ	480 695	χ0Ɛ
Ɛ	191 782	146	Ɛ	953 χ35	Ɛ85	Ɛ	50Ɛ 4χ4	χ05
Ɛ920	220 908	141	Ɛ960	9χ2 9Ɛχ	Ɛ80	Ɛ9χ0	55χ 2χ9	χ01
1	26Ɛ χ49	137	1	χ31 97χ	Ɛ77	1	5χ9 0χχ	9Ɛ8
2	2Ɛχ Ɛ84	133	2	χ80 935	Ɛ72	2	637 χχ6	9Ɛ2
3	34χ 0Ɛ7	12χ	3	Ɛ0Ɛ 8χ7	Ɛ6χ	3	686 898	9χχ
4	399 225	124	4	Ɛ5χ 855	Ɛ64	4	715 686	9χ5
5	428 349	120	5	Ɛχ9 7Ɛ9	Ɛ5Ɛ	5	764 46Ɛ	99Ɛ
6	477 469	116	6	ƐƐ0 038 758	Ɛ56	6	7Ɛ3 24χ	997
7	506 583	112	7	087 6Ɛ2	Ɛ51	7	842 025	992
8	555 695	108	8	116 643	Ɛ48	8	890 9Ɛ7	989
9	5χ4 7χ1	104	9	165 58Ɛ	Ɛ43	9	91Ɛ 784	983
χ	633 8χ5	0Ɛχ	χ	1Ɛ4 512	Ɛ3χ	χ	96χ 547	97Ɛ
Ɛ	682 9χ3	0Ɛ6	Ɛ	243 450	Ɛ35	Ɛ	9Ɛ9 306	976
Ɛ930	711 χ99	0Ɛ0	Ɛ970	292 385	Ɛ30	Ɛ9Ɛ0	χ48 080	971
1	760 Ɛ89	0χ8	1	321 2Ɛ5	Ɛ27	1	χ96 χ31	968
2	7Ɛ0 075	0χ2	2	370 220	Ɛ23	2	Ɛ25 799	963
3	83Ɛ 157	09χ	3	3ƐƐ 143	Ɛ19	3	Ɛ74 540	95χ
4	88χ 235	094	4	44χ 060	Ɛ14	4	ƐƐ2 003 29χ	955
5	919 309	08Ɛ	5	498 Ɛ74	Ɛ0Ɛ	5	052 033	950
6	968 398	087	6	527 χ83	Ɛ06	6	0χ0 983	947
7	9Ɛ7 463	081	7	576 989	Ɛ01	7	12Ɛ 70χ	942
8	χ46 524	078	8	605 88χ	χƐ8	8	17χ 450	939
9	χ95 5χ0	073	9	654 786	χƐ3	9	209 189	934
χ	Ɛ24 653	06Ɛ	χ	6χ3 679	χχƐ	χ	257 Ɛ01	92Ɛ
Ɛ	Ɛ73 702	065	Ɛ	732 568	χχ5	Ɛ	2χ6 830	927

N	Log N	d	N	Log N	d	N	Log N	d
ƐX00	ƐƐ2 335 557	4X 921	ƐX40	ƐƐ3 XX2 Ɛ07	4X 763	ƐX80	ƐƐ5 645 966	4X 5X7
1	384 278	918	1	Ɛ31 66X	75Ɛ	1	694 351	5X2
2	412 Ɛ94	914	2	Ɛ80 209	755	2	722 933	599
3	461 8X8	90X	3	ƐƐ4 00X 962	751	3	771 310	594
4	4Ɛ0 5Ɛ6	905	4	059 4Ɛ3	747	4	7ƐƐ 8X4	58Ɛ
5	53Ɛ 2ƐƐ	901	5	0X8 03X	743	5	84X 273	586
6	58X 000	8Ɛ7	6	136 781	73X	6	898 839	581
7	618 8Ɛ7	8Ɛ3	7	185 2ƐƐ	735	7	927 1ƐX	578
8	667 5XX	8X9	8	213 X34	730	8	975 776	574
9	6Ɛ6 297	8X5	9	262 564	727	9	X04 12X	56X
X	744 Ɛ80	8X0	X	2Ɛ1 08Ɛ	722	X	X52 698	566
Ɛ	793 860	896	Ɛ	33Ɛ 7Ɛ1	719	Ɛ	XX1 042	561
ƐX10	822 536	892	ƐX50	38X 30X	714	ƐX90	Ɛ2Ɛ 5X3	557
1	871 208	889	1	418 X22	70Ɛ	1	Ɛ79 Ɛ3X	553
2	8ƐƐ X95	884	2	467 531	707	2	ƐƐ6 008 491	54X
3	94X 759	87X	3	4Ɛ6 038	701	3	056 X1Ɛ	545
4	999 417	876	4	544 739	6Ɛ9	4	0X5 364	540
5	X28 091	871	5	593 236	6Ɛ3	5	133 8X4	537
6	X76 942	868	6	621 929	6XƐ	6	182 21Ɛ	533
7	Ɛ05 5XX	863	7	670 418	6X5	7	210 752	529
8	Ɛ54 251	85X	8	6ƐX Ɛ01	6X1	8	25Ɛ 07Ɛ	525
9	ƐX2 XXƐ	855	9	749 5X2	698	9	2X9 5X4	51Ɛ
X	ƐƐ3 031 744	850	X	798 07X	693	X	337 Ɛ03	517
Ɛ	080 394	848	Ɛ	826 751	68X	Ɛ	386 41X	512
ƐX20	10Ɛ 020	842	ƐX60	875 21Ɛ	684	ƐXX0	414 930	508
1	159 862	839	1	903 8X3	681	1	463 238	504
2	1X8 49Ɛ	834	2	952 364	677	2	4Ɛ1 740	4ƐƐ
3	237 113	830	3	9X0 X1Ɛ	672	3	540 03Ɛ	4Ɛ6
4	285 943	826	4	X2Ɛ 491	669	4	58X 535	4Ɛ2
5	314 569	822	5	X79 Ɛ3X	664	5	618 X27	4X8
6	363 18Ɛ	818	6	Ɛ08 5X2	660	6	667 313	4X3
7	3Ɛ1 9X7	814	7	Ɛ57 042	656	7	6Ɛ5 7Ɛ6	49Ɛ
8	440 5ƐƐ	80X	8	ƐX5 698	652	8	744 095	495
9	48Ɛ 209	806	9	ƐƐ5 034 12X	648	9	792 56X	491
X	519 X13	801	X	082 776	644	X	820 X3Ɛ	488
Ɛ	568 614	7Ɛ7	Ɛ	111 1ƐX	63Ɛ	Ɛ	86Ɛ 307	483
ƐX30	5Ɛ7 20Ɛ	7Ɛ3	ƐX70	15Ɛ 839	636	ƐXƐ0	8Ɛ9 78X	47X
1	645 X02	7XX	1	1XX 273	631	1	948 048	475
2	694 5Ɛ0	7X5	2	238 8X4	628	2	996 501	470
3	723 195	7X0	3	287 310	623	3	X24 971	467
4	771 975	797	4	315 933	61X	4	X73 218	463
5	800 550	792	5	364 351	615	5	Ɛ01 67Ɛ	459
6	84Ɛ 122	789	6	3Ɛ2 966	610	6	Ɛ4Ɛ Ɛ18	455
7	899 8XƐ	784	7	441 376	608	7	Ɛ9X 371	44Ɛ
8	928 473	780	8	48Ɛ 982	602	8	ƐƐ7 028 800	447
9	977 033	776	9	51X 384	5ƐX	9	077 047	442
X	X05 7X9	771	X	568 982	5Ɛ4	X	105 489	439
Ɛ	X54 35X	769	Ɛ	5Ɛ7 376	5Ɛ0	Ɛ	153 906	434

N	Log N	d	N	Log N	d	N	Log N	d
εε00	εε7 1χ2 13χ	4χ 42ε	εε40	εε8 933 χ8ε	4χ 275	εε80	εεχ 47ε 223	4χ 0εε
1	230 569	426	1	982 144	270	1	509 322	0ε6
2	27χ 993	422	2	χ10 3ε4	267	2	557 418	0ε2
3	309 1ε5	418	3	χ5χ 65ε	262	3	5χ5 50χ	0χ9
4	357 611	414	4	χχ8 901	259	4	633 5ε7	0χ4
5	3χ5 χ25	40ε	5	ε36 ε5χ	254	5	681 69ε	09ε
6	434 234	405	6	ε85 1ε2	250	6	70ε 77χ	096
7	482 639	401	7	εε9 013 442	246	7	759 854	091
8	510 χ3χ	3ε8	8	061 688	242	8	7χ7 925	089
9	55ε 236	3ε3	9	0χε 90χ	239	9	835 9ε2	083
χ	5χ9 629	3χε	χ	139 ε47	234	χ	883 χ75	07ε
ε	637 χ18	3χ5	ε	188 17ε	22ε	ε	911 ε34	076
εε10	686 201	3χ0	εε50	216 3χχ	226	εε90	95ε εχχ	071
1	714 5χ1	398	1	264 614	222	1	9χχ 05ε	068
2	762 979	393	2	2ε2 836	218	2	χ38 107	064
3	7ε1 150	389	3	340 χ52	214	3	χ86 16ε	05χ
4	83ε 519	385	4	38ε 066	20ε	4	ε14 209	056
5	889 8χ2	380	5	419 275	205	5	ε62 263	051
6	918 062	378	6	467 47χ	201	6	εε0 2ε4	048
7	966 41χ	372	7	4ε5 67ε	1ε9	7	εεε 03χ 340	043
8	9ε4 790	369	8	543 878	1ε3	8	088 383	03χ
9	χ42 ε39	365	9	591 χ6ε	1χχ	9	116 401	036
χ	χ91 2χ2	35ε	χ	620 059	1χ6	χ	164 437	031
ε	ε1ε 641	357	ε	66χ 243	1χ1	ε	1ε2 468	027
εε20	ε69 998	352	εε60	6ε8 424	197	εεχ0	240 493	023
1	εε8 12χ	348	1	746 5εε	193	1	28χ 4ε6	01ε
2	εε8 046 476	344	2	794 792	18ε	2	318 515	015
3	094 7εχ	340	3	822 961	185	3	366 52χ	010
4	122 ε3χ	336	4	870 ε26	180	4	3ε4 53χ	008
5	171 274	331	5	8εε 0χ6	178	5	442 546	003
6	1εε 5χ5	329	6	949 262	172	6	490 549	49 εεχ
7	249 912	323	7	997 414	16χ	7	51χ 547	εε5
8	298 035	31ε	8	χ25 582	165	8	568 540	εε0
9	326 354	316	9	χ73 727	160	9	5ε6 530	εχ7
χ	374 66χ	311	χ	ε01 887	158	χ	644 517	εχ3
ε	402 97ε	308	ε	ε4ε χ23	152	ε	692 4εχ	ε9χ
εε30	451 087	303	εε70	ε99 ε75	149	εεε0	720 498	ε95
1	49ε 38χ	2εχ	1	εεχ 028 102	145	1	76χ 471	ε90
2	529 688	2ε6	2	076 247	140	2	7ε8 441	ε87
3	577 982	2ε0	3	104 387	137	3	846 408	ε83
4	606 072	2χ8	4	152 502	132	4	894 38ε	ε79
5	654 35χ	2χ3	5	1χ0 634	129	5	922 348	ε75
6	6χ2 641	29χ	6	22χ 761	125	6	970 301	ε70
7	730 91ε	295	7	278 886	11ε	7	9εχ 271	ε67
8	77χ ε24	290	8	306 9χ5	117	8	χ48 218	ε62
9	809 284	287	9	354 ε00	112	9	χ96 17χ	ε5χ
χ	857 54ε	283	χ	3χ3 012	109	χ	ε24 118	ε54
ε	8χ5 812	279	ε	431 11ε	104	ε	ε72 070	ε50

Logarithms of Sines, Cosines, Tangents

S and T

The following tables of log sine, log cosine, log tangent were derived from the tables of Peters and Andoyer.

The values of S and T in terms of the circle were independently derived from Peters' extended values of log sine and log tangent.

One dozen and seven duodecimal places were calculated.

The tables may be read to six places by direct proportion or to nine places by direct proportion after increasing for log sine, log tangent and T (decreasing for log cosine and S) the book difference by $\frac{1 - \text{Interval}}{2}$ of the second difference.

This does not apply to the beginning of the log sine and log tangent tables, which may be read as follows:-

By direct proportion to five places from *.01* to *.04*
to four places from *.004* to *.01*

Using second difference, to eight places from *.03* to *.06*
to seven places from *.01* to *.03*

The tables of S and T may be read to seven places by direct proportion. Since their use has been found convenient, they are given for the half quadrant.

Note:

Log sin *.004*	= *Χ.36Χ 085 Ɛ36*	Log tan *.004*	= *Χ.36Χ 171 064*
Log sin *.01*	= *Χ.8Χ5 Χ04 788*	Log tan *.01*	= *Χ.8Χ6 5Ɛ8 Χ84*
Log sin *.03*	= *Ɛ.220 062 003*	Log tan *.03*	= *Ɛ.226 026 5Ɛ7*
Log sin *.04*	= *Ɛ.366 671 473*	Log tan *.04*	= *Ɛ.375 241 272*
Log sin *.06*	= *Ɛ.558 0Ɛ8 819*	Log tan *.06*	= *Ɛ.578 233 853*

Log Sines

Example:

Find log sin .0649 72497(2)

(a) To six places by direct proportion
(For angles greater than .04)

Log sin	.0649	Ɛ.593 506 7	
			899 Ɛ
Interval	.724X		
Add	.724X (899Ɛ)	536 0	
Log sin	.0649 724(X)	Ɛ.593 X40(7)	

(b) To nine places, using second difference
(For angles greater than .06)

Log sin	.0649	Ɛ.593 506 754		(1553)
Add to book diff.	$1553\ \frac{1 - .724X}{2}$		899 Ɛ45	
			35X	
Corrected difference			89X 2X3	
Multiply by	.724972	5Ɛ6 186		
Add to log sin .0649		Ɛ.593 X40 91X		

Example:

Find the angle whose log sine is Ɛ.593 X40 91X

(a) To seven places by direct proportion

Log sin	.0649	Ɛ.593 506(7)	
			899(Ɛ)
Difference		536(2)	
Int. $\frac{5362}{899Ɛ}$ =	.725(1)		
Angle is	.0649 725		

(b) To nine places, using second difference

Log sin	.0649	Ɛ.593 506 754		(1553)
Add to book diff.	$1553\ \frac{1 - .7251}{2}$		899 Ɛ45	
			35X	
Corrected difference			89X 2X3	
Int. $\frac{536186}{89X2X3}$ =	.72497(2)			
Angle is	.0649 72497			

Example:

Find log sin .2572 49724(X) (second half quadrant)

Log sin .2572 49724(X) = log cos .0649 72497(2)
Proceed as for log cosine
Log sin .2572 49724(X) = Ɛ.Ɛ98 638 697

Example:

Find the angle whose log sin is Ɛ.Ɛ98 638 697

This value being greater than Ɛ.X3X ƐƐ0 4Ɛ7 (log sin .16), the angle is in the second half quadrant
Proceed as for log cosine to find the angle whose log cos is Ɛ.Ɛ98 638 697
This angle is .0649 72497
Angle required = .3 - .0649 72497 = .2572 49725

Alternative Using S

(Preferable for angles less than *.06*)

Example:

Find log sin *.0649 72497(2)*

(a) To seven places by direct proportion

S	*.0649*	*.899 00Ɛ 92*	
			2X 09
Subtract	*.724X (2X09)*	*18 53*	
S	*.0649 724X*	*.898 ƐƐ3 3Ɛ*	
Add log	*.0649 724X*	*X.8Ɛ6 X49 52*	
Log sin	*.0649 724(X)*	*X.593 X40 9(1)*	

(b) To nine places, using second difference

S	*.0649*	*.899 00Ɛ 91X*		*(56)*
			2X 096	
Subtract from book diff. $56\,\frac{1 - .725}{2}$			*11*	
Corrected difference			*2X 085*	
Multiply by	*.72497*	*18 528*		
Subtract from S	*.0649*	*.898 ƐƐ3 3Ɛ2*		
Add log	*.0649 72497(2)*	*X.8Ɛ6 X49 528*		
Log sin	*.0649 72497(2)*	*Ɛ.593 X40 91X*		

Alternative Using Natural Sine

(Preferable for log sin less than *Ɛ.558 0Ɛ8*)

Example:

Find the angle whose log sin is *Ɛ.593 X40 91X*

(a) To seven places by direct proportion

Log *.3383*		*Ɛ.593 953(2)*	
			156(3)
Difference		*X9(7)*	
Interval *X97:1563* = *.749(0)*			
Nat sin is		*.338 374(9)*	
Nat sin	*.0649*	*.337 ƐƐX(Ɛ)*	
			605(9)
Difference		*375(X)*	
Interval *375X:6059* = *.724(9)*			
Angle is	*.0649 725*		

(b) To nine places, using second difference

Log *.3383*		*Ɛ.593 953 255*		*(54)*
			156 2Ɛ1	
Add to book diff. $54\,\frac{1 - .749}{2}$			*10*	
Corrected difference			*156 301*	
Int. $\frac{X9686}{156301}$ =	*.74899(5)*			
Nat sin is		*.338 374 899*		
Nat sin	*.0649*	*.337 ƐƐX X72*		*(XX)*
			605 8X1	
Difference		*375 X27*		
Add to book diff. $XX\,\frac{1 - .725}{2}$			*22*	
Int. $\frac{375X27}{605903}$ =	*.72497(3)*		*605 903*	
Angle is	*.0649 72497*			

Log Cosines

Example:

Find log cos *.0649 72497(2)*

(a) To six places by direct proportion

Log cos	*.0649*	*Ɛ.Ɛ98 68Ɛ 2*	
			88 5
Interval	*.724X*		
Subtract	*.724X (885)*	*52 8*	
Log cos	*.0649 724(X)*	*Ɛ.Ɛ98 638(6)*	

(b) To nine places, using second difference

Log cos	*.0649*	*Ɛ.Ɛ98 68Ɛ 233*		*(152)*
			88 48X	
Subtract from book diff.	*152* $\frac{1 - .725}{2}$		*35*	
Corrected difference			*88 455*	
Multiply by	*.72497*	*52 758*		
Sub. from log cos	*.0649*	*Ɛ.Ɛ98 638 697*		

Example:

Find the angle whose log cos is *Ɛ.Ɛ98 638 697*

(a) To seven places by direct proportion

Log cos	*.0649*	*Ɛ.Ɛ98 68Ɛ(23)*	
			88(49)
Difference		*52(77)*	
Interval *5277:8849* =	*.724(8)*		
Angle is	*.0649 725*		

(b) To nine places, using second difference

Log cos	*.0649*	*Ɛ.Ɛ98 68Ɛ 233*		*(152)*
			88 48X	
Subtract from book diff.	*152* $\frac{1 - .725}{2}$		*35*	
Corrected difference			*88 455*	
Interval *52758:88455* =	*.72497(5)*			
Angle is	*.0649 72497*			

Example:

Find log cos *.2572 49724(X)* (second half quadrant)

Log cos *.2572 49724(X)* = log sin *.0649 72497(2)*
Proceed as for log sine
Log cos *.2572 49724(X)* = *Ɛ.593 X40 91X*

Example:

Find the angle whose log cos is *Ɛ.593 X40 91X*

This value being less than *Ɛ.X3X ƐƐ0 4Ɛ7* (log cos *.16*), the angle is in the second half quadrant
Proceed as for log sine to find the angle whose log sin is *Ɛ.593 X40 91X*
This angle is *.0649 72497(2)*
Angle required is *.3* - *.0649 72497(2)* = *.2572 49725*

Log Tangents

Example:

Find log tan .0649 72497(2)

(a) To six places by direct proportion

Log tan	.0649	Ɛ.5Ɛ6 X37 5		
			966 4	
Interval	.724X			
Add	.724X (9664)	588 8		
Log tan	.0649 724(X)	Ɛ.5Ɛ7 404(1)		

(b) To nine places, using second difference

Log tan	.0649	Ɛ.5Ɛ6 X37 521		(1401)
			966 413	
Add to book diff. 1401 $\frac{1 - .724X}{2}$			325	
Corrected difference			966 738	
Multiply by	.724972	588 922		
Add to log tan .0649		Ɛ.5Ɛ7 404 243		

Example:

Find the angle whose log tan is Ɛ.5Ɛ7 404 243

(a) To seven places by direct proportion

Log tan	.0649	Ɛ.5Ɛ6 X37(5)	
			966(4)
Difference		588(9)	
Int. $\frac{5889}{9664}$ =	.725(0)		
Angle is	.0649 725		

(b) To nine places, using second difference

Log tan	.0649	Ɛ.5Ɛ6 X37 521		(1401)
			966 413	
Add to book diff. 1401 $\frac{1 - .7250}{2}$			325	
Corrected difference			966 738	
Int. $\frac{588922}{966738}$ =	.72497(2)			
Angle is	.0649 72497			

Example:

Find log tan .2572 49724(X) (second half quadrant)

Log tan .2572 49724(X) = -log tan .0649 72497(2)
Proceed as above
Log tan .0649 72497(2) = Ɛ.5Ɛ7 404 243
Log tan .2572 49724(X) = 0.604 7Ɛ7 979

Example:

Find the angle whose log tan is 0.604 7Ɛ7 979

This value being positive, the angle is in the second half quadrant
Proceed as above to find the angle whose log tan is -0.604 7Ɛ7 979, i. e., Ɛ.5Ɛ7 404 243
This angle is .0649 72497
Angle required is .3 - .0649 72497 = .2572 49725

Alternative Using T

(Preferable for angles less than .06)

Example:

Find log tan .0649 72497(2)

(a) To seven places by direct proportion

T	.0649	.900 540 6Ɛ	
			5X 3Ɛ
Add	.724X 5X3Ɛ	36 24	
T	.0649 724X	.900 576 93	
Add log	.0649 724X	X.8Ɛ6 X49 52	
Log tan	.0649 724(X)	Ɛ.5Ɛ7 404 2(5)	

(b) To nine places, using second difference

T	.0649	.900 540 6X8		(Ɛ9)
			5X 3Ɛ3	
Subtract from book diff.	Ɛ9 $\frac{1 - .725}{2}$		24	
Corrected difference			5X 38Ɛ	
Multiply by	.72497	36 22Ɛ		
Add to T	.0649	.900 576 917		
Add log	.0649 72497(2)	X.8Ɛ6 X49 528		
Log tan	.0649 72497(2)	Ɛ.5Ɛ7 404 243		

Alternative Using Natural Tangent

(Preferable for log tan less than Ɛ.578 233)

Example:

Find the angle whose log tan is Ɛ.5Ɛ7 404 243

(a) To seven places by direct proportion

Log .3535	Ɛ.5Ɛ7 283(9)	
		14X(1)
Difference	140(6)	
Interval 1406:14X1 = .Ɛ52(0)		
Nat tan is	.353 5Ɛ5(2)	
Nat tan .0649	.353 1X5(8)	
		697(2)
Difference	40Ɛ(6)	
Interval $\frac{40Ɛ6}{6972}$ = .724(X)		
Angle is .0649 725		

(b) To nine places, using second difference

Log .3535	Ɛ.5Ɛ7 283 87Ɛ		(4X)
		14X 13Ɛ	
Add to book diff. 4X $\frac{1 - .Ɛ52}{2}$		1	
Corrected difference		14X 140	
Int. $\frac{140584}{14X140}$ = .Ɛ5173(9)			
Nat tan is	.353 5Ɛ5 174		
Nat tan .0649	.353 1X5 7Ɛ3		(205)
		697 1X4	
Difference	40Ɛ 581		
Sub. from tan diff. 205 $\frac{1 - .725}{2}$		4Ɛ	
Int. $\frac{40Ɛ581}{697155}$ = .72497(3)		697 155	
Angle is .0649 72497			

N	Log Sin	d	N	Log Sin	d	N	Log Sin	d
.0000	———		.0040	X.36X 085 Ɛ36		.0080	X.6XƐ ƐƐX 017	
1	8.8X6 081 Ɛ3Ɛ		1	.380 491 35X		1	.6Ɛ7 252 X7Ɛ	
2	9.028 0X1 08X		2	.392 540 02X		2	.702 400 013	
3	.222 043 550		3	.3X4 269 Ɛ5X		3	.709 483 Ɛ72	
4	.36X 100 01Ɛ		4	.3Ɛ5 871 936		4	.714 465 33X	
5	.479 30Ɛ Ɛ20		5	.406 Ɛ65 0XƐ		5	.71Ɛ 366 467	
6	.564 062 165		6	.417 Ɛ60 590		6	.726 189 786	
7	.633 2X4 973		7	.428 873 830		7	.730 Ɛ15 445	
8	.6Ɛ0 11X 378		8	.439 2Ɛ5 679		8	.737 787 93X	
9	.75X 003 948		9	.449 678 188		9	.742 367 070	
X	.7ƐƐ 329 883		X	.459 790 956		X	.748 X75 351	
Ɛ	.855 66X 7XƐ		Ɛ	.469 648 174		Ɛ	.753 4Ɛ4 650	
.0010	.8X6 07Ɛ 393		.0050	.479 276 238		.0090	.759 X66 952	
1	.931 872 063		1	.488 866 462		1	.764 351 Ɛ83	
2	.975 301 32X		2	.498 027 661		2	.76X 773 Ɛ92	
3	.9Ɛ5 289 XX8		3	.4X7 188 040		3	.774 Ɛ12 778	
4	.X32 135 Ɛ42		4	.4Ɛ6 115 81Ɛ		4	.77Ɛ 1XƐ 882	
5	.X68 322 996		5	.504 X59 X7X		5	.785 408 Ɛ84	
6	.XX0 01X 5X1		6	.513 5X5 741		6	.78Ɛ 568 0Ɛ4	
7	.Ɛ11 73Ɛ 717		7	.521 Ɛ41 4X7		7	.795 64X 81Ɛ	
8	.Ɛ41 343 469		8	.530 2Ɛ5 546		8	.79Ɛ 676 467	
9	.Ɛ6Ɛ 25Ɛ 2Ɛ7		9	.53X 491 676		9	.7X5 628 89Ɛ	
X	.Ɛ97 683 1X7		X	.548 499 248		X	.7XƐ 527 32Ɛ	
Ɛ	X.002 575 873		Ɛ	.556 31Ɛ 671		Ɛ	.7Ɛ5 373 56Ɛ	
.0020	.028 092 663		.0060	.563 ƐX3 56Ɛ		.00X0	.7ƐƐ 14X 91X	
1	.050 54Ɛ 3XX		1	.571 6Ɛ3 630		1	.804 X76 6X8	
2	.073 883 X87		2	.57Ɛ 056 03Ɛ		2	.80X 734 330	
3	.095 Ɛ75 631		3	.588 455 055		3	.814 345 240	
4	.0Ɛ7 311 769		4	.595 6Ɛ6 449		4	.819 XXX 79X	
5	.117 7Ɛ0 014		5	.5X2 803 722		5	.823 5X9 Ɛ03	
6	.137 298 803		6	.5XƐ 782 12X		6	.829 044 2X7	
7	.156 051 472		7	.5Ɛ8 5Ɛ7 067		7	.832 636 X01	
8	.174 142 ƐƐ5		8	.605 2XƐ 48X		8	.837 Ɛ86 X76	
9	.191 616 620		9	.611 X67 Ɛ27		9	.841 475 680	
X	.1XX 32X 068		X	.61X 4Ɛ1 336		X	.846 903 Ɛ88	
Ɛ	.206 515 72Ɛ		Ɛ	.626 X07 X2X		Ɛ	.850 0Ɛ3 309	
.0030	.222 023 952		.0070	.633 1Ɛ7 Ɛ52		.00Ɛ0	.855 444 582	
1	.239 09X 462		1	.63Ɛ 485 850		1	.85X 738 82Ɛ	
2	.253 642 X29		2	.647 635 101		2	.863 994 Ɛ20	
3	.269 812 X07		3	.653 689 Ɛ42		3	.868 Ɛ96 268	
4	.283 344 5X1		4	.65Ɛ 610 002		4	.872 141 634	
5	.298 54X X03		5	.667 442 X09		5	.877 253 9Ɛ1	
6	.2Ɛ1 25X 113		6	.673 169 Ɛ13		6	.880 312 09Ɛ	
7	.305 69Ɛ XƐ5		7	.67X 990 746		7	.885 339 211	
8	.319 67Ɛ 768		8	.686 4Ɛ2 195		8	.88X 312 069	
9	.331 222 569		9	.691 Ɛ15 800		9	.893 255 6X5	
X	.344 56Ɛ 85X		X	.699 442 255		X	.898 148 750	
Ɛ	.357 504 X88		Ɛ	.6X4 876 853		Ɛ	.8X0 ƐƐ0 046	

N	Log Sin	d	N	Log Sin	d	N	Log Sin	d
.0100	χ.8χ5 χ04 788	4 986 ...	.0140	χ.χ31 874 876	3 737 ...	.0180	χ.Ɛ40 807 491	2 χ77 ...
1	.8χχ 78Ɛ 326	939 ...	1	.χ35 3χƐ Ɛ93	70χ ...	1	.Ɛ43 683 021	χ5χ ...
2	.8Ɛ3 508 849	8Ɛ1 ...	2	.χ38 χƐχ Ɛ43	6χ2 ...	2	.Ɛ46 521 χχ7	χ42 ...
3	.8Ɛ8 1Ɛ9 87χ	865 ...	3	.χ40 5χ1 Ɛ42	677 ...	3	.Ɛ49 364 2Ɛ0	χ25 ...
4	.900 χ63 119	81χ ...	4	.χ44 059 382	650 ...	4	.Ɛ50 18χ 239	χ09 ...
5	.905 681 6χ5	794 ...	5	.χ47 6χ9 426	625 ...	5	.Ɛ52 Ɛ97 Ɛ09	9Ɛ1 ...
6	.90χ 255 χ76	74χ ...	6	.χ4Ɛ 112 489	5Ɛχ ...	6	.Ɛ55 989 718	995 ...
7	.912 9χ4 906	706 ...	7	.χ52 710 8ƐƐ	593 ...	7	.Ɛ58 763 45χ	97χ ...
8	.917 4χχ χ71	682 ...	8	.χ56 0χ4 882	569 ...	8	.Ɛ5Ɛ 521 506	962 ...
9	.91Ɛ Ɛ70 Ɛ68	63χ ...	9	.χ59 652 751	544 ...	9	.Ɛ62 283 χ84	947 ...
χ	.924 5χƐ 80χ	5Ɛ8 ...	χ	.χ60 Ɛ96 899	51χ ...	χ	.Ɛ65 00χ Ɛ40	92Ɛ ...
Ɛ	.928 Ɛχ7 815	575 ...	Ɛ	.χ64 4Ɛ5 444	4Ɛ5 ...	Ɛ	.Ɛ67 93χ 899	914 ...
.0110	.931 561 761	534 ...	.0150	.χ67 9χχ 966	490 ...	.0190	.Ɛ6χ 653 4Ɛ7	8Ɛ9 ...
1	.935 χ96 1Ɛ0	4Ɛ3 ...	1	.χ6Ɛ 27Ɛ 395	467 ...	1	.Ɛ71 351 173	8χ2 ...
2	.93χ 389 χχ5	473 ...	2	.χ72 727 256	443 ...	2	.Ɛ74 034 063	888 ...
3	.942 841 58Ɛ	434 ...	3	.χ75 Ɛ6χ 8χ7	41Ɛ ...	3	.Ɛ76 900 35Ɛ	871 ...
4	.947 075 595	3Ɛ5 ...	4	.χ79 38χ 241	3Ɛ7 ...	4	.Ɛ79 572 031	857 ...
5	.94Ɛ 46χ 612	376 ...	5	.χ80 785 χ07	394 ...	5	.Ɛ80 209 468	841 ...
6	.953 825 180	338 ...	6	.χ83 Ɛ59 Ɛ25	370 ...	6	.Ɛ82 χ4χ 611	827 ...
7	.957 Ɛ61 Ɛ40	2ƐƐ ...	7	.χ87 30χ 8Ɛ2	349 ...	7	.Ɛ85 675 667	811 ...
8	.960 261 599	282 ...	8	.χ8χ 658 63χ	327 ...	8	.Ɛ88 286 773	7Ɛ7 ...
9	.964 524 387	246 ...	9	.χ91 983 652	304 ...	9	.Ɛ8χ χ81 χχχ	7χ1 ...
χ	.968 76χ Ɛ62	20Ɛ ...	χ	.χ95 088 032	2χ2 ...	χ	.Ɛ91 663 610	788 ...
Ɛ	.970 979 Ɛ6χ	193 ...	Ɛ	.χ98 36χ 294	280 ...	Ɛ	.Ɛ94 22Ɛ 690	772 ...
.0120	.974 Ɛ51 χ17	159 ...	.0160	.χ9Ɛ 62χ 4χχ	25χ ...	.01χ0	.Ɛ96 9χ2 261	759 ...
1	.979 0χƐ 141	123 ...	1	.χχ2 888 962	238 ...	1	.Ɛ99 53Ɛ 6Ɛ1	744 ...
2	.981 212 328	0χ9 ...	2	.χχ5 Ɛ05 756	217 ...	2	.Ɛχ0 083 968	72Ɛ ...
3	.985 2ƐƐ 985	074 ...	3	.χχ9 121 165	1Ɛ6 ...	3	.Ɛχ2 7Ɛ2 ƐƐ5	716 ...
4	.989 374 271	03Ɛ ...	4	.χƐ0 317 662	195 ...	4	.Ɛχ5 309 377	701 ...
5	.991 3Ɛ3 Ɛ74	007 ...	5	.χƐ3 4Ɛ1 115	174 ...	5	.Ɛχ7 χ0χ χ13	6χ8 ...
6	.995 3ƐƐ 648	3 Ɛ93 ...	6	.χƐ6 666 005	154 ...	6	.Ɛχχ 4Ɛ7 8χ4	694 ...
7	.999 393 453	Ɛ60 ...	7	.χƐ9 7Ɛχ 5Ɛ1	134 ...	7	.ƐƐ0 Ɛ90 145	67Ɛ ...
8	.9χ1 333 Ɛ22	Ɛ29 ...	8	.Ɛ00 932 94χ	114 ...	8	.ƐƐ3 650 110	667 ...
9	.9χ5 261 7Ɛ7	χƐ7 ...	9	.Ɛ03 χ47 107	0Ɛ4 ...	9	.ƐƐ6 0Ɛ7 956	653 ...
χ	.9χ9 159 005	χ85 ...	χ	.Ɛ06 Ɛ3Ɛ 750	094 ...	χ	.ƐƐ8 74Ɛ 3χχ	63Ɛ ...
Ɛ	.9Ɛ1 022 465	χ53 ...	Ɛ	.Ɛ0χ 014 703	075 ...	Ɛ	.ƐƐƐ 18χ 9χ1	627 ...
.0130	.9Ɛ4 χ76 267	χ22 ...	.0170	.Ɛ11 08χ 241	056 ...	.01Ɛ0	Ɛ.001 7Ɛ6 47Ɛ	613 ...
1	.9Ɛ8 898 Ɛ09	9Ɛ1 ...	1	.Ɛ14 124 7χ0	037 ...	1	.004 20χ 18Ɛ	600 ...
2	.χ00 68χ χƐ8	981 ...	2	.Ɛ17 160 1χχ	018 ...	2	.006 80χ 255	5χ8 ...
3	.χ04 450 714	951 ...	3	.Ɛ1χ 178 χƐ4	2 ƐƐχ ...	3	.009 1Ɛ6 817	594 ...
4	.χ08 1χ2 427	922 ...	4	.Ɛ21 177 139	Ɛ9Ɛ ...	4	.00Ɛ 78Ɛ 816	581 ...
5	.χ0Ɛ Ɛ04 6Ɛ6	8Ɛ3 ...	5	.Ɛ24 156 Ɛ3Ɛ	Ɛ81 ...	5	.012 151 38Ɛ	56χ ...
6	.χ13 7Ɛ7 7Ɛ2	884 ...	6	.Ɛ27 118 736	Ɛ63 ...	6	.014 6ƐƐ 838	557 ...
7	.χ17 47Ɛ Ɛ7χ	855 ...	7	.Ɛ2χ 080 356	Ɛ45 ...	7	.017 056 Ɛ12	544 ...
8	.χ1Ɛ 115 χ69	827 ...	8	.Ɛ31 006 20Ɛ	Ɛ28 ...	8	.019 59Ɛ 14χ	531 ...
9	.χ22 941 907	7Ɛχ ...	9	.Ɛ33 Ɛ32 542	Ɛ0χ ...	9	.01Ɛ Ɛ10 459	51χ ...
χ	.χ26 53Ɛ Ɛ4χ	790 ...	χ	.Ɛ36 χ41 356	χƐ1 ...	χ	.022 42χ 970	507 ...
Ɛ	.χ2χ 110 9χ6	763 ...	Ɛ	.Ɛ39 932 χ67	χ94 ...	Ɛ	.024 936 5Ɛ5	4Ɛ5 ...

N	Log Sin	d	N	Log Sin	d	N	Log Sin	d
.0200	Ɛ.027 22Ɛ 69χ	2 4χ2 6..	.0240	Ɛ.0Ɛ6 093 483	2 086 7..	.0280	Ɛ.172 679 208	1 973 0..
1	.029 712 149	490 1..	1	.0Ɛ8 15χ 043	078 0..	1	.174 430 2Ɛ0	966 Ɛ..
2	.02Ɛ Ɛχ2 2χ6	479 9..	2	.0Ɛχ 216 075	069 5..	2	.176 197 207	95χ 9..
3	.032 460 056	467 6..	3	.100 283 627	05χ Ɛ..	3	.177 Ɛ35 ƐƐ7	952 9..
4	.034 907 738	455 5..	4	.102 322 5χ8	050 6..	4	.179 888 91χ	946 8..
5	.037 161 072	443 4..	5	.104 373 048	042 2..	5	.17Ɛ 613 615	93χ 9..
6	.039 5χ4 559	431 5..	6	.106 3Ɛ5 253	033 χ..	6	.181 352 342	932 9..
7	.03Ɛ χ15 Ɛ11	41Ɛ 7..	7	.108 429 091	025 7..	7	.183 085 13Ɛ	926 Ɛ..
8	.042 235 669	409 χ..	8	.10χ 452 809	017 5..	8	.184 9Ɛ0 066	91Ɛ 0..
9	.044 643 502	3Ɛ8 2..	9	.110 46χ 10Ɛ	009 3..	9	.186 70Ɛ 159	913 3..
χ	.046 χ3Ɛ 767	3χ6 7..	χ	.112 477 460	1 ƐƐƐ 2..	χ	.188 422 473	907 5..
Ɛ	.049 226 331	395 1..	Ɛ	.114 476 704	ƐƐ1 2..	Ɛ	.18χ 129 χ4χ	8ƐƐ 8..
.0210	.04Ɛ 5ƐƐ 52χ	383 9..	.0250	.116 467 944	Ɛχ3 2..	.0290	.18Ɛ χ29 741	8Ɛ4 0..
1	.051 983 267	372 5..	1	.118 44Ɛ 021	Ɛ95 3..	1	.191 721 7χ6	8χ8 4..
2	.054 135 832	361 3..	2	.11χ 424 41Ɛ	Ɛ87 5..	2	.193 40χ 059	8χ0 9..
3	.056 496 Ɛ52	350 1..	3	.120 3χƐ 9ƐƐ	Ɛ79 8..	3	.195 0χχ 974	895 2..
4	.058 827 111	33Ɛ 1..	4	.122 369 641	Ɛ6Ɛ Ɛ..	4	.196 983 Ɛ88	889 7..
5	.05χ Ɛ66 234	32χ 1..	5	.124 319 5χ4	Ɛ62 3..	5	.198 651 732	882 1..
6	.061 294 402	319 3..	6	.126 27Ɛ 928	Ɛ54 7..	6	.19χ 313 883	876 7..
7	.063 5Ɛ1 738	308 5..	7	.128 214 50Ɛ	Ɛ47 0..	7	.19Ɛ Ɛ8χ 454	86Ɛ 2..
8	.065 8Ɛχ 11Ɛ	2Ɛ7 9..	8	.12χ 15Ɛ 609	Ɛ39 6..	8	.1χ1 839 6Ɛ8	863 9..
9	.067 ƐƐ5 χ69	2χ7 1..	9	.130 099 0χ0	Ɛ30 1..	9	.1χ3 4χ1 485	858 5..
χ	.06χ 2χ1 061	296 7..	χ	.132 009 202	Ɛ22 8..	χ	.1χ5 139 χ10	851 1..
Ɛ	.070 577 7Ɛ5	286 1..	Ɛ	.133 ƐƐƐ χ2Ɛ	Ɛ15 3..	Ɛ	.1χ6 98χ Ɛ66	845 9..
.0220	.072 841 9χ5	275 9..	.0260	.135 χ45 219	Ɛ08 0..	.02χ0	.1χ8 614 960	83χ 6..
1	.074 χƐ7 727	265 5..	1	.137 951 241	χƐχ 9..	1	.1χχ 253 44χ	833 4..
2	.077 161 0Ɛ1	255 3..	2	.139 84Ɛ Ɛ55	χƐ1 6..	2	.1χƐ χ86 87χ	828 2..
3	.079 3Ɛ6 3Ɛ4	245 1..	3	.13Ɛ 741 60χ	χχ4 4..	3	.1Ɛ1 6Ɛ2 χ82	821 0..
4	.07Ɛ 63Ɛ 525	235 0..	4	.141 625 χ9χ	χ97 3..	4	.1Ɛ3 313 χχχ	815 χ..
5	.081 874 573	225 0..	5	.143 501 237	χ8χ 2..	5	.1Ɛ4 Ɛ29 989	80χ 9..
6	.083 χ99 60χ	215 1..	6	.145 38Ɛ 511	χ81 2..	6	.1Ɛ6 738 76Ɛ	803 9..
7	.086 0Ɛ2 75Ɛ	205 3..	7	.147 250 797	χ74 3..	7	.1Ɛ8 340 4χ2	7Ɛ8 9..
8	.088 2Ɛ7 χ94	1Ɛ5 6..	8	.149 104 Ɛ01	χ67 4..	8	.1Ɛ9 Ɛ39 1Ɛ5	7Ɛ1 9..
9	.08χ 4Ɛ1 497	1χ5 9..	9	.14χ Ɛ70 336	χ5χ 5..	9	.1ƐƐ 72χ Ɛ35	7χ6 9..
χ	.090 697 252	196 2..	χ	.150 χ0χ 929	χ51 8..	χ	.201 315 931	79Ɛ χ..
Ɛ	.092 871 467	186 7..	Ɛ	.152 860 548	χ44 χ..	Ɛ	.202 χƐ5 830	795 0..
.0230	.094 χ38 002	177 1..	.0270	.154 6χ5 442	χ38 2..	.02Ɛ0	.204 68χ 880	78χ 2..
1	.096 ƐƐ3 180	167 8..	1	.156 521 67Ɛ	χ2Ɛ 6..	1	.206 258 χχ9	783 4..
2	.099 15χ χ44	158 4..	2	.158 351 0χ8	χ22 χ..	2	.207 χ20 33Ɛ	778 7..
3	.09Ɛ 2Ɛ7 2Ɛ2	149 1..	3	.15χ 173 Ɛ70	χ16 3..	3	.209 598 χ41	771 9..
4	.0χ1 444 426	139 χ..	4	.15Ɛ Ɛ8χ 337	χ09 9..	4	.20Ɛ 14χ 83χ	767 1..
5	.0χ3 582 300	12χ 9..	5	.161 998 06χ	χ01 3..	5	.210 8Ɛ5 97χ	760 5..
6	.0χ5 6Ɛ1 018	11Ɛ 8..	6	.163 799 3Ɛ4	9Ɛ4 χ..	6	.212 456 286	755 9..
7	.0χ7 810 850	110 8..	7	.165 592 1Ɛ6	9χ8 5..	7	.213 ƐχƐ Ɛχ4	74Ɛ 1..
8	.0χ9 921 478	101 8..	8	.167 37χ 718	9χ0 0..	8	.215 73Ɛ 159	744 6..
9	.0χƐ χ23 172	0Ɛ2 χ..	9	.169 15χ 803	993 9..	9	.217 283 7Ɛ4	739 Ɛ..
χ	.0Ɛ1 Ɛ16 00χ	0χ4 0..	χ	.16χ Ɛ32 515	987 5..	χ	.218 χ01 774	733 5..
Ɛ	.0Ɛ3 ƐƐχ 0χ2	095 3..	Ɛ	.170 8Ɛ9 χ26	97Ɛ 3..	Ɛ	.21χ 535 0χ2	728 Ɛ..

N	Log Sin	d	N	Log Sin	d	N	Log Sin	d
.0300	Ɛ.220 062 003	1 722 5..	.0340	Ɛ.280 X16 383	1 52Ɛ 1..	.0380	Ɛ.316 734 675	1 37X 2..
1	.221 784 559	718 0..	1	.282 345 537	525 X..	1	.317 XƐ2 941	375 X..
2	.223 2X0 571	711 7..	2	.283 86Ɛ 418	520 8..	2	.319 268 812	371 6..
3	.224 9Ɛ2 084	707 2..	3	.285 190 057	517 6..	3	.31X 61X 30Ɛ	369 3..
4	.226 4Ɛ9 31Ɛ	700 X..	4	.286 6X7 666	512 4..	4	.31Ɛ 987 657	365 0..
5	.227 ƐƐX 13X	6Ɛ6 6..	5	.287 ƐƐ9 X74	509 2..	5	.321 130 657	360 8..
6	.229 6Ɛ4 764	6Ɛ0 2..	6	.289 507 0Ɛ4	504 0..	6	.322 491 332	358 5..
7	.22Ɛ 1X4 X17	6X5 Ɛ..	7	.28X X0Ɛ 194	4ƐX Ɛ..	7	.323 829 907	354 2..
8	.230 88X 958	69Ɛ 8..	8	.290 30X 146	4Ɛ5 X..	8	.324 Ɛ82 002	350 0..
9	.232 36X 5X8	695 5..	9	.291 803 ƐƐ8	4Ɛ0 9..	9	.326 312 041	347 9..
X	.233 X43 Ɛ86	68Ɛ 3..	X	.293 0Ɛ4 99Ɛ	4X7 9..	X	.327 659 X28	343 7..
Ɛ	.235 513 335	685 1..	Ɛ	.294 5X0 721	4X2 9..	Ɛ	.328 9X1 5X0	33Ɛ 5..
.0310	.236 Ɛ98 4Ɛ3	67Ɛ 0..	.0350	.295 X83 433	499 9..	.0390	.32X 120 Ɛ46	337 3..
1	.238 657 500	674 X..	1	.297 361 143	494 9..	1	.32Ɛ 458 303	333 1..
2	.23X 110 397	66X 9..	2	.298 835 X7Ɛ	48Ɛ 9..	2	.330 78Ɛ 4Ɛ5	32Ɛ 0..
3	.23Ɛ 77Ɛ 180	664 9..	3	.29X 105 853	486 X..	3	.331 XƐX 543	326 Ɛ..
4	.241 223 XƐ1	65X 8..	4	.29Ɛ 590 6Ɛ1	481 Ɛ..	4	.333 225 44Ɛ	322 9..
5	.242 882 7X8	654 9..	5	.2X0 X52 642	479 0..	5	.334 548 236	31X 8..
6	.244 317 4X8	64X 9..	6	.2X2 30Ɛ 6Ɛ6	474 2..	6	.335 866 Ɛ23	316 8..
7	.245 966 22X	644 X..	7	.2X3 783 8Ɛ8	46Ɛ 3..	7	.336 Ɛ81 732	312 7..
8	.247 3XƐ 02Ɛ	63X X..	8	.2X5 033 078	466 5..	8	.338 294 286	30X 6..
9	.248 X29 Ɛ29	635 0..	9	.2X6 499 622	461 7..	9	.339 5X2 983	306 6..
X	.24X 462 Ɛ60	62Ɛ 1..	X	.2X7 93Ɛ 1X0	458 9..	X	.33X 8X9 447	302 6..
Ɛ	.24Ɛ X92 146	625 3..	Ɛ	.2X9 197 Ɛ9X	454 0..	Ɛ	.33Ɛ ƐXƐ X27	2ƐX 6..
.0320	.251 4Ɛ7 519	61Ɛ 5..	.0360	.2XX 630 045	44Ɛ 3..	.03X0	.341 2XX 573	2Ɛ6 6..
1	.252 Ɛ16 Ɛ17	615 8..	1	.2XƐ X7Ɛ 386	446 6..	1	.342 5X5 059	2Ɛ2 7..
2	.254 530 777	60Ɛ Ɛ..	2	.2Ɛ1 305 X09	441 9..	2	.343 897 791	2XX 7..
3	.255 Ɛ40 6Ɛ4	606 2..	3	.2Ɛ2 747 77X	439 1..	3	.344 Ɛ86 374	2X6 8..
4	.257 546 945	600 5..	4	.2Ɛ3 Ɛ84 885	434 4..	4	.346 271 025	2X2 9..
5	.258 Ɛ47 325	5Ɛ6 9..	5	.2Ɛ5 3Ɛ9 152	42Ɛ 8..	5	.347 553 986	29X X..
6	.25X 542 08Ɛ	5Ɛ1 1..	6	.2Ɛ6 828 X08	427 0..	6	.348 832 835	296 Ɛ..
7	.25Ɛ Ɛ33 235	5X7 5..	7	.2Ɛ8 053 X97	422 5..	7	.349 Ɛ09 814	293 1..
8	.261 51X 815	5X1 X..	8	.2Ɛ9 476 3X6	419 9..	8	.34Ɛ 1X0 943	28Ɛ 2..
9	.262 Ɛ00 664	598 3..	9	.2ƐX 894 161	415 2..	9	.350 470 01Ɛ	287 4..
X	.264 498 998	592 8..	X	.300 0X9 3X9	410 7..	X	.351 737 486	283 6..
Ɛ	.265 X6Ɛ 62Ɛ	589 1..	Ɛ	.301 4Ɛ9 Ɛ32	408 0..	Ɛ	.352 9ƐX Ɛ1Ɛ	27Ɛ 8..
.0330	.267 438 814	583 7..	.0370	.302 905 Ɛ9X	403 5..	.03Ɛ0	.354 07X 781	277 X..
1	.268 X00 385	57X 1..	1	.304 109 594	3ƐX Ɛ..	1	.355 336 650	274 1..
2	.26X 37X 536	574 7..	2	.305 508 541	3Ɛ6 5..	2	.356 5XX 766	270 3..
3	.26Ɛ 933 120	56Ɛ 2..	3	.306 902 X88	3Ɛ1 Ɛ..	3	.357 85X Ɛ26	268 6..
4	.271 2X2 371	565 9..	4	.308 0Ɛ4 X16	3X9 5..	4	.358 Ɛ07 56Ɛ	264 9..
5	.272 848 0X3	560 4..	5	.309 4X2 391	3X5 0..	5	.35X 170 298	261 0..
6	.274 1X8 527	556 Ɛ..	6	.30X 887 39X	3X0 6..	6	.35Ɛ 411 308	259 3..
7	.275 743 4Ɛ6	551 7..	7	.310 067 X63	398 1..	7	.360 66X 659	255 6..
8	.277 095 041	548 3..	8	.311 444 009	393 8..	8	.361 904 129	251 X..
9	.278 621 379	542 Ɛ..	9	.312 817 879	38Ɛ 3..	9	.362 Ɛ55 Ɛ57	24X 1..
X	.279 Ɛ64 316	539 7..	X	.313 ƐX7 057	386 Ɛ..	X	.364 1X4 141	246 5..
Ɛ	.27Ɛ 4X1 Ɛ08	534 4..	Ɛ	.315 371 Ɛ88	382 6..	Ɛ	.365 42X 700	242 9..

N	Log Sin	d	N	Log Sin	d	N	Log Sin	d
.0400	Ɛ.366 671 473	1 23Ɛ 18.	.0440	Ɛ.3Ɛ1 71Ɛ 0XX	1 125 1X.	.0480	Ɛ.434 573 Ɛ61	1 02X 05.
1	.367 8Ɛ0 638	237 5Ɛ.	1	.3Ɛ2 844 292	122 06.	1	.435 5X1 ƐƐ5	027 42.
2	.368 Ɛ28 030	233 X4.	2	.3Ɛ3 966 333	11X Ɛ3.	2	.436 609 415	024 7Ɛ.
3	.36X 15Ɛ X70	230 2X.	3	.3Ɛ4 X85 265	117 X1.	3	.437 632 012	021 ƐX.
4	.36Ɛ 390 157	228 76.	4	.3Ɛ5 ƐX1 081	114 91.	4	.438 653 ƐƐX	01Ɛ 3X.
5	.370 5Ɛ8 905	225 04.	5	.3Ɛ7 0Ɛ5 999	111 82.	5	.439 673 3X6	018 7Ɛ.
6	.371 821 954	221 54.	6	.3Ɛ8 207 608	10X 75.	6	.43X 68Ɛ ƐX3	016 01.
7	.372 X43 2X0	219 X6.	7	.3Ɛ9 316 163	107 69.	7	.43Ɛ 6X6 002	013 45.
8	.374 061 144	216 39.	8	.3ƐX 421 83Ɛ	104 63.	8	.440 6Ɛ9 456	010 89.
9	.375 277 51Ɛ	212 92.	9	.3ƐƐ 526 270	101 59.	9	.441 70X 133	00X 13.
X	.376 48X 247	20Ɛ 29.	X	.400 627 84Ɛ	0ƐX 56.	X	.442 718 267	007 59.
Ɛ	.377 699 520	207 85.	Ɛ	.401 726 1Ɛ1	0Ɛ7 53.	Ɛ	.443 723 846	004 X5.
.0410	.378 8X5 17Ɛ	204 24.	.0450	.402 821 728	0Ɛ4 52.	.0490	.444 728 6X2	002 32.
1	.379 XX9 400	200 83.	1	.403 916 052	0Ɛ1 52.	1	.445 72X X08	ƐƐƐ 80.
2	.37Ɛ 0XX 03Ɛ	1Ɛ9 25.	2	.404 X07 57Ɛ	0XX 54.	2	.446 72X 610	ƐƐ9 0Ɛ.
3	.380 2X7 296	1Ɛ5 88.	3	.405 XƐ5 Ɛ03	0X7 57.	3	.447 727 704	ƐƐ6 5Ɛ.
4	.381 4X0 Ɛ64	1Ɛ2 31.	4	.406 ƐX1 475	0X4 5Ɛ.	4	.448 722 0Ɛ8	ƐƐ3 Ɛ0.
5	.382 693 281	1XX 98.	5	.408 085 X6X	0X1 64.	5	.449 716 001	ƐƐ1 42.
6	.383 882 045	1X7 44.	6	.409 167 4Ɛ9	09X 6Ɛ.	6	.44X 707 428	ƐXX 95.
7	.384 X69 490	1X3 Ɛ2.	7	.40X 245 ƐƐ6	097 77.	7	.44Ɛ 6Ɛ6 186	ƐX8 2X.
8	.386 051 3Ɛ6	1X0 62.	8	.40Ɛ 321 774	094 85.	8	.450 6X2 467	ƐX5 83.
9	.387 231 X17	199 13.	9	.410 3Ɛ6 408	091 94.	9	.451 688 09Ɛ	ƐX3 19.
X	.388 40X Ɛ49	195 86.	X	.411 488 149	08X X4.	X	.452 66Ɛ 278	ƐX0 75.
Ɛ	.389 5X4 7X9	192 3X.	Ɛ	.412 556 Ɛ8X	087 Ɛ5.	Ɛ	.453 64Ɛ X09	Ɛ9X 11.
.0420	.38X 776 Ɛ91	18X Ɛ4.	.0460	.413 622 Ɛ23	085 08.	.04X0	.454 629 Ɛ23	Ɛ97 6Ɛ.
1	.38Ɛ 945 Ɛ16	187 70.	1	.414 6X7 ƐX3	082 1Ɛ.	1	.455 605 613	Ɛ95 09.
2	.390 Ɛ11 616	184 29.	2	.415 76X 1X0	07Ɛ 34.	2	.456 59X 6X8	Ɛ92 68.
3	.392 095 8X9	180 X7.	3	.416 829 52Ɛ	078 4Ɛ.	3	.457 571 177	Ɛ90 09.
4	.393 256 768	179 68.	4	.417 8X5 X22	075 66.	4	.458 541 251	Ɛ89 6X.
5	.394 414 230	176 2X.	5	.418 95Ɛ 491	072 83.	5	.459 50X 940	Ɛ87 11.
6	.395 58X 514	172 Ɛ1.	6	.419 X12 10X	06Ɛ X1.	6	.45X 495 X56	Ɛ84 75.
7	.396 741 430	16Ɛ 76.	7	.41X X81 Ɛ28	069 01.	7	.45Ɛ 45X 5X6	Ɛ82 19.
8	.397 8Ɛ0 Ɛ9X	168 41.	8	.41Ɛ Ɛ2X Ɛ3Ɛ	066 21.	8	.460 420 781	Ɛ7Ɛ 83.
9	.398 X59 3Ɛ2	165 09.	9	.420 Ɛ95 158	063 43.	9	.461 3X0 3Ɛ2	Ɛ79 29.
X	.39X 002 487	161 97.	X	.422 038 592	060 66.	X	.462 359 688	Ɛ76 95.
Ɛ	.39Ɛ 164 238	15X 66.	Ɛ	.423 099 039	059 8X.	Ɛ	.463 314 419	Ɛ74 41.
.0430	.3X0 302 89Ɛ	157 36.	.0470	.424 136 926	056 Ɛ4.	.04Ɛ0	.464 288 834	Ɛ71 XƐ.
1	.3X1 45X 04X	154 09.	1	.425 191 868	054 1X.	1	.465 23X 724	Ɛ6Ɛ 59.
2	.3X2 5Ɛ2 11Ɛ	150 X0.	2	.426 225 X55	051 46.	2	.466 1XX 0Ɛ9	Ɛ69 08.
3	.3X3 742 Ɛ28	149 76.	3	.427 277 301	04X 73.	3	.467 157 186	Ɛ66 79.
4	.3X4 890 688	146 50.	4	.428 305 X38	047 X1.	4	.468 101 958	Ɛ64 2X.
5	.3X5 X16 Ɛ93	143 28.	5	.429 351 856	045 11.	5	.469 066 042	Ɛ61 X0.
6	.3X6 Ɛ5X 25Ɛ	140 06.	6	.42X 396 969	042 41.	6	.46X 007 X4Ɛ	Ɛ5Ɛ 54.
7	.3X8 09X 303	138 X5.	7	.42Ɛ 419 185	03Ɛ 73.	7	Ɛ67 38Ɛ	Ɛ59 08.
8	.3X9 217 158	135 85.	8	.430 458 8ƐƐ	038 X6.	8	.46Ɛ Ɛ04 451	Ɛ56 81.
9	.3XX 350 9Ɛ7	132 67.	9	.431 495 763	036 1X.	9	.470 X5Ɛ 065	Ɛ54 37.
X	.3XƐ 483 475	12Ɛ 4Ɛ.	X	.432 50Ɛ 947	033 53.	X	.471 9Ɛ3 419	Ɛ51 Ɛ2.
Ɛ	.3Ɛ0 5Ɛ2 968	128 34.	Ɛ	.433 543 282	030 89.	Ɛ	.472 945 342	Ɛ4Ɛ 6X.

N	Log Sin	d	N	Log Sin	d	N	Log Sin	d
.0500	Ɛ.473 894 X25	Ɛ49 27.	.0540	Ɛ.4XƐ X23 772	X7Ɛ 32.	.0580	Ɛ.525 241 764	X01 68.
1	.474 822 097	Ɛ46 X4.	1	.4Ɛ0 8X2 X92	X79 23.	1	.526 043 224	9ƐƐ 87.
2	.475 768 Ɛ26	Ɛ44 63.	2	.4Ɛ1 760 111	X77 16.	2	X42 X99	9Ɛ9 X7.
3	.476 6Ɛ1 562	Ɛ42 23.	3	.4Ɛ2 617 27X	X75 0X.	3	.527 840 953	9Ɛ8 08.
4	.477 633 796	Ɛ3Ɛ X3.	4	.4Ɛ3 490 362	X73 02.	4	.528 638 X14	9Ɛ6 29.
5	.478 573 613	Ɛ39 65.	5	.4Ɛ4 343 389	X70 Ɛ7.	5	.529 433 0X9	9Ɛ4 4Ɛ.
6	.479 4Ɛ1 067	Ɛ37 27.	6	.4Ɛ5 1Ɛ4 346	X6X Ɛ1.	6	.52X 227 5X2	9Ɛ2 71.
7	.47X 428 322	Ɛ34 XX.	7	.4Ɛ6 063 25Ɛ	X68 X8.	7	.52Ɛ 01X 100	9Ɛ0 95.
8	.47Ɛ 361 210	Ɛ32 73.	8	Ɛ10 120	X66 X3.	8	X0X X51	9XX Ɛ8.
9	.480 293 941	Ɛ30 38.	9	.4Ɛ7 976 Ɛ54	X64 9Ɛ.	9	.530 7Ɛ9 X1Ɛ	9X9 21.
X	.481 204 102	Ɛ2X 02.	X	.4Ɛ8 81Ɛ 948	X62 98.	X	.531 5X7 032	9X7 46.
Ɛ	.482 132 122	Ɛ27 88.	Ɛ	.4Ɛ9 682 709	X60 95.	Ɛ	.532 392 495	9X5 6Ɛ.
.0510	.483 059 9Ɛ1	Ɛ25 54.	.0550	.4ƐX 523 465	X5X 93.	.0590	.533 177 Ɛ94	9X3 96.
1	Ɛ83 338	Ɛ23 21.	1	.4ƐƐ 382 1X3	X58 92.	1	Ɛ5Ɛ 936	9X2 01.
2	.484 XX6 54X	Ɛ20 XX.	2	.500 21X Ɛ11	X56 92.	2	.534 941 946	9X0 28.
3	.485 X07 435	Ɛ1X 79.	3	.501 075 837	X54 92.	3	.535 722 00Ɛ	99X 54.
4	.486 926 005	Ɛ18 48.	4	Ɛ0X 566	X52 94.	4	.536 500 555	998 81.
5	.487 842 487	Ɛ16 18.	5	.502 961 2X6	X50 95.	5	.537 299 168	996 XX.
6	.488 758 64Ɛ	Ɛ13 X9.	6	.503 7Ɛ2 044	X4X 98.	6	.538 074 051	995 18.
7	.489 670 522	Ɛ11 7Ɛ.	7	.504 640 X09	X48 9Ɛ.	7	X49 214	993 46.
8	.48X 582 112	Ɛ0Ɛ 51.	8	.505 489 805	X46 X3.	8	.539 820 682	991 75.
9	.48Ɛ 491 62X	Ɛ09 25.	9	.506 314 641	X44 X8.	9	.53X 5Ɛ2 21Ɛ	98Ɛ X5.
X	.490 39X 880	Ɛ06 Ɛ9.	X	.507 159 506	X42 Ɛ1.	X	.53Ɛ 382 074	98X 15.
Ɛ	.491 2X5 857	Ɛ04 92.	Ɛ	ƐX0 422	X40 Ɛ7.	Ɛ	.540 150 211	988 46.
.0520	.492 1XX 584	Ɛ02 68.	.0560	.508 X21 3X0	X3Ɛ 02.	.05X0	Ɛ18 676	986 77.
1	.493 0Ɛ1 052	Ɛ00 43.	1	.509 860 407	X39 0X.	1	.541 8X3 235	984 X9.
2	ƐƐ1 48X	XƐX 1Ɛ.	2	.50X 699 4X8	X37 16.	2	.542 668 113	983 20.
3	.494 XXƐ 683	XƐ7 Ɛ8.	3	.50Ɛ 514 64Ɛ	X35 23.	3	.543 42Ɛ 319	981 53.
4	.495 9X7 643	XƐ5 95.	4	.510 349 880	X33 30.	4	.544 1Ɛ0 854	97Ɛ 87.
5	.496 8X1 397	XƐ3 73.	5	.511 180 Ɛ88	X31 3X.	5	Ɛ70 507	979 ƐƐ.
6	.497 794 Ɛ11	XƐ1 52.	6	ƐƐ2 376	X2Ɛ 49.	6	.545 92X 502	978 34.
7	.498 686 438	XXƐ 32.	7	.512 X21 854	X29 59.	7	.546 6X6 848	976 69.
8	.499 575 761	XX9 13.	8	.513 84Ɛ 228	X27 69.	8	.547 461 326	974 X3.
9	.49X 462 892	XX6 Ɛ4.	9	.514 676 904	X25 7X.	9	.548 216 165	973 1X.
X	.49Ɛ 349 819	XX4 96.	X	.515 4X0 4XƐ	X23 90.	X	Ɛ89 34Ɛ	971 55.
Ɛ	.4X0 232 586	XX2 7X.	Ɛ	.516 304 1Ɛ2	X21 X2.	Ɛ	.549 93X 8X6	96Ɛ 91.
.0530	.4X1 115 166	XX0 61.	.0570	.517 126 018	X1Ɛ Ɛ5.	.05Ɛ0	.54X 6XX 5Ɛ9	96X 09.
1	ƐƐ5 783	X9X 46.	1	Ɛ45 Ɛ71	X1X 09.	1	.54Ɛ 458 694	968 46.
2	.4X2 X94 029	X98 30.	2	.518 964 042	X18 21.	2	.550 204 Ɛ39	966 83.
3	.4X3 970 329	X96 16.	3	.519 780 256	X16 36.	3	Ɛ6Ɛ 775	965 01.
4	.4X4 846 490	X94 01.	4	.51X 596 5ƐX	X14 4Ɛ.	4	.551 914 792	963 40.
5	.4X5 71X 4X4	X91 X9.	5	.51Ɛ 3XX XƐ9	X12 66.	5	.552 677 Ɛ93	961 7Ɛ.
6	.4X6 5Ɛ0 376	X8Ɛ 95.	6	.520 201 55X	X10 81.	6	.553 419 786	95Ɛ ƐX.
7	.4X7 480 114	X89 83.	7	.521 012 16Ɛ	X0X 98.	7	.554 179 773	95X 3X.
8	.4X8 349 947	X87 71.	8	X20 Ɛ36	X08 Ɛ4.	8	Ɛ17 Ɛ61	958 7Ɛ.
9	.4X9 215 460	X85 60.	9	.522 829 X83	X07 11.	9	.555 874 758	957 00.
X	.4XX 09X X65	X83 50.	X	.523 634 Ɛ9Ɛ	X05 2Ɛ.	X	.556 60Ɛ 765	955 42.
Ɛ	Ɛ62 367	X81 40.	Ɛ	.524 43X 291	X03 49.	Ɛ	.557 364 Ɛ8Ɛ	953 84.

N	Log Sin	d	N	Log Sin	d	N	Log Sin	d
.0600	Ɛ.558 0Ɛ8 819	952 078	.0640	Ɛ.588 927 36X	8XƐ 189	.0680	Ɛ.5Ɛ7 586 708	853 65Ɛ
1	X4X 895	950 4Ɛ0	1	.589 616 537	8X9 7ƐƐ	1	.5Ɛ8 21X 167	852 252
2	.559 79Ɛ 185	94X 92Ɛ	2	.58X 304 136	8X8 234	2	X70 3Ɛ9	850 X49
3	.55X 529 XƐ4	949 174	3	ƐƐ0 36X	8X6 873	3	.5Ɛ9 701 246	84Ɛ 64X
4	.55Ɛ 277 068	947 604	4	.58Ɛ 897 021	8X5 2Ɛ8	4	.5ƐX 350 894	84X 252
5	.560 002 670	945 X5X	5	.590 580 319	8X3 946	5	Ɛ9X Ɛ26	848 X61
6	948 50X	944 2ƐX	6	.591 264 063	8X2 39X	6	.5ƐƐ 827 987	847 672
7	.561 690 808	942 764	7	Ɛ46 441	8X0 X37	7	.600 473 439	846 289
8	.562 413 370	941 015	8	.592 827 278	89Ɛ 498	8	.601 0Ɛ9 706	844 XX8
9	.563 154 385	93Ɛ 490	9	.593 506 754	899 Ɛ45	9	942 5Ɛ2	843 711
X	X93 855	939 951	X	.594 1X4 699	898 5Ɛ5	X	.602 586 103	842 338
Ɛ	.564 811 5X6	938 219	Ɛ	X81 092	897 06Ɛ	Ɛ	.603 208 43Ɛ	840 Ɛ6X
.0610	.565 549 803	936 6XƐ	.0650	.595 758 141	895 72X	.0690	X49 3X9	83Ɛ 7X4
1	.566 284 2Ɛ2	934 Ɛ86	1	.596 431 86Ɛ	894 1Ɛ3	1	.604 688 Ɛ91	83X 421
2	ƐƐ9 278	933 468	2	.597 105 X62	892 881	2	.605 307 3Ɛ2	839 064
3	.567 930 724	931 954	3	998 723	891 354	3	Ɛ44 456	837 8XƐ
4	.568 662 478	930 246	4	.598 669 X77	88Ɛ X30	4	.606 780 145	836 53X
5	.569 392 702	92X 743	5	.599 339 8X7	88X 512	5	.607 3Ɛ6 683	835 193
6	.56X 101 245	929 045	6	.59X 008 1Ɛ9	888 ƐƐ9	6	.608 02Ɛ 856	833 X2X
7	X2X 28X	927 551	7	895 1Ɛ6	887 6X8	7	863 684	832 690
8	.56Ɛ 755 81Ɛ	925 X64	8	.59Ɛ 560 8X2	886 1X1	8	.609 496 154	831 335
9	.570 47Ɛ 683	924 380	9	.5X0 226 X83	884 89Ɛ	9	.60X 107 489	82Ɛ ƐX2
X	.571 1X3 X43	922 8X3	X	XXƐ 762	883 3X2	X	937 46Ɛ	82X 855
Ɛ	Ɛ06 726	921 20X	Ɛ	.5X1 772 Ɛ44	881 XXƐ	Ɛ	.60Ɛ 566 104	829 50Ɛ
.0620	.572 827 934	91Ɛ 741	.0660	.5X2 434 X33	880 600	.06X0	.610 193 613	828 18X
1	.573 547 475	91X 079	1	.5X3 0Ɛ5 433	87Ɛ 116	1	9ƐƐ 7X1	826 X51
2	.574 265 532	918 600	2	974 549	879 835	2	.611 626 632	825 718
3	Ɛ81 Ɛ32	916 Ɛ47	3	.5X4 632 182	878 35X	3	.612 250 14X	824 3X8
4	.575 898 X79	915 499	4	.5X5 2XX 520	876 X88	4	X74 536	823 080
5	.576 5Ɛ2 356	913 X34	5	Ɛ65 3X8	875 5Ɛ9	5	.613 697 5Ɛ6	821 959
6	.577 306 18X	912 396	6	.5X6 81X 9X5	874 136	6	.614 2Ɛ9 353	820 639
7	.578 018 564	910 942	7	.5X7 492 Ɛ1Ɛ	872 875	7	Ɛ19 990	81Ɛ 322
8	929 2X6	90Ɛ 2Ɛ2	8	.5X8 145 794	871 3ƐƐ	8	.615 739 0Ɛ2	81X 010
9	.579 638 598	909 869	9	9Ɛ6 Ɛ93	86Ɛ Ɛ49	9	.616 357 102	818 901
X	.57X 346 245	908 22X	X	.5X9 666 Ɛ20	86X 6X0	X	Ɛ73 X03	817 5Ɛ6
Ɛ	.57Ɛ 052 473	906 7Ɛ4	Ɛ	.5XX 315 600	869 238	Ɛ	.617 78Ɛ 3Ɛ9	816 2Ɛ5
.0630	959 067	905 184	.0670	Ɛ82 838	867 999	.06Ɛ0	.618 3X5 6Ɛ2	814 ƐƐ7
1	.580 662 22Ɛ	903 75X	1	.5XƐ 82X 615	866 543	1	ƐƐX 6X9	813 901
2	.581 365 989	902 139	2	.5Ɛ0 494 Ɛ58	865 0Ɛ1	2	.619 812 3XX	812 60Ɛ
3	.582 067 Ɛ06	900 721	3	.5Ɛ1 13X 049	863 865	3	.61X 424 9Ɛ9	811 322
4	968 627	8ƐƐ 111	4	9X1 8Ɛ2	862 421	4	.61Ɛ 036 11Ɛ	810 039
5	.583 667 738	8Ɛ9 705	5	.5Ɛ2 644 113	860 ƐX3	5	846 158	80X 958
6	.584 365 241	8Ɛ8 102	6	.5Ɛ3 2X5 0Ɛ6	85Ɛ 768	6	.620 454 XƐ4	809 67Ɛ
7	.585 061 343	8Ɛ6 706	7	Ɛ44 862	85X 336	7	.621 062 573	808 3X6
8	957 X49	8Ɛ5 113	8	.5Ɛ4 7X2 Ɛ98	858 Ɛ0X	8	86X 959	807 116
9	.586 650 Ɛ60	8Ɛ3 725	9	.5Ɛ5 43Ɛ XX6	857 6X6	9	.622 475 X73	805 X48
X	.587 344 685	8Ɛ2 142	X	.5Ɛ6 097 590	856 287	X	.623 07Ɛ 8ƐƐ	804 785
Ɛ	.588 036 807	8Ɛ0 763	Ɛ	931 857	854 X71	Ɛ	884 484	803 504

N	Log Sin	d	N	Log Sin	d	N	Log Sin	d
.0700	Ɛ.624 487 988	802 247	.0740	Ɛ.64Ɛ 822 936	776 321	.0780	Ɛ.675 595 Ɛ1X	733 046
1	.625 08X 013	800 Ɛ94	1	.650 399 057	775 199	1	.676 108 Ɛ64	732 014
2	88X ƐX7	7ƐƐ 923	2	Ɛ52 234	774 059	2	83X Ɛ78	730 ƐX6
3	.626 48X 90X	7ƐX 676	3	.651 706 291	772 Ɛ20	3	.677 36Ɛ Ɛ62	72Ɛ Ɛ7X
4	.627 089 384	7Ɛ9 413	4	.652 279 1Ɛ1	771 9X8	4	X9Ɛ Ɛ20	72X Ɛ56
5	886 797	7Ɛ8 172	5	X2X Ɛ99	770 876	5	.678 60X X76	729 Ɛ35
6	.628 482 949	7Ɛ6 Ɛ16	6	.653 59Ɛ 853	76Ɛ 749	6	.679 138 9XƐ	728 Ɛ16
7	.629 079 863	7Ɛ5 882	7	.654 14Ɛ 3X0	76X 621	7	865 905	727 XƐƐ
8	873 525	7Ɛ4 631	8	8Ɛ9 X01	769 4ƐƐ	8	.67X 391 804	726 XX7
9	.62X 467 Ɛ56	7Ɛ3 3X5	9	.655 467 300	768 39Ɛ	9	X28 6XƐ	725 X95
X	.62Ɛ 05Ɛ 33Ɛ	7Ɛ2 160	X	.656 013 69Ɛ	767 283	X	.67Ɛ 622 584	724 X87
Ɛ	851 49Ɛ	7Ɛ0 Ɛ20	Ɛ	77X 962	766 16X	Ɛ	.680 147 44Ɛ	723 X80
.0710	.630 442 3ƐƐ	7XƐ 8X4	.0750	.657 324 Ɛ10	765 059	.0790	86Ɛ 30Ɛ	722 X78
1	.631 032 0X3	7XX 66X	1	X89 Ɛ69	763 Ɛ4Ɛ	1	.681 392 187	721 X76
2	820 751	7X9 43X	2	.658 631 X28	762 X44	2	X24 041	720 X79
3	.632 409 Ɛ8Ɛ	7X8 211	3	.659 194 940	761 942	3	.682 614 XƐX	71Ɛ X81
4	ƐƐ6 1X0	7X6 ƐX8	4	936 682	760 841	4	.683 134 97Ɛ	71X X88
5	.633 7X1 188	7X5 987	5	.65X 497 303	75Ɛ 745	5	853 847	719 X97
6	.634 386 Ɛ53	7X4 769	6	.65Ɛ 036 X48	75X 650	6	.684 371 722	718 XX9
7	Ɛ6Ɛ 700	7X3 554	7	795 498	759 55X	7	X8X 60Ɛ	717 Ɛ01
8	.635 753 054	7X2 342	8	.660 332 X36	758 46Ɛ	8	.685 5X6 510	716 Ɛ18
9	.636 335 396	7X1 134	9	X8Ɛ 2X5	757 385	9	.686 101 428	715 Ɛ37
X	Ɛ16 50X	79Ɛ Ɛ2Ɛ	X	.661 626 66X	756 2X1	X	817 363	714 Ɛ58
Ɛ	.637 6Ɛ6 439	79X 928	Ɛ	.662 180 94Ɛ	755 200	Ɛ	.687 330 2ƐƐ	713 Ɛ80
.0720	.638 295 165	799 729	.0760	915 Ɛ4Ɛ	754 123	.07X0	X44 27Ɛ	712 ƐX7
1	X72 892	798 533	1	.663 46X 072	753 04X	1	.688 557 266	015
2	.639 64Ɛ 205	797 340	2	.664 001 100	751 Ɛ77	2	.689 069 27Ɛ	711 045
3	.63X 226 545	796 150	3	753 077	750 XX7	3	77X 304	710 07X
4	X00 695	794 Ɛ65	4	.665 2X3 Ɛ62	74Ɛ X1Ɛ	4	.68X 28X 382	70Ɛ 0Ɛ3
5	.63Ɛ 595 63X	793 982	5	X33 981	74X 957	5	999 475	70X 131
6	.640 169 400	792 7X1	6	.666 582 718	749 895	6	.68Ɛ 4X7 5X6	709 172
7	93Ɛ ƐX1	791 605	7	.667 110 3Ɛ1	748 817	7	ƐƐ4 758	708 1Ɛ4
8	.641 511 5X6	790 431	8	859 008	747 760	8	.690 700 950	707 23Ɛ
9	.642 0X1 X17	78Ɛ 25Ɛ	9	.668 3X4 768	746 6X7	9	.691 207 Ɛ8Ɛ	706 287
X	871 076	78X 092	X	Ɛ2Ɛ 253	745 637	X	912 256	705 316
Ɛ	.643 43Ɛ 148	788 Ɛ09	Ɛ	.669 674 88X	744 58X	Ɛ	.692 417 570	704 369
.0730	.644 008 055	787 947	.0770	.66X 1Ɛ9 258	743 523	.07Ɛ0	Ɛ1Ɛ 919	703 402
1	793 9X0	786 788	1	940 77Ɛ	742 481	1	.693 623 11Ɛ	702 45X
2	.645 35X 568	785 612	2	.66Ɛ 483 040	741 420	2	.694 125 579	701 4Ɛ9
3	Ɛ23 Ɛ7X	784 45X	3	.670 004 460	740 384	3	826 X76	700 55X
4	.646 6X8 418	783 2Ɛ0	4	744 824	73Ɛ 32X	4	.695 327 414	6ƐƐ 603
5	.647 26Ɛ 708	782 143	5	.671 283 Ɛ52	73X 297	5	X26 X17	6ƐX 669
6	X31 84Ɛ	780 Ɛ9Ɛ	6	X02 229	739 248	6	.696 525 484	6Ɛ9 717
7	.648 5Ɛ2 82X	77Ɛ X3X	7	.672 53Ɛ 475	738 201	7	.697 022 Ɛ9Ɛ	6Ɛ8 788
8	.649 172 668	77X 8X2	8	.673 077 676	737 177	8	71Ɛ 767	6Ɛ7 840
9	931 34X	779 747	9	7Ɛ2 831	736 135	9	.698 217 3X7	6Ɛ6 8Ɛ5
X	.64X 4XX X95	778 5Ɛ6	X	.674 328 966	735 0Ɛ6	X	912 0X0	6Ɛ5 972
Ɛ	.64Ɛ 067 48Ɛ	777 467	Ɛ	X61 X60	734 07X	Ɛ	.699 407 X52	6Ɛ4 X32

N	Log Sin	d	N	Log Sin	d	N	Log Sin	d
.0800	Ɛ.699 Ɛ00 884	6Ɛ3 XƐ4	.0840	Ɛ.701 114 80Ɛ	678 4Ɛ4	.0880	Ɛ.723 131 50X	644 146
1	.69X 5Ɛ4 778	6Ɛ2 Ɛ78	1	791 103	677 660	1	775 654	643 382
2	.69Ɛ 0X7 734	045	2	.702 248 763	676 80X	2	.724 1Ɛ8 X16	642 5ƐƐ
3	799 779	6Ɛ1 112	3	903 371	675 979	3	83Ɛ 415	641 83Ɛ
4	.6X0 28X 88Ɛ	6Ɛ0 1X4	4	.703 379 12X	674 Ɛ30	4	.725 281 054	640 X81
5	97X X73	6XƐ 278	5	X32 05X	0X4	5	901 Ɛ15	105
6	.6X1 46X 12Ɛ	6XX 352	6	.704 4X6 142	673 25Ɛ	6	.726 342 01X	63Ɛ 34Ɛ
7	Ɛ58 481	6X9 42X	7	Ɛ59 3X1	672 419	7	981 369	63X 597
8	.6X2 645 8XƐ	6X8 50Ɛ	8	.705 60Ɛ 7ƐX	671 599	8	.727 3ƐƐ 944	639 826
9	.6X3 132 1ƐX	6X7 5Ɛ1	9	.706 081 197	670 75X	9	X39 56X	638 X75
X	819 7XƐ	6X6 696	X	731 935	66Ɛ 923	X	.728 476 423	109
Ɛ	.6X4 304 285	6X5 782	Ɛ	.707 1X1 658	66X XXX	Ɛ	XƐ2 530	637 361
.0810	9X9 X47	6X4 870	.0850	850 546	078	.0890	.729 529 891	636 5Ɛ7
1	.6X5 492 6Ɛ7	6X3 960	1	.708 2ƐX 602	669 246	1	Ɛ64 288	635 855
2	Ɛ76 457	6X2 X55	2	967 848	668 418	2	.72X 599 Ɛ21	634 XƐ3
3	.6X6 659 2Ɛ0	6X1 Ɛ4X	3	.709 414 064	667 5Ɛ1	3	.72Ɛ 012 X14	154
4	.6X7 13Ɛ 23X	047	4	X7Ɛ 655	666 787	4	646 Ɛ68	633 3Ɛ6
5	820 285	6X0 147	5	.70X 526 220	665 963	5	.730 07X 362	632 660
6	.6X8 300 410	69Ɛ 249	6	Ɛ8Ɛ Ɛ83	664 Ɛ43	6	6Ɛ0 X02	631 907
7	99Ɛ 659	69X 351	7	.70Ɛ 634 Ɛ06	124	7	.731 122 709	630 Ɛ74
8	.6X9 479 9XX	699 458	8	.710 099 02X	663 307	8	753 681	222
9	Ɛ57 246	698 566	9	740 335	662 4Ɛ1	9	.732 183 8X3	62Ɛ 494
X	.6XX 633 7Ɛ0	697 676	X	.711 1X2 826	661 69X	X	7Ɛ3 177	62X 747
Ɛ	.6XƐ 10Ɛ 266	696 789	Ɛ	844 304	660 888	Ɛ	.733 221 902	629 X00
.0820	7X5 X33	695 8X2	.0860	.712 2X4 Ɛ90	65Ɛ X78	.08X0	84Ɛ 702	078
1	.6Ɛ0 27Ɛ 715	694 9ƐƐ	1	944 X48	070	1	.734 278 77X	628 334
2	954 514	693 Ɛ18	2	.713 3X3 XƐ8	65X 264	2	8X4 XƐ2	627 5Ɛ4
3	.6Ɛ1 428 430	03X	3	X42 160	659 460	3	.735 310 4X6	626 875
4	XƐƐ 46X	692 161	4	.714 49Ɛ 600	658 65X	4	937 15Ɛ	625 Ɛ38
5	.6Ɛ2 591 60Ɛ	691 287	5	Ɛ38 05X	657 85X	5	.736 361 097	201
6	.6Ɛ3 062 896	690 3Ɛ4	6	.715 593 8Ɛ8	656 X60	6	986 298	624 489
7	733 08X	68Ɛ 523	7	.716 02X 758	064	7	.737 3XX 765	623 755
8	.6Ɛ4 202 5Ɛ1	68X 655	8	684 800	655 26Ɛ	8	X12 2ƐX	622 X25
9	891 046	689 788	9	.717 119 X6Ɛ	654 477	9	.738 435 123	0Ɛ5
X	.6Ɛ5 35X 812	688 903	X	772 326	653 687	X	X57 218	621 389
Ɛ	X27 515	687 X40	Ɛ	.718 205 9Ɛ1	652 898	Ɛ	.739 478 5X5	620 662
.0830	.6Ɛ6 4Ɛ3 355	686 Ɛ80	.0870	858 689	651 XXƐ	.08Ɛ0	X99 047	61Ɛ 939
1	Ɛ7X 315	101	1	.719 2XX 578	105	1	.73X 4Ɛ8 984	016
2	.6Ɛ7 644 416	685 246	2	93Ɛ 681	650 321	2	Ɛ17 99X	61X 2Ɛ5
3	.6Ɛ8 109 660	684 391	3	.71X 38Ɛ 9X2	64Ɛ 53Ɛ	3	.73Ɛ 536 093	619 595
4	791 X31	683 51Ɛ	4	X1Ɛ 321	64X 75Ɛ	4	Ɛ53 668	618 879
5	.6Ɛ9 255 350	682 66X	5	.71Ɛ 469 X80	649 981	5	.740 570 325	617 Ɛ61
6	917 9ƐX	681 800	6	XƐ7 841	648 ƐX6	6	Ɛ88 286	248
7	.6ƐX 399 5ƐX	680 955	7	.720 544 827	210	7	.741 5X3 512	616 534
8	X5X 353	67Ɛ XƐ0	8	Ɛ90 X37	647 439	8	ƐƐ9 X46	615 823
9	.6ƐƐ 51X 243	04X	9	.721 618 274	646 669	9	.742 613 669	614 Ɛ13
X	Ɛ99 291	67X 1XX	X	.722 062 921	645 899	X	.743 028 580	206
Ɛ	.700 657 47Ɛ	679 350	Ɛ	6X8 5ƐX	644 Ɛ10	Ɛ	640 786	613 4ƐX

N	Log Sin	d	N	Log Sin	d	N	Log Sin	d
.0900	Ɛ.744 054 084	612 7Ɛ4	.0940	Ɛ.763 Ɛ69 96Ɛ	5ᘔ3 900	.0980	Ɛ.782 Ɛ52 287	577 145
1	666 878	611 ᘔƐ1	1	.764 551 66Ɛ	06ᘔ	1	.783 509 410	576 55ᘔ
2	.745 078 769	1ᘔᘔ	2	Ɛ34 719	5ᘔ2 41ᘔ	2	ᘔ83 96ᘔ	575 973
3	689 957	610 4ᘔᘔ	3	.765 516 Ɛ37	5ᘔ1 790	3	.784 439 721	18ᘔ
4	.746 09ᘔ 245	60Ɛ 7Ɛ0	4	ᘔƐ8 707	5ᘔ0 Ɛ44	4	9Ɛ2 8ᘔƐ	574 5ᘔ6
5	6ᘔ9 ᘔ35	60ᘔ ᘔƐ3	5	.766 499 64Ɛ	2Ɛ9	5	.785 367 295	573 ᘔ05
6	.747 0Ɛ8 928	1Ɛ9	6	ᘔ79 948	59Ɛ 673	6	91Ɛ 09ᘔ	224
7	706 Ɛ25	609 505	7	.767 459 3ƐƐ	59ᘔ ᘔ31	7	.786 292 302	572 646
8	.748 114 42ᘔ	608 811	8	ᘔ38 230	1ᘔᘔ	8	844 948	571 ᘔ68
9	721 03Ɛ	607 Ɛ21	9	.768 416 41ᘔ	599 56Ɛ	9	.787 1Ɛ6 7Ɛ4	290
ᘔ	.749 128 Ɛ60	232	ᘔ	9Ɛ3 989	598 930	ᘔ	767 ᘔ84	570 6Ɛ6
Ɛ	734 192	606 545	Ɛ	.769 390 6Ɛ9	0Ɛ4	Ɛ	.788 118 57ᘔ	56Ɛ Ɛ22
.0910	.74ᘔ 13ᘔ 717	605 859	.0950	968 7Ɛ1	597 478	.0990	688 4ᘔ0	34ᘔ
1	744 374	604 Ɛ74	1	.76ᘔ 344 069	596 844	1	.789 037 82ᘔ	56ᘔ 778
2	.74Ɛ 149 328	291	2	91ᘔ 8Ɛ1	00Ɛ	2	5ᘔ6 3ᘔ6	569 Ɛᘔ8
3	751 5Ɛ9	603 5ᘔƐ	3	.76Ɛ 2Ɛ4 900	595 399	3	Ɛ54 392	419
4	.750 154 Ɛᘔ8	602 90ᘔ	4	88ᘔ 099	594 769	4	.78ᘔ 501 7ᘔƐ	568 850
5	757 8Ɛ6	031	5	.770 262 846	593 Ɛ3ᘔ	5	ᘔ6ᘔ 43Ɛ	083
6	.751 159 927	601 355	6	836 784	312	6	.78Ɛ 416 502	567 4Ɛᘔ
7	75Ɛ 080	600 67ᘔ	7	.771 209 ᘔ96	592 6ᘔ5	7	981 ᘔ00	566 935
8	.752 15Ɛ 73ᘔ	5ƐƐ 9ᘔ5	8	7ᘔ0 57Ɛ	591 ᘔ80	8	.790 328 735	171
9	75Ɛ 523	113	9	.772 172 43Ɛ	257	9	892 8ᘔ6	565 5ᘔƐ
ᘔ	.753 15ᘔ 636	5Ɛᘔ 442	ᘔ	743 696	590 635	ᘔ	.791 238 295	564 ᘔ2Ɛ
Ɛ	758 ᘔ78	5Ɛ9 772	Ɛ	.773 114 10Ɛ	58Ɛ ᘔ14	Ɛ	7ᘔ1 104	26Ɛ
.0920	.754 156 62ᘔ	5Ɛ8 ᘔᘔ5	.0960	6ᘔ3 Ɛ23	1Ɛ5	.09ᘔ0	.792 145 373	563 6Ɛ2
1	753 513	21ᘔ	1	.774 073 118	58ᘔ 597	1	6ᘔ8 ᘔ65	562 Ɛ36
2	.755 14Ɛ 731	5Ɛ7 554	2	641 6Ɛ3	589 97ᘔ	2	.793 04Ɛ 99Ɛ	380
3	747 085	5Ɛ6 890	3	.775 00Ɛ 471	164	3	5Ɛ2 15Ɛ	561 806
4	.756 141 955	00ᘔ	4	598 615	588 550	4	Ɛ53 965	052
5	737 963	5Ɛ5 349	5	Ɛ64 Ɛ65	587 938	5	.794 4Ɛ4 9Ɛ7	560 4ᘔ0
6	.757 131 0Ɛ0	5Ɛ4 68Ɛ	6	.776 530 8ᘔ1	126	6	ᘔ55 297	55Ɛ 930
7	725 77Ɛ	5Ɛ3 ᘔ12	7	ᘔƐ7 ᘔ07	586 516	7	.795 3Ɛ5 007	17Ɛ
8	.758 119 591	156	8	.777 482 321	585 908	8	954 186	55ᘔ 612
9	710 727	5Ɛ2 4ᘔ2	9	ᘔ48 029	0ƐƐ	9	.796 2Ɛ2 798	559 ᘔ65
ᘔ	.759 103 009	5Ɛ1 82ᘔ	ᘔ	.778 411 128	584 4Ɛ3	ᘔ	850 641	2ƐƐ
Ɛ	6Ɛ4 837	5Ɛ0 Ɛ78	Ɛ	995 61Ɛ	583 8ᘔᘔ	Ɛ	.797 1ᘔ9 940	558 754
.0930	.75ᘔ 0ᘔ5 7Ɛ3	309	.0970	.779 359 309	0ᘔ5	.09Ɛ0	746 494	557 Ɛ20
1	695 Ɛ00	5ᘔƐ 65ᘔ	1	920 3Ɛ2	582 4ᘔ3	1	.798 0ᘔ2 484	449
2	.75Ɛ 085 55ᘔ	5ᘔᘔ 9Ɛ1	2	.77ᘔ 2ᘔ2 895	581 8ᘔ2	2	639 911	556 8ᘔ8
3	674 34Ɛ	147	3	864 577	0ᘔ3	3	Ɛ94 5Ɛ9	148
4	.760 062 496	5ᘔ9 4ᘔ1	4	.77Ɛ 225 65ᘔ	580 4ᘔ4	4	.799 52ᘔ 745	555 5ᘔ9
5	64Ɛ 977	5ᘔ8 83Ɛ	5	7ᘔ5 Ɛ42	57Ɛ 8ᘔ8	5	ᘔ84 132	554 ᘔ50
6	.761 038 5Ɛ6	5ᘔ7 Ɛ98	6	.780 165 82ᘔ	0Ɛ2	6	.79ᘔ 418 Ɛ82	2Ɛ5
7	624 592	339	7	724 920	57ᘔ 4Ɛ8	7	971 277	553 75ᘔ
8	.762 00Ɛ 90Ɛ	5ᘔ6 69Ɛ	8	.781 0ᘔ3 218	579 904	8	.79Ɛ 304 ᘔ15	004
9	5Ɛ6 3ᘔᘔ	5ᘔ5 ᘔ43	9	660 Ɛ20	113	9	857 ᘔ19	552 472
ᘔ	Ɛᘔ0 231	1ᘔ8	ᘔ	.782 01ᘔ 033	578 521	ᘔ	.7ᘔ0 1ᘔᘔ 28Ɛ	551 91Ɛ
Ɛ	.763 585 419	5ᘔ4 552	Ɛ	596 554	577 933	Ɛ	73Ɛ Ɛᘔᘔ	18ᘔ

N	Log Sin	d	N	Log Sin	d	N	Log Sin	d
.0X00	Ɛ.7X1 091 178	550 63Ɛ	.0X40	Ɛ.7ƐX 424 0Ɛ6	527 959	.0X80	Ɛ.816 X3Ɛ 7ƐX	504 88Ɛ
1	621 7Ɛ7	54Ɛ XƐ1	1	94Ɛ X53	262	1	.817 344 489	221
2	Ɛ71 6X8	364	2	.7ƐƐ 277 0Ɛ5	526 769	2	848 6XX	503 775
3	.7X2 500 X50	54X 819	3	7X1 862	074	3	.818 150 263	10X
4	X4Ɛ 669	093	4	.800 107 916	525 581	4	653 371	502 664
5	.7X3 399 740	549 54X	5	631 297	524 X90	5	Ɛ55 X15	501 ƐƐƐ
6	927 08X	548 X07	6	Ɛ56 167	39Ɛ	6	.819 457 X14	557
7	.7X4 273 X95	286	7	.801 47X 546	523 8XƐ	7	959 36Ɛ	500 XƐ5
8	800 15Ɛ	547 745	8	9X2 235	202	8	.81X 25X 264	453
9	.7X5 147 8X4	006	9	.802 305 437	522 715	9	75X 6Ɛ7	4ƐƐ 9Ɛ3
X	692 8XX	546 489	X	827 Ɛ50	029	X	.81Ɛ 05X 4XX	354
Ɛ	.7X6 019 177	545 950	Ɛ	.803 149 Ɛ79	521 542	Ɛ	559 842	4ƐX 8Ɛ6
.0X10	562 Ɛ07	215	.0X50	66Ɛ 4ƐƐ	520 X5X	.0X90	X58 538	258
1	XX8 120	544 69Ɛ	1	Ɛ90 359	376	1	.820 356 794	4Ɛ9 801
2	.7X7 430 7ƐƐ	543 Ɛ67	2	.804 4Ɛ0 713	51Ɛ 893	2	854 395	166
3	974 766	435	3	X10 3X6	1Ɛ2	3	.821 151 53Ɛ	4Ɛ8 711
4	.7X8 2Ɛ7 Ɛ9Ɛ	542 902	4	.805 32Ɛ 598	51X 711	4	64X 050	078
5	83X 8X1	193	5	84X 0X9	032	5	Ɛ46 108	4Ɛ7 624
6	.7X9 180 X74	541 663	6	.806 168 11Ɛ	519 555	6	.822 441 730	4Ɛ6 Ɛ93
7	702 517	540 Ɛ36	7	685 674	518 X78	7	938 703	541
8	.7XX 043 451	40X	8	ƐX2 530	3X0	8	.823 233 044	4Ɛ5 XƐ1
9	583 85Ɛ	53Ɛ 8X3	9	.807 4ƐX 910	517 907	9	728 Ɛ35	461
X	Ɛ03 542	179	X	X16 617	231	X	.824 022 396	4Ɛ4 X14
Ɛ	.7XƐ 442 6ƐƐ	53X 655	Ɛ	.808 331 848	516 75X	Ɛ	517 1XX	388
.0X20	981 154	539 Ɛ32	0X60	848 3X6	087	.0XX0	X0Ɛ 576	4Ɛ3 93Ɛ
1	.7Ɛ0 2ƐƐ 086	410	1	.809 162 471	515 5Ɛ5	1	.825 303 2Ɛ5	2Ɛ5
2	838 496	538 8Ɛ0	2	677 X66	514 Ɛ26	2	7Ɛ6 5XX	4Ɛ2 86Ɛ
3	.7Ɛ1 175 186	191	3	Ɛ90 990	456	3	.826 0X9 259	227
4	6Ɛ1 357	537 674	4	.80X 4X5 226	513 989	4	59Ɛ 484	4Ɛ1 7X3
5	.7Ɛ2 028 X0Ɛ	536 Ɛ57	5	9Ɛ8 ƐƐ3	300	5	X91 067	161
6	563 966	440	6	.80Ɛ 310 2Ɛ3	512 834	6	.827 382 208	4Ɛ0 720
7	X9X 1X6	535 926	7	822 Ɛ27	16X	7	872 928	0X0
8	.7Ɛ3 413 Ɛ10	212	8	.810 135 095	511 6X6	8	.828 162 X08	4XƐ 660
9	949 122	534 6ƐX	9	646 77Ɛ	021	9	652 468	023
X	.7Ɛ4 281 820	533 ƐX9	X	Ɛ57 7X0	510 55Ɛ	X	Ɛ41 48Ɛ	4XX 5X5
Ɛ	7Ɛ5 809	498	Ɛ	.811 468 13Ɛ	50Ɛ X99	Ɛ	.829 42Ɛ X74	4X9 Ɛ6X
.0X30	.7Ɛ5 129 0X5	532 989	.0X70	978 018	418	.0XƐ0	919 X22	533
1	65Ɛ X72	27X	1	.812 287 434	50X 95X	1	.82X 207 355	4X8 XƐ9
2	Ɛ92 130	531 772	2	796 192	29Ɛ	2	6Ɛ4 252	485
3	.7Ɛ6 503 8X2	067	3	.813 0X4 471	509 823	3	ƐX0 717	4X7 X51
4	X34 949	530 560	4	5Ɛ2 094	166	4	.82Ɛ 488 568	41X
5	.7Ɛ7 365 2X9	52Ɛ X58	5	XƐƐ 23X	508 6Ɛ0	5	973 986	4X6 9X9
6	895 145	354	6	.814 407 92X	037	6	.830 25X 773	378
7	.7Ɛ8 204 499	52X 851	7	913 965	507 583	7	744 ƐƐƐ	4X5 949
8	733 12X	151	8	.815 21Ɛ 328	506 Ɛ0Ɛ	8	.831 02X 878	31Ɛ
9	.7Ɛ9 061 27Ɛ	529 650	9	726 237	45X	9	513 Ɛ97	4X4 8Ɛ1
X	58X 90Ɛ	528 Ɛ53	X	.816 030 695	505 9X8	X	9Ɛ8 888	286
Ɛ	XƐ7 862	454	Ɛ	536 481	339	Ɛ	.832 2X0 Ɛ52	4X3 859

N	Log Sin	d	N	Log Sin	d	N	Log Sin	d
.0Ɛ00	Ɛ.832 784 7XƐ	4X3 234	.0Ɛ40	Ɛ.849 894 Ɛ05	483 058	.0Ɛ80	Ɛ.864 204 247	464 1X6
1	.833 067 X23	4X2 80Ɛ	1	.84X 157 Ɛ61	482 671	1	668 431	463 839
2	54X 632	1X6	2	61X 612	089	2	Ɛ10 06X	28Ɛ
3	X30 818	4X1 784	3	XX0 69Ɛ	481 6X6	3	.865 373 339	462 924
4	.834 312 3X0	161	4	.84Ɛ 362 185	103	4	816 061	378
5	7Ɛ3 541	4X0 741	5	823 288	480 722	5	.866 078 419	461 X12
6	.835 094 082	120	6	.850 0X3 9XX	140	6	51X 22Ɛ	468
7	574 1X2	49Ɛ 702	7	563 Ɛ2X	47Ɛ 761	7	97Ɛ 697	460 Ɛ04
8	X53 8X4	0X3	8	X23 68Ɛ	182	8	.867 220 59Ɛ	560
9	.836 332 987	49X 687	9	.851 2X2 851	47X 7X4	9	680 Ɛ3Ɛ	45Ɛ ƐƐ9
X	811 452	06Ɛ	X	761 435	208	X	Ɛ20 Ɛ38	657
Ɛ	.837 0XƐ 501	499 654	Ɛ	.852 01Ɛ 641	479 82Ɛ	Ɛ	.868 380 593	0Ɛ6
.0Ɛ10	588 Ɛ55	03X	.0Ɛ50	499 270	254	.0Ɛ90	81Ɛ 689	45X 756
1	X65 Ɛ93	498 626	1	956 504	478 87X	1	.869 07X 223	1Ɛ6
2	.838 342 5Ɛ9	011	2	.853 213 182	2X4	2	518 419	459 857
3	81X 60X	497 5ƐƐ	3	68Ɛ 466	477 910	3	976 074	2ƐX
4	.839 0Ɛ6 009	496 ƐX9	4	Ɛ47 176	339	4	.86X 213 372	458 960
5	590 ƐƐ6	599	5	.854 402 4Ɛ3	476 967	5	670 112	405
6	X67 593	495 Ɛ88	6	879 25X	395	6	Ɛ08 517	457 X69
7	.83X 341 55Ɛ	57X	7	.855 133 633	475 X04	7	.86Ɛ 364 384	513
8	816 Ɛ19	494 Ɛ70	8	5X9 437	434	8	7ƐƐ 897	456 Ɛ7X
9	.83Ɛ 0XƐ X89	564	9	X62 86Ɛ	474 X66	9	.870 056 855	624
X	584 431	493 Ɛ57	X	.856 317 715	498	X	4Ɛ1 279	091
Ɛ	X58 388	551	Ɛ	78Ɛ ƐƐ1	473 Ɛ0Ɛ	Ɛ	947 34X	455 73X
.0Ɛ20	.840 32Ɛ 919	492 Ɛ47	.0Ɛ60	.857 043 Ɛ00	542	.0ƐX0	.871 1X0 X88	1X7
1	802 864	543	1	4Ɛ7 442	472 Ɛ78	1	636 073	454 856
2	.841 095 1X7	491 Ɛ3X	2	96X 3ƐX	5Ɛ1	2	X8X 909	306
3	567 125	538	3	.858 220 9XƐ	028	3	.872 323 013	453 976
4	X38 661	490 Ɛ36	4	692 X17	471 664	4	776 989	427
5	.842 309 597	536	5	Ɛ44 47Ɛ	0X0	5	.873 00X 1Ɛ4	452 X99
6	799 Ɛ11	48Ɛ Ɛ35	6	.859 3Ɛ5 55Ɛ	470 719	6	461 091	54Ɛ
7	.843 069 X46	537	7	866 078	158	7	8Ɛ3 620	004
8	539 381	48X Ɛ38	8	.85X 116 214	46Ɛ 797	8	.874 145 624	451 677
9	X08 2Ɛ9	540	9	585 9XƐ	217	9	597 09Ɛ	131
X	.844 296 839	489 Ɛ44	X	X35 006	46X 858	X	X28 210	450 7X7
Ɛ	764 781	54X	Ɛ	.85Ɛ 2X3 862	299	Ɛ	.875 278 9Ɛ7	262
.0Ɛ30	.845 032 10Ɛ	488 Ɛ53	.0Ɛ70	751 Ɛ3Ɛ	469 921	.0ƐƐ0	709 059	44Ɛ 91X
1	4ƐƐ 062	55X	1	ƐƐƐ 860	364	1	Ɛ58 977	396
2	987 600	487 Ɛ66	2	.860 469 004	468 9X8	2	.876 3X8 151	44X X54
3	.846 253 566	573	3	915 9Ɛ0	432	3	836 ƐX5	511
4	71X Ɛ19	486 Ɛ82	4	.861 182 222	467 X79	4	.877 085 4Ɛ6	449 Ɛ91
5	ƐX5 X9Ɛ	590	5	62X 09Ɛ	503	5	513 487	650
6	.847 470 46Ɛ	485 Ɛ9Ɛ	6	X95 5X2	466 Ɛ50	6	960 Ɛ17	111
7	936 44X	5Ɛ1	7	.862 340 532	598	7	.878 1XX 028	448 792
8	.848 1ƐƐ X3Ɛ	003	8	7X6 Ɛ0X	026	8	636 7ƐX	255
9	684 X42	484 615	9	.863 050 Ɛ34	465 675	9	X82 X53	447 917
X	Ɛ49 457	029	X	4Ɛ6 5X9	105	X	.879 30X 76X	3X0
Ɛ	.849 411 484	483 641	Ɛ	95Ɛ 6Ɛ2	464 755	Ɛ	755 Ɛ4X	446 X64

N	Log Sin	d	N	Log Sin	d	N	Log Sin	d
.1000	Ɛ.879 Ɛχ0 9Ɛ2	446 529	.1040	Ɛ.893 270 38χ	429 949	.1080	Ɛ.8χ7 χ73 χ14	412 141
1	.87χ 427 31Ɛ	445 ƐƐ4	1	69χ 117	443	1	.8χ8 285 Ɛ55	411 866
2	871 313	67χ	2	Ɛ07 55χ	428 Ɛ3Ɛ	2	697 7ƐƐ	390
3	.87Ɛ 0Ɛ6 991	147	3	.894 334 499	638	3	χχ8 Ɛ8Ɛ	410 χƐ5
4	53Ɛ Ɛ18	444 813	4	760 Ɛ15	135	4	.8χ9 2Ɛ9 χ84	621
5	984 72Ɛ	2χ0	5	Ɛ89 04χ	427 833	5	70χ 4χ5	149
6	.880 208 χ0Ɛ	443 96χ	6	.895 3Ɛ4 881	331	6	Ɛ1χ 632	40Ɛ 874
7	650 779	43χ	7	81Ɛ ƐƐ2	426 χ31	7	.8χχ 32χ 2χ6	3χ2
8	χ93 ƐƐ7	442 Ɛ09	8	.896 046 χ23	532	8	739 688	40χ Ɛ0Ɛ
9	.881 316 Ɛ04	59χ	9	471 355	031	9	Ɛ48 597	63χ
χ	759 4χ2	06Ɛ	χ	897 386	425 734	χ	.8χƐ 357 015	169
Ɛ	Ɛ9Ɛ 551	441 742	Ɛ	.897 100 χƐχ	236	Ɛ	765 182	409 898
.1010	.882 421 093	214	.1050	526 134	424 939	.1090	Ɛ72 χ5χ	408
1	862 2χ7	440 8χ8	1	94χ χ71	440	1	.8Ɛ0 380 266	408 Ɛ3χ
2	.883 0χ2 Ɛ93	380	2	.898 173 2Ɛ1	423 Ɛ45	2	789 1χ4	66Ɛ
3	523 353	43Ɛ χ56	3	597 236	64Ɛ	3	Ɛ95 853	1χ2
4	963 1χ9	530	4	9Ɛχ 885	154	4	.8Ɛ1 3χ1 χ35	407 914
5	.884 1χ2 719	006	5	.899 221 χ19	422 85Ɛ	5	7χ9 749	449
6	621 723	43χ 6χ3	6	644 678	366	6	ƐƐ4 Ɛ96	406 Ɛ80
7	χ60 206	17χ	7	χ66 χ22	421 χ72	7	.8Ɛ2 3ƐƐ Ɛ56	6Ɛ6
8	.885 29χ 384	439 858	8	.89χ 288 894	57Ɛ	8	806 650	22Ɛ
9	718 020	335	9	6χχ 253	088	9	.8Ɛ3 010 87Ɛ	405 965
χ	Ɛ55 355	438 χ15	χ	Ɛ0Ɛ 31Ɛ	420 797	χ	416 624	4χ0
Ɛ	.886 392 16χ	4Ɛ3	Ɛ	.89Ɛ 32Ɛ χƐ6	2χ6	Ɛ	81Ɛ Ɛ04	018
.1020	80χ 661	437 Ɛ94	.1060	750 1χ0	41Ɛ 9Ɛ5	.10χ0	.8Ɛ4 024 Ɛ20	404 754
1	.887 046 635	675	1	Ɛ6Ɛ Ɛ95	505	1	429 674	291
2	482 0χχ	157	2	.8χ0 38Ɛ 49χ	017	2	831 945	403 χ0Ɛ
3	8Ɛ9 245	436 839	3	7χχ 4Ɛ5	41χ 728	3	.8Ɛ5 035 754	548
4	.888 133 χ82	321	4	.8χ1 009 021	23χ	4	439 0χ0	088
5	56χ 1χ3	435 χ04	5	427 25Ɛ	419 952	5	840 168	402 807
6	9χ3 Ɛχ7	4χχ	6	844 ƐƐ1	466	6	.8Ɛ6 042 973	347
7	.889 219 495	434 Ɛ93	7	.8χ2 062 457	418 Ɛ7χ	7	445 0Ɛχ	401 χ88
8	652 468	679	8	47Ɛ 415	693	8	846 Ɛ86	60χ
9	χ86 Ɛ25	164	9	897 χχ8	1χ9	9	.8Ɛ7 048 594	14Ɛ
χ	.88χ 2ƐƐ 089	433 850	χ	.8χ3 0Ɛ4 095	417 904	χ	449 723	400 892
Ɛ	732 919	339	Ɛ	50Ɛ 999	41Ɛ	Ɛ	84χ 3Ɛ5	416
.1030	Ɛ66 056	432 χ26	.1070	927 1Ɛ8	416 Ɛ37	.10Ɛ0	.8Ɛ8 04χ 80Ɛ	3ƐƐ Ɛ59
1	.88Ɛ 398 χ80	514	1	.8χ4 142 133	654	1	44χ 768	6χ3
2	80Ɛ 394	003	2	558 787	172	2	84χ 24Ɛ	227
3	.890 041 397	431 6Ɛ3	3	972 939	415 88Ɛ	3	.8Ɛ9 049 476	3Ɛχ 971
4	472 χ8χ	1χ3	4	.8χ5 188 608	3χχ	4	448 227	4Ɛ8
5	8χ4 071	430 894	5	5χ1 9Ɛ6	414 Ɛ0χ	5	846 723	044
6	.891 114 945	386	6	9Ɛ6 904	629	6	.8Ɛχ 044 767	3Ɛ9 78Ɛ
7	545 10Ɛ	42Ɛ χ79	7	.8χ6 20Ɛ 331	14Ɛ	7	442 336	317
8	974 Ɛ88	56Ɛ	8	623 480	413 870	8	83Ɛ 651	3Ɛ8 χ64
9	.892 1χ4 537	064	9	χ37 130	392	9	.8ƐƐ 038 4Ɛ5	5Ɛ3
χ	613 59Ɛ	42χ 759	χ	.8χ7 24χ 502	412 χƐ5	χ	434 χχ8	140
Ɛ	χ42 138	252	Ɛ	661 3Ɛ7	619	Ɛ	831 028	3Ɛ7 890

N	Log Sin	d	N	Log Sin	d	N	Log Sin	d
.1100	Ɛ.900 028 8Ɛ8	3Ɛ7 41Ɛ	.1140	Ɛ.913 788 X64	3X1 505	.1180	Ɛ.926 946 Ɛ49	388 326
1	424 117	3Ɛ6 Ɛ70	1	Ɛ6X 369	079	1	.927 113 273	387 Ɛ02
2	81Ɛ 087	700	2	.914 34Ɛ 426	3X0 834	2	49Ɛ 175	69Ɛ
3	.901 015 787	252	3	730 05X	3XX	3	866 854	278
4	40Ɛ X19	3Ɛ5 9X4	4	Ɛ10 448	39Ɛ Ɛ65	4	.928 031 Ɛ10	386 X56
5	805 801	536	5	.915 2Ɛ0 3Ɛ1	720	5	3Ɛ8 966	633
6	ƐƐƐ 137	08X	6	68Ɛ Ɛ11	299	6	783 399	213
7	.902 3Ɛ4 205	3Ɛ4 822	7	X6Ɛ 1XX	39X X55	7	Ɛ49 5Ɛ0	385 9Ɛ2
8	7X8 X27	377	8	.916 24X 043	612	8	.929 313 3X2	591
9	ƐX1 1X2	3Ɛ3 Ɛ10	9	628 655	191	9	698 973	172
X	.903 395 0Ɛ2	666	X	X06 826	399 94Ɛ	X	X61 Ɛ25	384 953
Ɛ	788 758	200	Ɛ	.917 1X4 575	509	Ɛ	.92X 226 878	535
.1110	Ɛ7Ɛ 958	3Ɛ2 957	.1150	581 X82	08X	.1190	5XƐ 1Ɛ1	116
1	.904 372 6Ɛ3	4Ɛ3	1	95X Ɛ50	398 849	1	973 307	383 8Ɛ9
2	764 ƐX6	04Ɛ	2	.918 137 799	40X	2	.92Ɛ 137 004	49Ɛ
3	Ɛ57 035	3Ɛ1 7X8	3	513 ƐX7	397 Ɛ8Ɛ	3	4ƐX 4X3	084
4	.905 348 821	346	4	8XƐ Ɛ76	751	4	881 567	382 867
5	739 Ɛ67	3Ɛ0 XX4	5	.919 087 707	314	5	.930 044 212	450
6	Ɛ2X X4Ɛ	643	6	462 X1Ɛ	396 X96	6	406 662	035
7	.906 31Ɛ 492	1X2	7	839 8Ɛ5	65Ɛ	7	788 697	381 81Ɛ
8	70Ɛ 674	3XƐ 942	8	.91X 014 354	222	8	Ɛ4X 2Ɛ6	405
9	XƐƐ 3Ɛ6	4X2	9	3XX 576	395 9X6	9	.931 30Ɛ 6ƐƐ	380 ƐXƐ
X	.907 2XX 898	044	X	784 360	570	X	690 6XX	797
Ɛ	699 920	3XX 7X5	Ɛ	Ɛ59 910	136	Ɛ	X51 285	382
.1120	X88 505	348	.1160	.91Ɛ 332 X46	394 900	.11X0	.932 211 647	37Ɛ Ɛ6Ɛ
1	.908 276 851	3X9 XXƐ	1	707 746	487	1	591 5Ɛ6	758
2	664 740	653	2	XX0 011	053	2	951 152	344
3	X52 193	1Ɛ7	3	.920 274 064	393 81X	3	.933 110 496	37X Ɛ33
4	.909 23Ɛ 38X	3X8 95Ɛ	4	647 882	3X7	4	48Ɛ 409	721
5	628 129	505	5	X1Ɛ 069	392 Ɛ74	5	849 Ɛ2X	310
6	X14 632	06Ɛ	6	.921 1Ɛ2 021	742	6	.934 008 23X	379 XƐƐ
7	.90X 200 6X1	3X7 816	7	584 763	310	7	386 139	6XƐ
8	5X8 2Ɛ7	381	8	956 X73	391 X9Ɛ	8	743 828	29Ɛ
9	993 678	3X6 Ɛ28	9	.922 128 952	66X	9	Ɛ00 Ɛ07	378 X90
X	.90Ɛ 17X 5X4	695	X	4ƐX 400	23X	X	.935 279 997	682
Ɛ	565 079	242	Ɛ	88Ɛ 63X	390 X0Ɛ	Ɛ	636 459	273
.1130	94Ɛ 2ƐƐ	3X5 9Ɛ0	.1170	.923 060 449	59Ɛ	.11Ɛ0	9Ɛ2 710	377 X66
1	.910 135 0XƐ	55X	1	430 X28	171	1	.936 16X 576	659
2	51X 649	108	2	800 Ɛ99	38Ɛ 943	2	526 013	251
3	903 755	3X4 878	3	Ɛ90 920	516	3	8X1 264	376 X44
4	.911 0X8 411	428	4	.924 360 236	0X9	4	.937 058 0X8	639
5	490 839	3X3 Ɛ98	5	72Ɛ 323	38X 881	5	412 725	232
6	874 815	74X	6	XƐ9 ƐX4	455	6	788 957	375 X27
7	.912 058 363	2ƐƐ	7	.925 288 439	02X	7	Ɛ42 782	621
8	43Ɛ 662	3X2 X72	8	656 467	389 803	8	.938 2Ɛ8 1X3	218
9	822 514	624	9	X24 06X	399	9	671 3ƐƐ	374 X13
X	.913 004 Ɛ38	198	X	.926 1Ɛ1 447	388 Ɛ74	X	X26 212	60X
Ɛ	3X7 114	3X1 950	Ɛ	57X 3ƐƐ	74X	Ɛ	.939 19X 820	207

N	Log Sin	d	N	Log Sin	d	N	Log Sin	d
.1200	Ɛ.939 552 X27	373 X02	.1240	Ɛ.94Ɛ 815 X99	360 0X2	.1280	Ɛ.961 57Ɛ 107	348 Ɛ1X
1	906 829	600	1	Ɛ75 Ɛ7Ɛ	35Ɛ 900	1	908 025	754
2	.93X 07X 229	1Ɛ9	2	.950 315 87Ɛ	517	2	.962 054 779	38X
3	431 426	372 9Ɛ8	3	675 196	135	3	3X0 Ɛ47	006
4	7X4 222	5Ɛ6	4	X14 30Ɛ	35X 953	4	728 Ɛ51	347 840
5	Ɛ56 818	1Ɛ4	5	.951 173 062	570	5	X74 791	477
6	.93Ɛ 308 X10	371 9Ɛ5	6	511 612	18Ɛ	6	.963 200 048	0Ɛ4
7	67X 805	5Ɛ4	7	86Ɛ 7X1	359 9XX	7	547 140	346 930
8	X30 1Ɛ9	1Ɛ5	8	.952 009 58Ɛ	60X	8	891 X70	569
9	.940 1X1 3Ɛ2	370 9Ɛ6	9	366 Ɛ99	229	9	.964 018 419	1X6
X	552 1X8	5Ɛ7	X	704 206	358 X4X	X	362 603	345 X24
Ɛ	902 7X3	1Ɛ9	Ɛ	X61 054	66X	Ɛ	6X8 427	662
.1210	.941 072 9X0	36Ɛ X00	.1250	.953 1Ɛ9 702	290	.1290	X31 X89	2X1
1	422 7X0	603	1	555 992	357 XƐ2	1	.965 177 16X	344 Ɛ1Ɛ
2	792 1X3	206	2	8Ɛ1 884	714	2	500 089	75Ɛ
3	Ɛ41 3X9	36X X0X	3	.954 049 398	336	3	844 828	39Ɛ
4	.942 2Ɛ0 1Ɛ7	613	4	3X4 712	356 Ɛ5X	4	Ɛ89 007	01Ɛ
5	65X 80X	217	5	73Ɛ 670	781	5	.966 311 026	343 85Ɛ
6	X08 X25	369 X21	6	X96 231	3X5	6	654 885	4X1
7	.943 176 846	627	7	.955 230 616	00X	7	998 166	123
8	524 271	231	8	586 624	355 833	8	.967 11Ɛ 289	342 964
9	891 4X2	368 X38	9	920 257	458	9	462 031	5X7
X	.944 03X 31X	644	X	.956 075 6Ɛ3	081	X	7X4 618	229
Ɛ	3X6 962	24Ɛ	Ɛ	40X 774	354 8X9	Ɛ	Ɛ26 845	341 X71
.1220	752 ƐƐ1	367 X57	.1260	763 461	513	.12X0	.968 268 6Ɛ6	6Ɛ4
1	XƐX X48	665	1	XƐ7 974	13X	1	5XX 1XX	338
2	.945 266 4Ɛ1	271	2	.957 24Ɛ XƐ2	353 965	2	92Ɛ 526	340 Ɛ81
3	611 762	366 X80	3	5X3 857	592	3	.969 070 4X7	806
4	978 622	68X	4	937 229	1ƐƐ	4	3Ɛ1 0Ɛ1	44Ɛ
5	.946 123 0Ɛ0	298	5	.958 08X 428	352 X27	5	731 540	095
6	489 388	365 XX8	6	421 253	655	6	X71 615	33Ɛ 91Ɛ
7	833 274	6Ɛ7	7	773 8X8	282	7	.96X 1Ɛ1 334	565
8	Ɛ98 96Ɛ	308	8	Ɛ05 Ɛ6X	351 XƐ1	8	530 899	1Ɛ1
9	.947 342 077	364 Ɛ18	9	.959 257 X5Ɛ	720	9	86Ɛ X8X	33X X37
X	6X6 Ɛ93	729	X	5X9 57Ɛ	34Ɛ	X	ƐXX 905	684
Ɛ	X4Ɛ 700	33Ɛ	Ɛ	93X 90X	350 Ɛ7Ɛ	Ɛ	.96Ɛ 329 389	310
.1230	.948 1Ɛ3 X3Ɛ	363 Ɛ51	.1270	.95X 08Ɛ 889	7XX	.12Ɛ0	667 699	339 Ɛ59
1	557 990	764	1	420 477	420	1	9X5 636	7X5
2	8ƐƐ 534	377	2	770 897	050	2	.970 123 21Ɛ	433
3	.949 062 8XƐ	362 Ɛ8X	3	Ɛ00 927	34Ɛ 882	3	460 652	081
4	405 879	7X2	4	.95Ɛ 250 5X9	4Ɛ3	4	799 713	338 90Ɛ
5	768 45Ɛ	3Ɛ6	5	59Ɛ XX0	126	5	Ɛ16 422	55X
6	Ɛ0X 855	010	6	92Ɛ 006	34X 959	6	.971 252 980	1X9
7	.94X 270 865	361 825	7	.960 079 963	590	7	58X Ɛ69	337 X39
8	612 48X	43Ɛ	8	408 333	203	8	906 9X6	689
9	973 909	055	9	756 536	349 X38	9	.972 042 473	318
X	.94Ɛ 114 962	360 86Ɛ	X	XX4 372	670	X	379 78Ɛ	336 Ɛ6X
Ɛ	475 611	488	Ɛ	.961 231 X22	2X5	Ɛ	6Ɛ4 739	7ƐƐ

N	Log Sin	d	N	Log Sin	d	N	Log Sin	d
.1300	Ɛ.972 X2Ɛ 338	336 450	.1340	Ɛ.983 X09 487	324 422	.1380	Ɛ.994 536 71X	312 X03
1	.973 165 788	0X2	1	.984 131 8X9	08Ɛ	1	849 521	685
2	49Ɛ 86X	335 935	2	455 978	323 938	2	Ɛ5Ɛ ƐX6	348
3	815 5X3	587	3	779 6Ɛ4	5X6	3	.995 272 332	010
4	Ɛ4X Ɛ6X	21Ɛ	4	XX1 09X	253	4	584 342	311 892
5	.974 284 189	334 X72	5	.985 204 331	322 Ɛ02	5	896 014	557
6	5Ɛ9 03Ɛ	706	6	527 233	771	6	ƐX7 56Ɛ	21Ɛ
7	931 745	35Ɛ	7	849 9X4	41Ɛ	7	.996 2Ɛ8 78X	310 XX3
8	.975 065 XX4	333 ƐƐ3	8	Ɛ70 203	090	8	609 671	768
9	399 X97	848	9	.986 292 293	321 93X	9	91X 219	432
X	711 723	4X2	X	5Ɛ4 011	5Ɛ0	X	.997 02X 64Ɛ	0Ɛ7
Ɛ	X45 005	139	Ɛ	915 601	25Ɛ	Ɛ	33X 746	30Ɛ 980
.1310	.976 178 142	332 992	.1350	.987 036 860	320 Ɛ11	.1390	64X 506	648
1	4XX Ɛ14	629	1	357 771	782	1	959 Ɛ52	312
2	821 541	285	2	678 333	433	2	.998 069 264	30X Ɛ98
3	Ɛ53 806	331 Ɛ20	3	998 766	0X6	3	378 240	865
4	.977 285 726	778	4	.988 0Ɛ8 850	31Ɛ 958	4	686 XX5	52Ɛ
5	5Ɛ7 2X2	414	5	418 5X8	60Ɛ	5	995 414	1Ɛ8
6	928 6Ɛ6	071	6	737 ƐƐ7	282	6	.999 0X3 610	309 X85
7	.978 059 767	330 90Ɛ	7	X57 279	31X Ɛ35	7	3Ɛ1 495	751
8	38X 476	568	8	.989 176 1Ɛ2	7XX	8	6ƐƐ 026	41X
9	6ƐX X22	206	9	494 9X0	462	9	X08 444	0X7
X	X2Ɛ 028	32Ɛ X64	X	7Ɛ3 242	116	X	.99X 115 52Ɛ	308 975
Ɛ	.979 15X X90	703	Ɛ	Ɛ11 358	319 08Ɛ	Ɛ	422 2X4	644
.1320	48X 593	362	.1360	.98X 22Ɛ 127	645	.13X0	72X 928	311
1	7Ɛ9 935	002	1	548 770	2ƐƐ	1	X37 039	307 ƐX1
2	Ɛ28 937	32X 861	2	865 X6Ɛ	318 Ɛ74	2	.99Ɛ 143 01X	870
3	.97X 257 598	502	3	Ɛ82 X23	830	3	44X 88X	53Ɛ
4	585 X9X	163	4	.98Ɛ 29Ɛ 653	4X6	4	756 209	20Ɛ
5	8Ɛ4 041	329 X04	5	5Ɛ7 Ɛ39	161	5	X61 418	306 X9Ɛ
6	.97Ɛ 021 X45	665	6	914 09X	317 X19	6	.9X0 168 2Ɛ7	770
7	34Ɛ 4XX	307	7	.990 02Ɛ XƐ7	694	7	472 X67	441
8	678 7Ɛ5	328 Ɛ6X	8	347 58Ɛ	351	8	779 2X8	111
9	9X5 763	810	9	662 920	00X	9	X83 3Ɛ9	305 9X4
X	.980 112 373	473	X	979 92X	316 887	X	.9X1 189 1X1	675
Ɛ	43X 826	116	Ɛ	.991 094 5Ɛ5	544	Ɛ	492 856	347
.1330	766 940	327 97Ɛ	.1370	3XX Ɛ39	202	.13Ɛ0	797 ƐX1	01X
1	X92 6ƐƐ	622	1	705 13Ɛ	315 X80	1	XX0 ƐƐƐ	304 8Ɛ1
2	.981 1ƐX 121	287	2	X1X ƐƐƐ	73X	2	.9X2 1X5 8Ɛ0	584
3	525 3X8	326 Ɛ31	3	.992 134 739	3Ɛ9	3	4XX 274	258
4	850 319	795	4	449 Ɛ36	079	4	7Ɛ2 510	303 ƐƐƐ
5	Ɛ76 XƐ2	43Ɛ	5	762 ƐƐ3	314 938	5	XƐ6 43Ɛ	804
6	.982 2X1 331	0X6	6	X77 92Ɛ	5Ɛ8	6	.9X3 1ƐX 043	498
7	607 417	325 950	7	.993 190 327	278	7	501 51Ɛ	171
8	931 167	5Ɛ6	8	4X4 5X3	313 Ɛ39	8	804 690	302 X47
9	.983 056 761	262	9	7Ɛ8 520	7ƐX	9	Ɛ07 517	720
X	37Ɛ X03	324 Ɛ0X	X	Ɛ10 11X	47Ɛ	X	.9X4 20X 037	3Ɛ6
Ɛ	6X4 911	776	Ɛ	.994 223 599	141	Ɛ	510 431	090

N	Log Sin	d	N	Log Sin	d	N	Log Sin	d
.1400	Ɛ.9X4 812 501	301 967	.1440	Ɛ.9Ɛ4 676 X95	2Ɛ1 24X	.1480	Ɛ.X04 104 863	2X1 032
1	Ɛ14 268	642	1	968 123	2Ɛ0 Ɛ39	1	3X5 895	2X0 933
2	.9X5 215 8XX	319	2	.9Ɛ5 059 060	827	2	686 608	634
3	517 007	300 ƐƐ4	3	349 887	516	3	967 040	336
4	817 ƐƐƐ	891	4	63X 1X1	206	4	.X05 047 376	037
5	Ɛ18 890	568	5	92X 3X7	2XƐ XƐ5	5	327 3Ɛ1	29Ɛ 93X
6	.9X6 219 238	246	6	.9Ɛ6 01X 2X0	7X6	6	607 12Ɛ	640
7	519 482	2ƐƐ Ɛ22	7	309 X86	495	7	8X6 76Ɛ	342
8	819 3X4	7ƐƐ	8	5Ɛ9 35Ɛ	186	8	Ɛ85 XƐ1	046
9	Ɛ18 ƐX3	499	9	8X8 525	2XX X77	9	.X06 264 Ɛ37	29X 949
X	.9X7 218 480	177	X	Ɛ97 3X0	768	X	543 884	650
Ɛ	517 637	2ƐX X55	Ɛ	.9Ɛ7 285 Ɛ48	45X	Ɛ	822 314	354
.1410	816 490	733	.1450	574 3X6	14Ɛ	.1490	Ɛ00 668	059
1	Ɛ15 003	413	1	862 535	2X9 X42	1	.X07 19X 705	299 960
2	.9X8 213 416	0Ɛ2	2	Ɛ50 377	734	2	478 465	666
3	511 508	2Ɛ9 991	3	.9Ɛ8 239 XXƐ	426	3	755 Ɛ0Ɛ	36X
4	80Ɛ 299	671	4	527 315	11X	4	X33 279	074
5	Ɛ08 94X	351	5	814 433	2X8 X11	5	.X08 110 331	298 979
6	.9X9 206 09Ɛ	032	6	Ɛ01 244	705	6	3X9 0XX	683
7	503 111	2Ɛ8 913	7	.9Ɛ9 1X9 949	3Ɛ8	7	685 771	38X
8	7ƐƐ X24	5Ɛ3	8	496 145	0Ɛ1	8	961 Ɛ3Ɛ	093
9	XƐ8 417	296	9	782 236	2X7 9X6	9	.X09 03X 012	297 99Ɛ
X	.9XX 1Ɛ4 6Ɛ1	2Ɛ7 Ɛ77	X	X6X 020	69X	X	315 9Ɛ1	6X5
Ɛ	4Ɛ0 668	859	Ɛ	.9ƐX 155 6ƐX	393	Ɛ	5Ɛ1 496	3Ɛ1
.1420	7X8 305	53Ɛ	.1460	440 X91	089	.14X0	888 887	0Ɛ8
1	XX3 844	223	1	727 Ɛ5X	2X6 983	1	Ɛ63 983	296 X04
2	.9XƐ 19X X67	2Ɛ6 Ɛ05	2	X12 921	679	2	.X0X 23X 787	710
3	495 970	7X9	3	.9ƐƐ 0Ɛ9 39X	373	3	515 297	419
4	790 559	491	4	3X3 751	06X	4	7XƐ 6Ɛ4	125
5	X86 X2X	174	5	689 7ƐƐ	2X5 964	5	X85 819	295 X33
6	.9Ɛ0 180 ƐX2	2Ɛ5 X5X	6	973 563	661	6	.X0Ɛ 15Ɛ 650	73Ɛ
7	476 X40	741	7	.X00 059 004	357	7	435 18Ɛ	449
8	770 581	427	8	342 35Ɛ	054	8	70X 618	157
9	X65 9X8	110	9	627 3Ɛ3	2X4 94Ɛ	9	9X3 773	294 X65
X	.9Ɛ1 15X XƐ8	2Ɛ4 9Ɛ6	X	910 142	648	X	.X10 078 618	774
Ɛ	453 8Ɛ2	6X0	Ɛ	ƐƐ4 78X	345	Ɛ	351 190	482
.1430	748 392	386	.1470	.X01 298 Ɛ13	042	.14Ɛ0	625 652	191
1	X40 758	071	1	580 Ɛ55	2X3 940	1	8Ɛ9 823	293 XX1
2	.9Ɛ2 134 809	2Ɛ3 957	2	864 895	639	2	Ɛ91 704	7Ɛ0
3	428 564	643	3	Ɛ48 312	337	3	.X11 265 2Ɛ4	4ƐƐ
4	71Ɛ ƐX7	32Ɛ	4	.X02 22Ɛ 649	035	4	538 7Ɛ3	210
5	X13 316	016	5	512 682	2X2 934	5	80Ɛ X03	292 Ɛ20
6	.9Ɛ3 106 330	2Ɛ2 902	6	7Ɛ5 3Ɛ6	633	6	XX2 923	831
7	3Ɛ9 032	5XƐ	7	X97 X29	331	7	.X12 175 554	542
8	6XƐ 621	298	8	.X03 17X 15X	032	8	447 X96	253
9	9X1 8Ɛ9	2Ɛ1 Ɛ85	9	460 190	2X1 931	9	71X 129	291 Ɛ64
X	.9Ɛ4 093 882	873	X	741 Ɛ01	631	X	9Ɛ0 091	876
Ɛ	385 535	560	Ɛ	X23 532	331	Ɛ	.X13 081 947	588

N	Log Sin	d	N	Log Sin	d	N	Log Sin	d
.1500	ε.χ13 353 313	291 29ε	.1540	ε.χ22 1ε8 950	281 997	.1580	ε.χ30 892 548	272 8ε3
1	624 5ε2	290 εε1	1	47χ 727	6εε	1	ε45 23ε	626
2	8ε5 5χ3	904	2	740 226	422	2	.χ31 1ε7 865	35χ
3	ε86 2χ7	617	3	χ01 648	146	3	46χ 003	093
4	.χ14 256 902	32χ	4	.χ23 082 792	280 χ6ε	4	720 096	271 χ06
5	527 030	042	5	343 641	793	5	991 χχ0	73ε
6	7ε7 072	28ε 956	6	604 214	4ε7	6	.χ32 043 61ε	474
7	χ86 χ08	66χ	7	884 70ε	221	7	2ε4 χ93	1χ9
8	.χ15 156 476	383	8	ε44 930	27ε ε46	8	566 080	270 ε22
9	425 839	098	9	.χ24 204 876	86ε	9	816 εχ2	857
χ	6ε4 915	28χ 9ε0	χ	484 525	595	χ	χ87 839	591
ε	983 705	706	ε	743 χεχ	2εε	ε	.χ33 138 20χ	307
.1510	.χ16 052 20ε	420	.1550	χ03 1ε9	026	.1590	3χ8 515	042
1	320 62ε	135	1	.χ25 082 223	27χ 94ε	1	658 557	26ε 977
2	5χχ 764	289 χ4ε	2	340 ε72	677	2	908 312	6ε3
3	878 5ε3	766	3	5εε 629	3χ2	3	ε77 χ05	429
4	ε46 159	481	4	879 χ0ε	109	4	.χ34 227 232	165
5	.χ17 213 61χ	197	5	ε37 ε18	279 χ34	5	496 397	26χ χχ0
6	4χ0 7ε5	288 χε3	6	.χ26 1ε5 950	760	6	745 277	817
7	769 6χ8	80χ	7	473 4ε0	489	7	9ε3 χ92	554
8	χ36 2ε6	526	8	730 979	1ε4	8	.χ35 062 426	28ε
9	.χ18 102 820	242	9	9χ9 ε71	278 ε22	9	310 6ε5	008
χ	38χ χ62	287 ε5χ	χ	.χ27 066 χ93	84χ	χ	57χ 701	269 945
ε	656 χ00	877	ε	323 721	577	ε	828 446	681
.1520	922 677	594	.1560	5χ0 098	2χ4	.15χ0	χ95 ε07	3εχ
1	εχχ 04ε	2ε1	1	858 380	012	1	.χ36 143 305	138
2	.χ19 275 340	00χ	2	ε14 392	277 940	2	3ε0 441	268 χ76
3	540 34χ	286 927	3	.χ28 190 112	66χ	3	659 2ε7	7ε3
4	807 075	646	4	447 780	398	4	905 χχχ	531
5	χ91 6εε	364	5	702 ε58	107	5	ε72 41ε	26ε
6	.χ1χ 157 χ63	082	6	97χ 063	276 χ35	6	.χ37 21χ 68χ	267 εχχ
7	421 ε25	285 9χ1	7	.χ29 034 χ98	765	7	486 678	929
8	6χ7 906	700	8	2χε 641	494	8	732 3χ5	667
9	971 406	41ε	9	565 ε15	203	9	999 χ50	3χ7
χ	.χ1ε 036 825	13ε	χ	820 118	275 ε34	χ	.χ38 045 237	127
ε	2εε 964	284 χ5χ	ε	χ96 050	863	ε	2ε0 362	266 χ66
.1530	584 802	77ε	.1570	.χ2χ 14ε 8ε3	594	.15ε0	557 208	7χ5
1	849 381	49χ	1	405 287	304	1	801 9ε1	526
2	ε11 85ε	200	2	67χ 58ε	035	2	χ68 317	267
3	.χ20 195 χ5ε	283 ε20	3	933 604	274 966	3	.χ39 112 582	265 εχ7
4	459 97ε	841	4	εχ8 36χ	698	4	378 569	928
5	721 600	562	5	.χ2ε 260 χ46	409	5	622 295	669
6	9χ4 ε62	284	6	515 253	13ε	6	887 942	3χχ
7	.χ21 068 226	282 εχ6	7	789 392	273 χ71	7	ε31 130	130
8	32ε 210	909	8	χ41 243	7χ3	8	.χ3χ 196 260	264 χ71
9	5ε1 ε19	62χ	9	.χ30 0ε4 χ26	516	9	43ε 111	7ε4
χ	874 547	351	χ	368 340	248	χ	6χ3 905	536
ε	ε36 898	074	ε	61ε 588	272 ε80	ε	948 23ε	278

.1600 εε0 4ε7

N	Log Cos	d	N	Log Cos	d	N	Log Cos	d
.0000	0.000 000 000	07Ɛ	.0040	Ɛ.ƐƐƐ Ɛ14 χ92	5 427	.0080	Ɛ.ƐƐƐ 857 651	χ 797
1	Ɛ.ƐƐƐ ƐƐƐ Ɛ41	1Ɛχ	1	Ɛ0Ɛ 667	565	1	848 χ76	915
2	ƐƐƐ 943	339	2	Ɛ06 102	6χ5	2	83χ 161	χ55
3	ƐƐƐ 606	477	3	Ɛ00 619	823	3	82Ɛ 308	Ɛ93
4	ƐƐƐ 14Ɛ	5Ɛ6	4	χƐ6 9Ɛ6	962	4	820 335	Ɛ 112
5	ƐƐχ 755	735	5	χƐ1 054	χχ0	5	811 223	251
6	ƐƐχ 020	873	6	χχ7 174	6 020	6	801 Ɛ92	38Ɛ
7	ƐƐ9 369	9Ɛ2	7	χχ1 154	159	7	7Ɛ2 803	50Ɛ
8	ƐƐ8 577	Ɛ30	8	χ96 ƐƐ7	299	8	7χ3 2Ɛ4	649
9	ƐƐ7 647	1 06Ɛ	9	χ90 91χ	417	9	793 867	788
χ	ƐƐ6 598	1χχ	χ	χ86 503	556	χ	784 09Ɛ	907
Ɛ	ƐƐ5 3χχ	329	Ɛ	χ7Ɛ Ɛ69	695	Ɛ	774 394	χ46
.0010	ƐƐ4 081	467	.0050	χ75 494	814	.0090	764 54χ	Ɛ85
1	ƐƐ2 816	5χ6	1	χ6χ 880	952	1	754 585	10 103
2	ƐƐ1 230	724	2	χ63 Ɛ2χ	χ91	2	744 482	243
3	ƐχƐ 708	863	3	χ59 059	7 00Ɛ	3	734 23Ɛ	381
4	Ɛχ9 χ65	9χ2	4	χ52 04χ	14Ɛ	4	723 χ7χ	500
5	Ɛχ8 083	Ɛ20	5	χ46 χƐƐ	289	5	713 57χ	63Ɛ
6	Ɛχ6 163	2 05Ɛ	6	χ3Ɛ 832	408	6	702 Ɛ3Ɛ	77χ
7	Ɛχ4 104	19χ	7	χ34 426	546	7	6Ɛ2 381	8Ɛ9
8	Ɛχ1 Ɛ26	318	8	χ28 χχ0	685	8	6χ1 684	χ38
9	Ɛ9Ɛ 80χ	457	9	χ21 417	804	9	690 848	Ɛ76
χ	Ɛ99 373	596	χ	χ15 813	943	χ	67Ɛ 892	11 0Ɛ6
Ɛ	Ɛ96 999	714	Ɛ	χ09 χ90	χ81	Ɛ	66χ 798	234
.0020	Ɛ94 285	853	.0060	χ02 00Ɛ	8 000	.00χ0	659 564	373
1	Ɛ91 632	991	1	9Ɛ6 00Ɛ	13Ɛ	1	648 1Ɛ1	4Ɛ2
2	Ɛ8χ 861	Ɛ11	2	9χ9 χ90	27χ	2	636 8ƐƐ	631
3	Ɛ87 950	3 04Ɛ	3	9χ1 812	3Ɛ8	3	625 28χ	770
4	Ɛ84 901	189	4	995 416	538	4	613 71χ	8χƐ
5	Ɛ81 734	309	5	988 χ9χ	675	5	601 χ2Ɛ	χ2χ
6	Ɛ7χ 427	446	6	980 425	7Ɛ5	6	5Ɛ0 001	Ɛ69
7	Ɛ76 Ɛχ1	586	7	973 830	933	7	59χ 054	12 0χ7
8	Ɛ73 617	704	8	966 χƐ9	χ73	8	587 Ɛ69	227
9	Ɛ6Ɛ Ɛ13	843	9	95χ 046	ƐƐ1	9	575 942	365
χ	Ɛ68 290	982	χ	951 055	9 12Ɛ	χ	563 599	4χ5
Ɛ	Ɛ64 50χ	Ɛ00	Ɛ	943 Ɛ26	26Ɛ	Ɛ	551 0Ɛ4	623
.0030	Ɛ60 60χ	4 03Ɛ	.0070	936 877	3χ9	.00Ɛ0	53χ 691	763
1	Ɛ58 58Ɛ	179	1	929 48χ	528	1	527 Ɛ2χ	8χ1
2	Ɛ54 412	2Ɛ9	2	91Ɛ Ɛ62	667	2	515 249	χ20
3	Ɛ50 115	437	3	912 4Ɛ7	7χ5	3	502 429	Ɛ5Ɛ
4	Ɛ47 89χ	575	4	904 912	925	4	4χƐ 48χ	13 09Ɛ
5	Ɛ43 325	6Ɛ5	5	8Ɛ6 Ɛχ9	χ63	5	498 3χƐ	219
6	Ɛ3χ 830	833	6	8χ9 146	Ɛχ2	6	485 192	358
7	Ɛ35 ƐƐ9	971	7	89Ɛ 164	χ 120	7	471 χ36	497
8	Ɛ31 248	χƐ0	8	891 044	260	8	45χ 55Ɛ	616
9	Ɛ28 358	5 02Ɛ	9	882 9χ4	39χ	9	446 Ɛ45	756
χ	Ɛ23 329	16χ	χ	874 606	519	χ	433 3χƐ	894
Ɛ	Ɛ1χ 17Ɛ	2χ9	Ɛ	866 0χ9	658	Ɛ	41Ɛ 717	χ13

N	Log Cos	d	N	Log Cos	d	N	Log Cos	d
.0100	Ɛ.ƐƐƐ 407 904	13 Ɛ52	.0140	Ɛ.ƐƐX 9X5 343	19 319	.0180	Ɛ.ƐƐX 1XƐ 8X4	22 6Ɛ8
1	3Ɛ3 972	14 091	1	988 026	459	1	189 1X8	837
2	39Ɛ 8X1	210	2	96X 789	598	2	166 571	978
3	387 691	350	3	951 1Ɛ1	717	3	143 7Ɛ5	XƐ7
4	373 341	48X	4	933 696	857	4	120 8ƐX	23 037
5	35X X73	609	5	915 X3Ɛ	996	5	0Ɛ9 883	176
6	346 466	749	6	8Ɛ8 065	Ɛ15	6	096 709	2Ɛ6
7	331 919	887	7	89X 150	1X 054	7	073 413	436
8	319 052	X06	8	880 0Ɛ8	194	8	04Ɛ Ɛ99	576
9	304 248	Ɛ46	9	861 Ɛ24	313	9	028 623	6Ɛ5
X	2XƐ 302	15 084	X	843 811	453	X	004 Ɛ2X	835
Ɛ	296 23X	204	Ɛ	825 37X	592	Ɛ	.ƐƐ9 ƐX1 2Ɛ5	975
.0110	281 036	343	.0150	806 9X8	711	.0190	Ɛ79 540	XƐ5
1	267 8Ɛ3	482	1	7X8 297	851	1	Ɛ55 647	24 034
2	252 431	600	2	789 646	990	2	Ɛ31 613	174
3	238 X31	740	3	76X 876	Ɛ10	3	Ɛ09 45Ɛ	2Ɛ4
4	223 2Ɛ1	87Ɛ	4	74Ɛ 966	1Ɛ 04Ɛ	4	XX5 167	434
5	209 632	9ƐƐ	5	730 917	18X	5	X80 933	574
6	1Ɛ3 833	Ɛ39	6	711 749	30X	6	X58 37Ɛ	6Ɛ3
7	199 8Ɛ6	16 078	7	6Ɛ2 43Ɛ	449	7	X33 888	833
8	183 83X	1Ɛ8	8	692 ƐƐ2	589	8	X0Ɛ 055	973
9	169 642	336	9	673 625	708	9	9X6 2X2	XƐ3
X	153 308	476	X	653 Ɛ19	848	X	981 3XƐ	25 033
Ɛ	138 X52	5Ɛ5	Ɛ	634 291	987	Ɛ	958 378	173
.0120	122 459	734	.0160	614 506	Ɛ06	.01X0	933 205	2Ɛ2
1	107 925	873	1	5Ɛ4 600	20 046	1	909 Ɛ13	432
2	0Ɛ1 072	9Ɛ3	2	594 576	185	2	8X4 6X1	573
3	096 27Ɛ	Ɛ31	3	574 3Ɛ1	305	3	87Ɛ 12X	6Ɛ2
4	07Ɛ 34X	17 071	4	554 0X8	445	4	855 638	832
5	064 299	1Ɛ0	5	533 863	584	5	82Ɛ X06	972
6	049 0X9	32Ɛ	6	513 29Ɛ	703	6	806 054	XƐ2
7	031 97X	46X	7	4Ɛ2 798	843	7	7X0 162	26 032
8	016 510	5X9	8	491 Ɛ55	983	8	776 130	171
9	.ƐƐX ƐƐX Ɛ23	729	9	471 192	Ɛ02	9	74Ɛ Ɛ7Ɛ	2Ɛ2
X	ƐX3 3Ɛ6	867	X	450 290	21 041	X	725 889	432
Ɛ	Ɛ87 74Ɛ	9X7	Ɛ	42Ɛ 24Ɛ	181	Ɛ	6ƐƐ 457	572
.0130	Ɛ6Ɛ 964	Ɛ27	.0170	40X 08X	301	.01Ɛ0	694 XX5	6Ɛ1
1	Ɛ53 X39	18 065	1	3X8 989	440	1	66X 3Ɛ4	832
2	Ɛ37 994	1X5	2	387 549	580	2	643 782	972
3	Ɛ1Ɛ 7XƐ	324	3	365 Ɛ89	6ƐƐ	3	618 X10	XƐ1
4	Ɛ03 487	463	4	344 48X	83Ɛ	4	5Ɛ1 Ɛ1Ɛ	27 032
5	XX7 024	5X2	5	322 84Ɛ	97Ɛ	5	586 XX9	172
6	X8X 642	722	6	300 X90	XƐX	6	55Ɛ 937	2Ɛ2
7	X71 Ɛ20	861	7	29X Ɛ92	22 03X	7	534 645	432
8	X55 27Ɛ	9X0	8	278 Ɛ54	17X	8	509 213	572
9	X38 49Ɛ	Ɛ1Ɛ	9	256 996	2Ɛ9	9	4X1 861	6Ɛ2
X	X1Ɛ 580	19 05Ɛ	X	234 699	438	X	476 16Ɛ	832
Ɛ	X02 521	19X	Ɛ	212 261	579	Ɛ	44X 539	972

N	Log Cos	d	N	Log Cos	d	N	Log Cos	d
.0200	Ɛ.ƐƐ9 422 787	27 XƐ2	.0240	Ɛ.ƐƐ8 481 490	31 308	.0280	Ɛ.ƐƐ7 347 359	36 746
1	3Ɛ6 895	28 033	1	450 184	449	1	310 813	887
2	38X 862	172	2	41X 937	589	2	295 Ɛ48	X08
3	362 6Ɛ0	2Ɛ3	3	3X9 36X	70X	3	25Ɛ 140	Ɛ49
4	336 3Ɛ9	433	4	377 860	84Ɛ	4	224 1Ɛ3	37 08X
5	309 Ɛ86	573	5	346 011	990	5	1X9 125	210
6	2X1 613	6Ɛ3	6	314 241	Ɛ10	6	171 Ɛ15	351
7	274 Ɛ20	833	7	2X2 331	32 051	7	136 784	493
8	248 2X9	974	8	270 2X0	191	8	0ƐƐ 2Ɛ1	614
9	21Ɛ 535	XƐ4	9	23X 10Ɛ	313	9	083 899	755
X	1Ɛ2 641	29 034	X	207 9Ɛ8	453	X	048 144	897
Ɛ	185 609	174	Ɛ	195 565	594	Ɛ	010 469	X18
.0210	158 455	2Ɛ4	.0250	162 Ɛ91	714	.0290	.ƐƐ6 Ɛ94 651	Ɛ5X
1	12Ɛ 161	435	1	130 479	856	1	Ɛ58 6Ɛ3	38 09X
2	101 928	575	2	0Ɛ9 823	996	2	Ɛ20 615	221
3	094 373	6Ɛ5	3	086 X49	Ɛ17	3	XX4 3Ɛ4	362
4	066 87X	835	4	053 Ɛ32	33 058	4	X68 052	4X3
5	039 045	976	5	020 X96	199	5	X2Ɛ 76Ɛ	625
6	00Ɛ 28Ɛ	XƐ6	6	.ƐƐ7 ƐX9 8Ɛ9	31X	6	9Ɛ3 146	766
7	.ƐƐ8 ƐX1 395	2X 036	7	Ɛ76 59Ɛ	45X	7	976 5X0	8X8
8	Ɛ73 35Ɛ	177	8	Ɛ43 141	5X0	8	939 8Ɛ4	X29
9	Ɛ45 1X4	2Ɛ7	9	Ɛ0Ɛ 761	720	9	900 X87	Ɛ6Ɛ
X	Ɛ16 XX9	437	X	X98 041	861	X	883 Ɛ18	39 0Ɛ1
Ɛ	XX8 672	578	Ɛ	X64 3X0	9X2	Ɛ	846 X27	232
.0220	X7X 0Ɛ6	6Ɛ8	.0260	X30 5ƐX	Ɛ23	.02X0	809 7Ɛ5	374
1	X4Ɛ 5ƐX	838	1	9Ɛ8 697	34 064	1	790 441	4Ɛ5
2	X20 982	979	2	984 633	1X5	2	752 Ɛ48	637
3	9Ɛ2 005	XƐ9	3	950 44X	326	3	715 511	778
4	983 108	2Ɛ 03X	4	918 124	467	4	697 955	8ƐX
5	954 08X	17X	5	8X3 879	5X8	5	65X 057	X40
6	924 Ɛ10	2ƐX	6	86Ɛ 291	729	6	620 217	Ɛ82
7	8Ɛ5 812	43Ɛ	7	836 764	86X	7	5X2 255	3X 103
8	886 393	57Ɛ	8	801 XƐ6	9XƐ	8	564 152	245
9	856 X14	700	9	789 107	Ɛ30	9	525 Ɛ09	386
X	827 314	840	X	754 197	35 071	X	4X7 743	509
Ɛ	7Ɛ7 694	981	Ɛ	71Ɛ 126	1Ɛ2	Ɛ	469 236	64X
.0230	787 913	Ɛ01	.0270	6X5 Ɛ34	334	.02Ɛ0	42X 7X8	790
1	757 X12	30 042	1	670 800	474	1	3Ɛ0 018	912
2	727 990	182	2	637 348	5Ɛ5	2	371 306	X53
3	6Ɛ7 80X	303	3	601 953	737	3	332 473	Ɛ95
4	687 507	443	4	588 218	878	4	2Ɛ3 49X	3Ɛ 117
5	657 084	584	5	552 560	9Ɛ9	5	274 383	259
6	626 700	705	6	518 763	Ɛ3X	6	235 126	39Ɛ
7	5Ɛ5 Ɛ27	845	7	4X2 825	36 07Ɛ	7	1Ɛ5 947	521
8	585 372	985	8	468 766	201	8	176 426	663
9	554 5X9	Ɛ07	9	432 565	341	9	136 983	7X4
X	523 6X2	31 047	X	3Ɛ8 224	483	X	0Ɛ7 19Ɛ	926
Ɛ	4Ɛ2 657	187	Ɛ	381 961	604	Ɛ	077 475	X69

N	Log Cos	d	N	Log Cos	d	N	Log Cos	d
.0300	Ɛ.ƐƐ6 037 608	3Ɛ ƐχΧ	.0340	Ɛ.ƐƐ4 751 136	45 483	.0380	Ɛ.ƐƐ3 08Ɛ 073	4χ 98Ɛ
1	.ƐƐ5 ƐƐ7 61χ	40 130	1	707 873	605	1	040 2χ4	Ɛ13
2	Ɛ77 4χχ	273	2	682 26χ	749	2	.ƐƐ2 ƐƐ1 391	4Ɛ 057
3	Ɛ37 237	3Ɛ4	3	638 721	88Ɛ	3	Ɛ62 336	19χ
4	χƐ6 χ43	536	4	5Ɛ2 χ52	χ12	4	Ɛ13 158	322
5	χ76 509	679	5	569 040	Ɛ55	5	χ83 χ36	466
6	χ35 χ50	7Ɛχ	6	523 0χ7	46 098	6	χ34 590	5χ9
7	9Ɛ5 252	940	7	499 00Ɛ	21χ	7	9χ4 Ɛχ3	731
8	974 512	χ83	8	452 9Ɛ1	362	8	955 472	875
9	933 64Ɛ	41 004	9	408 64Ɛ	4χ4	9	905 7Ɛ9	9Ɛ9
χ	8Ɛ2 647	147	χ	382 167	627	χ	875 χ00	Ɛ41
Ɛ	871 500	289	Ɛ	337 740	76χ	Ɛ	825 χ7Ɛ	50 084
.0310	830 233	40Ɛ	.0350	2Ɛ0 Ɛ92	8Ɛ1	.0390	795 9Ɛ7	208
1	7χχ χ24	551	1	266 2χ1	χ34	1	745 7χƐ	350
2	769 493	693	2	21Ɛ 469	Ɛ78	2	6Ɛ5 45Ɛ	494
3	727 χ00	816	3	194 4Ɛ1	47 0Ɛχ	3	664 Ɛ87	618
4	6χ6 1χ6	957	4	149 3Ɛ3	241	4	614 56Ɛ	760
5	664 44Ɛ	χ9χ	5	102 172	384	5	583 χ0Ɛ	8χ4
6	622 571	42 020	6	076 9χχ	507	6	533 127	χ27
7	5χ0 551	163	7	02Ɛ 4χ3	64χ	7	4χ2 300	Ɛ70
8	55χ 3χχ	2χ4	8	.ƐƐ3 Ɛχ3 χ55	792	8	451 350	51 0Ɛ4
9	518 106	427	9	Ɛ58 283	914	9	400 258	238
χ	495 89Ɛ	56χ	χ	Ɛ10 56Ɛ	χ58	χ	36Ɛ 020	37Ɛ
Ɛ	453 331	6χƐ	Ɛ	χ84 713	Ɛ9χ	Ɛ	319 861	504
.0320	410 842	832	.0360	χ38 735	48 122	.03χ0	288 359	648
1	38χ 010	974	1	9Ɛ0 613	265	1	236 911	790
2	347 258	χƐ7	2	964 36χ	3χ9	2	1χ5 141	914
3	304 361	43 039	3	917 Ɛ81	52Ɛ	3	153 429	χ58
4	281 324	17Ɛ	4	88Ɛ 652	673	4	101 591	Ɛχ1
5	23χ 165	302	5	842 Ɛ9Ɛ	7Ɛ6	5	06Ɛ 5Ɛ0	52 124
6	1Ɛ6 χ63	444	6	7Ɛ6 3χ5	939	6	019 488	269
7	173 61Ɛ	587	7	769 668	χ81	7	.ƐƐ1 Ɛ87 21Ɛ	3Ɛ1
8	130 054	709	8	720 7χ7	49 004	8	Ɛ34 χ2χ	536
9	0χ8 547	850	9	693 7χ3	147	9	χχ2 4Ɛ4	679
χ	064 8Ɛ7	992	χ	646 658	28χ	χ	χ4Ɛ χ37	802
Ɛ	020 Ɛ25	Ɛ14	Ɛ	5Ɛ9 38χ	412	Ɛ	9Ɛ9 235	946
.0330	.ƐƐ4 Ɛ99 011	44 058	.0370	56Ɛ Ɛ78	556	.03Ɛ0	966 4χƐ	χ8Ɛ
1	Ɛ54 Ɛ75	199	1	522 622	698	1	913 620	53 012
2	Ɛ10 998	321	2	494 Ɛ46	820	2	880 60χ	158
3	χ88 677	463	3	447 326	964	3	829 472	29Ɛ
4	χ44 214	5χ5	4	3Ɛ9 582	χχ7	4	796 193	424
5	9ƐƐ 82Ɛ	728	5	36Ɛ 697	4χ 02χ	5	742 96Ɛ	569
6	977 103	86Ɛ	6	321 669	172	6	6χƐ 402	6Ɛ0
7	932 454	9Ɛ1	7	293 4Ɛ7	2Ɛ6	7	657 912	836
8	8χ9 663	Ɛ34	8	245 201	439	8	604 098	979
9	864 72Ɛ	45 077	9	1Ɛ6 984	581	9	570 31Ɛ	Ɛ03
χ	81Ɛ 674	1Ɛχ	χ	168 403	704	χ	518 418	54 047
Ɛ	796 476	340	Ɛ	119 8ƐƐ	848	Ɛ	484 391	18Ɛ

N	Log Cos	d	N	Log Cos	d	N	Log Cos	d
.0400	Ɛ.ƐƐ1 430 202	54 314	.0440	Ɛ.ƐχƐ 5Ɛ3 212	59 899	.0480	Ɛ.Ɛχ9 596 800	63 2χ7
1	397 χχχ	459	1	555 535	χ22	1	533 515	432
2	343 651	5χ1	2	4Ɛ7 713	Ɛ69	2	490 0χ3	578
3	2χƐ 070	726	3	459 766	5χ 0Ɛ2	3	428 727	703
4	256 546	86χ	4	3ƐƐ 674	237	4	385 024	84Ɛ
5	201 898	9Ɛ3	5	361 439	382	5	321 395	995
6	168 χχ5	Ɛ38	6	303 077	507	6	279 600	Ɛ20
7	113 Ɛ69	55 081	7	264 770	651	7	215 6χ0	64 067
8	07χ χχ8	205	8	206 11Ɛ	797	8	171 635	1Ɛ2
9	025 8χ3	34χ	9	167 544	921	9	109 443	339
χ	.ƐƐ0 Ɛ90 555	493	χ	108 823	χ67	χ	065 106	484
Ɛ	Ɛ37 082	618	Ɛ	069 978	ƐƐ0	Ɛ	000 842	60Ɛ
.0410	χχ1 666	760	.0450	00χ 988	5Ɛ 136	.0490	.Ɛχ8 Ɛ58 233	757
1	χ47 Ɛ06	8χ6	1	.Ɛχχ Ɛ6Ɛ 852	281	1	χƐ3 698	8χ1
2	9Ɛ2 220	χ2χ	2	Ɛ10 591	406	2	χ4χ 9Ɛ7	χ28
3	958 3Ɛ2	Ɛ73	3	χ71 187	550	3	9χ5 Ɛ8Ɛ	Ɛ74
4	902 43Ɛ	56 0Ɛ8	4	χ11 837	697	4	941 017	65 0ƐƐ
5	868 343	241	5	972 160	820	5	897 Ɛ18	246
6	812 102	386	6	912 540	966	6	832 892	391
7	777 938	50Ɛ	7	872 796	χƐ0	7	789 501	518
8	721 429	654	8	812 8χ6	60 037	8	723 Ɛχ5	664
9	686 995	799	9	772 86Ɛ	181	9	67χ 541	7χƐ
χ	630 1Ɛ8	922	χ	712 6χχ	306	χ	614 952	937
Ɛ	595 496	χ67	Ɛ	672 3χ4	451	Ɛ	56Ɛ 017	χ81
.0420	53χ 62Ɛ	ƐƐ0	.0460	611 Ɛ53	597	.04χ0	505 156	66 009
1	4χ3 63Ɛ	57 136	1	571 578	722	1	45Ɛ 149	155
2	448 505	27χ	2	510 χ56	867	2	3Ɛ4 ƐƐ4	2χ0
3	3Ɛ1 247	404	3	470 1χƐ	9Ɛ2	3	34χ 914	427
4	355 χ43	548	4	40Ɛ 3Ɛ9	Ɛ38	4	2χ4 4χ9	573
5	2Ɛχ 4Ɛ7	692	5	36χ 481	61 083	5	239 Ɛ36	6ƐƐ
6	262 χ25	818	6	309 3Ɛχ	208	6	193 437	846
7	207 209	960	7	268 1Ɛ2	353	7	128 7Ɛ1	991
8	16Ɛ 469	χχ6	8	206 χ5Ɛ	49χ	8	081 χ20	Ɛ19
9	113 583	58 02Ɛ	9	165 581	624	9	016 Ɛ03	67 065
χ	077 554	174	χ	103 Ɛ59	76χ	χ	Ɛχ7 Ɛ6Ɛ χ5χ	1Ɛ1
Ɛ	01Ɛ 3χ0	2Ɛχ	Ɛ	062 3χƐ	8Ɛ5	Ɛ	Ɛ04 869	338
.0430	.ƐχƐ Ɛ83 0χ2	443	.0470	000 6Ɛ6	χ3Ɛ	.04Ɛ0	χ59 531	483
1	Ɛ26 85Ɛ	588	1	.Ɛχ9 Ɛ5χ 877	Ɛ86	1	9Ɛ2 06χ	610
2	χ8χ 293	712	2	χƐ8 8Ɛ1	62 110	2	946 65χ	757
3	χ31 781	857	3	χ56 7χ1	257	3	89χ Ɛ03	8χ3
4	994 Ɛ26	9χ1	4	9Ɛ4 546	3χ2	4	833 220	χ2Ɛ
5	938 145	Ɛ26	5	952 164	528	5	787 3Ɛ1	Ɛ77
6	89Ɛ 21Ɛ	59 06Ɛ	6	8χƐ 838	672	6	71Ɛ 436	68 102
7	842 170	1Ɛ5	7	849 186	7Ɛχ	7	673 334	24Ɛ
8	7χ4 Ɛ77	33Ɛ	8	7χ6 588	944	8	607 0χ5	396
9	747 838	484	9	743 844	χ8χ	9	55χ 90Ɛ	522
χ	6χχ 374	60χ	χ	6χ0 976	63 016	χ	4Ɛ2 3χ9	66χ
Ɛ	650 966	754	Ɛ	639 960	160	Ɛ	445 93Ɛ	7Ɛ7

N	Log Cos	d	N	Log Cos	d	N	Log Cos	d
.0500	Ɛ.ƐX7 399 144	68 942	.0540	Ɛ.ƐX4 ƐƐ8 X3X	72 430	.0580	Ɛ.ƐX2 634 153	77 Ɛ73
1	330 402	X8X	1	Ɛ46 60X	578	1	578 1X0	78 102
2	283 534	69 016	2	X94 052	707	2	500 09X	251
3	216 51X	163	3	X21 547	853	3	443 X49	3X0
4	169 377	2XX	4	96X 8Ɛ4	9X2	4	387 669	52Ɛ
5	100 089	437	5	8Ɛ7 Ɛ12	Ɛ2X	5	30Ɛ 13X	67X
6	052 852	583	6	844 ƐX4	73 079	6	252 680	809
7	.ƐX6 ƐX5 28Ɛ	70Ɛ	7	791 Ɛ27	205	7	195 X73	958
8	Ɛ37 780	857	8	71X 922	354	8	119 117	XX7
9	X89 Ɛ25	9X4	9	667 58X	4X1	9	060 230	79 036
X	X20 141	Ɛ30	X	5Ɛ4 0X9	62X	X	.ƐX1 ƐX3 1Ɛ6	185
Ɛ	972 211	6X 078	Ɛ	540 67Ɛ	779	Ɛ	Ɛ26 031	314
.0510	904 155	205	.0550	488 Ɛ02	906	.0590	X68 919	463
1	855 Ɛ50	351	1	415 1Ɛ8	X53	1	9XƐ 476	5Ɛ3
2	7X7 7ƐƐ	499	2	361 365	ƐX2	2	931 X83	742
3	739 322	626	3	2X9 383	74 12Ɛ	3	874 341	891
4	68X 8Ɛ8	772	4	235 254	279	4	7Ɛ6 670	X20
5	620 146	8ƐX	5	180 Ɛ97	407	5	738 850	Ɛ70
6	571 448	X48	6	108 790	555	6	67X 8X0	7X 0ƐƐ
7	502 600	Ɛ93	7	054 237	6X3	7	600 7X1	24X
8	453 629	6Ɛ 121	8	.ƐX3 Ɛ9Ɛ 754	831	8	542 553	39X
9	3X4 508	268	9	Ɛ26 Ɛ23	97X	9	484 175	52X
X	335 260	3Ɛ6	X	X72 165	Ɛ09	X	405 847	678
Ɛ	285 X66	542	Ɛ	9Ɛ9 258	75 057	Ɛ	347 18Ɛ	809
.0520	216 524	68Ɛ	.0560	944 201	1X5	.05X0	288 582	958
1	166 X55	817	1	88Ɛ 018	332	1	209 826	XX7
2	0Ɛ7 23X	965	2	815 8X6	481	2	14X 93Ɛ	7Ɛ 037
3	047 495	XƐ1	3	760 425	610	3	08Ɛ 904	187
4	.ƐX5 Ɛ97 5X4	70 039	4	6X6 X15	759	4	010 739	316
5	Ɛ27 567	187	5	631 278	8X8	5	.ƐX0 Ɛ51 423	466
6	X77 3X0	313	6	577 590	X35	6	X91 Ɛ79	5Ɛ6
7	X07 089	461	7	501 757	Ɛ84	7	X12 583	746
8	956 828	5X9	8	447 793	76 113	8	952 X39	895
9	8X6 23Ɛ	736	9	391 680	261	9	893 164	X26
X	835 705	883	X	317 41Ɛ	3XƐ	X	813 33X	Ɛ75
Ɛ	784 X42	X10	Ɛ	261 030	539	Ɛ	753 385	80 105
.0530	714 032	Ɛ59	.0570	1X6 6Ɛ3	688	.05Ɛ0	693 280	255
1	663 095	71 0X6	1	130 027	816	1	613 027	3X5
2	5Ɛ1 ƐXƐ	234	2	075 411	965	2	552 842	535
3	540 977	380	3	.ƐX2 ƐƐX 668	XƐ4	3	492 309	685
4	48Ɛ 5Ɛ7	509	4	Ɛ43 774	77 041	4	411 844	815
5	41X 0XX	657	5	X88 733	191	5	351 02Ɛ	965
6	368 653	7X4	6	X11 562	31Ɛ	6	290 286	XƐ6
7	2Ɛ6 X6Ɛ	931	7	956 243	46X	7	20Ɛ 390	81 045
8	245 13X	X7X	8	89X 995	5Ɛ8	8	14X 347	196
9	193 280	72 007	9	823 399	747	9	089 171	326
X	121 275	155	X	767 852	896	X	007 X47	476
Ɛ	06Ɛ 120	2X2	Ɛ	6XƐ Ɛ78	X25	Ɛ	.Ɛ9Ɛ Ɛ46 591	607

N	Log Cos	d	N	Log Cos	d	N	Log Cos	d
.0600	Ɛ.Ɛ9Ɛ X84 Ɛ86	81 757	.0640	Ɛ.Ɛ99 129 458	87 3X3	.0680	Ɛ.Ɛ96 1X3 14X	91 099
1	X03 42Ɛ	8X7	1	062 075	534	1	112 071	230
2	941 744	X38	2	.Ɛ98 Ɛ96 741	687	2	040 X41	384
3	87Ɛ 908	Ɛ88	3	Ɛ0Ɛ 076	819	3	.Ɛ95 Ɛ6Ɛ 679	518
4	7Ɛ9 940	82 118	4	X43 459	96Ɛ	4	X9X 161	670
5	737 824	269	5	977 6XX	Ɛ02	5	X08 6Ɛ1	804
6	675 577	3ƐX	6	8XƐ 7X8	88 053	6	936 XX9	957
7	5Ɛ3 179	54X	7	823 755	1X6	7	865 152	XƐ0
8	530 82Ɛ	69Ɛ	8	757 56Ɛ	338	8	793 262	92 044
9	46X 150	82Ɛ	9	68Ɛ 233	48X	9	701 21X	197
X	3X7 521	980	X	602 965	621	X	62Ɛ 043	330
Ɛ	324 761	Ɛ11	Ɛ	536 344	773	Ɛ	558 913	484
.0610	261 850	83 062	.0650	469 791	905	.0690	486 44Ɛ	619
1	19X 7XX	1Ɛ2	1	3X0 X88	X58	1	3Ɛ3 X32	770
2	117 5Ɛ8	343	2	314 030	ƐXƐ	2	321 282	905
3	054 275	494	3	247 041	89 140	3	24X 579	X59
4	.Ɛ9X Ɛ90 9X1	625	4	179 Ɛ01	294	4	177 720	ƐƐ1
5	Ɛ09 378	775	5	0Ɛ0 829	426	5	0X4 72Ɛ	93 146
6	X45 803	907	6	023 403	578	6	011 5X5	29X
7	981 XƐ8	X58	7	.Ɛ97 Ɛ55 X47	710	7	.Ɛ94 Ɛ3X 307	433
8	8ƐX 060	ƐX8	8	X88 337	862	8	X66 X94	587
9	836 074	84 13X	9	9ƐX 695	9Ɛ4	9	993 509	720
X	771 Ɛ36	28Ɛ	X	930 8X1	Ɛ48	X	8ƐƐ 9X9	874
Ɛ	6X9 867	41Ɛ	Ɛ	862 955	8X 09X	Ɛ	828 135	X09
.0620	625 448	571	.0660	794 877	231	.06X0	754 328	Ɛ62
1	560 X97	703	1	706 646	384	1	680 386	94 0Ɛ6
2	498 394	853	2	638 282	517	2	5X8 290	24Ɛ
3	413 741	9X5	3	569 967	66X	3	514 041	3X4
4	34X 958	Ɛ36	4	49Ɛ 2Ɛ9	801	4	43Ɛ 859	538
5	285 X22	85 087	5	410 6Ɛ8	954	5	367 321	692
6	200 957	218	6	341 964	XX7	6	292 84Ɛ	826
7	137 73Ɛ	36X	7	272 X79	8Ɛ 03X	7	1ƐX 025	97Ɛ
8	072 391	500	8	1X3 X3Ɛ	191	8	125 266	Ɛ14
9	.Ɛ99 ƐX8 X91	651	9	114 86X	325	9	050 352	95 069
X	Ɛ23 440	7X2	X	045 545	477	X	.Ɛ93 Ɛ77 2X5	203
Ɛ	X59 85X	934	Ɛ	.Ɛ96 Ɛ76 08X	60Ɛ	Ɛ	XX2 0X2	357
.0630	993 Ɛ26	X85	.0670	XX6 67Ɛ	762	.06Ɛ0	X08 947	4Ɛ0
1	90X 061	86 017	1	X16 Ɛ19	8Ɛ6	1	933 457	646
2	844 046	169	2	947 223	X49	2	859 X11	79Ɛ
3	779 X99	2ƐX	3	877 396	ƐX0	3	784 232	934
4	6Ɛ3 79Ɛ	450	4	7X7 326	90 133	4	6XX 4ƐX	X89
5	629 34Ɛ	5X2	5	717 283	288	5	614 631	96 023
6	562 969	733	6	646 ƐƐ7	41X	6	53X 60X	178
7	498 236	886	7	576 799	572	7	464 452	311
8	411 570	X17	8	4X6 227	706	8	38X 141	467
9	346 755	Ɛ69	9	415 721	85X	9	2Ɛ3 896	600
X	27Ɛ 7X8	87 0ƐƐ	X	344 X83	9Ɛ1	X	219 296	756
Ɛ	1Ɛ4 6X9	251	Ɛ	274 092	Ɛ44	Ɛ	142 740	8Ɛ0

N	Log Cos	d	N	Log Cos	d	N	Log Cos	d
.0700	Ɛ.Ɛ93 067 χ50	96 χ45	.0740	Ɛ.Ɛ8Ɛ 939 182	χ0 86χ	.0780	Ɛ.Ɛ88 414 35χ	χ6 754
1	.Ɛ92 Ɛ91 007	Ɛ9χ	1	858 514	χ05	1	329 806	8Ɛ3
2	χƐ6 029	97 135	2	777 70Ɛ	Ɛ62	2	242 Ɛ13	χ50
3	χ1χ χƐ4	28χ	3	696 769	χ1 0Ɛ8	3	158 083	Ɛχχ
4	943 826	423	4	5Ɛ5 671	255	4	071 095	χ7 148
5	868 403	57χ	5	514 418	3Ɛ1	5	.Ɛ87 Ɛ85 Ɛ49	2χ6
6	790 χ45	713	6	433 027	548	6	χ9χ 863	444
7	6Ɛ5 332	86χ	7	351 69Ɛ	6χ4	7	9Ɛ3 41Ɛ	5χ1
8	619 684	χ03	8	26Ɛ ƐƐ7	840	8	907 χ3χ	740
9	541 881	Ɛ59	9	18χ 377	998	9	820 2Ɛχ	89χ
χ	465 924	98 0Ɛ4	χ	0χ8 59Ɛ	Ɛ34	χ	734 620	χ38
Ɛ	389 830	249	Ɛ	006 667	χ2 090	Ɛ	648 7χ4	Ɛ96
.0710	2Ɛ1 5χ3	3χ3	.0750	.Ɛ8χ Ɛ24 597	228	.0790	560 80χ	χ8 135
1	215 200	53χ	1	χ42 36Ɛ	385	1	474 695	292
2	138 882	693	2	95Ɛ Ɛχ6	520	2	388 403	431
3	060 1χƐ	82χ	3	879 686	679	3	29Ɛ Ɛ92	590
4	.Ɛ91 Ɛ83 581	984	4	797 009	815	4	1Ɛ3 602	729
5	χχ6 7Ɛ9	Ɛ1Ɛ	5	6Ɛ4 3Ɛ4	971	5	106 χ95	889
6	χ09 89χ	99 074	6	611 643	Ɛ0χ	6	01χ 208	χ26
7	930 826	20Ɛ	7	52χ 735	χ3 066	7	.Ɛ86 Ɛ31 3χ2	Ɛ86
8	853 617	366	8	447 68Ɛ	202	8	χ44 418	χ9 123
9	776 271	500	9	364 489	35Ɛ	9	957 2Ɛ5	283
χ	698 971	656	χ	281 12χ	4Ɛ8	χ	86χ 032	421
Ɛ	5ƐƐ 317	7Ɛ1	Ɛ	199 832	654	Ɛ	780 811	580
.0720	521 726	948	.0760	0Ɛ6 19χ	7Ɛ1	.07χ0	693 251	71Ɛ
1	443 99χ	χχ2	1	012 5χ9	949	1	5χ5 732	879
2	365 χƐ8	9χ 039	2	.Ɛ89 Ɛ2χ 860	χχ6	2	4Ɛ7 χ75	χ19
3	287 χ7Ɛ	193	3	χ46 976	χ4 043	3	40χ 058	Ɛ77
4	1χ9 8χ8	32Ɛ	4	962 933	19Ɛ	4	320 0χ1	χχ 116
5	10Ɛ 579	485	5	87χ 754	339	5	231 Ɛ87	275
6	031 0Ɛ4	620	6	796 417	495	6	143 912	415
7	.Ɛ90 Ɛ52 694	776	7	6Ɛ1 Ɛ42	632	7	055 4Ɛ9	573
8	χ73 Ɛ1χ	912	8	609 510	790	8	.Ɛ85 Ɛ66 Ɛ46	713
9	995 208	χ69	9	524 940	928	9	χ78 433	871
χ	8Ɛ6 35Ɛ	9Ɛ 003	χ	440 014	χ85	χ	989 782	χ11
Ɛ	817 358	15Ɛ	Ɛ	357 14Ɛ	χ5 022	Ɛ	89χ 971	Ɛ71
.0730	738 1Ɛ9	2Ɛ5	.0770	272 129	180	.07Ɛ0	7χƐ χ00	χƐ 10Ɛ
1	658 Ɛ04	451	1	188 Ɛ69	319	1	700 8Ɛ1	26Ɛ
2	579 673	5χ8	2	0χ3 850	475	2	611 642	40Ɛ
3	49χ 087	743	3	.Ɛ88 ƐƐχ 397	614	3	522 233	56χ
4	3Ɛχ 544	89Ɛ	4	Ɛ14 983	770	4	432 885	709
5	31χ 865	χ35	5	χ2Ɛ 213	90χ	5	343 178	869
6	23χ χ30	Ɛ92	6	945 505	χ67	6	253 50Ɛ	χ09
7	15χ χ5χ	χ0 128	7	85Ɛ 65χ	χ6 005	7	163 702	Ɛ68
8	07χ 932	284	8	775 655	162	8	073 756	Ɛ0 108
9	.Ɛ8Ɛ Ɛ9χ 66χ	41Ɛ	9	68Ɛ 4Ɛ3	300	9	.Ɛ84 Ɛ83 64χ	268
χ	χƐχ 24Ɛ	577	χ	5χ5 1Ɛ3	45χ	χ	χ93 3χ2	407
Ɛ	χ19 894	712	Ɛ	4Ɛχ 955	5Ɛ7	Ɛ	9χ2 Ɛ97	568

N	Log Cos	d	N	Log Cos	d	N	Log Cos	d
.0800	Ɛ.Ɛ84 8Ɛ2 62Ɛ	Ɛ0 707	.0840	Ɛ.Ɛ80 Ɛ90 X46	Ɛ6 74Ɛ	.0880	Ɛ.Ɛ79 068 233	100 870
1	801 Ɛ24	867	1	X96 2Ɛ7	8Ɛ3	1	.Ɛ78 Ɛ67 583	X15
2	711 279	X08	2	99Ɛ 604	X54	2	X66 76X	Ɛ7X
3	620 471	Ɛ67	3	8X4 770	ƐƐ7	3	965 7Ɛ0	101 123
4	52Ɛ 506	Ɛ1 108	4	7X9 775	Ɛ7 159	4	864 689	287
5	43X 3ƐX	267	5	6Ɛ2 618	300	5	763 402	431
6	349 153	408	6	5Ɛ7 318	462	6	661 Ɛ91	596
7	257 947	568	7	4ƐƐ X76	605	7	560 5Ɛ7	73Ɛ
8	166 39Ɛ	708	8	404 471	768	8	45X X78	8X4
9	074 893	869	9	308 905	90X	9	359 194	X49
X	.Ɛ83 Ɛ83 026	X09	X	210 ƐƐ7	X71	X	257 347	ƐƐ3
Ɛ	X91 219	Ɛ69	Ɛ	115 146	Ɛ8 014	Ɛ	155 354	102 157
.0810	99Ɛ 270	Ɛ2 10X	.0850	019 132	177	.0890	053 1Ɛ9	302
1	8X9 162	26Ɛ	1	.Ɛ7Ɛ Ɛ20 Ɛ77	319	1	.Ɛ77 Ɛ50 XƐ7	466
2	7Ɛ6 XƐ3	40Ɛ	2	X24 85X	481	2	X4X 651	610
3	704 6X4	56Ɛ	3	928 399	624	3	948 041	776
4	612 135	710	4	82Ɛ 975	786	4	845 487	91Ɛ
5	51Ɛ 625	872	5	733 1XƐ	92X	5	742 768	X85
6	428 973	X11	6	636 481	X91	6	63Ɛ 8X3	103 02Ɛ
7	335 Ɛ62	Ɛ73	7	539 5Ɛ0	Ɛ9 035	7	538 874	194
8	242 ƐXƐ	Ɛ3 113	8	440 577	197	8	435 6X0	33Ɛ
9	14Ɛ X98	275	9	343 3X0	33Ɛ	9	332 361	4X4
X	058 823	415	X	246 061	4X2	X	22X X79	64X
Ɛ	.Ɛ82 Ɛ65 40X	577	Ɛ	148 77Ɛ	646	Ɛ	127 42Ɛ	7Ɛ4
.0820	X71 X53	717	.0860	04Ɛ 135	7X9	.08X0	023 837	95X
1	97X 338	879	1	.Ɛ7X Ɛ51 548	950	1	.Ɛ76 Ɛ1Ɛ X99	Ɛ04
2	886 67Ɛ	X19	2	X53 7Ɛ8	XƐ5	2	X17 Ɛ95	104 06X
3	792 862	Ɛ7Ɛ	3	955 903	ƐX 057	3	913 Ɛ27	215
4	69X 8X3	Ɛ4 120	4	857 868	200	4	80Ɛ 912	37X
5	5X6 783	282	5	759 668	363	5	707 554	525
6	4Ɛ2 501	423	6	65Ɛ 305	507	6	603 02Ɛ	690
7	3ƐX 09X	584	7	560 9ƐX	66Ɛ	7	4ƐX 55Ɛ	835
8	305 716	726	8	462 34Ɛ	813	8	3Ɛ5 926	9X0
9	210 ƐƐ0	887	9	363 738	977	9	2Ɛ0 Ɛ46	Ɛ47
X	118 325	X29	X	264 981	Ɛ1X	X	1X7 ƐƐƐ	105 0Ɛ2
Ɛ	023 4Ɛ8	Ɛ8X	Ɛ	165 X63	ƐƐ 083	Ɛ	0X2 Ɛ09	257
.0830	.Ɛ81 Ɛ2X 52X	Ɛ5 130	.0870	066 9X0	227	.08Ɛ0	.Ɛ75 Ɛ99 872	403
1	X35 3ƐX	292	1	.Ɛ79 Ɛ67 775	38Ɛ	1	X94 46Ɛ	56X
2	940 128	433	2	X68 3X6	533	2	98X Ɛ01	714
3	846 8Ɛ5	596	3	968 X73	698	3	885 3X9	87Ɛ
4	751 31Ɛ	737	4	869 397	840	4	77Ɛ 72X	X26
5	657 7X4	899	5	769 757	9X4	5	675 904	Ɛ91
6	561 Ɛ07	X3Ɛ	6	669 973	Ɛ48	6	56Ɛ 933	106 138
7	468 088	ƐX1	7	569 X27	100 0Ɛ2	7	465 7Ɛ7	2X3
8	372 0X7	Ɛ6 143	8	469 935	255	8	35Ɛ 514	44X
9	277 Ɛ64	2X5	9	369 6X0	3ƐX	9	255 086	5Ɛ5
X	181 87Ɛ	447	X	269 2X2	563	X	14X 691	761
Ɛ	087 434	5XX	Ɛ	168 93Ɛ	708	Ɛ	043 Ɛ30	908

N	Log Cos	d	N	Log Cos	d	N	Log Cos	d
.0900	Ɛ.Ɛ74 Ɛ39 224	106 χ73	.0940	Ɛ.Ɛ70 800 427	111 164	.0980	Ɛ.Ɛ68 272 012	117 549
1	χ32 371	107 01χ	1	6χƐ 283	311	1	156 685	6Ɛ9
2	927 353	187	2	599 Ɛ72	480	2	03χ Ɛ88	86χ
3	820 188	331	3	488 6Ɛ2	62Ɛ	3	.Ɛ67 Ɛ23 31χ	χ20
4	714 χ57	499	4	377 083	798	4	χ07 4Ɛχ	Ɛ90
5	609 57χ	645	5	265 4χ7	947	5	8χƐ 52χ	118 143
6	501 Ɛ35	7Ɛ1	6	153 760	χƐ6	6	793 3χ7	2Ɛ3
7	3Ɛ6 344	958	7	041 866	112 064	7	677 0Ɛ4	465
8	2χχ 5χ8	Ɛ04	8	.Ɛ6Ɛ ƐƐƐ 802	212	8	55χ 84Ɛ	617
9	1χ2 6χ4	108 070	9	χ19 5Ɛ0	382	9	442 234	788
χ	096 634	218	χ	907 22χ	530	χ	325 668	93χ
Ɛ	.Ɛ73 Ɛ8χ 418	384	Ɛ	7Ɛ4 8Ɛχ	69χ	Ɛ	208 92χ	χƐ0
.0910	χ82 054	530	.0950	6χ2 220	84χ	.0990	0χƐ χ3χ	119 061
1	975 724	698	1	58Ɛ 592	9Ɛ9	1	.Ɛ66 Ɛ92 999	213
2	869 048	844	2	478 795	Ɛ67	2	χ75 786	385
3	760 404	9Ɛ1	3	365 82χ	113 116	3	958 401	538
4	653 613	Ɛ58	4	252 714	286	4	83χ χ85	6χ9
5	546 677	109 105	5	13Ɛ 44χ	435	5	721 398	85Ɛ
6	439 572	272	6	028 015	5χ4	6	603 739	χ11
7	330 300	419	7	.Ɛ6χ Ɛ14 631	753	7	4χ5 928	Ɛ84
8	222 χχ3	587	8	χ00 χ9χ	902	8	387 964	11χ 136
9	115 518	732	9	8χ9 198	χ72	9	269 82χ	2χ8
χ	007 9χ6	8χ0	χ	795 326	114 021	χ	14Ɛ 542	45Ɛ
Ɛ	.Ɛ72 χƐχ 106	χ48	Ɛ	681 305	191	Ɛ	031 0χ3	611
.0920	9Ɛ0 27χ	ƐƐ5	.0960	569 134	340	.09χ0	.Ɛ65 Ɛ12 692	784
1	8χ2 285	10χ 161	1	454 9Ɛ4	4Ɛ0	1	9Ɛ3 Ɛ0χ	936
2	794 124	30Ɛ	2	340 504	660	2	895 194	χχ9
3	685 χ15	477	3	227 χ64	80Ɛ	3	776 2χ7	11Ɛ 060
4	577 55χ	624	4	113 255	97Ɛ	4	657 247	213
5	468 Ɛ36	791	5	.Ɛ69 ƐƐχ 496	Ɛ2Ɛ	5	538 034	385
6	35χ 365	93Ɛ	6	χχ5 567	115 09Ɛ	6	418 86Ɛ	539
7	24Ɛ 626	χχ7	7	990 488	24Ɛ	7	2Ɛ9 332	6χƐ
8	140 73Ɛ	10Ɛ 055	8	877 239	3ƐƐ	8	199 843	863
9	031 6χ6	202	9	761 χ3χ	56Ɛ	9	079 Ɛχ0	χ15
χ	.Ɛ71 Ɛ22 4χ4	36Ɛ	χ	648 48Ɛ	720	χ	.Ɛ64 Ɛ5χ 187	Ɛ89
Ɛ	χ13 135	518	Ɛ	532 96Ɛ	88Ɛ	Ɛ	χ3χ 1Ɛχ	120 140
.0930	903 819	686	.0970	419 0χ0	χ40	.09Ɛ0	91χ 07χ	2Ɛ3
1	7Ɛ4 153	834	1	303 260	ƐƐ0	1	7Ɛ9 987	467
2	6χ4 51Ɛ	9χ1	2	1χ9 270	116 161	2	699 520	61χ
3	594 73χ	Ɛ4χ	3	093 10Ɛ	311	3	578 Ɛ02	792
4	484 7Ɛ0	110 0Ɛ9	4	.Ɛ68 Ɛ78 9Ɛχ	481	4	458 330	945
5	374 6Ɛ3	265	5	χ62 539	632	5	337 5χ7	χƐ9
6	264 44χ	414	6	947 Ɛ07	7χ3	6	216 6χχ	121 071
7	154 036	582	7	831 324	954	7	0Ɛ5 639	224
8	043 674	72Ɛ	8	716 590	Ɛ04	8	.Ɛ63 Ɛ94 415	398
9	.Ɛ70 Ɛ32 Ɛ45	899	9	5ƐƐ 688	075	9	χ73 039	551
χ	χ22 268	χ48	χ	4χ4 613	226	χ	951 6χ8	704
Ɛ	911 420	ƐƐ5	Ɛ	389 3χ9	397	Ɛ	82Ɛ Ɛχ4	878

N	Log Cos	d	N	Log Cos	d	N	Log Cos	d
.0X00	Ɛ.Ɛ63 70X 328	121 X30	.0X40	Ɛ.Ɛ5X 949 060	128 420	.0X80	Ɛ.Ɛ55 966 028	132 Ɛ22
1	5X8 4Ɛ8	ƐX4	1	820 840	597	1	833 106	133 0X1
2	486 514	122 159	2	6Ɛ4 265	752	2	700 025	260
3	364 377	311	3	587 713	90X	3	588 985	41Ɛ
4	242 066	485	4	45X X05	X86	4	455 566	59X
5	11Ɛ 7X1	63X	5	331 Ɛ3Ɛ	129 041	5	321 Ɛ88	759
6	.Ɛ62 ƐƐ9 163	7Ɛ2	6	204 XƐX	1ƐX	6	1XX 42Ɛ	918
7	X96 571	967	7	097 900	375	7	076 713	X98
8	973 806	Ɛ20	8	.Ɛ59 Ɛ6X 547	530	8	.Ɛ54 Ɛ42 837	134 057
9	850 8X6	123 094	9	X41 017	6X9	9	X0X 7X0	216
X	729 812	249	X	913 52X	865	X	896 586	395
Ɛ	606 585	402	Ɛ	7X5 885	X21	Ɛ	762 1Ɛ1	555
.0X10	4X3 183	576	.0X50	677 X64	Ɛ99	.0X90	629 858	715
1	37Ɛ 809	730	1	549 X87	12X 155	1	4Ɛ5 143	895
2	258 099	8X4	2	41Ɛ 932	312	2	380 46X	X54
3	134 3Ɛ5	X5X	3	2Ɛ1 620	48X	3	247 616	135 014
4	010 557	124 013	4	183 152	646	4	112 602	194
5	.Ɛ61 XX8 544	188	5	054 708	803	5	.Ɛ53 Ɛ99 42X	354
6	984 378	341	6	.Ɛ58 Ɛ25 Ɛ05	980	6	X64 096	514
7	860 037	4Ɛ7	7	9Ɛ7 145	Ɛ38	7	92X 782	694
8	737 740	670	8	888 209	12Ɛ 0Ɛ5	8	7Ɛ5 0XX	854
9	613 090	826	9	759 114	272	9	67Ɛ 456	X15
X	4XX 466	99Ɛ	X	629 X62	42X	X	545 641	Ɛ95
Ɛ	385 687	Ɛ55	Ɛ	4ƐX 634	5X8	Ɛ	40Ɛ 668	136 155
.0X20	260 732	125 10Ɛ	.0X60	38Ɛ 048	764	.0XX0	295 513	316
1	137 623	284	1	25Ɛ 4X4	922	1	15Ɛ 1Ɛ9	496
2	012 35Ɛ	43X	2	12Ɛ 782	X9Ɛ	2	024 923	657
3	.Ɛ60 XX8 Ɛ21	5Ɛ4	3	.Ɛ57 ƐƐƐ 8X3	130 058	3	.Ɛ52 XXX 288	818
4	983 529	76X	4	X8Ɛ 847	215	4	973 670	999
5	859 97Ɛ	924	5	95Ɛ 632	393	5	838 893	Ɛ59
6	734 057	X9Ɛ	6	82Ɛ 25Ɛ	550	6	701 936	137 11X
7	60X 178	126 054	7	6ƐX 90Ɛ	709	7	586 818	2X0
8	4X4 124	20Ɛ	8	58X 202	888	8	44Ɛ 538	460
9	379 Ɛ15	384	9	459 536	X44	9	314 098	622
X	253 751	540	X	328 6Ɛ2	131 003	X	198 676	7X3
Ɛ	129 211	6Ɛ5	Ɛ	1Ɛ7 6XƐ	180	Ɛ	060 X93	964
.0X30	002 718	871	.0X70	086 52Ɛ	33Ɛ	.0XƐ0	.Ɛ51 Ɛ25 12Ɛ	Ɛ26
1	.Ɛ5Ɛ X97 X67	X26	1	.Ɛ56 Ɛ55 1Ɛ0	4Ɛ8	1	9X9 205	138 0X7
2	971 041	ƐX2	2	X23 8Ɛ4	676	2	871 11X	269
3	846 05Ɛ	127 158	3	8Ɛ2 23X	834	3	734 X71	42X
4	71X Ɛ03	313	4	780 606	9Ɛ3	4	5Ɛ8 643	5Ɛ0
5	5Ɛ3 7Ɛ0	48X	5	64X 813	Ɛ70	5	480 053	772
6	488 322	644	6	518 863	132 12Ɛ	6	343 4X1	934
7	360 89X	800	7	3X6 734	2XX	7	206 769	XƐ5
8	235 09X	977	8	274 446	467	8	089 874	139 078
9	109 323	Ɛ32	9	141 Ɛ9Ɛ	627	9	.Ɛ50 Ɛ50 7Ɛ8	23X
X	.Ɛ5X ƐX1 3Ɛ1	128 0X9	X	00Ɛ 574	7X5	X	X13 57X	3ƐƐ
Ɛ	X75 304	264	Ɛ	.Ɛ55 X98 98Ɛ	963	Ɛ	896 17Ɛ	582

N	Log Cos	d	N	Log Cos	d	N	Log Cos	d
.0Ɛ00	Ɛ.Ɛ50 758 7Ɛ9	139 745	.0Ɛ40	Ɛ.Ɛ47 320 261	144 493	.0Ɛ80	Ɛ.Ɛ41 86Ɛ 770	14Ɛ 356
1	61Ɛ 074	907	1	197 98X	659	1	720 416	525
2	4X1 369	X89	2	053 331	823	2	590 XƐ1	6Ɛ3
3	363 4X0	13X 050	3	.Ɛ46 Ɛ0X 70X	9X9	3	441 3ƐX	881
4	225 450	212	4	985 921	Ɛ74	4	2Ɛ1 739	X50
5	0X7 23X	395	5	840 969	145 13Ɛ	5	161 8X9	150 01X
6	.Ɛ4Ɛ Ɛ68 X65	558	6	6Ɛ7 82X	304	6	011 88Ɛ	1X8
7	X2X 509	71Ɛ	7	572 526	490	7	.Ɛ40 X81 6X3	377
8	8XƐ 9XX	8X1	8	429 056	656	8	931 328	546
9	771 109	X65	9	2X3 600	821	9	7X0 9X2	715
X	632 264	13Ɛ 028	X	159 99Ɛ	9X8	X	650 289	8X3
Ɛ	4Ɛ3 238	1XƐ	Ɛ	013 ƐƐ3	Ɛ73	Ɛ	4ƐƐ 5X6	X73
.0Ɛ10	374 049	372	.0Ɛ50	.Ɛ45 X8X 040	146 13X	.0Ɛ90	36X 733	151 041
1	234 897	535	1	943 Ɛ02	305	1	219 6Ɛ2	211
2	0Ɛ5 362	6Ɛ9	2	7Ɛ9 7Ɛ9	490	2	088 4X1	3X0
3	.Ɛ4X Ɛ75 865	880	3	673 329	658	3	.Ɛ3Ɛ Ɛ37 101	56Ɛ
4	X35 ƐX5	X44	4	528 891	823	4	9X5 752	73Ɛ
5	8Ɛ6 161	140 007	5	3X2 06X	9XX	5	854 013	90X
6	776 156	190	6	257 280	Ɛ76	6	702 305	X99
7	635 Ɛ86	352	7	110 306	147 142	7	570 428	152 06X
8	4Ɛ5 834	517	8	.Ɛ44 Ɛ85 184	309	8	41X 37X	239
9	375 319	69Ɛ	9	X39 X77	495	9	288 141	409
X	234 83X	863	X	8Ɛ2 5X2	661	X	135 934	599
Ɛ	0Ɛ3 Ɛ97	X26	Ɛ	766 Ɛ41	829	Ɛ	.Ɛ3X ƐX3 357	768
.0Ɛ20	.Ɛ49 Ɛ73 171	ƐXƐ	.0Ɛ60	61Ɛ 314	9Ɛ5	.0ƐX0	X50 7XƐ	939
1	X32 182	141 174	1	493 51Ɛ	Ɛ81	1	8Ɛ9 X72	Ɛ09
2	8Ɛ1 00X	337	2	347 55X	148 149	2	766 Ɛ65	153 09X
3	76Ɛ 893	500	3	1ƐƐ 411	315	3	613 X87	26X
4	62X 393	685	4	073 0Ɛ8	4X2	4	480 819	43X
5	4X8 90X	849	5	.Ɛ43 Ɛ26 816	66Ɛ	5	329 39Ɛ	60X
6	367 081	X11	6	99X 167	836	6	195 991	7X0
7	225 270	Ɛ97	7	851 531	X04	7	042 1Ɛ1	970
8	0X3 295	142 15Ɛ	8	704 729	Ɛ90	8	.Ɛ39 XXX 441	Ɛ40
9	.Ɛ48 Ɛ61 136	324	9	577 759	149 159	9	956 501	154 112
X	X1X X12	4X9	X	42X 600	325	X	802 3XƐ	2X3
Ɛ	898 525	672	Ɛ	2X1 297	4Ɛ3	Ɛ	66X 108	473
.0Ɛ30	755 X73	837	.0Ɛ70	153 9X4	680	.0ƐƐ0	515 855	645
1	613 238	X00	1	006 324	849	1	381 210	816
2	490 438	Ɛ86	2	.Ɛ42 X78 697	X16	2	228 5Ɛ6	9X7
3	349 472	143 14Ɛ	3	92X 881	ƐX3	3	093 80Ɛ	Ɛ79
4	206 323	314	4	7X0 89X	14X 170	4	.Ɛ38 Ɛ3X 852	155 14X
5	083 00Ɛ	49X	5	652 72X	33X	5	9X5 704	320
6	.Ɛ47 Ɛ3Ɛ 731	664	6	504 3Ɛ0	508	6	850 3X4	4Ɛ1
7	9Ɛ8 089	829	7	375 XX4	695	7	6Ɛ6 XƐ3	684
8	874 460	9Ɛ3	8	227 40Ɛ	863	8	561 42Ɛ	855
9	730 669	Ɛ79	9	098 768	X31	9	407 796	X27
X	5X8 6Ɛ0	144 142	X	.Ɛ41 Ɛ49 937	ƐƐX	X	271 96Ɛ	ƐƐ9
Ɛ	464 56X	309	Ɛ	9ƐX 939	14Ɛ 189	Ɛ	117 972	18Ɛ

N	Log Cos	d	N	Log Cos	d	N	Log Cos	d
.1000	Ɛ.Ɛ37 Ɛ81 7χ3	156 361	.1040	Ɛ.Ɛ32 050 885	161 4Ɛχ	.1080	Ɛ.Ɛ27 χ93 005	168 7Ɛ4
1	χ27 442	533	1	.Ɛ31 χχƐ 387	693	1	926 411	994
2	890 Ɛ0Ɛ	706	2	949 8Ɛ4	86Ɛ	2	779 639	Ɛ73
3	736 405	899	3	7χ8 045	χ45	3	610 686	169 153
4	59Ɛ 728	χ6Ɛ	4	646 200	162 021	4	463 533	332
5	444 879	157 041	5	4χ4 19Ɛ	1Ɛ7	5	2Ɛ6 201	512
6	2χ9 838	215	6	341 Ɛχ4	393	6	148 8χƐ	6Ɛ2
7	152 623	3χ7	7	19Ɛ 811	569	7	.Ɛ26 Ɛ9Ɛ 1Ɛ9	892
8	.Ɛ36 ƐƐ7 238	57χ	8	039 264	745	8	χ31 527	χ71
9	χ5Ɛ 87χ	751	9	.Ɛ30 χ96 71Ɛ	921	9	883 676	16χ 052
χ	904 129	924	χ	933 9Ɛχ	χƐ8	χ	715 624	232
Ɛ	768 405	χƐ8	Ɛ	790 Ɛ02	163 094	Ɛ	567 3Ɛ2	412
.1010	610 509	158 08χ	.1050	629 χ2χ	26Ɛ	.1090	3Ɛ8 Ɛχ0	5Ɛ2
1	474 43Ɛ	262	1	486 77Ɛ	447	1	24χ 5χχ	793
2	318 199	436	2	323 334	623	2	09Ɛ χ17	974
3	17Ɛ 963	608	3	17Ɛ 911	7ƐƐ	3	.Ɛ25 Ɛ31 063	Ɛ54
4	023 357	7χ1	4	018 112	997	4	982 10Ɛ	16Ɛ 135
5	.Ɛ35 χ86 776	974	5	.Ɛ2Ɛ χ74 337	Ɛ73	5	812 Ɛ96	316
6	929 χ02	Ɛ49	6	910 384	164 150	6	663 880	4Ɛ7
7	790 χ75	159 120	7	768 234	328	7	4Ɛ4 385	697
8	633 955	2Ɛ4	8	603 Ɛ08	504	8	344 8χχ	879
9	496 661	488	9	45Ɛ 604	6χ1	9	195 031	χ5Ɛ
χ	339 195	660	χ	2Ɛ6 Ɛ23	87χ	χ	025 192	170 03Ɛ
Ɛ	19Ɛ 735	835	Ɛ	152 265	χ56	Ɛ	.Ɛ24 χ75 153	221
.1020	041 Ɛ00	χ08	.1060	.Ɛ2χ Ɛχ9 40Ɛ	165 034	.10χ0	904 Ɛ32	403
1	.Ɛ34 χχ4 0Ɛ4	Ɛχ2	1	χ44 397	210	1	754 72Ɛ	5χ4
2	946 112	15χ 176	2	89Ɛ 187	3χ9	2	5χ4 147	787
3	7χ7 Ɛ58	34χ	3	735 99χ	586	3	433 580	968
4	649 80χ	524	4	590 414	764	4	282 814	Ɛ4χ
5	4χƐ 2χ6	6Ɛ8	5	426 870	941	5	111 886	171 130
6	350 7χχ	891	6	280 Ɛ2Ɛ	Ɛ1χ	6	.Ɛ23 Ɛ60 756	312
7	1Ɛ1 Ɛ19	χ66	7	117 011	166 0Ɛ8	7	9χƐ 444	4Ɛ4
8	053 073	15Ɛ 03Ɛ	8	.Ɛ29 Ɛ70 Ɛ15	295	8	839 Ɛ50	697
9	.Ɛ33 χƐ4 034	214	9	χ06 840	473	9	688 475	87χ
χ	954 χ20	3χ9	χ	860 389	651	χ	516 7Ɛ7	χ60
Ɛ	7Ɛ5 633	583	Ɛ	6Ɛ5 938	82Ɛ	Ɛ	364 957	172 042
.1030	656 070	759	.1070	54Ɛ 109	χ09	.10Ɛ0	1Ɛ2 915	226
1	4Ɛ6 513	932	1	3χ4 300	Ɛχ7	1	040 6χƐ	408
2	356 7χ1	Ɛ07	2	239 315	167 186	2	.Ɛ22 χ8χ 2χ3	5χƐ
3	1Ɛ6 896	160 0χ1	3	092 14Ɛ	363	3	917 8Ɛ4	793
4	056 7Ɛ5	278	4	.Ɛ28 Ɛ26 9χ8	542	4	765 121	975
5	.Ɛ32 χƐ6 539	451	5	97Ɛ 466	720	5	5Ɛ2 368	Ɛ59
6	956 0χ8	627	6	813 946	8ƐƐ	6	43Ɛ 40Ɛ	173 141
7	7Ɛ5 681	801	7	668 047	χ9χ	7	288 28χ	324
8	654 χ80	997	8	500 169	168 078	8	114 Ɛ66	507
9	4Ɛ4 0χ5	Ɛ72	9	354 0Ɛ1	258	9	.Ɛ21 Ɛ61 65Ɛ	6χƐ
χ	353 133	161 148	χ	1χ7 χ55	436	χ	9χ9 Ɛ70	893
Ɛ	1Ɛ1 Ɛχ7	322	Ɛ	03Ɛ 61Ɛ	616	Ɛ	836 299	χ77

N	Log Cos	d	N	Log Cos	d	N	Log Cos	d
.1100	Ɛ.Ɛ21 682 422	174 05Ɛ	.1140	Ɛ.Ɛ17 014 375	17Ɛ 684	.1180	Ɛ.Ɛ10 302 098	187 278
1	50X 383	243	1	.Ɛ16 X54 8Ɛ1	871	1	136 X20	46X
2	356 140	427	2	895 040	X5Ɛ	2	.Ɛ0Ɛ Ɛ6Ɛ 572	661
3	1X1 915	610	3	715 1X1	180 048	3	9X3 Ɛ11	854
4	029 305	7Ɛ4	4	555 155	235	4	818 279	X47
5	.Ɛ20 X74 711	999	5	394 Ɛ20	423	5	650 432	188 03X
6	8ƐƐ 934	Ɛ81	6	214 6Ɛ9	611	6	484 3Ɛ4	231
7	746 973	175 166	7	054 0X8	7ƐƐ	7	2Ɛ8 183	424
8	591 809	34Ɛ	8	.Ɛ15 X93 4X9	9X8	8	12Ɛ 95Ɛ	618
9	418 47X	533	9	912 701	Ɛ97	9	.Ɛ0X Ɛ63 343	80Ɛ
X	262 Ɛ47	719	X	751 726	181 185	X	996 734	X03
Ɛ	0X9 42X	902	Ɛ	590 561	373	Ɛ	809 931	ƐƐ7
.1110	.Ɛ1Ɛ Ɛ33 728	XX8	.1150	40Ɛ 1XX	562	.1190	640 936	189 1XX
1	979 840	176 090	1	249 848	750	1	473 748	3X2
2	803 770	276	2	088 0Ɛ8	93Ɛ	2	2X6 366	597
3	649 4Ɛ6	460	3	.Ɛ14 Ɛ06 379	Ɛ2X	3	118 98Ɛ	78Ɛ
4	493 056	646	4	944 44Ɛ	182 119	4	.Ɛ09 Ɛ4Ɛ 200	983
5	318 610	82Ɛ	5	782 332	307	5	981 439	Ɛ77
6	161 9X1	X15	6	600 027	4Ɛ7	6	7Ɛ3 482	18X 170
7	.Ɛ1X ƐX6 Ɛ88	ƐƐƐ	7	439 730	6X6	7	625 312	365
8	X2Ɛ Ɛ89	177 1X6	8	277 046	895	8	456 Ɛ69	55X
9	874 9X3	38Ɛ	9	0Ɛ4 371	X85	9	288 60Ɛ	752
X	6Ɛ9 614	576	X	.Ɛ13 Ɛ31 4X8	183 074	X	0Ɛ9 X79	948
Ɛ	542 05X	760	Ɛ	96X 434	264	Ɛ	.Ɛ08 ƐƐƐ 131	Ɛ40
.1120	386 4ƐX	947	.1160	7X7 190	454	.11X0	960 1Ɛ1	18Ɛ 136
1	20X 773	Ɛ31	1	623 938	643	1	791 077	330
2	052 842	178 118	2	460 2Ɛ5	834	2	601 947	524
3	.Ɛ19 X96 726	304	3	298 681	X23	3	432 423	71Ɛ
4	91X 422	4XX	4	114 85X	184 014	4	262 904	914
5	761 Ɛ34	695	5	.Ɛ12 Ɛ50 846	204	5	092 Ɛ20	Ɛ0X
6	5X5 45Ɛ	880	6	988 642	3Ɛ5	6	.Ɛ07 Ɛ03 0X2	190 104
7	428 79Ɛ	X67	7	804 249	5X5	7	932 Ɛ9X	2ƐX
8	26Ɛ 934	179 053	8	63Ɛ 864	795	8	762 8X0	4Ɛ4
9	0Ɛ2 8X1	23Ɛ	9	477 08Ɛ	987	9	592 3X8	6XƐ
X	.Ɛ18 Ɛ35 662	426	X	2Ɛ2 304	Ɛ77	X	401 8Ɛ9	8X5
Ɛ	978 238	612	Ɛ	129 349	185 169	Ɛ	231 014	X9Ɛ
.1130	7ƐX 826	7Ɛ9	.1170	.Ɛ11 Ɛ64 1X0	359	.11Ɛ0	060 135	191 097
1	641 029	9X6	1	99X X43	54Ɛ	1	.Ɛ06 X8Ɛ 05X	291
2	483 243	Ɛ91	2	815 4Ɛ4	740	2	8Ɛ9 989	488
3	305 272	17X 17X	3	64Ɛ 974	932	3	728 501	683
4	147 0Ɛ4	366	4	486 042	Ɛ23	4	556 X3X	87X
5	.Ɛ17 Ɛ88 94X	552	5	300 11Ɛ	186 115	5	385 180	X75
6	X0X 3Ɛ8	73Ɛ	6	136 006	306	6	1Ɛ3 307	192 071
7	84Ɛ 879	927	7	Ɛ10 Ɛ6Ɛ 900	4Ɛ9	7	021 256	269
8	690 Ɛ52	Ɛ14	8	9X5 403	6XX	8	.Ɛ05 X4X ƐX9	464
9	512 03X	17Ɛ 101	9	81X 915	8X1	9	878 745	65Ɛ
X	352 Ɛ39	2XX	X	654 034	X93	X	6X6 0X6	858
Ɛ	193 84Ɛ	496	Ɛ	489 161	187 085	Ɛ	513 44X	X54

N	Log Cos	d	N	Log Cos	d	N	Log Cos	d
.1200	Ɛ.Ɛ05 340 5Ɛ6	193 04Ɛ	.1240	Ɛ.XƐX 104 097	19Ɛ 016	.1280	Ɛ.XƐ2 804 X35	1X7 1X5
1	169 567	249	1	.XƐ9 Ɛ25 081	218	1	619 850	3Ɛ1
2	.Ɛ04 Ɛ96 31X	444	2	945 X65	41X	2	432 45Ɛ	5Ɛ9
3	X02 X96	641	3	766 647	621	3	246 X62	807
4	82Ɛ 455	839	4	587 026	823	4	05Ɛ 257	X13
5	657 818	X36	5	3X7 403	X26	5	.XƐ1 X73 444	1X8 020
6	483 9X2	194 034	6	207 599	1X0 029	6	887 424	229
7	2XƐ 96X	230	7	027 570	230	7	69Ɛ 1Ɛ7	437
8	117 73X	429	8	.XƐ8 X47 340	433	8	4Ɛ2 980	643
9	.Ɛ03 Ɛ43 311	626	9	866 Ɛ09	636	9	306 339	852
X	96X 8X7	824	X	686 493	839	X	119 6X7	X5Ɛ
Ɛ	796 083	X21	Ɛ	4X5 856	X41	Ɛ	.XƐ0 Ɛ30 848	1X9 069
.1210	601 262	195 01X	.1250	304 X15	1X1 045	.1290	943 79Ɛ	276
1	428 244	219	1	123 990	248	1	756 525	485
2	253 027	416	2	.XƐ7 Ɛ42 744	450	2	569 060	693
3	079 811	614	3	961 2Ɛ4	654	3	37Ɛ 589	8X2
4	.Ɛ02 XX4 1Ɛ9	812	4	77Ɛ 860	858	4	191 8X7	XXƐ
5	90X 5X7	X11	5	59X 004	X60	5	.XXƐ ƐX3 9Ɛ8	1XX 0ƐƐ
6	734 796	196 00X	6	3Ɛ8 164	1X2 065	6	9Ɛ5 8Ɛ9	309
7	55X 788	209	7	216 0ƐƐ	269	7	807 5Ɛ0	518
8	384 57Ɛ	408	8	033 X52	472	8	619 094	727
9	1XX 173	607	9	.XƐ6 X51 5X0	677	9	42X 569	936
X	013 768	805	X	86X Ɛ25	87Ɛ	X	23Ɛ 833	Ɛ46
Ɛ	.Ɛ01 X38 Ɛ63	X04	Ɛ	688 266	X85	Ɛ	050 8X9	1XƐ 155
.1220	862 15Ɛ	197 003	.1260	4X5 3X1	1X3 089	.12X0	.XXX X61 754	364
1	687 158	202	1	302 314	293	1	872 3Ɛ0	574
2	4XƐ Ɛ56	402	2	11Ɛ 041	498	2	682 X38	784
3	314 754	601	3	.XƐ5 Ɛ37 765	6X2	3	493 274	994
4	139 153	801	4	954 083	8X8	4	2X3 4X0	ƐX4
5	.Ɛ00 Ɛ61 552	X00	5	770 397	XƐ1	5	0Ɛ3 4Ɛ8	1Ɛ0 1Ɛ5
6	985 752	198 000	6	588 4X6	1X4 0Ɛ7	6	.XX9 Ɛ03 303	404
7	7X9 752	200	7	3X4 3XƐ	302	7	912 XƐƐ	616
8	611 552	400	8	200 0X9	507	8	722 4X5	826
9	435 152	600	9	017 7X2	712	9	531 87Ɛ	X36
X	258 752	801	X	.XƐ4 X33 090	918	X	340 X45	1Ɛ1 048
Ɛ	07Ɛ Ɛ51	X01	Ɛ	84X 374	Ɛ23	Ɛ	14Ɛ 9Ɛ9	259
.1230	.XƐƐ XX3 150	199 001	.1270	665 451	1X5 12X	.12Ɛ0	.XX8 Ɛ5X 760	46X
1	906 14Ɛ	202	1	480 323	334	1	969 2Ɛ2	67Ɛ
2	728 Ɛ49	403	2	296 ƐXƐ	540	2	777 833	891
3	54Ɛ 746	604	3	0Ɛ1 66Ɛ	746	3	585 Ɛ62	XX2
4	372 142	805	4	.XƐ3 Ɛ07 Ɛ25	952	4	394 080	1Ɛ2 0Ɛ5
5	194 539	X06	5	922 193	Ɛ59	5	1X1 Ɛ87	306
6	.XƐX ƐƐ6 733	19X 007	6	738 236	1X6 165	6	.XX7 ƐXƐ 881	518
7	X18 728	209	7	552 091	370	7	9Ɛ9 365	72X
8	83X 51Ɛ	40X	8	367 921	578	8	806 837	941
9	660 111	610	9	181 365	784	9	613 X26	Ɛ53
X	481 701	812	X	.XƐ2 Ɛ96 7X1	990	X	420 Ɛ63	1Ɛ3 166
Ɛ	2X2 XXƐ	X14	Ɛ	9XƐ X11	Ɛ98	Ɛ	229 9Ɛ9	379

N	Log Cos	d	N	Log Cos	d	N	Log Cos	d
.1300	Ɛ.XX7 036 640	1Ɛ3 58Ɛ	.1340	Ɛ.X9Ɛ 190 365	1ƐƐ ƐX8	.1380	Ɛ.X93 040 X94	208 849
1	.XX6 X43 071	7X3	1	.X9X Ɛ90 379	200 205	1	.X92 X34 247	X73
2	84Ɛ 48X	9Ɛ6	2	990 174	423	2	827 394	209 098
3	657 694	1Ɛ4 009	3	78Ɛ 951	642	3	61X 2Ɛ8	302
4	463 687	220	4	58Ɛ 30Ɛ	860	4	410 ƐƐ6	528
5	26Ɛ 467	434	5	38X 66Ɛ	X7Ɛ	5	203 68X	751
6	077 033	648	6	189 7Ɛ0	201 099	6	.X91 ƐƐ5 Ɛ39	978
7	.XX5 X82 5X7	860	7	.X99 Ɛ88 713	2Ɛ8	7	9X8 181	ƐX2
8	889 947	X74	8	987 417	518	8	79X 19Ɛ	20X 208
9	694 X93	1Ɛ5 088	9	785 XƐƐ	736	9	58Ɛ Ɛ93	433
X	49Ɛ X07	2X0	X	584 385	956	X	381 760	659
Ɛ	2X6 727	4Ɛ5	Ɛ	382 62Ɛ	Ɛ76	Ɛ	173 103	885
.1310	0Ɛ1 232	709	.1350	180 675	202 195	.1390	.X90 Ɛ64 43X	XƐ0
1	.XX4 XƐ7 725	922	1	.X98 Ɛ7X 4X0	3Ɛ4	1	955 54X	20Ɛ 116
2	901 X03	Ɛ37	2	978 0X8	615	2	746 434	342
3	707 X88	1Ɛ6 150	3	775 693	835	3	537 0Ɛ2	56X
4	511 938	365	4	572 X5X	X55	4	327 744	795
5	317 593	57Ɛ	5	370 005	203 075	5	117 Ɛ6Ɛ	X02
6	121 014	793	6	168 Ɛ50	296	6	.X8Ɛ Ɛ08 169	210 029
7	.XX3 Ɛ26 441	9XX	7	.X97 Ɛ65 876	4Ɛ7	7	8Ɛ8 140	255
8	92Ɛ 653	1Ɛ7 003	8	962 37Ɛ	717	8	6X7 XX7	482
9	734 650	219	9	75X 864	939	9	497 625	6XX
X	539 433	434	X	556 Ɛ27	Ɛ59	X	286 Ɛ37	917
Ɛ	341 ƐƐƐ	649	Ɛ	352 Ɛ8X	204 17Ɛ	Ɛ	076 220	Ɛ44
.1320	146 572	864	.1360	14X X0Ɛ	3X1	.13X0	.X8X X65 298	211 170
1	.XX2 Ɛ4X 90X	X7X	1	.X96 Ɛ46 62X	602	1	854 128	39X
2	952 X50	1Ɛ8 095	2	942 028	823	2	642 94X	607
3	756 977	2XƐ	3	739 405	X46	3	431 343	834
4	55X 688	507	4	534 57Ɛ	205 068	4	21Ɛ 70Ɛ	X62
5	362 181	721	5	32Ɛ 513	28X	5	009 869	212 090
6	165 660	939	6	126 245	4Ɛ0	6	.X89 9Ɛ7 799	2ƐX
7	.XX1 Ɛ68 923	Ɛ54	7	.X95 Ɛ20 955	713	7	7X5 49Ɛ	528
8	96Ɛ 98Ɛ	1Ɛ9 170	8	917 242	935	8	592 Ɛ73	756
9	772 81Ɛ	387	9	711 509	Ɛ59	9	380 419	985
X	575 454	5X3	X	507 570	206 17Ɛ	X	169 654	ƐƐ3
Ɛ	377 X71	7ƐX	Ɛ	301 3Ɛ1	3X2	Ɛ	.X88 Ɛ56 661	213 222
.1330	17X 273	X17	.1370	0Ɛ7 00Ɛ	606	.13Ɛ0	943 43Ɛ	451
1	.XX0 Ɛ80 458	1ƐX 034	1	.X94 XƐ0 605	829	1	72Ɛ ƐXX	680
2	982 424	24Ɛ	2	8X5 998	X51	2	518 52X	8XƐ
3	784 195	468	3	69X Ɛ47	207 075	3	304 83Ɛ	Ɛ1X
4	585 929	685	4	493 X92	298	4	0Ɛ0 921	214 14X
5	387 264	8X1	5	288 7Ɛ6	501	5	.X87 X98 793	37X
6	188 583	XƐƐ	6	081 2Ɛ5	724	6	884 415	5XX
7	.X9Ɛ 289 684	1ƐƐ 117	7	.X93 X75 791	94X	7	66Ɛ X27	81X
8	98X 569	335	8	869 X43	Ɛ71	8	457 209	X4X
9	78Ɛ 234	552	9	661 X92	208 197	9	242 37Ɛ	215 07X
X	58Ɛ 8X2	770	X	455 8Ɛ7	3ƐƐ	X	029 301	2XƐ
Ɛ	390 132	989	Ɛ	249 4Ɛ8	624	Ɛ	.X86 X14 012	520

N	Log Cos	d	N	Log Cos	d	N	Log Cos	d
.1400	Ɛ.X86 7ƐX 6Ɛ2	215 750	.1440	Ɛ.X7X 077 053	222 910	.1480	Ɛ.X71 223 4X7	230 167
1	5X4 Ɛ62	982	1	.X79 X54 343	Ɛ4X	1	.X70 ƐƐ3 340	3Ɛ1
2	38Ɛ 1X0	ƐƐ2	2	831 3Ɛ5	223 187	2	982 Ɛ4Ɛ	636
3	175 1XX	216 225	3	60X 22X	405	3	752 515	881
4	.X85 Ɛ5X Ɛ85	455	4	3X6 X25	643	4	521 854	Ɛ08
5	944 730	688	5	183 3X2	880	5	2Ɛ0 948	231 151
6	72X 064	8Ɛ9	6	.X78 Ɛ5Ɛ 722	XƐX	6	07Ɛ 7Ɛ7	399
7	513 367	Ɛ2Ɛ	7	937 824	224 139	7	.X6Ɛ X4X 41X	624
8	2Ɛ8 438	217 162	8	713 6X7	377	8	818 9Ɛ6	86X
9	0X1 296	394	9	4XƐ 330	5Ɛ6	9	5X7 148	XƐ6
X	.X84 X85 Ɛ02	606	X	286 936	835	X	375 252	232 142
Ɛ	86X 4Ɛ8	839	Ɛ	062 101	X73	Ɛ	143 110	389
.1410	652 87Ɛ	X70	.1450	.X77 X39 24X	225 0Ɛ3	.1490	.X6X Ɛ10 943	615
1	436 X0Ɛ	218 0X3	1	814 157	332	1	89X 32X	861
2	21X 928	317	2	5XX X25	571	2	667 689	XX9
3	002 611	549	3	385 474	7Ɛ1	3	434 7X0	233 136
4	.X83 9X6 084	782	4	15Ɛ 883	X31	4	201 666	382
5	789 502	9Ɛ5	5	.X76 Ɛ35 X52	226 071	5	.X69 Ɛ8X 2X4	60Ɛ
6	570 709	219 028	6	90Ɛ 9X1	2Ɛ1	6	956 895	858
7	353 6X1	261	7	6X5 6Ɛ0	532	7	723 039	XX5
8	136 440	495	8	47Ɛ 17X	772	8	4XƐ 154	234 133
9	.X82 Ɛ18 Ɛ67	70X	9	254 608	9Ɛ3	9	277 021	380
X	8ƐƐ 459	942	X	029 815	227 034	X	042 861	60X
Ɛ	6X1 717	Ɛ77	Ɛ	.X75 X02 7X1	275	Ɛ	.X68 X0X 253	858
.1420	483 760	21X 1XƐ	.1460	797 528	4Ɛ6	.14X0	795 5Ɛ7	XX6
1	265 571	425	1	570 032	737	1	560 711	235 134
2	047 148	65X	2	344 4Ɛ7	97X	2	327 599	383
3	.X81 X28 6XX	893	3	118 739	ƐƐƐ	3	0Ɛ2 216	611
4	809 X17	Ɛ09	4	.X74 XƐ0 73X	228 241	4	.X67 X78 805	861
5	5XX Ɛ0X	21Ɛ 143	5	884 4Ɛ9	483	5	842 Ɛ64	XXƐ
6	38Ɛ 987	379	6	658 036	705	6	609 075	236 13Ɛ
7	170 60X	5Ɛ2	7	42Ɛ 531	948	7	392 Ɛ36	38X
8	.X80 Ɛ51 018	829	8	202 7X5	Ɛ8Ɛ	8	158 768	619
9	931 3XƐ	X64	9	.X73 Ɛ95 816	229 212	9	.X66 Ɛ22 14Ɛ	86X
X	711 547	220 09X	X	968 604	455	X	8X7 4X1	XƐX
Ɛ	4Ɛ1 469	315	Ɛ	73Ɛ 16Ɛ	698	Ɛ	670 5X3	237 149
.1430	291 154	54Ɛ	.1470	511 693	91Ɛ	.14Ɛ0	435 456	39Ɛ
1	070 805	787	1	2X3 974	Ɛ63	1	1ƐX 077	62X
2	.X7Ɛ X50 03X	X02	2	075 X11	22X 1X7	2	.X65 Ɛ82 649	880
3	82Ɛ 238	221 03X	3	.X72 X47 826	42Ɛ	3	946 989	Ɛ10
4	60X 1ƐX	275	4	819 3Ɛ7	673	4	70X X79	238 162
5	3X8 Ɛ45	4Ɛ1	5	5XX 944	8Ɛ7	5	492 917	3Ɛ3
6	187 654	729	6	380 049	Ɛ40	6	256 524	645
7	.X7X Ɛ65 Ɛ27	966	7	151 109	22Ɛ 185	7	019 X9Ɛ	896
8	944 181	ƐX1	8	.X71 Ɛ21 Ɛ44	409	8	.X64 9X1 205	Ɛ29
9	722 1X0	222 21X	9	8Ɛ2 737	653	9	764 298	239 17X
X	4ƐƐ Ɛ82	457	X	683 0X4	898	X	527 11X	411
Ɛ	299 727	694	Ɛ	453 408	Ɛ21	Ɛ	2X9 909	664

N	Log Cos	d	N	Log Cos	d	N	Log Cos	d
.1500	Ɛ.χ64 070 265	239 8Ɛ6	.1540	Ɛ.χ56 789 3χ5	247 75Ɛ	.1580	Ɛ.χ48 Ɛ65 χƐ7	255 93χ
1	.χ63 χ32 56Ɛ	Ɛ49	1	541 846	9ƐƐ	1	910 179	Ɛχ9
2	7Ɛ4 622	23χ 1χ0	2	2Ɛ5 χ47	248 060	2	676 190	256 258
3	576 442	433	3	069 9χ7	300	3	41Ɛ Ɛ34	506
4	338 00Ɛ	687	4	.χ55 χ21 6χ7	562	4	185 62χ	776
5	0Ɛ9 544	91Ɛ	5	795 145	803	5	.χ47 Ɛ2χ χ74	χ26
6	.χ62 χ7χ 825	Ɛ73	6	548 542	χ65	6	894 04χ	257 096
7	83Ɛ 872	23Ɛ 206	7	2ƐƐ 699	249 107	7	638 Ɛ74	345
8	600 668	45Ɛ	8	072 592	369	8	3χ1 82Ɛ	5Ɛ6
9	381 209	6Ɛ4	9	.χ54 χ25 225	60χ	9	146 235	867
χ	141 715	948	χ	797 817	872	χ	.χ46 χχχ 58χ	Ɛ17
Ɛ	.χ61 Ɛ01 989	Ɛχ1	Ɛ	549 Ɛ65	Ɛ13	Ɛ	852 673	258 188
.1510	881 9χ8	240 236	.1550	300 052	24χ 177	.1590	5Ɛ6 4χ7	439
1	641 772	48Ɛ	1	071 χ97	41χ	1	35χ 06χ	6χƐ
2	401 2χ3	725	2	.χ53 χ23 679	681	2	101 57Ɛ	960
3	180 77χ	97Ɛ	3	794 ƐƐ8	924	3	.χ45 χ64 81Ɛ	259 012
4	.χ60 Ɛ3Ɛ 9ƐƐ	241 014	4	546 294	Ɛ89	4	807 809	284
5	8Ɛχ 9χ7	26Ɛ	5	2Ɛ7 307	24Ɛ 230	5	56χ 545	536
6	679 738	504	6	068 097	494	6	311 00Ɛ	7χ9
7	438 234	760	7	.χ52 χ18 803	738	7	073 422	χ5Ɛ
8	1Ɛ6 694	9Ɛ6	8	789 087	9χ1	8	.χ44 χ15 583	25χ 113
9	.χ5Ɛ Ɛ74 89χ	242 050	9	539 2χ6	250 046	9	777 470	385
χ	932 84χ	2χ8	χ	2χ9 260	2χχ	χ	519 0χ7	639
Ɛ	6Ɛ0 562	543	Ɛ	058 Ɛ72	554	Ɛ	27χ 66χ	8Ɛ1
.1520	46χ 01Ɛ	79Ɛ	.1560	.χ51 χ08 61χ	7Ɛ9	.15χ0	01Ɛ 979	Ɛ64
1	227 440	χ36	1	777 χ21	χ63	1	.χ43 980 χ15	25Ɛ 219
2	.χ5χ Ɛχ4 606	243 092	2	526 Ɛ7χ	251 108	2	721 7Ɛ8	490
3	961 534	32χ	3	295 χ72	372	3	482 328	746
4	71χ 206	587	4	044 700	619	4	222 7χ2	9Ɛχ
5	496 83Ɛ	823	5	.χ50 9Ɛ3 0χ3	883	5	.χ42 Ɛ82 9χ4	260 073
6	253 018	χ7Ɛ	6	761 420	Ɛ2χ	6	922 931	328
7	00Ɛ 159	244 119	7	50Ɛ 4Ɛ2	252 194	7	682 605	5χ1
8	.χ59 987 040	375	8	279 31χ	440	8	422 024	857
9	742 887	613	9	026 χ9χ	6χ7	9	181 389	Ɛ11
χ	4Ɛχ 274	870	χ	.χ4Ɛ 994 3Ɛ3	952	χ	.χ41 Ɛ20 478	261 187
Ɛ	275 604	Ɛ0χ	Ɛ	741 661	ƐƐχ	Ɛ	87Ɛ 2Ɛ1	442
.1530	030 6Ɛ6	245 168	.1570	4χχ 663	253 266	.15Ɛ0	619 χ6Ɛ	6Ɛ8
1	.χ58 9χ7 54χ	406	1	257 3Ɛ9	512	1	378 373	972
2	762 144	664	2	003 χχ7	77Ɛ	2	116 601	262 02χ
3	518 6χ0	903	3	.χ4χ 970 328	χ27	3	.χ40 χ74 593	2χ5
4	292 999	Ɛ61	4	718 501	254 094	4	812 2χχ	560
5	048 χ38	246 201	5	484 429	340	5	56Ɛ 94χ	818
6	.χ57 χ02 837	45Ɛ	6	230 0χ9	5χχ	6	309 132	χ94
7	778 398	6ƐƐ	7	.χ49 Ɛ97 6ƐƐ	858	7	066 25χ	263 151
8	531 899	95χ	8	942 χ63	Ɛ05	8	.χ3Ɛ χ03 109	408
9	2χ6 Ɛ3Ɛ	ƐƐχ	9	6χ9 Ɛ5χ	255 173	9	75Ɛ 901	685
χ	05Ɛ Ɛ41	247 25χ	χ	454 9χ7	421	χ	4Ɛ8 238	942
Ɛ	.χ56 χ14 8χ3	4Ɛχ	Ɛ	1ƐƐ 586	68Ɛ	Ɛ	254 4Ɛ6	ƐƐƐ

.1600 .χ3χ Ɛ20 4Ɛ7

N	Log Tan	d	N	Log Tan	d	N	Log Tan	d
.0000	——		.0040	χ.36χ 171 064		.0080	χ.6Ɛ0 362 586	
1	8·8χ6 081 ƐƐƐ		1	.380 581 8Ɛ2		1	.6Ɛ7 606 004	
2	9·028 0χ1 347		2	.392 635 Ɛ29		2	.702 781 χ73	
3	.222 043 Ɛ46		3	.3χ4 369·541		3	.709 854 866	
4	.36χ 100 χ90		4	.3Ɛ5 976 Ɛ40		4	.714 845 005	
5	.479 311 387		5	.407 074 057		5	.71Ɛ 755 244	
6	.564 064 144		6	.418 075 418		6	.726 587 7Ɛ3	
7	.633 2χ7 606		7	.428 992 697		7	.731 322 842	
8	.6Ɛ0 121 χ01		8	.439 41χ 682		8	.737 Ɛχ4 646	
9	.75χ 008 301		9	.449 7χ7 46χ		9	.742 793 405	
χ	.7ƐƐ 333 2χ7		χ	.459 906 453		χ	.749 2Ɛ1 273	
Ɛ	.855 675 401		Ɛ	.469 788 208		Ɛ	.753 940 278	
.0010	.8χ6 087 312		.0050	.479 400 965		.0090	.75χ 302 404	
1	.931 87Ɛ 448		1	.488 9Ɛ7 7χ1		1	.764 7Ɛ9 5Ɛχ	
2	.975 310 0Ɛχ		2	.498 183 733		2	.76Ɛ 02Ɛ 711	
3	.9Ɛ5 29χ 3χ0		3	.4χ7 32χ Ɛχ3		3	.775 39χ 539	
4	.χ32 148 099		4	.4Ɛ6 283 791		4	.77Ɛ 687 χ04	
5	.χ68 336 913		5	.505 012 Ɛ7Ɛ		5	.785 8Ɛ5 606	
6	.χχ0 034 43χ		6	.513 765 Ɛ0Ɛ		6	.78Ɛ χ65 176	
7	.Ɛ11 757 613		7	.522 109 081		7	.795 Ɛ58 45χ	
8	.Ɛ41 361 543		8	.530 488 666		8	.79Ɛ Ɛ94 9χ3	
9	.Ɛ6Ɛ 27Ɛ 6χ9		9	.53χ 670 25Ɛ		9	.7χ5 Ɛ58 053	
χ	.Ɛ97 6χ5 χ34		χ	.548 683 635		χ	.7χƐ χ67 659	
Ɛ	χ.002 59χ χ95		Ɛ	.556 511 7χ1		Ɛ	.7Ɛ5 904 992	
.0020	.028 0Ɛχ 39χ		.0060	.564 1χ1 560		.00χ0	.7ƐƐ 6Ɛ1 376	
1	.050 579 978		1	.571 8Ɛ9 622		1	.805 42χ 4Ɛ7	
2	.073 8Ɛ5 227		2	.57Ɛ 268 170		2	.80Ɛ 0Ɛ9 631	
3	.095 Ɛχ9 8χ1		3	.588 673 443		3	.814 91Ɛ Ɛ72	
4	.0Ɛ7 348 χ68		4	.595 921 033		4	.81χ 497 080	
5	.117 82χ 4χ0		5	.5χ2 χ36 843		5	.823 Ɛχ8 094	
6	.137 31χ 397		6	.5χƐ χ01 906		6	.829 654 2χ6	
7	.156 096 492		7	.5Ɛ8 843 437		7	.833 058 968	
8	.174 18Ɛ 59χ		8	.605 544 591		8	.838 5Ɛχ Ɛ0χ	
9	.191 666 709		9	.612 109 χχ1		9	.841 χƐƐ 93χ	
χ	.1χχ 381 998		χ	.61χ 760 2χ0		χ	.847 360 5χƐ	
Ɛ	.206 571 221		Ɛ	.627 083 Ɛ04		Ɛ	.850 762 215	
.0030	.222 083 344		.0070	.633 481 296		.00Ɛ0	.855 Ɛ05 χƐ1	
1	.239 141 χ93		1	.63Ɛ 758 382		1	.85Ɛ 210 901	
2	.253 7χχ 617		2	.647 915 15Ɛ		2	.864 47Ɛ 893	
3	.269 882 8Ɛ1		3	.653 977 647		3	.869 693 χ40	
4	.283 3Ɛ8 903		4	.65Ɛ 907 2Ɛ1		4	.872 852 167	
5	.298 607 69χ		5	.667 747 χ20		5	.877 977 602	
6	.2Ɛ1 31Ɛ 4χ3		6	.673 480 988		6	.880 χ48 Ɛ09	
7	.305 765 χƐ8		7	.67Ɛ 0Ɛ1 5χ1		7	.885 χ87 397	
8	.319 74χ 520		8	.686 821 152		8	.88χ χ73 70χ	
9	.331 2Ɛ6 211		9	.692 252 χ18		9	.893 χ0χ 761	
χ	.344 648 532		χ	.699 789 84Ɛ		χ	.898 915 360	
Ɛ	.357 5χ6 909		Ɛ	.6χ5 010 766		Ɛ	.8χ1 790 52Ɛ	

N	Log Tan	d	N	Log Tan	d	N	Log Tan	d
.0100	X.8X6 5Ɛ8 X84	4 99X ...	.0140	X.X32 X8Ɛ 533	3 754 ...	.0180	X.Ɛ42 617 7X9	2 X9X ...
1	.8XƐ 397 574	951 ...	1	.X36 623 Ɛ6X	728 ...	1	.Ɛ45 4Ɛ5 X35	X81 ...
2	.8Ɛ4 128 Ɛ69	905 ...	2	.X3X 150 376	700 ...	2	.Ɛ48 377 536	X65 ...
3	.8Ɛ8 X32 1XX	879 ...	3	.X41 850 951	694 ...	3	.Ɛ4Ɛ 220 6Ɛ7	X48 ...
4	.901 6XƐ 998	832 ...	4	.X45 325 8X8	669 ...	4	.Ɛ52 069 53Ɛ	X30 ...
5	.906 322 832	7X8 ...	5	.X48 993 5X6	642 ...	5	.Ɛ54 X9X 246	X14 ...
6	.90X Ɛ0Ɛ 610	763 ...	6	.X50 416 423	618 ...	6	.Ɛ57 8Ɛ3 00Ɛ	9Ɛ9 ...
7	.913 672 ƐX9	71X ...	7	.X53 X32 76X	5Ɛ2 ...	7	.Ɛ5X 6Ɛ0 048	9X1 ...
8	.918 191 X1Ɛ	696 ...	8	.X57 424 786	588 ...	8	.Ɛ61 491 529	985 ...
9	.920 868 920	653 ...	9	.X5X 9Ɛ0 82X	562 ...	9	.Ɛ64 257 461	96X ...
X	.925 300 508	611 ...	X	.X62 353 088	538 ...	X	.Ɛ67 006 012	953 ...
Ɛ	.929 911 597	58Ɛ ...	Ɛ	.X65 890 086	513 ...	Ɛ	.Ɛ69 959 5X4	938 ...
.0110	.932 2X0 727	549 ...	.0150	.X69 1X3 Ɛ7X	4XƐ ...	.0190	.Ɛ70 695 Ɛ77	921 ...
1	.936 82X 4Ɛ9	509 ...	1	.X70 693 0ƐƐ	486 ...	1	.Ɛ73 3Ɛ7 728	906 ...
2	.93Ɛ 137 673	489 ...	2	.X73 Ɛ59 810	462 ...	2	.Ɛ76 102 651	8Ɛ0 ...
3	.943 604 75X	449 ...	3	.X77 400 032	43X ...	3	.Ɛ78 9Ɛ2 Ɛ00	895 ...
4	.947 X52 2X4	40X ...	4	.X7X 83X 497	416 ...	4	.Ɛ7Ɛ 688 X87	87Ɛ ...
5	.950 260 ƐX1	390 ...	5	.X82 055 0Ɛ0	3Ɛ3 ...	5	.Ɛ82 348 735	865 ...
6	.954 631 549	352 ...	6	.X85 448 398	390 ...	6	.Ɛ84 ƐƐ2 251	84Ɛ ...
7	.958 984 246	315 ...	7	.X88 818 473	369 ...	7	.Ɛ87 841 99Ɛ	835 ...
8	.961 099 960	298 ...	8	.X8Ɛ Ɛ85 649	346 ...	8	.Ɛ8X 477 71X	820 ...
9	.965 376 945	260 ...	9	.X93 310 029	324 ...	9	.Ɛ91 097 808	806 ...
X	.969 617 856	225 ...	X	.X96 634 115	301 ...	X	.Ɛ93 8X2 221	7Ɛ1 ...
Ɛ	.971 841 118	1XX ...	Ɛ	.X99 936 003	29Ɛ ...	Ɛ	.Ɛ96 493 314	797 ...
.0120	.975 XƐƐ 57X	173 ...	.0160	.XX1 015 ƐX4	27X ...	.01X0	.Ɛ99 06Ɛ 057	782 ...
1	.979 ƐX3 418	139 ...	1	.XX4 294 362	258 ...	1	.Ɛ9Ɛ 831 79X	769 ...
2	.982 121 276	104 ...	2	.XX7 531 1X0	237 ...	2	.ƐX2 39Ɛ 288	754 ...
3	.986 225 705	08Ɛ ...	3	.XXX 768 975	216 ...	3	.ƐX4 Ɛ33 X87	73Ɛ ...
4	.98X 2Ɛ4 Ɛ23	056 ...	4	.XƐ1 983 577	1Ɛ5 ...	4	.ƐX7 673 93Ɛ	727 ...
5	.992 34Ɛ 897	022 ...	5	.XƐ4 Ɛ79 472	195 ...	5	.ƐXX 19Ɛ 009	712 ...
6	.996 372 55X	3 ƐXƐ ...	6	.XƐ8 152 926	175 ...	6	.ƐƐ0 8Ɛ1 84Ɛ	6ƐX ...
7	.99X 361 694	Ɛ77 ...	7	.XƐƐ 307 X15	154 ...	7	.ƐƐ3 3XƐ ƐX2	6X5 ...
8	.9X2 319 612	Ɛ45 ...	8	.Ɛ02 460 9Ɛ5	135 ...	8	.ƐƐ5 X95 ƐX0	691 ...
9	.9X6 262 894	Ɛ12 ...	9	.Ɛ05 595 Ɛ35	115 ...	9	.ƐƐ8 567 997	679 ...
X	.9XX 175 80X	XX1 ...	X	.Ɛ08 6XƐ 480	0Ɛ5 ...	X	.ƐƐƐ 025 722	665 ...
Ɛ	.9Ɛ2 056 917	X6Ɛ ...	Ɛ	.Ɛ0Ɛ 7X5 474	096 ...	Ɛ	Ɛ.001 68Ɛ 546	652 ...
.0130	.9Ɛ5 Ɛ06 504	X3X ...	.0170	.Ɛ12 880 174	077 ...	.01Ɛ0	.004 121 596	63X ...
1	.9Ɛ9 945 090	X0X ...	1	.Ɛ15 937 X13	058 ...	1	.006 75Ɛ 997	626 ...
2	.X01 753 124	999 ...	2	.Ɛ18 994 861	03X ...	2	.009 186 693	613 ...
3	.X05 530 Ɛ25	96X ...	3	.Ɛ1Ɛ X12 Ɛ27	01Ɛ ...	3	.00Ɛ 799 X07	5ƐƐ ...
4	.X09 29X Ɛ60	93X ...	4	.Ɛ22 X32 86Ɛ	001 ...	4	.012 199 8Ɛ7	5X8 ...
5	.X11 019 692	90Ɛ ...	5	.Ɛ25 X34 2Ɛ1	2 ƐX3 ...	5	.014 786 4X3	595 ...
6	.X14 929 170	8X0 ...	6	.Ɛ28 X17 866	Ɛ85 ...	6	.017 15Ɛ Ɛ01	582 ...
7	.X18 60X 05X	872 ...	7	.Ɛ2Ɛ 9X1 385	Ɛ67 ...	7	.019 722 489	56Ɛ ...
8	.X20 280 7XX	844 ...	8	.Ɛ32 949 277	Ɛ4X ...	8	.020 091 Ɛ36	558 ...
9	.X23 Ɛ05 428	817 ...	9	.Ɛ35 897 768	Ɛ31 ...	9	.022 62X 7Ɛ7	546 ...
X	.X27 720 58X	7X9 ...	X	.Ɛ38 808 878	Ɛ13 ...	X	.024 Ɛ74 800	533 ...
Ɛ	.X2Ɛ 30X 485	781 ...	Ɛ	.Ɛ3Ɛ 720 806	XƐ6 ...	Ɛ	.027 4X8 078	520 ...

N	Log Tan	d	N	Log Tan	d	N	Log Tan	d
.0200	Ɛ.029 X08 Ɛ13	2 50X 5..	.0240	Ɛ.029 811 ƐƐ3	2 0Ɛ7 X..	0280	Ɛ.177 331 X6Ɛ	1 9X9 8..
1	.030 317 474	4Ɛ8 1..	1	.0ƐƐ 909 X7Ɛ	0X9 4..	1	.179 11Ɛ 699	9X1 7..
2	.032 813 644	4X5 Ɛ..	2	.101 9Ɛ7 339	09X Ɛ..	2	.17X Ɛ01 27Ɛ	995 7..
3	.035 0Ɛ9 566	493 9..	3	.103 X96 279	090 6..	3	.180 896 X76	989 8..
4	.037 591 33Ɛ	481 9..	4	.105 Ɛ66 949	082 2..	4	.182 664 727	981 9..
5	.039 X53 0X8	46Ɛ X..	5	.108 029 037	073 Ɛ..	5	.184 426 4Ɛ0	975 Ɛ..
6	.040 302 Ɛ46	45X 0..	6	.10X 0X1 011	065 9..	6	.186 1X0 429	96X 1..
7	.042 760 ƐƐ1	448 3..	7	.110 146 95Ɛ	057 7..	7	.187 Ɛ4X 577	962 3..
8	.044 ƐX9 380	436 8..	8	.112 1X2 529	049 6..	8	.189 8Ɛ0 975	956 7..
9	.047 423 Ɛ89	425 1..	9	.114 230 001	03Ɛ 6..	9	.18Ɛ 647 480	94X X..
X	.049 849 125	413 7..	X	.116 26Ɛ 664	031 6..	X	.191 396 330	943 2..
Ɛ	.050 060 924	402 3..	Ɛ	.118 2X1 15Ɛ	023 8..	Ɛ	.193 119 5X1	937 7..
.0210	.052 463 095	3Ɛ1 0..	.0250	.11X 304 972	015 9..	.0290	.194 X55 0Ɛ0	930 0..
1	.054 854 106	39Ɛ X..	1	.120 31X 765	008 0..	1	.196 785 0Ɛ3	924 5..
2	.057 033 Ɛ06	38X 8..	2	.122 326 7Ɛ8	1 ƐƐX 3..	2	.198 4X9 645	918 Ɛ..
3	.059 402 79Ɛ	379 8..	3	.124 324 Ɛ72	ƐƐ0 7..	3	.19X 206 580	911 5..
4	.05Ɛ 780 453	368 9..	4	.126 315 70Ɛ	ƐX3 0..	4	.19Ɛ Ɛ17 Ɛ35	906 0..
5	.061 Ɛ29 1XƐ	357 Ɛ..	5	.128 2Ɛ8 70Ɛ	Ɛ95 5..	5	.1X1 821 Ɛ83	8ƐX 7..
6	.064 285 133	347 2..	6	.12X 292 02Ɛ	Ɛ87 Ɛ..	6	.1X3 520 739	8Ɛ3 3..
7	.066 610 363	336 6..	7	.130 259 Ɛ30	Ɛ7X 5..	7	.1X5 213 X74	8X7 Ɛ..
8	.068 946 980	325 Ɛ..	8	.132 218 488	Ɛ71 0..	8	.1X6 XƐƐ X04	8X0 7..
9	.06Ɛ 070 885	315 4..	9	.134 189 53X	Ɛ63 8..	9	.1X8 7X0 5ƐƐ	895 4..
X	.071 386 173	304 Ɛ..	X	.136 131 181	Ɛ56 4..	X	.1XX 475 XƐ4	88X 2..
Ɛ	.073 68Ɛ 143	2Ɛ4 7..	Ɛ	.138 087 64Ɛ	Ɛ49 1..	Ɛ	.1Ɛ0 144 13Ɛ	883 0..
.0220	.075 983 8XƐ	2X4 4..	.0260	.13X 014 81Ɛ	Ɛ3Ɛ Ɛ..	.02X0	.1Ɛ1 X07 167	877 X..
1	.078 068 129	294 2..	1	.13Ɛ Ɛ54 767	Ɛ32 9..	1	.1Ɛ3 683 008	870 9..
2	.07X 340 330	284 0..	2	.141 X87 522	Ɛ25 8..	2	.1Ɛ5 333 932	865 8..
3	.080 604 3XƐ	274 0..	3	.143 9Ɛ1 181	Ɛ18 7..	3	.1Ɛ6 Ɛ99 571	85X 7..
4	.082 878 419	264 0..	4	.145 909 977	Ɛ0Ɛ 8..	4	.1Ɛ8 838 155	853 7..
5	.084 Ɛ20 4X5	254 2..	5	.147 819 57X	Ɛ02 8..	5	.1ƐX 48Ɛ 933	848 8..
6	.087 174 6ƐX	244 4..	6	.149 720 240	XƐ5 9..	6	.200 118 554	841 8..
7	.089 3Ɛ8 Ɛ49	234 7..	7	.14Ɛ 616 033	XX8 Ɛ..	7	.201 95X 249	836 X..
8	.08Ɛ 631 701	224 Ɛ..	8	.151 503 007	XX0 2..	8	.203 595 063	82Ɛ Ɛ..
9	.091 856 683	215 4..	9	.153 3X3 22X	X93 5..	9	.205 205 028	825 1..
X	.093 X6Ɛ Ɛ3Ɛ	205 X..	X	.155 276 752	X86 8..	X	.206 X2X 1XX	81X 4..
Ɛ	.096 075 994	1Ɛ6 5..	Ɛ	.157 141 422	X7X 0..	Ɛ	.208 648 5Ɛ6	813 6..
.0230	.098 270 2XƐ	1X7 0..	.0270	.158 ƐƐƐ 50Ɛ	X71 5..	.02Ɛ0	.20X 260 094	808 9..
1	.09X 457 36Ɛ	197 9..	1	.15X X70 X7Ɛ	X64 X..	1	.20Ɛ X68 X91	802 1..
2	.0X0 633 074	188 6..	2	.160 915 960	X58 4..	2	.211 66Ɛ 034	7Ɛ7 5..
3	.0X2 7ƐƐ 6X5	179 4..	3	.162 772 21X	X4Ɛ Ɛ..	3	.213 266 58X	7Ɛ0 9..
4	.0X4 978 Ɛ1Ɛ	16X 3..	4	.164 602 11Ɛ	X43 5..	4	.214 X57 361	7X6 2..
5	.0X6 Ɛ27 239	15Ɛ 2..	5	.166 445 70X	X37 1..	5	.216 641 5Ɛ7	79Ɛ 7..
6	.0X9 086 518	150 3..	6	.168 280 851	X2X 9..	6	.218 221 160	795 0..
7	.0XƐ 216 855	141 4..	7	.16X 0XƐ 591	X22 5..	7	.219 9Ɛ6 259	78X 6..
8	.0Ɛ1 358 106	132 6..	8	.16Ɛ Ɛ11 Ɛ72	X16 2..	8	.21Ɛ 584 933	784 0..
9	.0Ɛ3 48X 785	123 9..	9	.171 928 259	X0X 0..	9	.221 148 X30	779 7..
X	.0Ɛ5 5Ɛ2 528	115 1..	X	.173 736 2Ɛ1	X01 X..	X	.222 906 595	773 2..
Ɛ	.0Ɛ7 707 646	106 5..	Ɛ	.175 538 155	9Ɛ5 9..	Ɛ	.224 479 82X	768 9..

N	Log Tan	d	N	Log Tan	d	N	Log Tan	d
.0300	Ɛ.226 026 5Ɛ7	1 762 5..	.0340	Ɛ.288 285 249	1 574 6..	.0380	Ɛ.323 665 601	1 409 0..
1	.227 788 Ɛ3Ɛ	758 1..	1	.289 839 884	56Ɛ 4..	1	.324 X72 659	404 9..
2	.229 325 083	751 9..	2	.28Ɛ 1X9 16X	566 3..	2	.326 277 441	400 7..
3	.22X X76 X49	747 6..	3	.290 753 536	561 2..	3	.327 677 Ɛ94	3Ɛ8 5..
4	.230 602 498	741 3..	4	.292 0Ɛ4 814	558 2..	4	.328 X74 4ƐƐ	3Ɛ4 3..
5	.232 143 831	737 0..	5	.293 650 X34	553 1..	5	.32X 268 821	3Ɛ0 1..
6	.233 87X 914	730 X..	6	.294 ƐX4 009	54X 1..	6	.32Ɛ 658 962	3X7 Ɛ..
7	.235 3XƐ 785	726 8..	7	.296 532 185	545 1..	7	.330 X44 924	3X3 X..
8	.236 Ɛ16 446	720 7..	8	.297 X77 355	540 2..	8	.332 228 750	39Ɛ 8..
9	.238 636 Ɛ58	716 5..	9	.299 3Ɛ7 568	537 2..	9	.333 608 444	397 7..
X	.23X 151 540	710 4..	X	.29X 932 833	532 3..	X	.334 9X4 028	393 6..
Ɛ	.23Ɛ 861 X35	706 4..	Ɛ	.2X0 264 ƐX1	529 4..	Ɛ	.336 177 721	38Ɛ 6..
.0310	.241 368 280	700 4..	.0350	.2X1 792 461	524 6..	.0390	.337 547 14Ɛ	387 5..
1	.242 X68 698	6Ɛ6 4..	1	.2X3 0Ɛ6 X62	51Ɛ 7..	1	.338 912 714	383 5..
2	.244 562 Ɛ04	6Ɛ0 4..	2	.2X4 616 613	516 9..	2	.33X 096 056	37Ɛ 5..
3	.246 053 380	6X6 5..	3	.2X5 Ɛ31 362	511 Ɛ..	3	.33Ɛ 455 578	377 5..
4	.247 739 907	6X0 6..	4	.2X7 443 2Ɛ9	509 1..	4	.340 810 XX0	373 5..
5	.249 21X 35X	696 7..	5	.2X8 950 490	504 4..	5	.341 Ɛ84 427	36Ɛ 5..
6	.24X 8Ɛ4 Ɛ37	690 9..	6	.2XX 254 907	4ƐƐ 7..	6	.343 333 9Ɛ7	367 6..
7	.250 385 899	686 Ɛ..	7	.2XƐ 754 415	4Ɛ6 X..	7	.344 69Ɛ 432	363 7..
8	.251 X50 841	681 1..	8	.2Ɛ1 04Ɛ 223	4Ɛ2 1..	8	.345 X42 Ɛ36	35Ɛ 7..
9	.253 511 X23	677 4..	9	.2Ɛ2 541 35Ɛ	4X9 4..	9	.347 1X2 727	357 8..
X	.254 Ɛ89 282	671 7..	X	.2Ɛ3 X2X 831	4X4 8..	X	.348 53X 426	353 X..
Ɛ	.256 63X X14	667 X..	Ɛ	.2Ɛ5 313 487	4X0 0..	Ɛ	.349 892 256	34Ɛ Ɛ..
.0320	.258 0X6 897	662 2..	.0360	.2Ɛ6 7Ɛ3 510	497 4..	.03X0	.34Ɛ 022 216	348 1..
1	.259 748 Ɛ07	658 6..	1	.2Ɛ8 08X 973	492 8..	1	.350 36X 348	344 3..
2	.25Ɛ 1X5 51Ɛ	652 X..	2	.2Ɛ9 561 65Ɛ	48X 1..	2	.351 6Ɛ2 650	340 4..
3	.260 838 353	649 2..	3	.2ƐX X2Ɛ 7Ɛ8	485 6..	3	.352 X32 Ɛ47	338 7..
4	.262 285 621	643 7..	4	.300 2Ɛ5 233	480 Ɛ..	4	.354 16Ɛ 654	334 9..
5	.263 909 181	63X 0..	5	.301 776 172	478 4..	5	.355 4X4 395	330 Ɛ..
6	.265 347 228	634 5..	6	.303 032 623	473 X..	6	.356 815 36X	329 2..
7	.266 97Ɛ 816	62X Ɛ..	7	.304 4X6 42Ɛ	46Ɛ 3..	7	.357 Ɛ42 5Ɛ6	325 5..
8	.268 3XX 781	625 5..	8	.305 955 7ƐƐ	466 9..	8	.359 267 Ɛ15	321 8..
9	.269 X14 119	61Ɛ Ɛ..	9	.307 200 57X	462 3..	9	.35X 589 727	319 Ɛ..
X	.26Ɛ 434 0X1	616 6..	X	.308 662 951	459 X..	X	.35Ɛ 8X7 650	316 2..
Ɛ	.270 X4X 705	611 0..	Ɛ	.309 Ɛ00 765	455 4..	Ɛ	.361 001 8X6	312 5..
.0330	.272 45Ɛ 803	607 8..	.0370	.30Ɛ 356 023	450 Ɛ..	.03Ɛ0	.362 314 293	30X 9..
1	.273 X67 410	602 3..	1	.310 7X6 Ɛ72	448 6..	1	.363 623 02Ɛ	307 1..
2	.275 469 75Ɛ	5Ɛ8 Ɛ..	2	.312 033 5Ɛ7	444 1..	2	.364 92X 158	303 5..
3	.276 X66 665	5Ɛ3 6..	3	.313 477 762	43Ɛ 8..	3	.366 031 673	2ƐƐ 9..
4	.278 45X 159	5XX 3..	4	.314 8Ɛ7 454	437 4..	4	.367 331 398	2Ɛ8 1..
5	.279 X48 474	5X4 Ɛ..	5	.316 132 8Ɛ6	433 0..	5	.368 629 52X	2Ɛ4 5..
6	.27Ɛ 431 424	59Ɛ 8..	6	.317 565 932	42X 8..	6	.369 921 Ɛ06	2Ɛ0 X..
7	.280 X11 061	596 5..	7	.318 994 569	426 4..	7	.36Ɛ 012 948	2X9 3..
8	.282 3X7 59Ɛ	591 2..	8	.31X 1ƐX X08	422 0..	8	.370 300 051	2X5 7..
9	.283 978 84X	588 0..	9	.31Ɛ 620 XƐ5	419 9..	9	.371 5X5 839	2X2 0..
X	.285 344 862	582 9..	X	.320 X3X 853	415 6..	X	.372 887 925	29X 6..
Ɛ	.286 907 651	579 7..	Ɛ	.322 254 289	411 3..	Ɛ	.373 Ɛ66 32Ɛ	296 Ɛ..

N	Log Tan	d	N	Log Tan	d	N	Log Tan	d
.0400	Ɛ.375 241 272	1 293 49.	.0440	Ɛ.402 127 χ97	1 182 χ8.	.0480	Ɛ.446 Ɛ99 361	1 091 33.
1	.376 514 74χ	28Ɛ χ5.	1	.403 2χχ 959	17Ɛ χ8.	1	.448 06χ 6χ0	08χ 85.
2	.377 7χ4 59χ	288 42.	2	.404 46χ 820	178 χ9.	2	.449 139 332	088 17.
3	.378 χ70 χ00	284 χ1.	3	.405 627 6ƐƐ	175 Ɛ0.	3	.44χ 205 4χ8	085 6χ.
4	.37χ 135 810	281 41.	4	.406 7χ1 609	172 Ɛ5.	4	.44Ɛ 28χ Ɛ97	083 03.
5	.37Ɛ 3Ɛ7 029	279 χ4.	5	.407 954 560	16Ɛ ƐƐ.	5	.450 352 010	080 59.
6	.380 674 χ6Ɛ	276 48.	6	.408 Ɛ04 550	169 06.	6	.451 412 5χ3	079 Ɛ3.
7	.381 92Ɛ 333	272 Ɛ2.	7	.40χ 071 5Ɛ3	166 12.	7	.452 490 522	077 4Ɛ.
8	.382 Ɛχ2 258	26Ɛ 5χ.	8	.40Ɛ 217 720	163 20.	8	.453 547 χ21	074 χ8.
9	.384 251 838	268 07.	9	.410 37χ 928	160 30.	9	.454 600 8Ɛ1	072 47.
χ	.385 4Ɛ9 8Ɛ2	264 76.	χ	.411 51Ɛ 028	159 40.	χ	.455 673 161	06Ɛ χ6.
Ɛ	.386 762 45χ	261 27.	Ɛ	.412 678 434	156 52.	Ɛ	.456 723 005	069 46.
.0410	.387 χ03 714	259 9χ.	.0450	.413 812 960	153 66.	.0490	.457 790 470	066 χ8.
1	.389 061 4Ɛ6	256 52.	1	.414 966 401	150 7χ.	1	.458 837 330	064 4χ.
2	.38χ 2Ɛ7 χ1Ɛ	253 08.	2	.415 χƐ6 Ɛχχ	149 94.	2	.459 89Ɛ 815	061 Ɛ2.
3	.38Ɛ 54χ χχ4	24Ɛ 84.	3	.417 044 938	146 Ɛ0.	3	.45χ 941 735	05Ɛ 56.
4	.390 79χ 725	248 41.	4	.418 18Ɛ 83χ	144 08.	4	.45Ɛ 9χ1 0χ1	059 00.
5	.391 χ26 Ɛ3χ	245 00.	5	.419 313 909	141 26.	5	.460 χ3χ 0χ5	056 67.
6	.393 06Ɛ Ɛ43	241 81.	6	.41χ 454 Ɛ78	13χ 46.	6	.461 χ94 756	054 12.
7	.394 2Ɛ1 755	23χ 43.	7	.41Ɛ 593 420	137 66.	7	.462 Ɛ28 885	051 7Ɛ.
8	.395 52Ɛ Ɛ89	237 07.	8	.420 70χ χ8Ɛ	134 88.	8	.463 Ɛ7χ 482	04Ɛ 29.
9	.396 767 042	233 90.	9	.421 843 759	131 Ɛ0.	9	.465 009 75χ	048 98.
χ	.397 99χ 951	230 58.	χ	.422 975 65Ɛ	12Ɛ 14.	χ	.466 056 526	046 48.
Ɛ	.399 00Ɛ 313	229 25.	Ɛ	.423 χχ4 7χ7	128 3χ.	Ɛ	.467 0χ0 9Ɛ2	043 Ɛ9.
.0420	.39χ 238 563	225 Ɛ3.	.0460	.425 010 Ɛ90	125 65.	.04χ0	.468 124 98χ	041 6Ɛ.
1	.39Ɛ 462 498	222 83.	1	.426 136 627	122 91.	1	.469 166 486	03Ɛ 22.
2	.3χ0 685 111	21Ɛ 55.	2	.427 259 346	11Ɛ ƐƐ.	2	.46χ 1χ5 6Ɛ4	038 96.
3	.3χ1 8χ4 662	218 28.	3	.428 379 340	119 2χ.	3	.46Ɛ 222 463	036 50.
4	.3χ2 Ɛ00 925	215 01.	4	.429 496 626	116 5χ.	4	.470 258 964	034 06.
5	.3χ4 115 936	211 97.	5	.42χ 5Ɛ1 010	113 90.	5	.471 290 χ07	031 81.
6	.3χ5 327 6χƐ	20χ 73.	6	.42Ɛ 704 910	111 02.	6	.472 302 61Ɛ	02Ɛ 39.
7	.3χ6 536 223	207 50.	7	.430 815 937	10χ 36.	7	.473 331 9Ɛ5	028 Ɛ6.
8	.3χ7 741 731	204 2Ɛ.	8	.431 924 0χ0	107 6Ɛ.	8	.474 35χ 961	026 74.
9	.3χ8 945 χ2χ	201 10.	9	.432 χ2Ɛ 797	104 χ5.	9	.475 385 4χƐ	024 34.
χ	.3χ9 Ɛ46 Ɛ33	1Ɛ9 Ɛ2.	χ	.433 Ɛ34 635	102 21.	χ	.476 3χ9 82Ɛ	021 Ɛ4.
Ɛ	.3χƐ 144 χ58	1Ɛ6 96.	Ɛ	.435 036 84χ	0ƐƐ 5χ.	Ɛ	.477 40Ɛ 770	01Ɛ 75.
.0430	.3Ɛ0 33Ɛ 7Ɛ9	1Ɛ3 7Ɛ.	.0470	.436 136 230	0Ɛ8 98.	.04Ɛ0	.478 42Ɛ 302	019 37.
1	.3Ɛ1 533 3χƐ	1Ɛ0 65.	1	.437 232 ƐƐ1	0Ɛ6 17.	1	.479 448 676	016 Ɛχ.
2	.3Ɛ2 723 χ48	1χ9 51.	2	.438 329 164	0Ɛ3 57.	2	.47χ 463 65χ	014 82.
3	.3Ɛ3 911 367	1χ6 3Ɛ.	3	.439 420 720	0Ɛ0 99.	3	.47Ɛ 478 283	012 47.
4	.3Ɛ4 χƐ7 762	1χ3 2χ.	4	.43χ 511 4Ɛ3	0χχ 1Ɛ.	4	.480 48χ 739	010 11.
5	.3Ɛ6 09χ χ49	1χ0 1Ɛ.	5	.43Ɛ 5ƐƐ 6Ɛ2	0χ7 63.	5	.481 49χ 851	009 98.
6	.3Ɛ7 27Ɛ 040	199 11.	6	.440 6χ7 130	0χ4 χ9.	6	.482 4χ8 615	007 64.
7	.3Ɛ8 458 154	196 04.	7	.441 790 000	0χ2 33.	7	.483 4Ɛ4 058	005 31.
8	.3Ɛ9 632 1χ1	192 Ɛ9.	8	.442 872 332	09Ɛ 7χ.	8	.484 4Ɛ9 368	002 Ɛχ.
9	.3Ɛχ 805 17Ɛ	18Ɛ Ɛ4.	9	.443 951 Ɛ1χ	099 07.	9	.485 500 356	000 89.
χ	.3ƐƐ 995 101	188 Ɛ0.	χ	.444 χ2χ Ɛ92	096 55.	χ	.486 501 031	ƐƐχ 59.
Ɛ	.400 Ɛ62 003	185 χ9.	Ɛ	.445 Ɛ05 522	093 χ3.	Ɛ	.487 4ƐƐ 603	ƐƐ8 29.

N	Log Tan	d	N	Log Tan	d	N	Log Tan	d
.0500	Ɛ.488 4Ɛ7 8X1	ƐƐ5 ƐƐ.	.0540	Ɛ.506 X26 935	Ɛ31 74.	.0580	Ɛ.542 809 611	X79 63.
1	.489 4Ɛ1 895	ƐƐ3 91.	1	.507 958 483	Ɛ2Ɛ 7Ɛ.	1	.543 687 044	X77 97.
2	.48X 4X5 5Ɛ2	ƐƐ1 65.	2	.508 888 080	Ɛ29 87.	2	.544 542 X00	X76 10.
3	.48Ɛ 497 045	ƐXƐ 39.	3	.509 7Ɛ5 933	Ɛ27 93.	3	.545 3Ɛ8 Ɛ06	X74 46.
4	.490 486 41X	ƐX9 12.	4	.50X 721 66X	Ɛ25 X0.	4	.546 271 368	X72 80.
5	.491 473 547	ƐX6 X8.	5	.50Ɛ 647 477	Ɛ23 XX.	5	.547 123 Ɛ70	X70 Ɛ7.
6	.492 45X 415	ƐX4 83.	6	.510 56Ɛ 362	Ɛ21 Ɛ9.	6	Ɛ94 Ɛ22	X6Ɛ 32.
7	.493 443 053	ƐX2 5Ɛ.	7	.511 491 334	Ɛ20 08.	7	.548 X44 249	X69 6X.
8	.494 425 651	ƐX0 38.	8	.512 3Ɛ1 3ƐX	Ɛ1X 18.	8	.549 8Ɛ1 936	X67 X7.
9	.495 405 X18	Ɛ9X 16.	9	.513 30Ɛ 585	Ɛ18 29.	9	.54X 759 7XƐ	X66 24.
X	.496 3X3 Ɛ81	Ɛ97 Ɛ5.	X	.514 227 85Ɛ	Ɛ16 3Ɛ.	X	.54Ɛ 603 X38	X64 62.
Ɛ	.497 37Ɛ Ɛ11	Ɛ95 94.	Ɛ	.515 142 04Ɛ	Ɛ14 51.	Ɛ	.550 468 464	X62 X1.
.0510	.498 355 858	Ɛ93 74.	.0550	.516 056 562	Ɛ12 64.	.0590	.551 30Ɛ 277	X61 20.
1	.499 329 3X7	Ɛ91 56.	1	Ɛ68 ƐX7	Ɛ10 78.	1	.552 170 480	X5Ɛ 60.
2	.49X 2ƐX 94X	Ɛ8Ɛ 38.	2	.517 X79 768	Ɛ0X 90.	2	.553 00Ɛ X83	X59 X0.
3	.49Ɛ 28X 113	Ɛ89 1Ɛ.	3	.518 988 474	Ɛ08 X5.	3	X69 88X	X58 21.
4	.4X0 257 309	Ɛ87 03.	4	.519 895 312	Ɛ06 ƐƐ.	4	.554 905 XX5	X56 63.
5	.4X1 222 341	Ɛ84 X8.	5	.51X 7X0 30Ɛ	Ɛ05 16.	5	.555 760 518	X54 X5.
6	.4X2 1X7 203	Ɛ82 91.	6	.51Ɛ 6X5 474	Ɛ03 31.	6	.556 5Ɛ5 371	X53 28.
7	.4X3 169 Ɛ21	Ɛ80 78.	7	.520 5X8 792	Ɛ01 49.	7	.557 448 633	X51 6Ɛ.
8	.4X4 12X 6X5	Ɛ7X 63.	8	.521 4XX 071	XƐƐ 66.	8	.558 29X 12Ɛ	X4Ɛ Ɛ3.
9	.4X5 0X9 122	Ɛ78 4Ɛ.	9	.522 3X9 71X	XƐ9 84.	9	.559 12X 066	X4X 38.
X	.4X6 065 621	Ɛ76 39.	X	.523 2X7 361	XƐ7 X2.	X	Ɛ78 429	X48 81.
Ɛ	.4X7 01Ɛ 9Ɛ1	Ɛ74 26.	Ɛ	.524 1X3 186	XƐ6 01.	Ɛ	.55X X05 042	X47 07.
.0520	Ɛ94 060	Ɛ72 15.	.0560	.525 099 19Ɛ	XƐ4 21.	.05X0	.55Ɛ 850 0Ɛ4	X45 51.
1	.4X8 Ɛ46 1Ɛ9	Ɛ70 05.	1	Ɛ91 3XƐ	XƐ2 41.	1	.560 695 60Ɛ	X43 98.
2	.4X9 XƐ6 250	Ɛ69 Ɛ5.	2	.526 X83 802	XƐ0 62.	2	.561 519 395	X42 24.
3	.4XX X64 1XX	Ɛ67 X7.	3	.527 974 226	XXX 84.	3	.562 35Ɛ 615	X40 70.
4	.4XƐ X10 05X	Ɛ65 99.	4	.528 862 X67	XX8 X6.	4	.563 1X0 117	X3X Ɛ8.
5	.4Ɛ0 975 X30	Ɛ63 90.	5	.529 74Ɛ 910	XX7 09.	5	.564 01Ɛ 0X5	X39 46.
6	.4Ɛ1 919 731	Ɛ61 83.	6	.52X 636 9X6	XX5 31.	6	X58 546	X37 93.
7	.4Ɛ2 87Ɛ 36Ɛ	Ɛ5Ɛ 78.	7	.52Ɛ 520 0Ɛ9	XX3 55.	7	.565 894 285	X36 22.
8	.4Ɛ3 81X Ɛ35	Ɛ59 71.	8	.530 403 656	XX1 7X.	8	.566 70X 4X9	X34 71.
9	.4Ɛ4 778 653	Ɛ57 68.	9	.531 2X5 244	X9Ɛ X4.	9	.567 543 002	X33 00.
X	.4Ɛ5 714 114	Ɛ55 63.	X	.532 185 090	X9X 0Ɛ.	X	.568 376 010	X31 51.
Ɛ	.4Ɛ6 669 745	Ɛ53 5X.	Ɛ	.533 063 181	X98 36.	Ɛ	.569 1X7 521	X2Ɛ X1.
.0530	.4Ɛ7 601 134	Ɛ51 57.	.0570	Ɛ3Ɛ 525	X96 62.	.05Ɛ0	.56X 017 33X	X2X 32.
1	.4Ɛ8 552 6XX	Ɛ4Ɛ 55.	1	.534 X15 Ɛ46	X94 8X.	1	X45 669	X28 84.
2	.4Ɛ9 4X2 03Ɛ	Ɛ49 53.	2	.535 8XX 832	X92 Ɛ7.	2	.56Ɛ 872 2Ɛ7	X27 17.
3	.4ƐX 42Ɛ 572	Ɛ47 52.	3	.536 781 7XƐ	X91 25.	3	.570 699 469	X25 6X.
4	.4ƐƐ 376 X95	Ɛ45 52.	4	.537 652 X45	X8Ɛ 54.	4	.571 502 Ɛ4X	X24 01.
5	.500 300 3Ɛ6	Ɛ43 52.	5	.538 522 386	X89 83.	5	.572 326 Ɛ65	X22 55.
6	.501 243 923	Ɛ41 54.	6	.539 3XƐ ƐƐ8	X87 Ɛ3.	6	.573 149 500	X20 XX.
7	.502 185 265	Ɛ3Ɛ 56.	7	.53X 277 Ɛ28	X86 23.	7	Ɛ6X 3X2	X1Ɛ 43.
8	.503 104 808	Ɛ39 59.	8	.53Ɛ 142 161	X84 54.	8	.574 989 817	X19 99.
9	.504 042 1X0	Ɛ37 61.	9	.540 006 6X7	X82 86.	9	.575 7X7 5X7	X18 33.
X	Ɛ79 7Ɛ0	Ɛ35 65.	X	X89 349	X80 Ɛ8.	X	.576 603 91X	X16 8X.
Ɛ	.505 XƐ3 247	Ɛ33 6X.	Ɛ	.541 94X 315	X7Ɛ 2Ɛ.	Ɛ	.577 41X 5ƐƐ	X15 25.

N	Log Tan	d	N	Log Tan	d	N	Log Tan	d
.0600	Ɛ.578 233 853	X13 813	.0640	Ɛ.5XƐ 7Ɛ9 Ɛ11	976 571	.0680	Ɛ.621 3X3 57X	924 738
1	.579 047 466	X12 197	1	.5Ɛ0 574 482	975 133	1	.622 108 026	923 482
2	X59 641	X10 767	2	.5Ɛ1 329 5Ɛ5	973 8ƐƐ	2	X2Ɛ 578	922 211
3	.57X 86X 1X8	X0Ɛ 140	3	.5Ɛ2 0X1 2Ɛ4	972 490	3	.623 751 789	920 Ɛ66
4	.57Ɛ 679 328	X09 720	4	X53 784	971 068	4	.624 472 733	91Ɛ 902
5	.580 486 X48	X08 107	5	.5Ɛ3 804 830	96Ɛ 847	5	.625 192 435	91X 664
6	.581 292 Ɛ53	X06 6Ɛ8	6	.5Ɛ4 574 477	96X 431	6	XƐ0 X99	919 40X
7	.582 099 64Ɛ	X05 0Ɛ2	7	.5Ɛ5 322 8X8	969 021	7	.626 80X 2X7	918 179
8	XX2 741	X03 6Ɛ4	8	.5Ɛ6 08Ɛ 909	967 814	8	.627 526 464	916 Ɛ30
9	.583 8X6 235	X02 0ƐƐ	9	X37 521	966 413	9	.628 241 394	915 8X8
X	.584 6X8 334	X00 712	X	.5Ɛ7 7X1 934	965 015	X	Ɛ57 080	914 669
Ɛ	.585 4X8 X46	9ƐƐ 129	Ɛ	.5Ɛ8 546 949	963 823	Ɛ	.629 86Ɛ 729	913 432
.0610	.586 2X7 Ɛ73	9Ɛ9 750	.0650	.5Ɛ9 2XX 570	962 433	.0690	.62X 582 Ɛ5Ɛ	912 1ƐƐ
1	.587 0X5 703	9Ɛ8 179	1	.5ƐX 050 9X3	961 04Ɛ	1	.62Ɛ 295 15X	910 Ɛ92
2	XX1 880	9Ɛ6 7XƐ	2	9Ɛ1 X32	95Ɛ 870	2	ƐX6 130	90Ɛ 969
3	.588 898 46Ɛ	9Ɛ5 228	3	.5ƐƐ 751 6X2	95X 495	3	.630 8Ɛ5 X99	90X 748
4	.589 691 697	9Ɛ3 86Ɛ	4	.600 4XƐ Ɛ77	959 103	4	.631 604 625	909 530
5	.58X 485 346	9Ɛ2 2Ɛ8	5	.601 249 07X	957 938	5	.632 311 Ɛ55	908 318
6	.58Ɛ 277 642	9Ɛ0 950	6	ƐX4 9Ɛ6	956 575	6	.633 01X 271	907 109
7	.590 068 392	9XƐ 3X9	7	.602 93Ɛ 36Ɛ	955 1Ɛ8	7	925 37X	905 Ɛ02
8	X57 77Ɛ	9X9 X50	8	.603 694 567	953 X43	8	.634 62Ɛ 280	904 900
9	.591 845 60Ɛ	9X8 42X	9	.604 428 3XX	952 693	9	.635 333 Ɛ80	903 702
X	.592 631 Ɛ09	9X6 Ɛ71	X	.605 17X X81	951 32X	X	.636 037 682	902 509
Ɛ	.593 418 X7X	9X5 62Ɛ	Ɛ	Ɛ10 1XƐ	94Ɛ Ɛ89	Ɛ	939 Ɛ8Ɛ	901 318
.0620	.594 202 4X9	9X4 0Ɛ2	.0660	.606 860 178	94X 831	.06X0	.637 63Ɛ 2X7	900 12Ɛ
1	ƐX6 59Ɛ	9X2 77Ɛ	1	.607 5XX 9X9	949 49X	1	.638 33Ɛ 416	8ƐX Ɛ47
2	.595 989 15X	9X1 253	2	.608 338 287	948 151	2	.639 03X 361	8Ɛ9 968
3	.596 76X 3Ɛ1	99Ɛ 92Ɛ	3	.609 084 418	946 X08	3	938 109	8Ɛ8 790
4	.597 54X 120	99X 413	4	X0Ɛ 224	945 688	4	.63X 634 899	8Ɛ7 5Ɛ8
5	.598 328 533	998 Ɛ00	5	.60X 754 8Ɛ0	944 352	5	.63Ɛ 330 295	8Ɛ6 42X
6	.599 105 433	997 5Ɛ3	6	.60Ɛ 499 042	943 020	6	.640 026 703	8Ɛ5 264
7	XX0 X26	996 0XƐ	7	.610 220 062	941 8Ɛ3	7	91Ɛ 967	8Ɛ4 0X1
8	.59X 876 Ɛ15	994 7Ɛ2	8	Ɛ61 955	940 590	8	.641 613 X48	8Ɛ2 Ɛ24
9	.59Ɛ 64Ɛ 707	993 2ƐX	9	.611 8X2 325	93Ɛ 272	9	.642 306 970	8Ɛ1 96X
X	.5X0 422 X05	991 X10	X	.612 621 597	939 Ɛ57	X	Ɛ28 71X	8Ɛ0 7Ɛ9
Ɛ	.5X1 1Ɛ4 815	990 528	Ɛ	.613 35Ɛ 532	938 847	Ɛ	.643 8X9 317	8XƐ 650
.0630	Ɛ85 141	98Ɛ 049	.0670	.614 098 179	937 540	.06Ɛ0	.644 598 967	8XX 4X7
1	.5X2 954 18X	989 775	1	X13 6Ɛ9	936 238	1	.645 287 252	8X9 347
2	.5X3 721 943	988 2X5	2	.615 749 935	934 Ɛ3X	2	Ɛ74 599	8X8 1XX
3	.5X4 4XX 028	986 X21	3	.616 482 873	933 845	3	.646 860 787	8X7 056
4	.5X5 274 X49	985 560	4	.617 1Ɛ6 4Ɛ8	932 555	4	.647 547 821	8X5 Ɛ06
5	.5X6 03X 3X9	984 0X7	5	Ɛ28 X51	931 269	5	.648 231 727	8X4 97Ɛ
6	X02 494	982 836	6	.618 85X 0ƐX	92Ɛ Ɛ87	6	Ɛ16 4X6	8X3 837
7	.5X7 785 10X	981 38Ɛ	7	.619 58X 085	92X 8X9	7	.649 7ƐX 121	8X2 6Ɛ7
8	.5X8 546 499	97Ɛ Ɛ2X	8	.61X 2Ɛ8 972	929 613	8	.64X 4X0 818	8X1 581
9	.5X9 306 407	97X 692	9	.61Ɛ 026 385	928 344	9	.64Ɛ 182 199	8X0 449
X	.5XX 084 X99	979 241	X	952 709	927 078	X	X62 626	89Ɛ 31X
Ɛ	X42 11X	977 9Ɛ3	Ɛ	.620 679 785	925 9Ɛ5	Ɛ	.650 741 944	89X 1Ɛ3

N	Log Tan	d	N	Log Tan	d	N	Log Tan	d
.0700	Ɛ.651 41Ɛ Ɛ37	899 091	.0740	Ɛ.67Ɛ XX5 774	856 Ɛ8Ɛ	.0780	Ɛ.6X9 181 780	819 79X
1	.652 0Ɛ9 008	897 Ɛ72	1	.680 740 743	855 ƐX2	1	99Ɛ 35X	818 907
2	994 Ɛ7X	896 X57	2	.681 396 725	854 ƐƐX	2	.6XX 5Ɛ8 065	817 X36
3	.653 66Ɛ X15	895 945	3	.682 02Ɛ 723	01X	3	.6XƐ 213 X9Ɛ	816 Ɛ68
4	.654 345 75X	894 836	4	883 741	853 040	4	X2X X47	0X2
5	.655 01X 394	893 730	5	.683 516 781	852 067	5	.6Ɛ0 644 Ɛ29	815 21X
6	8Ɛ1 Ɛ04	892 62X	6	.684 168 828	851 094	6	.6Ɛ1 25X 147	814 35X
7	.656 584 532	891 52Ɛ	7	9Ɛ9 900	850 106	7	X72 4X5	813 4X1
8	.657 255 X61	890 434	8	.685 649 X06	84Ɛ 13Ɛ	8	.6Ɛ2 685 986	812 627
9	Ɛ26 295	88Ɛ 342	9	.686 298 Ɛ45	84X 177	9	.6Ɛ3 298 3Ɛ1	811 773
X	.658 7Ɛ5 617	88X 254	X	Ɛ27 100	849 1Ɛ7	X	XX9 Ɛ64	810 903
Ɛ	.659 483 86Ɛ	889 169	Ɛ	.687 774 2Ɛ7	848 23Ɛ	Ɛ	.6Ɛ4 6ƐX 867	80Ɛ X56
.0710	.65X 150 X18	888 087	.0750	.688 400 536	847 285	.0790	.6Ɛ5 30X 701	80X ƐƐ1
1	X18 XX3	886 ƐX8	1	.689 047 7ƐƐ	846 313	1	Ɛ19 6Ɛ2	149
2	.65Ɛ 6X3 X8Ɛ	885 Ɛ11	2	891 Ɛ12	845 365	2	.6Ɛ6 727 83Ɛ	809 2X9
3	.660 369 9X0	884 X3Ɛ	3	.68X 517 277	844 3Ɛ9	3	.6Ɛ7 334 Ɛ28	808 450
4	.661 032 81Ɛ	883 970	4	.68Ɛ 15Ɛ 674	843 457	4	Ɛ41 378	807 5Ɛ6
5	8Ɛ6 58Ɛ	882 8X5	5	9X2 Ɛ0Ɛ	842 4Ɛ6	5	.6Ɛ8 748 972	806 764
6	.662 579 274	881 822	6	.690 625 405	841 559	6	.6Ɛ9 353 516	805 913
7	.663 23X X96	880 763	7	.691 266 962	840 605	7	Ɛ59 229	804 X86
8	XƐƐ 639	87Ɛ 6X8	8	XX7 367	83Ɛ 672	8	.6ƐX 762 0Ɛ3	040
9	.664 77Ɛ 125	87X 634	9	.692 726 X19	83X 723	9	.6ƐƐ 366 133	803 1ƐX
X	.665 439 759	879 585	X	.693 365 540	839 799	X	Ɛ69 331	802 379
Ɛ	.666 0Ɛ7 122	878 519	Ɛ	ƐX3 119	838 854	Ɛ	.700 76Ɛ 6XX	801 540
.0720	973 63Ɛ	877 475	.0760	.694 81Ɛ 971	837 914	.07X0	.701 371 02X	800 705
1	.667 62X XƐ4	876 415	1	.695 457 685	836 997	1	Ɛ71 733	7ƐƐ 893
2	.668 2X5 309	875 378	2	.696 092 460	835 X61	2	.702 771 406	7ƐX X62
3	Ɛ5X 685	874 325	3	908 301	834 Ɛ2X	3	.703 370 268	034
4	.669 812 9XX	873 293	4	.697 541 22Ɛ	833 ƐƐƐ	4	Ɛ6X 2X0	7Ɛ9 20X
5	.66X 486 081	872 246	5	.698 175 22X	093	5	.704 767 4XX	7Ɛ8 3X7
6	.66Ɛ 138 307	871 202	6	9X8 301	832 16X	6	.705 363 895	7Ɛ7 586
7	9X9 509	870 180	7	.699 61X 46Ɛ	831 249	7	Ɛ5Ɛ 25Ɛ	7Ɛ6 767
8	.670 659 689	86Ɛ 142	8	.69X 24Ɛ 6Ɛ8	830 32Ɛ	8	.706 755 X06	7Ɛ5 951
9	.671 308 80Ɛ	86X 108	9	X7Ɛ X27	82Ɛ 414	9	.707 34Ɛ 757	7Ɛ4 Ɛ39
X	Ɛ76 917	869 096	X	.69Ɛ 6XƐ 23Ɛ	82X 500	X	Ɛ44 694	128
Ɛ	.672 823 9Ɛ1	868 067	Ɛ	.6X0 319 73Ɛ	829 5Ɛ0	Ɛ	.708 738 800	7Ɛ3 319
.0730	.673 48Ɛ X58	867 040	.0770	Ɛ47 12Ɛ	828 6X3	.07Ɛ0	.709 32Ɛ Ɛ19	7Ɛ2 511
1	.674 136 X98	866 019	1	.6X1 773 812	827 799	1	Ɛ22 42X	7Ɛ1 709
2	9X0 XƐ5	864 ƐƐX	2	.6X2 39Ɛ 3XƐ	826 897	2	.70X 713 Ɛ37	7Ɛ0 908
3	.675 645 XƐ3	863 ƐX2	3	.6X3 006 086	825 996	3	.70Ɛ 304 843	7XƐ Ɛ08
4	.676 2X9 X95	862 Ɛ89	4	82Ɛ X60	824 X9Ɛ	4	XƐ4 74Ɛ	110
5	Ɛ50 X62	861 Ɛ79	5	.6X4 454 93Ɛ	823 ƐX5	5	.710 6X3 85Ɛ	7XX 316
6	.677 7Ɛ2 X1Ɛ	860 Ɛ70	6	.6X5 078 924	0Ɛ4	6	.711 291 Ɛ75	7X9 524
7	.678 453 98Ɛ	85Ɛ Ɛ67	7	89Ɛ X18	822 205	7	X7Ɛ 499	7X8 734
8	.679 0Ɛ3 936	85X Ɛ65	8	.6X6 502 021	821 319	8	.712 668 011	7X7 948
9	952 89Ɛ	859 Ɛ67	9	.6X7 123 33X	820 435	9	.713 253 959	7X6 Ɛ61
X	.67X 5Ɛ0 846	858 Ɛ71	X	943 773	81Ɛ 553	X	X3X 8ƐX	17X
Ɛ	.67Ɛ 249 7Ɛ7	857 Ɛ79	Ɛ	.6X8 563 106	81X 676	Ɛ	.714 624 X78	7X5 399

N	Log Tan	d	N	Log Tan	d	N	Log Tan	d
.0800	Ɛ.715 20χ 255	7χ4 5ƐƐ	.0840	Ɛ.740 143 984	773 045	.0880	Ɛ.766 085 297	744 9Ɛ6
1	9Ɛ2 854	7χ3 824	1	8Ɛ6 χ09	772 352	1	80χ 091	197
2	.716 596 478	7χ2 χ4Ɛ	2	.741 469 15Ɛ	771 661	2	.767 352 268	743 579
3	.717 179 307	07Ɛ	3	.742 01χ 800	770 975	3	χ95 825	742 962
4	95Ɛ 386	7χ1 2χƐ	4	78Ɛ 575	089	4	.768 618 587	148
5	.718 540 675	7χ0 523	5	.743 33Ɛ 642	76Ɛ 3χ4	5	.769 15χ 713	741 536
6	.719 120 Ɛ98	79Ɛ 759	6	χχχ χ26	76χ 701	6	8χ0 049	740 925
7	900 735	79χ 997	7	.744 659 527	769 χ22	7	.76χ 420 972	116
8	.71χ 49Ɛ 510	017	8	.745 207 349	144	8	Ɛ60 χ88	73Ɛ 509
9	.71Ɛ 079 527	799 25χ	9	974 491	768 469	9	.76Ɛ 6χ0 395	73χ 903
χ	856 785	798 4χ3	χ	.746 520 93χ	767 795	χ	.770 21Ɛ 098	0ƐƐ
Ɛ	.720 433 068	797 72Ɛ	Ɛ	.747 088 513	766 Ɛ01	Ɛ	959 197	739 4Ɛ9
.0810	.721 00χ 797	796 97χ	.0850	833 414	232	.0890	.771 496 694	738 8Ɛ9
1	7χ5 555	00Ɛ	1	.748 399 646	765 565	1	.772 013 391	0ƐƐ
2	.722 37Ɛ 564	795 263	2	Ɛ42 ƐχƐ	764 898	2	74Ɛ 490	737 503
3	Ɛ54 807	794 4Ɛχ	3	.749 6χ7 887	015	3	.773 286 993	736 90χ
4	.723 729 105	793 758	4	.74χ 24Ɛ 8χ0	763 351	4	χ01 6χ1	116
5	.724 300 861	792 9Ɛ8	5	9Ɛ3 031	762 691	5	.774 537 7Ɛ7	735 525
6	χ93 659	05χ	6	.74Ɛ 555 702	761 χ14	6	.775 071 120	734 935
7	.725 665 6Ɛ7	791 304	7	.750 0Ɛ7 516	158	7	7χ5 χ55	148
8	.726 236 9ƐƐ	790 56Ɛ	8	858 672	760 4χ3	8	.776 319 Ɛχ1	733 561
9	χ07 36χ	78Ɛ 81Ɛ	9	.751 3Ɛ8 Ɛ55	75Ɛ 830	9	χ51 542	732 978
χ	.727 596 Ɛ89	78χ χ8Ɛ	χ	Ɛ58 785	75χ Ɛ80	χ	.777 584 2Ɛχ	195
Ɛ	.728 165 χ58	144	Ɛ	.752 6Ɛ7 745	311	Ɛ	.778 0Ɛ6 493	731 5Ɛ4
.0820	933 Ɛχ0	789 3Ɛ9	.0860	.753 255 χ56	759 666	.08χ0	827 χ87	730 χ16
1	.729 501 399	788 677	1	9Ɛ3 500	758 χ00	1	.779 358 8χ1	238
2	.72χ 089 χ54	787 936	2	.754 550 300	159	2	χ88 Ɛ19	72Ɛ 662
3	855 78χ	786 ƐƐ9	3	.755 0χ8 459	757 4Ɛ8	3	.77χ 5Ɛ8 57Ɛ	72χ χ89
4	.72Ɛ 420 787	282	4	843 955	756 859	4	.77Ɛ 127 448	2Ɛ7
5	Ɛχ6 χ49	785 548	5	.756 39χ 5Ɛ2	001	5	855 743	729 726
6	.730 770 395	784 817	6	Ɛ34 5Ɛ3	755 367	6	.780 383 269	728 Ɛ58
7	.731 334 ƐƐ0	783 χχ7	7	.757 689 95χ	754 713	7	χƐ0 205	38Ɛ
8	χƐ8 χ97	17χ	8	.758 222 471	753 χ82	8	.781 618 594	727 805
9	.732 680 055	782 454	9	976 333	232	9	.782 144 199	041
χ	.733 242 4χ9	781 730	χ	.759 509 565	752 5χ6	χ	86Ɛ 21χ	726 47χ
Ɛ	χ04 019	780 χ0χ	Ɛ	.75χ 05Ɛ Ɛ4Ɛ	751 95χ	Ɛ	.783 395 698	725 8Ɛχ
.0830	.734 584 χ27	0Ɛ0	.0870	7Ɛ1 8χ9	116	.08Ɛ0	χƐƐ 396	13Ɛ
1	.735 144 Ɛ17	77Ɛ 393	1	.75Ɛ 342 χ03	750 494	1	.784 624 515	724 583
2	904 2χχ	77χ 67χ	2	χ93 297	74Ɛ 854	2	.785 148 χ98	723 χ09
3	.736 482 968	779 966	3	.760 622 Ɛ2Ɛ	017	3	870 8χ5	255
4	.737 040 712	055	4	.761 171 Ɛ46	74χ 39χ	4	.786 393 Ɛ3χ	722 6χ2
5	7Ɛ9 767	778 347	5	900 324	749 766	5	χƐ6 620	721 Ɛ32
6	.738 375 χƐ2	777 640	6	.762 449 χ8χ	748 Ɛ32	6	.787 618 552	384
7	Ɛ31 532	776 936	7	Ɛ96 χ00	302	7	.788 139 916	720 818
8	.739 6χ8 268	033	8	.763 723 102	747 692	8	85χ 532	071
9	.73χ 262 29Ɛ	775 333	9	.764 26χ 794	746 χ67	9	.789 37χ 5χ3	71Ɛ 508
χ	χ17 612	774 635	χ	9Ɛ5 63Ɛ	240	χ	χ99 χχƐ	71χ 967
Ɛ	.73Ɛ 590 047	773 939	Ɛ	.765 53Ɛ 87Ɛ	745 618	Ɛ	.78χ 5Ɛ8 856	206

N	Log Tan	d	N	Log Tan	d	N	Log Tan	d
.0900	Ɛ.78Ɛ 116 X60	719 667	.0940	Ɛ.7Ɛ3 369 545	6Ɛ4 X63	.0980	Ɛ.816 8X0 276	692 691
1	834 507	718 Ɛ0Ɛ	1	X62 3X8	37Ɛ	1	.817 372 947	056
2	.790 351 416	374	2	.7Ɛ4 556 767	6Ɛ3 89Ɛ	2	X44 9X1	691 622
3	X69 78X	717 820	3	.7Ɛ5 04X 446	1ƐX	3	.818 516 403	690 ƐX9
4	.791 585 3XX	089	4	741 644	6Ɛ2 720	4	ƐX7 3Ɛ0	578
5	.792 0X0 477	716 539	5	.7Ɛ6 234 164	044	5	.819 677 968	68Ɛ Ɛ46
6	7Ɛ6 9Ɛ4	715 9X9	6	926 1X8	6Ɛ1 569	6	.81X 147 8Ɛ2	518
7	.793 310 7X1	261	7	.7Ɛ7 417 755	6Ɛ0 X95	7	817 20X	68X XXƐ
8	X25 X42	714 716	8	Ɛ08 62X	401	8	.81Ɛ 2X6 0Ɛ9	483
9	.794 53X 558	713 Ɛ91	9	.7Ɛ8 5Ɛ8 X2Ɛ	6XƐ 930	9	974 580	689 X59
X	.795 052 529	449	X	.7Ɛ9 0X8 75Ɛ	260	X	.820 442 419	433
Ɛ	765 976	712 909	Ɛ	797 9ƐƐ	6XX 792	Ɛ	Ɛ0Ɛ 850	688 X11
.0910	.796 278 683	189	.0950	.7ƐX 286 591	106	.0990	.821 598 661	3Ɛ0
1	98X 850	711 651	1	974 697	6X9 640	1	.822 064 X51	687 98Ɛ
2	.797 4X0 2X1	710 Ɛ14	2	.7ƐƐ 462 117	6X8 Ɛ77	2	730 820	371
3	ƐƐ1 1Ɛ5	39Ɛ	3	Ɛ4Ɛ 092	4Ɛ4	3	.823 1Ɛ7 Ɛ91	686 954
4	.798 701 594	70Ɛ 868	4	.800 637 586	6X7 X32	4	882 925	339
5	.799 211 240	135	5	.801 123 3Ɛ8	373	5	.824 349 062	685 923
6	920 375	70X 606	6	80X 76Ɛ	6X6 8Ɛ5	6	X12 985	30Ɛ
7	.79X 42X 97Ɛ	709 X98	7	.802 2Ɛ5 464	239	7	.825 498 094	684 8Ɛ9
8	Ɛ38 857	370	8	99Ɛ 6X1	6X5 782	8	Ɛ60 991	2X7
9	.79Ɛ 646 007	708 845	9	.803 485 263	109	9	.826 625 078	683 897
X	.7X0 152 850	121	X	Ɛ6X 370	6X4 656	X	.827 0X8 953	28X
Ɛ	85X 971	707 5ƐƐ	Ɛ	.804 652 X06	6X3 ƐX5	Ɛ	770 021	682 881
.0920	.7X1 366 370	706 X9X	.0960	.805 136 9XƐ	535	.09X0	.828 232 8X2	275
1	X71 24X	37Ɛ	1	81X 324	6X2 X87	1	8Ɛ4 Ɛ57	681 871
2	.7X2 577 609	705 862	2	.806 301 1XƐ	41X	2	.829 376 808	268
3	.7X3 081 26Ɛ	148	3	9X3 609	6X1 974	3	X37 X74	680 866
4	786 3Ɛ7	704 632	4	.807 485 381	30X	4	.82X 4Ɛ8 71X	265
5	.7X4 28X X29	703 Ɛ1X	5	Ɛ66 68Ɛ	6X0 867	5	Ɛ78 983	67Ɛ 866
6	992 947	409	6	.808 647 336	206	6	.82Ɛ 638 629	267
7	.7X5 496 154	702 8ƐX	7	.809 127 540	69Ɛ 765	7	.830 0Ɛ7 894	67X 86Ɛ
8	Ɛ98 X52	1XƐ	8	807 0X5	106	8	776 543	275
9	.7X6 69Ɛ 041	701 6X4	9	.80X 2X6 1XƐ	69X 66X	9	.831 234 7Ɛ8	679 87Ɛ
X	.7X7 1X0 725	700 Ɛ99	X	984 859	013	X	8Ɛ2 477	286
Ɛ	8X1 702	495	Ɛ	.80Ɛ 462 870	699 579	Ɛ	.832 36Ɛ 741	678 895
.0930	.7X8 3X1 Ɛ97	6ƐƐ 992	.0970	Ɛ40 229	698 Ɛ25	.09Ɛ0	X28 416	2X3
1	XX1 969	291	1	.810 619 152	493	1	.833 4X4 6Ɛ9	677 8Ɛ4
2	.7X9 5X1 03X	6ƐX 793	2	.811 0Ɛ5 625	697 X43	2	Ɛ60 3Ɛ1	307
3	.7XX 09Ɛ 811	095	3	791 468	3Ɛ3	3	.834 617 6Ɛ8	676 919
4	799 8X6	6Ɛ9 59X	4	.812 268 85Ɛ	696 966	4	.835 092 415	333
5	.7XƐ 297 284	6Ɛ8 XX4	5	943 605	31Ɛ	5	748 748	675 949
6	994 168	3Ɛ1	6	.813 419 924	695 894	6	.836 202 495	364
7	.7Ɛ0 490 559	6Ɛ7 8ƐX	7	XƐ3 5Ɛ8	250	7	877 839	674 983
8	Ɛ88 257	20X	8	.814 588 848	694 808	8	.837 330 600	3X1
9	.7Ɛ1 683 465	6Ɛ6 720	9	.815 061 454	188	9	9X4 9X1	673 X01
X	.7Ɛ2 179 Ɛ85	033	X	735 620	693 748	X	.838 458 7X2	423
Ɛ	873 ƐƐ8	6Ɛ5 549	Ɛ	.816 209 168	10X	Ɛ	Ɛ10 005	672 X47

N	Log Tan	d	N	Log Tan	d	N	Log Tan	d
.0χ00	Ɛ.839 582 χ50	672 46Ɛ	.0χ40	Ɛ.85Ɛ 697 057	654 178	.0χ80	Ɛ.881 095 793	637 7Ɛ0
1	.83χ 035 2ƐƐ	671 χ95	1	.860 12Ɛ 213	653 839	1	711 383	303
2	6χ7 194	501	2	782 χ50	2ƐƐ	2	.882 148 686	636 χ14
3	.83Ɛ 158 695	670 Ɛ2χ	3	.861 216 14Ɛ	652 982	3	783 49χ	529
4	809 603	558	4	868 Ɛ11	447	4	.883 1Ɛ9 χ07	042
5	.840 279 Ɛ5Ɛ	66Ɛ Ɛ88	5	.862 2ƐƐ 358	651 Ɛ11	5	833 χ49	635 758
6	929 Ɛ27	5Ɛχ	6	951 269	598	6	.884 269 5χ5	273
7	.841 399 525	030	7	.863 3χ2 845	065	7	8χ2 858	634 991
8	χ48 555	66χ 665	8	χ33 8χχ	650 732	8	.885 317 629	4χχ
9	.842 4Ɛ6 ƐƐχ	09χ	9	.864 484 420	202	9	94Ɛ Ɛ17	009
χ	Ɛ65 098	669 715	χ	Ɛ14 622	64Ɛ 892	χ	.886 383 Ɛ24	633 729
Ɛ	.843 612 7Ɛ1	152	Ɛ	.865 564 2Ɛ4	363	Ɛ	9Ɛ7 651	24Ɛ
.0χ10	.844 07Ɛ 943	668 790	.0χ50	ƐƐ3 657	64χ χ37	.0χ90	.887 42χ 8χ0	632 971
1	728 513	20Ɛ	1	.866 642 492	50Ɛ	1	χ61 651	496
2	.845 194 722	667 850	2	.867 090 9χ1	649 Ɛχ5	2	.888 493 Ɛ27	631 ƐƐχ
3	840 372	292	3	71χ 986	67Ɛ	3	Ɛ05 Ɛ25	725
4	.846 2χ7 644	666 915	4	.868 168 445	158	4	.889 537 64χ	250
5	952 359	35Ɛ	5	7Ɛ5 5χ1	648 836	5	Ɛ68 89χ	630 978
6	.847 3Ɛ8 6Ɛ8	665 9χ5	6	.869 242 217	314	6	.88χ 599 656	4χ6
7	χ62 4χ1	431	7	88χ 52Ɛ	647 9Ɛ4	7	.88Ɛ 009 Ɛ40	015
8	.848 507 912	664 χ79	8	.86χ 316 323	495	8	639 Ɛ55	62Ɛ 746
9	Ɛ70 78Ɛ	509	9	961 7Ɛ8	646 Ɛ78	9	.890 069 69Ɛ	276
χ	.849 615 098	663 Ɛ58	χ	.86Ɛ 3χ8 774	660	χ	698 955	62χ 9χ9
Ɛ	.84χ 079 034	5χχ	Ɛ	χ33 214	145	Ɛ	.891 107 742	520
.0χ20	720 622	041	.0χ60	.870 479 359	645 830	.0χχ0	736 062	056
1	.84Ɛ 183 663	662 694	1	Ɛ02 Ɛ89	317	1	.892 164 0Ɛ8	629 78Ɛ
2	826 137	12Ɛ	2	.871 548 2χ4	644 χ04	2	791 887	306
3	.850 288 266	661 785	3	Ɛ91 0χ8	4Ɛ3	3	.893 1Ɛχ Ɛ91	628 χ43
4	929 χ2Ɛ	221	4	.872 615 59Ɛ	643 Ɛχ2	4	827 χ14	580
5	.851 38Ɛ 050	660 87Ɛ	5	.873 059 581	692	5	.894 254 394	0Ɛχ
6	χ2Ɛ 90Ɛ	31χ	6	6χ1 053	185	6	880 492	627 83χ
7	.852 490 029	65Ɛ 97Ɛ	7	.874 124 218	642 878	7	.895 2χ8 110	380
8	Ɛ2Ɛ 9χ8	420	8	766 χ94	370	8	913 490	626 Ɛ01
9	.853 58Ɛ 208	65χ χ83	9	.875 1χ9 244	641 χ66	9	.896 33χ 391	644
χ	.854 02χ 08Ɛ	528	χ	82Ɛ 0χχ	562	χ	964 χ15	189
Ɛ	688 5Ɛ7	659 Ɛ92	Ɛ	.876 270 650	059	Ɛ	.897 38χ Ɛχ2	625 912
.0χ30	.855 126 589	639	.0χ70	8Ɛ1 6χ9	640 757	.0χƐ0	9Ɛ4 8Ɛ4	458
1	784 006	0χ6	1	.877 332 244	255	1	.898 41χ 150	624 Ɛχ5
2	.856 221 0Ɛ0	658 753	2	972 499	63Ɛ 956	2	χ43 135	731
3	879 843	203	3	.878 3Ɛ2 233	457	3	.899 467 866	27Ɛ
4	.857 315 χ46	657 873	4	χ31 68χ	63χ Ɛ59	4	χ8Ɛ Ɛ25	623 χ0χ
5	971 6Ɛ9	326	5	.879 470 627	661	5	.89χ 4Ɛ3 933	55Ɛ
6	.858 408 χ23	656 998	6	χχƐ 088	166	6	Ɛ17 292	0Ɛ0
7	χ63 7ƐƐ	451	7	.87χ 529 232	639 86Ɛ	7	.89Ɛ 53χ 382	622 843
8	.859 4Ɛχ 050	655 Ɛ08	8	Ɛ66 χχ1	378	8	Ɛ61 005	396
9	Ɛ53 Ɛ58	582	9	.87Ɛ 5χ4 259	638 χ83	9	.8χ0 583 39Ɛ	621 ƐƐƐ
χ	.85χ 5χ9 51χ	03Ɛ	χ	.880 021 120	592	χ	Ɛχ5 30χ	685
Ɛ	.85Ɛ 042 559	654 6Ɛχ	Ɛ	659 6Ɛ2	0χ1	Ɛ	.8χ1 606 993	220

N	Log Tan	d	N	Log Tan	d	N	Log Tan	d
.0Ɛ00	Ɛ.8χ2 027 ƐƐ3	620 978	.0Ɛ40	Ɛ.902 574 864	607 52χ	.0Ɛ80	Ɛ.922 554 697	5Ɛ3 541
1	648 96Ɛ	515	1	Ɛ80 192	10Ɛ	1	Ɛ48 018	161
2	.8χ3 069 284	074	2	.903 587 2χ1	606 8Ɛ0	2	.923 53Ɛ 179	5Ɛ2 982
3	689 338	61Ɛ 813	3	Ɛ91 Ɛ91	493	3	Ɛ31 Ɛ3Ɛ	5χ5
4	.8χ4 0χ8 Ɛ4Ɛ	374	4	.904 598 464	077	4	.924 524 524	207
5	708 303	61χ Ɛ16	5	Ɛχ2 51Ɛ	605 860	5	Ɛ16 72Ɛ	5Ɛ1 χ30
6	.8χ5 127 219	678	6	.905 5χ8 17Ɛ	446	6	.925 508 55Ɛ	655
7	745 895	220	7	ƐƐ1 605	030	7	χƐ9 ƐƐ4	27Ɛ
8	.8χ6 163 χƐ5	619 986	8	.906 5Ɛ6 635	604 818	8	.926 4χƐ 273	5Ɛ0 χχ6
9	781 87Ɛ	52Ɛ	9	ƐƐƐ 251	406	9	χχ0 159	712
χ	.8χ7 19Ɛ 1χχ	096	χ	.907 603 657	603 ƐƐ3	χ	.927 490 86Ɛ	33χ
Ɛ	7Ɛ8 284	618 843	Ɛ	.908 007 64χ	7χ2	Ɛ	χ80 Ɛχ9	5χƐ Ɛ69
.0Ɛ10	.8χ8 214 Ɛ07	3Ɛ1	.0Ɛ50	60Ɛ 230	392	.0Ɛ90	.928 470 Ɛ56	797
1	831 2Ɛ8	617 Ɛ5Ɛ	1	.909 012 602	602 Ɛ83	1	χ60 731	407
2	.8χ9 249 257	70χ	2	615 585	775	2	.929 44Ɛ Ɛ38	037
3	864 965	27Ɛ	3	.90χ 018 13χ	367	3	χ3χ Ɛ73	5χχ 869
4	.8χχ 280 024	616 χ31	4	61χ 4χ5	601 Ɛ60	4	.92χ 429 820	49Ɛ
5	896 χ55	5χ4	5	.90Ɛ 020 445	755	5	χ18 0ƐƐ	113
6	.8χƐ 2Ɛ1 439	158	6	621 Ɛ9χ	34Ɛ	6	.92Ɛ 406 212	5χ9 947
7	907 595	615 910	7	.910 023 329	600 Ɛ46	7	9Ɛ3 Ɛ59	580
8	.8Ɛ0 321 2χ5	487	8	624 273	741	8	.930 3χ1 519	1Ɛ6
9	936 770	042	9	.911 024 9Ɛ4	33Ɛ	9	98χ 713	5χ8 χ32
χ	.8Ɛ1 34Ɛ 7Ɛ2	614 7ƐƐ	χ	625 133	5ƐƐ Ɛ39	χ	.931 377 545	66χ
Ɛ	964 3Ɛ1	377	Ɛ	.912 025 070	737	Ɛ	963 ƐƐ3	2χ6
.0Ɛ20	.8Ɛ2 378 768	613 Ɛ37	.0Ɛ60	624 7χ7	338	.0Ɛχ0	.932 350 299	5χ7 Ɛ25
1	990 6χ3	6Ɛ5	1	.913 023 Ɛ23	5Ɛχ Ɛ39	1	938 202	763
2	.8Ɛ3 3χ4 198	276	2	622 χ60	73χ	2	.933 323 965	3χ3
3	9Ɛ7 452	612 χ38	3	.914 021 59χ	342	3	90Ɛ 148	023
4	.8Ɛ4 40χ 28χ	5ƐƐ	4	61Ɛ 920	5Ɛ9 Ɛ45	4	.934 2Ɛ6 16Ɛ	5χ6 865
5	χ20 889	182	5	.915 019 865	74χ	5	8χ0 χ14	4χ8
6	.8Ɛ5 432 χ4Ɛ	611 947	6	617 3Ɛ3	355	6	.935 287 300	12Ɛ
7	χ44 796	511	7	.916 014 748	5Ɛ8 Ɛ5Ɛ	7	871 42Ɛ	5χ5 973
8	.8Ɛ6 456 0χ7	098	8	611 6χ7	767	8	.936 257 1χ2	5Ɛ9
9	χ67 183	610 864	9	.917 00χ 252	373	9	840 79Ɛ	242
χ	.8Ɛ7 477 χ27	431	χ	606 605	5Ɛ7 Ɛ82	χ	.937 225 χ21	5χ4 χ8χ
Ɛ	χ88 258	60Ɛ ƐƐƐ	Ɛ	.918 002 587	790	Ɛ	80χ 8χƐ	715
.0Ɛ30	.8Ɛ8 498 257	78Ɛ	.0Ɛ70	5Ɛχ 157	3χ1	.0ƐƐ0	.938 1Ɛ3 404	363
1	χχ7 χ26	35χ	1	ƐƐ5 538	5Ɛ6 ƐƐ0	1	797 767	5χ3 ƐƐ0
2	.8Ɛ9 4Ɛ7 184	60χ Ɛ30	2	.919 5Ɛ0 528	803	2	.939 17Ɛ 757	83Ɛ
3	Ɛ06 0Ɛ4	702	3	Ɛχ7 12Ɛ	415	3	763 396	48χ
4	.8Ɛχ 514 7Ɛ6	296	4	.91χ 5χ1 544	029	4	.93χ 146 864	11Ɛ
5	Ɛ22 χ90	609 χ6χ	5	Ɛ97 571	5Ɛ5 842	5	729 983	5χ2 970
6	.8ƐƐ 530 93χ	643	6	.91Ɛ 591 1Ɛ3	457	6	.93Ɛ 110 733	602
7	Ɛ3χ 381	21χ	7	Ɛ86 64χ	071	7	6Ɛ3 135	256
8	.900 547 59Ɛ	608 9Ɛ5	8	.920 57Ɛ 6ƐƐ	5Ɛ4 88χ	8	.940 095 38Ɛ	5χ1 χχ9
9	Ɛ54 394	592	9	Ɛ74 389	4χ5	9	677 278	743
χ	.901 560 966	170	χ	.921 568 872	103	χ	.941 058 9ƐƐ	398
Ɛ	Ɛ68 Ɛ16	607 94χ	Ɛ	Ɛ60 975	5Ɛ3 922	Ɛ	63χ 197	033

N	Log Tan	d	N	Log Tan	d	N	Log Tan	d
.1000	Ɛ.942 01Ɛ 20χ	5χ0 88Ɛ	.1040	Ɛ.961 21Ɛ 706	58Ɛ 245	.1080	Ɛ.97Ɛ Ɛχ0 χ0Ɛ	57χ 935
1	5ƐƐ χ99	527	1	7χχ 94Ɛ	58χ Ɛ17	1	.980 55Ɛ 744	63χ
2	Ɛχ0 404	185	2	.962 179 866	7χχ	2	Ɛ1χ 182	343
3	.943 580 589	59Ɛ χ22	3	748 454	481	3	.981 498 505	049
4	Ɛ60 3χƐ	682	4	.963 116 915	156	4	χ56 552	579 953
5	.944 53Ɛ χ71	322	5	6χ4 χ6Ɛ	589 χ2χ	5	.982 414 2χ5	65χ
6	Ɛ1Ɛ 193	59χ Ɛ83	6	.964 072 899	704	6	991 943	366
7	.945 4Ɛχ 156	825	7	640 3χ1	39Ɛ	7	.983 34Ɛ 0χ9	074
8	χ98 97Ɛ	487	8	.965 009 780	076	8	908 161	578 981
9	.946 477 246	12Ɛ	9	596 836	588 952	9	.984 284 Ɛ22	68Ɛ
χ	χ55 375	599 994	χ	Ɛ63 588	630	χ	841 5Ɛ1	39χ
Ɛ	.947 433 149	638	Ɛ	.966 52Ɛ ƐƐ8	309	Ɛ	.985 1Ɛ9 98Ɛ	0χƐ
.1010	χ10 785	2χ3	.1050	χƐ8 305	587 Ɛχ9	.1090	775 χ7χ	577 9ƐƐ
1	.948 3χ9 χ68	598 Ɛ4χ	1	.967 484 2Ɛ2	887	1	.986 131 879	710
2	986 9Ɛ6	7Ɛ6	2	χ4Ɛ Ɛ79	568	2	6χ9 389	423
3	.949 363 5Ɛ0	463	3	.968 417 525	24χ	3	.987 064 7Ɛ0	136
4	93Ɛ χ53	110	4	9χ2 773	586 Ɛ2Ɛ	4	61Ɛ 926	576 χ49
5	.94χ 317 Ɛ63	597 97Ɛ	5	.969 369 6χ2	812	5	Ɛ96 773	762
6	8Ɛ3 922	62χ	6	934 2Ɛ4	4Ɛ6	6	.988 551 315	478
7	.94Ɛ 28Ɛ 350	29Ɛ	7	.96χ 2Ɛχ 7χχ	19χ	7	Ɛ07 791	191
8	866 62Ɛ	596 Ɛ4Ɛ	8	884 988	585 χ83	8	.989 481 962	575 χχ8
9	.950 241 57χ	802	9	.96Ɛ 24χ 84Ɛ	76χ	9	χ37 84χ	804
χ	818 180	475	χ	814 3Ɛ9	454	χ	.98χ 3Ɛ1 452	51Ɛ
Ɛ	.951 1Ɛ2 635	128	Ɛ	.970 199 851	140	Ɛ	966 971	239
.1020	788 761	595 9χ1	.1060	762 991	584 χ28	.10χ0	.98Ɛ 31Ɛ Ɛχχ	574 Ɛ57
1	.952 162 542	656	1	.971 127 7Ɛ9	716	1	894 Ɛ45	876
2	737 Ɛ98	311	2	6Ɛ0 313	403	2	.990 249 7ƐƐ	594
3	.953 111 2χ9	594 Ɛ87	3	.972 074 716	0Ɛ3	3	802 193	2Ɛ5
4	6χ6 274	844	4	638 809	583 9χ2	4	.991 176 488	015
5	.954 07χ χƐ8	501	5	.973 000 5χƐ	693	5	72χ 4χ1	573 938
6	653 3Ɛ9	17χ	6	584 082	384	6	.992 0χ2 219	659
7	.955 027 577	593 χ39	7	Ɛ47 446	075	7	655 876	380
8	5ƐƐ 3Ɛ4	6Ɛ8	8	.974 50χ 4ƐƐ	582 969	8	.993 009 036	0χ5
9	Ɛ92 χƐ0	379	9	χ91 268	661	9	580 11Ɛ	572 χ09
χ	.956 566 269	03χ	χ	.975 453 909	355	χ	Ɛ32 Ɛ28	732
Ɛ	Ɛ39 2χ7	592 8ƐƐ	Ɛ	χ16 062	04χ	Ɛ	.994 4χ5 65χ	458
.1030	.957 50Ɛ Ɛχ6	583	.1070	.976 398 0Ɛ0	581 944	.10Ɛ0	χ57 χƐ6	183
1	χχ2 569	246	1	959 χ34	63Ɛ	1	.995 40χ 079	571 χχƐ
2	.958 474 7Ɛ3	591 Ɛ0Ɛ	2	.977 31Ɛ 473	336	2	97Ɛ Ɛ68	816
3	χ46 702	794	3	8χ0 7χ9	033	3	.996 331 782	544
4	.959 418 296	45χ	4	.978 261 820	580 930	4	8χ3 106	272
5	9χ9 734	125	5	822 550	62χ	5	.997 254 378	570 Ɛχ0
6	.95χ 37χ 859	590 9Ɛ1	6	.979 1χ2 Ɛ7χ	329	6	805 358	90Ɛ
7	94Ɛ 64χ	679	7	763 2χ7	028	7	.998 176 067	63Ɛ
8	.95Ɛ 320 107	348	8	.97χ 123 313	57Ɛ 929	8	726 6χ6	370
9	8Ɛ0 453	015	9	6χ3 040	629	9	.999 096 χ56	0χ2
χ	.960 280 468	58Ɛ 8χ5	χ	.97Ɛ 062 669	330	χ	646 Ɛ38	56Ɛ χ13
Ɛ	850 151	575	Ɛ	621 999	032	Ɛ	ƐƐ6 94Ɛ	747

N	Log Tan	d	N	Log Tan	d	N	Log Tan	d
.1100	Ɛ.99χ 566 496	56Ɛ 47χ	.1140	Ɛ.9Ɛ8 774 6χƐ	560 Ɛ89	.1180	Ɛ.χ16 644 χ71	553 5χ2
1	Ɛ15 954	1Ɛ3	1	.9Ɛ9 115 678	92Ɛ	1	Ɛ98 453	370
2	.99Ɛ 484 Ɛ47	56χ Ɛ27	2	676 3χ7	692	2	.χ17 5ƐƐ 803	140
3	χ33 χ72	862	3	.9Ɛχ 016 χ79	435	3	χ82 943	552 Ɛ10
4	.9χ0 3χ2 714	598	4	577 2Ɛ2	19Ɛ	4	.χ18 415 853	8χ0
5	951 0Ɛ0	313	5	Ɛ17 491	55Ɛ Ɛ43	5	968 533	672
6	.9χ1 2ƐƐ 403	04Ɛ	6	.9ƐƐ 477 414	8χχ	6	.χ19 2Ɛχ Ɛχ5	444
7	869 452	569 988	7	χ17 102	654	7	851 429	216
8	.9χ2 217 21χ	706	8	.χ00 376 756	3ƐƐ	8	.χ1χ 1χ3 643	551 Ɛχ9
9	784 924	443	9	915 Ɛ55	167	9	735 630	981
χ	.9χ3 132 167	183	χ	.χ01 275 100	55χ Ɛ14	χ	.χ1Ɛ 087 3Ɛ1	756
Ɛ	69Ɛ 32χ	568 Ɛ02	Ɛ	814 014	881	Ɛ	618 Ɛ47	52Ɛ
.1110	.9χ4 048 230	843	.1150	.χ02 172 895	62Ɛ	.1190	Ɛ6χ 476	305
1	5Ɛ4 χ73	583	1	711 304	399	1	.χ20 4ƐƐ 77Ɛ	09Ɛ
2	Ɛ61 436	306	2	.χ03 06Ɛ 6χ1	149	2	χ50 85χ	550 χ76
3	.9χ5 509 740	048	3	609 82χ	559 χƐχ	3	.χ21 3χ1 714	852
4	χ75 788	567 98Ɛ	4	Ɛ67 728	869	4	932 366	62Ɛ
5	.9χ6 421 557	713	5	.χ04 505 395	61Ɛ	5	.χ22 282 995	407
6	989 06χ	458	6	χ62 9Ɛ4	392	6	813 1χ0	1χ5
7	.9χ7 334 506	1χ1	7	.χ05 400 186	144	7	.χ23 163 385	54Ɛ Ɛ84
8	89Ɛ 6χ7	566 Ɛ27	8	959 30χ	558 χƐ7	8	6Ɛ3 349	962
9	.9χ8 246 612	872	9	.χ06 2Ɛ6 205	86Ɛ	9	.χ24 043 0χƐ	742
χ	7Ɛ1 284	5Ɛχ	χ	852 χ74	624	χ	592 831	523
Ɛ	.9χ9 157 882	345	Ɛ	.χ07 1χƐ 498	39χ	Ɛ	ƐƐ2 154	303
.1120	702 007	093	.1160	747 876	154	.11χ0	.χ25 471 457	0χ4
1	.9χχ 068 09χ	565 χ21	1	.χ08 0χ3 χ0χ	557 Ɛ0χ	1	χ00 53Ɛ	54χ χ87
2	611 χƐƐ	76χ	2	63Ɛ 918	886	2	.χ26 34Ɛ 406	86χ
3	Ɛ77 669	4Ɛχ	3	Ɛ97 5χ2	642	3	89χ 074	651
4	.9χƐ 520 Ɛ67	24χ	4	.χ09 533 024	3ƐƐ	4	.χ27 228 705	435
5	χ86 1Ɛ5	564 Ɛ9χ	5	χ8χ 423	178	5	776 Ɛ3χ	219
6	.9Ɛ0 42Ɛ 193	92Ɛ	6	.χ0χ 425 59Ɛ	556 Ɛ37	6	.χ28 105 157	003
7	993 Ɛ02	681	7	980 516	8Ɛ5	7	653 15χ	549 9χ9
8	.9Ɛ1 338 583	414	8	.χ0Ɛ 317 20Ɛ	674	8	Ɛχ0 Ɛ47	794
9	8χ0 997	167	9	871 883	435	9	.χ29 52χ 71Ɛ	57Ɛ
χ	.9Ɛ2 244 Ɛ42	563 χƐƐ	χ	.χ10 208 0Ɛ8	1Ɛ6	χ	χ78 09χ	367
Ɛ	7χ8 χ41	854	Ɛ	762 2Ɛ2	555 Ɛ76	Ɛ	.χ2χ 405 445	153
.1130	.9Ɛ3 150 695	5χ9	.1170	.χ11 0Ɛ8 268	93χ	.11Ɛ0	952 598	548 Ɛ40
1	6Ɛ4 082	343	1	651 Ɛχ6	6ƐƐ	1	.χ2Ɛ 29Ɛ 518	92χ
2	.9Ɛ4 057 405	09χ	2	Ɛχ7 6χ5	484	2	828 246	718
3	5Ɛχ 4χ3	562 χ36	3	.χ12 540 Ɛ69	247	3	.χ30 174 962	508
4	Ɛ61 319	792	4	χ96 1Ɛ4	010	4	701 26χ	2Ɛ7
5	.9Ɛ5 503 χχƐ	52χ	5	.χ13 42Ɛ 204	554 996	5	.χ31 049 565	0χ7
6	χ66 419	289	6	983 Ɛ9χ	75Ɛ	6	595 650	547 χ98
7	.9Ɛ6 408 6χ6	026	7	.χ14 318 739	526	7	Ɛ21 528	88χ
8	96χ 710	561 986	8	871 063	2Ɛ2	8	.χ32 469 1Ɛ6	680
9	.9Ɛ7 310 496	725	9	.χ15 205 355	07χ	9	9Ɛ4 876	472
χ	871 ƐƐƐ	486	χ	759 413	553 χ46	χ	.χ33 340 128	266
Ɛ	.9Ɛ8 213 485	226	Ɛ	.χ16 0Ɛ1 259	814	Ɛ	887 392	05χ

N	Log Tan	d	N	Log Tan	d	N	Log Tan	d
.1200	Ɛ.X34 212 430	546 X53	.1240	Ɛ.X51 711 X02	53Ɛ 0Ɛ8	.1280	Ɛ.X6X 976 292	534 103
1	759 283	848	1	.X52 050 XƐX	53X Ɛ17	1	.X6Ɛ 2XX 395	533 Ɛ45
2	.X35 0X3 Ɛ0Ɛ	641	2	58Ɛ X15	936	2	822 31X	988
3	62X 550	439	3	Ɛ0X 74Ɛ	756	3	.X70 156 0X6	80Ɛ
4	Ɛ74 989	233	4	.X53 449 2X5	576	4	689 8Ɛ5	653
5	.X36 4ƐƐ 000	02Ɛ	5	987 85Ɛ	396	5	.X71 001 348	498
6	X45 02Ɛ	545 X27	6	.X54 306 035	1Ɛ8	6	534 824	321
7	.X37 38X X56	825	7	844 231	01X	7	X67 Ɛ45	167
8	914 67Ɛ	622	8	.X55 182 24Ɛ	539 X40	8	.X72 39Ɛ 0Ɛ0	532 ƐƐ0
9	.X38 25X 0X1	420	9	700 08Ɛ	864	9	912 0X0	X38
X	7X3 501	21Ɛ	X	.X56 039 933	687	X	.X73 244 Ɛ18	883
Ɛ	.X39 128 720	01X	Ɛ	577 3ƐX	4Ɛ0	Ɛ	777 79Ɛ	70Ɛ
.1210	671 73X	544 X1X	.1250	XƐ4 8XX	314	.1290	.X74 0XX 2XX	557
1	ƐƐ6 558	820	1	.X57 432 002	13X	1	620 845	3X4
2	.X3X 53Ɛ 178	620	2	96Ɛ 140	538 Ɛ64	2	Ɛ53 029	232
3	X83 798	422	3	.X58 2X8 0X4	98X	3	.X75 485 25Ɛ	080
4	.X3Ɛ 407 ƐƐX	225	4	824 X72	7Ɛ6	4	9Ɛ7 31Ɛ	531 Ɛ0Ɛ
5	950 223	028	5	.X59 161 668	621	5	.X76 329 22X	95X
6	.X40 294 24Ɛ	543 X2Ɛ	6	69X 089	44X	6	85X Ɛ88	7XX
7	818 07X	834	7	.X5X 016 517	277	7	.X77 190 776	63Ɛ
8	.X41 15Ɛ 8Ɛ2	639	8	552 792	0X5	8	702 1Ɛ5	48Ɛ
9	6X3 32Ɛ	443	9	X8X 877	537 Ɛ12	9	.X78 033 684	321
X	.X42 026 772	248	X	.X5Ɛ 406 789	942	X	564 9X5	173
Ɛ	569 9ƐX	054	Ɛ	942 50Ɛ	770	Ɛ	X95 Ɛ58	005
.1220	XƐ0 X52	542 X5X	.1260	.X60 27X 07Ɛ	5X1	.12X0	.X79 406 Ɛ61	530 X59
1	.X43 433 8Ɛ0	867	1	7Ɛ5 660	411	1	937 9ƐX	8Ɛ0
2	976 557	673	2	.X61 130 X71	242	2	.X7X 268 6XX	745
3	.X44 2Ɛ9 00X	481	3	668 0Ɛ3	073	3	799 233	59X
4	83Ɛ 48Ɛ	28X	4	ƐX3 166	536 XX6	4	.X7Ɛ 109 811	433
5	.X45 181 759	099	5	.X62 51X 050	919	5	63X 044	289
6	703 836	541 XX8	6	X54 969	750	6	Ɛ6X 311	124
7	.X46 045 722	8Ɛ7	7	.X63 38Ɛ 4Ɛ9	584	7	.X80 49X 435	52Ɛ Ɛ7Ɛ
8	587 419	708	8	905 X81	3Ɛ8	8	X0X 3Ɛ4	X16
9	Ɛ08 Ɛ25	518	9	.X64 240 279	232	9	.X81 33X 20X	873
X	.X47 44X 441	32X	X	776 4XƐ	067	X	869 X81	70Ɛ
Ɛ	98Ɛ 76Ɛ	140	Ɛ	.X65 0Ɛ0 556	535 XX2	Ɛ	.X82 199 590	569
.1230	.X48 310 8XƐ	540 Ɛ52	.1270	626 438	918	.12Ɛ0	708 Ɛ39	406
1	851 841	966	1	Ɛ60 154	754	1	.X83 038 343	265
2	.X49 192 5X7	77X	2	.X66 495 8X8	590	2	567 5X8	104
3	713 165	592	3	X0Ɛ 278	408	3	X96 6Ɛ0	52X Ɛ64
4	.X4X 053 737	3X7	4	.X67 344 684	245	4	.X84 405 654	X03
5	593 Ɛ22	200	5	879 909	083	5	934 457	864
6	Ɛ14 122	017	6	.X68 1Ɛ2 990	534 Ɛ01	6	.X85 263 0ƐƐ	705
7	.X4Ɛ 454 139	53Ɛ X32	7	727 891	941	7	791 804	567
8	993 Ɛ6Ɛ	849	8	.X69 060 612	77Ɛ	8	.X86 100 16Ɛ	40X
9	.X50 313 7Ɛ8	665	9	595 191	600	9	62X 579	270
X	853 261	482	X	Ɛ09 791	440	X	Ɛ58 829	113
Ɛ	.X51 192 723	29Ɛ	Ɛ	.X6X 442 011	281	Ɛ	.X87 486 940	529 Ɛ77

N	Log Tan	d
.1300	Ɛ.X87 9Ɛ4 8Ɛ7	529 X20
1	.X88 322 717	885
2	850 3X0	72X
3	.X89 179 Ɛ0X	595
4	6X7 4X3	43Ɛ
5	.X8X 014 922	2X6
6	542 008	152
7	X6Ɛ 15X	528 ƐƐX
8	.X8Ɛ 398 158	X68
9	905 004	914
X	.X90 231 918	782
Ɛ	75X 49X	631
.1310	.X91 086 Ɛ0Ɛ	4X0
1	5Ɛ3 3XƐ	34Ɛ
2	Ɛ1Ɛ 73X	200
3	.X92 447 93X	070
4	973 9XX	527 Ɛ21
5	.X93 29Ɛ 90Ɛ	993
6	807 6X2	845
7	.X94 133 327	6Ɛ8
8	65X X23	56Ɛ
9	Ɛ86 392	423
X	.X95 4Ɛ1 7Ɛ5	298
Ɛ	X18 X91	150
.1320	.X96 344 021	006
1	86Ɛ 027	526 X80
2	.X97 195 XX7	936
3	700 821	7Ɛ2
4	.X98 027 413	669
5	551 X80	525
6	X78 3X5	3X2
7	.X99 3X2 787	25Ɛ
8	908 X26	119
9	.X9X 232 Ɛ43	525 Ɛ97
X	758 Ɛ1X	X56
Ɛ	.X9Ɛ 082 974	916
.1330	5X8 68X	795
1	Ɛ12 263	656
2	.XX0 437 8Ɛ9	517
3	961 214	398
4	.XX1 286 5Ɛ0	25X
5	7XƐ 84X	121
6	.XX2 114 96Ɛ	524 ƐX3
7	639 952	X68
8	Ɛ62 7ƐX	92Ɛ
9	.XX3 487 529	7Ɛ5
X	9Ɛ0 122	679
Ɛ	.XX4 314 79Ɛ	543

N	Log Tan	d
.1340	Ɛ.XX4 839 122	524 40X
1	.XX5 161 530	294
2	685 804	15Ɛ
3	ƐX9 963	028
4	.XX6 511 98Ɛ	523 XƐ3
5	X35 882	981
6	.XX7 359 643	84X
7	881 291	718
8	.XX8 1X4 9X9	5X6
9	708 393	476
X	.XX9 02Ɛ 849	345
Ɛ	552 Ɛ92	215
.1350	X76 1X7	0X5
1	.XXX 399 290	522 Ɛ77
2	900 247	X48
3	.XXƐ 223 093	91Ɛ
4	745 9Ɛ2	7Ɛ1
5	.XƐ0 068 5X3	684
6	58Ɛ 067	558
7	XƐ1 603	430
8	.XƐ1 413 X33	305
9	936 138	19X
X	.XƐ2 258 316	074
Ɛ	77X 38X	521 Ɛ4Ɛ
.1360	.XƐ3 0X0 319	X25
1	602 142	900
2	Ɛ23 X42	799
3	.XƐ4 445 61Ɛ	675
4	967 094	551
5	.XƐ5 288 625	42Ɛ
6	7X9 X54	30X
7	.XƐ6 10Ɛ 162	1X7
8	630 349	087
9	Ɛ51 414	520 Ɛ66
X	.XƐ7 472 37X	X46
Ɛ	993 204	926
.1370	.XƐ8 2Ɛ3 Ɛ2X	808
1	814 736	6X9
2	.XƐ9 135 223	58Ɛ
3	655 7Ɛ2	472
4	Ɛ76 064	355
5	.XƐX 496 3Ɛ9	239
6	9Ɛ6 636	120
7	.XƐƐ 316 756	006
8	836 760	51Ɛ XXX
9	.Ɛ00 156 64X	995
X	676 423	87X
Ɛ	Ɛ96 0X1	765

N	Log Tan	d
.1380	Ɛ.Ɛ01 4Ɛ5 846	51Ɛ 650
1	X15 296	538
2	.Ɛ02 334 812	425
3	854 037	311
4	.Ɛ03 173 348	1ƐX
5	692 546	0X8
6	ƐƐ1 632	51X Ɛ97
7	.Ɛ04 510 609	X85
8	X2Ɛ 492	974
9	.Ɛ05 34X 246	864
X	868 XXX	755
Ɛ	.Ɛ06 187 643	645
.1390	6X6 088	537
1	.Ɛ07 004 603	429
2	522 X30	31Ɛ
3	X41 14Ɛ	212
4	.Ɛ08 35Ɛ 361	105
5	879 466	519 ƐƐ9
6	.Ɛ09 197 463	XƐ1
7	6Ɛ5 354	9X7
8	.Ɛ0X 013 13Ɛ	89Ɛ
9	530 X1X	796
X	X4X 5Ɛ4	690
Ɛ	.Ɛ0Ɛ 368 084	587
.13X0	885 64Ɛ	483
1	.Ɛ10 1X2 Ɛ12	37X
2	700 290	277
3	.Ɛ11 019 547	173
4	536 6ƐX	072
5	X53 770	518 Ɛ6Ɛ
6	.Ɛ12 370 71Ɛ	X69
7	889 588	969
8	.Ɛ13 1X6 335	868
9	702 ƐX1	767
X	.Ɛ14 01Ɛ 748	669
Ɛ	538 1Ɛ5	569
.13Ɛ0	X54 762	46Ɛ
1	.Ɛ15 371 011	371
2	889 382	273
3	.Ɛ16 1X5 635	176
4	701 7XƐ	079
5	.Ɛ17 019 868	517 Ɛ82
6	535 82X	X86
7	X51 6Ɛ4	98Ɛ
8	.Ɛ18 369 483	895
9	885 158	79X
X	.Ɛ19 1X0 936	6X5
Ɛ	6Ɛ8 41Ɛ	5Ɛ0

N	Log Tan	d	N	Log Tan	d	N	Log Tan	d
.1400	Ɛ.Ɛ1X 013 X0Ɛ	517 4Ɛ7	.1440	Ɛ.Ɛ36 5ƐƐ X41	513 Ɛ5Ɛ	.1480	Ɛ.Ɛ52 XX1 378	511 199
1	52Ɛ 306	403	1	Ɛ13 9X0	X87	1	.Ɛ53 3Ɛ2 555	124
2	X46 709	310	2	.Ɛ37 427 867	9Ɛ2	2	903 679	06Ɛ
3	.Ɛ1Ɛ 361 X19	219	3	93Ɛ 659	91Ɛ	3	.Ɛ54 214 728	510 ƐƐ6
4	879 036	126	4	.Ɛ38 253 378	849	4	725 722	Ɛ43
5	.Ɛ20 194 160	034	5	767 005	775	5	.Ɛ55 036 665	X8Ɛ
6	6XƐ 194	516 Ɛ42	6	.Ɛ39 07X 77X	6X4	6	547 534	X19
7	.Ɛ21 006 116	X52	7	592 262	612	7	X58 351	966
8	520 Ɛ68	961	8	XX5 874	542	8	.Ɛ56 369 0Ɛ7	8Ɛ4
9	X37 909	871	9	.Ɛ3X 3Ɛ9 1Ɛ6	470	9	879 9XƐ	843
X	.Ɛ22 352 57X	781	X	910 666	3X1	X	.Ɛ57 18X 632	792
Ɛ	869 13Ɛ	692	Ɛ	.Ɛ3Ɛ 223 X47	311	Ɛ	69Ɛ 204	721
.1410	.Ɛ23 183 811	5X4	.1450	737 158	242	.1490	ƐXƐ 925	671
1	69X 1Ɛ5	4Ɛ5	1	.Ɛ40 04X 39X	174	1	.Ɛ58 500 396	602
2	ƐƐ4 6XX	408	2	561 552	0X5	2	X10 998	553
3	.Ɛ24 50X XƐ6	31Ɛ	3	X74 637	018	3	.Ɛ59 321 32Ɛ	4X4
4	X25 215	233	4	.Ɛ41 387 653	512 Ɛ4X	4	831 813	436
5	.Ɛ25 33Ɛ 448	146	5	89X 5X1	X82	5	.Ɛ5X 142 049	388
6	855 592	05X	6	.Ɛ42 1Ɛ1 463	9Ɛ6	6	652 415	320
7	.Ɛ26 16Ɛ 630	515 Ɛ74	7	704 259	92Ɛ	7	Ɛ62 735	272
8	685 5X4	X89	8	.Ɛ43 016 Ɛ88	862	8	.Ɛ5Ɛ 472 9X7	206
9	Ɛ9Ɛ 471	9X2	9	529 82X	799	9	982 ƐƐ1	15Ɛ
X	.Ɛ27 4Ɛ5 253	8Ɛ9	X	X40 407	712	X	.Ɛ60 293 150	0Ɛ3
Ɛ	X0X Ɛ50	814	Ɛ	.Ɛ44 352 Ɛ19	648	Ɛ	7X3 243	049
.1420	.Ɛ28 324 764	730	.1460	865 565	583	.14X0	.Ɛ61 0Ɛ3 290	50Ɛ ƐX2
1	83X 294	647	1	.Ɛ45 177 Ɛ28	4ƐX	1	603 272	Ɛ38
2	.Ɛ29 153 91Ɛ	563	2	68X 426	436	2	Ɛ13 1XX	X93
3	669 282	480	3	ƐX0 860	372	3	.Ɛ62 423 081	X2X
4	Ɛ82 742	39X	4	.Ɛ46 4Ɛ3 012	2XƐ	4	932 XXƐ	986
5	.Ɛ2X 497 Ɛ20	2Ɛ7	5	X05 301	228	5	.Ɛ63 242 875	922
6	9Ɛ1 217	216	6	.Ɛ47 317 529	166	6	752 597	87X
7	.Ɛ2Ɛ 306 431	135	7	829 693	0X3	7	.Ɛ64 062 255	817
8	81Ɛ 566	053	8	.Ɛ48 13Ɛ 776	023	8	571 X70	775
9	.Ɛ30 134 5Ɛ9	514 Ɛ74	9	651 799	511 Ɛ61	9	X81 625	712
X	649 571	X94	X	Ɛ63 73X	XX1	X	.Ɛ65 391 137	672
Ɛ	Ɛ62 445	9Ɛ4	Ɛ	.Ɛ49 475 61Ɛ	X21	Ɛ	8X0 7X9	610
.1430	.Ɛ31 477 239	916	.1470	987 440	961	.14Ɛ0	.Ɛ66 1Ɛ0 1Ɛ9	56Ɛ
1	98Ɛ Ɛ53	838	1	.Ɛ4X 299 1X1	8X3	1	6ƐƐ 768	50Ɛ
2	.Ɛ32 2X4 78Ɛ	75X	2	7XX X84	824	2	.Ɛ67 00Ɛ 077	470
3	7Ɛ9 329	680	3	.Ɛ4Ɛ 100 6X8	766	3	51X 527	410
4	.Ɛ33 111 9X9	5X4	4	612 252	6X8	4	X29 937	371
5	626 391	507	5	Ɛ23 93X	62Ɛ	5	.Ɛ68 339 0X8	314
6	Ɛ3X 898	430	6	.Ɛ50 435 369	573	6	848 400	275
7	.Ɛ34 453 108	354	7	946 920	4Ɛ6	7	.Ɛ69 157 675	218
8	967 460	279	8	.Ɛ51 258 216	43Ɛ	8	666 891	180
9	.Ɛ35 27Ɛ 719	1X3	9	769 655	383	9	Ɛ75 X51	122
X	793 900	10X	X	.Ɛ52 07X X18	309	X	.Ɛ6X 484 Ɛ73	087
Ɛ	.Ɛ36 0X7 X0X	033	Ɛ	590 125	253	Ɛ	994 03X	030

N	Log Tan	d	N	Log Tan	d	N	Log Tan	d
.1500	Ɛ.Ɛ6Ɛ 2X3 06X	50X Ɛ94	.1540	Ɛ.Ɛ87 62Ɛ 568	509 535	.1580	Ɛ.ƐX3 928 651	508 631
1	7Ɛ2 042	Ɛ3Ɛ	1	Ɛ38 XX1	4ƐX	1	.ƐX4 235 082	613
2	.Ɛ70 100 Ɛ81	XX4	2	.Ɛ88 446 39Ɛ	482	2	741 695	5Ɛ6
3	60Ɛ X65	X4X	3	953 861	447	3	.ƐX5 04X 08Ɛ	599
4	Ɛ1X 8Ɛ3	9Ɛ5	4	.Ɛ89 261 0X8	410	4	556 668	581
5	.Ɛ71 429 6X8	961	5	76X 4Ɛ8	396	5	X63 029	564
6	938 449	909	6	.Ɛ8X 077 892	361	6	.ƐX6 36Ɛ 591	54X
7	.Ɛ72 247 156	875	7	585 033	327	7	877 Ɛ1Ɛ	532
8	755 X0Ɛ	821	8	X92 35X	2Ɛ2	8	.ƐX7 184 451	518
9	.Ɛ73 064 630	78Ɛ	9	.Ɛ8Ɛ 39Ɛ 650	27X	9	690 969	502
X	573 1ƐƐ	739	X	8X8 90X	247	X	Ɛ99 26Ɛ	4X8
Ɛ	X81 938	6X7	Ɛ	.Ɛ90 1Ɛ5 Ɛ55	213	Ɛ	.ƐX8 4X5 757	493
.1510	.Ɛ74 390 423	656	.1550	703 168	1X0	.1590	9Ɛ2 02X	47Ɛ
1	89X X79	604	1	.Ɛ91 010 348	169	1	.ƐX9 2ƐX 4X9	466
2	.Ɛ75 1X9 481	575	2	519 4Ɛ5	138	2	806 953	452
3	6Ɛ7 X36	524	3	X26 631	106	3	.ƐXX 113 1X5	440
4	.Ɛ76 006 35X	495	4	.Ɛ92 333 737	095	4	61Ɛ 625	428
5	514 833	446	5	840 810	065	5	Ɛ27 X51	417
6	X23 079	3Ɛ7	6	.Ɛ93 149 875	034	6	.ƐXƐ 434 268	404
7	.Ɛ77 331 474	36X	7	656 8X9	005	7	940 670	3Ɛ3
8	83Ɛ 822	320	8	Ɛ63 8Ɛ2	508 Ɛ95	8	.ƐƐ0 248 X63	3X2
9	.Ɛ78 149 Ɛ42	292	9	.Ɛ94 470 887	Ɛ67	9	755 245	391
X	658 214	246	X	979 832	Ɛ39	X	.ƐƐ1 061 616	382
Ɛ	Ɛ66 45X	1ƐX	Ɛ	.Ɛ95 286 76Ɛ	Ɛ0Ɛ	Ɛ	569 998	372
.1520	.Ɛ79 474 658	173	.1560	793 67X	XX1	.15X0	X76 14X	363
1	982 80Ɛ	127	1	.Ɛ96 0X0 55Ɛ	X75	1	.ƐƐ2 382 4Ɛ1	354
2	.Ɛ7X 290 936	0X0	2	5X9 414	X48	2	88X 845	346
3	79X X16	056	3	XƐ6 260	X20	3	.ƐƐ3 196 Ɛ8Ɛ	338
4	.Ɛ7Ɛ 0X8 X70	010	4	.Ɛ97 403 080	9Ɛ5	4	6X3 307	330
5	5Ɛ6 X80	509 Ɛ87	5	90Ɛ X75	98X	5	ƐXƐ 637	322
6	Ɛ04 X47	Ɛ41	6	.Ɛ98 218 843	963	6	.ƐƐ4 4Ɛ7 959	316
7	.Ɛ80 412 988	XƐX	7	725 5X6	939	7	X04 073	30X
8	920 886	X75	8	.Ɛ99 032 323	914	8	.ƐƐ5 310 381	303
9	.Ɛ81 22X 73Ɛ	X32	9	53Ɛ 037	8XX	9	818 684	2Ɛ8
X	738 571	9XƐ	X	X47 925	886	X	.ƐƐ6 124 980	2Ɛ1
Ɛ	.Ɛ82 046 360	969	Ɛ	.Ɛ9X 354 5XƐ	861	Ɛ	631 071	2X7
.1530	554 109	926	.1570	861 250	83X	.15Ɛ0	Ɛ39 358	2X2
1	X61 X33	8X4	1	.Ɛ9Ɛ 169 X8X	816	1	.ƐƐ7 445 63X	299
2	.Ɛ83 36Ɛ 717	864	2	676 6X4	7Ɛ4	2	951 917	294
3	879 37Ɛ	823	3	Ɛ83 298	791	3	.ƐƐ8 259 ƐXƐ	290
4	.Ɛ84 186 ƐX2	7X2	4	.ƐX0 48Ɛ X69	770	4	766 27Ɛ	288
5	694 784	763	5	998 619	749	5	.ƐƐ9 072 547	285
6	ƐX2 327	724	6	.ƐX1 2X5 166	729	6	57X 810	282
7	.Ɛ85 4XƐ X4Ɛ	6X5	7	7Ɛ1 893	709	7	X86 X92	280
8	9Ɛ9 534	666	8	.ƐX2 0ƐX 3X0	6X8	8	.ƐƐX 393 152	27X
9	.Ɛ86 306 Ɛ9X	628	9	606 X88	689	9	89Ɛ 410	279
X	814 606	5XƐ	X	Ɛ13 555	669	X	.ƐƐƐ 1X7 689	278
Ɛ	.Ɛ87 121 ƐƐ5	573	Ɛ	.ƐX3 420 002	64Ɛ	Ɛ	6Ɛ3 945	277
						.1600	.000 000 000	

N	S	d	N	S	d	N	S	d
.0000	.8X6 081 Ɛ67	28	.0040	.8X6 047 71X	1 94X	.0080	.8X5 Ɛ60 5Ɛ0	3 671
1	081 Ɛ3Ɛ	7Ɛ	1	045 990	9X2	1	Ɛ58 Ɛ3Ɛ	704
2	081 X80	113	2	043 ƐXX	X35	2	Ɛ55 437	758
3	081 969	166	3	042 175	X89	3	Ɛ51 89Ɛ	7XƐ
4	081 803	1ƐX	4	040 2X8	Ɛ21	4	Ɛ4X 0Ɛ0	843
5	081 605	252	5	03X 387	Ɛ73	5	Ɛ46 469	897
6	081 373	2X5	6	038 414	2 008	6	Ɛ42 792	92X
7	081 08X	339	7	036 408	05Ɛ	7	Ɛ3X X64	982
8	080 951	390	8	034 369	0Ɛ3	8	Ɛ37 0X2	X15
9	080 581	423	9	032 276	146	9	Ɛ33 289	X69
X	080 15X	478	X	030 130	199	X	Ɛ2Ɛ 420	Ɛ01
Ɛ	07Ɛ 8X2	50Ɛ	Ɛ	029 Ɛ53	232	Ɛ	Ɛ27 51Ɛ	Ɛ54
.0010	07Ɛ 393	562	.0050	027 921	285	.0090	Ɛ23 587	ƐX7
1	07X X31	5Ɛ6	1	025 658	318	1	Ɛ1Ɛ 5X0	4 040
2	07X 437	649	2	023 340	370	2	Ɛ17 560	092
3	079 9XX	6X1	3	020 Ɛ90	403	3	Ɛ13 48X	126
4	079 309	735	4	01X 789	457	4	Ɛ0Ɛ 364	17X
5	078 794	788	5	018 332	4XƐ	5	Ɛ07 1X6	212
6	078 008	820	6	015 X43	542	6	Ɛ02 Ɛ94	265
7	077 3X8	873	7	013 501	596	7	XƐX 9ƐƐ	2Ɛ8
8	076 735	907	8	010 Ɛ27	629	8	XƐ6 633	350
9	075 X2X	95X	9	00X 4ƐX	681	9	XƐ2 2X3	3X4
X	075 090	9Ɛ2	X	007 X39	714	X	XX9 XƐƐ	437
Ɛ	074 29X	X45	Ɛ	005 325	768	Ɛ	XX5 684	48Ɛ
.0020	073 455	X99	.0060	002 779	7ƐƐ	.00X0	XX1 1Ɛ5	522
1	072 578	Ɛ31	1	.8X5 ƐƐƐ Ɛ7X	853	1	X98 893	576
2	071 647	Ɛ84	2	ƐƐ9 327	8X7	2	X94 319	60X
3	070 683	1 017	3	ƐƐ6 640	93X	3	X8Ɛ 90Ɛ	661
4	06Ɛ 668	06Ɛ	4	ƐƐ3 902	992	4	X87 26X	6Ɛ4
5	06X 5Ɛ9	103	5	ƐƐ0 Ɛ30	X25	5	X82 776	749
6	069 4Ɛ6	156	6	ƐXX 107	X79	6	X7X 029	79Ɛ
7	068 360	1XX	7	ƐX7 24X	Ɛ10	7	X75 44X	834
8	067 172	242	8	ƐX4 33X	Ɛ64	8	X70 816	887
9	065 Ɛ30	295	9	ƐX1 396	ƐƐ8	9	X67 Ɛ4Ɛ	91X
X	064 857	328	X	Ɛ9X 39X	3 04Ɛ	X	X63 231	972
Ɛ	063 52Ɛ	380	Ɛ	Ɛ97 34Ɛ	0X2	Ɛ	X5X 47Ɛ	X06
.0030	062 16Ɛ	414	.0070	Ɛ94 269	136	.00Ɛ0	X55 675	X59
1	060 957	467	1	Ɛ91 133	18X	1	X50 818	XƐ0
2	05Ɛ 4Ɛ0	4ƐX	2	Ɛ89 Ɛ65	221	2	X47 928	Ɛ45
3	059 ƐƐ2	553	3	Ɛ86 944	275	3	X42 9X3	Ɛ98
4	058 65Ɛ	5X5	4	Ɛ83 68Ɛ	308	4	X39 X07	5 02Ɛ
5	057 076	63X	5	Ɛ80 383	360	5	X34 998	083
6	055 638	691	6	Ɛ79 023	3Ɛ4	6	X2Ɛ 915	117
7	053 Ɛ67	724	7	Ɛ75 82Ɛ	447	7	X26 7ƐX	16X
8	052 443	778	8	Ɛ72 3X4	49Ɛ	8	X21 650	202
9	050 887	80Ɛ	9	Ɛ6X Ɛ05	532	9	X18 44X	255
X	04Ɛ 078	863	X	Ɛ67 593	585	X	X13 1Ɛ5	2X9
Ɛ	049 415	8Ɛ7	Ɛ	Ɛ64 00X	61X	Ɛ	X09 Ɛ08	340

N	S	d	N	S	d	N	S	d
.0100	.8X5 X04 788	5 394	.0140	.8X5 7Ɛ8 041	7 0Ɛ8	.0180	.8X5 53X 759	8 X21
1	9ƐƐ 3Ɛ4	428	1	7Ɛ0 Ɛ45	14Ɛ	1	531 938	X74
2	9Ɛ5 Ɛ88	47Ɛ	2	7X5 9Ɛ6	1X4	2	524 X84	Ɛ09
3	9Ɛ0 709	513	3	79X 812	236	3	517 Ɛ77	Ɛ5Ɛ
4	9X7 1Ɛ6	566	4	793 598	28Ɛ	4	50Ɛ 018	ƐƐ4
5	9X1 850	5ƐX	5	788 309	322	5	502 024	9 047
6	998 252	651	6	780 ƐX7	375	6	4Ɛ4 Ɛ99	09Ɛ
7	992 801	6X6	7	775 832	409	7	4X7 XƐX	132
8	989 117	738	8	76X 425	461	8	49X 988	186
9	983 59Ɛ	790	9	762 Ɛ84	4Ɛ4	9	491 802	219
X	979 X0Ɛ	824	X	757 690	548	X	484 5X5	272
Ɛ	974 1X7	877	Ɛ	750 144	5X0	Ɛ	477 333	304
.0110	96X 530	90Ɛ	.0150	744 764	633	.0190	46X 02Ɛ	359
1	964 821	963	1	739 131	687	1	460 892	3Ɛ0
2	95X X7X	9Ɛ6	2	731 666	71X	2	453 4X2	444
3	955 084	X4X	3	725 Ɛ48	772	3	446 05X	497
4	94Ɛ 236	XX1	4	71X 396	805	4	438 783	52Ɛ
5	945 355	Ɛ35	5	712 791	85X	5	42Ɛ 254	582
6	93Ɛ 420	Ɛ88	6	706 Ɛ33	8Ɛ0	6	421 892	617
7	935 454	6 020	7	6ƐƐ 243	945	7	414 277	669
8	92Ɛ 434	074	8	6Ɛ3 4ƐX	998	8	406 80X	702
9	925 380	107	9	6X7 722	X2Ɛ	9	3Ɛ9 108	755
X	91Ɛ 275	15Ɛ	X	69Ɛ 8Ɛ3	X83	X	3XƐ 573	7X9
Ɛ	915 116	1Ɛ2	Ɛ	693 X30	Ɛ17	Ɛ	3X1 986	840
.0120	90X Ɛ24	246	.0160	687 Ɛ15	Ɛ6X	.01X0	394 146	894
1	904 89X	299	1	67Ɛ Ɛ67	8 002	1	386 472	927
2	8ƐX 601	331	2	673 Ɛ65	056	2	378 747	980
3	8Ɛ4 290	385	3	667 Ɛ0Ɛ	0X9	3	36X 987	X12
4	8X9 Ɛ07	418	4	65Ɛ X22	141	4	360 Ɛ75	X67
5	8X3 6XƐ	470	5	653 8X1	194	5	353 10X	XƐX
6	899 23Ɛ	503	6	647 709	228	6	345 210	Ɛ52
7	892 938	557	7	63Ɛ 4X1	280	7	337 27X	ƐX5
8	888 3X1	5XƐ	8	633 221	313	8	329 295	X 039
9	881 9Ɛ2	642	9	626 Ɛ0X	367	9	31Ɛ 258	091
X	877 370	696	X	61X 763	3ƐX	X	311 187	124
Ɛ	870 896	729	Ɛ	612 365	452	Ɛ	303 063	178
.0130	866 169	781	.0170	605 Ɛ13	4X6	.01Ɛ0	2Ɛ4 XX7	210
1	85Ɛ 5X8	815	1	5Ɛ9 629	539	1	2X6 897	263
2	854 993	868	2	5Ɛ1 0Ɛ0	591	2	298 634	2Ɛ7
3	84X 127	8ƐƐ	3	5X4 71Ɛ	624	3	28X 339	34X
4	843 428	954	4	598 0Ɛ7	678	4	27Ɛ ƐXƐ	3X2
5	838 694	9X6	5	58Ɛ 63Ɛ	710	5	271 809	436
6	831 8XX	X3Ɛ	6	582 Ɛ2Ɛ	763	6	263 393	489
7	826 X6Ɛ	X92	7	576 388	7Ɛ7	7	254 Ɛ06	521
8	81Ɛ Ɛ99	Ɛ25	8	569 791	84Ɛ	8	246 5X5	575
9	815 074	Ɛ7X	9	560 Ɛ42	8X2	9	238 030	608
X	80X 0Ɛ6	7 010	X	554 260	935	X	229 624	660
Ɛ	803 0X6	065	Ɛ	547 527	98X	Ɛ	21X Ɛ84	6Ɛ4

N	S	d	N	S	d	N	S	d
.0200	.8X5 210 490	X 747	.0240	.8X4 X31 381	10 473	.0280	.8X4 5X1 384	12 1X1
1	201 945	79Ɛ	1	X20 Ɛ0X	507	1	58Ɛ 1X3	234
2	1Ɛ3 166	833	2	X10 603	55X	2	578 Ɛ6Ɛ	288
3	1X4 533	886	3	X00 065	5Ɛ2	3	566 8X3	320
4	195 869	91X	4	9XƐ 673	646	4	554 583	374
5	186 Ɛ4Ɛ	971	5	99Ɛ 029	69X	5	542 20Ɛ	407
6	178 19X	X06	6	98X 54Ɛ	731	6	52Ɛ X04	460
7	169 394	X58	7	979 X1X	785	7	519 564	4Ɛ2
8	15X 538	XƐ1	8	969 255	819	8	507 072	547
9	14Ɛ 647	Ɛ44	9	958 638	870	9	4Ɛ4 727	59X
X	140 703	Ɛ98	X	947 988	904	X	4X2 149	632
Ɛ	131 727	Ɛ 02Ɛ	Ɛ	937 084	958	Ɛ	48Ɛ 717	686
.0210	122 6Ɛ8	083	.0250	926 328	9XƐ	.0290	479 051	71X
1	113 635	117	1	915 539	X43	1	466 533	771
2	104 51X	16X	2	904 6Ɛ6	X97	2	453 982	805
3	0Ɛ5 370	202	3	8Ɛ3 81Ɛ	Ɛ2X	3	441 179	859
4	0X6 16X	256	4	8X2 8Ɛ1	Ɛ82	4	42X 520	8Ɛ0
5	096 Ɛ14	2XX	5	891 92Ɛ	11 016	5	417 830	944
6	087 826	341	6	880 915	06X	6	404 XX8	998
7	078 4X5	394	7	86Ɛ 867	101	7	3Ɛ2 110	X30
8	069 111	429	8	85X 766	155	8	39Ɛ 2X0	X83
9	059 8X4	480	9	849 611	1X8	9	388 419	Ɛ17
X	04X 424	513	X	838 425	241	X	375 502	Ɛ6Ɛ
Ɛ	03X Ɛ11	568	Ɛ	827 1X4	294	Ɛ	362 553	13 003
.0220	02Ɛ 565	5ƐƐ	.0260	815 Ɛ10	327	.02X0	34Ɛ 550	056
1	01Ɛ Ɛ66	652	1	804 7X5	380	1	338 4Ɛ6	0XX
2	010 514	6X6	2	7Ɛ3 425	413	2	325 408	142
3	000 X2X	73X	3	7X2 012	467	3	312 286	196
4	.8X4 ƐƐ1 2Ɛ0	792	4	790 767	4ƐX	4	2ƐƐ 0Ɛ0	229
5	ƐX1 71X	825	5	77Ɛ 269	552	5	2X7 X83	281
6	Ɛ91 XƐ5	879	6	769 917	5X6	6	294 802	315
7	Ɛ82 238	911	7	758 331	63X	7	281 4X9	369
8	Ɛ72 527	964	8	746 8Ɛ3	691	8	26X 140	400
9	Ɛ62 783	9Ɛ8	9	735 222	725	9	256 940	454
X	Ɛ52 987	X50	X	723 6Ɛ9	779	X	243 4X8	4X8
Ɛ	Ɛ42 Ɛ37	XX3	Ɛ	711 Ɛ40	811	Ɛ	230 000	540
.0230	Ɛ33 054	Ɛ37	.0270	700 32Ɛ	864	.02Ɛ0	218 680	593
1	Ɛ23 119	Ɛ8Ɛ	1	6XX 687	8Ɛ8	1	205 0X9	627
2	Ɛ13 14X	10 022	2	698 98Ɛ	94Ɛ	2	1Ɛ1 682	67Ɛ
3	Ɛ03 128	076	3	687 040	9X4	3	19X 003	713
4	XƐ3 072	10X	4	675 258	X37	4	186 4Ɛ0	766
5	XX2 Ɛ64	161	5	663 421	X8X	5	172 946	7ƐƐ
6	X92 X03	1Ɛ5	6	651 553	Ɛ23	6	15Ɛ 147	851
7	X82 80X	249	7	63Ɛ 630	Ɛ76	7	147 4Ɛ6	8X6
8	X72 581	2X1	8	629 676	12 00X	8	133 810	93X
9	X62 2X0	334	9	617 688	062	9	11Ɛ X92	991
X	X51 Ɛ68	387	X	605 606	0Ɛ5	X	108 101	X25
Ɛ	X41 7X1	420	Ɛ	5Ɛ3 511	149	Ɛ	0Ɛ4 298	X79

N	S	d	N	S	d	N	S	d
.0300	.8X4 0X0 41Ɛ	13 Ɛ10	.0340	.8X3 72X 441	15 842	.0380	.8X3 107 350	17 578
1	088 50Ɛ	Ɛ64	1	714 7ƐƐ	897	1	0XƐ 994	60Ɛ
2	074 567	ƐƐ8	2	6ƐX Ɛ24	92X	2	094 385	663
3	060 56Ɛ	14 050	3	6X5 1Ɛ6	982	3	078 922	6Ɛ7
4	048 51Ɛ	0X4	4	68Ɛ 434	X16	4	061 227	74Ɛ
5	034 437	137	5	675 61X	X6X	5	045 698	7X2
6	020 300	18Ɛ	6	65Ɛ 770	Ɛ01	6	029 XƐ6	837
7	008 131	223	7	645 86Ɛ	Ɛ55	7	012 27Ɛ	88X
8	.8X3 ƐƐ3 Ɛ0X	277	8	62Ɛ 916	ƐXX	8	.8X2 ƐƐ6 5Ɛ1	923
9	Ɛ9Ɛ 853	30X	9	615 928	16 041	9	Ɛ9X 88X	976
X	Ɛ87 545	363	X	5ƐƐ 8X7	094	X	Ɛ82 Ɛ14	X0X
Ɛ	Ɛ73 1X2	3Ɛ6	Ɛ	5X5 813	129	Ɛ	Ɛ67 106	X62
.0310	Ɛ5X 9X8	44X	.0350	58Ɛ 6X6	181	.0390	Ɛ4Ɛ 264	XƐ6
1	Ɛ46 55X	4X1	1	575 525	214	1	Ɛ33 36X	Ɛ4X
2	Ɛ32 079	536	2	55Ɛ 311	268	2	Ɛ17 420	ƐX1
3	Ɛ19 743	589	3	545 065	300	3	XƐƐ 43Ɛ	18 036
4	Ɛ05 176	621	4	52X 965	354	4	XX3 405	089
5	XƐ0 755	674	5	514 611	3X8	5	X87 338	122
6	X98 0X1	709	6	4ƐX 225	43Ɛ	6	X6Ɛ 216	175
7	X83 594	760	7	4X3 9X6	494	7	X53 061	209
8	X6X X34	7Ɛ4	8	489 512	527	8	X36 X54	261
9	X56 240	848	9	472 ƐX7	57Ɛ	9	X1X 7Ɛ3	2Ɛ5
X	X41 5Ɛ4	8X0	X	458 628	613	X	X02 4ƐX	349
Ɛ	X28 914	933	Ɛ	442 015	667	Ɛ	9X6 171	3X1
.0320	X13 ƐX1	988	.0360	427 56X	6ƐX	.03X0	989 990	434
1	9ƐƐ 215	X1Ɛ	1	410 X70	753	1	971 558	489
2	9X6 3Ɛ6	X72	2	3Ɛ6 319	7X6	2	955 08Ɛ	520
3	991 544	Ɛ07	3	39Ɛ 733	83X	3	938 76Ɛ	575
4	978 639	Ɛ5Ɛ	4	384 XƐ5	892	4	920 1Ɛ6	608
5	963 69X	ƐƐ2	5	36X 223	926	5	903 7XX	660
6	94X 6X8	15 046	6	353 4Ɛ9	97X	6	8X7 14X	6Ɛ5
7	935 662	09X	7	338 73Ɛ	X11	7	88X 655	748
8	920 584	131	8	321 92X	X66	8	871 Ɛ09	7X0
9	907 453	186	9	306 X84	XƐ9	9	855 329	833
X	8ƐƐ 289	219	X	2XƐ Ɛ87	Ɛ51	X	838 6Ɛ6	888
Ɛ	899 070	271	Ɛ	295 036	ƐX5	Ɛ	81Ɛ X2X	920
.0330	883 9ƐƐ	305	.0370	27X 051	17 039	.03Ɛ0	803 10X	974
1	86X 6Ɛ6	358	1	263 014	091	1	7X6 356	X07
2	855 35X	3Ɛ1	2	247 Ɛ43	124	2	789 54Ɛ	X60
3	83Ɛ Ɛ69	444	3	230 X1Ɛ	179	3	770 6XƐ	XƐ3
4	826 725	498	4	215 862	210	4	753 7Ɛ8	Ɛ48
5	811 249	530	5	1ƐX 652	264	5	736 870	Ɛ9Ɛ
6	7Ɛ7 919	584	6	1X3 3XX	2Ɛ8	6	719 891	19 033
7	7X2 355	617	7	188 0Ɛ2	350	7	700 85X	087
8	788 93X	670	8	170 962	3X4	8	6X3 793	11Ɛ
9	773 28X	703	9	155 57X	437	9	686 674	173
X	759 787	757	X	13X 143	490	X	669 501	207
Ɛ	744 030	7XƐ	Ɛ	122 873	523	Ɛ	650 2Ɛ6	25Ɛ

N	S	d	N	S	d	N	S	d
.0400	.8X2 633 057	19 2Ɛ3	.0440	.8X1 XX9 660	1Ɛ 032	.0480	.8X1 2Ɛ2 851	20 973
1	615 964	347	1	X8X 62X	085	1	291 X9X	X08
2	5Ɛ8 619	39X	2	X6Ɛ 565	11X	2	271 092	X60
3	59Ɛ 23Ɛ	433	3	X50 447	171	3	250 232	XƐ4
4	581 X08	487	4	X31 296	206	4	22Ɛ 33X	Ɛ48
5	564 541	51X	5	X12 090	25X	5	20X 3Ɛ2	ƐX0
6	547 023	573	6	9Ɛ2 X32	2Ɛ1	6	1X9 412	21 034
7	529 670	606	7	993 741	346	7	188 39X	088
8	510 066	65X	8	974 3Ɛ7	399	8	167 312	120
9	4Ɛ2 608	6Ɛ3	9	955 01X	432	9	146 1Ɛ2	174
X	494 Ɛ15	746	X	935 7X8	486	X	125 03X	209
Ɛ	477 38Ɛ	79X	Ɛ	916 322	519	Ɛ	103 X31	260
.0410	459 7Ɛ1	832	.0450	8Ɛ6 X05	572	.0490	0X2 791	2Ɛ5
1	43Ɛ Ɛ7Ɛ	887	1	897 453	606	1	081 498	349
2	422 2Ɛ4	91X	2	877 X49	659	2	060 14Ɛ	3X1
3	404 596	972	3	858 3Ɛ0	6Ɛ2	3	03X 96X	435
4	3X6 824	X06	4	838 8ƐX	746	4	019 535	489
5	388 X1X	X5X	5	819 174	79X	5	.8X0 ƐƐ8 068	521
6	36X Ɛ80	XƐ2	6	7Ɛ9 596	832	6	Ɛ96 747	575
7	351 08X	Ɛ46	7	799 964	886	7	Ɛ75 192	60X
8	333 144	Ɛ9X	8	77X 09X	919	8	Ɛ53 784	661
9	315 166	1X 031	9	75X 381	972	9	Ɛ32 123	6Ɛ6
X	2Ɛ7 135	086	X	73X 60Ɛ	X06	X	Ɛ10 629	749
Ɛ	299 06Ɛ	11X	Ɛ	71X 805	X5X	Ɛ	XXX XX0	7X2
.0420	27X Ɛ51	172	.0460	6ƐX 967	XƐ3	.04X0	X89 2ƐX	836
1	260 99Ɛ	205	1	69X X74	Ɛ46	1	X67 684	88X
2	242 796	25X	2	67X Ɛ2X	Ɛ9X	2	X45 9Ɛ6	922
3	224 538	2Ɛ2	3	65X Ɛ50	20 032	3	X24 094	977
4	206 246	345	4	63X Ɛ1X	086	4	X02 319	X0X
5	1X7 Ɛ01	39X	5	61X X54	11Ɛ	5	9X0 50Ɛ	X63
6	189 723	432	6	5ƐX 935	172	6	97X 668	XƐ7
7	16Ɛ 2Ɛ1	485	7	59X 783	207	7	958 771	Ɛ4X
8	150 X28	51X	8	57X 578	25X	8	936 823	ƐX3
9	132 50X	571	9	55X 31X	2Ɛ3	9	914 840	22 037
X	113 Ɛ59	606	X	53X 027	346	X	8Ɛ2 805	090
Ɛ	0Ɛ5 553	65X	Ɛ	519 8X1	39Ɛ	Ɛ	890 735	123
.0430	096 XƐ5	6Ɛ1	.0470	4Ɛ9 502	433	.04Ɛ0	86X 612	178
1	078 404	746	1	499 08Ɛ	486	1	848 456	20Ɛ
2	059 87X	799	2	478 805	51Ɛ	2	826 247	264
3	03Ɛ 0X1	832	3	458 2X6	573	3	803 ƐX3	2Ɛ8
4	020 46Ɛ	885	4	437 933	607	4	7X1 8X7	350
5	001 7X6	91X	5	417 328	65Ɛ	5	77Ɛ 557	3X4
6	.8X1 ƐX2 X88	971	6	3Ɛ6 889	6Ɛ3	6	759 173	439
7	Ɛ84 117	X05	7	396 196	747	7	736 936	490
8	Ɛ65 312	X5X	8	375 64Ɛ	7X0	8	714 466	525
9	Ɛ46 474	XƐ1	9	354 X6Ɛ	833	9	6Ɛ1 Ɛ41	579
X	Ɛ27 583	Ɛ46	X	334 238	887	X	68Ɛ 584	611
Ɛ	Ɛ08 639	Ɛ99	Ɛ	313 571	920	Ɛ	668 Ɛ73	665

N	S	d	N	S	d	N	S	d
.0500	.8X0 646 50X	22 6Ɛ9	.0540	.89Ɛ 928 721	24 447	.0580	.89X Ɛ59 145	26 199
1	623 X11	752	1	904 296	4X0	1	Ɛ32 Ɛ68	231
2	601 27Ɛ	7X5	2	89Ɛ 9Ɛ6	533	2	Ɛ08 937	285
3	59X 696	83X	3	877 483	588	3	XX2 672	31X
4	577 X58	892	4	852 XƐ7	620	4	X78 354	373
5	555 186	926	5	82X 497	674	5	X51 ƐX1	406
6	532 460	97X	6	805 X23	708	6	X27 797	45Ɛ
7	50Ɛ 6X2	X13	7	7X1 317	761	7	X01 338	4Ɛ3
8	4X8 88Ɛ	X66	8	778 776	7Ɛ5	8	996 X45	548
9	485 X25	XƐƐ	9	753 Ɛ81	849	9	970 4Ɛ9	5X0
X	462 Ɛ26	Ɛ53	X	72Ɛ 334	8X2	X	945 Ɛ19	634
Ɛ	43Ɛ Ɛ93	ƐX7	Ɛ	706 652	936	Ɛ	91Ɛ 4X5	689
.0510	418 ƐX8	23 040	0550	6X1 918	98X	.0590	8Ɛ4 X18	721
1	3Ɛ5 Ɛ68	093	1	678 Ɛ4X	X22	1	88X 2Ɛ7	775
2	392 X95	128	2	654 128	X77	2	863 742	80X
3	36Ɛ 969	180	3	62Ɛ 271	Ɛ0X	3	838 Ɛ34	862
4	348 7X9	214	4	606 363	Ɛ64	4	812 292	8Ɛ6
5	325 595	268	5	5X1 3ƐƐ	ƐƐ7	5	7X7 598	94Ɛ
6	302 329	301	6	578 404	25 050	6	780 849	9X3
7	29Ɛ 028	354	7	553 374	0X4	7	755 X66	X38
8	277 894	3X9	8	52X 290	138	8	72Ɛ 02X	X90
9	254 4X7	441	9	505 154	190	9	704 15X	Ɛ24
X	231 066	495	X	49Ɛ Ɛ84	225	X	699 236	Ɛ79
Ɛ	209 791	52X	Ɛ	476 95Ɛ	279	Ɛ	672 279	27 011
.0520	1X6 263	582	.0560	451 6X2	312	.05X0	647 268	065
1	182 8X1	615	1	428 390	365	1	620 203	0ƐX
2	15Ɛ 288	66X	2	403 027	3ƐX	2	5Ɛ5 105	152
3	137 81X	703	3	399 829	452	3	589 Ɛ73	1X7
4	114 117	756	4	374 397	4X7	4	562 988	23Ɛ
5	0Ɛ0 581	7XƐ	5	34X XƐ0	53Ɛ	5	537 749	293
6	088 992	843	6	325 571	593	6	510 476	328
7	065 14Ɛ	897	7	2ƐƐ Ɛ9X	627	7	4X5 14X	380
8	041 474	92Ɛ	8	296 573	680	8	479 98X	415
9	019 745	984	9	270 XƐ3	714	9	452 575	469
X	.89Ɛ ƐƐ5 981	X17	X	247 39Ɛ	769	X	427 108	501
Ɛ	Ɛ91 Ɛ66	X70	Ɛ	221 832	800	Ɛ	3ƐƐ 807	556
.0530	Ɛ6X 0Ɛ6	Ɛ04	.0570	1Ɛ8 032	855	.05Ɛ0	394 271	5XX
1	Ɛ46 1Ɛ2	Ɛ59	1	192 399	8X9	1	368 883	643
2	Ɛ22 255	ƐƐ0	2	168 6Ɛ0	942	2	341 240	697
3	XƐX 265	24 045	3	142 96X	996	3	315 765	72Ɛ
4	X96 220	099	4	118 Ɛ94	X2X	4	2XX 036	784
5	X72 143	132	5	0Ɛ3 166	X83	5	282 472	818
6	X4X 011	185	6	089 2X3	Ɛ17	6	256 856	871
7	X25 X48	21X	7	063 388	Ɛ6Ɛ	7	22X ƐX5	905
8	X01 82X	272	8	039 419	26 003	8	203 2X0	959
9	999 578	306	9	013 416	058	9	197 543	9Ɛ2
X	975 272	35Ɛ	X	.89X ƐX9 37X	0Ɛ0	X	16Ɛ 751	X47
Ɛ	950 Ɛ13	3Ɛ2	Ɛ	Ɛ83 28X	145	Ɛ	143 906	X9X

N	S	d	N	S	d	N	S	d
.0600	.89χ 117 χ28	27 Ɛ34	.0640	.899 224 823	29 893	.0680	.898 27Ɛ 578	2Ɛ 637
1	0χƐ χƐ4	Ɛ87	1	1Ɛ6 Ɛ50	926	1	24Ɛ Ɛ41	68Ɛ
2	083 Ɛ29	28 020	2	189 226	980	2	220 472	724
3	057 Ɛ09	075	3	15Ɛ 466	χ14	3	1Ɛ0 94χ	778
4	02Ɛ χ54	109	4	131 652	χ68	4	181 192	811
5	003 947	161	5	103 7χ6	Ɛ01	5	151 581	866
6	.899 Ɛ97 7χ6	1Ɛ6	6	095 8χ5	Ɛ56	6	121 917	8Ɛχ
7	Ɛ6Ɛ 5Ɛ0	24χ	7	067 94Ɛ	Ɛχχ	7	0Ɛ2 019	953
8	Ɛ43 362	2χ3	8	039 961	2χ 042	8	082 286	9χ7
9	Ɛ17 07Ɛ	337	9	00Ɛ 91Ɛ	098	9	052 49Ɛ	χ41
χ	χχχ 944	390	χ	.898 Ɛχ1 843	12Ɛ	χ	022 65χ	χ95
Ɛ	χ82 574	424	Ɛ	Ɛ73 714	185	Ɛ	.897 ƐƐ2 785	Ɛ29
.0610	χ56 150	478	.0650	Ɛ45 54Ɛ	219	.0690	Ɛ82 858	Ɛ83
1	χ29 894	511	1	Ɛ17 332	271	1	Ɛ52 895	30 017
2	χ01 383	566	2	χχ9 081	306	2	Ɛ22 87χ	06Ɛ
3	994 χ19	5Ɛχ	3	χ7χ 977	35χ	3	χƐ2 80Ɛ	104
4	968 41Ɛ	652	4	χ50 619	3Ɛ4	4	χ82 707	159
5	93Ɛ 989	6χ7	5	χ22 225	447	5	χ52 56χ	1Ɛ2
6	913 2χ2	73Ɛ	6	9Ɛ3 99χ	4χ1	6	χ22 378	246
7	8χ6 763	794	7	985 4Ɛ9	534	7	9Ɛ2 132	29Ɛ
8	879 Ɛ8Ɛ	828	8	956 Ɛ85	58χ	8	981 χ53	334
9	851 363	881	9	928 5Ɛ7	622	9	951 71Ɛ	389
χ	824 6χ2	915	χ	8Ɛ9 Ɛ95	676	χ	921 352	421
Ɛ	7Ɛ7 989	96χ	Ɛ	88Ɛ 51Ɛ	70Ɛ	Ɛ	8Ɛ0 Ɛ31	475
.0620	78Ɛ 01Ɛ	χ02	.0660	860 χ10	764	.06χ0	880 678	50Ɛ
1	762 219	χ56	1	832 268	7Ɛ8	1	850 169	563
2	735 383	χχƐ	2	803 670	851	2	81Ɛ 806	5Ɛ8
3	708 494	Ɛ44	3	794 χ1Ɛ	8χ6	3	7χƐ 20χ	650
4	69Ɛ 550	Ɛ98	4	766 135	93χ	4	77χ 77χ	6χ6
5	672 574	29 031	5	737 3Ɛ7	993	5	74χ 094	73χ
6	645 543	085	6	708 624	χ27	6	719 556	792
7	618 47χ	119	7	699 7Ɛ9	χ80	7	6χ8 984	828
8	5χƐ 361	172	8	66χ 939	Ɛ14	8	678 158	880
9	582 1χƐ	207	9	63Ɛ χ25	Ɛ69	9	647 498	915
χ	554 Ɛχ4	25Ɛ	χ	610 χ78	2Ɛ 002	χ	616 783	969
Ɛ	527 945	2Ɛ4	Ɛ	5χ1 χ76	056	Ɛ	5χ5 χ16	χ03
.0630	4Ɛχ 651	348	.0670	572 χ20	0χƐ	.06Ɛ0	575 013	χ57
1	491 305	3χ0	1	543 931	144	1	544 178	χχƐ
2	463 Ɛ25	435	2	514 7χ9	198	2	513 289	Ɛ45
3	436 6Ɛ0	48χ	3	4χ5 611	231	3	4χ2 344	Ɛ99
4	409 222	522	4	476 3χ0	285	4	471 367	31 032
5	39Ɛ 900	577	5	447 117	31χ	5	440 335	087
6	372 345	60Ɛ	6	417 9Ɛ9	373	6	40Ɛ 26χ	11Ɛ
7	344 936	663	7	3χ8 646	407	7	39χ 14Ɛ	174
8	317 293	6Ɛ9	8	379 23Ɛ	460	8	368 Ɛ97	209
9	2χ9 796	750	9	349 99Ɛ	4Ɛ4	9	337 98χ	262
χ	280 046	7χ6	χ	31χ 4χ7	549	χ	306 728	2Ɛ6
Ɛ	252 460	839	Ɛ	2χχ Ɛ5χ	5χ2	Ɛ	295 432	34Ɛ

N	S	d	N	S	d	N	S	d
.0700	.897 264 0X3	31 3X4	.0740	.896 196 403	33 157	.0780	.895 056 129	34 Ɛ14
1	232 8ƐƐ	439	1	163 268	1Ɛ0	1	021 215	Ɛ68
2	201 482	491	2	130 078	244	2	.894 ƐX8 269	35 002
3	18Ɛ ƐƐ1	526	3	0Ɛ8 X34	29X	3	Ɛ73 267	057
4	15X 687	57Ɛ	4	085 756	332	4	Ɛ3X 210	0Ɛ0
5	129 108	614	5	052 424	387	5	Ɛ05 120	145
6	0Ɛ7 6Ɛ4	668	6	01Ɛ 059	421	6	X8Ɛ Ɛ97	199
7	086 048	701	7	.895 ƐX7 838	475	7	X56 9ƐX	233
8	054 547	756	8	Ɛ74 383	50X	8	X21 787	288
9	022 9Ɛ1	7XƐ	9	Ɛ40 X75	563	9	9X8 4ƐƐ	321
X	.896 ƐƐ1 202	844	X	Ɛ09 512	5Ɛ7	X	973 19X	376
Ɛ	Ɛ7Ɛ 57X	898	Ɛ	X95 Ɛ17	651	Ɛ	939 X24	40Ɛ
.0710	Ɛ49 8X2	931	.0750	X62 486	6X6	.0790	904 615	464
1	Ɛ17 Ɛ71	986	1	X2X 9X0	73X	1	88Ɛ 171	4Ɛ9
2	XX6 1X7	X1X	2	9Ɛ7 262	793	2	855 874	552
3	X74 389	X74	3	983 68Ɛ	829	3	820 322	5X7
4	X42 515	Ɛ08	4	94Ɛ X62	881	4	7X6 937	640
5	X10 609	Ɛ61	5	918 1X1	916	5	771 2Ɛ7	695
6	99X 668	ƐƐ6	6	8X4 487	96Ɛ	6	737 822	72X
7	968 672	32 04Ɛ	7	870 718	X04	7	702 0Ɛ4	784
8	936 623	0X3	8	838 914	X59	8	688 530	818
9	904 540	138	9	804 X77	XƐ2	9	652 914	871
X	892 404	191	X	790 Ɛ85	Ɛ46	X	619 063	907
Ɛ	860 233	226	Ɛ	759 03Ɛ	ƐX0	Ɛ	5X3 358	95Ɛ
.0720	82X 009	27Ɛ	.0760	725 05Ɛ	34 035	.07X0	569 5Ɛ9	9Ɛ5
1	7Ɛ7 94X	313	1	6Ɛ1 026	089	1	533 804	X49
2	785 637	369	2	678 Ɛ59	123	2	4Ɛ9 977	XX3
3	753 28X	401	3	644 X36	177	3	483 X94	Ɛ38
4	720 X89	456	4	610 87Ɛ	210	4	449 Ɛ58	Ɛ90
5	6XX 633	4XƐ	5	598 66Ɛ	266	5	413 Ɛ88	36 026
6	678 144	543	6	564 405	2ƐX	6	399 Ɛ62	07Ɛ
7	645 801	599	7	530 107	353	7	363 XX3	114
8	613 224	631	8	4Ɛ7 974	3X8	8	329 98Ɛ	169
9	5X0 7Ɛ3	686	9	483 588	441	9	2Ɛ3 822	203
X	56X 129	71Ɛ	X	44Ɛ 147	496	X	279 61Ɛ	257
Ɛ	537 60X	774	Ɛ	416 871	52Ɛ	Ɛ	243 384	2Ɛ0
.0730	504 X56	808	.0770	3X2 342	584	.07Ɛ0	209 094	346
1	492 24X	862	1	369 97X	619	1	192 94X	39X
2	45Ɛ 5X8	8Ɛ6	2	335 361	672	2	158 570	434
3	428 8Ɛ2	94Ɛ	3	300 8XƐ	707	3	122 138	489
4	3Ɛ5 Ɛ63	9X4	4	288 1X4	760	4	0X7 86Ɛ	522
5	383 17Ɛ	X39	5	253 644	7Ɛ5	5	071 349	577
6	350 342	X92	6	21X X4Ɛ	84X	6	036 992	610
7	319 470	Ɛ26	7	1X6 201	8X3	7	000 382	665
8	2X6 546	Ɛ80	8	171 51X	937	8	.893 Ɛ85 919	6ƐX
9	273 586	33 014	9	138 7X3	991	9	Ɛ4Ɛ 21Ɛ	754
X	240 572	069	X	103 X12	X26	X	Ɛ14 687	7X8
Ɛ	209 505	102	Ɛ	08X ƐX8	X7Ɛ	Ɛ	X99 X9Ɛ	842

N	S	d	N	S	d	N	S	d
.0800	.893 ᘔ63 259	36 897	.0840	.892 7Ɛ9 580	38 665	.0880	.891 4ᘔ0 872	3ᘔ 439
1	ᘔ28 582	930	1	780 Ɛ17	6Ɛ9	1	462 435	492
2	9Ɛ1 852	985	2	744 41ᘔ	753	2	423 Ɛ63	527
3	976 ᘔ89	ᘔ1ᘔ	3	707 887	7ᘔ8	3	3ᘔ5 638	581
4	940 06Ɛ	ᘔ74	4	68Ɛ 09Ɛ	842	4	367 077	616
5	905 1Ɛ7	Ɛ08	5	652 459	896	5	328 661	670
6	88ᘔ 2ᘔƐ	Ɛ62	6	615 783	930	6	2ᘔ9 ƐƐ1	705
7	853 349	ƐƐ7	7	598 ᘔ53	986	7	26Ɛ 4ᘔ8	75ᘔ
8	818 352	37 050	8	560 089	ᘔ1ᘔ	8	230 94ᘔ	7Ɛ4
9	7ᘔ1 302	0ᘔ5	9	523 26Ɛ	ᘔ74	9	1Ɛ2 156	849
ᘔ	766 219	13ᘔ	ᘔ	4ᘔ6 3Ɛ7	Ɛ09	ᘔ	173 509	8ᘔ3
Ɛ	72Ɛ 09Ɛ	194	Ɛ	469 4ᘔᘔ	Ɛ63	Ɛ	134 826	939
.0810	6Ɛ3 Ɛ07	228	.0850	430 547	ƐƐ7	.0890	0Ɛ5 ᘔᘔ9	991
1	678 89Ɛ	282	1	3Ɛ3 550	39 051	1	077 118	ᘔ27
2	641 619	317	2	376 4ƐƐ	0ᘔ7	2	038 2Ɛ1	ᘔ81
3	606 302	370	3	339 414	13Ɛ	3	.890 ƐƐ9 430	Ɛ16
4	58ᘔ Ɛ52	405	4	300 295	195	4	Ɛ7ᘔ 516	Ɛ70
5	553 749	45Ɛ	5	283 100	22Ɛ	5	Ɛ3Ɛ 566	3Ɛ 005
6	518 2ᘔᘔ	4Ɛ3	6	245 ᘔ91	283	6	Ɛ00 561	05ᘔ
7	4ᘔ0 9Ɛ7	549	7	208 80ᘔ	319	7	ᘔ81 503	0Ɛ4
8	465 46ᘔ	5ᘔ2	8	18Ɛ 4Ɛ1	372	8	ᘔ42 40Ɛ	149
9	429 ᘔ88	637	9	152 13Ɛ	408	9	ᘔ03 282	1ᘔ3
ᘔ	3Ɛ2 451	691	ᘔ	114 933	461	ᘔ	984 09Ɛ	238
Ɛ	376 980	725	Ɛ	097 492	4Ɛ6	Ɛ	944 ᘔ63	292
.0820	33Ɛ 257	77Ɛ	.0860	059 Ɛ98	550	.08ᘔ0	905 791	328
1	303 698	814	1	020 648	5ᘔ5	1	886 465	380
2	287 ᘔ84	869	2	.891 Ɛᘔ3 063	63ᘔ	2	847 0ᘔ5	417
3	250 217	902	3	Ɛ65 625	694	3	807 88ᘔ	46Ɛ
4	214 515	958	4	Ɛ27 Ɛ51	729	4	788 41Ɛ	506
5	198 779	9Ɛ1	5	ᘔᘔᘔ 424	782	5	748 Ɛ15	55ᘔ
6	160 988	ᘔ46	6	ᘔ70 862	818	6	709 577	5Ɛ5
7	124 Ɛ42	ᘔ9Ɛ	7	ᘔ33 046	871	7	689 Ɛ82	649
8	0ᘔ9 063	Ɛ34	8	9Ɛ5 395	906	8	64ᘔ 535	6ᘔ4
9	071 12Ɛ	Ɛ8ᘔ	9	977 68Ɛ	960	9	60ᘔ ᘔ51	738
ᘔ	035 161	38 023	ᘔ	939 92Ɛ	9Ɛ5	ᘔ	58Ɛ 315	793
Ɛ	.892 ƐƐ9 13ᘔ	078	Ɛ	8ƐƐ Ɛ36	ᘔ4ᘔ	Ɛ	54Ɛ 742	828
.0830	Ɛ81 082	111	.0870	882 0ᘔ8	ᘔᘔ4	.08Ɛ0	50Ɛ Ɛ16	881
1	Ɛ44 Ɛ71	167	1	844 204	Ɛ39	1	490 255	917
2	Ɛ08 ᘔ06	200	2	806 287	Ɛ93	2	450 53ᘔ	970
3	ᘔ90 806	255	3	788 2Ɛ4	3ᘔ 028	3	410 78ᘔ	ᘔ06
4	ᘔ54 571	2ᘔᘔ	4	74ᘔ 288	081	4	390 984	ᘔ5Ɛ
5	ᘔ18 283	344	5	710 207	117	5	350 Ɛ25	ᘔƐ5
6	99Ɛ Ɛ3Ɛ	398	6	692 0Ɛ0	170	6	311 030	Ɛ4Ɛ
7	963 763	432	7	653 Ɛ40	206	7	291 0ᘔ1	Ɛᘔ4
8	927 331	488	8	615 936	25Ɛ	8	251 0Ɛ9	40 03ᘔ
9	8ᘔᘔ ᘔ65	520	9	597 697	2Ɛ4	9	211 07Ɛ	093
ᘔ	872 545	576	ᘔ	559 3ᘔ3	34ᘔ	ᘔ	190 Ɛᘔ8	128
Ɛ	835 Ɛ8Ɛ	60Ɛ	Ɛ	51Ɛ 055	3ᘔ3	Ɛ	150 ᘔ80	183

.0900 .890 110 8Ɛ9

N	T	d
.0000	.8χ6 081 Ɛ67	54
1	081 ƐƐƐ	13χ
2	082 139	226
3	082 363	311
4	082 674	3Ɛ8
5	082 χ70	4χ3
6	083 353	58χ
7	083 921	675
8	084 396	760
9	084 Ɛ36	848
χ	085 782	932
Ɛ	086 4Ɛ4	χ1χ
.0010	087 312	Ɛ05
1	088 217	ƐƐ0
2	089 207	1 097
3	08χ 2χ2	182
4	08Ɛ 464	269
5	090 711	354
6	091 χ65	43Ɛ
7	093 2χ4	527
8	094 80Ɛ	611
9	096 220	6Ɛ9
χ	097 919	7χ4
Ɛ	099 501	88Ɛ
.0020	09Ɛ 190	976
1	0χ0 Ɛ46	χ61
2	0χ2 9χ7	Ɛ48
3	0χ4 933	2 033
4	0χ6 966	11Ɛ
5	0χ8 χ85	205
6	0χƐ 08χ	2Ɛ1
7	0Ɛ1 37Ɛ	398
8	0Ɛ3 757	483
9	0Ɛ6 01χ	56χ
χ	0Ɛ8 588	655
Ɛ	0ƐƐ 021	740
.0030	101 761	827
1	104 388	913
2	107 09Ɛ	9Ɛ9
3	109 χ98	χχ5
4	110 981	Ɛ90
5	113 951	3 077
6	116 χ08	162
7	119 Ɛ6χ	249
8	121 1Ɛ7	335
9	124 530	41Ɛ
χ	127 94Ɛ	507
Ɛ	12Ɛ 256	5Ɛ1
.0040	.8χ6 132 847	3 699
1	136 324	784
2	139 χχ8	870
3	141 758	956
4	145 4Ɛ2	χ41
5	149 333	Ɛ29
6	151 260	4 014
7	155 274	0Ɛχ
8	159 372	1χ7
9	161 559	291
χ	165 82χ	378
Ɛ	169 Ɛχ6	464
.0050	172 44χ	54χ
1	176 998	636
2	17Ɛ 412	721
3	183 Ɛ33	808
4	188 73Ɛ	8Ɛ3
5	191 432	99Ɛ
6	196 211	χ86
7	19Ɛ 097	Ɛ70
8	1χ4 047	5 058
9	1χ9 0χ3	143
χ	1Ɛ2 226	22Ɛ
Ɛ	1Ɛ7 455	315
.0060	200 76χ	401
1	205 Ɛ6Ɛ	4χ8
2	20Ɛ 457	593
3	214 χ2χ	67χ
4	21χ 4χ8	766
5	224 052	850
6	229 8χ2	938
7	233 61χ	χ23
8	239 441	Ɛ0χ
9	243 34Ɛ	ƐƐ6
χ	249 345	6 0χ1
Ɛ	253 426	187
.0070	259 5Ɛ1	274
1	263 865	35χ
2	26χ 003	445
3	274 448	531
4	27χ 979	618
5	285 395	703
6	28Ɛ χ98	7χƐ
7	296 687	895
8	2χ1 360	981
9	2χ8 121	χ68
χ	2Ɛ2 Ɛ89	Ɛ54
Ɛ	2Ɛ9 Ɛ21	7 03χ
.0080	.8χ6 304 Ɛ5Ɛ	7 126
1	310 085	212
2	317 297	2Ɛ8
3	322 593	3χ4
4	329 977	48χ
5	335 245	577
6	340 800	661
7	348 261	749
8	353 9χχ	834
9	35Ɛ 622	91Ɛ
χ	367 341	χ07
Ɛ	373 148	χƐ1
.0090	37Ɛ 039	Ɛ9χ
1	387 017	8 084
2	393 09Ɛ	170
3	39Ɛ 24Ɛ	257
4	3χ7 4χ6	342
5	3Ɛ3 828	42χ
6	400 056	515
7	408 56Ɛ	600
8	414 Ɛ6Ɛ	6χ7
9	421 656	793
χ	42χ 229	87χ
Ɛ	436 χχ7	966
.00χ0	443 851	χ51
1	450 6χ2	Ɛ38
2	459 61χ	9 024
3	466 642	10Ɛ
4	473 751	1Ɛ6
5	480 947	2χ1
6	48χ 028	389
7	497 3Ɛ5	475
8	4χ4 86χ	55Ɛ
9	4Ɛ2 209	647
χ	4χƐ 854	733
Ɛ	509 387	81χ
.00Ɛ0	516 Ɛχ5	905
1	524 8χχ	9Ɛ0
2	532 69χ	χ98
3	540 576	Ɛ84
4	54χ 53χ	χ 06Ɛ
5	558 5χ9	156
6	566 743	241
7	574 984	329
8	583 0Ɛ1	415
9	591 506	500
χ	59Ɛ χ06	5χ7
Ɛ	5χχ 3Ɛ1	693

N	T	d	N	T	d	N	T	d
.0100	.8X6 5Ɛ8 X84	X 77X	.0140	.8X6 X12 8ƐX	12 222	.0180	.8X7 34X X75	15 897
1	607 642	865	1	X24 Ɛ20	309	1	364 750	983
2	616 2X7	951	2	X37 229	3Ɛ4	2	37X 513	X6Ɛ
3	625 038	X39	3	X49 621	4X1	3	394 382	Ɛ57
4	633 X75	Ɛ24	4	X5Ɛ Ɛ02	588	4	3XX 319	16 044
5	642 999	Ɛ 00Ɛ	5	X72 48X	674	5	404 361	12Ɛ
6	651 9X8	0Ɛ7	6	X84 Ɛ42	760	6	41X 490	218
7	660 XX3	1X2	7	X97 6X2	847	7	434 6X8	303
8	670 085	28X	8	XXX 329	933	8	44X 9XƐ	3Ɛ0
9	67Ɛ 353	376	9	Ɛ01 060	X1Ɛ	9	465 19Ɛ	498
X	68X 709	460	X	Ɛ13 X7Ɛ	Ɛ07	X	47Ɛ 677	584
Ɛ	699 Ɛ69	549	Ɛ	Ɛ26 986	ƐƐ2	Ɛ	496 03Ɛ	670
.0110	6X9 4Ɛ6	633	.0150	Ɛ39 978	13 09X	.0190	4Ɛ0 6XƐ	758
1	6Ɛ8 Ɛ29	720	1	Ɛ50 X56	187	1	507 247	844
2	708 649	806	2	Ɛ64 021	271	2	521 X8Ɛ	931
3	718 253	8Ɛ3	3	Ɛ77 292	35X	3	538 800	X18
4	727 Ɛ46	99X	4	Ɛ8X 630	445	4	553 618	Ɛ05
5	737 924	X85	5	ƐX1 X75	532	5	56X 521	ƐƐ1
6	747 7X9	Ɛ71	6	ƐƐ5 3X7	619	6	585 512	17 099
7	757 75X	10 058	7	.8X7 008 X04	705	7	5X0 5XƐ	186
8	767 7Ɛ6	144	8	020 509	7Ɛ0	8	5Ɛ7 775	272
9	777 93X	230	9	034 0Ɛ9	899	9	612 X27	359
X	787 Ɛ6X	317	X	047 996	984	X	62X 184	446
Ɛ	798 285	402	Ɛ	05Ɛ 75X	X71	Ɛ	645 60X	533
.0120	7X8 687	4XX	.0160	073 60Ɛ	Ɛ58	.01X0	660 Ɛ41	61X
1	7Ɛ8 Ɛ75	596	1	087 567	14 044	1	678 55Ɛ	707
2	809 54Ɛ	681	2	09Ɛ 5XƐ	130	2	694 066	7Ɛ3
3	81X 010	769	3	0Ɛ3 71Ɛ	217	3	6XƐ 859	89Ɛ
4	82X 779	855	4	107 936	304	4	707 538	988
5	83Ɛ 412	940	5	120 03X	3Ɛ0	5	723 304	X74
6	850 152	X27	6	134 42X	497	6	73Ɛ 178	Ɛ60
7	860 Ɛ79	Ɛ13	7	148 905	583	7	757 118	18 049
8	871 X90	ƐƐƐ	8	161 288	670	8	773 165	134
9	882 X8Ɛ	11 0X7	9	175 938	757	9	78Ɛ 299	221
X	893 Ɛ76	192	X	18X 493	843	X	7X7 4ƐX	30X
Ɛ	8X5 148	279	Ɛ	1X3 116	92Ɛ	Ɛ	803 808	3Ɛ6
.0130	8Ɛ6 405	366	.0170	1Ɛ7 X45	X17	.01Ɛ0	820 002	4X2
1	907 76Ɛ	451	1	210 860	Ɛ03	1	838 4X4	58X
2	919 000	538	2	225 763	ƐXƐ	2	854 X72	677
3	92X 538	624	3	23X 752	15 097	3	871 529	763
4	93Ɛ Ɛ60	710	4	253 829	183	4	88X 090	850
5	951 670	7Ɛ8	5	268 9Ɛ0	26Ɛ	5	8X6 920	938
6	963 268	8X3	6	282 05Ɛ	357	6	903 658	X24
7	974 Ɛ4Ɛ	98Ɛ	7	297 3Ɛ6	443	7	920 480	Ɛ11
8	986 91X	X76	8	2Ɛ0 839	52Ɛ	8	939 391	ƐƐ9
9	998 794	Ɛ63	9	306 168	617	9	956 38X	19 0X6
X	9XX 737	12 04X	X	31Ɛ 783	703	X	973 474	192
Ɛ	X00 785	135	Ɛ	335 286	7XƐ	Ɛ	990 646	27Ɛ

N	T	d	N	T	d	N	T	d
.0200	.8X7 9X9 905	19 367	.0240	.8X8 56Ɛ XƐ1	20 X55	.0280	.8X9 256 028	24 564
1	X07 070	453	1	590 946	Ɛ42	1	27X 590	652
2	X24 503	540	2	5Ɛ1 888	21 02Ɛ	2	2X3 022	740
3	X41 X43	629	3	612 8Ɛ7	118	3	307 762	829
4	X5Ɛ 470	715	4	633 X13	205	4	330 38Ɛ	917
5	X78 Ɛ85	801	5	655 018	2Ɛ2	5	355 0X6	X05
6	X96 786	8XX	6	676 30X	39Ɛ	6	379 XXƐ	XƐ2
7	XƐ4 474	997	7	697 6X9	488	7	3X2 9X1	ƐX0
8	Ɛ12 24Ɛ	X83	8	6Ɛ8 Ɛ75	575	8	407 981	25 089
9	Ɛ30 112	Ɛ70	9	71X 52X	662	9	430 X4X	177
X	Ɛ4X 082	1X 058	X	73Ɛ Ɛ90	74Ɛ	X	456 005	264
Ɛ	Ɛ68 11X	145	Ɛ	761 71Ɛ	838	Ɛ	47Ɛ 269	353
.0210	Ɛ86 263	231	.0250	783 357	926	.0290	484 600	440
1	ƐX4 494	31X	1	7X5 081	X12	1	509 X40	529
2	.8X8 002 7Ɛ2	406	2	806 X93	Ɛ00	2	533 369	618
3	020 ƐƐ8	4Ɛ3	3	828 993	ƐX8	3	558 985	705
4	03Ɛ 4XƐ	5X0	4	84X 97Ɛ	22 096	4	582 48X	7Ɛ3
5	059 X8Ɛ	688	5	870 X55	183	5	5X8 081	8X1
6	078 557	775	6	893 018	270	6	611 962	98X
7	097 110	862	7	8Ɛ5 288	359	7	637 730	X78
8	0Ɛ5 972	94X	8	917 625	447	8	661 5X8	Ɛ66
9	114 700	X37	9	939 X70	534	9	687 552	26 054
X	133 537	Ɛ24	X	960 3X4	621	X	6Ɛ1 5X6	141
Ɛ	152 45Ɛ	1Ɛ 010	Ɛ	982 X05	70X	Ɛ	717 727	230
.0220	171 46Ɛ	0Ɛ9	.0260	9X5 513	7Ɛ7	.02X0	741 957	319
1	190 568	1X6	1	X08 10X	8X5	1	768 074	407
2	1XƐ 752	293	2	X2X 9Ɛ3	991	2	792 47Ɛ	4Ɛ5
3	20X X25	37Ɛ	3	X51 784	X80	3	7Ɛ8 974	5X3
4	22X 184	468	4	X74 644	Ɛ68	4	823 357	691
5	249 650	554	5	X97 5Ɛ0	23 056	5	849 X28	77Ɛ
6	268 ƐX4	642	6	XƐX 646	143	6	874 5X7	868
7	288 626	72X	7	Ɛ21 789	230	7	89Ɛ 253	957
8	2X8 154	817	8	Ɛ44 9Ɛ9	31X	8	905 ƐXX	X45
9	307 96Ɛ	904	9	Ɛ68 117	407	9	930 X33	Ɛ32
X	327 673	9Ɛ0	X	Ɛ8Ɛ 522	4Ɛ4	X	957 965	27 021
Ɛ	347 463	X9X	Ɛ	ƐƐ2 X16	5X2	Ɛ	982 986	10X
.0230	367 341	Ɛ86	.0270	.8X9 016 3Ɛ8	68Ɛ	.02Ɛ0	9X9 X94	1Ɛ9
1	387 307	20 073	1	039 X87	778	1	X15 091	2X6
2	3X7 37X	160	2	061 643	866	2	X40 377	395
3	407 51X	249	3	085 2X9	954	3	X67 750	482
4	427 767	335	4	0X9 041	X40	4	X93 012	571
5	447 XX0	423	5	110 X81	Ɛ2X	5	XƐX 583	65Ɛ
6	468 303	50Ɛ	6	134 9XƐ	24 018	6	Ɛ26 022	749
7	488 812	5Ɛ9	7	158 X07	105	7	Ɛ51 76Ɛ	837
8	4X9 20Ɛ	6X5	8	180 Ɛ10	1Ɛ3	8	Ɛ79 3X6	925
9	509 8Ɛ4	792	9	1X5 103	2X0	9	ƐX5 10Ɛ	X13
X	52X 486	87Ɛ	X	209 3X3	389	X	.8XX 010 Ɛ22	Ɛ02
Ɛ	54Ɛ 145	968	Ɛ	231 770	478	Ɛ	038 X24	ƐXƐ

N	T	d	N	T	d	N	T	d
.0300	.8XX 064 X13	28 09X	.0340	.8XX E99 307	2E 840	.0380	.8E0 038 298	33 414
1	090 XE1	188	1	.8XE 008 E47	930	1	06E 6E0	504
2	0E9 079	276	2	038 877	X1X	2	0X2 EE4	5E4
3	125 333	365	3	068 695	E09	3	116 5X8	6X3
4	151 698	452	4	098 5X2	EE8	4	14X 08E	793
5	179 E2X	541	5	108 59X	30 0X7	5	181 862	883
6	1X6 46E	62E	6	138 685	196	6	1E5 525	973
7	212 X9X	71X	7	168 85E	286	7	229 298	X63
8	23E 5E8	808	8	198 E25	374	8	261 13E	E53
9	268 204	8E6	9	209 299	463	9	295 092	34 042
X	294 XEX	9X4	X	239 740	553	X	309 114	133
E	301 8X2	X93	E	26X 093	641	E	341 247	222
.0310	32X 775	E81	.0350	29X 714	731	.0390	375 469	312
1	357 736	29 070	1	30E 245	81E	1	3X9 77E	403
2	384 7X6	15X	2	33E X64	90E	2	421 E82	4E2
3	3E1 944	248	3	370 773	9EX	3	456 474	5X2
4	41X E90	337	4	3X1 571	XXX	4	48X X56	693
5	448 307	425	5	412 45E	E98	5	503 529	782
6	475 730	513	6	443 437	31 088	6	538 0XE	873
7	4X3 043	602	7	474 503	177	7	570 962	962
8	510 645	6E1	8	4X5 67X	266	8	5X5 704	X53
9	53X 136	79E	9	516 924	355	9	61X 557	E42
X	567 915	88X	X	548 079	445	X	653 499	35 033
E	595 5X3	978	E	579 502	534	E	688 510	123
.0320	603 35E	X66	.0360	5XX X36	623	.03X0	701 633	214
1	631 205	E56	1	620 459	713	1	736 847	303
2	65E 15E	2X 043	2	651 E70	802	2	76E E4X	3E4
3	689 1X2	133	3	683 772	8E1	3	7X5 342	4X4
4	6E7 315	221	4	6E5 463	9X1	4	81X 826	594
5	725 536	30E	5	727 244	X90	5	854 1EX	684
6	753 845	3EX	6	759 114	E80	6	889 882	775
7	782 043	4X9	7	78E 094	32 06E	7	903 437	865
8	7E0 530	598	8	801 143	15X	8	939 0X0	955
9	81X E08	686	9	833 2X1	24X	9	972 X35	X46
X	849 592	775	X	865 52E	339	X	9X8 87E	E36
E	878 147	864	E	897 868	429	E	X22 7E5	36 026
.0330	8X6 9XE	952	.0370	90X 095	519	.03E0	X58 81E	117
1	915 741	X41	1	940 5E2	608	1	X92 936	207
2	944 582	E30	2	972 EEX	6E7	2	E08 E41	2E8
3	973 4E2	2E 01X	3	9X5 6E5	7X7	3	E43 239	3X8
4	9X2 510	10X	4	X18 2X0	897	4	E79 625	499
5	X11 61X	1E8	5	X4X E77	986	5	EE3 E02	589
6	X40 816	2X7	6	X81 941	X76	6	.8E1 02X 48E	679
7	X6E E01	396	7	XE4 7E7	E66	7	064 E48	76E
8	X9E 297	485	8	E27 761	33 055	8	09E 6E7	85X
9	E0X 760	573	9	E5X 7E6	145	9	116 355	950
X	E3X 113	663	X	E91 93E	235	X	151 0X5	X3E
E	E69 776	751	E	.8E0 004 E74	324	E	187 E24	E31

N	T	d	N	T	d	N	T	d
.0400	.8Ɛ1 202 X55	37 021	.0440	.8Ɛ2 4Ɛ6 449	3X 868	.0480	.8Ɛ3 918 051	42 533
1	239 X76	112	1	535 0Ɛ5	959	1	95X 584	626
2	274 Ɛ88	202	2	573 X52	X4Ɛ	2	9X0 ƐXX	719
3	2Ɛ0 18X	2Ɛ4	3	5Ɛ2 8X1	Ɛ40	3	X23 707	810
4	327 482	3X4	4	631 821	3Ɛ 032	4	X66 317	902
5	362 866	494	5	670 853	124	5	XX9 019	9Ɛ5
6	39X 13X	586	6	6XƐ 977	216	6	Ɛ2Ɛ X12	XX8
7	415 704	676	7	72X Ɛ91	308	7	Ɛ72 8ƐX	Ɛ9Ɛ
8	451 17X	767	8	76X 299	3Ɛ9	8	ƐƐ5 899	43 092
9	488 925	857	9	7X9 696	4XƐ	9	.8Ɛ4 038 96Ɛ	185
X	504 580	949	X	828 Ɛ85	5X1	X	07Ɛ Ɛ34	277
Ɛ	540 309	X3X	Ɛ	868 566	693	Ɛ	103 1XƐ	36Ɛ
.0410	578 147	Ɛ2X	.0450	8X8 039	785	.0490	146 55X	462
1	5Ɛ4 075	38 01Ɛ	1	927 802	876	1	189 X00	554
2	630 094	110	2	967 478	969	2	211 354	648
3	668 1X4	201	3	9X7 225	X5X	3	254 9X0	73X
4	6X4 3X5	2Ɛ2	4	X27 083	Ɛ51	4	298 51X	832
5	720 697	3X3	5	X67 014	40 042	5	320 150	925
6	758 X7X	495	6	XX7 056	134	6	363 X75	X18
7	795 353	585	7	Ɛ27 18X	227	7	3X7 891	Ɛ0Ɛ
8	811 918	676	8	Ɛ67 3Ɛ5	319	8	42Ɛ 7X0	44 002
9	84X 392	767	9	ƐX7 712	40X	9	473 7X2	0Ɛ6
X	886 Ɛ39	858	X	.8Ɛ3 027 Ɛ20	501	X	4Ɛ7 898	1X8
Ɛ	903 795	949	Ɛ	068 421	5Ɛ3	Ɛ	53Ɛ X84	2X0
.0420	940 522	X3Ɛ	.0460	0X8 X14	6X5	.04X0	584 164	393
1	979 361	Ɛ2Ɛ	1	129 4Ɛ9	797	1	608 537	487
2	9Ɛ6 290	39 021	2	16X 094	889	2	650 X02	57X
3	X33 2Ɛ1	112	3	1XX 961	980	3	695 380	671
4	X70 403	203	4	22Ɛ 721	X72	4	719 X31	764
5	XX9 606	2Ɛ4	5	270 593	Ɛ64	5	762 595	858
6	Ɛ26 8ƐX	3X6	6	2Ɛ1 537	41 056	6	7X7 231	94Ɛ
7	Ɛ64 0X4	497	7	332 591	149	7	82Ɛ Ɛ80	X43
8	ƐX1 57Ɛ	588	8	373 71X	23Ɛ	8	874 X03	Ɛ36
9	.8Ɛ2 01X Ɛ47	679	9	3Ɛ4 959	331	9	8Ɛ9 939	45 02X
X	058 604	76Ɛ	X	436 08X	424	X	942 967	121
Ɛ	096 173	860	Ɛ	477 4Ɛ2	516	Ɛ	987 X88	215
.0430	113 X13	952	.0470	4Ɛ8 X08	609	.04Ɛ0	X11 0X1	308
1	151 765	X42	1	53X 415	6ƐƐ	1	X56 3X9	400
2	18Ɛ 5X7	Ɛ35	2	57Ɛ Ɛ14	7Ɛ1	2	X9Ɛ 7X9	4Ɛ3
3	209 520	3X 025	3	601 705	8X4	3	Ɛ25 0X0	5X7
4	247 545	118	4	643 3X9	996	4	Ɛ6X 687	69Ɛ
5	285 661	208	5	685 183	X89	5	ƐƐ4 166	792
6	303 869	2ƐX	6	707 050	Ɛ80	6	.8Ɛ5 039 938	887
7	341 Ɛ67	3Ɛ0	7	749 010	42 072	7	083 603	979
8	380 357	4X1	8	78Ɛ 082	165	8	109 380	X72
9	3ƐX 838	593	9	811 227	257	9	153 232	Ɛ65
X	439 20Ɛ	684	X	853 482	34X	X	199 197	46 05X
Ɛ	477 893	776	Ɛ	895 810	441	Ɛ	223 235	151

N	T	d	N	T	d	N	T	d
.0500	.8Ɛ5 269 386	46 245	.0540	.8Ɛ6 92Ɛ 8χ3	49 Ɛχ4	.0580	.8Ɛ8 524 ƐƐ2	51 996
1	2Ɛ3 60Ɛ	338	1	979 887	4χ 09χ	1	576 988	χ91
2	339 947	431	2	χ07 965	193	2	608 859	Ɛ88
3	384 178	525	3	χ55 Ɛ38	288	3	65χ 825	52 082
4	40χ 6χ1	618	4	χχ4 204	381	4	6Ɛ0 8χ7	179
5	455 0Ɛ9	711	5	Ɛ32 585	476	5	742 χ64	273
6	49Ɛ 80χ	805	6	Ɛ80 χ3Ɛ	570	6	795 117	36χ
7	526 413	8Ɛ8	7	.8Ɛ7 00Ɛ 3χƐ	665	7	827 485	465
8	571 10Ɛ	9Ɛ1	8	059 χ54	75χ	8	879 92χ	55Ɛ
9	5Ɛ7 Ɛ00	χχ5	9	0χ8 5Ɛ2	854	9	910 289	656
χ	642 9χ5	Ɛ99	χ	137 246	949	χ	962 923	751
Ɛ	689 982	47 091	Ɛ	185 Ɛ93	χ43	Ɛ	9Ɛ5 474	847
.0510	714 χ53	185	.0550	214 χ16	Ɛ38	.0590	χ48 0ƐƐ	943
1	760 018	279	1	263 952	4Ɛ 031	1	χ9χ χ42	χ39
2	7χ7 295	372	2	2Ɛ2 983	127	2	Ɛ31 87Ɛ	Ɛ34
3	832 647	466	3	341 χχχ	221	3	Ɛ84 7Ɛ3	53 02Ɛ
4	879 χƐ1	55χ	4	391 10Ɛ	316	4	.8Ɛ9 017 822	126
5	905 44Ɛ	652	5	420 425	40Ɛ	5	06χ 948	221
6	950 χχ1	747	6	46Ɛ 834	505	6	101 Ɛ69	318
7	998 628	83Ɛ	7	4ƐƐ 139	5ƐƐ	7	155 285	412
8	χ24 267	933	8	54χ 738	6Ɛ5	8	1χ8 697	50χ
9	χ6Ɛ Ɛ9χ	χ28	9	59χ 231	7χχ	9	23Ɛ Ɛχ5	605
χ	χƐ7 χ06	Ɛ20	χ	629 χ1Ɛ	8χ4	χ	293 5χχ	701
Ɛ	Ɛ43 926	48 015	Ɛ	679 703	99χ	Ɛ	327 0χƐ	7Ɛ7
.0520	Ɛ8Ɛ 93Ɛ	109	.0560	709 4χ1	χ93	.05χ0	37χ 8χ6	8Ɛ2
1	.8Ɛ6 017 χ48	202	1	759 374	Ɛ89	1	412 598	9χχ
2	064 04χ	2Ɛ6	2	7χ9 341	50 083	2	466 386	χχ5
3	0Ɛ0 344	3χƐ	3	839 404	179	3	4Ɛχ 26Ɛ	Ɛχ0
4	138 733	4χ3	4	889 581	273	4	552 24Ɛ	54 097
5	185 016	598	5	919 834	369	5	5χ6 326	193
6	211 5Ɛ2	691	6	969 Ɛχ1	462	6	63χ 4Ɛ9	28χ
7	25χ 083	785	7	9Ɛχ 443	559	7	692 787	386
8	2χ6 848	87χ	8	χ4χ 9χ0	653	8	726 Ɛ51	481
9	333 506	972	9	χ9Ɛ 433	748	9	77Ɛ 412	578
χ	380 278	χ68	χ	ƐƐƐ Ɛ7Ɛ	843	χ	813 98χ	674
Ɛ	409 124	Ɛ60	Ɛ	Ɛ80 802	939	Ɛ	868 442	76Ɛ
.0530	456 084	49 055	.0570	.8Ɛ8 011 53Ɛ	χ33	.05Ɛ0	900 ƐƐ1	867
1	4χ3 119	14χ	1	062 372	Ɛ29	1	955 858	962
2	530 267	242	2	0Ɛ3 29Ɛ	51 023	2	9χχ 5Ɛχ	χ5χ
3	579 4χ9	338	3	144 302	11χ	3	χ43 458	Ɛ56
4	606 825	430	4	195 420	213	4	χ98 3Ɛ2	55 051
5	654 055	525	5	226 633	30χ	5	Ɛ31 443	149
6	6χ1 57χ	61χ	6	277 941	404	6	Ɛ86 590	245
7	72χ Ɛ98	714	7	309 145	4ƐƐ	7	.8Ɛχ 01Ɛ 815	340
8	778 6Ɛ0	808	8	35χ 644	5Ɛ5	8	074 Ɛ55	439
9	806 2Ɛ8	901	9	3Ɛ0 039	6χƐ	9	10χ 392	534
χ	853 ƐƐ9	9Ɛ6	χ	441 728	7χ6	χ	163 906	630
Ɛ	8χ1 9Ɛ3	χƐ0	Ɛ	493 312	8χ0	Ɛ	1Ɛ9 336	727

N	T	d	N	T	d	N	T	d
.0600	.8ƐX 252 X61	55 824	.0640	.900 0Ɛ7 386	59 711	.0680	.902 098 42X	61 662
1	2X8 685	920	1	154 X97	80X	1	139 X90	761
2	342 3X5	X17	2	1Ɛ2 6X5	907	2	19Ɛ 631	861
3	398 200	Ɛ14	3	250 3Ɛ0	X06	3	241 292	95Ɛ
4	432 114	56 010	4	2XX 1Ɛ6	Ɛ02	4	2X3 031	X5Ɛ
5	488 124	107	5	348 0Ɛ8	5X 001	5	344 X90	Ɛ5X
6	522 22Ɛ	204	6	3X6 0Ɛ9	0ƐX	6	3X6 X2X	62 059
7	578 433	300	7	444 1Ɛ7	1Ɛ7	7	448 X87	159
8	612 733	3Ɛ8	8	4X2 3Ɛ2	2Ɛ6	8	4XƐ 024	258
9	668 Ɛ2Ɛ	4Ɛ4	9	540 6X8	3Ɛ3	9	551 280	358
X	703 423	5Ɛ1	X	59X X9Ɛ	4Ɛ1	X	5Ɛ3 618	457
Ɛ	759 X14	6X8	Ɛ	639 390	5XX	Ɛ	655 X73	556
.0610	7Ɛ4 500	7X5	.0650	697 97X	6X9	.0690	6Ɛ8 409	656
1	84Ɛ 0X5	8X2	1	736 467	7X6	1	75X X63	756
2	8X5 987	999	2	795 051	8X5	2	801 5Ɛ9	855
3	940 764	X96	3	833 936	9X2	3	864 252	955
4	997 63X	Ɛ93	4	892 718	XX0	4	906 ƐX7	X54
5	X32 611	57 08Ɛ	5	931 5Ɛ8	Ɛ9Ɛ	5	969 X3Ɛ	Ɛ54
6	X89 6X0	187	6	990 597	5Ɛ 098	6	X10 993	63 054
7	Ɛ24 867	284	7	X2Ɛ 673	196	7	X73 X27	154
8	Ɛ7Ɛ Ɛ2Ɛ	380	8	X8X 849	295	8	Ɛ16 Ɛ7Ɛ	253
9	.8ƐƐ 017 2XƐ	479	9	Ɛ29 Ɛ22	393	9	Ɛ7X 212	353
X	072 768	576	X	Ɛ89 2Ɛ5	491	X	.903 021 565	454
Ɛ	10X 122	672	Ɛ	.901 028 786	58Ɛ	Ɛ	084 9Ɛ9	553
.0620	165 794	76Ɛ	.0660	088 155	689	.06X0	128 350	653
1	201 343	867	1	127 822	788	1	18Ɛ 9X3	753
2	258 ƐXX	964	2	187 3XX	886	2	233 536	853
3	2Ɛ4 952	X62	3	227 074	984	3	297 189	953
4	350 7Ɛ4	Ɛ59	4	286 X38	X83	4	33X Ɛ20	X53
5	3X8 751	58 057	5	326 8ƐƐ	Ɛ81	5	3X2 973	Ɛ54
6	444 7X8	154	6	386 880	60 080	6	446 907	64 053
7	4X0 940	250	7	426 940	17X	7	4XX 95X	154
8	538 Ɛ90	349	8	486 XƐX	279	8	552 XƐ2	254
9	595 319	447	9	527 177	377	9	5Ɛ7 146	355
X	631 764	543	X	587 532	476	X	65Ɛ 49Ɛ	454
Ɛ	68X 0X7	640	Ɛ	627 9X8	575	Ɛ	703 933	555
.0630	726 727	739	.0670	688 361	673	.06Ɛ0	768 288	656
1	783 264	837	1	728 X14	772	1	810 922	756
2	81Ɛ X9Ɛ	933	2	789 586	871	2	875 478	856
3	878 812	X31	3	82X 237	96Ɛ	3	91X 112	957
4	915 643	Ɛ2X	4	88X ƐX6	X6X	4	982 X69	X57
5	972 571	59 027	5	92Ɛ X54	Ɛ6X	5	X27 904	Ɛ58
6	X0Ɛ 598	125	6	990 X02	61 068	6	X90 860	65 059
7	X68 701	221	7	X31 X6X	166	7	Ɛ35 8Ɛ9	159
8	Ɛ05 922	31Ɛ	8	X93 014	266	8	Ɛ9X X56	25X
9	Ɛ63 041	418	9	Ɛ34 27X	365	9	.904 044 0Ɛ4	35Ɛ
X	.900 000 459	516	X	Ɛ95 623	464	X	0X9 453	45Ɛ
Ɛ	059 973	613	Ɛ	.902 036 X87	563	Ɛ	152 8Ɛ2	561

N	T	d	N	T	d	N	T	d
.0700	.904 1Ɛ8 253	65 661	.0740	.906 459 241	69 713	.0780	.908 841 98Ɛ	71 841
1	261 8Ɛ4	762	1	506 954	816	1	8Ɛ3 610	945
2	307 456	863	2	574 56X	918	2	965 355	X4Ɛ
3	371 0Ɛ9	964	3	622 286	X20	3	X17 1X4	Ɛ53
4	416 X61	X64	4	690 0X6	Ɛ22	4	X89 137	72 058
5	480 905	Ɛ66	5	73X 008	6X 025	5	Ɛ3Ɛ 193	161
6	526 86Ɛ	66 067	6	7X8 031	128	6	ƐƐ1 334	266
7	590 916	169	7	856 159	22Ɛ	7	.909 063 59X	36Ɛ
8	636 X83	269	8	904 388	332	8	115 949	474
9	6X1 130	36X	9	972 6ƐX	435	9	188 201	579
X	747 49X	470	X	X20 Ɛ33	539	X	23X 77X	682
Ɛ	7Ɛ1 94X	571	Ɛ	X8Ɛ 470	63Ɛ	Ɛ	2Ɛ1 240	787
.0710	858 2ƐƐ	672	.0750	Ɛ39 XXƐ	743	.0790	363 X07	891
1	902 971	774	1	ƐX8 632	846	1	416 698	995
2	969 525	875	2	.907 057 278	949	2	489 471	X9Ɛ
3	X14 19X	976	3	106 005	X50	3	540 350	ƐX5
4	X7X Ɛ54	X78	4	174 X55	Ɛ54	4	5Ɛ3 335	73 0X9
5	Ɛ25 X10	Ɛ79	5	223 9X9	6Ɛ 057	5	666 422	1Ɛ3
6	Ɛ90 989	67 07Ɛ	6	292 X44	15Ɛ	6	719 615	2Ɛ9
7	.905 037 X48	181	7	341 ƐX3	262	7	790 912	402
8	0X3 009	282	8	3Ɛ1 245	366	8	844 114	507
9	14X 28Ɛ	383	9	460 5XƐ	469	9	8Ɛ7 61Ɛ	612
X	1Ɛ5 652	486	X	50Ɛ X58	570	X	96Ɛ 031	716
Ɛ	260 Ɛ18	587	Ɛ	57Ɛ 408	675	Ɛ	X22 747	821
.0720	308 4X3	689	.0760	62X X81	778	.07X0	X96 368	926
1	373 Ɛ70	78Ɛ	1	69X 639	880	1	Ɛ4X 092	X30
2	41Ɛ 73Ɛ	890	2	74X 2Ɛ9	983	2	.90X 001 Ɛ02	Ɛ36
3	487 40Ɛ	993	3	7ƐX 080	X88	3	075 X38	74 03Ɛ
4	533 1X2	X94	4	869 Ɛ48	Ɛ8Ɛ	4	129 X77	146
5	59Ɛ 076	Ɛ96	5	919 Ɛ17	70 093	5	1X2 001	24Ɛ
6	647 050	68 098	6	989 ƐXX	197	6	256 250	355
7	6Ɛ3 128	19Ɛ	7	X3X 185	29Ɛ	7	30X 5X5	460
8	75Ɛ 307	2X0	8	XXX 464	3X3	8	382 X45	565
9	807 5X7	3X3	9	Ɛ5X 847	4X7	9	437 3XX	670
X	873 98X	4X4	X	.908 00Ɛ 132	5Ɛ0	X	4XƐ X5X	775
Ɛ	920 272	5X7	Ɛ	07Ɛ 722	6Ɛ3	Ɛ	564 613	880
.0730	988 859	6X9	.0770	130 215	7Ɛ7	.07Ɛ0	619 293	986
1	X35 346	7Ɛ0	1	1X0 X10	900	1	692 059	X91
2	XX1 Ɛ36	8Ɛ1	2	251 710	X04	2	746 Ɛ2X	Ɛ97
3	Ɛ4X 827	9Ɛ4	3	302 514	Ɛ08	3	7ƐƐ Ɛ05	75 0X1
4	ƐƐ7 61Ɛ	XƐ7	4	373 420	71 011	4	874 ƐX6	1X7
5	.906 064 516	ƐƐ9	5	424 431	115	5	92X 191	2Ɛ2
6	111 513	69 0ƐƐ	6	495 546	21X	6	9X3 483	3Ɛ9
7	17X 612	202	7	546 764	322	7	X58 880	503
8	227 814	304	8	5Ɛ7 X86	426	8	Ɛ12 183	60X
9	294 Ɛ18	407	9	669 2Ɛ0	52Ɛ	9	Ɛ87 791	714
X	342 323	50X	X	71X 81Ɛ	634	X	.90Ɛ 041 2X5	81Ɛ
Ɛ	3XƐ 831	610	Ɛ	790 253	738	Ɛ	0Ɛ6 Ɛ04	926

N	T	d	N	T	d	N	T	d
.0800	.90Ɛ 170 82χ	75 χ30	.0840	.911 828 736	7χ 0χ7	.0880	.914 434 63Ɛ	82 433
1	226 65χ	Ɛ37	1	8χ6 821	1Ɛ4	1	4Ɛ6 χ72	543
2	2χ0 595	76 043	2	964 χ15	302	2	579 3Ɛ5	653
3	356 618	149	3	χ23 117	40Ɛ	3	63Ɛ χ48	762
4	410 765	254	4	χχ1 526	518	4	702 5χχ	871
5	486 9Ɛ9	35Ɛ	5	Ɛ5Ɛ χ42	625	5	785 25Ɛ	981
6	541 158	466	6	.912 01χ 467	732	6	848 020	χ91
7	5Ɛ7 602	571	7	098 Ɛ99	840	7	90χ χƐ1	Ɛχ1
8	671 Ɛ73	678	8	157 819	949	8	991 χ92	83 020
9	728 62Ɛ	784	9	216 566	χ56	9	χ54 Ɛ82	200
χ	7χ3 1Ɛ3	88Ɛ	χ	295 400	Ɛ64	χ	Ɛ18 182	30Ɛ
Ɛ	859 χ82	996	Ɛ	354 364	7Ɛ 072	Ɛ	Ɛ9Ɛ 491	420
.0810	914 858	χχ1	.0850	413 416	17Ɛ	.0890	.915 062 8Ɛ1	52Ɛ
1	98Ɛ 739	Ɛχ9	1	492 595	288	1	126 220	640
2	χ46 726	77 0Ɛ4	2	551 861	396	2	1χ9 860	74Ɛ
3	Ɛ01 81χ	1ƐƐ	3	611 037	4χ4	3	271 3χƐ	860
4	Ɛ78 χ19	307	4	690 51Ɛ	5Ɛ2	4	335 04Ɛ	970
5	.910 034 124	413	5	74Ɛ Ɛ11	700	5	3Ɛ8 9ƐƐ	χ80
6	0χƐ 537	51χ	6	80Ɛ 611	809	6	480 87Ɛ	Ɛ90
7	166 χ55	626	7	88Ɛ 21χ	917	7	544 84Ɛ	84 0χ1
8	222 47Ɛ	731	8	94χ Ɛ35	χ26	8	608 930	1Ɛ0
9	299 Ɛ20	83χ	9	χ0χ 95Ɛ	Ɛ33	9	690 Ɛ20	302
χ	355 82χ	945	χ	χ8χ 892	80 041	χ	755 222	411
Ɛ	411 573	χ50	Ɛ	Ɛ4χ 913	14Ɛ	Ɛ	819 633	522
.0820	489 403	Ɛ59	.0860	.913 00χ χ62	25χ	.08χ0	8χ1 Ɛ55	633
1	545 360	78 065	1	08Ɛ 100	368	1	966 588	744
2	601 405	170	2	14Ɛ 468	476	2	χ2Ɛ 110	853
3	679 575	279	3	20Ɛ 922	584	3	χƐ3 963	965
4	735 832	384	4	290 2χ6	692	4	Ɛ78 708	χ76
5	7Ɛ1 ƐƐ6	491	5	350 978	7χ1	5	.916 041 582	Ɛ86
6	86χ 487	599	6	411 559	8Ɛ0	6	106 548	85 097
7	926 χ64	6χ5	7	492 249	9Ɛχ	7	18Ɛ 623	1χ8
8	9χ3 549	7Ɛ1	8	553 047	Ɛ08	8	254 80Ɛ	2Ɛ9
9	χ60 13χ	8Ɛχ	9	613 Ɛ53	81 017	9	319 Ɛ08	40χ
χ	Ɛ18 χ38	χ06	χ	694 Ɛ6χ	126	χ	3χ3 316	51Ɛ
Ɛ	Ɛ95 842	Ɛ12	Ɛ	756 094	234	Ɛ	468 835	630
.0830	.911 052 754	79 01Ɛ	.0870	817 308	343	.08Ɛ0	532 265	741
1	10Ɛ 773	127	1	898 64Ɛ	452	1	5Ɛ7 9χ6	853
2	188 89χ	233	2	959 χχ1	560	2	681 639	964
3	245 Ɛ11	341	3	χ1Ɛ 441	670	3	747 3χ1	χ75
4	303 252	449	4	χχ0 χƐ1	77χ	4	811 256	Ɛ86
5	380 69Ɛ	555	5	Ɛ62 66Ɛ	88χ	5	897 220	86 098
6	43χ 034	662	6	.914 024 339	998	6	961 2Ɛ8	1χχ
7	4Ɛ7 696	76Ɛ	7	0χ6 115	χχ8	7	χ27 4χ6	2ƐƐ
8	575 245	878	8	168 001	ƐƐ6	8	χƐ1 7χ5	410
9	632 Ɛ01	985	9	229 ƐƐ7	82 106	9	Ɛ77 ƐƐ5	522
χ	6Ɛ0 886	χ91	χ	2Ɛ0 101	215	χ	.917 042 517	634
Ɛ	76χ 757	Ɛ9Ɛ	Ɛ	372 316	325	Ɛ	108 Ɛ4Ɛ	746

.0900 .917 193 695

Natural Logarithms

The natural logarithm of a number may be obtained from the tables on pages *274-275* by dividing the number by its first two figures to give a result commencing *1.0*, then interpolating as with the common log table.

Example: Find ln π:*4*

π:*4* =	*.951 202 424 0*		
Divide by *.95*	*1.001 5X4 080 X*		
ln *1.001*	*.000 ƐƐƐ 600*		(*ƐƐ9*)
		ƐƐX 603	
Add to book diff. *ƐƐ9* $\frac{1 - .5X4}{2}$		*309 3*	
Corrected difference		*ƐƐX 910*	
Multiply by *.5X4 080 X*	*5X3 547 7*		
Add to ln *1.001*	*.001 5X2 Ɛ47 7*		
ln *.95* = ln *95* - ln *100*	*-.2XX XƐ2 735 0*		
Add to ln *1.0015* etc.	*-.2X9 50Ɛ 7X9 5*		

Note: The extended value of ln π:*4* is:- *-.2X9 50Ɛ 7X9 2XX*

Example:- Find the number whose natural logarithm is:- *.2X9 50Ɛ 7X9*

From the table below, the number lies between *.9* and *.X*

	-.2X9 50Ɛ 7X9		
Subtract ln *.9*	*-.355 146 095*		
	+.067 836 4X8		
ln *1.069*	*.067 1XX 660*		(*XƐ5*)
		Ɛ56 207	
Difference	*647 X48*		
Approx. interval $\frac{648}{Ɛ56}$ = *.684*			
Add to book diff. *XƐ5* $\frac{1 - .684}{2}$		*251*	
Corrected book difference		*Ɛ56 458*	
Interval $\frac{647\ X48}{Ɛ56\ 458}$ =	*.683 171*		
Number is	*1.069 683 171*		
Multiply by *.9*	*.951 202 424*		

N	ln	N	ln	N	ln	N	ln
.10	*-2.599 Ɛ03 5Ɛ8*	*.20*	*-1.960 1Ɛ1 135*	*.40*	*-1.122 49X 872*	*.90*	*-.355 146 095*
.11	*-2.4X3 731 306*	*.22*	*-1.865 X1X X42*	*.44*	*-1.028 108 57Ɛ*	*.96*	*-.297 82X 25Ɛ*
.12	*-2.3Ɛ7 668 04Ɛ*	*.24*	*-1.779 955 788*	*.48*	*- .Ɛ40 043 305*	*.X0*	*-.223 075 302*
.13	*-2.318 3Ɛ0 510*	*.26*	*-1.69X 69X 049*	*.50*	*- .X60 987 786*	*.X6*	*-.172 8XX 728*
.14	*-2.244 979 523*	*.28*	*-1.607 067 060*	*.54*	*- .989 354 798*	*.Ɛ0*	*-.106 432 6Ɛ5*
.15	*-2.178 065 347*	*.2X*	*-1.53X 352 X83*	*.58*	*- .900 640 600*	*.Ɛ6*	*-.061 662 3Ɛ2*
.16	*-2.0Ɛ5 337 20X*	*.30*	*-1.477 624 947*	*.60*	*- .839 912 483*		
.17	*-2.037 X1Ɛ 394*	*.32*	*-1.3ƐX 108 Ɛ11*	*.66*	*- .743 540 191*		
.18	*-1.Ɛ83 266 437*	*.34*	*-1.345 553 Ɛ74*	*.70*	*- .657 476 Ɛ16*		
.19	*-1.Ɛ12 X9Ɛ 861*	*.36*	*-1.295 189 39X*	*.76*	*- .578 1ƐƐ 398*		
.1X	*-1.X66 623 82X*	*.38*	*-1.228 911 367*	*.80*	*- .4X4 788 3XX*		
.1Ɛ	*-1.X01 853 527*	*.3X*	*-1.183 Ɛ41 064*	*.86*	*- .417 X74 212*		

Exponential Function

The tables of the exponential function given on pages *276-277* were calculated from the expansions of e^N and e^{-N} for N = *.01*, *.02*, *.03*, etc., and for N = *.1*, *.2*, *.3*, etc., the remainder of the table being obtained by multiplication. One dozen and three places were calculated and checked against the hyperbolic functions.

The table may be interpolated for nine place results by the use of the Everett coefficients for second differences. The necessary coefficients may be obtained by direct proportion from the table of coefficients given on pages *296-29Ɛ*.

Example: Find the value of $e^{\pi:4}$ $\pi:4$ = *.951 202 424 0*

		d_2 +	E_0 & E_1 −
$e^{.95}$	*2.237 515 9Ɛ5*	*223 753*	*.040 18Ɛ*
$e^{.96}$	*2.259 9χ1 166*	*225 9χ0*	*.023 925*
The interval n =	*.120 242 40*		
$(1 - n)e^{.95}$	*1.Ɛ8χ 938 654 Ɛ*		
$n\ e^{.96}$	*.26Ɛ 278 604 1*		
$E_0\ d_2$	− *8 963 7*		
$E_1\ d_2$	− *5 134 χ*		
$e^{\pi:4}$	*2.239 Ɛχ3 180(7)*		

Example: Find the value of $e^{-\pi:4}$

$e^{-.95}$	*.558 468 612*	*55 849*	*.040 18Ɛ*
$e^{-.96}$	*.552 Ɛ30 681*	*55 2Ɛ4*	*.023 925*
$(1 - n)e^{-.95}$	*.4Ɛ3 7χ3 Ɛ98 9*		
$n\ e^{-.96}$	*.064 25χ χ23 5*		
$E_0\ d_2$	− *1 9Ɛ7 2*		
$E_1\ d_2$	− *1 06Ɛ 8*		
$e^{-\pi:4}$	*.557 χ3Ɛ Ɛ55(4)*		

Note: From the following extended values, results may be obtained beyond the scope of the tables by multiplication.

N	e^N	e^{-N}
1	*2.875 236 069 822*	*.44Ɛ 842 160 565*
2	*7.480 357 353 108*	*.175 χ38 Ɛχ7 463*
3	*18.103 983 χ73 774*	*.072 047 481 194*
4	*46.721 72χ 518 696*	*.027 796 255 80χ*
5	*104.4Ɛ5 Ɛ32 577 884*	*.00Ɛ 787 49χ 657*
6	*297.518 Ɛ56 612 χ69*	*.004 349 620 941*
7	*774.772 120 Ɛ2Ɛ*	*.001 6χχ χ46 795 χ07*
8	*1 884.Ɛ5Ɛ 499 Ɛ8Ɛ*	*.000 6Ɛ5 829 587 021*
9	*4 833.101 03χ 492*	*.000 268 5ƐƐ 595 653*
χ	*10 8Ɛ6.570 χ87 χ10*	*.000 0Ɛ3 691 7Ɛχ 133*
Ɛ	*2χ 796.184 χ73 391*	*.000 041 χ55 135 χχ0*
10	*7χ 22χ.95Ɛ 6χ4 597*	*.000 016 41χ 952 627*
π	*1Ɛ.183 149 Ɛ4χ 352*	*.062 810 09χ 483*
π:*4*	*2.239 Ɛχ3 180 294*	*.557 χ3Ɛ Ɛ55 45Ɛ*

N	Natural Log	N	Natural Log	N	Natural Log
		41	3.X85 095 183 857 E5X 6	81	4.6X9 125 952 E63 7X5 6
2	.839 912 483 369 XE2 1	2	3.XE3 E86 127 E91 816 6	2	4.702 9X7 647 005 X50 7
3	1.122 49X 871 651 348 X	3	3.E22 240 51E 279 960 3	3	4.718 44X 425 987 089 1
4	1.477 624 946 717 9X4 3	4	3.E4E 8EX 635 124 69X X	4	4.731 898 5XE 33E 708 8
5	1.739 137 X32 411 X72 3	5	3.E78 7E8 167 301 2E4 2	5	4.746 E18 030 XXE 995 8
6	1.960 1E1 134 9EE 23X E	6	3.EX4 E6X 657 XX1 914 7	6	4.75E E52 9X2 627 852 5
7	1.E42 648 6X1 X29 E8E 3	7	4.010 808 935 0E6 465 7	7	4.774 98X 72X 38E 3EE 2
8	2.0E5 337 209 X85 896 4	8	4.037 983 8XE 8E3 865 7	8	4.789 610 XE8 492 590 E
9	2.244 979 523 0X2 695 8	9	4.062 486 491 X99 756 4	9	4.7X2 063 185 891 18X 4
X	2.376 X4X 2E5 77E 964 4	X	4.088 541 X42 296 X56 1	X	4.7E6 50X 62X 66E 1X6 4
E	2.493 690 E02 8X4 5E3 5	E	4.0E1 E99 697 738 4XE X	E	4.80X 794 174 395 444 5
10	2.599 E03 5E8 169 131 1	50	4.117 03E 42X 57X EX3 3	90	4.822 880 E1E 24E 806 9
1	2.694 295 8XX 608 8E6 7	1	4.13E 70E 701 XE3 651 0	1	4.836 795 86E 158 130 6
2	2.780 35X E65 197 X81 4	2	4.163 831 2X6 029 360 1	2	4.84X 51E 1E8 464 357 8
3	2.85E 616 6X3 X63 1EE 1	3	4.187 406 004 E10 664 E	3	4.862 099 9E3 X70 0X4 E
4	2.933 049 691 233 788 5	4	4.1XX 672 417 94E 570 8	4	4.875 696 173 061 757 8
5	2.9EE 961 869 828 613 6	5	4.211 411 720 X1X 768 X	5	4.888 E14 47E 339 079 0
6	2.X82 68E 9X6 450 587 9	6	4.233 882 037 6X3 832 4	6	4.8X0 198 955 247 648 5
7	2.E3E EX7 820 448 409 6	7	4.255 860 X77 896 5X2 0	7	4.8E3 2XE 4EE 603 X53 5
8	2.EE4 760 778 E29 856 5	8	4.277 386 5E4 344 3E7 8	8	4.906 254 305 644 948 2
9	3.064 E27 353 47E 318 1	9	4.298 652 33X 843 32X 1	9	4.919 053 211 6XE 390 3
X	3.111 3X3 386 052 4X5 6	X	4.2E9 496 997 5X9 933 7	X	4.92E 8XE E5X XX6 3X2 0
E	3.176 173 689 1E1 EX1 3	E	4.319 XE1 XE0 50E XX1 1	E	4.942 3XX 34E 656 5X2 9
20	3.217 815 X7E 517 023 2	60	4.33X 0E4 730 E68 370 0	X0	4.954 951 8E1 928 X95 4
1	3.276 273 864 823 924 5	1	4.359 XE7 2E1 5X7 435 7	1	4.967 161 X05 588 EX6 9
2	3.311 EX8 171 976 7X8 8	2	4.379 511 605 788 84X 3	2	4.979 421 E85 261 543 1
3	3.367 258 194 733 X22 6	3	4.398 752 516 275 071 3	3	4.98E 555 5X7 076 632 1
4	3.3EX 071 428 545 973 6	4	4.3E7 610 566 E64 1E1 9	4	4.9X1 543 769 397 252 2
5	3.44X 82E 57X E28 E64 0	5	4.416 119 5X4 712 582 8	5	4.9E3 3XE 697 035 796 8
6	3.499 328 E67 211 0E1 2	6	4.434 486 X23 407 E35 6	6	4.X05 118 488 27X 557 0
7	3.525 E1X X22 87E 46X 0	7	4.452 4X5 462 2E8 515 8	7	4.X16 909 172 155 457 4
8	3.570 95E E54 5X1 67X 7	8	4.470 185 503 645 63X 8	8	4.X28 384 89E 0E9 462 9
9	3.5E5 E6E 774 335 940 3	9	4.489 736 X46 185 16E 4	9	4.X39 90X 0EX 521 210 5
X	3.639 674 130 E96 505 7	X	4.4X6 989 1E8 993 197 4	X	4.X4E 123 EX4 188 65X E
E	3.67E 784 514 23E X41 6	E	4.503 90E 42X 88E 08E 6	E	4.X60 411 254 462 2X4 3
30	3.700 3X2 269 7EX 479 E	70	4.520 550 099 E97 100 4	E0	4.X71 594 4EX X51 724 5
1	3.73E 7EE 142 41X 958 1	1	4.538 X99 6X0 03X 485 8	1	4.X82 634 302 276 398 9
2	3.779 8EX 0X3 7E6 2EE 7	2	4.555 141 910 239 975 9	2	4.X93 573 33E 044 494 2
3	3.7E6 774 560 05X 043 5	3	4.571 10X 230 57X 2E0 X	3	4.XX4 394 006 E45 894 9
4	3.832 473 040 297 748 6	4	4.588 X08 110 76X 289 8	4	4.XE5 098 X77 6E2 2X9 9
5	3.869 076 935 625 2X5 3	5	4.5X4 444 46E 996 XEE X	5	4.E05 888 3X9 377 145 9
6	3.8X2 839 816 829 20X 2	6	4.5EE 807 818 862 43X 0	6	4.E16 364 801 EE1 220 2
7	3.917 42E 448 X8E X83 7	7	4.616 922 390 436 885 X	7	4.E26 930 267 75X 136 E
8	3.94E 0E5 849 400 397 7	8	4.631 798 413 909 985 5	8	4.E37 1X9 25X 957 825 8
9	3.981 XE5 355 4E4 547 E	9	4.648 3E9 694 310 7E6 X	9	4.E47 559 X29 180 124 1
X	3.9E3 X85 E50 55E X93 4	X	4.662 991 63X X98 889 5	X	4.E57 804 373 879 993 2
E	3.X25 07E 177 72X 997 3	E	4.679 123 652 85X 27E 9	E	4.E67 966 7E1 2E1 2XX 0
40	3.X55 528 342 884 E15 3	80	4.693 23X 806 032 X07 4	100	4.E77 X06 EE4 316 262 1

N	Natural Log	d	N	Natural Log	d	N	Natural Log	d
1.000	.000 000 000	ƐƐƐ 600	1.040	.03Ɛ 418 X95	Ɛ80 9X8	1.080	.079 517 X36	Ɛ44 730
1.001	.000 ƐƐƐ 600	ƐƐX 603	1.041	.040 399 881	Ɛ7Ɛ X66	1.081	.07X 460 566	Ɛ43 85X
1.002	.001 ƐƐX 003	ƐƐ9 606	1.042	.041 359 727	Ɛ7X Ɛ26	1.082	.07Ɛ 3X4 204	Ɛ42 98Ɛ
1.003	.002 ƐƐ7 609	ƐƐ8 610	1.043	.042 318 651	Ɛ79 ƐX7	1.083	.080 326 Ɛ93	Ɛ41 Ɛ02
1.004	.003 ƐƐ4 019	ƐƐ7 619	1.044	.043 296 638	06Ɛ	1.084	.081 268 X95	035
1.005	.004 ƐXƐ 636	ƐƐ6 626	1.045	.044 253 6X7	Ɛ78 135	1.085	.082 1X9 Ɛ0X	Ɛ40 16Ɛ
1.006	.005 ƐX6 060	ƐƐ5 636	1.046	.045 20Ɛ 820	Ɛ77 1ƐƐ	1.086	.083 12X 079	Ɛ3Ɛ 2X6
1.007	.006 Ɛ9Ɛ 696	ƐƐ4 648	1.047	.046 186 X1Ɛ	Ɛ76 289	1.087	.084 069 363	Ɛ3X 423
1.008	.007 Ɛ94 122	ƐƐ3 660	1.048	.047 141 0X8	Ɛ75 357	1.088	.084 ƐX7 786	Ɛ39 561
1.009	.008 Ɛ87 782	ƐƐ2 676	1.049	.048 0Ɛ6 443	Ɛ74 428	1.089	.085 Ɛ25 127	Ɛ38 6X2
1.00X	.009 Ɛ7X 238	ƐƐ1 692	1.04X	.049 06X 86Ɛ	Ɛ73 4ƐX	1.08X	.086 X61 809	Ɛ37 824
1.00Ɛ	.00X Ɛ6Ɛ 90X	ƐƐ0 6XƐ	1.04Ɛ	.04X 022 169	Ɛ72 593	1.08Ɛ	.087 999 431	Ɛ36 967
1.010	.00Ɛ Ɛ60 3Ɛ9	ƐXƐ 70Ɛ	1.050	.04X Ɛ94 740	Ɛ71 668	1.090	.088 914 198	Ɛ35 XƐ1
1.011	.010 Ɛ4Ɛ Ɛ08	ƐXX 731	1.051	.04Ɛ Ɛ46 1X8	Ɛ70 744	1.091	.089 84X 089	038
1.012	.011 Ɛ3X 639	ƐX9 755	1.052	.050 XƐ6 930	Ɛ6Ɛ 822	1.092	.08X 783 105	Ɛ34 185
1.013	.012 Ɛ28 192	ƐX8 77X	1.053	.051 X66 552	Ɛ6X 902	1.093	.08Ɛ 6Ɛ7 28X	Ɛ33 312
1.014	.013 Ɛ14 950	ƐX7 7X6	1.054	.052 X15 254	Ɛ69 9X2	1.094	.090 62X 5X0	Ɛ32 463
1.015	.014 Ɛ00 536	ƐX6 813	1.055	.053 983 036	Ɛ68 X86	1.095	.091 560 X43	Ɛ31 5Ɛ4
1.016	.015 XX7 149	ƐX5 843	1.056	.054 92Ɛ Ɛ00	Ɛ67 Ɛ6Ɛ	1.096	.092 492 437	Ɛ30 748
1.017	.016 X90 990	ƐX4 874	1.057	.055 897 X6Ɛ	055	1.097	.093 402 Ɛ83	Ɛ2Ɛ 8X0
1.018	.017 X75 644	ƐX3 8X7	1.058	.056 842 Ɛ04	Ɛ66 141	1.098	.094 332 863	Ɛ2X X38
1.019	.018 X59 32Ɛ	ƐX2 921	1.059	.057 7X9 045	Ɛ65 230	1.099	.095 261 69Ɛ	Ɛ29 Ɛ93
1.01X	.019 X40 050	ƐX1 958	1.05X	.058 752 275	Ɛ64 31Ɛ	1.09X	.096 18Ɛ 672	131
1.01Ɛ	.01X X21 9X8	ƐX0 995	1.05Ɛ	.059 6Ɛ6 594	Ɛ63 411	1.09Ɛ	.097 0Ɛ8 7X3	Ɛ28 291
1.020	.01Ɛ X02 781	Ɛ9Ɛ X13	1.060	.05X 659 9X5	Ɛ62 505	1.0X0	.098 024 X74	Ɛ27 431
1.021	.020 ƐX2 594	Ɛ9X X55	1.061	.05Ɛ 600 2XX	Ɛ61 5ƐX	1.0X1	.098 Ɛ50 2X5	Ɛ26 595
1.022	.021 981 429	Ɛ99 X98	1.062	.060 561 8X8	Ɛ60 6Ɛ5	1.0X2	.099 X76 87X	Ɛ25 739
1.023	.022 95Ɛ 305	Ɛ98 Ɛ21	1.063	.061 502 3X1	Ɛ5Ɛ 7Ɛ1	1.0X3	.09X 9X0 3Ɛ7	Ɛ24 8X3
1.024	.023 938 226	Ɛ97 Ɛ67	1.064	.062 461 Ɛ92	Ɛ5X 8Ɛ1	1.0X4	.09Ɛ 905 09X	Ɛ23 X4X
1.025	.024 914 191	Ɛ96 ƐƐ3	1.065	.063 400 883	Ɛ59 9Ɛ0	1.0X5	.0X0 828 Ɛ28	Ɛ22 Ɛ28
1.026	.025 8XƐ 184	043	1.066	.064 35X 673	Ɛ58 XƐ3	1.0X6	.0X1 74Ɛ Ɛ24	167
1.027	.026 885 207	Ɛ95 092	1.067	.065 2Ɛ7 566	Ɛ57 Ɛ26	1.0X7	.0X2 672 08Ɛ	Ɛ21 317
1.028	.027 85X 299	Ɛ94 125	1.068	.066 253 560	100	1.0X8	.0X3 593 3X6	Ɛ20 48X
1.029	.028 832 402	Ɛ93 179	1.069	.067 1XX 660	Ɛ56 207	1.0X9	.0X4 4Ɛ3 874	Ɛ1Ɛ 641
1.02X	.029 805 57Ɛ	Ɛ92 213	1.06X	.068 144 867	Ɛ55 314	1.0XX	.0X5 413 ƐƐ5	Ɛ1X 7Ɛ6
1.02Ɛ	.02X 797 792	Ɛ91 26Ɛ	1.06Ɛ	.069 099 Ɛ7Ɛ	Ɛ54 423	1.0XƐ	.0X6 331 XXƐ	Ɛ19 972
1.030	.02Ɛ 768 X41	Ɛ90 309	1.070	.06X 032 3X2	Ɛ53 534	1.0Ɛ0	.0X7 24Ɛ 861	Ɛ18 Ɛ2X
1.031	.030 739 14X	Ɛ8Ɛ 368	1.071	.06X Ɛ85 916	Ɛ52 645	1.0Ɛ1	.0X8 168 78Ɛ	0X8
1.032	.031 708 4Ɛ6	Ɛ8X 40X	1.072	.06Ɛ Ɛ18 35Ɛ	Ɛ51 75X	1.0Ɛ2	.0X9 084 877	Ɛ17 268
1.033	.032 696 904	Ɛ89 472	1.073	.070 X69 XƐ9	Ɛ50 873	1.0Ɛ3	.0X9 Ɛ9Ɛ ƐƐ3	Ɛ16 429
1.034	.033 664 176	Ɛ88 516	1.074	.071 9ƐX 770	Ɛ4Ɛ 98Ɛ	1.0Ɛ4	.0XX XƐ6 350	Ɛ15 5Ɛ0
1.035	.034 630 690	Ɛ87 582	1.075	.072 94X 53Ɛ	Ɛ4X XX8	1.0Ɛ5	.0XƐ X0Ɛ 940	Ɛ14 775
1.036	.035 5Ɛ8 052	Ɛ86 62Ɛ	1.076	.073 899 427	007	1.0Ɛ6	.0Ɛ0 924 4Ɛ5	Ɛ13 93Ɛ
1.037	.036 582 681	Ɛ85 69X	1.077	.074 827 432	Ɛ49 127	1.0Ɛ7	.0Ɛ1 838 234	Ɛ12 Ɛ07
1.038	.037 548 15Ɛ	Ɛ84 74Ɛ	1.078	.075 774 559	Ɛ48 249	1.0Ɛ8	.0Ɛ2 74Ɛ 13Ɛ	094
1.039	.038 510 8XX	Ɛ83 801	1.079	.076 700 7X6	Ɛ47 372	1.0Ɛ9	.0Ɛ3 661 213	Ɛ11 263
1.03X	.039 494 4XƐ	Ɛ82 876	1.07X	.077 647 Ɛ58	Ɛ46 497	1.0ƐX	.0Ɛ4 572 476	Ɛ10 433
1.03Ɛ	.03X 457 165	Ɛ81 930	1.07Ɛ	.078 592 433	Ɛ45 603	1.0ƐƐ	.0Ɛ5 482 8X9	Ɛ0Ɛ 605

N	e^N	d_2 +	N	e^N	d_2 +	N	e^N	d_2 +
.00	1.000 000 000	100 001	.40	1.48Ɛ 750 456	148 Ɛ77	.80	1.Ɛ45 826 824	1Ɛ4 584
.01	.010 060 201	101 006	.41	.4X4 510 612	14X 452	.81	.Ɛ65 17Ɛ 55Ɛ	1Ɛ6 51Ɛ
.02	.020 201 408	102 022	.42	.4Ɛ9 41Ɛ 020	14Ɛ 943	.82	.Ɛ84 90X 7Ɛ5	1Ɛ8 492
.03	.030 464 635	103 047	.43	.512 479 371	151 24X	.83	.ƐX4 656 321	1ƐX 468
.04	.040 80X 8X9	104 082	.44	.527 668 950	152 767	.84	2.004 5X0 2Ɛ5	200 45Ɛ
.05	.051 079 023	105 108	.45	.540 9XX X96	154 0X1	.85	.024 726 728	202 476
.06	.061 630 465	106 165	.46	.556 285 101	155 62X	.86	.044 X73 415	204 4X8
.07	.072 0X9 X50	107 210	.47	.56Ɛ 8Ɛ4 956	156 Ɛ91	.87	.065 404 5XX	206 543
.08	.082 872 647	108 288	.48	.585 47Ɛ 580	158 54X	.88	.085 Ɛ60 106	208 5Ɛ8
.09	.093 543 50X	109 355	.49	.59Ɛ 1X2 734	159 Ɛ1Ɛ	.89	.0X6 904 21X	20X 693
.0X	.0X4 321 726	10X 434	.4X	.5Ɛ5 063 807	15Ɛ 507	.8X	.107 876 X05	210 789
.0Ɛ	.0Ɛ5 20X 176	10Ɛ 521	.4Ɛ	.60Ɛ 084 1X5	160 Ɛ0Ɛ	.8Ɛ	.128 X3X 179	212 8X6
.10	.106 206 127	110 622	.50	.625 245 692	162 526	.90	.14X 214 217	214 X23
.11	.117 312 6ƐX	111 733	.51	.63Ɛ 569 4X5	163 Ɛ58	.91	.16Ɛ 803 098	216 Ɛ83
.12	.128 530 804	112 853	.52	.655 X35 254	165 5X4	.92	.191 408 Ɛ20	219 143
.13	.139 861 561	113 988	.53	.670 466 5X7	167 049	.93	.1Ɛ3 22Ɛ XX7	21Ɛ 325
.14	.14Ɛ 0X6 086	114 Ɛ0Ɛ	.54	.687 042 987	168 706	.94	.215 272 197	221 52X
.15	.160 643 6ƐX	116 066	.55	.6X1 987 871	16X 19X	.95	.237 515 9Ɛ5	223 753
.16	.172 0Ɛ7 198	117 211	.56	.6Ɛ8 87X 935	16Ɛ 88X	.96	.259 9X1 166	225 9X0
.17	.183 885 X87	118 389	.57	.713 921 687	171 393	.97	.280 492 2Ɛ7	228 050
.18	.195 570 Ɛ43	119 558	.58	.72X Ɛ35 7Ɛ0	172 XƐ5	.98	.2X3 1XƐ 498	22X 321
.19	.1X7 375 557	11X 739	.59	.746 300 80X	174 632	.99	.306 136 99X	230 615
.1X	.1Ɛ9 298 6X8	11Ɛ 92Ɛ	.5X	.761 840 25X	176 186	.9X	.329 2Ɛ2 8Ɛ5	232 933
.1Ɛ	.20Ɛ 31Ɛ 568	120 Ɛ33	.5Ɛ	.779 335 X74	177 934	.9Ɛ	.350 6X1 543	235 06Ɛ
.20	.221 483 35Ɛ	122 149	.60	.794 ƐX7 402	179 501	.X0	.374 105 240	237 414
.21	.233 749 29Ɛ	123 377	.61	.7Ɛ0 X16 251	17Ɛ 0X4	.X1	.397 964 351	239 798
.22	.245 Ɛ36 596	124 5Ɛ4	.62	.808 X04 184	180 8X1	.X2	.3ƐƐ 841 03X	23Ɛ Ɛ86
.23	.258 448 285	125 846	.63	.824 Ɛ72 998	182 4Ɛ9	.X3	.423 959 8Ɛ1	242 399
.24	.26X X83 7ƐX	126 XXX	.64	.841 2X3 XX9	184 130	.X4	.448 0Ɛ8 941	244 812
.25	.281 626 021	128 163	.65	.859 799 12X	185 980	.X5	.470 6X0 5X3	247 070
.26	.294 2Ɛ4 5X7	129 431	.66	.876 258 12Ɛ	187 627	.X6	.495 30Ɛ 2Ɛ5	249 533
.27	.2X7 0Ɛ0 3X2	12X 710	.67	.892 XX2 757	189 2XƐ	.X7	.4ƐX 187 53X	24Ɛ X20
.28	.2ƐX 016 8X9	12Ɛ X03	.68	.8XƐ 8Ɛ6 472	18X Ɛ93	.X8	.523 293 5X3	252 32Ɛ
.29	.311 070 ƐƐ7	131 108	.69	.908 899 160	190 88X	.X9	.548 631 977	254 866
.2X	.324 238 411	132 425	.6X	.925 X50 718	192 5X8	.XX	.572 024 9Ɛ5	257 205
.2Ɛ	.337 536 050	133 755	.6Ɛ	.943 196 680	194 31Ɛ	.XƐ	.597 873 038	259 789
.30	.34X 967 424	134 X98	.70	.960 6Ɛ4 943	196 071	.Ɛ0	.601 75X X48	260 179
.31	.362 311 694	136 233	.71	.97X 1X9 077	197 X20	.Ɛ1	.627 8X6 X15	262 791
.32	.375 9Ɛ1 Ɛ77	137 5X0	.72	.997 X79 20Ɛ	199 7XƐ	.Ɛ2	.652 095 573	265 210
.33	.389 609 X3X	138 962	.73	.9Ɛ5 926 Ɛ52	19Ɛ 593	.Ɛ3	.678 729 321	267 875
.34	.3X1 362 663	13X 137	.74	.X13 974 268	1X1 39X	.Ɛ4	.6X3 428 944	26X 346
.35	.3Ɛ5 235 403	13Ɛ 525	.75	.X31 ƐX2 960	1X3 200	.Ɛ5	.70X 396 6Ɛ1	270 X3Ɛ
.36	.409 247 688	140 927	.76	.X50 3Ɛ4 654	1X5 041	.Ɛ6	.735 5Ɛ5 299	273 563
.37	.421 39X 678	142 13X	.77	.X6X 9XƐ 389	1X6 XX1	.Ɛ7	.760 X87 428	276 0XƐ
.38	.435 673 7X6	143 569	.78	.X89 590 ƐX3	1X8 95Ɛ	.Ɛ8	.788 613 666	278 864
.39	.449 X90 281	144 9XƐ	.79	.XX8 35Ɛ 558	1XX 838	.Ɛ9	.7Ɛ4 418 548	27Ɛ 444
.3X	.462 431 747	146 244	.7X	.Ɛ07 318 749	1Ɛ0 733	.ƐX	.820 4X0 872	282 051
.3Ɛ	.476 Ɛ19 255	147 6Ɛ3	.7Ɛ	.Ɛ26 486 471	1Ɛ2 64Ɛ	.ƐƐ	.848 827 029	284 886
						1.00	.875 236 06X	287 525

N	e-N	d_2 +	N	e-N	d_2 +	N	e-N	d_2 +
.00	1.000 000 000	100 001	.40	.872 1ƐƐ 042	87 221	.80	.61Ɛ 227 377	61 Ɛ23
.01	.ƐƐ0 05Ɛ X00	ƐƐ 008	.41	.865 720 610	86 572	.81	.615 065 Ɛ71	61 507
.02	.ƐX0 1ƐX 808	ƐX 020	.42	.859 108 550	85 912	.82	.60X Ɛ46 072	60 XƐ5
.03	.Ɛ90 457 634	Ɛ9 047	.43	.850 77X 1X2	85 078	.83	.604 X87 068	60 4XX
.04	.Ɛ80 7Ɛ1 4X7	Ɛ8 080	.44	.844 2Ɛ4 XƐ0	84 430	.84	.5ƐX X68 550	5Ɛ XX6
.05	.Ɛ71 043 41X	Ɛ7 106	.45	.837 XƐ4 02X	83 7Ɛ1	.85	.5Ɛ4 XX9 91X	5Ɛ 4Ɛ0
.06	.Ɛ61 590 457	Ɛ6 159	.46	.82Ɛ 776 959	82 Ɛ78	.86	.5XX Ɛ8X 598	5X XƐ9
.07	.Ɛ52 013 631	Ɛ5 202	.47	.823 500 644	82 350	.87	.5X5 10X 153	5X 511
.08	.Ɛ42 74Ɛ X09	Ɛ4 277	.48	.817 308 67Ɛ	81 732	.88	.59Ɛ 2X8 21Ɛ	59 Ɛ30
.09	.Ɛ33 380 460	Ɛ3 338	.49	.80Ɛ 196 228	80 Ɛ1X	.89	.595 524 217	59 552
.0X	.Ɛ24 0X4 22Ɛ	Ɛ2 410	.4X	.803 124 8Ɛ3	80 313	.8X	.58Ɛ 7Ɛ9 765	58 Ɛ81
.0Ɛ	.Ɛ14 XƐX 40X	Ɛ1 4Ɛ1	.4Ɛ	.7Ɛ7 133 691	7Ɛ 714	.8Ɛ	.585 Ɛ30 074	58 5Ɛ3
.10	.Ɛ05 X05 X9X	Ɛ0 5X0	.50	.7XƐ 201 Ɛ83	7X Ɛ21	.90	.580 2ƐX Ɛ76	58 030
.11	.XƐ6 X01 Ɛ4X	XƐ 6X2	.51	.7X3 34Ɛ 396	7X 335	.91	.576 725 XX8	57 674
.12	.XX7 XX9 6X0	XX 7Ɛ0	.52	.797 556 Ɛ22	79 757	.92	.570 ƐX8 492	57 0ƐX
.13	.X99 083 X22	X9 909	.53	.78Ɛ 820 205	78 Ɛ82	.93	.567 505 Ɛ76	56 752
.14	.X8X 347 X71	X8 X36	.54	.783 Ɛ62 46X	78 3Ɛ7	.94	.561 X7X 1Ɛ0	56 1X8
.15	.X7Ɛ 6Ɛ8 936	X7 Ɛ70	.55	.778 360 Ɛ0X	77 837	.95	.558 488 612	55 849
.16	.X70 Ɛ55 76Ɛ	X7 0Ɛ6	.56	.770 817 1X5	77 083	.96	.552 Ɛ30 681	55 2Ɛ4
.17	.X62 499 69X	X6 24Ɛ	.57	.765 148 543	76 514	.97	.549 629 X24	54 963
.18	.X53 Ɛ07 858	X5 3Ɛ2	.58	.759 734 1Ɛ5	75 974	.98	.544 17Ɛ Ɛ2X	54 418
.19	.X45 61Ɛ 208	X4 562	.59	.752 195 81Ɛ	75 21Ɛ	.99	.53X 966 450	53 X97
.1X	.X37 217 11X	X3 723	.5X	.746 8Ɛ0 464	74 68Ɛ	.9X	.535 5X4 849	53 55Ɛ
.1Ɛ	.X28 XƐ6 753	X2 8Ɛ0	.5Ɛ	.73Ɛ 47Ɛ 778	73 Ɛ49	.9Ɛ	.530 276 5X5	53 028
.20	.X1X 878 X78	X1 X89	.60	.734 102 X19	73 410	.X0	.526 Ɛ9Ɛ 369	52 6ƐƐ
.21	.X10 721 06X	X1 073	.61	.728 9Ɛ9 48X	72 8X1	.X1	.521 956 830	52 195
.22	.X02 666 313	X0 267	.62	.721 766 820	72 178	.X2	.518 764 288	51 877
.23	.9Ɛ4 68Ɛ 823	9Ɛ 46X	.63	.716 586 12X	71 658	.X3	.513 603 59Ɛ	51 361
.24	.9X6 794 5X1	9X 67X	.64	.70Ɛ 457 094	70 Ɛ46	.X4	.50X 4Ɛ4 053	50 X50
.25	.998 977 X19	99 899	.65	.704 398 Ɛ84	70 43Ɛ	.X5	.505 435 557	50 544
.26	.98Ɛ 038 Ɛ32	98 Ɛ04	.66	.6Ɛ9 38Ɛ 2Ɛ3	6Ɛ 939	.X6	.500 407 3X3	50 040
.27	.981 396 Ɛ4Ɛ	98 13Ɛ	.67	.6Ɛ2 431 35Ɛ	6Ɛ 244	.X7	.4Ɛ7 429 26Ɛ	4Ɛ 744
.28	.973 811 0X7	97 381	.68	.6X7 542 64Ɛ	6X 755	.X8	.4Ɛ2 49X 87Ɛ	4Ɛ 24X
.29	.966 122 604	96 614	.69	.6X0 702 494	6X 070	.X9	.4X9 59Ɛ 519	4X 95Ɛ
.2X	.958 70X 535	95 871	.6X	.695 930 389	69 595	.XX	.4X4 72X Ɛ16	4X 472
.2Ɛ	.94Ɛ 190 117	94 Ɛ1X	.6Ɛ	.68Ɛ 007 857	68 Ɛ00	.XƐ	.49Ɛ 908 985	49 Ɛ92
.30	.941 926 817	94 193	.70	.684 350 025	68 436	.Ɛ0	.496 Ɛ34 806	49 6Ɛ4
.31	.934 555 4XX	93 456	.71	.679 740 829	67 974	.Ɛ1	.492 1XX 13Ɛ	49 21Ɛ
.32	.927 257 617	92 727	.72	.672 Ɛ99 1X5	67 2ƐƐ	.Ɛ2	.489 4Ɛ0 893	48 94Ɛ
.33	.91X 030 26Ɛ	91 X04	.73	.668 4X0 X60	66 84X	.Ɛ3	.484 840 176	48 485
.34	.910 X96 907	91 0XX	.74	.661 X4Ɛ 365	66 1X6	.Ɛ4	.480 017 Ɛ22	48 002
.35	.903 X12 451	90 3X2	.75	.657 463 X54	65 747	.Ɛ5	.477 43Ɛ 890	47 744
.36	.8Ɛ6 X1X 379	8Ɛ 6X2	.76	.650 Ɛ22 08X	65 0Ɛ3	.Ɛ6	.472 8XƐ 182	47 290
.37	.8X9 XƐ5 987	8X 9Ɛ1	.77	.646 645 3Ɛ7	64 664	.Ɛ7	.46X 1X5 944	46 X1X
.38	.8X1 060 186	8X 106	.78	.640 211 188	64 022	.Ɛ8	.465 727 324	46 573
.39	.894 294 68Ɛ	89 42Ɛ	.79	.635 X40 Ɛ7Ɛ	63 5X5	.Ɛ9	.461 0Ɛ3 277	46 110
.3X	.887 596 403	88 75X	.7X	.62Ɛ 714 357	62 Ɛ71	.ƐX	.458 705 31X	45 871
.3Ɛ	.87X 964 895	87 X97	.7Ɛ	.625 44X 6X4	62 546	.ƐƐ	.454 161 032	45 416
						1.00	.44Ɛ 842 160	44 Ɛ85

Circular Measure

The following tables of sin N, cos N, sinh N, cosh N, N being in radians, were calculated from the expansions of the functions for N = *.1*, *.2*, *.3*, etc., and n = *.01*, *.02*, *.03*, etc., the remainder of the tables being obtained by multiplication.

$$\sin (N + n) = \sin N \cos n + \cos N \sin n$$
$$\cos (N + n) = \cos N \cos n - \sin N \sin n$$

$$\sinh (N + n) = \sinh N \cosh n + \cosh N \sinh n$$
$$\cosh (N + n) = \cosh N \cosh n + \sinh N \sinh n$$

results being checked for the corresponding formulae for sin (N - n), cos (N - n), sinh (N - n), cosh (N - n). One dozen and three places were calculated.

The tables may be interpolated for nine place results by the use of the Everett coefficients for second differences. The necessary coefficients may be obtained by direct proportion from the table of coefficients given on pages *296-29Ɛ*.

Note: From the following extended values, results may be obtained beyond the scope of the table, by multiplication.

N	Sine	Cosine	Sinh	Cosh
1.0	*+.X12 08X X92 234*	*+.659 786 059 Ɛ61*	*1.212 8Ɛ7 Ɛ64 73X*	*1.662 53X 105 0X3*
2.0	*+.XXƐ 323 699 086*	*-.4ƐƐ 127 966 91X*	*3.763 26Ɛ 193 X33*	*3.919 0X8 17Ɛ 296*
3.0	*+.183 X32 104 X40*	*-.ƐX6 859 908 705*	*X.026 X7X 2Ɛ7 2Ɛ0*	*X.098 Ɛ05 778 484*
4.0	*-.90Ɛ 908 185 774*	*-.7X1 5Ɛ5 488 186*	*23.358 Ɛ88 141 544*	*23.384 762 397 152*
5.0	*-.Ɛ61 030 65Ɛ 568*	*+.34X 202 8Ɛ7 1XX*	*62.253 193 64X 715*	*62.262 95X Ɛ29 170*
6.0	*-.342 9Ɛ6 259 799*	*+.Ɛ63 211 143 771*	*149.868 404 5Ɛ7 074*	*149.870 752 017 9Ɛ5*

Example: Find sin $\frac{\pi}{4}$ $\qquad \frac{\pi}{4}$ = .951 202 424 0

		d_2 -	E_0 & E_1 -
sin .95	.859 079 X45	85 907	.040 18Ɛ
sin .96	.865 623 415	86 562	.023 925
The interval n =	.120 242 40		
(1 - n) sin .95	.77X 251 7Ɛ4 6		
n sin .96	.09Ɛ 813 483 X		
E_0 d_2	+ 2 X03 0		
E_1 d_2	+ 1 791 0		
sin $\frac{\pi}{4}$	.859 X69 550 4		

Example: Find cos $\frac{\pi}{4}$

cos .95	.85X 858 2X9	85 X86	.040 18Ɛ
cos .96	.852 244 917	85 223	.023 925
(1 - n) cos .95	.77Ɛ 83X 25X 2		
n cos .96	.09X 226 X43 3		
E_0 d_2	+ 2 X09 8		
E_1 d_2	+ 1 761 6		
cos $\frac{\pi}{4}$	.859 X69 650 7		

Note: $\frac{1}{\sqrt{2}}$ = .859 X69 650 3ƐX

Example: Find sinh $\frac{\pi}{4}$ $\qquad \frac{\pi}{4}$ = .951 202 424 0

		d_2 +	E_0 & E_1 -
sinh .95	.X4Ɛ 624 7Ɛ1	X4 Ɛ64	.040 18Ɛ
sinh .96	.X63 536 352	X6 355	.023 925
(1 - n) sinh .95	.949 688 339 7		
n sinh .96	.103 60X 9Ɛ0 3		
E_0 d_2	- 3 594 3		
E_1 d_2	- 2 04Ɛ 7		
sinh $\frac{\pi}{4}$	.X51 091 713 0		

Example: Find cosh $\frac{\pi}{4}$

cosh .95	1.3X7 XƐ1 203	13X 7Ɛ1	.040 18Ɛ
cosh .96	1.3Ɛ6 466 X13	13Ɛ 648	.023 925
(1 - n) cosh .95	1.241 270 316 4		
n cosh .96	.167 869 813 8		
E_0 d_2	- 5 38Ɛ 5		
E_1 d_2	- 3 0Ɛ2 3		
cosh $\frac{\pi}{4}$	1.3X8 Ɛ11 688 4		

Note: The sum of the above results is 2.239 ƐX3 17Ɛ 4

The extended value of $e^{\pi:4}$ 2.239 ƐX3 180 294

N	Sine	d_2 -	N	Sine	d_2 -	N	Sine	d_2 -
.00	.000 000 000	000	.40	.3E1 486 168	3E 149	.80	.750 662 408	75 066
.01	.00E EEE X00	1 000	.41	.400 875 05E	40 086	.81	.759 E45 X14	9E3
.02	.01E EEX 800	2 000	.42	.410 023 X88	41 002	.82	.767 373 629	76 737
.03	.02E EE7 600	EEE	.43	.41E 351 8E3	E36	.83	.774 726 707	77 472
.04	.03E EE1 401	4 000	.44	.42X 639 7X4	42 X62	.84	.781 X22 333	78 1X2
.05	.04E EX3 202	EEX	.45	.439 8X2 833	43 98E	.85	.78E 061 979	E05
.06	.05E E90 005	5 EE8	.46	.448 E03 XE3	44 8XE	.86	.798 224 4EX	79 822
.07	.06E E72 X10	6 EE8	.47	.458 0X0 484	45 80E	.87	.7X5 329 419	7X 532
.08	.07E E4X 81E	7 EE5	.48	.467 233 246	46 722	.88	.7E2 373 X06	7E 237
.09	.08E E1X 635	8 EE2	.49	.476 33E 4X6	47 633	.89	.7EE 33E 178	E33
.0X	.09E XX1 459	9 EX9	.4X	.485 400 113	48 541	.8X	.808 246 5E7	80 824
.0E	.0XE X56 294	X EX6	.4E	.494 434 3EE	49 442	.8E	.815 091 212	81 508
.10	.0EE X00 125	E EX0	.50	.4X3 41E 265	4X 342	.90	.821 X56 521	82 1X5
.11	.10E 955 E96	10 E96	.51	.4E2 377 989	4E 236	.91	.82X 759 647	X75
.12	.11E 89X X71	11 E89	.52	.501 285 277	50 129	.92	.837 399 8E8	83 739
.13	.12E 811 97E	12 E81	.53	.510 142 638	51 014	.93	.843 E56 430	84 3E6
.14	.13E 731 908	13 E73	.54	.51X E6X 9X5	XE6	.94	.850 64X 76X	85 063
.15	.14E 639 8X2	14 E64	.55	.529 945 258	52 995	.95	.859 079 X45	907
.16	.15E 530 914	15 E53	.56	.538 688 936	53 867	.96	.865 623 415	86 562
.17	.16E 409 9E3	16 E41	.57	.547 378 769	54 738	.97	.871 E02 443	87 1E0
.18	.17E 28E E51	17 E28	.58	.556 013 X64	55 601	.98	.87X 316 281	X30
.19	.18E 136 183	18 E14	.59	.564 815 75X	56 480	.99	.886 662 28E	88 666
.1X	.19X E83 4X1	19 XE8	.5X	.573 380 E94	57 339	.9X	.892 921 833	89 291
.1E	.1XX 9E2 903	1X X9E	.5E	.581 X91 091	58 1X8	.9E	.89X E13 E06	XE1
.20	.1EX 803 246	1E X80	.60	.590 544 EX2	59 054	.X0	.8X7 038 2X8	8X 703
.21	.20X 5E3 909	20 X5E	.61	.59X E5E X5E	XE5	.X1	.8E3 091 E87	8E 308
.22	.21X 383 531	21 X39	.62	.5X9 518 X23	5X 951	.X2	.8EE 058 55X	E05
.23	.22X 131 318	22 X12	.63	.5E7 X37 056	5E 7X4	.X3	.906 E53 028	90 6E4
.24	.239 X78 2E1	23 9X8	.64	.606 2E5 6X5	60 62E	.X4	.912 979 002	91 298
.25	.249 79E 49X	24 979	.65	.614 713 705	61 470	.X5	.91X 711 900	X70
.26	.259 499 90X	25 94E	.66	.622 X90 275	62 2X9	.X6	.926 394 74X	92 638
.27	.269 172 3XE	26 916	.67	.631 1X6 738	63 11X	.X7	.931 E84 E60	93 1E9
.28	.278 X20 176	27 8X2	.68	.63E 459 XX1	E45	.X8	.939 6X2 175	968
.29	.288 662 25E	28 865	.69	.649 669 301	64 967	.X9	.945 127 622	94 513
.2X	.298 277 69E	29 829	.6X	.657 813 976	65 780	.XX	.950 698 578	95 068
.2E	.2X7 X63 2E2	2X 7X5	.6E	.665 914 86E	66 591	.XE	.957 E74 466	7E7
.30	.2E7 620 320	2E 762	.70	.673 96E 193	67 397	.E0	.963 376 759	96 337
.31	.307 169 7X8	30 717	.71	.681 95X 320	68 195	.E1	.96X 6X2 715	X69
.32	.316 886 559	31 688	.72	.68E 8X1 294	E89	.E2	.975 933 824	97 592
.33	.326 371 842	32 636	.73	.699 777 27E	69 977	.E3	.980 XX9 361	98 0XE
.34	.335 X26 4E1	33 5X3	.74	.6X7 5X3 4XE	6X 75X	.E4	.987 E86 9XE	7E7
.35	.345 467 779	34 547	.75	.6E5 360 E81	6E 536	.E5	.992 E87 842	99 2E9
.36	.354 X74 4EX	35 4X6	.76	.703 06E 119	70 306	.E6	.999 XXE 398	9X9
.37	.364 447 955	36 445	.77	.710 908 E6E	71 090	.E7	.9X4 935 145	9X 493
.38	.373 9X4 967	37 39X	.78	.71X 4E5 931	X4E	.E8	.9XE 6X0 61E	E69
.39	.383 306 59E	38 330	.79	.728 030 864	72 803	.E9	.9E6 368 E48	9E 636
.3X	.392 7XE XX3	39 27E	.7X	.735 6E4 E94	73 56X	.EX	.X00 E55 X3E	X0 0E5
.3E	.3X2 058 128	3X 205	.7E	.743 105 956	74 310	.EE	.X07 662 839	765
						1.00	.X12 08X X92	X1 208

N	Cosine	d2 -	N	Cosine	d2 -	N	Cosine	d2 -
.00	1.000 000 000	100 000	.40	.Ɛ40 X76 3X5	Ɛ4 0X7	.80	.952 01X 953	95 201
.01	.ƐƐƐ Ɛ60 000	ƐƐ ƐƐ4	.41	.Ɛ38 Ɛ05 76X	Ɛ3 8XƐ	.81	.946 687 959	94 669
.02	.ƐƐƐ X00 008	ƐX0	.42	.Ɛ34 X61 244	4X5	.82	.93Ɛ 060 2Ɛ6	93 Ɛ05
.03	.ƐƐƐ 760 034	Ɛ74	.43	.Ɛ30 905 435	090	.83	.933 560 94X	354
.04	.ƐƐƐ 400 0X8	Ɛ40	.44	.Ɛ28 676 556	Ɛ2 866	.84	.927 98X 04X	92 799
.05	.ƐƐX Ɛ60 220	XƐ4	.45	.Ɛ24 334 X11	433	.85	.920 124 771	012
.06	.ƐƐX 600 460	X60	.46	.Ɛ1Ɛ Ɛ00 X55	Ɛ1 ƐXƐ	.86	.914 3X9 282	91 43X
.07	.ƐƐ9 Ɛ60 840	9Ɛ4	.47	.Ɛ17 596 XXX	759	.87	.908 5X0 555	90 859
.08	.ƐƐ9 401 228	940	.48	.Ɛ12 Ɛ7Ɛ 3X6	2Ɛ6	.88	.900 702 Ɛ8Ɛ	06Ɛ
.09	.ƐƐ8 761 X94	875	.49	.Ɛ0X 472 5X8	Ɛ0 X47	.89	.8Ɛ4 755 556	8Ɛ 475
.0X	.ƐƐ7 X02 X87	79Ɛ	.4X	.Ɛ05 874 963	587	.8X	.8X8 718 668	8X 871
.0Ɛ	.ƐƐ6 Ɛ64 29Ɛ	6Ɛ5	.4Ɛ	.Ɛ00 Ɛ86 753	0Ɛ7	.8Ɛ	.8X0 610 Ɛ09	061
.10	.ƐƐ6 005 ƐƐX	600	.50	.XƐ8 1X8 448	XƐ 81X	.90	.894 437 309	89 442
.11	.ƐƐ4 Ɛ68 319	4Ɛ6	.51	.XƐ3 31X 523	331	.91	.888 194 287	88 819
.12	.ƐƐ3 X0Ɛ 142	3X0	.52	.XXX 361 289	XX X35	.92	.87Ɛ X64 628	87 ƐX5
.13	.ƐƐ2 772 787	275	.53	.XX5 2Ɛ5 1ƐX	52X	.93	.873 668 9X4	367
.14	.ƐƐ1 416 Ɛ57	142	.54	.XX0 15X 801	016	.94	.867 1X5 9Ɛ5	86 719
.15	.ƐXƐ Ɛ80 1X5	ƐX ƐƐ6	.55	.X96 Ɛ16 1XX	X9 6Ɛ0	.95	.85X 858 2X9	85 X86
.16	.ƐXX 626 439	X62	.56	.X91 7X4 0X7	179	.96	.852 244 917	223
.17	.ƐX8 Ɛ91 82Ɛ	8Ɛ8	.57	.X88 384 X27	X8 839	.97	.845 768 122	84 576
.18	.ƐX7 43X 325	743	.58	.X82 X78 Ɛ2X	2X6	.98	.839 006 Ɛ73	83 900
.19	.ƐX5 7X8 298	57X	.59	.X79 484 947	X7 947	.99	.830 3X2 104	039
.1X	.ƐX3 X57 891	3X4	.5X	.X73 9X4 X19	39X	.9X	.823 6Ɛ6 218	82 36Ɛ
.1Ɛ	.ƐX2 008 XX2	201	.5Ɛ	.X6X 219 711	X6 X21	.9Ɛ	.816 947 Ɛ81	81 695
.20	.ƐX0 07Ɛ XƐ2	006	.60	.X64 567 5X4	456	.X0	.809 Ɛ18 251	80 9Ɛ0
.21	.Ɛ9X 034 XƐ8	Ɛ9 X02	.61	.X5X 80Ɛ 021	X5 X7Ɛ	.X1	.801 027 731	102
.22	.Ɛ97 XƐ0 100	7XƐ	.62	.X54 988 79Ɛ	499	.X2	.7Ɛ4 076 Ɛ0Ɛ	7Ɛ 407
.23	.Ɛ95 869 715	585	.63	.X4X X60 X80	X4 XX5	.X3	.7X7 046 XX2	7X 704
.24	.Ɛ93 529 765	352	.64	.X44 X50 278	4X3	.X4	.799 Ɛ58 371	79 9Ɛ5
.25	.Ɛ91 0Ɛ0 463	10X	.65	.X3X 957 191	X3 X96	.X5	.790 9XƐ X47	09Ɛ
.26	.Ɛ8X 776 053	Ɛ8 X77	.66	.X34 77X 210	477	.X6	.783 786 442	78 377
.27	.Ɛ88 142 988	813	.67	.X2X 4Ɛ9 994	X2 X4X	.X7	.776 4X4 682	77 64X
.28	.Ɛ85 612 XXX	561	.68	.X24 156 70X	416	.X8	.769 147 274	76 914
.29	.Ɛ82 9X6 66Ɛ	298	.69	.X19 911 02X	X1 98Ɛ	.X9	.75Ɛ 933 152	75 Ɛ93
.2X	.Ɛ80 081 Ɛ54	008	.6X	.X13 3X5 77Ɛ	33X	.XX	.752 465 059	245
.2Ɛ	.Ɛ79 261 431	Ɛ7 926	.6Ɛ	.X08 998 Ɛ92	X0 899	.XƐ	.744 Ɛ21 91Ɛ	74 4Ɛ2
.30	.Ɛ76 344 ƐX4	632	.70	.X02 2XƐ 708	22Ɛ	.Ɛ0	.737 526 0XƐ	73 752
.31	.Ɛ73 331 125	333	.71	.9Ɛ7 722 013	9Ɛ 770	.Ɛ1	.729 X76 929	72 9X7
.32	.Ɛ70 221 Ɛ33	021	.72	.9Ɛ0 X74 96X	0X7	.Ɛ2	.720 354 780	034
.33	.Ɛ69 017 920	Ɛ6 901	.73	.9X6 128 61X	9X 612	.Ɛ3	.712 780 59Ɛ	71 278
.34	.Ɛ65 916 X08	590	.74	.99Ɛ 301 878	99 Ɛ30	.Ɛ4	.704 Ɛ37 142	70 4Ɛ3
.35	.Ɛ62 51Ɛ 524	251	.75	.994 3Ɛ8 ƐX6	43X	.Ɛ5	.6Ɛ7 241 3Ɛ2	6Ɛ 724
.36	.Ɛ5Ɛ 029 9XƐ	Ɛ5 Ɛ02	.76	.989 416 X96	98 941	.Ɛ6	.6X9 497 Ɛ3X	6X 949
.37	.Ɛ57 642 374	764	.77	.982 358 045	235	.Ɛ7	.69Ɛ 683 939	69 Ɛ67
.38	.Ɛ53 Ɛ61 195	3Ɛ4	.78	.977 200 Ɛ7Ɛ	97 71Ɛ	.Ɛ8	.691 801 791	180
.39	.Ɛ50 386 802	038	.79	.96Ɛ Ɛ8X 396	96 Ɛ28	.Ɛ9	.683 892 465	68 389
.3X	.Ɛ48 6Ɛ7 1Ɛ3	Ɛ4 86Ɛ	.7X	.964 880 7Ɛ5	488	.ƐX	.675 8Ɛ6 970	67 58Ɛ
.3Ɛ	.Ɛ44 932 Ɛ35	492	.7Ɛ	.959 498 748	95 948	.ƐƐ	.667 873 8X8	66 786
						1.00	.659 786 05X	65 978

N	Sinh	d_2 +	N	Sinh	d_2 +	N	Sinh	d_2 +
.00	.000 000 000	000	.40	.40X 886 808	40 X89	.80	.873 2ƐƐ 834	87 331
.01	.010 000 200	1 000	.41	.41Ɛ 4Ɛ6 001	41 Ɛ50	.81	.886 068 8Ɛ5	88 607
.02	.020 001 400	2 000	.42	.430 167 346	43 017	.82	.898 XX2 381	89 8XƐ
.03	.030 004 600	3 001	.43	.440 X5Ɛ 6X6	44 0X6	.83	.8XƐ 9X5 738	8X Ɛ9Ɛ
.04	.040 00X 801	4 000	.44	.451 797 Ɛ30	45 17X	.84	.902 977 X92	90 299
.05	.050 018 X02	5 002	.45	.462 559 534	46 256	.85	.915 X1X 505	91 5X2
.06	.060 030 005	6 004	.46	.473 365 192	47 337	.86	.928 Ɛ52 51X	92 8Ɛ7
.07	.070 049 210	7 004	.47	.484 1Ɛ8 167	48 421	.87	.940 159 22X	94 016
.08	.080 071 41Ɛ	8 007	.48	.495 097 561	49 509	.88	.953 437 Ɛ54	95 344
.09	.090 0X1 635	9 00X	.49	.4X6 004 264	4X 601	.89	.966 7Ɛ0 002	96 680
.0X	.0X0 11X 859	X 013	.4X	.4Ɛ6 Ɛ7Ɛ 568	4Ɛ 6Ɛ8	.8X	.97X 03X 730	97 X05
.0Ɛ	.0Ɛ0 165 X94	Ɛ 016	.4Ɛ	.507 Ɛ86 368	50 7ƐX	.8Ɛ	.991 565 063	99 157
.10	.100 200 125	10 020	.50	.519 021 966	51 901	.90	.9X4 Ɛ68 731	9X 4Ɛ7
.11	.110 266 396	11 027	.51	.52X 10Ɛ 065	52 X13	.91	.9Ɛ8 64X 6Ɛ6	9Ɛ 866
.12	.120 321 672	12 031	.52	.53Ɛ 24Ɛ 177	53 Ɛ24	.92	.X10 210 325	X1 022
.13	.130 3XX 97Ɛ	13 040	.53	.550 423 1Ɛ1	55 044	.93	.X23 X72 Ɛ76	X2 3X9
.14	.140 48Ɛ 108	14 049	.54	.561 650 26Ɛ	56 164	.94	.X37 7Ɛ7 Ɛ24	X3 77Ɛ
.15	.150 583 4X2	15 059	.55	.572 913 491	57 293	.95	.X4Ɛ 624 7Ɛ1	X4 Ɛ64
.16	.160 690 915	16 068	.56	.584 031 986	58 403	.96	.X63 536 352	X6 355
.17	.170 7Ɛ4 1Ɛ4	17 080	.57	.595 3X8 682	59 53Ɛ	.97	.X77 532 248	X7 753
.18	.180 932 753	18 094	.58	.5X6 800 8Ɛ9	5X 681	.98	.X8Ɛ 615 895	X8 Ɛ63
.19	.190 X89 186	19 0X8	.59	.5Ɛ8 073 5Ɛ5	5Ɛ 808	.99	.XX3 7X6 285	XX 37Ɛ
.1X	.1X1 040 8X5	1X 104	.5X	.609 585 XƐ9	60 959	.9X	.XƐ7 X65 034	XƐ 7X8
.1Ɛ	.1Ɛ1 212 508	1Ɛ 122	.5Ɛ	.61X Ɛ39 15X	61 XƐ4	.9Ɛ	.Ɛ10 213 58Ɛ	Ɛ1 021
.20	.201 403 251	20 141	.60	.630 552 2Ɛ3	63 055	.X0	.Ɛ24 672 Ɛ47	Ɛ2 469
.21	.211 614 117	21 160	.61	.642 00X 4X1	64 203	.X1	.Ɛ39 004 970	Ɛ3 902
.22	.221 846 141	22 186	.62	.653 72X 892	65 372	.X2	.Ɛ51 64X 497	Ɛ5 165
.23	.231 X9X 331	23 1X9	.63	.665 2Ɛ4 435	66 531	.X3	.Ɛ66 189 167	Ɛ6 61X
.24	.242 155 70X	24 217	.64	.676 Ɛ24 509	67 6Ɛ2	.X4	.Ɛ7X X02 455	Ɛ7 XX1
.25	.252 435 102	25 242	.65	.688 800 093	68 881	.X5	.Ɛ93 733 624	Ɛ9 374
.26	.262 739 938	26 275	.66	.69X 544 51X	69 X55	.X6	.ƐX8 561 Ɛ67	ƐX 857
.27	.272 X68 827	27 2X7	.67	.6Ɛ0 336 7ƐX	6Ɛ 034	.X7	1.001 48Ɛ 145	100 14Ɛ
.28	.283 202 X01	28 320	.68	.702 197 Ɛ12	70 21X	.X8	.016 4Ɛ8 472	101 650
.29	.293 585 2Ɛ7	29 359	.69	.714 0X9 444	71 40Ɛ	.X9	.02Ɛ 627 22Ɛ	102 Ɛ64
.2X	.2X3 974 Ɛ4X	2X 398	.6X	.726 070 185	72 609	.XX	.044 858 Ɛ50	104 486
.2Ɛ	.2Ɛ4 192 Ɛ79	2Ɛ 419	.6Ɛ	.738 0X5 513	73 80X	.XƐ	.059 Ɛ93 137	105 9ƐƐ
.30	.304 620 405	30 462	.70	.74X 192 46Ɛ	74 X1X	.Ɛ0	.073 413 121	107 342
.31	.314 X9X 0Ɛ3	31 4XƐ	.71	.760 334 225	76 034	.Ɛ1	.088 95X 449	108 897
.32	.325 389 290	32 538	.72	.772 550 013	77 256	.Ɛ2	.0X2 3Ɛ2 450	10X 240
.33	.335 8XX 9X5	33 590	.73	.784 823 057	78 482	.Ɛ3	.0Ɛ7 Ɛ54 693	10Ɛ 7Ɛ7
.34	.346 243 X8X	34 624	.74	.796 Ɛ72 561	79 6Ɛ9	.Ɛ4	.111 806 511	111 181
.35	.356 811 597	35 682	.75	.7X9 37Ɛ 564	7X 938	.Ɛ5	.127 589 510	112 75Ɛ
.36	.367 214 766	36 721	.76	.7ƐƐ 847 2X3	7Ɛ Ɛ85	.Ɛ6	.141 463 06X	114 146
.37	.377 852 456	37 786	.77	.812 192 ƐX7	81 21X	.Ɛ7	.157 450 952	115 747
.38	.388 307 910	38 831	.78	.824 79Ɛ Ɛ09	82 47Ɛ	.Ɛ8	.171 554 181	117 156
.39	.398 9Ɛ9 9Ɛ7	39 8X0	.79	.837 26Ɛ 2XX	83 728	.Ɛ9	.187 772 746	118 779
.3X	.3X9 529 782	3X 953	.7X	.849 X02 1Ɛ7	84 9X0	.ƐX	.1X1 XX9 888	11X 1Ɛ0
.3Ɛ	.3ƐX 098 2X0	3Ɛ X0X	.7Ɛ	.860 619 XX4	86 063	.ƐƐ	.1Ɛ8 342 ƐƐX	11Ɛ 835
						1.00	1.212 8Ɛ7 Ɛ65	121 290

N	Cosh	d_2 +	N	Cosh	d_2 +	N	Cosh	d_2 +
.00	1.000 000 000	100 002	.40	1.080 X85 84X	108 0XX	.80	1.292 526 Ɛ20	129 253
.01	.000 060 001	006	.41	.085 016 611	502	.81	.29Ɛ 112 866	Ɛ13
.02	.000 200 008	022	.42	.089 273 896	928	.82	.2X7 X28 433	12X 7X5
.03	.000 460 035	046	.43	.091 619 887	109 164	.83	.2Ɛ4 870 7X5	12Ɛ 487
.04	.000 800 0X8	082	.44	.095 X90 X20	5X9	.84	.301 824 422	130 184
.05	.001 060 221	106	.45	.09X 451 562	X47	.85	.30X 908 223	X92
.06	.001 600 460	162	.46	.0X2 Ɛ1Ɛ Ɛ2Ɛ	10X 2Ɛ3	.86	.317 Ɛ20 XƐ6	131 7Ɛ3
.07	.002 060 841	206	.47	.0X7 6Ɛ8 7XƐ	771	.87	.325 267 380	132 529
.08	.002 801 228	282	.48	.0Ɛ0 3X4 020	10Ɛ 03Ɛ	.88	.332 724 173	133 272
.09	.003 461 X95	347	.49	.0Ɛ5 19X 490	51Ɛ	.89	.340 114 218	134 014
.0X	.004 202 X89	421	.4X	.0ƐX 0X4 25Ɛ	X0Ɛ	.8X	.349 838 295	984
.0Ɛ	.005 064 2X2	507	.4Ɛ	.103 0Ɛ9 X39	110 311	.8Ɛ	.357 495 116	135 74Ɛ
.10	.006 006 002	602	.50	.108 223 928	824	.90	.365 267 6X6	136 528
.11	.007 068 324	708	.51	.111 45X 43Ɛ	111 147	.91	.373 174 5X2	137 319
.12	.008 20Ɛ 152	822	.52	.116 7X6 099	67Ɛ	.92	.381 1Ɛ8 7Ɛ7	138 121
.13	.009 472 7X2	947	.53	.120 043 3Ɛ6	112 006	.93	.38Ɛ 378 Ɛ31	Ɛ39
.14	.00X 816 Ɛ79	X84	.54	.125 5Ɛ2 719	560	.94	.399 676 1X4	139 968
.15	.010 080 218	101 008	.55	.12Ɛ 074 3X0	Ɛ08	.95	.3X7 XƐ1 203	13X 7Ɛ1
.16	.011 626 483	164	.56	.134 848 Ɛ6Ɛ	113 487	.96	.3Ɛ6 466 X13	13Ɛ 648
.17	.013 091 892	30X	.57	.13X 535 005	X53	.97	.404 Ɛ60 06Ɛ	140 4Ɛ8
.18	.014 83X 3XƐ	485	.58	.144 334 XƐ2	114 436	.98	.413 795 803	141 37X
.19	.016 4X8 391	650	.59	.14X 249 215	X25	.99	.422 550 715	142 256
.1X	.018 257 X03	827	.5X	.154 276 361	115 429	.9X	.431 449 881	143 147
.1Ɛ	.01X 109 060	X11	.5Ɛ	.15X 3Ɛ8 916	X41	.9Ɛ	.440 489 Ɛ74	144 04X
.20	.020 080 10X	102 009	.60	.164 655 110	116 466	.X0	.44Ɛ 652 2Ɛ5	Ɛ66
.21	.022 135 185	214	.61	.16X X07 970	XX2	.X1	.45X 95Ɛ 5X0	145 X98
.22	.024 2Ɛ0 454	431	.62	.175 295 4Ɛ2	117 52Ɛ	.X2	.46X 1Ɛ2 763	146 X20
.23	.026 569 Ɛ54	658	.63	.17Ɛ 87X 563	Ɛ88	.X3	.479 790 746	147 97Ɛ
.24	.028 92X 0Ɛ0	893	.64	.186 37Ɛ 5X0	118 63X	.X4	.489 2Ɛ6 4X8	148 931
.25	.02Ɛ 1Ɛ0 Ɛ1Ɛ	Ɛ20	.65	.190 Ɛ99 057	119 0ƐƐ	.X5	.498 Ɛ68 Ɛ7Ɛ	149 8Ɛ8
.26	.031 776 86X	103 179	.66	.197 913 811	792	.X6	.4X8 969 34X	14X 898
.27	.034 243 776	426	.67	.1X2 767 Ɛ59	11X 278	.X7	.4Ɛ8 8Ɛ8 3Ɛ5	14Ɛ 891
.28	.036 X13 XX8	6X1	.68	.1X9 71X 561	973	.X8	.508 997 131	150 89Ɛ
.29	.039 6X7 8ƐƐ	971	.69	.1Ɛ4 7XƐ 918	11Ɛ 480	.X9	.519 006 748	151 902
.2X	.040 483 483	104 049	.6X	.1ƐƐ 9X0 553	Ɛ9Ɛ	.XX	.529 387 X65	152 93X
.2Ɛ	.043 363 094	337	.6Ɛ	.207 0Ɛ1 169	120 711	.XƐ	.539 89Ɛ Ɛ00	153 990
.30	.046 347 020	635	.70	.212 522 494	121 253	.Ɛ0	.54X 347 927	154 X36
.31	.049 433 5X1	945	.71	.219 X74 X52	9X8	.Ɛ1	.55X Ɛ48 588	155 XƐ6
.32	.050 624 8X7	105 063	.72	.225 529 1Ɛ8	122 555	.Ɛ2	.56Ɛ 8X3 123	156 Ɛ90
.33	.053 91Ɛ 054	394	.73	.231 103 XƐ7	123 111	.Ɛ3	.580 794 84X	158 07X
.34	.057 11X 795	712	.74	.238 X01 907	8X1	.Ɛ4	.591 822 433	159 184
.35	.05X 623 X28	X64	.75	.244 823 3Ɛ8	124 484	.Ɛ5	.5X2 X09 1X0	15X 2X3
.36	.062 032 Ɛ23	106 203	.76	.250 769 371	125 078	.Ɛ6	.5Ɛ4 152 230	15Ɛ 416
.37	.065 748 221	577	.77	.258 818 3X2	882	.Ɛ7	.605 636 696	160 565
.38	.069 367 X96	937	.78	.264 9Ɛ1 095	126 4X1	.Ɛ8	.617 07Ɛ 4X5	161 70X
.39	.071 092 486	107 10Ɛ	.79	.271 0Ɛ0 269	127 111	.Ɛ9	.628 865 X02	162 887
.3X	.074 203 Ɛ85	4Ɛ1	.7X	.279 516 552	952	.ƐX	.63X 5Ɛ2 ƐX6	163 X62
.3Ɛ	.078 X40 Ɛ75	8X5	.7Ɛ	.285 X68 589	128 5X8	.ƐƐ	.650 4X4 030	165 04Ɛ
						1.00	1.662 53X 105	166 256

Exponential, Sine, Cosine Integrals

The following tables of the exponential, sine and cosine integrals are given, for ease of interpolation, in the form

$$Ei(N) - \ln(N),\ Ei(-N) - \ln(N),\ Si(N),\ Ci(N) - \ln(N)$$

ln(N) being the logarithm of N to base e.

The values were calculated from the expansions

$$Ei(N) - \ln(N) = C + N + \frac{N^2}{2\ 2!} + \frac{N^3}{3\ 3!} + \frac{N^4}{4\ 4!} + \frac{N^5}{5\ 5!} + \ldots$$

$$Ei(-N) - \ln(N) = C - N + \frac{N^2}{2\ 2!} - \frac{N^3}{3\ 3!} + \frac{N^4}{4\ 4!} - \frac{N^5}{5\ 5!} + \ldots$$

$$Si(N) = N - \frac{N^3}{3\ 3!} + \frac{N^5}{5\ 5!} - \ldots$$

$$Ci(N) - \ln(N) = C - \frac{N^2}{2\ 2!} + \frac{N^4}{4\ 4!} - \ldots$$

where C is Euler's constant.

They were also obtained, for comparison, by interpolation, from the values published by Glaisher (Phil: Trans: vol. 160). One dozen and three places were calculated.

The tables may be interpolated for nine place results by the use of the Everett coefficients for second differences. The necessary coefficients may be obtained by direct proportion from the table of coefficients given on pages *296-29Ɛ*. For the natural logarithms, see pages *274-275*.

Example: Find Ei $\frac{\pi}{4}$ $\qquad \frac{\pi}{4}$ = .951 202 424 0

		d_2 +	E_0 & E_1 -
(Ei - ln).95	1.669 75Ɛ 4Ɛ8	X3 610	.040 18Ɛ
(Ei - ln).96	1.683 X76 124	X4 148	.023 925
The interval n =	.120 242 40		
(1 - n)(Ei - ln).95	+1.491 476 ƐX6 1		
n (Ei - ln).96	+ .19X 023 997 4		
E_0 d_2	- 3 536 3		
E_1 d_2	- 1 ƐƐ2 4		
	1.66Ɛ 495 454 X		
ln $\frac{\pi}{4}$	- .2X9 50Ɛ 7X9 3		
Ei $\frac{\pi}{4}$	+1.381 Ɛ85 867 7		

Note: The extended value of Ei $\frac{\pi}{4}$ is:- +1.381 Ɛ85 867 210

Example: Find Ei $\left(-\frac{\pi}{4}\right)$

(Ei - ln)(-.95)	- .0Ɛ0 X77 523	37 521	.040 18Ɛ
(Ei - ln)(-.96)	- .0Ɛ9 232 2X5	37 2Ɛ3	.023 925
(1 - n)(Ei - ln)(-.95)	- .09Ɛ Ɛ50 636 6		
n (Ei - ln)(-.96)	- .011 8XƐ 441 0		
E_0 d_2	- 1 263 0		
E_1 d_2	- 840 9		
	- .0Ɛ1 841 95Ɛ 3		
ln $\frac{\pi}{4}$	- .2X9 50Ɛ 7X9 3		
Ei $\left(-\frac{\pi}{4}\right)$	- .39Ɛ 151 548 6		

Note: The extended value of Ei $\left(-\frac{\pi}{4}\right)$ is:- -.39Ɛ 151 548 068

Example: Find Si $\frac{\pi}{4}$

		d_2 -	E_0 & E_1 -
Si .95	.912 560 624	2Ɛ 492	.040 18Ɛ
Si .96	.921 307 217	2Ɛ 807	.023 925
(1 - n) Si .95	+ .826 XX2 X75 5		
n Si .96	+ .0X8 731 486 2		
E_0 d_2	+ ƐX0 2		
E_1 d_2	+ 6X6 6		
Si $\frac{\pi}{4}$	.913 615 X06 3		

Note: The extended value of Si $\frac{\pi}{4}$ is:- .913 615 X06 945

Example: Find Ci $\frac{\pi}{4}$

(Ci - ln).95	.516 183 21X	51 358	.040 18Ɛ
(Ci - ln).96	.511 799 716	51 131	.023 925
(1 - n)(Ci - ln).95	+ .476 363 01X 3		
n (Ci - ln).96	+ .05Ɛ 4Ɛ1 0Ɛ2 6		
E_0 d_2	+ 1 85X 9		
E_1 d_2	+ Ɛ94 8		
	.515 856 944 2		
ln $\frac{\pi}{4}$	- .2X9 50Ɛ 7X9 3		
Ci $\frac{\pi}{4}$	+ .228 347 156 Ɛ		

Note: The extended value of Ci $\frac{\pi}{4}$ is:- +.228 347 156 93X

N	Ei N - ln N	d_2 +	N	Ei N - ln N	d_2 +	N	Ei N - ln N	d_2 +
.00	.6Ɛ1 518 8X7	60 000	.40	.Ɛ35 276 260	76 236	.80	1.459 X1X 156	95 78X
.01	.701 548 967	402	.41	.Ɛ47 5X1 772	755	.81	.472 Ɛ31 433	96 24Ɛ
.02	.711 619 229	806	.42	.Ɛ59 983 819	77 078	.82	.488 11X 95Ɛ	913
.03	.721 74X 2Ɛ5	61 012	.43	.Ɛ70 220 940	5X4	.83	.4X1 3X2 Ɛ9X	97 3X1
.04	.731 920 393	420	.44	.Ɛ82 735 447	Ɛ12	.84	.4Ɛ6 742 5ƐX	X76
.05	.741 Ɛ53 891	833	.45	.Ɛ95 105 X64	78 445	.85	.50Ɛ Ɛ79 X94	98 552
.06	.752 228 X02	62 046	.46	.ƐX7 752 906	980	.86	.525 491 900	99 034
.07	.762 563 Ɛ79	463	.47	.ƐƐX 258 528	79 300	.87	.53X X82 760	720
.08	.772 941 597	882	.48	1.010 X1Ɛ 44X	842	.88	.554 551 120	9X 20Ɛ
.09	.783 181 877	63 0X4	.49	.023 65Ɛ ƐƐ2	7X 18X	.89	.56X 0Ɛ9 8XƐ	907
.0X	.793 665 03Ɛ	508	.4X	.036 35X 924	719	.8X	.583 945 185	9Ɛ 406
.0Ɛ	.7X3 ƐXƐ 90Ɛ	937	.4Ɛ	.049 118 173	7Ɛ 071	.8Ɛ	.599 66Ɛ X65	Ɛ0X
.10	.7Ɛ4 59X 316	64 164	.50	.05Ɛ Ɛ54 673	608	.90	.5Ɛ3 476 653	X0 61X
.11	.805 030 X85	598	.51	.072 X50 57Ɛ	Ɛ68	.91	.609 361 85Ɛ	X1 131
.12	.815 728 010	X13	.52	.085 X08 433	80 511	.92	.623 329 Ɛ98	84X
.13	.826 287 Ɛ6X	65 24Ɛ	.53	.098 X44 7Ɛ8	X78	.93	.639 397 Ɛ63	X2 372
.14	.836 X91 157	68Ɛ	.54	.0XƐ Ɛ41 X39	81 42Ɛ	.94	.653 528 2X0	X9Ɛ
.15	.847 73Ɛ X13	Ɛ15	.55	.103 100 4X9	9X1	.95	.669 75Ɛ 4Ɛ8	X3 610
.16	.858 454 5X4	66 35X	.56	.116 340 93X	82 360	.96	.683 X76 124	X4 148
.17	.869 213 513	7XX	.57	.129 643 52Ɛ	921	.97	.69X 274 X98	88Ɛ
.18	.87X 039 030	67 03Ɛ	.58	.140 X08 X41	83 2X8	.98	.6Ɛ4 758 51Ɛ	X5 415
.19	.88X Ɛ09 788	494	.59	.154 255 63Ɛ	875	.99	.70Ɛ 125 377	Ɛ67
.1X	.89Ɛ X45 7Ɛ8	931	.5X	.167 765 XƐ2	84 248	.9X	.725 798 17X	X6 702
.1Ɛ	.8Ɛ0 X29 559	68 191	.5Ɛ	.17Ɛ 13X 5Ɛ1	824	.9Ɛ	.740 335 683	X7 262
.20	.901 X79 48Ɛ	634	.60	.192 797 914	85 203	.X0	.756 Ɛ7X 22X	X09
.21	.912 Ɛ75 X35	X9X	.61	.1X6 2ƐX 23X	7X7	.X1	.771 8XX 7X2	X8 57X
.22	.924 11Ɛ 279	69 34X	.62	.1Ɛ9 XX6 34Ɛ	86 194	.X2	.788 707 714	X9 133
.23	.935 331 X4Ɛ	7ƐX	.63	.211 758 634	786	.X3	.7X3 611 779	8Ɛ5
.24	.946 5Ɛ2 21Ɛ	6X 074	.64	.225 495 4X3	87 17X	.X4	.7ƐX 605 517	XX 47Ɛ
.25	.957 920 663	531	.65	.239 299 510	77X	.X5	.815 6X7 734	XƐ 04Ɛ
.26	.969 0Ɛ9 418	9Ɛ0	.66	.251 169 0Ɛ7	88 180	.X6	.830 878 9X0	826
.27	.97X 544 Ɛ81	6Ɛ 275	.67	.265 104 X62	788	.X7	.847 Ɛ39 872	Ɛ0 406
.28	.98Ɛ X3Ɛ 99Ɛ	73Ɛ	.68	.279 129 395	89 198	.X8	.863 2XX Ɛ4X	ƐƐ2
.29	.9X1 3X6 338	70 00Ɛ	.69	.291 21X XX4	7Ɛ2	.X9	.87X 751 218	Ɛ1 7X1
.2X	.9Ɛ2 X00 8X4	4X1	.6X	.2X5 39X 1X5	8X 20X	.XX	.896 0X5 087	Ɛ2 399
.2Ɛ	.X04 487 731	977	.6Ɛ	.2Ɛ9 627 6Ɛ4	832	.XƐ	.8Ɛ1 72Ɛ 313	Ɛ9Ɛ
.30	.X16 003 335	71 256	.70	.311 943 835	8Ɛ 259	.Ɛ0	.909 268 53X	Ɛ3 7X6
.31	.X27 7Ɛ0 193	735	.71	.326 12Ɛ 013	888	.Ɛ1	.924 X99 34Ɛ	Ɛ4 3Ɛ8
.32	.X39 44X 766	72 020	.72	.33X 5X6 079	90 302	.Ɛ2	.940 802 558	Ɛ5 014
.33	.X4Ɛ 15Ɛ 159	509	.73	.352 Ɛ31 425	940	.Ɛ3	.958 620 779	837
.34	.X60 Ɛ22 059	9Ɛ8	.74	.367 549 511	91 382	.Ɛ4	.974 534 615	Ɛ6 465
.35	.X72 957 955	73 2Ɛ2	.75	.380 036 97Ɛ	X09	.Ɛ5	.990 542 916	Ɛ7 097
.36	.X84 844 943	7X8	.76	.394 7Ɛ6 036	92 45Ɛ	.Ɛ6	.9X8 648 0Ɛ2	916
.37	.X96 7X5 519	74 0XX	.77	.3X9 447 750	XƐ3	.Ɛ7	.X04 849 1X4	Ɛ8 55X
.38	.XX8 7ƐX 1X1	5Ɛ1	.78	.402 170 159	93 552	.Ɛ8	.X20 Ɛ46 834	Ɛ9 1X9
.39	.XƐX 887 456	XƐ8	.79	.416 Ɛ68 0Ɛ8	ƐƐ6	.Ɛ9	.X39 341 471	X44
.3X	.Ɛ10 X09 607	75 408	.7X	.42Ɛ X38 051	94 661	.ƐX	.X55 835 Ɛ32	ƐX 6X3
.3Ɛ	.Ɛ23 004 Ɛ84	91Ɛ	.7Ɛ	.444 9X0 647	95 115	.ƐƐ	.X72 229 096	ƐƐ 350

1.00 1.X8X 91Ɛ 58X ƐƐƐ

N	Ei(-N) - ln N	d_2 +	N	Ei(-N) - ln N	d_2 +	N	Ei(-N) - ln N	d_2 +
.00	+.6Ɛ1 518 8X7	60 000	.40	+.32X 101 207	49 X02	.80	+.010 239 544	3X 908
.01	.6X1 548 827	5Ɛ 802	.41	.31Ɛ X90 036	6X8	.81	+.003 546 149	674
.02	.691 618 369	406	.42	.311 8X8 551	397	.82	-.005 32X 7Ɛ6	424
.03	.681 747 2Ɛ5	011	.43	.303 752 243	087	.83	.011 Ɛ65 115	193
.04	.671 915 252	5X 821	.44	.2Ɛ5 645 000	48 97X	.84	.01X 761 461	39 Ɛ45
.05	.661 Ɛ41 X10	432	.45	.2X7 584 737	671	.85	.027 31Ɛ 864	8Ɛ8
.06	.652 208 X00	044	.46	.299 550 923	369	.86	.033 X60 36Ɛ	672
.07	.642 531 X34	59 862	.47	.28Ɛ 565 278	066	.87	.040 563 404	428
.08	.632 8Ɛ4 70X	47Ɛ	.48	.281 605 877	47 965	.88	.049 029 031	1X5
.09	.623 114 863	09Ɛ	.49	.273 6Ɛ2 01Ɛ	668	.89	.055 675 675	38 Ɛ64
.0X	.613 591 X97	58 904	.4X	.265 825 X2Ɛ	36X	.8X	.062 085 155	923
.0Ɛ	.603 XX7 X13	529	.4Ɛ	.257 9X4 ƐX9	075	.8Ɛ	.06X 657 Ɛ12	6X5
.10	.5Ɛ4 45X 278	159	.50	.249 ƐXƐ 220	46 980	.90	-.076 ƐƐ2 1X6	468
.11	.5X4 X68 87X	57 987	.51	.240 240 213	690	.91	.083 510 012	232
.12	.595 513 047	5ƐƐ	.52	.232 517 896	39Ɛ	.92	.08Ɛ 921 808	37 ƐƐ8
.13	.586 014 X13	234	.53	.224 839 738	0Ɛ2	.93	.098 257 406	984
.14	.576 771 X13	56 X72	.54	.216 ƐX5 690	45 X06	.94	.0X4 685 240	753
.15	.567 365 885	6Ɛ0	.55	.209 397 42X	722	.95	.0Ɛ0 X77 523	521
.16	.557 Ɛ24 227	332	.56	.1ƐƐ 812 8XX	43X	.96	.0Ɛ9 232 2X5	2Ɛ3
.17	.548 898 XƐƐ	55 Ɛ78	.57	.1Ɛ2 093 5X8	15X	.97	.105 571 974	087
.18	.539 617 74Ɛ	802	.58	.1X4 599 444	44 X79	.98	.111 876 378	36 X59
.19	.52X 3XƐ ƐX1	451	.59	.196 Ɛ28 159	7X2	.99	.119 243 Ɛ23	835
.1X	.51Ɛ 219 884	0X1	.5X	.189 4ƐƐ 654	506	.9X	.126 196 X55	60Ɛ
.1Ɛ	.510 0X0 648	54 936	.5Ɛ	.17Ɛ Ɛ17 455	231	.9Ɛ	.132 3Ɛ3 378	3X9
.20	.500 Ɛ28 146	58X	.60	.172 577 487	43 Ɛ60	.X0	-.13X 595 4Ɛ2	187
.21	.4Ɛ1 Ɛ68 212	229	.61	.165 05Ɛ 459	889	.X1	.146 741 461	35 Ɛ69
.22	.4X2 Ɛ70 507	53 X87	.62	.157 787 0Ɛ8	600	.X2	.152 873 463	948
.23	.494 008 687	728	.63	.14X 336 357	332	.X3	.15X 96Ɛ 719	732
.24	.485 0Ɛ8 373	393	.64	.140 Ɛ28 928	067	.X4	.166 X32 261	515
.25	.476 23Ɛ 432	038	.65	.133 762 364	42 9X3	.X5	.172 X7Ɛ 490	300
.26	.467 415 529	52 8X6	.66	.126 41X 783	721	.X6	.17X X93 3ƐƐ	0X9
.27	.458 642 30X	557	.67	.119 119 703	45X	.X7	.186 X72 241	34 X94
.28	.449 901 646	20X	.68	.10Ɛ X5X XX1	1X0	.X8	.192 X18 1XƐ	885
.29	.43Ɛ 012 Ɛ90	51 X81	.69	.102 822 45Ɛ	41 Ɛ23	.X9	.19X 949 494	674
.2X	.430 376 397	73Ɛ	.6X	.0Ɛ5 627 940	869	.XX	.1X6 846 105	467
.2Ɛ	.421 76Ɛ 321	3Ɛ8	.6Ɛ	.0X8 472 X8X	5Ɛ2	.XƐ	.1Ɛ2 70X 48Ɛ	25X
.30	.412 ƐƐ5 663	07X	.70	.09Ɛ 33Ɛ 60X	33Ɛ	.Ɛ0	-.1ƐX 55X 5Ɛ7	052
.31	.404 490 X63	50 93Ɛ	.71	.092 249 489	08X	.Ɛ1	.206 376 691	33 X49
.32	.3Ɛ5 9Ɛ8 ƐX2	607	.72	.085 198 416	40 X1Ɛ	.Ɛ2	.212 15X 91X	845
.33	.3X7 375 728	291	.73	.078 168 182	771	.Ɛ3	.219 Ɛ0Ɛ 322	642
.34	.398 982 543	4Ɛ Ɛ60	.74	.06Ɛ 178 69Ɛ	505	.Ɛ4	.225 848 2X4	43Ɛ
.35	.38X 41Ɛ 2ƐX	832	.75	.062 209 501	25X	.Ɛ5	.231 551 X27	241
.36	.37Ɛ Ɛ07 8X7	504	.76	.055 29X 581	3Ɛ ƐƐ8	.Ɛ6	.239 224 329	042
.37	.371 643 798	199	.77	.048 3XƐ 639	955	.Ɛ7	.244 X83 7X9	32 X45
.38	.363 20X 866	4X X77	.78	.03Ɛ 540 44X	6Ɛ3	.Ɛ8	.250 6Ɛ0 224	848
.39	.354 X24 7XƐ	754	.79	.032 710 952	456	.Ɛ9	.258 2X6 013	653
.3X	.346 689 288	435	.7X	.025 920 6Ɛ0	1Ɛ9	.ƐX	.263 X69 36Ɛ	459
.3Ɛ	.338 380 19X	117	.7Ɛ	.018 Ɛ6Ɛ 647	3X Ɛ62	.ƐƐ	.26Ɛ 5ƐX 26X	267
						1.00	-.277 118 Ɛ02	073

N	Si N	d_2 -	N	Si N	d_2 -	N	Si N	d_2 -
.00	.000 000 000	000	.40	.3Ɛ8 558 537	13 9X6	.80	.797 ƐƐ2 51Ɛ	26 725
.01	.00Ɛ ƐƐƐ Ɛ40	400	.41	.408 292 730	14 18Ɛ	.81	.7X7 078 X33	X81
.02	.01Ɛ ƐƐƐ 680	800	.42	.417 Ɛ24 756	572	.82	.7Ɛ6 1X8 486	27 219
.03	.02Ɛ ƐƐX 600	1 000	.43	.427 902 20X	955	.83	.805 2Ɛ0 900	571
.04	.03Ɛ ƐƐ8 540	400	.44	.437 5Ɛ6 Ɛ29	15 137	.84	.814 389 785	906
.05	.04Ɛ ƐƐ5 080	7ƐƐ	.45	.447 296 711	518	.85	.823 43X 944	28 058
.06	.05Ɛ ƐƐ0 001	2 000	.46	.456 Ɛ60 999	8ƐX	.86	.832 483 X67	3X8
.07	.06Ɛ ƐX4 Ɛ42	3ƐX	.47	.466 811 367	16 097	.87	.841 4X0 7X2	737
.08	.07Ɛ Ɛ97 685	800	.48	.476 467 85X	477	.88	.850 490 9X2	X85
.09	.08Ɛ Ɛ87 608	ƐƐ9	.49	.486 0X7 896	854	.89	.85Ɛ 454 119	29 211
.0X	.09Ɛ Ɛ74 552	3 3ƐX	.4X	.495 911 07X	17 032	.8X	.86X 3XX 243	557
.0Ɛ	.0XƐ Ɛ5X 09X	7Ɛ7	.4Ɛ	.4X5 51Ɛ 430	408	.8Ɛ	.879 316 X12	8X0
.10	.0ƐƐ Ɛ40 02Ɛ	ƐƐ8	.50	.4Ɛ5 112 396	7X4	.90	.888 215 901	2X 021
.11	.10Ɛ Ɛ19 Ɛ84	4 3Ɛ6	.51	.504 8X9 758	Ɛ7X	.91	.897 0X6 78Ɛ	364
.12	.11Ɛ XƐ3 723	7Ɛ5	.52	.514 468 Ɛ60	18 351	.92	.8X5 Ɛ49 2Ɛ5	6X3
.13	.12Ɛ X84 689	ƐƐ1	.53	.524 010 013	727	.93	.8Ɛ4 981 338	X20
.14	.13Ɛ X50 642	5 3Ɛ2	.54	.533 756 55Ɛ	XƐ9	.94	.903 786 55Ɛ	2Ɛ 15X
.15	.14Ɛ X13 205	7XX	.55	.543 283 ƐXX	19 28X	.95	.912 560 624	492
.16	.15Ɛ 990 19X	ƐX7	.56	.552 994 36Ɛ	65Ɛ	.96	.921 307 217	807
.17	.16Ɛ 943 188	6 3X6	.57	.562 487 091	X30	.97	.930 042 203	Ɛ3Ɛ
.18	.17Ɛ 8XƐ 990	7X1	.58	.571 Ɛ5Ɛ Ɛ83	1X 1Ɛ9	.98	.93X 949 270	30 26Ɛ
.19	.18Ɛ 851 9Ɛ3	Ɛ9Ɛ	.59	.581 616 878	586	.99	.949 624 06X	59Ɛ
.1X	.19Ɛ 7X8 X37	7 395	.5X	.591 072 ƐX7	954	.9X	.958 28X 489	907
.1Ɛ	.1XƐ 738 6X6	794	.5Ɛ	.5X0 6Ɛ0 582	1Ɛ 11X	.9Ɛ	.966 Ɛ03 ƐX1	31 035
.20	.1ƐƐ 680 781	Ɛ88	.60	.5Ɛ0 10X X3Ɛ	4X4	.X0	.975 708 680	358
.21	.20Ɛ 5Ɛ8 890	8 386	.61	.5ƐƐ 709 X14	86X	.X1	.984 29Ɛ X03	682
.22	.21Ɛ 528 615	77X	.62	.60Ɛ 0X9 13Ɛ	20 030	.X2	.992 X41 684	9X4
.23	.22Ɛ 44Ɛ 7X0	Ɛ76	.63	.61X 668 436	3Ɛ4	.X3	.9X1 571 561	32 103
.24	.23Ɛ 365 9Ɛ1	9 36Ɛ	.64	.62X 007 339	774	.X4	.9Ɛ0 06Ɛ 337	422
.25	.24Ɛ 272 853	764	.65	.639 545 688	Ɛ35	.X5	.9ƐX 736 8XƐ	73X
.26	.25Ɛ 171 Ɛ51	Ɛ5X	.66	.648 X62 XX2	21 2Ɛ3	.X6	.X09 18Ɛ 725	X56
.27	.26Ɛ 063 2Ɛ1	X 351	.67	.658 35Ɛ 005	672	.X7	.X17 7Ɛ1 705	33 169
.28	.27X Ɛ46 300	744	.68	.667 835 676	X28	.X8	.X26 1X0 538	481
.29	.28X X1X 787	Ɛ3X	.69	.677 0XX 2ƐƐ	22 1X5	.X9	.X34 757 XXX	791
.2X	.29X 8X4 114	Ɛ 32X	.6X	.686 540 95Ɛ	55X	.XX	.X43 09Ɛ 88Ɛ	XX0
.2Ɛ	.2XX 75X 333	721	.6Ɛ	.695 970 X61	912	.XƐ	.X51 5XƐ 790	34 1X8
.30	.2ƐX 604 X31	Ɛ13	.70	.6X5 17X 251	23 086	.Ɛ0	.X5Ɛ X87 4X5	4Ɛ5
.31	.30X 45Ɛ 618	10 303	.71	.6Ɛ4 564 577	436	.Ɛ1	.X6X 32X 905	7Ɛ8
.32	.31X 2X5 Ɛ00	6Ɛ4	.72	.703 927 467	7X8	.Ɛ2	.X78 759 529	Ɛ00
.33	.32X 11Ɛ 8Ɛ0	XX4	.73	.713 086 76Ɛ	Ɛ57	.Ɛ3	.X86 Ɛ53 251	35 201
.34	.339 Ɛ44 7Ɛ8	11 293	.74	.722 401 Ɛ18	24 303	.Ɛ4	.X95 313 974	4ƐƐ
.35	.349 958 431	681	.75	.731 714 Ɛ82	670	.Ɛ5	.XX3 65X Ɛ98	7Ɛ8
.36	.359 75X 5X5	X6X	.76	.740 X03 578	X18	.Ɛ6	.XƐ1 970 604	XƐ3
.37	.369 54X 8XƐ	12 258	.77	.750 089 156	25 180	.Ɛ7	.Ɛ00 048 139	36 1X8
.38	.379 328 959	645	.78	.75Ɛ 329 774	523	.Ɛ8	.Ɛ0X 2X9 686	49Ɛ
.39	.389 0Ɛ4 382	X2Ɛ	.79	.76X 564 86Ɛ	888	.Ɛ9	.Ɛ18 514 734	78X
.3X	.398 X68 Ɛ78	13 216	.7X	.779 776 09X	26 027	.ƐX	.Ɛ26 705 014	X7X
.3Ɛ	.3X8 80X 558	601	.7Ɛ	.788 961 4X2	387	.ƐƐ	.Ɛ34 87X 636	37 166
						1.00	.Ɛ42 9Ɛ8 XƐ2	450

N	Ci N - ln N	d_2 -	N	Ci N - ln N	d_2 -	N	Ci N - ln N	d_2 -
.00	.6Ɛ1 518 8X7	60 000	.40	.671 797 963	5X 01X	.80	.574 Ɛ48 503	54 242
.01	.6Ɛ1 4X8 8X7	5Ɛ ƐƐX	.41	.66Ɛ 794 823	59 Ɛ18	.81	.571 0Ɛ0 702	052
.02	.6Ɛ1 418 8X9	ƐƐ6	.42	.669 733 787	X17	.82	.569 200 86Ɛ	53 X60
.03	.6Ɛ1 2X8 8Ɛ5	ƐXX	.43	.667 634 914	912	.83	.565 278 Ɛ78	868
.04	.6Ɛ1 118 913	ƐX0	.44	.665 498 14Ɛ	805	.84	.561 2X1 619	671
.05	.6Ɛ0 XX8 951	Ɛ8X	.45	.663 2X1 981	6Ɛ6	.85	.559 272 609	473
.06	.6Ɛ0 818 X01	Ɛ76	.46	.661 049 XƐ9	5X3	.86	.555 1Ɛ0 146	273
.07	.6Ɛ0 4X8 XƐ7	Ɛ5X	.47	.65X 958 652	48Ɛ	.87	.551 096 610	072
.08	.6Ɛ0 119 053	Ɛ40	.48	.658 609 918	374	.88	.548 Ɛ29 X24	52 X67
.09	.6XƐ 8X9 26Ɛ	Ɛ1Ɛ	.49	.656 221 82X	254	.89	.544 92X 391	861
.0X	.6XƐ 419 568	XƐ4	.4X	.653 998 4X8	133	.8X	.540 698 099	652
.0Ɛ	.6XX XX9 971	X90	.4Ɛ	.651 4Ɛ6 033	00Ɛ	.8Ɛ	.538 3Ɛ3 353	441
.10	.6XX 51X 2X6	X5Ɛ	.50	.64X Ɛ76 76Ɛ	58 XX3	.90	.534 078 188	230
.11	.6X9 XXX 980	X2X	.51	.648 59X 404	976	.91	.52Ɛ 8XX 991	015
.12	.6X9 41Ɛ 628	9Ɛ7	.52	.645 Ɛ65 2X3	845	.92	.527 48Ɛ 581	51 9ƐX
.13	.6X8 8Ɛ0 499	97X	.53	.643 493 539	712	.93	.523 01X 373	79Ɛ
.14	.6X8 121 590	93Ɛ	.54	.640 965 081	596	.94	.51X 717 586	57Ɛ
.15	.6X7 4Ɛ2 944	900	.55	.63X 19X 22Ɛ	45X	.95	.516 183 21X	358
.16	.6X6 824 3Ɛ8	876	.56	.637 576 Ɛ3Ɛ	319	.96	.511 799 716	131
.17	.6X5 XƐ6 1Ɛ6	82X	.57	.634 8Ɛ7 532	197	.97	.509 162 XX1	50 Ɛ07
.18	.6X5 128 386	7X1	.58	.631 Ɛ9Ɛ 94X	052	.98	.504 697 361	897
.19	.6X4 2ƐX 975	74Ɛ	.59	.62Ɛ 228 114	57 Ɛ04	.99	.4ƐƐ Ɛ7X Ɛ46	668
.1X	.6X3 431 815	6Ɛ6	.5X	.628 418 596	976	.9X	.4Ɛ7 412 083	433
.1Ɛ	.6X2 504 Ɛ7Ɛ	660	.5Ɛ	.625 571 0X2	823	.9Ɛ	.4Ɛ2 814 989	1ƐƐ
.20	.6X1 538 885	601	.60	.622 669 Ɛ87	690	.X0	.4X9 Ɛ87 494	4Ɛ Ɛ83
.21	.6X0 510 Ɛ8X	560	.61	.61Ɛ 70Ɛ 3X0	534	.X1	.4X5 2XX 018	944
.22	.69Ɛ 445 933	4Ɛ7	.62	.618 715 281	395	.X2	.4X0 580 X18	705
.23	.69X 31Ɛ 1X1	451	.63	.615 683 989	234	.X3	.497 804 113	481
.24	.699 155 1ƐX	3X2	.64	.612 597 261	092	.X4	.492 9Ɛ7 Ɛ49	239
.25	.697 ƐƐƐ X35	331	.65	.60Ɛ 453 663	56 Ɛ26	.X5	.489 Ɛ60 746	4X ƐƐ1
.26	.696 867 33Ɛ	279	.66	.608 274 Ɛ3Ɛ	979	.X6	.485 076 352	964
.27	.695 543 588	202	.67	.605 03Ɛ 65X	80X	.X7	.480 141 1Ɛ6	713
.28	.694 180 613	144	.68	.601 96Ɛ 56Ɛ	657	.X8	.477 179 547	482
.29	.692 95X 516	083	.69	.5ƐX 644 X25	4X3	.X9	.472 167 416	229
.2X	.691 499 356	5X ƐƐƐ	.6X	.5Ɛ7 283 9Ɛ8	325	.XX	.469 107 078	49 Ɛ92
.2Ɛ	.68Ɛ Ɛ79 197	Ɛ35	.6Ɛ	.5Ɛ3 X68 666	167	.XƐ	.464 018 948	936
.30	.68X 5ƐX 0X3	X66	.70	.5Ɛ0 5Ɛ7 169	55 ƐX7	.Ɛ0	.45X XX0 8X2	697
.31	.688 ƐX0 145	995	.71	.5X9 0XƐ 885	X22	.Ɛ1	.455 917 161	435
.32	.687 523 412	903	.72	.5X5 74X 57Ɛ	857	.Ɛ2	.450 704 1X7	192
.33	.685 X07 998	828	.73	.5X2 153 61X	68Ɛ	.Ɛ3	.447 464 05Ɛ	48 Ɛ28
.34	.684 251 736	749	.74	.59X 702 ƐXX	4ƐƐ	.Ɛ4	.442 176 ƐX7	880
.35	.682 638 947	66X	.75	.597 019 07Ɛ	328	.Ɛ5	.438 X41 273	613
.36	.680 985 4XX	586	.76	.593 499 X24	152	.Ɛ6	.433 67X Ɛ28	362
.37	.67Ɛ 073 687	4X0	.77	.58Ɛ 905 637	54 Ɛ78	.Ɛ7	.42X 270 43Ɛ	0Ɛ0
.38	.679 303 384	3Ɛ3	.78	.588 098 292	998	.Ɛ8	.424 X15 862	47 X38
.39	.677 4Ɛ4 88X	303	.79	.584 416 151	7Ɛ8	.Ɛ9	.41Ɛ 533 249	781
.3X	.675 647 X91	20Ɛ	.7X	.580 6ƐƐ 414	615	.ƐX	.416 005 073	504
.3Ɛ	.673 740 X85	116	.7Ɛ	.578 950 082	429	.ƐƐ	.410 64Ɛ 595	247
						1.00	.407 04X 870	46 Ɛ85

Factorial Function

The values of the factorial function were calculated from the logarithmic values given by Gauss and checked with the twelve place table in the British Association Mathematical Tables, vol. 1. One dozen and three duodecimal places were calculated.

In order to interpolate between the values given, the second difference is tabulated and, since there is a small fourth difference which is not negligible, the second difference has been modified, i. e., decreased by an amount *.226* d_4. For the principle of throwback, see Nautical Almanac, 1937.

The table may be interpolated for nine place results by the use of the Everett coefficients for second differences. The necessary coefficients may be obtained by direct proportion from the table of coefficients given on pages *296-29Ɛ*.

Example: Find the factorial of *1*:π, i. e., *.39X 058 288 7*

		d_2	E_0 & E_1
.39!	= *.X8Ɛ 833 641*	*103 591*	*.039 968*
.3X!	= *.X8X 094 433*	*101 Ɛ99*	*.060 371*
The interval n	= *.X05 828 87*		
(*1* - n)(*.39*!)	= *.190 X33 067 1*		
n (*.3X*!)	= *.8Ɛ9 583 Ɛ29 2*		
E_0 d_2	=- *3 XXX 0*		
E_1 d_2	=- *6 136 7*		
$\left(\frac{1}{\pi}\right)!$	= *.X8X 3X8 Ɛ6Ɛ 8*		

Example: Find the factorial of $1 - \frac{1}{\pi}$, i. e., *.821 Ɛ63 933 5*

		d_2	E_0 & E_1
.82!	= *.XX4 014 055*	*91 961*	*.060 371*
.83!	= *.XX6 179 3X0*	*91 7ƐƐ*	*.039 968*
The interval n	= *.1Ɛ6 393 35*		
(*1* - n)(*.82*!)	= *.910 5X1 840 1*		
n (*.83*!)	= *.193 X53 15X 7*		
E_0 d_2	=- *4 715 Ɛ*		
E_1 d_2	=- *2 XX6 4*		
$\left(1 - \frac{1}{\pi}\right)!$	= *.XX4 429 39X 5*		

The product of the above results is *.987 X70 Ɛ95 8*

Since $(X)!\ (1-X)! = \frac{\pi X(1 - X)}{\sin \pi X}$

$$\left(\frac{1}{\pi}\right)!\ \left(1-\frac{1}{\pi}\right)! = \frac{1 - \frac{1}{\pi}}{\sin 1} = \frac{.821\ Ɛ63\ 933\ 5}{.X12\ 08X\ X92\ 2} = .987\ X70\ Ɛ95\ 2$$

N	N!	d2 +	N	N!	d2 +	N	N!	d2 +
.00	1.000 000 000	1Ɛ8 9Ɛ9	.40	.X87 09X 64Ɛ	ƐƐ 152	.80	.X9Ɛ Ɛ3Ɛ 001	92 115
.01	.ƐƐ5 1X4 467	1Ɛ3 575	.41	.X85 841 029	Ɛ9 8Ɛ8	.81	.XX1 Ɛ40 673	91 Ɛ27
.02	.ƐXX 580 30X	1XX 31X	.42	.X84 4X1 315	Ɛ8 4ƐX	.82	.XX4 014 055	91 961
.03	.ƐX3 Ɛ46 510	1X5 263	.43	.X83 239 Ɛ0Ɛ	Ɛ7 156	.83	.XX6 179 3X0	91 7ƐƐ
.04	.Ɛ99 6Ɛ5 9Ɛ3	1X0 37Ɛ	.44	.X82 091 86Ɛ	Ɛ5 X47	.84	.XX8 3Ɛ4 32Ɛ	91 680
.05	.Ɛ93 445 694	197 662	.45	.X81 01Ɛ 466	Ɛ4 790	.85	.XXX 700 944	91 565
.06	.Ɛ89 370 X51	192 Ɛ03	.46	.X80 061 841	Ɛ3 566	.86	.XƐ0 X9X 906	91 471
.07	.Ɛ83 46Ɛ 148	18X 516	.47	.X7Ɛ 197 590	Ɛ2 391	.87	.XƐ3 34X 142	91 39Ɛ
.08	.Ɛ79 737 993	186 095	.48	.X7X 403 700	Ɛ1 246	.88	.XƐ5 88X 962	91 330
.09	.Ɛ73 Ɛ8X 726	181 9Ɛ4	.49	.X79 720 X84	Ɛ0 14X	.89	.XƐ8 2X0 8Ɛ8	91 2X4
.0X	.Ɛ6X 5X3 2X3	179 867	.4X	.X78 Ɛ2X 3X5	XƐ 09X	.8X	.XƐX 983 Ɛ3X	91 279
.0Ɛ	.Ɛ65 175 738	175 869	.4Ɛ	.X78 426 9Ɛ2	XX 076	.8Ɛ	.Ɛ01 538 441	91 273
.10	.Ɛ5Ɛ Ɛ01 86X	171 9Ɛ2	.50	.X77 X11 482	X9 097	.90	.Ɛ04 182 000	91 28Ɛ
.11	.Ɛ56 9ƐƐ 802	16X 076	.51	.X77 4X5 037	X8 142	.91	.Ɛ06 X98 X53	91 308
.12	.Ɛ51 X67 839	166 471	.52	.X77 064 93Ɛ	X7 230	.92	.Ɛ09 884 ƐƐ7	91 367
.13	.Ɛ49 07X 152	162 996	.53	.X76 90Ɛ 881	X6 361	.93	.Ɛ10 742 50Ɛ	91 425
.14	.Ɛ44 433 469	15Ɛ 424	.54	.X76 660 Ɛ71	X5 514	.94	.Ɛ13 691 250	91 505
.15	.Ɛ3Ɛ 948 012	157 Ɛ91	.55	.X76 497 781	X4 707	.95	.Ɛ16 6Ɛ1 49X	91 604
.16	.Ɛ37 3Ɛ8 773	154 855	.56	.X76 3Ɛ6 XX6	X3 93Ɛ	.96	.Ɛ19 7X3 135	91 724
.17	.Ɛ33 001 Ɛ92	151 62X	.57	.X76 3Ɛ9 Ɛ56	X2 ƐƐ1	.97	.Ɛ20 966 4Ɛ9	91 864
.18	.Ɛ2X 958 X43	14X 50Ɛ	.58	.X76 4X4 003	X2 2X1	.98	.Ɛ23 ƐƐƐ 528	91 X03
.19	.Ɛ26 842 226	147 4Ɛ5	.59	.X76 670 35X	X1 60X	.99	.Ɛ27 326 363	91 Ɛ82
.1X	.Ɛ22 872 Ɛ25	144 59Ɛ	.5X	.X76 91X 10X	X0 973	.9X	.Ɛ2X 723 163	92 160
.1Ɛ	.Ɛ1X X28 225	141 780	.5Ɛ	.X77 068 838	X0 153	.9Ɛ	.Ɛ31 ƐƐ2 108	92 35X
.20	.Ɛ17 123 106	13X X55	.60	.X77 497 505	9Ɛ 56X	.X0	.Ɛ35 553 413	92 576
.21	.Ɛ13 558 X60	138 219	.61	.X77 9X5 748	9X 9ƐX	.X1	.Ɛ38 Ɛ87 099	92 7Ɛ2
.22	.Ɛ0Ɛ Ɛ0X X33	135 68X	.62	.X78 392 794	9X 283	.X2	.Ɛ40 691 558	92 X48
.23	.Ɛ08 5Ɛ6 4Ɛ2	133 022	.63	.X78 X59 XXX	99 781	.X3	.Ɛ44 26X 869	93 101
.24	.Ɛ05 214 ƐƐ2	130 657	.64	.X79 602 990	99 0Ɛ1	.X4	.Ɛ47 Ɛ1Ɛ 082	93 395
.25	.Ɛ01 Ɛ64 166	12X 16X	.65	.X7X 244 96Ɛ	98 655	.X5	.Ɛ4Ɛ 862 875	93 687
.26	.XƐX X21 4X6	127 957	.66	.X7X Ɛ63 3X9	98 02Ɛ	.X6	.Ɛ53 679 Ɛ37	93 998
.27	.XƐ7 X06 599	125 617	.67	.X7Ɛ 959 X61	97 636	.X7	.Ɛ57 568 Ɛ99	94 107
.28	.XƐ4 Ɛ15 102	123 366	.68	.X80 82Ɛ Ɛ55	97 071	.X8	.Ɛ5Ɛ 530 14X	94 453
.29	.XƐ2 146 ƐX9	121 183	.69	.X81 799 106	96 71X	.X9	.Ɛ63 587 756	94 7ƐX
.2X	.XXƐ 49X 072	11Ɛ 066	.6X	.X82 820 99X	96 1Ɛ5	.XX	.Ɛ67 6Ɛ7 965	94 Ɛ83
.2Ɛ	.XX8 950 1Ɛ6	119 010	.6Ɛ	.X83 93X 873	95 900	.XƐ	.Ɛ6Ɛ 900 Ɛ3Ɛ	95 366
.30	.XX6 31Ɛ 364	117 037	.70	.X84 Ɛ32 451	95 435	.Ɛ0	.Ɛ73 Ɛ9Ɛ 484	95 767
.31	.XX3 X05 562	115 120	.71	.X86 1ƐƐ 46X	94 Ɛ98	.Ɛ1	.Ɛ78 353 577	95 Ɛ85
.32	.XX1 604 896	113 281	.72	.X87 561 469	94 768	.Ɛ2	.Ɛ80 7X1 638	96 402
.33	.X9Ɛ 317 2X3	111 498	.73	.X88 998 01Ɛ	94 365	.Ɛ3	.Ɛ85 105 Ɛ02	96 857
.34	.X99 13Ɛ 1X0	10Ɛ 765	.74	.X8X 2X6 Ɛ40	93 Ɛ8Ɛ	.Ɛ4	.Ɛ89 705 028	97 10Ɛ
.35	.X97 072 855	109 XX4	.75	.X8Ɛ 889 X36	93 821	.Ɛ5	.Ɛ92 19Ɛ 265	97 5X0
.36	.X95 0Ɛ4 206	108 291	.76	.X91 344 556	93 49X	.Ɛ6	.Ɛ96 950 X86	97 X8X
.37	.X93 241 X5Ɛ	106 727	.77	.X92 X92 55X	93 182	.Ɛ7	.Ɛ9Ɛ 59X 579	98 396
.38	.X91 496 231	105 027	.78	.X94 6Ɛ3 72X	92 X91	.Ɛ8	.ƐX4 304 44Ɛ	98 900
.39	.X8Ɛ 833 641	103 591	.79	.X96 3X7 794	92 805	.Ɛ9	.ƐX9 107 024	99 243
.3X	.X8X 094 433	101 Ɛ99	.7X	.X98 172 448	92 564	.ƐX	.ƐƐ1 ƐX6 X45	99 7X3
.3Ɛ	.X88 637 213	100 646	.7Ɛ	.X9X 00Ɛ 66X	92 328	.ƐƐ	.ƐƐ6 Ɛ64 450	9X 161
						1.00	1.000 000 000	9X 738

Digamma Function

The values of the Digamma function were obtained from those given by Gauss. Twelve duodecimal places were calculated.

In order to interpolate between the values given, the second difference is tabulated and since there is a small fourth difference which is not negligible, this second difference has been modified, that is, the second difference has been decreased by .226 d_4. For the principle of throwback, see Nautical Almanac, 1937. The table may be interpolated for nine place results by the use of the Everett coefficients for second differences. The necessary coefficients may be obtained by direct proportion from the table of Everett coefficients given on pages 296-29Ɛ.

Notation. In the following examples the expression for the Digamma function $\frac{d}{dN} \log_e N!$ is written DN.

<u>Example:</u> Find DN when N = 4:5 i. e., $.\dot{9}72\ \dot{4}$

		d_2 -	E_0 & E_1 -
D .97	+ .34X 841 Ɛ7X	63 6Ɛ7	.06X Ɛ3Ɛ
D .98	+ .357 639 36Ɛ	62 X40	.047 367
The interval n =	$.249\ \dot{7}24\ \dot{9}$		
(1 - n) D .97	+ .288 681 6Ɛ0 X		
n D .98	+ .083 XX4 314 7		
$E_0\ d_2$	+ 3 764 Ɛ		
$E_1\ d_2$	+ 2 48Ɛ 6		
D 4:5	+ .350 56Ɛ X39 X		

<u>Example:</u> Find DN when N = 3:X i. e., $.3\dot{7}2\ \dot{4}9$

D .37	- .207 104 874	125 07Ɛ	.06X Ɛ3Ɛ
D .38	- .1Ɛ5 608 4X3	122 803	.047 367
The interval n =	$.249\ \dot{7}24\ \dot{9}$		
(1 - n) D .37	- .178 09X Ɛ83 2		
n D .38	- .048 374 0Ɛ7 X		
$E_0\ d_2$	+ 8 381 X		
$E_1\ d_2$	+ 5 565 3		
D 3:X	- .204 441 353 Ɛ		

<u>Example:</u> Find DN when N = 3:5 i. e., $.\dot{7}24\ \dot{9}$

D .72	+ .159 827 471	85 912	.092 713
D .73	+ .167 Ɛ91 8Ɛ6	84 796	.080 927
The interval n =	$.4\dot{9}7\ 2\dot{4}9\ 7$		
(1 - n) D .72	+ .0X8 264 51X 2		
n D .73	+ .075 713 122 5		
$E_0\ d_2$	+ 6 619 8		
$E_1\ d_2$	+ 5 777 8		
D 3:5	+ .161 987 815 Ɛ		

Note: Since D(N + 1) = DN + 1:N, we have D 8:5 = .901 987 815 Ɛ

Also, $D(2N) - \log_e 2 = 1:2\left[DN + D(N - 1:2)\right]$

D 8:5	+ .901 987 815 Ɛ	D 4:5	+ .350 56Ɛ X39 X
log 2	+ .839 912 483 4	D 3:X	- .204 441 353 X
D 8:5 - log 2	+ .084 075 352 7	1:2(D 4:5 + D 3:X)	+ .084 075 353 0

N	Digamma	d_2 -	N	Digamma	d_2 -	N	Digamma	d_2 -
.00	-.6Ɛ1 518 8X7	24X 212	.40	-.170 1X2 908	115 6Ɛ9	.80	+.222 111 162	77 4Ɛ9
.01	.695 957 4X9	243 925	.41	.15Ɛ 078 X72	113 504	.81	.22Ɛ 9Ɛ8 120	76 571
.02	.67X 419 X5Ɛ	239 639	.42	.14X 066 531	111 36X	.82	.239 628 724	75 646
.03	.663 119 X91	233 544	.43	.139 165 36Ɛ	10Ɛ 273	.83	.247 1X3 69X	74 73Ɛ
.04	.648 051 488	229 635	.44	.128 373 471	109 214	.84	.254 8X5 Ɛ11	73 853
.05	.631 1Ɛ2 539	223 903	.45	.117 68X 797	107 20Ɛ	.85	.262 334 6X8	72 987
.06	.616 577 32Ɛ	21X 161	.46	.106 XƐ1 11Ɛ	105 25Ɛ	.86	.26Ɛ 910 4Ɛ4	71 Ɛ1X
.07	.5ƐƐ Ɛ5X 2ƐƐ	214 784	.47	.0Ɛ6 418 913	103 343	.87	.279 236 399	71 08Ɛ
.08	.5X5 755 X8Ɛ	20Ɛ 364	.48	.0X5 X47 859	101 479	.88	.286 6XƐ 1XX	70 25Ɛ
.09	.58Ɛ 560 X39	206 0Ɛ5	.49	.095 578 070	ƐƐ 643	.89	.293 XƐ3 95X	6Ɛ 447
.0X	.575 571 Ɛ15	200 ƐXƐ	.4X	.085 1X7 Ɛ14	Ɛ9 858	.8X	.2X1 249 079	6X 651
.0Ɛ	.55Ɛ 784 014	1Ɛ8 045	.4Ɛ	.074 Ɛ15 621	Ɛ7 XƐX	.8Ɛ	.2XX 533 944	69 874
.10	-.545 Ɛ92 189	1Ɛ3 233	.50	-.064 93Ɛ 038	Ɛ6 1X9	.90	.2Ɛ7 770 953	68 XƐ3
.11	.530 593 5X7	1XX 56X	.51	.054 85X 848	Ɛ4 522	.91	.304 940 X68	68 14X
.12	.517 183 3X2	1X5 X29	.52	.044 872 989	Ɛ2 8X1	.92	.311 X64 X30	67 400
.13	.501 Ɛ59 036	1X1 426	.53	.034 979 7Ɛ8	Ɛ1 0X4	.93	.31X Ɛ21 5XƐ	66 68X
.14	.4X8 Ɛ14 122	198 Ɛ57	.54	.024 Ɛ75 71X	XƐ 52Ɛ	.94	.327 Ɛ33 699	65 973
.15	.494 068 192	194 7Ɛ6	.55	.015 260 Ɛ77	X9 9Ɛ8	.95	.334 X9Ɛ X11	65 072
.16	.47Ɛ 394 X63	190 57X	.56	-.005 636 219	X8 305	.96	.341 9X3 08Ɛ	64 388
.17	.466 892 119	188 461	.57	+.006 104 42Ɛ	X6 852	.97	.34X 841 Ɛ7X	63 6Ɛ7
.18	.452 357 85X	184 460	.58	.015 758 219	X5 21X	.98	.357 639 36Ɛ	62 X40
.19	.439 ƐX5 865	180 571	.59	.025 106 9X0	X3 823	.99	.364 391 91X	62 19X
.1X	.425 9Ɛ4 244	178 78Ɛ	.5X	.034 591 934	X2 265	.9X	.371 084 0X8	61 551
.1Ɛ	.411 972 416	174 XƐ2	.5Ɛ	.043 976 617	X0 923	.9Ɛ	.379 914 Ɛ21	60 918
.20	-.3Ɛ9 XƐƐ 501	171 316	.60	+.053 07X 58Ɛ	9Ɛ 417	.X0	.386 505 038	60 0Ɛ8
.21	.3X6 1Ɛ0 923	169 836	.61	.062 2X3 120	99 Ɛ45	.X1	.393 055 053	5Ɛ 4Ɛ0
.22	.392 64Ɛ 9X1	166 24Ɛ	.62	.071 429 921	98 6X7	.X2	.39Ɛ 745 778	5X 8Ɛ8
.23	.37Ɛ 055 10X	162 955	.63	.080 497 X30	97 282	.X3	.3X8 197 5X1	5X 117
.24	.367 801 1Ɛ0	15Ɛ 547	.64	.08Ɛ 46X 871	95 X90	.X4	.3Ɛ4 78Ɛ 2X9	59 549
.25	.354 508 838	158 223	.65	.09X 367 818	94 70Ɛ	.X5	.401 125 664	58 993
.26	.341 370 506	154 ƐX1	.66	.0X9 190 068	93 380	.X6	.409 623 046	58 22Ɛ
.27	.32X 369 194	151 X39	.67	.0Ɛ7 Ɛ21 131	92 062	.X7	.415 X84 3Ɛ7	57 699
.28	.317 4Ɛ7 8Ɛ8	14X 971	.68	.106 7X0 14X	90 973	.X8	.422 28X 089	56 Ɛ59
.29	.304 795 1X9	147 979	.69	.115 38X 3X9	8Ɛ 6Ɛ4	.X9	.42X 638 9ƐX	56 430
.2X	.2Ɛ1 ƐƐX 473	144 X55	.6X	.123 XX8 Ɛ49	8X 463	.XX	.436 951 2Ɛ9	55 914
.2Ɛ	.29Ɛ 568 5XX	142 000	.6Ɛ	.132 539 241	89 23Ɛ	.XƐ	.443 00Ɛ XX2	55 20X
.30	-.289 058 741	13Ɛ 232	.70	+.140 Ɛ00 2Ɛ0	88 044	.Ɛ0	.44Ɛ 235 476	54 714
.31	.276 887 Ɛ1Ɛ	138 529	.71	.14Ɛ 3Ɛ7 310	86 X76	.Ɛ1	.457 406 334	54 030
.32	.264 633 840	135 8X5	.72	.159 827 471	85 912	.Ɛ2	.463 543 17Ɛ	53 559
.33	.252 515 260	133 121	.73	.167 Ɛ91 8Ɛ6	84 796	.Ɛ3	.46Ɛ 628 667	52 X96
.34	.240 529 9Ɛ5	130 615	.74	.176 273 560	83 684	.Ɛ4	.477 67Ɛ 078	52 423
.35	.22X 672 Ɛ78	129 Ɛ84	.75	.184 491 738	82 598	.Ɛ5	.483 67Ɛ 263	51 981
.36	.218 926 117	127 5X6	.76	.192 629 333	81 514	.Ɛ6	.48Ɛ 629 687	51 32X
.37	.207 104 874	125 07Ɛ	.77	.1X0 703 610	80 475	.Ɛ7	.497 546 77X	50 8X8
.38	.1Ɛ5 608 4X3	122 803	.78	.1XX 719 42Ɛ	7Ɛ 43X	.Ɛ8	.4X3 412 Ɛ84	50 274
.39	.1X4 032 929	120 3Ɛ4	.79	.1Ɛ8 673 X07	7X 426	.Ɛ9	.4XƐ 24Ɛ 113	4Ɛ 851
.3X	.192 779 579	11X 051	.7X	.206 54Ɛ Ɛ74	79 435	.ƐX	.4Ɛ7 037 610	4Ɛ 238
.3Ɛ	.181 422 270	117 953	.7Ɛ	.214 36X 8X2	78 466	.ƐƐ	.502 994 88Ɛ	4X 832
						1.00	.50X 6X3 315	4X 237

Bessel Functions

The following tables of Bessel functions were obtained by summation of the series:-

$$J_0\,(2N) = 1 - N^2 + \frac{N^4}{2!2!} - \frac{N^6}{3!3!} \cdots$$

$$J_1\,(2N) = N - \frac{N^3}{1!2!} + \frac{N^5}{2!3!} - \frac{N^7}{3!4!} \cdots$$

$$J_{1:2}\,N = \sqrt{\frac{2}{\pi N}}\,\sin N$$

One dozen and three duodecimal places were calculated. The tables may be interpolated for nine place results by the use of the Everett coefficients for second differences. The necessary coefficients may be obtained by direct proportion from the table of coefficients given on pages 296-29Ɛ.

Example: Find $J_0 \frac{\pi}{4}$ $\frac{\pi}{4}$ = .951 202 424 0

		d_2 -	E_0 & E_1 -
J_0 .95	.X28 064 062	48 0X5	.040 18Ɛ
J_0 .96	.X23 80X 541	47 973	.023 925
The interval n =	.120 242 40		
$(1 - n)\ J_0$ .95	.928 918 521 3		
$n\ J_0$ .96	.0ƐX X34 465 4		
$E_0\ d_2$	+ 1 68Ɛ 7		
$E_1\ d_2$	+ X91 5		
$J_0 \frac{\pi}{4}$	.X27 753 327 7		

Note: The extended value of $J_0 \frac{\pi}{4}$ is:- .X27 753 327 579

Example: Find $J_1 \frac{\pi}{4}$

J_1 .95	.443 173 403	32 X20	.040 18Ɛ
J_1 .96	.447 966 2X5	33 168	.023 925
$(1 - n)\ J_1$ .95	.3Ɛ2 112 07X 5		
$n\ J_1$ .96	.051 5Ɛ5 385 7		
$E_0\ d_2$	+ 1 0ƐX 4		
$E_1\ d_2$	+ 766 6		
$J_1 \frac{\pi}{4}$	.443 709 0X8 X		

Note: The extended value of $J_1 \frac{\pi}{4}$ is:- .443 709 0X8 47X

The same method may be used for interpolating the $J_{1:2}$ table where the second difference, which is modified, has been given.

N	$J_{1:2}$	d_2 -	N	$J_{1:2}$	d_2 -	N	$J_{1:2}$	d_2 -
.00	.000 000 000		.40	.551 438 674	139 889	.80	.730 228 890	8Χ 083
.01	.096 Χ89 747		.41	.558 Χ05 294	135 690	.81	.733 Ɛ22 9ΧΧ	89 4Ɛ1
.02	.116 593 999		.42	.564 258 387	131 74Ɛ	.82	.737 74Ɛ 611	88 946
.03	.146 ƐΧ7 161		.43	.56Ɛ 579 894	129 Χ65	.83	.73Ɛ 2ΧƐ 4Χ6	202
.04	.171 917 439		.44	.576 771 2Χ9	126 3Ɛ3	.84	.742 983 174	87 6Χ2
.05	.194 Χ41 Ɛ7Χ		.45	.581 83Χ 481	122 Ɛ5Χ	.85	.746 38Ɛ 357	86 ƐΧ3
.06	.1Ɛ5 42Ɛ 080		.46	.588 7Χ4 673	11Ɛ 904	.86	.749 910 553	506
.07	.213 Χ46 635		.47	.593 62Χ Ɛ20	118 852	.87	.751 187 240	85 Χ49
.08	.230 980 Χ52		.48	.59Χ 358 6Ɛ8	115 970	.88	.754 578 098	3ΧΧ
.09	.248 565 Ɛ2Ɛ		.49	.5Χ4 Ɛ70 4ΧΧ	113 045	.89	.757 8Χ3 741	84 96Χ
.0Χ	.263 057 735		.4Χ	.5ΧƐ 671 222	110 484	.8Χ	.75Χ Ɛ46 435	347
.0Ɛ	.278 83Ɛ Χ32		.4Ɛ	.5Ɛ6 061 660	109 Χ56	.8Ɛ	.762 124 999	83 940
.10	.291 670 314		.50	.600 544 014	107 570	.90	.765 23Ɛ 5ƐΧ	351
.11	.2Χ5 847 409		.51	.606 91Χ ƐΧΧ	105 1Ɛ9	.91	.768 292 Χ86	82 978
.12	.2Ɛ9 27Ɛ Ɛ89		.52	.610 Ɛ20 95Ɛ	102 Ɛ6Ɛ	.92	.76Ɛ 263 593	3ƐΧ
.13	.310 225 285		.53	.617 17Ɛ 737	100 Χ39	.93	.772 171 89Ɛ	81 Χ54
.14	.322 777 950		.54	.621 249 672	ƐΧ Χ14	.94	.774 ƐƐΧ 150	503
.15	.334 761 Ɛ91		.55	.627 218 771	Ɛ8 ΧƐ1	.95	.777 985 0Ɛ7	80 Ɛ86
.16	.346 236 819		.56	.631 0ΧΧ 95Χ	Ɛ7 083	.96	.77Χ 68Ɛ 094	660
.17	.357 447 5ƐƐ		.57	.636 Χ85 Χ64	Ɛ5 343	.97	.781 314 610	149
.18	.368 216 5Ɛ8		.58	.640 767 808	Ɛ3 6Χ6	.98	.783 Χ99 9Ɛ8	7Ɛ 847
.19	.378 79Ɛ 585		.59	.646 355 Χ69	Ɛ1 Ɛ25	.99	.786 5Χ3 556	357
.1Χ	.388 991 025		.5Χ	.64Ɛ Χ52 189	Ɛ0 436	.9Χ	.789 029 956	7Χ Χ78
.1Ɛ	.398 819 387		.5Ɛ	.655 45Χ 058	ΧΧ Χ14	.9Ɛ	.78Ɛ 5Ɛ5 298	5ΧΧ
.20	.3Χ8 326 98Χ		.60	.65Χ 977 0Ɛ8	Χ9 475	.Χ0	.791 Ɛ02 229	12Ɛ
.21	.3Ɛ7 718 953		.61	.664 1Χ6 88Χ	Χ7 Ɛ94	.Χ1	.794 351 04Χ	79 880
.22	.406 813 907		.62	.669 52Χ 474	Χ6 769	.Χ2	.796 722 1Χ8	41Ɛ
.23	.415 631 Χ2Ɛ		.63	.672 787 498	Χ5 3Ɛ3	.Χ3	.798 Χ35 Ɛ26	78 Ɛ89
.24	.424 18Ɛ 198		.64	.677 93Ɛ 0Ɛ7	Χ4 0Χ5	.Χ4	.79Ɛ 090 895	745
.25	.432 681 Χ92		.65	.680 Χ0Χ 81Ɛ	Χ2 Χ41	.Χ5	.7Χ1 26Χ ΧƐ9	30Ɛ
.26	.440 922 8ƐΧ		.66	.685 9Ɛ7 4Ɛ0	Χ1 839	.Χ6	.7Χ3 390 Χ11	77 ΧΧ1
.27	.44Χ 944 Ɛ4Ɛ		.67	.68Χ 902 533	Χ0 694	.Χ7	.7Χ5 436 Χ42	681
.28	.458 73Χ 5Ɛ3		.68	.693 728 Χ92	9Ɛ 585	.Χ8	.7Χ7 425 3Ɛ1	269
.29	.466 318 312		.69	.698 473 Χ58	9Χ 509	.Χ9	.7Χ9 358 6Ɛ1	76 Χ61
.2Χ	.473 8ΧΧ 156		.6Χ	.6Χ1 120 506	99 4Χ2	.ΧΧ	.7ΧƐ 214 Ɛ4Χ	661
.2Ɛ	.481 083 0Χ2		.6Ɛ	.6Χ5 8ΧƐ 683	98 504	.ΧƐ	.7Ɛ1 016 945	268
.30	.48Χ 269 351		.70	.6ΧΧ 3Χ2 32Χ	97 572	.Ɛ0	.7Ɛ2 962 492	75 Χ7Ɛ
.31	.497 272 276		.71	.6Ɛ2 9Ɛ9 616	96 663	.Ɛ1	.7Ɛ4 634 15Ɛ	698
.32	.4Χ4 0Χ2 802		.72	.6Ɛ7 33Χ 251	95 797	.Ɛ2	.7Ɛ6 250 34Ɛ	300
.33	.4Ɛ0 946 9Ɛ7		.73	.6ƐƐ 7Χ5 2Χ4	94 94Ɛ	.Ɛ3	.7Ɛ7 9Ɛ3 23Χ	74 Ɛ29
.34	.4Ɛ9 42Χ 43Ɛ		.74	.703 Ɛ77 59Ɛ	93 Ɛ41	.Ɛ4	.7Ɛ9 4Χ1 1ƐƐ	761
.35	.505 958 503		.75	.708 275 949	16Ɛ	.Ɛ5	.7ƐΧ Ɛ16 61Χ	39Ɛ
.36	.512 117 861		.76	.710 4Χ0 Ɛ41	92 412	.Ɛ6	.800 497 659	021
.37	.51Χ 332 633		.77	.714 635 916	91 6ΧΧ	.Ɛ7	.801 9Χ4 676	73 869
.38	.526 3ΧΧ 92Χ		.78	.718 6Ɛ8 ƐƐ8	90 9Ɛ8	.Ɛ8	.803 239 Χ25	4ƐΧ
.39	.532 312 011		.79	.720 6ΧƐ 496	136	.Ɛ9	.804 61Ɛ 895	153
.3Χ	.53Χ 0Χ5 580		.7Χ	.724 611 835	8Ɛ 4Χ4	.ƐΧ	.805 94Χ 5Ɛ1	72 9Ɛ1
.3Ɛ	.545 932 124		.7Ɛ	.728 464 6Χ5	8Χ 87Ɛ	.ƐƐ	.807 006 517	653
						1.00	.808 20Ɛ 9ΧΧ	2Ɛ9

N	J_0	d_2 -	N	J_0	d_2 -	N	J_0	d_2 -
.00	1.000 000 000	60 000	.40	.Ɛ80 3ƐX 285	59 033	.80	.X85 327 013	50 447
.01	.ƐƐƐ Ɛ90 000	5Ɛ ƐƐ9	.41	.Ɛ7X 40Ɛ 61X	58 X95	.81	.X81 575 9X0	167
.02	.ƐƐƐ Ɛ00 003	ƐƐ3	.42	.Ɛ78 383 X9X	932	.82	.X79 774 602	4Ɛ X85
.03	.ƐƐƐ 990 013	ƐX3	.43	.Ɛ76 29Ɛ 628	786	.83	.X75 923 35Ɛ	79X
.04	.ƐƐƐ 800 040	Ɛ90	.44	.Ɛ74 15X 5Ɛ0	616	.84	.X71 X42 51X	4XX
.05	.ƐƐƐ 590 099	Ɛ73	.45	.Ɛ71 Ɛ80 Ɛ5X	463	.85	.X69 Ɛ12 1XƐ	1Ɛ9
.06	.ƐƐƐ 300 183	Ɛ53	.46	.Ɛ6Ɛ 947 065	2X7	.86	.X65 Ɛ52 883	4X Ɛ02
.07	.ƐƐX Ɛ90 316	Ɛ29	.47	.Ɛ69 674 X85	125	.87	.X61 Ɛ44 455	805
.08	.ƐƐX 800 540	Ɛ00	.48	.Ɛ67 346 780	57 Ɛ62	.88	.X59 XX7 422	504
.09	.ƐƐX 390 866	X89	.49	.Ɛ64 Ɛ80 515	995	.89	.X55 9ƐƐ XX7	1ƐƐ
.0X	.ƐƐ9 Ɛ01 103	X53	.4X	.Ɛ62 75X 495	803	.8X	.X51 886 371	49 XƐ3
.0Ɛ	.ƐƐ9 591 709	X14	.4Ɛ	.Ɛ60 2X0 852	62X	.8Ɛ	.X49 702 944	7X4
.10	.ƐƐ9 002 ƐƐƐ	98Ɛ	.50	.Ɛ59 987 5X1	451	.90	.X45 4Ɛ1 733	490
.11	.ƐƐ8 593 122	944	.51	.Ɛ57 416 X9Ɛ	26Ɛ	.91	.X41 253 052	176
.12	.ƐƐ7 Ɛ04 201	8Ɛ3	.52	.Ɛ54 X0Ɛ 12X	086	.92	.X38 Ɛ67 3Ɛ7	48 X56
.13	.ƐƐ7 395 5X9	859	.53	.Ɛ52 368 2Ɛ3	56 X97	.93	.X34 832 906	737
.14	.ƐƐ6 807 138	801	.54	.Ɛ4Ɛ 86X 5X1	8X6	.94	.X30 471 69X	410
.15	.ƐƐ5 Ɛ99 086	75X	.55	.Ɛ49 115 ƐX5	6XX	.95	.X28 064 062	0X5
.16	.ƐƐ5 30Ɛ 476	6Ɛ3	.56	.Ɛ46 526 XƐƐ	4Ɛ2	.96	.X23 80X 541	47 973
.17	.ƐƐ4 5X2 173	644	.57	.Ɛ43 8X1 523	2XX	.97	.X1Ɛ 329 069	642
.18	.ƐƐ3 815 428	591	.58	.Ɛ41 001 859	0X3	.98	.X16 X00 153	307
.19	.ƐƐ2 9X9 110	515	.59	.Ɛ3X 287 XƐ0	55 X95	.99	.X12 447 Ɛ32	46 Ɛ88
.1X	.ƐƐ1 Ɛ21 49Ɛ	455	.5X	.Ɛ37 4Ɛ8 26X	883	.9X	.X09 X48 945	847
.1Ɛ	.ƐƐ0 ƐƐ6 415	38Ɛ	.5Ɛ	.Ɛ34 692 965	668	.9Ɛ	.X05 402 Ɛ11	503
.20	.ƐƐ0 02Ɛ Ɛ80	302	.60	.Ɛ31 813 9Ɛ4	448	.X0	.X00 932 796	177
.21	.ƐXƐ 006 425	231	.61	.Ɛ2X 8ƐƐ 5Ɛ7	226	.X1	.9Ɛ8 218 2X4	45 X28
.22	.ƐX9 Ɛ41 659	155	.62	.Ɛ27 951 Ɛ94	54 ƐƐX	.X2	.9Ɛ3 677 Ɛ86	695
.23	.ƐX8 X19 738	078	.63	.Ɛ24 94Ɛ 573	991	.X3	.9XX X92 193	341
.24	.ƐX7 856 75Ɛ	5X Ɛ94	.64	.Ɛ21 8Ɛ4 181	759	.X4	.9X6 263 05Ɛ	44 ƐX2
.25	.ƐX6 634 7XX	XX9	.65	.Ɛ1X 804 232	522	.X5	.9X1 5XX Ɛ45	844
.26	.ƐX5 373 950	9Ɛ9	.66	.Ɛ17 67Ɛ 981	2X3	.X6	.998 8Ɛ2 1X7	49Ɛ
.27	.ƐX4 054 0Ɛ5	903	.67	.Ɛ14 4X3 229	060	.X7	.993 Ɛ70 Ɛ6X	137
.28	.ƐX2 895 757	809	.68	.Ɛ11 272 635	53 X16	.X8	.98Ɛ 1X7 7Ɛ6	43 988
.29	.ƐX1 478 5Ɛ0	706	.69	.Ɛ09 ƐXX 027	787	.X9	.986 39X 676	618
.2X	.ƐX0 000 93Ɛ	600	.6X	.Ɛ06 891 X52	534	.XX	.981 549 Ɛ1X	264
.2Ɛ	.Ɛ9X 6X6 68X	4Ɛ3	.6Ɛ	.Ɛ03 522 345	299	.XƐ	.978 676 11X	42 XXX
.30	.Ɛ99 131 Ɛ26	3X1	.70	.Ɛ00 11Ɛ 55Ɛ	040	.Ɛ0	.973 75Ɛ 430	730
.31	.Ɛ97 71X ƐX1	284	.71	.XƐ8 885 735	52 998	.Ɛ1	.96X 802 012	36Ɛ
.32	.Ɛ96 069 994	168	.72	.XƐ5 398 Ɛ33	733	.Ɛ2	.965 822 445	41 ƐX9
.33	.Ɛ94 55X 61Ɛ	042	.73	.XƐ1 X59 72X	485	.Ɛ3	.960 800 88Ɛ	820
.34	.Ɛ92 9Ɛ1 224	59 Ɛ16	.74	.XXX 488 000	212	.Ɛ4	.957 759 4Ɛ5	454
.35	.Ɛ91 1X5 Ɛ13	9X8	.75	.XX6 X64 1Ɛ0	51 Ɛ59	.Ɛ5	.952 674 887	082
.36	.Ɛ8Ɛ 540 X16	871	.76	.XX3 3XX 443	8X0	.Ɛ6	.949 54X Ɛ97	40 8Ɛ0
.37	.Ɛ89 83X 068	736	.77	.X9Ɛ 8X2 9Ɛ6	61X	.Ɛ7	.944 3X4 5Ɛ7	516
.38	.Ɛ87 X99 784	5Ɛ3	.78	.X98 145 94Ɛ	355	.Ɛ8	.93Ɛ 129 701	137
.39	.Ɛ86 09Ɛ 8X9	46Ɛ	.79	.X94 557 54Ɛ	088	.Ɛ9	.935 Ɛ92 690	3Ɛ 958
.3X	.Ɛ84 244 563	320	.7X	.X90 918 083	50 9Ɛ8	.ƐX	.930 927 903	574
.3Ɛ	.Ɛ82 34Ɛ X29	18X	.7Ɛ	.X89 047 9ƐƐ	724	.ƐƐ	.927 641 582	191
						1.00	.922 318 070	3X 9X1

N	J_1	d_2 -	N	J_1	d_2 -	N	J_1	d_2 -
.00	.000 000 000	000	.40	.1Ɛ8 027 Ɛ14	15 882	.80	.394 706 6X3	29 9X2
.01	.005 ƐƐƐ Ɛ30	460	.41	.201 922 3Ɛ1	16 0Ɛ7	.81	.399 736 30Ɛ	2X 164
.02	.00Ɛ ƐƐƐ 600	900	.42	.207 602 793	531	.82	.3X2 737 993	525
.03	.015 ƐƐX 390	1 160	.43	.211 288 644	963	.83	.3X7 70X Ɛ32	8X2
.04	.01Ɛ ƐƐ8 000	5ƐƐ	.44	.216 Ɛ37 752	17 195	.84	.3Ɛ0 673 3XƐ	2Ɛ 05Ɛ
.05	.025 ƐƐ4 231	X60	.45	.220 78Ɛ 687	606	.85	.3Ɛ5 5X8 809	413
.06	.02Ɛ ƐXX 602	2 2ƐƐ	.46	.226 407 ƐƐ6	X35	.86	.3ƐX 4Ɛ2 814	786
.07	.035 ƐX2 694	75Ɛ	.47	.230 028 6Ɛ0	18 261	.87	.403 389 055	Ɛ36
.08	.03Ɛ Ɛ94 007	ƐƐ9	.48	.235 830 Ɛ45	690	.88	.408 233 560	30 2X3
.09	.045 Ɛ82 541	3 459	.49	.23Ɛ 418 90X	XƐ5	.89	.411 069 784	650
.0X	.04Ɛ Ɛ69 61X	8Ɛ8	.4X	.244 ƐX7 79X	19 31Ɛ	.8X	.415 X73 358	9Ɛ3
.0Ɛ	.055 Ɛ50 9ƐƐ	4 156	.4Ɛ	.24X 759 34Ɛ	743	.8Ɛ	.41X 848 139	31 155
.10	.05Ɛ Ɛ30 046	5Ɛ4	.50	.254 2Ɛ1 379	Ɛ66	.90	.423 5XƐ 985	4Ɛ6
.11	.065 Ɛ06 899	X53	.51	.259 X27 441	1X 386	.91	.428 322 117	853
.12	.06Ɛ X98 699	5 2Ɛ0	.52	.263 543 13Ɛ	7X5	.92	.431 022 816	ƐX7
.13	.075 X65 1X9	74X	.53	.269 040 254	1Ɛ 005	.93	.435 8Ɛ1 32X	32 341
.14	.07Ɛ X28 16Ɛ	ƐX5	.54	.272 71X 364	41Ɛ	.94	.43X 549 701	691
.15	.085 9X5 148	6 443	.55	.278 199 055	837	.95	.443 173 403	X20
.16	.08Ɛ 957 8X2	89Ɛ	.56	.281 838 10Ɛ	20 04Ɛ	.96	.447 966 2X5	33 168
.17	.095 903 759	7 136	.57	.287 277 136	463	.97	.450 526 01Ɛ	4Ɛ0
.18	.09Ɛ 864 49X	591	.58	.290 895 8ƐX	874	.98	.455 072 465	832
.19	.0X5 7Ɛ0 84X	X28	.59	.296 293 80X	21 085	.99	.459 787 079	Ɛ73
.1X	.0XƐ 747 192	8 282	.5X	.29Ɛ 870 655	492	.9X	.462 267 91X	34 2XƐ
.1Ɛ	.0Ɛ5 688 454	717	.5Ɛ	.2X5 228 00X	89Ɛ	.9Ɛ	.466 914 290	625
.20	.0ƐƐ 600 ƐƐƐ	Ɛ70	.60	.2XX 781 8X4	22 0X6	.X0	.46Ɛ 348 219	958
.21	.105 528 7Ɛ6	9 404	.61	.2Ɛ4 0Ɛ5 494	4X9	.X1	.473 947 40X	35 089
.22	.10Ɛ 446 ƐX9	858	.62	.2Ɛ9 606 797	8Ɛ2	.X2	.478 311 532	3Ɛ6
.23	.115 357 744	X 0XƐ	.63	.302 XƐ5 1X8	23 0Ɛ3	.X3	.480 862 260	721
.24	.11Ɛ 25X 1Ɛ0	541	.64	.308 380 706	4Ɛ1	.X4	.485 179 469	X45
.25	.125 152 317	991	.65	.311 824 733	8XƐ	.X5	.489 65X 831	36 165
.26	.12Ɛ 037 671	Ɛ 224	.66	.317 064 X71	24 0X6	.X6	.491 Ɛ05 X50	484
.27	.134 Ɛ11 7X3	673	.67	.320 481 105	4X1	.X7	.496 336 7X7	79Ɛ
.28	.13X 998 262	Ɛ01	.68	.325 874 X78	893	.X8	.49X 730 963	XƐ2
.29	.144 852 X20	10 351	.69	.32Ɛ 043 Ɛ58	25 084	.X9	.4X2 XƐ0 029	37 205
.2X	.14X 6Ɛ9 249	79X	.6X	.334 3X9 Ɛ74	476	.XX	.4X7 234 0XX	512
.2Ɛ	.154 552 X98	11 026	.6Ɛ	.339 72X 716	861	.XƐ	.4XƐ 540 859	81X
.30	.15X 397 701	472	.70	.342 X45 617	26 049	.Ɛ0	.4Ɛ3 811 7XX	Ɛ21
.31	.164 20X X74	8Ɛ9	.71	.348 136 48Ɛ	433	.Ɛ1	.4Ɛ7 X66 81X	38 223
.32	.16X 030 52X	12 142	.72	.351 400 Ɛ10	816	.Ɛ2	.500 083 627	521
.33	.173 X3Ɛ X62	587	.73	.356 660 937	ƐƐ7	.Ɛ3	.504 263 Ɛ13	818
.34	.179 838 X0Ɛ	X10	.74	.35Ɛ 895 767	27 397	.Ɛ4	.508 407 7X3	Ɛ10
.35	.183 622 Ɛ68	13 251	.75	.364 XX3 200	771	.Ɛ5	.510 532 563	39 201
.36	.189 3Ɛ5 X74	694	.76	.36X 085 0X4	Ɛ4Ɛ	.Ɛ6	.514 620 122	4XX
.37	.193 175 2X8	Ɛ14	.77	.373 232 039	28 321	.Ɛ7	.518 690 3Ɛ3	796
.38	.198 Ɛ20 808	14 354	.78	.378 388 871	6Ɛ3	.Ɛ8	.520 702 XXX	X78
.39	.1X2 873 994	792	.79	.381 4X9 9Ɛ2	X85	.Ɛ9	.524 6Ɛ7 729	3X 159
.3X	.1X8 5Ɛ2 38X	15 00Ɛ	.7X	.386 5X2 06X	29 251	.ƐX	.528 672 20Ɛ	436
.3Ɛ	.1Ɛ2 317 975	448	.7Ɛ	.38Ɛ 669 095	619	.ƐƐ	.530 5XX 477	711
						1.00	.534 4X8 012	9X2

Interpolation Coefficients

Everett coefficients for even order differences for an interval n. The coefficients for second difference (d_2) and for fourth difference (d_4) are exact.

n	d_2 E_0 -	d_2 E_1 -	d_4 E_0 +	d_4 E_1 +	d_6 E_0 -	d_6 E_1 -	d_8 E_0 +	d_8 E_1 +
.1	.0362	.01ƐX	.006 7Ɛ3 6	.004 912 6	.001 364 54	.001 028 73	.000 333	.000 287
.2	.0614	.03X8	.010 154	.009 328	.002 491 85	.001 Ɛ91 4Ɛ	.000 614	.000 533
.3	.07X6	.0576	.014 2XX 6	.011 357 6	.003 31X 44	.002 9Ɛ2 6Ɛ	.000 849	.000 762
.4	.08X8	.0714	.016 Ɛ68	.014 714	.003 X42 Ɛ7	.003 618 19	.000 X02	.000 937
.5	.092X	.0832	.018 345 6	.016 Ɛ80 6	.004 221 9X	.003 ƐX1 89	.000 XƐ0	.000 X62
.6	.09	.09	.018 3	.018 3	.004 276	.004 276	.000 Ɛ0Ɛ	.000 Ɛ0Ɛ

Bessel coefficients for average differences for an interval n. The coefficients for second, fourth and sixth differences are exact.

n	B_2 -	B_4 +	B_6 -	B_8 +
.1	.056	.00Ɛ 506	.002 391 07	.000 5ƐX
.2	.0X	.019 48	.004 463 14	.000 Ɛ47
.3	.116	.025 646	.006 110 Ɛ3	.001 3XƐ
.4	.14	.02Ɛ 68	.007 45Ɛ 14	.001 739
.5	.156	.033 306	.008 203 67	.001 952
.6	.16	.034 6	.008 53	.001 X19

Interpolation Without Differences

Four point Lagrange coefficients for interpolating between V_0 and V_1 for an interval n. The coefficients are exact. For use when d_4 is negligible.

n	V_{-1}	V_0	V_1	V_2
.1	-.0362	+.Ɛ506	+.1056	-.01ƐX
.2	-.0614	+.X840	+.2180	-.03X8
.3	-.07X6	+.9X16	+.3346	-.0576
.4	-.08X8	+.8X80	+.4540	-.0714
.5	-.092X	+.7X26	+.5736	-.0832
.6	-.09	+.69	+.69	-.09

Six point Lagrange coefficients for interpolating between V_0 and V_1 for an interval n. The coefficients are exact. For use when d_6 is negligible.

n	V_{-2}	V_{-1}	V_0	V_1	V_2	V_3
.1	+.006 7Ɛ3 6	-.054 07Ɛ 6	+.Ɛ69 52Ɛ	+.107 4X1	-.030 256 6	+.004 912 6
.2	+.010 154	-.094 668	+.XƐ3 794	+.223 168	-.05Ɛ 754	+.009 328
.3	+.014 2XX 6	-.102 21X 6	+.X19 969	+.347 323	-.088 4Ɛ7 6	+.011 357 6
.4	+.016 Ɛ68	-.119 Ɛ14	+.927 4X8	+.473 854	-.0Ɛ0 8X8	+.014 714
.5	+.018 345 6	-.124 Ɛ99 6	+.820 367	+.5X0 265	-.10X 938 6	+.016 Ɛ80 6
.6	+.018 3	-.120 9	+.704 6	+.704 6	-.120 9	+.018 3

Everett Central Difference Coefficients

for Second Differences

by Intervals of .001

The following table gives the six place values of the two Everett coefficients for second differences for intervals (n) from .000 to .ƐƐƐ, from the formulae:-

$$-\frac{n(n-1)(n-2)}{3!} \quad \text{and} \quad \frac{(n-1)n(n-1)}{3!}$$

The numerical coefficients are always negative.

Intermediate values may be obtained by direct proportion.

Example:

Find the coefficients for an interval of 2:5, i. e., $.497\dot{2}49\dot{7}$

E_0 .497	.092 70X	E_1 .497	.080 901
E_0 .498	.092 729	E_1 .498	.080 X07
Difference	1Ɛ	Difference	106
$.\dot{2}49\dot{7}$ (1Ɛ)	5	$.\dot{2}49\dot{7}$ (106)	26
Added to E_0 .497	.092 713	Added to E_1 .497	.080 927

n	E0	E1		n	E0	E1		n	E0	E1	
.000	.000 000	.000 000	.000	.040	.013 40Ɛ	.007 ƐƐ1	.Ɛ80	.080	.025 471	.013 Ɛ4Ɛ	.Ɛ40
.001	400	200	.ƐƐƐ	.041	78Ɛ	.008 1Ɛ1	.Ɛ7Ɛ	.081	7Ɛ4	.014 148	.Ɛ3Ɛ
.002	7ƐX	400	.ƐƐX	.042	Ɛ4X	3Ɛ0	.Ɛ7X	.082	Ɛ35	345	.Ɛ3X
.003	ƐƐ8	600	.ƐƐ9	.043	.014 308	5XƐ	.Ɛ79	.083	.026 275	542	.Ɛ39
.004	.001 3Ɛ4	800	.ƐƐ8	.044	686	7XX	.Ɛ78	.084	5Ɛ4	740	.Ɛ38
.005	7Ɛ0	X00	.ƐƐ7	.045	X42	9XX	.Ɛ77	.085	933	939	.Ɛ37
.006	ƐX6	.001 000	.ƐƐ6	.046	.015 1Ɛ9	ƐX9	.Ɛ76	.086	.027 070	Ɛ36	.Ɛ36
.007	.002 3X0	200	.ƐƐ5	.047	574	.009 1X8	.Ɛ75	.087	3X9	.015 133	.Ɛ35
.008	794	400	.ƐƐ4	.048	929	3X7	.Ɛ74	.088	724	330	.Ɛ34
.009	Ɛ88	600	.ƐƐ3	.049	.016 0X1	5X6	.Ɛ73	.089	X5Ɛ	528	.Ɛ33
.00X	.003 37X	800	.ƐƐ2	.04X	455	7X5	.Ɛ72	.08X	.028 195	725	.Ɛ32
.00Ɛ	770	X00	.ƐƐ1	.04Ɛ	807	9X4	.Ɛ71	.08Ɛ	50X	922	.Ɛ31
.010	Ɛ60	.002 000	.ƐƐ0	.050	Ɛ79	ƐX3	.Ɛ70	.090	842	Ɛ1Ɛ	.Ɛ30
.011	.004 350	200	.ƐXƐ	.051	.017 329	.00X 1X2	.Ɛ6Ɛ	.091	Ɛ74	.016 117	.Ɛ2Ɛ
.012	73X	400	.ƐXX	.052	699	3X1	.Ɛ6X	.092	.029 2X6	314	.Ɛ2X
.013	Ɛ28	600	.ƐX9	.053	X48	5X0	.Ɛ69	.093	617	510	.Ɛ29
.014	.005 314	800	.ƐX8	.054	.018 1Ɛ5	79Ɛ	.Ɛ68	.094	948	708	.Ɛ28
.015	700	X00	.ƐX7	.055	562	99X	.Ɛ67	.095	.02X 077	905	.Ɛ27
.016	XX7	ƐƐƐ	.ƐX6	.056	90X	Ɛ98	.Ɛ66	.096	3X5	Ɛ01	.Ɛ26
.017	.006 290	.003 1ƐƐ	.ƐX5	.057	.019 075	.00Ɛ 197	.Ɛ65	.097	712	.017 0Ɛ9	.Ɛ25
.018	675	3ƐƐ	.ƐX4	.058	41X	396	.Ɛ64	.098	X3Ɛ	2Ɛ5	.Ɛ24
.019	X58	5ƐƐ	.ƐX3	.059	783	594	.Ɛ63	.099	.02Ɛ 166	4Ɛ2	.Ɛ23
.01X	.007 23Ɛ	7ƐƐ	.ƐX2	.05X	Ɛ27	793	.Ɛ62	.09X	490	6XX	.Ɛ22
.01Ɛ	621	9ƐƐ	.ƐX1	.05Ɛ	.01X 28X	991	.Ɛ61	.09Ɛ	7Ɛ6	8X5	.Ɛ21
.020	X01	ƐƐƐ	.ƐX0	.060	630	Ɛ90	.Ɛ60	.0X0	Ɛ1Ɛ	XX1	.Ɛ20
.021	.008 1X1	.004 1ƐX	.Ɛ9Ɛ	.061	991	.010 18X	.Ɛ5Ɛ	.0X1	.030 242	.018 099	.Ɛ1Ɛ
.022	580	3ƐX	.Ɛ9X	.062	.01Ɛ 131	389	.Ɛ5X	.0X2	565	295	.Ɛ1X
.023	959	5ƐX	.Ɛ99	.063	490	587	.Ɛ59	.0X3	887	491	.Ɛ19
.024	.009 136	7ƐX	.Ɛ98	.064	82X	786	.Ɛ58	.0X4	ƐX8	688	.Ɛ18
.025	512	9ƐX	.Ɛ97	.065	Ɛ88	984	.Ɛ57	.0X5	.031 308	884	.Ɛ17
.026	8X9	ƐƐ9	.Ɛ96	.066	.020 324	Ɛ82	.Ɛ56	.0X6	627	X7Ɛ	.Ɛ16
.027	.00X 082	.005 1Ɛ9	.Ɛ95	.067	67Ɛ	.011 180	.Ɛ55	.0X7	945	.019 076	.Ɛ15
.028	457	3Ɛ9	.Ɛ94	.068	X15	37Ɛ	.Ɛ54	.0X8	.032 062	272	.Ɛ14
.029	82Ɛ	5Ɛ9	.Ɛ93	.069	.021 16Ɛ	579	.Ɛ53	.0X9	37Ɛ	469	.Ɛ13
.02X	.00Ɛ 002	7Ɛ8	.Ɛ92	.06X	503	777	.Ɛ52	.0XX	696	664	.Ɛ12
.02Ɛ	394	9Ɛ8	.Ɛ91	.06Ɛ	857	975	.Ɛ51	.0XƐ	9Ɛ0	85Ɛ	.Ɛ11
.030	765	ƐƐ8	.Ɛ90	.070	ƐX9	Ɛ73	.Ɛ50	.0Ɛ0	.033 106	X56	.Ɛ10
.031	Ɛ34	.006 1Ɛ7	.Ɛ8Ɛ	.071	.022 33Ɛ	.012 171	.Ɛ4Ɛ	.0Ɛ1	41X	.01X 051	.Ɛ0Ɛ
.032	.010 303	3Ɛ7	.Ɛ8X	.072	68Ɛ	36Ɛ	.Ɛ4X	.0Ɛ2	732	248	.Ɛ0X
.033	691	5Ɛ6	.Ɛ89	.073	X1Ɛ	568	.Ɛ49	.0Ɛ3	X45	443	.Ɛ09
.034	X5X	7Ɛ6	.Ɛ88	.074	.023 16X	766	.Ɛ48	.0Ɛ4	.034 157	639	.Ɛ08
.035	.011 226	9Ɛ5	.Ɛ87	.075	4Ɛ7	964	.Ɛ47	.0Ɛ5	468	834	.Ɛ07
.036	5Ɛ1	ƐƐ5	.Ɛ86	.076	844	Ɛ62	.Ɛ46	.0Ɛ6	777	X2Ɛ	.Ɛ06
.037	977	.007 1Ɛ4	.Ɛ85	.077	Ɛ90	.013 15Ɛ	.Ɛ45	.0Ɛ7	X87	.01Ɛ 025	.Ɛ05
.038	.012 140	3Ɛ4	.Ɛ84	.078	.024 317	359	.Ɛ44	.0Ɛ8	.035 195	21Ɛ	.Ɛ04
.039	504	5Ɛ3	.Ɛ83	.079	661	556	.Ɛ43	.0Ɛ9	4X2	416	.Ɛ03
.03X	887	7Ɛ3	.Ɛ82	.07X	9X6	754	.Ɛ42	.0ƐX	7XX	610	.Ɛ02
.03Ɛ	.013 04X	9Ɛ2	.Ɛ81	.07Ɛ	.025 12X	951	.Ɛ41	.0ƐƐ	XƐ6	806	.Ɛ01
	E1	E0	n		E1	E0	n		E1	E0	n

n	E_0	E_1		n	E_0	E_1		n	E_0	E_1	
.100	.036 200	.01Ɛ X00	.Ɛ00	.140	.045 88Ɛ	.027 731	.X80	.180	.054 131	.033 28Ɛ	.X40
.101	506	ƐƐ6	.XƐƐ	.141	Ɛ59	923	.X7Ɛ	.181	386	476	.X3Ɛ
.102	80X	.020 1Ɛ0	.XƐX	.142	.046 226	Ɛ14	.X7X	.182	619	661	.X3X
.103	Ɛ12	3X6	.XƐ9	.143	4Ɛ3	.028 105	.X79	.183	86Ɛ	848	.X39
.104	.037 215	59Ɛ	.XƐ8	.144	77X	2Ɛ6	.X78	.184	Ɛ01	X33	.X38
.105	517	795	.XƐ7	.145	X45	4X7	.X77	.185	.055 152	.034 01X	.X37
.106	818	98X	.XƐ6	.146	.047 10Ɛ	697	.X76	.186	3X2	204	.X36
.107	Ɛ18	Ɛ84	.XƐ5	.147	394	888	.X75	.187	631	3XƐ	.X35
.108	.038 217	.021 179	.XƐ4	.148	658	X78	.X74	.188	87Ɛ	595	.X34
.109	515	373	.XƐ3	.149	91Ɛ	.029 069	.X73	.189	Ɛ09	77Ɛ	.X33
.10X	812	568	.XƐ2	.14X	ƐX1	259	.X72	.18X	.056 155	965	.X32
.10Ɛ	Ɛ0Ɛ	761	.XƐ1	.14Ɛ	.048 262	449	.X71	.18Ɛ	3X1	Ɛ4Ɛ	.X31
.110	.039 206	956	.XƐ0	.150	523	639	.X70	.190	628	.035 135	.X30
.111	501	Ɛ4Ɛ	.XXƐ	.151	7X2	829	.X6Ɛ	.191	871	31X	.X2Ɛ
.112	7Ɛ6	.022 144	.XXX	.152	X61	X19	.X6X	.192	XƐ7	503	.X2X
.113	XXƐ	338	.XX9	.153	.049 11Ɛ	.02X 009	.X69	.193	.057 13Ɛ	6X9	.X29
.114	.03X 1X3	531	.XX8	.154	398	1Ɛ8	.X68	.194	382	892	.X28
.115	496	725	.XX7	.155	654	3X7	.X67	.195	605	X77	.X27
.116	788	91X	.XX6	.156	90Ɛ	597	.X66	.196	846	.036 060	.X26
.117	X79	Ɛ12	.XX5	.157	Ɛ86	786	.X65	.197	X87	244	.X25
.118	.03Ɛ 169	.023 107	.XX4	.158	.04X 23Ɛ	975	.X64	.198	.058 107	429	.X24
.119	459	2ƐƐ	.XX3	.159	4Ɛ4	Ɛ64	.X63	.199	346	611	.X23
.11X	747	4Ɛ3	.XX2	.15X	767	.02Ɛ 153	.X62	.19X	585	7Ɛ5	.X22
.11Ɛ	X35	6X7	.XX1	.15Ɛ	X1X	341	.X61	.19Ɛ	802	999	.X21
.120	.040 121	89Ɛ	.XX0	.160	.04Ɛ 090	530	.X60	.1X0	X3Ɛ	Ɛ81	.X20
.121	409	X92	.X9Ɛ	.161	341	71X	.X5Ɛ	.1X1	.059 076	.037 165	.X1Ɛ
.122	6Ɛ4	.024 086	.X9X	.162	5Ɛ1	909	.X5X	.1X2	2Ɛ1	349	.X1X
.123	99X	27X	.X99	.163	861	XƐ7	.X59	.1X3	527	530	.X19
.124	.041 083	471	.X98	.164	Ɛ0Ɛ	.030 0X5	.X58	.1X4	761	713	.X18
.125	367	665	.X97	.165	.050 179	293	.X57	.1X5	995	8Ɛ7	.X17
.126	64X	858	.X96	.166	425	481	.X56	.1X6	.05X 008	X9X	.X16
.127	930	X4Ɛ	.X95	.167	691	66X	.X55	.1X7	23Ɛ	.038 080	.X15
.128	.042 012	.025 042	.X94	.168	938	858	.X54	.1X8	471	263	.X14
.129	2Ɛ2	235	.X93	.169	ƐX2	X45	.X53	.1X9	6X2	446	.X13
.12X	592	428	.X92	.16X	.051 247	.031 033	.X52	.1XX	912	628	.X12
.12Ɛ	871	61Ɛ	.X91	.16Ɛ	4Ɛ0	220	.X51	.1XƐ	Ɛ41	80X	.X11
.130	Ɛ4Ɛ	812	.X90	.170	753	409	.X50	.1Ɛ0	.05Ɛ 170	9Ɛ0	.X10
.131	.043 227	X04	.X8Ɛ	.171	9Ɛ6	5Ɛ6	.X4Ɛ	.1Ɛ1	399	Ɛ92	.X0Ɛ
.132	503	ƐƐ7	.X8X	.172	.052 058	7X2	.X4X	.1Ɛ2	606	.039 174	.X0X
.133	79Ɛ	.026 1X9	.X89	.173	2Ɛ8	98Ɛ	.X49	.1Ɛ3	832	355	.X09
.134	X75	39Ɛ	.X88	.174	558	Ɛ78	.X48	.1Ɛ4	X59	537	.X08
.135	.044 14X	591	.X87	.175	7Ɛ8	.032 164	.X47	.1Ɛ5	.060 084	718	.X07
.136	423	783	.X86	.176	X56	350	.X46	.1Ɛ6	2X9	8Ɛ9	.X06
.137	6Ɛ6	975	.X85	.177	.053 0Ɛ3	538	.X45	.1Ɛ7	512	X9X	.X05
.138	989	Ɛ67	.X84	.178	350	724	.X44	.1Ɛ8	735	.03X 07Ɛ	.X04
.139	.045 05Ɛ	.027 159	.X83	.179	5X7	910	.X43	.1Ɛ9	958	25Ɛ	.X03
.13X	330	34X	.X82	.17X	842	XƐ8	.X42	.1ƐX	Ɛ7X	440	.X02
.13Ɛ	600	540	.X81	.17Ɛ	X98	.033 0X3	.X41	.1ƐƐ	.061 1X0	620	.X01
	E_1	E_0	n		E_1	E_0	n		E_1	E_0	n

n	E_0	E_1		n	E_0	E_1		n	E_0	E_1	
.200	.061 400	.03X 800	.X00	.240	.069 54Ɛ	.045 X71	.980	.280	.074 5Ɛ1	.050 X0Ɛ	.940
.201	620	9X0	.9ƐƐ	.241	737	.046 045	.97Ɛ	.281	768	Ɛ94	.93Ɛ
.202	83X	Ɛ80	.9ƐX	.242	922	218	.97X	.282	921	.051 159	.93X
.203	X58	.03Ɛ 15Ɛ	.9Ɛ9	.243	Ɛ09	3XX	.979	.283	X96	322	.939
.204	.062 075	33Ɛ	.9Ɛ8	.244	.06X 0Ɛ3	581	.978	.284	.075 04X	4X6	.938
.205	292	51X	.9Ɛ7	.245	298	754	.977	.285	201	66Ɛ	.937
.206	4X9	6Ɛ9	.9Ɛ6	.246	480	926	.976	.286	373	833	.936
.207	704	898	.9Ɛ5	.247	664	XƐ8	.975	.287	525	9Ɛ7	.935
.208	919	X77	.9Ɛ4	.248	846	.047 08X	.974	.288	696	Ɛ7X	.934
.209	Ɛ32	.040 055	.9Ɛ3	.249	X28	25Ɛ	.973	.289	846	.052 142	.933
.20X	.063 146	234	.9Ɛ2	.24X	.06Ɛ 009	431	.972	.28X	9Ɛ5	305	.932
.20Ɛ	35X	412	.9Ɛ1	.24Ɛ	1X9	602	.971	.28Ɛ	Ɛ64	488	.931
.210	570	5Ɛ0	.9Ɛ0	.250	389	793	.970	.290	.076 112	64Ɛ	.930
.211	782	78X	.9XƐ	.251	567	964	.96Ɛ	.291	27X	811	.92Ɛ
.212	993	967	.9XX	.252	745	Ɛ35	.96X	.292	427	993	.92X
.213	ƐX3	Ɛ45	.9X9	.253	922	.048 105	.969	.293	592	Ɛ55	.929
.214	.064 1Ɛ2	.041 122	.9X8	.254	XƐƐ	295	.968	.294	739	.053 117	.928
.215	400	2ƐƐ	.9X7	.255	.070 096	465	.967	.295	8X3	299	.927
.216	60X	498	.9X6	.256	271	635	.966	.296	X48	45X	.926
.217	816	675	.9X5	.257	447	805	.965	.297	ƐƐ0	61Ɛ	.925
.218	X22	852	.9X4	.258	620	994	.964	.298	.077 154	7X0	.924
.219	.065 029	X2X	.9X3	.259	7Ɛ4	Ɛ64	.963	.299	2Ɛ7	961	.923
.21X	233	.042 007	.9X2	.25X	987	.049 133	.962	.29X	459	Ɛ21	.922
.21Ɛ	439	1X3	.9X1	.25Ɛ	Ɛ5X	301	.961	.29Ɛ	5ƐX	.054 0X1	.921
.220	641	37Ɛ	.9X0	.260	.071 130	490	.960	.2X0	75Ɛ	261	.920
.221	845	556	.99Ɛ	.261	301	65X	.95Ɛ	.2X1	8ƐX	421	.91Ɛ
.222	X48	732	.99X	.262	491	829	.95X	.2X2	X59	5X1	.91X
.223	.066 04X	909	.999	.263	661	9Ɛ7	.959	.2X3	ƐƐ8	760	.919
.224	24Ɛ	XX5	.998	.264	830	Ɛ84	.958	.2X4	.078 155	91Ɛ	.918
.225	450	.043 080	.997	.265	9ƐX	.04X 152	.957	.2X5	2Ɛ2	X9X	.917
.226	650	256	.996	.266	X87	31Ɛ	.956	.2X6	44X	.055 058	.916
.227	84X	431	.995	.267	.072 153	4X8	.955	.2X7	5X5	216	.915
.228	X48	608	.994	.268	31Ɛ	675	.954	.2X8	740	394	.914
.229	.067 046	7X2	.993	.269	4X6	842	.953	.2X9	895	552	.913
.22X	242	978	.992	.26X	670	X0X	.952	.2XX	X2X	710	.912
.22Ɛ	43X	Ɛ52	.991	.26Ɛ	835	Ɛ97	.951	.2XƐ	Ɛ82	889	.911
.230	635	.044 128	.990	.270	9Ɛ9	.04Ɛ 163	.950	.2Ɛ0	.079 116	X46	.910
.231	82X	301	.98Ɛ	.271	Ɛ81	32Ɛ	.94Ɛ	.2Ɛ1	268	.056 003	.90Ɛ
.232	X24	496	.98X	.272	.073 144	4Ɛ6	.94X	.2Ɛ2	3ƐX	180	.90X
.233	.068 018	670	.989	.273	306	682	.949	.2Ɛ3	550	338	.909
.234	210	844	.988	.274	487	849	.948	.2Ɛ4	6X0	4Ɛ4	.908
.235	402	X19	.987	.275	648	X14	.947	.2Ɛ5	830	670	.907
.236	5Ɛ4	ƐƐ2	.986	.276	807	Ɛ9Ɛ	.946	.2Ɛ6	97X	828	.906
.237	7X5	.045 186	.985	.277	986	.050 165	.945	.2Ɛ7	Ɛ09	9X3	.905
.238	996	35X	.984	.278	Ɛ44	330	.944	.2Ɛ8	.07X 056	Ɛ5X	.904
.239	Ɛ85	532	.983	.279	.074 102	4Ɛ6	.943	.2Ɛ9	1X3	.057 115	.903
.23X	.069 174	706	.982	.27X	27X	680	.942	.2ƐX	32X	290	.902
.23Ɛ	362	89X	.981	.27Ɛ	436	845	.941	.2ƐƐ	476	446	.901
	E_1	E_0	n		E_1	E_0	n		E_1	E_0	n

n	E_0	E_1		n	E_0	E_1		n	E_0	E_1	
.300	.07X 600	.057 600	.900	.340	.083 60Ɛ	.061 9Ɛ1	.880	.380	.087 671	.067 94Ɛ	.840
.301	746	776	.8ƐƐ	.341	725	Ɛ57	.87Ɛ	.381	75X	XX2	.83Ɛ
.302	88Ɛ	92Ɛ	.8ƐX	.342	83Ɛ	.062 0ƐƐ	.87X	.382	845	.068 035	.83X
.303	X13	XX5	.8Ɛ9	.343	953	264	.879	.383	930	187	.839
.304	Ɛ56	.058 05X	.8Ɛ8	.344	X68	408	.878	.384	X16	31X	.838
.305	.07Ɛ 099	213	.8Ɛ7	.345	Ɛ7Ɛ	571	.877	.385	Ɛ00	470	.837
.306	21Ɛ	387	.8Ɛ6	.346	.084 092	714	.876	.386	ƐX5	601	.836
.307	360	540	.8Ɛ5	.347	1X4	878	.875	.387	.088 089	752	.835
.308	4X0	6Ɛ4	.8Ɛ4	.348	2Ɛ5	X1Ɛ	.874	.388	170	8X4	.834
.309	620	868	.8Ɛ3	.349	405	Ɛ82	.873	.389	253	X34	.833
.30X	75Ɛ	X1Ɛ	.8Ɛ2	.34X	515	.063 125	.872	.38X	335	Ɛ85	.832
.30Ɛ	899	X93	.8Ɛ1	.34Ɛ	624	287	.871	.38Ɛ	417	.069 115	.831
.310	X16	.059 146	.8Ɛ0	.350	733	429	.870	.390	4Ɛ8	265	.830
.311	Ɛ53	2Ɛ9	.8XƐ	.351	841	58Ɛ	.86Ɛ	.391	598	3Ɛ4	.82Ɛ
.312	.080 08Ɛ	46Ɛ	.8XX	.352	949	731	.86X	.392	677	543	.82X
.313	206	622	.8X9	.353	X56	892	.869	.393	756	692	.829
.314	340	794	.8X8	.354	Ɛ61	X33	.868	.394	834	820	.828
.315	476	945	.8X7	.355	.085 068	Ɛ93	.867	.395	911	96Ɛ	.827
.316	5XƐ	XƐ7	.8X6	.356	172	.064 134	.866	.396	9X9	XƐ9	.826
.317	723	.05X 068	.8X5	.357	278	294	.865	.397	X85	.06X 046	.825
.318	857	219	.8X4	.358	380	434	.864	.398	Ɛ61	193	.824
.319	98X	38X	.8X3	.359	484	593	.863	.399	.089 037	320	.823
.31X	Ɛ00	53X	.8X2	.35X	588	732	.862	.39X	111	469	.822
.31Ɛ	.081 031	6XƐ	.8X1	.35Ɛ	68X	891	.861	.39Ɛ	1X6	5Ɛ5	.821
.320	161	85Ɛ	.8X0	.360	790	X30	.860	.3X0	27Ɛ	741	.820
.321	291	X0X	.89Ɛ	.361	891	Ɛ8X	.85Ɛ	.3X1	352	889	.81Ɛ
.322	400	Ɛ7X	.89X	.362	992	.065 128	.85X	.3X2	426	X14	.81X
.323	52Ɛ	.05Ɛ 129	.899	.363	X91	286	.859	.3X3	4Ɛ8	Ɛ5Ɛ	.819
.324	658	298	.898	.364	Ɛ90	424	.858	.3X4	58X	.06Ɛ 0X6	.818
.325	785	447	.897	.365	.086 08Ɛ	581	.857	.3X5	65Ɛ	230	.817
.326	8Ɛ1	5Ɛ5	.896	.366	188	71X	.856	.3X6	72Ɛ	377	.816
.327	X18	763	.895	.367	285	876	.855	.3X7	7ƐƐ	500	.815
.328	Ɛ43	911	.894	.368	381	X13	.854	.3X8	88X	646	.814
.329	.082 069	X7X	.893	.369	479	Ɛ6Ɛ	.853	.3X9	959	78Ɛ	.813
.32X	192	.060 028	.892	.36X	574	.066 106	.852	.3XX	X26	914	.812
.32Ɛ	2Ɛ7	195	.891	.36Ɛ	66X	262	.851	.3XƐ	XƐ3	X58	.811
.330	41Ɛ	342	.890	.370	763	3Ɛ9	.850	.4Ɛ0	Ɛ80	ƐX0	.810
.331	542	4XX	.88Ɛ	.371	858	554	.84Ɛ	.4Ɛ1	.08X 048	.070 124	.80Ɛ
.332	664	656	.88X	.372	950	6XX	.84X	.4Ɛ2	113	267	.80X
.333	785	802	.889	.373	X43	844	.849	.4Ɛ3	199	3XƐ	.809
.334	8X6	96X	.888	.374	Ɛ36	99X	.848	.4Ɛ4	263	531	.808
.335	X06	Ɛ15	.887	.375	.087 028	Ɛ34	.847	.4Ɛ5	328	674	.807
.336	Ɛ26	.061 080	.886	.376	119	.067 089	.846	.4Ɛ6	3Ɛ0	7Ɛ6	.806
.337	.083 044	227	.885	.377	209	222	.845	.4Ɛ7	474	938	.805
.338	162	392	.884	.378	2Ɛ9	377	.844	.4Ɛ8	537	X79	.804
.339	27Ɛ	538	.883	.379	3X8	50Ɛ	.843	.4Ɛ9	5Ɛ9	ƐƐƐ	.803
.33X	398	6X2	.882	.37X	497	663	.842	.4ƐX	67Ɛ	.071 13Ɛ	.802
.33Ɛ	4Ɛ4	848	.881	.37Ɛ	584	7Ɛ7	.841	.4ƐƐ	740	280	.801
	E_1	E_0	n		E_1	E_0	n		E_1	E_0	n

n	E_0	E_1		n	E_0	E_1		n	E_0	E_1	
.400	.08X 800	.071 400	.800	.440	.090 X8Ɛ	.076 531	.780	.480	.092 331	.07Ɛ 08Ɛ	.740
.401	880	540	.7ƐƐ	.441	Ɛ23	658	.77Ɛ	.481	360	1X0	.73Ɛ
.402	93Ɛ	67Ɛ	.7ƐX	.442	Ɛ77	783	.77X	.482	389	2Ɛ1	.73X
.403	9Ɛ9	7ƐX	.7Ɛ9	.443	.091 00X	8XX	.779	.483	3Ɛ7	401	.739
.404	X77	939	.7Ɛ8	.444	060	X14	.778	.484	423	511	.738
.405	Ɛ34	X78	.7Ɛ7	.445	0Ɛ2	Ɛ39	.777	.485	44Ɛ	620	.737
.406	ƐƐ0	ƐƐ6	.7Ɛ6	.446	143	.077 063	.776	.486	476	730	.736
.407	.08Ɛ 068	.072 134	.7Ɛ5	.447	194	188	.775	.487	4X1	83X	.735
.408	123	271	.7Ɛ4	.448	224	2Ɛ0	.774	.488	507	949	.734
.409	199	3XX	.7Ɛ3	.449	273	415	.773	.489	531	X57	.733
.40X	253	527	.7Ɛ2	.44X	301	539	.772	.48X	556	Ɛ64	.732
.40Ɛ	308	664	.7Ɛ1	.44Ɛ	34Ɛ	660	.771	.48Ɛ	57X	.080 072	.731
.410	380	7X0	.7Ɛ0	.450	399	783	.770	.490	5X2	17Ɛ	.730
.411	434	918	.7XƐ	.451	426	8X6	.76Ɛ	.491	605	287	.72Ɛ
.412	4X7	X53	.7XX	.452	472	X08	.76X	.492	627	393	.72X
.413	559	Ɛ8X	.7X9	.453	4Ɛ9	Ɛ2X	.769	.493	649	49Ɛ	.729
.414	60Ɛ	.073 105	.7X8	.454	544	.078 050	.768	.494	66X	5X6	.728
.415	680	23Ɛ	.7X7	.455	58X	171	.767	.495	68Ɛ	6Ɛ1	.727
.416	731	375	.7X6	.456	614	292	.766	.496	6XƐ	7Ɛ7	.726
.417	7X0	4XƐ	.7X5	.457	659	3Ɛ3	.765	.497	70X	901	.725
.418	84Ɛ	625	.7X4	.458	6X1	513	.764	.498	729	X07	.724
.419	8ƐX	75X	.7X3	.459	725	633	.763	.499	747	Ɛ10	.723
.41X	968	892	.7X2	.45X	768	752	.762	.49X	765	.081 015	.722
.41Ɛ	X15	X07	.7X1	.45Ɛ	7XX	871	.761	.49Ɛ	782	119	.721
.420	X81	Ɛ3Ɛ	.7X0	.460	830	990	.760	.4X0	79Ɛ	221	.720
.421	Ɛ29	.074 072	.79Ɛ	.461	871	XXX	.75Ɛ	.4X1	7Ɛ7	325	.71Ɛ
.422	Ɛ94	1X6	.79X	.462	8Ɛ2	.079 008	.75X	.4X2	812	428	.71X
.423	.090 03Ɛ	319	.799	.463	932	126	.759	.4X3	828	52Ɛ	.719
.424	0X5	44Ɛ	.798	.464	971	243	.758	.4X4	843	631	.718
.425	14X	581	.797	.465	9Ɛ0	360	.757	.4X5	858	733	.717
.426	1Ɛ3	6Ɛ3	.796	.466	X2X	478	.756	.4X6	871	835	.716
.427	257	825	.795	.467	X67	594	.755	.4X7	885	936	.715
.428	2ƐX	956	.794	.468	XX4	6Ɛ0	.754	.4X8	899	X37	.714
.429	360	X87	.793	.469	Ɛ20	807	.753	.4X9	8Ɛ0	Ɛ37	.713
.42X	402	ƐƐ8	.792	.46X	Ɛ58	922	.752	.4XX	903	.082 037	.712
.42Ɛ	464	.075 128	.791	.46Ɛ	Ɛ93	X39	.751	.4XƐ	914	137	.711
.430	505	258	.790	.470	.092 009	Ɛ53	.750	.4Ɛ0	926	236	.710
.431	565	387	.78Ɛ	.471	043	.07X 069	.74Ɛ	.4Ɛ1	937	335	.70Ɛ
.432	604	4Ɛ6	.78X	.472	078	182	.74X	.4Ɛ2	947	433	.70X
.433	663	625	.789	.473	0Ɛ1	297	.749	.4Ɛ3	956	531	.709
.434	701	753	.788	.474	124	3Ɛ0	.748	.4Ɛ4	965	62Ɛ	.708
.435	75X	881	.787	.475	158	504	.747	.4Ɛ5	974	728	.707
.436	7Ɛ7	9XƐ	.786	.476	18X	618	.746	.4Ɛ6	981	825	.706
.437	853	Ɛ18	.785	.477	200	72Ɛ	.745	.4Ɛ7	98Ɛ	921	.705
.438	8XƐ	.076 045	.784	.478	232	842	.744	.4Ɛ8	997	X19	.704
.439	946	172	.783	.479	263	955	.743	.4Ɛ9	9X3	Ɛ14	.703
.43X	9X0	29X	.782	.47X	293	X67	.742	.4ƐX	9XƐ	.083 00Ɛ	.702
.43Ɛ	X36	406	.781	.47Ɛ	302	Ɛ79	.741	.4ƐƐ	9Ɛ6	106	.701
	E_1	E_0	n		E_1	E_0	n		E_1	E_0	n

n	E_0	E_1		n	E_0	E_1		n	E_0	E_1	
.500	.092 X00	.083 200	.700	.540	.092 74Ɛ	.086 871	.680	.580	.091 7Ɛ1	.089 80Ɛ	.640
.501	X06	2Ɛ6	.6ƐƐ	.541	731	94X	.67Ɛ	.581	772	88X	.63Ɛ
.502	X0Ɛ	3XƐ	.6ƐX	.542	713	X27	.67X	.582	732	948	.63X
.503	X13	4X4	.6Ɛ9	.543	6Ɛ4	Ɛ03	.679	.583	6Ɛ1	X07	.639
.504	X17	599	.6Ɛ8	.544	695	Ɛ9Ɛ	.678	.584	670	X84	.638
.505	X1Ɛ	691	.6Ɛ7	.545	675	.087 076	.677	.585	62X	Ɛ41	.637
.506	X22	784	.6Ɛ6	.546	655	151	.676	.586	5X8	ƐƐX	.636
.507	X24	878	.6Ɛ5	.547	634	228	.675	.587	565	.08X 076	.635
.508	X25	96Ɛ	.6Ɛ4	.548	612	302	.674	.588	522	132	.634
.509	X26	X61	.6Ɛ3	.549	5Ɛ0	397	.673	.589	49X	1X9	.633
.50X	X27	Ɛ53	.6Ɛ2	.54X	58X	470	.672	.58X	456	264	.632
.50Ɛ	X27	.084 045	.6Ɛ1	.54Ɛ	567	545	.671	.58Ɛ	411	31Ɛ	.631
.510	X26	136	.6Ɛ0	.550	543	619	.670	.590	388	395	.630
.511	X25	227	.6XƐ	.551	51Ɛ	6Ɛ1	.66Ɛ	.591	342	44X	.62Ɛ
.512	X23	317	.6XX	.552	4Ɛ6	784	.66X	.592	2Ɛ7	503	.62X
.513	X21	407	.6X9	.553	490	857	.669	.593	270	577	.629
.514	X1X	4Ɛ6	.6X8	.554	467	929	.668	.594	225	62Ɛ	.628
.515	X16	5X5	.6X7	.555	440	9ƐƐ	.667	.595	199	6X3	.627
.516	X12	694	.6X6	.556	415	X91	.666	.596	150	756	.626
.517	X09	782	.6X5	.557	3XX	Ɛ62	.665	.597	103	808	.625
.518	X04	870	.6X4	.558	382	.088 032	.664	.598	076	87X	.624
.519	9ƐX	959	.6X3	.559	355	102	.663	.599	028	930	.623
.51X	9Ɛ4	X46	.6X2	.55X	328	192	.662	.59X	.090 Ɛ99	9X1	.622
.51Ɛ	9X9	Ɛ33	.6X1	.55Ɛ	2ƐX	261	.661	.59Ɛ	Ɛ4X	X51	.621
.520	9X1	.085 01Ɛ	.6X0	.560	290	330	.660	.5X0	XƐƐ	Ɛ01	.620
.521	995	106	.69Ɛ	.561	261	3ƐX	.65Ɛ	.5X1	X6Ɛ	Ɛ71	.61Ɛ
.522	989	1Ɛ1	.69X	.562	232	488	.65X	.5X2	X1X	020	.61X
.523	97Ɛ	298	.699	.563	202	555	.659	.5X3	989	08Ɛ	.619
.524	971	383	.698	.564	192	622	.658	.5X4	937	139	.618
.525	963	468	.697	.565	161	6XƐ	.657	.5X5	8X5	1X6	.617
.526	954	552	.696	.566	12Ɛ	777	.656	.5X6	852	254	.616
.527	945	637	.695	.567	0Ɛ9	842	.655	.5X7	7ƐƐ	300	.615
.528	934	720	.694	.568	087	909	.654	.5X8	768	368	.614
.529	924	804	.693	.569	054	994	.653	.5X9	713	414	.613
.52X	913	8X7	.692	.56X	020	X5X	.652	.5XX	67Ɛ	47Ɛ	.612
.52Ɛ	901	98Ɛ	.691	.56Ɛ	.091 ƐX8	Ɛ24	.651	.5XƐ	626	526	.611
.530	8XƐ	X72	.690	.570	Ɛ73	ƐX9	.650	.5Ɛ0	590	.08Ɛ 590	.610
.531	898	Ɛ54	.68Ɛ	.571	Ɛ3X	.089 072	.64Ɛ	.5Ɛ1	536	636	.60Ɛ
.532	884	.086 036	.68X	.572	Ɛ04	136	.64X	.5Ɛ2	49Ɛ	69Ɛ	.60X
.533	870	117	.689	.573	X8X	1ƐX	.649	.5Ɛ3	444	744	.609
.534	858	1Ɛ8	.688	.574	X53	281	.648	.5Ɛ4	3X8	7X8	.608
.535	842	299	.687	.575	X18	344	.647	.5Ɛ5	350	850	.607
.536	829	379	.686	.576	9X0	406	.646	.5Ɛ6	2Ɛ3	8Ɛ3	.606
.537	812	459	.685	.577	963	488	.645	.5Ɛ7	256	956	.605
.538	7Ɛ8	538	.684	.578	926	54X	.644	.5Ɛ8	1Ɛ8	9Ɛ8	.604
.539	7X0	617	.683	.579	8X9	60Ɛ	.643	.5Ɛ9	15X	X5X	.603
.53X	784	6Ɛ6	.682	.57X	86Ɛ	68Ɛ	.642	.5ƐX	0ƐƐ	XƐƐ	.602
.53Ɛ	768	794	.681	.57Ɛ	830	74Ɛ	.641	.5ƐƐ	060	Ɛ60	.601
	E_1	E_0	n		E_1	E_0	n	.600	.090 000	.090 000	.600